SILICON PROCESSING

FOR

THE VLSI ERA

VOLUME 3:

THE SUBMICRON MOSFET

SILICON PROCESSING

FOR

THE VLSI ERA

VOLUME 3:

THE SUBMICRON MOSFET

STANLEY WOLF Ph.D.
Professor, Department of Electrical Engineering
California State University, Long Beach
Long Beach, California

LATTICE PRESS

Sunset Beach, California

Published by:

Lattice Press,
Post Office Box 340
Sunset Beach, California 90742, U.S.A.

Cover design by Roy Montibon, Visionary Art Resources, Inc., Los Angeles, CA.

Library of Congress Cataloging in Publication Data
Wolf, Stanley

Silicon Processing for the VLSI Era
 Volume 3 : The Submicron MOSFET

Includes Index
1. Integrated circuits-Very large scale
 integration. 2. Silicon. I. Title

ISBN 0-961672-5-3

9 8 7 6 5 4 3 2 1

PRINTED IN THE UNITED STATES OF AMERICA

CONTENTS

CONTENTS

PREFACE

SILICON PROCESSING FOR THE VLSI ERA now represents a series of texts designed to provide a comprehensive and up-to-date treatment of this important and rapidly changing field. The volume in hand is the third of this series. Volumes 1 (*Process Technology*) and 2 (*Process Integration*) were published in 1986 and 1990, respectively. Volume 1 deals with the individual processes employed in the fabrication of silicon VLSI circuits, such as epitaxial growth, thermal oxidation of silicon, CVD and PVD of amorphous and polycrystalline films, diffusion and ion implantation of dopants in silicon, microlithography, and patterning technology. Volume 2 describes how the individual processes of Volume 1 are combined in various ways to produce MOS and bipolar VLSI and ULSI circuits. The task of integrating these various fabrication processes together is referred to as *process integration*.

Here, we treat the topics of submicron MOSFET device physics and the relationship between such device physics and submicron MOSFET fabrication. That is, an understanding of device physics has become even more important now that MOSFETs have crossed the long-channel frontier into the submicron realm. Device aspects that could once be ignored (because they cause only second-order effects in large MOS devices) are now significant. Many device effects observed in submicron MOSFETs are impacted by the process technology used to fabricate them. Some of such effects include: short-channel effect on V_T; RSCE (reverse-short-channel effect on V_T); DIBL (drain-induced barrier lowering); narrow-width effect; reverse-narrow-width effect; subsurface punchthrough in NMOSFETs; punchthrough in PMOSFETs; impact of the V_T-adjust implant on subthreshold swing, S_t; boron penetration of gate oxides in p^+-poly-gate PMOSFETs - and the polysilicon depletion effect that this causes; GIDL (gate-induced drain leakage); impact of process technology on the reliability and wearout of thin gate oxides, including damage from plasma processing; hot-carrier degradation and drain-engineered MOSFET structures developed to combat the problem (including LDDs, LATID, "halo" implants, and asymmetrical MOSFETs); well-engineering by high-energy implants (including retrograde-well CMOS); ROXNOX (re-oxidized-nitrided oxides); and very-lightly-nitrided gate oxides. These and many other phenomena associated with submicron MOS fabrication can only be understood in the context of short-channel MOSFET physics. Only with such an understanding can the relationship between circuit behavior, device design, and process technology of submicron MOSFETs be grasped. Consequently, by gaining such an understanding process engineers (and other microelectronic professionals) will be better able to contribute to the task of successfully designing and manufacturing submicron ICs. One of our main purposes is thus to provide a text that treats both the topics of submicron MOSFET device physics and the phenomena associated with fabricating such devices.

Chapter 1 introduces the process and device models employed in the early days of the semiconductor industry. Such models were based on empirical data and/or simplified physical equations (e.g., differential equations in their one-dimensional form). In the submicron era, however, the more general forms of these differential equations must be used to obtain accurate predictive capability of both the fabrication processes and the device physics. Since this generally means that partial differential equations in two- or three-dimensional form must be solved, this can only be carried out by numerical analysis, performed with the aid of high-speed digital computers. Thus, chapter 2 outlines the methodology of this approach.

 To facilitate the discussion of submicron MOSFET device physics, we divide the topic up into three chapters: The first of these, chapter 3, deals with basic MOS theory and the MOS capacitor. The next, chapter 4, covers long-channel MOSFETs and the circuit models developed to predict the drain current characteristics of such devices. Finally, chapter 5 describes the characteristics of the short-channel (i.e., submicron) MOSFET. This is the longest chapter of the book, and it includes the following topics: DIBL, subsurface punchthrough, the drain current in saturation, simplified short-channel MOSFET circuit models, MOSFET scaling, and submicron PMOSFETs.

Chapter 6 is concerned with isolation issues in integrated circuits with an emphasis on CMOS technology. Chapter 7 covers thin gate oxides, primarily with respect to their reliability and growth. Chapter 8 deals with well formation in CMOS. Chapter 9 focuses on hot-carrier effects in MOS ICs, as well as on device structures and processing techniques that mitigate the detrimental aspect of such phenomena on MOSFETs. Problems are included at the end of each chapter to assist readers in gauging how well they have assimilated the material in the text.

A book of this length and diversity would not have been possible without the indirect and direct assistance of many other workers. From an indirect perspective, virtually all the information presented here is based on the research efforts of countless numbers of scientists and engineers. Their contributions are recognized to a small degree by citing some of their articles in the references given at the end of each chapter. Likewise, the direct help came in a variety of forms, and was generously provided by many people. The text is a much better work as a result of this aid, and the author expresses heartfelt thanks to those who gave of their time, energy, and intellect.

Roy Montibon of Visionary Art Resources, Inc., Los Angeles, CA designed this cover, as well as those of Volumes 1 and 2.

Stanley Wolf

P.S. Additional copies of the books can be obtained from:

Lattice Press
Post Office Box 340-V
Sunset Beach, CA 90742

For your convenience an order form is provided on the final leaf of the book.

CHAPTER 1

THE ROLE OF PROCESS AND DEVICE MODELS

IN MICROELECTRONICS TECHNOLOGY

Experimentation through trial-and-error (*empiricism*) is one way of advancing technology. Progress in such traditional materials-based industries as glass and steel relied on this approach until the early 20th century. However, as evidenced by the centuries-long evolution of these technologies, empirically driven progress is very slow. One reason is that new discoveries are codified merely as 'recipes' (i.e., as a set of explicit instructions for achieving a specific outcome). Unfortunately, recipes give no indication of the outcome if the variables of the procedure are altered. Thus, with empiricism alone, neither empirical results nor the 'recipes' point the way toward further advances.

The rate of technological progress can be radically increased by combining empirical investigations with scientific modeling. In this approach, theoretical behavior is inferred from experimental data, and models of the phenomena or systems being investigated are developed from these theories. Such models not only provide an understanding of the observed phenomena, but also offer a means for predicting behavior under conditions not yet experimentally attempted. Since scientific modeling has been one of the foundations of the rapid progress in microelectronics, we need to expand upon the role of such models, and how they are derived.

1.1 MODELS IN MICROELECTRONIC TECHNOLOGY

A *model*, in the technological sense, is *a schematic description or analogy of a phenomenon or system, that accounts for its known or inferred properties, and may be used for further study of its properties.* Whenever possible, models used in microelectronics are *physically based* (i.e., the phenomenon being modeled is represented by some well-understood physical effect). However, if the physics of the phenomenon being studied is unknown it may be necessary to resort to an *empirically based model.**
In such cases, the relationship between the variables of the phenomena are experiment-

---

* The term *model* for an empirically derived description is probably not really appropriate. Maybe the term *empirical functional relationship* would be more apt. However, since the term *empirical model* is used frequently in the literature, we will use it as well.

1

ally determined. The quantitative empirical model in this case is often a closed-form mathematical expression fitted to the experimental data.

Models can contribute to technological progress in two ways:

1. Physically based models can provide a basic explanation or visualization of the phenomenon, device, or system under study, even if the effect being modeled it is not directly observable.

2. Both physically or empirically based models can serve as vehicles for *simulating* process or device behavior. That is, the behavior of a real process or device can be examined by studying the characteristics or operation of the analogous system (model). However, the simulation task is carried out by conducting 'paper' (or more recently 'computer') experiments. This can be comparatively less expensive and faster than performing actual experiments. Although, while simulation obviously does not replace fabrication, it does reduce the trial and error needed to converge to a stable process. Moreover, it allows exploration of the process window to help find an optimum device structure or set of process conditions. The major challenge is to develop models that can quickly, inexpensively, and accurately simulate actual semiconductor process and device phenomena.

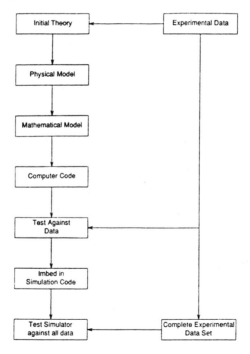

Fig. 1-1 Algorithm for creating new process models and embedding them in the process simulation code.[1] This paper was originally presented at the Spring 1989 Meeting of the Electrochemical Society, Inc. held in Los Angeles.

1.1.1 Development of Physically Based Models

Generally, physically based models are developed in three stages (Fig. 1-1). First, a concept of the mechanisms and relations which capture the essence of the observed phenomena must be deduced (this results in a *qualitative* model). In this form, the model can provide insight or even a visualization of the phenomenon or device being studied. This is especially important in microelectronics, where the phenomena being investigated are usually not directly observable. Two examples of such *qualitative models* are: (1) the depiction of the Bohr model of the atom as a nucleus surrounded by electrons occupying well-defined orbits (Fig. 1-2a); and (2) the description of drift current in a semiconductor bar as the motion of discrete particles of electric charge, e.g., electrons and holes, moving in response to an applied electric field (Fig. 1-2b).

In the second stage, the qualitative model has to be translated into a set of equations or computational operations (resulting in a *quantitative* model). To be useful for simulation applications, such quantitative forms of the model must be available. Examples of mathematical expressions that quantitatively depict some aspects of the two models above are: (1) the equation expressing the energy of an electron when it occupies one of

a)

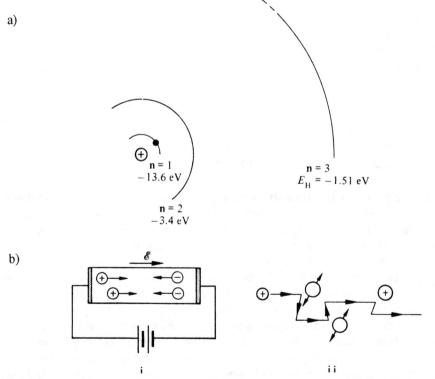

b)

Fig. 1-2 (a) Depiction of the Bohr model of the atom as a nucleus surrounded by electrons occupying well-defined orbits; (b) Visualization of electric current (drift): (*i*) motion of carriers in a biased semiconductor bar; (*ii*) drifting hole on a microscopic scale.

the orbits in the model of the Bohr atom; and (2) the relationship between the electron drift current density, $J_{n\text{drift}}$ and the electric field $\mathcal{E}$, electron density n, electric charge per electron q, and electron mobility in a solid μ_n, or $J_{n\text{drift}} = qn\mu_n\mathcal{E}$.

Finally, the solution of the equations constituting the *quantitative* form of the model must be found and the results compared to data from actual experiments (to ensure that the simulation correctly emulates the observed phenomena).

In microelectronics, quantitative physical models frequently take the form of differential equations. Differential equations are classified according to the number of variables involved. If only one independent variable exists, it is known as an 'ordinary' differential equation. If the differential equation is expressed in terms of two or more independent variables, it is called a 'partial' differential equation (PDE). Many of the phenomena encountered in semiconductor device behavior or process technology are modeled by such *partial differential equations*.

It should also be mentioned that the task of simulating submicron device and process phenomena involves more than merely evaluating the model equations or carrying out computational operations. That is, simulating such behavior has become a complex discipline involving computer science, numerical analysis, and computer graphics (as described in chap. 2).

In addition, we should also note that simulation can play a role in aiding the manufacture of devices in several other ways. First, it can improve the probability of a first pass success for new products and processes. Second, the manufacturability of existing processes can be improved through *process centering* (i.e., finding the mix of process conditions that yields not only the correct result, but also the smallest variation from that result in the face of changes in the process conditions). In this same vein, by simulating the variation of device behavior versus changes in manufacturing conditions, the allowable limits of process variation at that point can also be identified.

1.1.2 Development of Empirically Based Models

1.1.2.1 Empirically Based *versus* Physically Based Models.
We noted that *physically based* models are developed by linking the behavior under study to an analogous physical phenomenon for which a quantitative relationship is known. For example, the motion of an electron in a vacuum subjected to an electric field can be modeled as the acceleration of a particle of mass m_e which is subjected to a force $q\mathcal{E}$ due to the electric field. Such models, when based on sound physical principles, are preferred over *empirically based* models (which provide quantitative predictive capability based only on empirically derived data). That is, physically based models are more likely to produce useful simulations even when the experimental conditions being simulated are outside of the range of conditions explored in actual experiments. In addition, when there are no generally available techniques for accurately measuring the data being simulated (the condition that exists, for example, in the case of two-dimensional doping profiles in submicron devices), obtaining simulation results from a model based on a physical foundation is the only avenue outside of empiricism for helping to design a new process or device structure.

Generally speaking, semiconductor *device* behavior can be more accurately simulated than the phenomena of *IC fabrication processes*. The physics of semiconductor devices are relatively well understood, allowing robust physically based models to be correctly implemented.* On the other hand, the physics of many IC processes is still not well understood, and physically based models of such processes may not be available. Hence, process simulation is more likely to be forced to rely upon empirical models.

Another point should be mentioned. The physically based models often rely on experimentally determined values of some parameter in the model equation. For example, the mobilities of the mobile charge carriers in the device equations (μ_n and μ_p), and the intrinsic diffusion coefficient D (in the Fick's 2nd Law equation) are experimentally determined. Although theoretical work is continuing to calculate these parameters from first principles, the simulation programs in current use depend on experimentally determined values of these parameters.

1.1.2.2 Deriving Empirically Based Models. As noted earlier, quantitative *empirically based models* are merely representations of experimental data, and have little, or no physical foundations. That is, to establish such models, data from previously conducted experiments is used to create such models in one of the following two forms:

   1. The empirical results are assembled and stored in a *data base* in a computer. Sometimes the data is organized in tabular form, such as a *look-up table*. Tabular quantities however, are the least useful form for using data for simulation. For example, in such form no information is provided about how to carry out accurate interpolation should it be necessary to approximate an unknown value between two data points.

   2. A closed-form equation relating the set of experimental parameters can be developed from the experimental data by curve fitting a mathematical function to a set of experimental results. That is, experimental results are plotted using an appropriate graphical format, and a closed-form mathematical expression is chosen to be a function that represents this plotted data. Curve fitting techniques are employed to find the parameter values which make the selected function best fit the experimental data points.

We should remark that there are two basic approaches for fitting data with an approximating function. The first involves passing an assumed polynomial through every data point. This approach is not used because an *n*th-order polynomial for *n + 1* data points is too complex for large *n* values. In addition, experimental data are subject to errors, and thus passing a polynomial though every point is not appropriate.

---

* It should be noted, however, that obtaining a solution of the set of device equations is generally a complex procedure. Thus, while the path toward accurate device simulations is will marked, it may still be difficult to attain the goal in specific cases.

The second method is the standard approach of curve fitting data. The given data set is plotted and a mathematical function is selected to represent the plotted points.* The chosen function is fitted to the data set by having it pass as close as possible (but not necessarily through), every data point. The most popular method for finding the parameters of the assumed function that gives this best fit is known as the *least-squares method* (for it involves approximating a function such that the sum of the squares of the differences between the curve and the data points given is a minimum). There are other methods of curve fitting, all of which are denoted by the general term *regression analysis*. Figure 1-3 depicts a graphical interpretation of the least squares method.

If an attempt is made to fit a straight line of the form $y = a + bx$ to a set of data, the procedure for finding the most probable values for the coefficients a and b (i.e., the *regression coefficients*) is known as *linear regression*. If the assumed functional approximation is nonlinear, a *nonlinear regression* procedure must be used to find the regression coefficients.

1.1.2.3 Role of Empirical Models in Semiconductor Simulation.
Despite the fact that they are not physically based, empirical models can still be very useful. First, there may be no other option available for simulating phenomena for which the physical basis is not yet understood. Second, when embedded as part of a process or device simulation program, empirical models can serve as convenient storehouses for experimental data. Third, obtaining simulation results from models of this type is usually quick and straightforward. Fourth, empirical models may be able to provide an exact simulation for some particular experimental conditions. Finally, even if the conditions being simulated fall between the actual experimental data points, interpolation is still likely to give reasonably accurate results.

However, since physical principles do not underlie the quantitative expressions which constitute these models, their main limitation is that the results they provide cannot be extrapolated to conditions outside of the ranges of previously conducted experiments. Hence, these models cannot be reliably used to characterize new processes beyond these ranges of process conditions.

It should also be emphasized that many, if not most, models used in semiconductor process and device simulation are, in fact, *semi-empirical* models. That is, where possible, phenomena are modeled with physically based equations and parameters relating to these phenomena. However, some effects are not well understood, or their parameter values cannot yet be derived from physical principles. Hence, empirical parameters are used in these instances. As an example, the MOSFET dc circuit models used in SPICE (described in chaps. 4 and 5) contain empirically determined parameters in the expressions they use to model the effects of carrier mobility degradation, carrier velocity saturation, and drain-induced barrier lowering on the drain current.

---

* For example, the plotted data is examined for obvious trends such as linear, quadratic, or higher order behavior. If logarithmic or exponential behavior is suspected, the data may be plotted on a semilog and/or log-log scale. Based on the trends observed, one of these functional forms is chosen as the function to be fitted to the data.

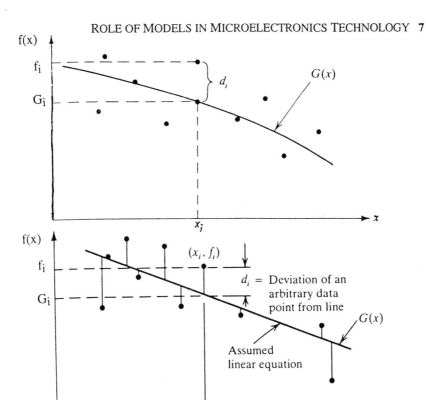

Fig. 1-3 (a) Graphical interpretation of the least-squares method. (b) Schematic representation of linear regression.

1.1.2.4 Examples of Quantitative Empirically Based Models. Some examples of empirically based semiconductor process models are the following:

1. When silicon is oxidized in dry O_2 to grow SiO_2 at thicknesses less than 350Å, the growth is 'anomalous' (i.e., it does not obey the conventional Deal-Grove model). By analyzing a vast amount of data, Reisman-Nicollian were able to derive an empirical model for this thickness regime.[2] Their thin-oxide-growth power-law model predicts that the oxide thickness t_{ox} is given by a general power law of the form, $t_{ox} = a (t_g + \tau)^b$, where a and b are constants, and t_g is the time for growth measured in a given experiment (Fig. 1-4a, see chap. 7). This result is contrasted with the Deal and Grove model, where oxide thickness is the solution of a quadratic equation.

2. When boron is ion implanted in single crystal silicon, channeling effects are observed (i.e., the penetration of some boron ions is deeper than in non-crystalline silicon). In an attempt to model these effects, an exponential tail of fixed decay length (independent of dose energy or crystal orientation) can be added

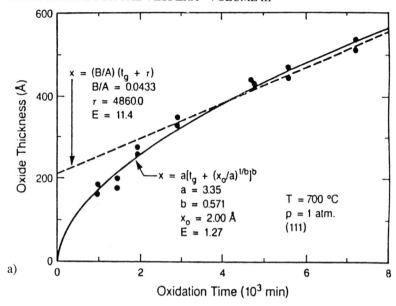

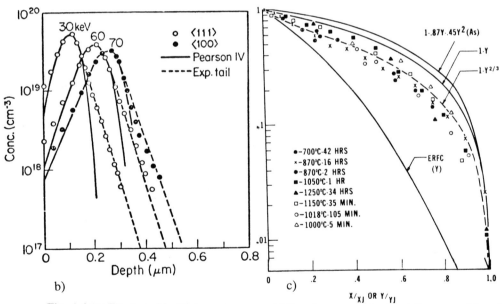

Fig. 1-4 (a) Fits to oxide thickness versus oxidation time using the Deal-Grove model and the power-law model expression.[2] Reprinted with permission of the Journal of Electronic Materials. (b) Boron as-implanted profiles in <111> and <100> silicon in a random direction. Pearson IV and modified Pearson IV distributions for representation of these profiles.[3] (© 1983 IEEE). (c) Boron diffusion profiles normalized to C_S and x_j.[4] (© North-Holland).

to the Pearson-IV distribution function curves used to simulate boron implantation processes into non-crystalline silicon (Fig. 1-4b). The decay length of this exponential tail is empirically determined to be 450Å. This empirical model is an option available in the SUPREM III program.[3]

3. The extent of boron or arsenic diffusion in silicon under high boron concentration (*extrinsic*) conditions can be simulated with a physically based model. However, this requires obtaining the solution of Fick's 2nd Law equation in nonlinear form by numerical analysis (see chap. 2). In some cases, one may wish to estimate extrinsic diffusion processes without having to resort to numerical analysis. A closed-form analytical solution that still yields a reasonably accurate result would be useful for such circumstances. Closed-form solutions to the one-dimensional diffusion equation, expressed as a polynomial have been empirically derived by fitting a polynomial expression to experimental data for extrinsic diffusion of B and As into Si (Fig. 1-4c).[4]

1.1.2.5 PREDICT-1: A Process Simulator Based on Empirical Models.

Although virtually all process simulators (e.g., SUPREM-III, SUPREM-IV, FEDSS) use empirically based models to some degree, the process simulator PREDICT-1[5] has been organized to deliberately exploit the benefits of empirical models. First, the empirical models it employs are derived from a large data base of experimental results. Extensive analysis of sufficient data is conducted to ensure that valid model equations are extracted. Continued verification of the modeling software is performed with each addition to the data set. Second, since universal empirical models which can simulate all conditions usually do not exist, PREDICT-1 employs a decision tree architecture (Fig. 1-5). That is, when a particular process is to be simulated, the decision tree structure of the program selects the empirical model that has been shown to be valid over the range of processing parameters being simulated. Since the models can be separated as tree branches, it allows for their verification independently of other models.

1.2 MATHEMATICAL FORMULATION OF THE PHYSICALLY-BASED MODELS OF SEMICONDUCTOR PROCESSES AND DEVICES

Despite the fact that empirical models play a useful role in simulating semiconductor processes and devices, they are chiefly employed when physically based models are either too complex or not available. In fact, a major ongoing theme of semiconductor research is to develop new physical models to replace empirical models. We also noted that physically based models are used to provide insight about process physics and device behavior. Since the main purpose of our books is to discuss the physics of submicron devices and processing, the remainder of our discussion will be devoted to

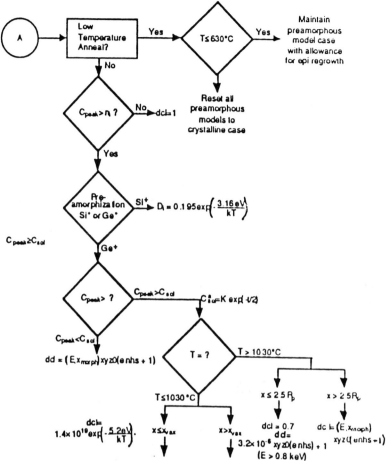

Fig. 1-5 Example of the "tree architecture" used in the PREDICT-1 simulator.[5] (© 1988 IEEE).

such physically based models. In this chapter, the emphasis will be on the mathematical forms such models assume, and the methods used to treat these mathematical relations.

As stated earlier, many of the fundamental equations utilized to provide quantitative relationships for the models in IC technology are *partial differential equations* (PDEs). Obviously, in order to use these equations for simulation purposes it must be possible to solve them. While finding the solution of such PDEs generally requires complex numerical procedures that must be carried out with the aid of a computer (as described in chap. 2), under some circumstances less elaborate methods can provide solutions. Specifically, by using suitable approximations, the form of the PDEs can be simplified to a degree that closed-form analytic solutions exist. Such analytic solutions are very attractive since they allow a particular regime of operation to be continuously explored (in a mathematical sense), and because they can provide solutions without costly and time-consuming computer calculations.

When such simplifying approximations are employed, however, the range of applicability of the solutions is reduced to a limited set of process conditions or device structures. However, it turns out that such simplified equation forms were adequate for semiconductor devices fabricated down to about the 2 μm device generations. On the other hand, to model the physics of smaller devices it became necessary to use the PDEs in their multidimensional forms. Coincidentally, at about the time the simplified forms of the model equations had to be abandoned, high-speed computing hardware became widely available. This was fortuitous, since such computing power was needed to implement the numerical procedures for solving the equations in their more complex form. This transition away from the simplified equations (and the resultant closed-form analytic solutions) and the implications this has on the approach that must then be used to simulate devices and processes should be described in more detail.

The remaining sections of this chapter will address this topic. We will proceed by first introducing the two PDEs in their general form, and then go on to answer the following questions:

1. How can the general forms of the model equations be simplified so that their closed-form solutions can be obtained?

2. Under what circumstances is it valid to invoke the approximations used to simplify the equations?

3. Why are the closed-form analytical solutions of the model equations so attractive, and what important roles do they still play in studying and simulating ICs?

4. Why do such simplified forms eventually have to be abandoned in order to retain the ability to accurately simulate submicron process and device behavior?

The answers to these questions will provide the background for the material of chap. 2. That is, the discussion of this chapter should make it clear why numerical procedures are necessary for simulating submicron process and device behavior.

1.2.1 The Physically Based Model of Impurity Diffusion in Silicon - Fick's Second Law Equation

Thermally driven *diffusion** of impurities in a semiconductor is one of the key steps in fabricating integrated circuits. A detailed description of the physics of dopant diffusion in silicon is presented in Vol. 1. Here, however, we merely introduce the mathematical formulation of the physical model of diffusion, namely, the PDE known as Fick's 2nd Law equation. It is presented at this point because we will use it as one of the two examples for illustrating the analytical and numerical methods needed to obtain solutions of such PDEs.

Assume that a wafer of silicon contains a known, nonuniform distribution of impurities (e.g., B, P, or As) at some initial time. It is observed that measurable

---

* *Diffusion* is defined as the net tendency of objects in random motion to move from regions of high concentration to low concentration.

redistribution of the impurities occurs as a result of heating the sample above about 600°C. How can this phenomenon be modeled?

The *qualitative physical model* of diffusion assumes that at high temperatures the impurities undergo random movement in the silicon lattice, and that such movement causes the impurities to redistribute themselves from regions of higher to lower concentration. In *quantitative* form, the model postulates that the extent of such redistribution can be found by solving Fick's 1st and 2nd Laws of Diffusion.

Specifically, the *quantitative model of diffusion* states that if the concentration of impurities (e.g., number/cm^{-3}) is known at all locations in a wafer at some initial time (the initial condition), and we wish to predict the concentration at a specific location at some later time t_1, this can be achieved by solving Fick's 2nd Law Equation for the concentration at that location and time. The Fick's 2nd Law equation, in its general three-dimensional form is

$$\partial C/\partial t \ = \ - \operatorname{div} F_D \qquad\qquad (1-1)$$

where the flux of impurities F_D according to Fick's first law is

$$F_D \ = \ - D \ \nabla C \qquad\qquad (1-2)$$

In these equations C is the impurity concentration in the silicon, and D is the concentration-dependent diffusion coefficient.

To be able to obtain specific solutions of the Fick's 2nd Law equation, in addition to the initial condition, we must also know: (1) the concentration values at the boundaries of the wafer during the time of the diffusion (the boundary conditions); and (2) the value of the diffusion coefficient D at each location and time in the wafer during the diffusion. Information about the value of D can be obtained from another model, which may be physically or empirically based.**

If the above information is known and a method is available for solving Eq. 1-1, then the simulated value of the impurity concentration can be obtained by applying the solution method to Eq. 1-1.

1.2.2 The Physically Based Model of Semiconductor Device Behavior

The goal of device simulation is to accurately predict the electrical behavior of semi-conductor devices. For the purposes of circuit analysis and design, such behavior is generally expressed in terms of the variables of circuit theory (namely, the terminal currents and terminal voltages of the device). Examples of such circuit-related device behavior are: (1) the relationship between the current and voltage in a *pn* diode (one model of which is the *ideal diode equation*); and (2) the static output characteristics of bipolar transistor and MOSFET devices. In MOSFETs such output characteristics are

---

** In practice, as noted earlier, empirical values of D are used in such process simulators as SUPREM III. There is an attempt being made to develop physical based models of D.

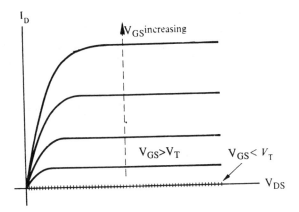

Fig. 1-6 Output I-V characteristics (I_D versus V_{DS}) of a MOSFET with V_{GS} as the parameter.

expressed as the dependence of the drain current I_D on such terminal voltages as V_{GS} and V_{DS}. Figure 1-6 is an example of a set of experimental I_D versus V_{DS} curves for a MOSFET (with V_{GS} as the parameter). An appropriate device model should be able to accurately simulate such a set of experimental I-V output characteristics.

The physically based model of semiconductor devices assumes that electrical device behavior, in general, can be simulated by solving a set of five fundamental, nonlinear, partial-differential equations (often referred to as the *classical semiconductor equations*). These constitute a complete set of equations which describe the carrier, current, and field distributions, and are written in general form as follows:

1. The Poisson equation: $-\nabla^2\varphi = \nabla\mathcal{E} = q(n - p + N_D - N_A)/\kappa_{si}\varepsilon_0$ (1 - 3)

which describes the electrostatic potential (and the electric field) within the device. (Here φ is the electrostatic potential, $\mathcal{E}$ is the electric field, and N_D and N_A are the donor and acceptor concentrations.)

2. & 3. The continuity equations for electrons and holes;

$$\partial n/\partial t = (\nabla J_n /q) - R \qquad (1 - 4a)$$

$$\partial p/\partial t = (\nabla J_p /q) - R \qquad (1 - 4b)$$

where J_n and J_p are the electron and hole current densities, respectively, and R is the net recombination rate of the carrier being considered.

4. & 5. The equations for the electron and hole current densities;

$$J_n = qn\,\mu_n\,\mathcal{E} + q\,D_n\,\nabla n \qquad (1 - 5a)$$

$$J_p = q\,p\,\mu_p\,\mathcal{E} - q\,D_p\,\nabla p \qquad (1 - 5b)$$

In the first term on the right side of Eqs. 1-5a and b the current is proportional to the electric field and thus represents the drift of carriers with the electric field. In the second term the current is proportional to the gradient of the carrier concentration, e.g., ∇n. Hence, it represents the diffusion of carriers from regions of high to low concentration. Equations 1-5 are referred to as the *drift-diffusion current equations.*

This set of equations can be solved for dc or time-domain (transient) conditions. It is generally agreed that device modeling programs can do an excellent job of simulating device characteristics provided accurate information is available on the doping concentration and the device structure.

Some of the parameters of these five equations must be obtained by solving additional auxiliary equations, including the equations that provide the mobile charge concentrations n and p in the device and the equations that yield R. For example, the equations that give the concentration of mobile charges at *equilibrium*, n_0 and p_0 (assuming Boltzmann statistics) are most frequently expressed in terms of the intrinsic carrier concentration n_i, the *Fermi energy* (also called the *Fermi level*) E_F, and the *intrinsic Fermi level* E_i, as follows:

$$n_0 = n_i \exp (E_F - E_i)/kT \quad \text{and} \quad p_0 = n_i \exp (E_i - E_F)/kT \qquad (1 - 6)$$

However, since Eq. 1-3 is expressed in terms of the electrostatic potential φ instead of the energy E, it is useful to express Eqs. 1-6 in terms of φ and the Fermi potential φ_F instead of E_i and E_F. This can be done by noting that the electrostatic potential φ is related to the potential energy by $-q\varphi = E$ (see chap. 3 for more discussion on this). In addition, the electric field $\mathcal{E}$ is defined as the negative gradient of the electrostatic potential (written in one-dimension as $\mathcal{E} = -d\varphi/dx$), and $\mathcal{E}$ can also be expressed in terms of energy as represented using the energy-band representation, $\mathcal{E} = (1/q)(dE_i/dx)$. Thus, these two terms can be equated, as $-d\varphi/dx = (1/q)(dE_i/dx)$. This means we can define φ in terms of E_i, as $\varphi = -E_i/q$, and the *Fermi potential* φ_F in terms of E_F, as $\varphi_F = -E_F/q$. This allows us to express Eqs. 1-6 in another form, namely:

$$n_0 = n_i \exp (q[\varphi - \varphi_F]/kT) \quad \text{and} \quad p_0 = n_i \exp (q[\varphi_F - \varphi]/kT) \qquad (1 - 7)$$

However, under *nonequilibrium conditions* the Fermi level parameter is not meaningful. Thus, neither Eqs. 1-6 nor 1-7 are valid in such cases. Nevertheless, in some cases of non-equilibrium it is still possible to express n and p with relationships similar to those of Eqs. 1-6 and 1-7 by defining two quantities (E_{Fn} and E_{Fp}) to replace the Fermi level in Eqs. 1-6, and another two quantities (φ_{Fn} and φ_{Fp}), to replace the Fermi potential in Eqs. 1-7. By doing this we can write:

$$n = n_i \exp [E_{Fn} - E_i]/kT = n_i \exp (q[\varphi - \varphi_{Fn}]/kT)$$
and
$$p = n_i \exp [E_i - E_{Fp}]/kT = n_i \exp (q[\varphi_{Fp} - \varphi]/kT)$$

$$(1 - 8)$$

where E_{Fn} and E_{Fp} are called the *quasi-Fermi energies* for electrons and holes, respectively, and φ_{Fn} and φ_{Fp} are the corresponding *quasi-Fermi potentials*.

The term R in Eqs. 1-4a and 1-4b must be calculated by another auxiliary equation. In such indirect bandgap semiconductors as Si and Ge the recombination process is calculated using an equation derived by Shockley, Read, and Hall (and the process itself is frequently referred to as SRH recombination). This expression is

$$R = \frac{pn - n_i^2}{\tau_p\,(n + n_i) + \tau_n\,(p + n_i)} \qquad (1-9)$$

where τ_n and τ_p are the electron and hole lifetimes (which are independent of doping concentration at low doping levels, but decrease at high doping concentrations). Empirical expressions for τ_p and τ_n are used in process simulation programs for these parameters. At low doping, the values most commonly used for τ_n and τ_p in Si are 3.95×10^{-5} sec and 3.52×10^{-5} sec, respectively.

Note that for the case of low-level injection (i.e., when the excess minority carrier concentration, $\Delta n_p = n - n_0$ or $\Delta p_n = p - p_0$, is much less than the concentration of the dominant equilibrium species), then Eq. 1-9 is reduced for *p*-type material to

$$R \sim \Delta n_p/\tau_n \qquad (1-9a)$$

and for *n*-type material to

$$R \sim \Delta p_n/\tau_p \qquad (1-9b)$$

Equations 1-9a and 1-9b state that for low-level injection conditions the net recombination rate is proportional to the excess minority carrier concentration.[*]

1.2.3 The Poisson Equation

Of the five classical semiconductor device equations, we will focus on the Poisson equation (Eq. 1-3), where φ is the electrostatic potential, q the electronic charge, $\kappa_{Si}\varepsilon_0$ the permittivity of Si, N_D the donor doping concentration, N_A the acceptor doping concentration, n the electron concentration and p the hole concentration. We single out the Poisson equation for several reasons: (1) it is a fundamental physical equation, being essentially the third Maxwell's equation; (2) it relates the electrostatic potential and electric field to the charge density in a device; (3) as noted above, it is one of the 5 coupled equations that must be solved to simulate general semiconductor device operation; and (4) in it's two-dimensional form, it is a second-order, non-linear, time-

---

[*] The current density equations (Eqs. 1-5a & b) can be derived from the even more fundamental *Boltzmann transport equation (BTE)*. However, the classical hole-current-density and electron-current-density equations listed above have been adequate for most devices down to the mid-submicron range, and have been the work-horse model in nearly all of industry for device analysis of conventional FET and bipolar structures down to about 0.5 μm. Nevertheless, in order to simulate devices with minimum feature sizes smaller than 0.5 μm (and especially as device dimensions approach 0.25 μm and smaller),[6] it may be necessary to invoke the full BTE instead. This topic is beyond the scope of our text.

invariant, partial-differential equation. This makes it another useful example of a PDE that can be solved with numerical analysis techniques - in this case involving only spatial discretization.*

1.3 CLOSED-FORM ANALYTICAL SOLUTIONS *VERSUS* NUMERICAL SOLUTIONS OF THE PDEs THAT ARE THE PHYSICALLY BASED MODELS OF MICROELECTRONICS

Assume we have a differential equation that represents the quantitative physically based model of some phenomenon in a device or process. To obtain quantitative predictive results from the model it must be possible to solve the equation. Generally, two approaches are available for obtaining a solution: (1) using analytic techniques (i.e., techniques from calculus) to find a *closed-form analytical solution;* and (2) finding the solution using *numerical analysis.* Let us compare the solutions obtained using each of these approaches, first from a mathematical point of view, and then from a perspective of their usefulness in solving differential equations for simulation applications.

1.3.1 Closed-Form Analytical Solutions - Mathematical Aspects

A closed-form analytical solution of a differential equation is determined using *analytic* techniques, such as separation of variables followed by integration.** An analytic solution may consist of one or more functions from elementary calculus (including rational algebraic, trigonometric, exponential, or logarithmic functions). It may also take the form of an infinite series. In either case, when an analytic solution is substituted into the differential equation, an identity results. The analytic solution also makes it possible to find the *exact value* of the dependent variable for a given value of the independent variable. Finally, if the analytical solution consists of a continuous function over the range of interest, it can be used to provide a continuous set of dependent variable values.

1.3.2 Numerical Solutions - Mathematical Aspects

A numerical solution of a differential equation is obtained using numerical techniques instead of employing the techniques of calculus. For example, when an integration is called for in an analytic procedure used for obtaining the solution of a differential equation, a numerical approximation to the integration step may be used instead. Or, the differentials of the differential equation being solved may be replaced with finite difference expressions. Upon making such changes to the differential equation, the

* Note that Maxwell's third equation, $\nabla D = \rho$ becomes the Poisson equation if the permittivity is constant throughout the device region.

** *Analytic* is defined as: using, subjected to, or capable of being subjected to a methodology of calculus.

resulting equation can be solved using only algebraic techniques. Solutions obtained using such approaches give an *approximate* value of the dependent variable for a given value of the independent variable(s). In addition, values of the dependent variable are only provided for the discrete values of the independent variable chosen. However, if the error of the approximate value of the numerical solution is zero, the analytical and numerical solutions are identical. In chap. 2 we describe the numerical techniques used to model the PDEs of semiconductor devices and processes.

1.3.3 Comparing the Analytical and Numerical Solutions in Semiconductor Simulation Applications

Now that we have compared the two solution types from a mathematical perspective we can comment on their roles in simulation applications. First, based on the previous discussion, it is obvious that if an analytical solution of a PDE can be discovered, and this solution is found to give good agreement with experimental observations of the device or process phenomenon being simulated, the analytic solution of the *PDE in that form* will provide the most accurate simulation. However, if approximations had to be made to reduce the PDE to its simplified form so that an analytic solution could be found, and these approximations do not realistically reflect the actual conditions of the problem being considered, then the analytic solution may not provide the most accurate simulation of that problem. In that case, solutions obtained using numerical analysis offer the possibility of providing more accurate predictive capability.

That is, we stated that the numerical solution is an approximation of the analytical solution. But, if approximations with respect to actual device or process phenomena had to be made to simplify the PDE so that an analytic solution could be obtained, the analytic solution in that case *is also in fact approximate.* When the PDE is posed in a form which invokes fewer of these approximations, it more realistically mirrors the actual conditions in the device or process being simulated. In that case, it may no longer be possible to find an analytic solution of the PDE. To solve the equation in that form, numerical analysis is the only option. It is true that to obtain sufficient accuracy, extensive computation may be needed, but it will be possible for a solution to be obtained. For this reason, in simulation applications that require high accuracy in the submicron era, the closed-form analytic models are tending to be replaced by numerically obtained simulations - that is by models which can more accurately represent realistically complex problems: e.g., nonlinear, time-dependent conditions. In the last sections of this chapter we indicate under what circumstances the analytic solutions become inadequate for the most accurate device and process simulations.

1.3.4 Role of Analytical Solutions in Submicron Semiconductor Technology

Do not be misled from the above discussion that numerically obtained solutions will eliminate the need for analytic solutions in semiconductor technology. That is, analytic solutions still play many important roles in both visualization and simulation applications. First, analytic solutions can normally be obtained with much less computation than can numerical solutions. (In the extreme solving three-dimensional forms of the semiconductor PDEs may even require the use of a supercomputer to obtain a numerical solution. Even the numerical solution of coupled two-dimensional PDEs can be a very computationally intensive task.) Thus, where it is possible to find analytic solutions that provide reasonably accurate predictive capability, they will be used. Several examples include:

1. Use of engineering (analytic based) models to predict I-V behavior of devices in circuit analysis simulators (SPICE). When simulating the transient response of digital circuits, the device currents and capacitances between various nodes for a given bias condition must be carried out thousands of times. Thus, a model that is computationally efficient, yet sufficiently accurate, must be available so that such a simulation can be quickly and inexpensively performed. Simple analytical models resulting from applying various approximations to the basic semiconductor device equations are widely used to calculate I_D to a first order. Higher order effects are then accounted for through the introduction of physical and empirical parameters into these models. These model parameters are optimally extracted from the data in a curve fitting fashion as described in section 1.1.1.2. Hence, such models are referred to as semiempirical analytical models. We will discuss the topic of the I_D models for MOSFETs in more detail in chaps. 3, 4, and 5.

2. Use of the analytical models to select device and process conditions in which it is known that such models provide good agreement with measured data. For example, such solutions may provide a reasonably accurate first order approximation of the doping profiles for some diffusion processes (e.g., a low-dose implant and subsequent drive-in). Such low-concentration profiles may be encountered in such applications as channel and field implants.

3. During the exploratory phase of new process or device development it is generally useful to examine the problem from the simplest and most intuitive point of view. In such cases, accurate simulation is not as important as short computation times, as the latter will permit a larger experimental space to be explored. If analytical models are available, they can be used for this purpose. Such models may yield both an initial estimate of the magnitude of the process parameters to be used and a simple picture of the physics behind the technique. Such insight may also help to design a numerical analysis approach that is computationally efficient. For example, initial simulations in one-dimension may be adequate to predict trends rather than exact values when various options are being examined. At that point the use of complex 2-D simulation programs could be a waste of time and computer resources. The use of more sophisticated tools might only be needed after the feasibility of an idea has been demonstrated.

4. Analytic solutions can also provide insight into the mechanisms being simulated that cannot be easily gained from examining numerical solutions. That is, by inspecting the mathematical function that represents the analytical model, trends about the phenomena being modeled can often easily be visualized. While some of these insights may be quantitatively inaccurate, they are usually qualitatively correct. On the other hand, numerical analysis solves the differential equation that governs the phenomenon being examined one point at a time. Thus, it may not be easy to use such a solution to visualize trends for cases which have not been numerically treated.

In this sense analytic solutions can serve as a sort of bridge between the purely qualitative models and the more accurate simulation results obtained from numerical analysis. This is especially important when topics as complex as diffusion in semiconductors are first being introduced to students. For example, the Gaussian function as a representative of the diffusion profile after drive-in (and the concepts of $\sqrt{Dt}$ and the dependence of D on temperature), help develop a picture of the evolution of a doping profile with time and temperature T during a diffusion process. It also gives a rough visualization of the fact that the surface concentration decreases with time, and that the profile broadens.

It should also be noted that new analytic models can also be developed with the aid of numerical analysis techniques. Let us illustrate this procedure by considering the development of an analytical model of the threshold-voltage shift in a MOSFET as a function of decreasing channel length.

To begin, we recall that numerical analysis can be used to obtain solutions of the Poisson equation in two-dimensions. Such solutions may be employed to calculate the change in threshold voltage of short-channel devices. Comparisons of the numerically simulated results with experimentally measured shifts in V_T are then used to confirm the accuracy of the numerical simulation. This establishes the numerical simulation-based solutions as benchmarks for calculating V_T changes in short channel MOSFETs.

With this quantitative benchmark in hand, simplifications of the Poisson equation can be sought which will allow closed-form analytic solutions to be obtained. The analytic solutions of such simplified forms of the Poisson equation are then used to calculate the shift in threshold voltage as L is decreased. These results are compared to the results obtained from the numerical analysis to establish the range of parameters over which the analytic model is likely to yield accurate estimates of the V_T shift. If good agreement over some range of values is found, the analytic model developed becomes a computationally efficient vehicle for simulating the change V_T shift in short channel devices over that range of channel lengths and bias voltages.

The development of analytic solutions in this manner is described in more detail in chap. 5, where a variety of analytical solutions for such short-channel MOSFET effects as V_T roll-off (and roll-up), drain-induced barrier lowering (DIBL), gate-electric-field-induced carrier mobility degradation, and channel length modulation are presented.

1.3.5 Analytic Solutions of Fick's 2nd Law Equation

If the Fick's 2nd Law equation is simplified to a one-dimensional form, and the diffusion coefficient is constant everywhere throughout the device region during the time of the diffusion process, the more general form of the equation (Eq. 1-1) is reduced to the following form:

$$\partial C(x,t)\,/\partial t\ =\ D\,\partial^2 C(x,t)\,/\partial x^2 \qquad\qquad (1 - 10)$$

The equation in this form is known as the one-dimensional *simple* Fick's 2nd Law equation, and we observe this is a *linear* partial-differential equation. Analytical solutions are available for the simple Fick's 2nd Law equation under certain boundary and initial conditions. Two of these closely approximate the conditions that exist in two important types of diffusion processes that are performed during IC fabrication.

These two boundary conditions that permit a closed-form solution of the simple Fick's equation to be obtained are: (1) the impurity concentration at the surface of the Si (i.e., $x = 0$) during diffusion is constant at a value C_S, and the impurity concentration at large distances from the surface (i.e., $x = \infty$) is zero; and (2) the total concentration of impurities in the Si remains constant during the diffusion, and the impurity concentration at large distances from the surface (i.e., $x = \infty$) is again zero. The initial condition at $t = 0$ for both cases is the same; namely $C(x, 0) = 0$ (which states that the dopant concentration in the host semiconductor is initially zero). The solution for these two cases which satisfies both the initial and boundary conditions is:

$$C(x,t) = C_S\ \mathrm{erfc}[x/2\sqrt{Dt}] \qquad\qquad (1 - 11)$$

for the constant concentration C_S case, and

$$C(x,t) = C_S\,[\exp(-x^2/4Dt)] = (Q/\sqrt{\pi Dt})[\exp(-x^2/4Dt)] \qquad (1 - 12)$$

for the case of a constant dose Q per cm^2 of impurity in the silicon. The former case, in which Eq. 1-11 is called the *erfc solution* has been used to model the so-called *chemical predeposition* process, while the latter, in which Eq. 1-12 is called a *Gaussian solution*, the so-called *drive-in* step. These concentration distributions can be plotted on both linear and logarithmic scales, normalized to the surface concentration. As an example, this is done for three different diffusion times in Figs. 1-7a and 1-7b for Eq. 1-11, and in Figs. 1-8a and 1-8b for Eq. 1-12. Note that the penetration depth of the dopant increases only as the square root of the diffusion time (e.g., as shown in Fig. 1-8b, to double the depth of a given value of $C(x)$, one must quadruple the diffusion time). It is also important to realize that in the case of the Gaussian distribution we have also introduced the time variable into our other normalizing parameter, the surface concentration C_S.

We should also note that both the erfc Eq. 1-11 and the Gaussian distribution Eq. 1-12 are functions of a normalized distance $x/2\sqrt{Dt}$. Thus, if we also normalize the dopant concentration with the surface concentration, each distribution can be represented with a single curve valid for all diffusion times. Such normalized impurity concentrations are shown in Fig. 1-9a on a linear axis, and in Fig. 1-9b on a log axis. The combination of parameters $2\sqrt{Dt}$ used to normalize the x-axis of Figs. 1-9a and 1-9b represents the characteristic diffusion length associated with a particular diffusion cycle and describes the depth of penetration of the dopant.

The closed-form solutions given by Eqs. 1-11 and 1-12 were widely used to model dopant diffusion in silicon devices during the 1960's. At that time bipolar device

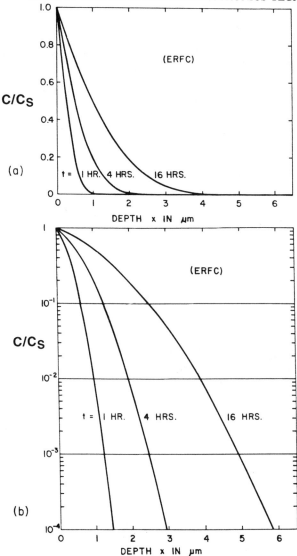

Fig. 1-7 Normalized impurity-concentration erfc profiles versus distance into the substrate for three different diffusion times (a) Linear presentation. (b) Log-linear presentation.

technology was still dominant and was being used to fabricate medium-scale-integration (MSI) ICs.* The bipolar devices were fabricated with a double-diffused process, and the analytical solutions of the 1-D simple Fick's 2nd Law equation given above were used to predict the process dependencies of such double-diffused profiles. For these early

---

* MOS technology had not yet overcome its isolation and threshold control issues, and for systems designed with MSI parts, the superior off-chip drive capabilities of the bipolar transistor provided critical system leverage.

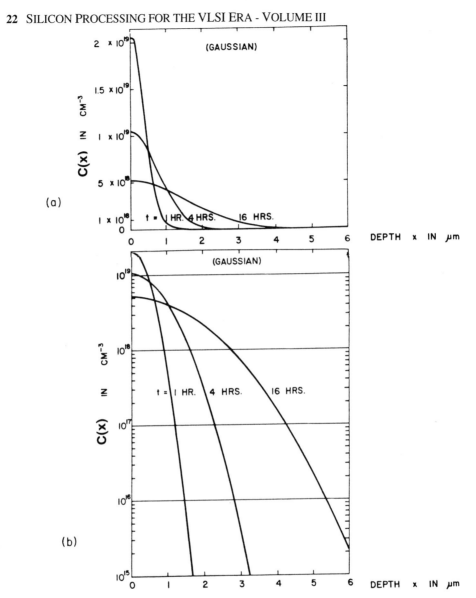

Fig. 1-8 Gaussian impurity-concentration erfc profiles versus distance into the substrate for three different diffusion times (a) Linear presentation. (b) Log-linear presentation.

bipolar device structures, the analytical solutions given by Eqs. 1-11 and 1-12 could predict the device impurity doping profiles (i.e., the one-dimensional variation of C versus depth at the conclusion of a particular diffusion process) with reasonable accuracy.**

** This was due primarily to the relatively gross feature sizes of those devices. This meant that: (1) The junction depths were sufficiently deep that the dopant surface concentrations during drive-in were reduced below the intrinsic carrier concentrations at the process

1.3.6 Analytical Solutions of the One-Dimensional Form of the Poisson Equation in the Depletion Approximation

In three- (or even two-) dimensional form, an exact analytical solution of the Poisson equation is not possible. Instead, the equation can only be approximately solved using numerical methods. Nevertheless, by making a number of assumptions (which happen to be appropriate for some important semiconductor device structures), the equation can be simplified to a degree where closed-form solutions can be obtained. This was the approach used for modeling large-dimension FET device structures in the early days of the semiconductor industry. It is, in fact, still the basis of the device equations used to

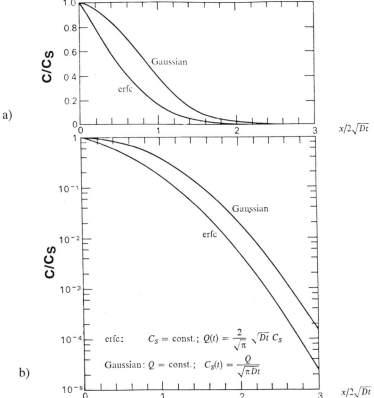

Fig. 1-9 The erfc and Gaussian impurity distributions versus normalized distance $x/2\sqrt{Dt}$. Note that by using this representation these distributions can be represented with a single curve valid for all diffusion times. C/C_S is displayed (a) on a linear axis, and (b) on a log axis.

* (cont.) temperatures. Thus, the approximations invoked to allow the Gaussian solution were valid during a large fraction of the diffusion time; (2) In planar transistor structures whose minimum feature sizes exceed 5 μm, two-dimensional diffusion effects occur over such a small fraction of the total device area that they have only a minor impact on measured device behavior. Hence, they can be ignored in the model.

model long-channel MOSFETs (as we shall describe in detail in chap. 4). Here let us briefly discuss the simplification procedure is it applies to case of MOS device structures.

In the ideal MOS *capacitor* structure described in chap. 3 (Fig. 3-1), the electric field is normal to the oxide surface, and hence only a one-dimensional variation in electrostatic potential φ exists (i.e., $\partial\varphi/\partial y$ and $\partial\varphi/\partial z = 0$). In addition, if we assume: (1) uniform doping exists in the semiconductor; (2) ($N_A \gg N_D$); and (3) we invoke the depletion approximation ($n = p = 0$ in the depletion region), the Poisson equation in the semiconductor region of a MOS capacitor, under the oxide under depletion biasing becomes

$$d^2\varphi/dx^2 = q\, N_A/\kappa_{si}\, \varepsilon_0 \qquad (1\text{-}13)$$

The Poisson equation in this form is an ordinary, linear differential equation that can easily be integrated twice to yield a closed-form solution of $\varphi(x)$ in the semiconductor. That is, assuming $\varphi = 0$ far below the wafer surface (e.g., at $x = \infty$),

$$\varphi(x) = \varphi_{surf}\,(1 - x/d)^2 \qquad (1\text{-}14)$$

where φ_{surf} is the value of $\varphi(x)$ at the surface ($x = 0$), and d is the depletion depth (i.e., the depth to which the mobile charge density is negligible, or where

$$d = [\kappa_{si}\varepsilon_0(2\varphi_{surf})/kTN_A]^{1/2} \qquad (1\text{-}15)$$

Although Eq. 1-14 was derived here for the case of a MOS capacitor, we shall see in chap. 4 that the solution of Eq. 1-13 as given by Eq. 1-14 is also used to calculate the electrostatic potential in long-channel MOSFETs, even when $V_{DS} \neq 0$. This is justified in such devices by invoking the *gradual-channel approximation* (see section 4.3.1, chap 4). When this approximation is valid the simplified MOSFET device models are able to simulate the experimentally observed drain current (I_D) values quite closely. However, as devices shrink to sizes in which they have submicron gate lengths, this approximation is no longer satisfied. In such cases if the simplified equation is used to simulate I_D, agreement with experimental results is poor, and the model must be modified to account for the discrepancy between predicted and measured behavior.

1.4 CIRCUMSTANCES UNDER WHICH THE ANALYTIC SOLUTIONS OF THESE PDES BECOME INADEQUATE FOR SIMULATION PURPOSES

1.4.1 The Inadequacy of the Analytic Solutions of Fick's 2nd Law Equation for Simulating Diffusion in Submicron Device Structures

If dopant diffusion exhibited only simple behavior, then erfc-type concentration profiles after constant-source depositions and approximately Gaussian-shaped profiles after ion implantation and diffusion would be found in silicon substrates. However, careful

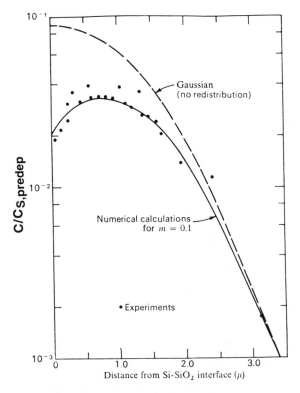

Fig. 1-10 Redistribution of diffused boron layer after thermal oxidation.[7]

comparison of experiments with the doping profiles predicted using the two classical solutions (Eqs. 1-11 and 1-12) revealed that several physical effects occurring during diffusion caused the profiles to be significantly different from those predicted by the closed-form functions. Furthermore, it became evident that such physical effects would play an increasingly greater role in the diffusion process as planar-process-fabricated device structures (both bipolar and MOS) were shrunk to the micron range and smaller. Some examples of the effects that cause the experimental doping profiles to deviate from those predicted by Eqs. 1-11 and 1-12, are:

1. If an oxide layer is grown during the drive-in step, the preference of the boron to be in SiO_2 rather than silicon gives rise to a doping profile in which the concentration of boron near the silicon surface is much lower than that predicted by the Gaussian solution (as shown in Fig. 1-10).

2. When the doping concentration is higher than the intrinsic carrier concentration at the diffusion temperature, the doping profile after predeposition does not match the erfc profile predicted by Eq. 1-11, but instead exhibits a form as shown Fig. 1-10 for the case of boron diffusion. This apparently occurs because D becomes a function of the concentration $(D = f[C])$, and the simple

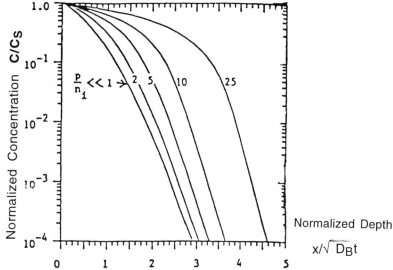

Fig. 1-11 Measured boron doping profile after predeposition step and the profile predicted using the erfc solution of the diffusion equation.[10] Reprinted with permission of the American Physical Society.

form of Fick's 2nd Law is no longer valid. Instead, the equation that must be solved is $\partial C/\partial t = \partial/\partial x [D(C) \, \partial C/\partial x]$, which is a non-linear PDE).

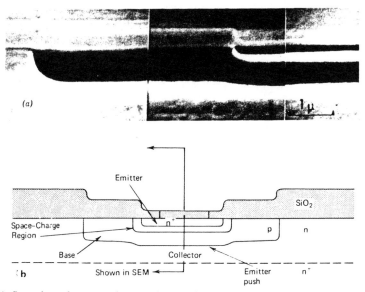

Fig. 1-12 (a) Scanning electron micrograph showing cross section through a bipolar transistor. (b) Sketch identifying the regions shown. The boron-doped base region has been pushed ahead (emitter push) by the concentration-dependent diffusion effects associated with heavy phosphorus doping in the emitter.[11] Reprinted with permission of John Wiley & Sons.

3. In the cross-section of a typical double-diffused bipolar device having a phosphorus-doped emitter (Fig. 1-12), another diffusion-related disparity is observed. The base-collector diffusion depth is deeper under the emitter than under the base regions. This indicates that the boron diffusion is affected by the high-concentration phosphorus emitter region (i.e., the boron diffusivity is now a function of the phosphorus concentration).

In device regions where these (and other) effects cause the diffusion coefficient to become position dependent, or where diffusion must be simulated as a two-dimensional effect, numerical methods with the aid of computers must be used to obtain solutions.

1.4.2 The Inadequacy of Using a One-Dimensional Form of the Poisson Equation and the Depletion Approximation to Model Submicron MOSFET Behavior.

In submicron MOSFETs the approximations used to reduce the Poisson equation to a one-dimensional form given as Eq. 1-13 are not valid, and thus Eq. 1-13 does not accurately model the electrostatic potential in submicron MOSFETs. First, in submicron MOSFETs the electric field has lateral components that cannot be ignored when a non-zero drain-source bias is applied. Second, the doping in the channel region is usually not uniform with depth below the oxide. Finally, the mobile charge concentrations in the depletion region are not zero (i.e., the depletion approximation does not hold, even when the device is biased in depletion).

Instead, the Poisson equation in at least two-dimensional form must be used to simulate φ and $\mathcal{E}$ in submicron MOSFETs. The 2-D form of the Poisson equation under the above conditions for the semiconductor region of the MOSFET is

$$\frac{\partial^2 \varphi\,(x,y)}{\partial x^2} + \frac{\partial^2 \varphi\,(x,y)}{\partial y^2} = \left(\frac{\rho}{\kappa_{Si}\varepsilon_0}\right) \tag{1 - 16}$$

or

$$\frac{\partial^2 \varphi}{\partial x^2} + \frac{\partial^2 \varphi}{\partial y^2} = -\left(\frac{q}{\kappa_{Si}\varepsilon_0}\right)\left[-N_A + p_{po}\,e^{-q\varphi/kT} + N_D - n_{po}\,e^{q\varphi/kT}\right] \tag{1 - 17}$$

Note that the Poisson equation in this form relates the space-charge potential of mobile and fixed charges with mobile charge densities given by Boltzmann statistics. In this form it is a second-order, exponentially non-linear, partial-differential equation. The solution of Eq. 1-17 [i.e., $\varphi\,(x,y)$ in the semiconductor region of the MOSFET] for an appropriate set of boundary conditions can only be found using numerical analysis. We will discuss such solution techniques of this equation in chap. 2.

REFERENCES

1. R.S. Fair, *Ext. Abs. Electrochem. Soc. Mtg,* Spring 1989, Abs. No. 141, May 1989, p. 197.
2. A. Reisman et al., *J. Electron. Mat.* **16**, p. 45, (1987)

3. C.P. Ho et al., "VLSI Process Modeling - SUPREM III," *IEEE Trans. Electron Dev.,* November 1983, p. 1438.

4. R.S. Fair, "Concentration Profiles of Diffused Dopants in Silicon,", in *Impurity Doping Processes in Silicon,* ed. F.F. Y. Wang, North-Holland, Amsterdam, 1981, chap. 7.

5. R.S. Fair, "Low-Thermal Budget Process Modeling with the PREDICT Computer Program," *IEEE Trans. Electron Dev.,* March 1988, p. 285.

6. D.C. Cole et al., "The Use of Simulation in Semiconductor Technology Development," *Solid-State Electronics,* **33**, No. 6, June 1990, p. 591.

7. T. Kato and Y. Nishi, *Jap. Jnl. Appl. Phys.,* **3**, 377 (1964).

8. R. Dutton, "Modeling Silicon Integrated Circuits," *IEEE Trans. Electron Dev.,* **ED-30**, September 1983, p. 975.

9. E.S. Meieran and T.I. Kamins, *Solid-State Electronics,* **16**, 545 (1973).

10. P.M. Fahey, P.B. Griffin, and J.D. Plummer, "Point Defects and Dopant Diffusion in Silicon," *Rev. Mod. Phys.,* April 1989.

11. R.S. Muller and T.I. Kamins, *Device Electronics for Integrated Circuits,* 2nd Ed., New York, John Wiley & Sons, 1986.

PROBLEMS

1. (a) Describe the difference between physically based and empirically based models. (b) Describe the difference between an analytical solution and a numerical solution of the partial differential equation which serves as the model of some process or device phenomenon. Elaborate on the perspective that many of the so-called physically based models of process and device phenomena should more aptly be termed hybrid (empirical-physical) models, i.e., insofar as they employ both physical models and empirically determined parameter values.

2. The intrinsic diffusion coefficient for boron in silicon is 2×10^{-14} cm^2/sec at 1000°C. Use this fact and the definition of D which states that $D = a(\Delta x)^2$ [where Δx is the lattice spacing in silicon, and a is the fraction of atoms in the volume of silicon (per unit area of lattice multiplied by a thickness Δx) which will move per unit time into an adjacent volume], to estimate the rate at which boron atoms move from lattice site to lattice site in Si at 1000°C.

3 The diffusion coefficient of boron in silicon can be written as $D_0 \exp(-E_a/kT)$, where D_0 is 2 cm^2/sec, E_a is 3.5 eV, and $k = 8.62 \times 10^{-5}$ eV/K. Using this information, verify the value of D given in Problem 1.

4. Assume that inversion in a MOS-C occurs when the surface potential is twice the value of What is the maximum depletion width at room temperature where the *p*-type Si is doped at $N_A = 10^{16}$ cm^{-2}?

5. Calculate $\varphi(x)$ versus x from x = 0 to x = d at 0.1 μm intervals for the structure given in Problem 4 when a gate bias is applied that just causes inversion. Plot these values, and compare with the plot shown in Fig. 3.9.

CHAPTER 2

NUMERICAL METHODS FOR SOLVING
THE PARTIAL DIFFERENTIAL EQUATIONS
WHICH MODEL THE PHYSICS OF SUBMICRON
DEVICES AND PROCESSES

As described in chap. 1, the process and device models employed during the early days of the semiconductor industry were either: (1) *empirically based* or; (2) *based on simplified physical equations.* That is, one-dimensional forms of the fundamental differential equations (such as the Poisson equation or the diffusion equation) were used as the *quantitative physically based models* because exact closed-form solutions of such simplified equations exist, and these analytical functions can be evaluated without the aid of computers. However, it was also pointed out that such closed-form analytical solutions are limited in scope and applicability. Specifically, such elementary models become inadequate for predicting the behavior of submicron processes and devices. The simplifying approximations that permit the partial differential equations (PDEs) to be reduced to one-dimensional, linear, differential-equation forms (for which closed-form solutions exist) no longer match the actual conditions that exist in submicron devices.

Instead, to obtain accurate predictive capability in the submicron era it has become necessary to solve the PDEs in their nonlinear form in two or three dimensions. The only way to obtain the solutions of such PDEs is to use numerical analysis[1-4,20] - performed with the aid of high-speed digital computers, interactive computer graphics, and advanced discrete mathematical analysis methods. Unlike closed-form solutions, numerical solutions are not limited by the complexity of the differential equations or by the physical model they represent.

Some may still claim that numerical solutions of differential equations are inaccurate because they are merely an approximation to the exact solution. However - as was pointed out in chap. 1 - this view neglects to mention that the so-called exact solutions are generally constrained by various assumptions and simplifications. On the other hand, the accuracy obtained when using numerical methods is limited only by the power of the computer being used. While some numerical simulation applications require the use of supercomputers, simulation packages have been developed in recent years which are capable of giving quite reasonable results on the more powerful desk-top computers and workstations.

The advantage of using numerical methods lies in their versatility and simplicity. Thus, it is now possible to tackle the most complex of engineering problems for which solutions were nowhere in sight even a few decades ago. It is likely that the semiconductor industry will rely ever more heavily on this type of simulation as the real cost of computing power continues to decrease.

Despite the fact that numerical analysis of process and device equations has become a basic methodology of research and development engineers, most textbooks on IC fabrication and device physics still focus their presentations on the closed-form models mentioned above. We have noted that this approach is no longer sufficient, and that results obtainable only from numerical solutions must now be used to explain process and device behavior. From this perspective it is important that the reader has some insight into the methods used in numerical analysis. We have therefore decided to include this chapter at the outset of the book as an introduction to the topic.

We also recognize that the users of the computer simulation programs are generally not specialists in most of the aspects involved with the procedure of numerical analysis. This is not surprising, considering the complexity of the assumptions, algorithms, and implementations of the programs they use. So, to impart some flavor of numerical analysis without overwhelming the reader with mathematical complexity, the discussion will be kept at a very basic level. However, a list of references is provided for those who wish to probe deeper.

The Synergy Between Submicron Devices & the Capability of Simulating their Behavior. The mathematical methods used to discretize the differential equations and to solve the large number of simultaneous discrete equations that result, require the manipulation of massive amounts of data. Hence, in practice, numerical analysis can only be carried out with the aid of high-speed computer hardware as well as software packages that have the ability to: (1) represent the structures of the devices in the computer; (2) discretize the appropriate differential equations that describe the process or device behavior; (3) solve the resulting set of discretized algebraic equations; and (4) display the solution results in a manner that allows the user to best interpret them (e.g., in tabular, graphical, contour plot, or 3-D-perspective form). Furthermore, such software packages can only be used effectively in device and process design by making the numerical computations transparent to the device or process engineer - while still allowing any interaction with the data. Currently available simulation programs leave the engineer free to focus on design issues instead of the numerical algorithms. Usually, the engineer need only understand of the physics of device or process to apply the simulation programs accurately. Nevertheless, by acquiring some knowledge of the numerical methods used in such simulation software packages, one becomes a much more astute user of such software.

If used properly, simulation can help in cutting development costs. One opinion is that as much as 40% cost saving is possible.[2] However, the cost savings depends considerably on the skill of the persons using the simulation programs. That is, to obtain the maximum cost savings, experience and insight are still important. This is because the following tasks must be carried out by the user of the programs: (1) correctly specifying the relevant regions to be simulated in the complicated device structures; (2) selecting the appropriate material parameters and models; (3) varying appropriate process and device operating conditions to obtain optimum device performance; and (4) ensuring that accurate numerical answers are produced. If these tasks are not competently performed, the results of the simulation may either be less accurate, or the costs will be excessive. In addition, a basic understanding of the physics incorporated in the simulation program is helpful to the user in understanding the limitations of computer program. One of the goals of this text is provide such an understanding of the process and device physics.

The ability to accurately simulate submicron processes and behavior is based on a fascinating synergistic linkage between the advances in simulation of semiconductor devices and processes and improvements in computer power. That is, these two endeavors influence and complement each other. Simulating the fabrication and behavior of semiconductor devices aids in developing smaller and faster devices, which in turn, improves available computational resources. Greater computing power means more accurate simulations can be constructed, which are presently needed as devices shrink to submicron regimes, thereby requiring new physical effects to be taken into account.

2.1 NUMERICAL SOLUTIONS OF DIFFERENTIAL EQUATIONS

As we noted in chap. 1, the solution of some differential equations can be expressed in the form of analytical closed-form expressions. An example is Eq. 1-10, which is a solution of the one-dimensional Poisson equation of the form of Eq. 1-9. On the other hand, there are many differential equations for which no solution exists as a simple closed-form expression. A method for obtaining an approximate solution of such equations is through a numerical procedure. For example, for the following differential equation there is no simple formula (in terms of elementary functions)

$$\frac{dy}{dx} = (x^2 - y^2) \tag{2-1}$$

However, one way to obtain a solution is to replace the differential equation by the *difference equation*

$$\Delta y = (x^2 - y^2) \Delta x \tag{2-2}$$

For the solution starting at (0,2) (i.e., which represents a specific boundary condition for this equation) - that is, $y = 2$ for $x = 0$ - we select a Δx, say 0.1, and compute $\Delta y = (0 - 4)(0.1) = -0.4$, so that our next point is (0.1, 1.6). Here, with the same Δx, we find $\Delta y = (0.01 - 2.56)(0.1) = -0.255$, so that our next point is (0.2, 1.345). Thus, the value of y at each selected point x can be approximately computed using this method. The results of such a process are shown in Table 2-1 and Fig. 2-1.

SOLUTION OF $y' = x^2 - y^2$ WITH $\Delta x = 0.1$

x	y	x^2	y^2	$x^2 - y^2$	$\Delta y = (x^2 - y^2)\Delta x$
0	2	0	4	-4	-0.4
0.1	1.6	0.01	2.56	-2.55	-0.255
0.2	1.345	0.04	1.81	-1.77	-0.177
0.3	1.168	0.09	1.36	-1.27	-0.127
0.4	1.041	0.16	1.08	-0.92	-0.092
0.5	0.949	–	–	–	–

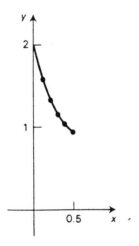

Fig. 2-1 Solutions of $dy/dx = x^2 - y^2$ found numerically, as in Table 2-1.

   The simple numerical procedure illustrated above (i.e., finding the particular solution of a differential equation by replacing it with a difference equation, and then solving the difference equation numerically) is known as the *Euler method* of numerically solving differential equations. The Euler method, or some variant of it, is widely applied. To improve the accuracy of the approximate solutions obtained, one can decrease the size of Δx. The procedure can also be generalized to higher order differential equations. We will describe how similar numerical procedures can be used to solve the PDEs that are the physically based models of IC processes and devices.

2.2 NUMERICAL METHODS FOR SOLVING NONLINEAR PARTIAL DIFFERENTIAL EQUATIONS

Process and device simulators calculate values of solution variables at discrete locations within a domain. If these variables also change with time the solution at each location must also be determined at each discrete time interval. In process simulators the concentrations of dopants at each location and time step are usually the quantities being sought, whereas in device simulators it is the electrostatic potential φ and the mobile carrier concentrations n and p that are the quantities being determined. The values of φ, n, and p may then be used to calculate the currents flowing in the devices. The discrete points within the domain being simulated form the nodes of a mesh. Relationships between the values at discrete points are established by discretization procedures. The nonlinear coupling between equations is handled by an iteration strategy that involves solving sequences of linear subproblems. As a result, the numerical performance of a device simulator is determined by the combination of the characteristics of the mesh, the discretization procedure, the nonlinear iteration strategy, and the linear system solvers.

The overall approach to solving nonlinear PDEs using numerical analysis is as follows:

1. An appropriate grid for the device domain under consideration is specified, i.e., the domain is divided up into a sufficiently large number of discrete regions. If the PDE is also time dependent, the time interval of the process or device effect being analyzed is also broken up into a number of sufficiently small time increments.

2. The differential equation is transformed into an algebraic equation which is an approximation of the original differential equation. This allows a discrete algebraic equation to be written for each grid location or discrete region.

3. The resulting set of discrete equations is organized into a standard matrix format suitable for computer manipulation to solve the equations.

4. If these discrete equations are nonlinear, they must first be linearized.

5. The linearized set of equations are then solved, using linear matrix solution techniques.

6. If a time-dependent PDE is being solved, the time is advanced by an incremental step after the linearized equations have been solved for the previous time step. The PDE is then solved again at all the grid locations for the new time step, using the previous solution to find the solution during the next time interval. At the end of the last time increment, the variable values at each grid location represent the solution of the PDE at that time.

7. The final solutions of the PDE at each of the grid locations is finally processed into a form that is either: (a) suitable for visualization by the user; or (b) suitable as the input to the next process step or device event in the simulation, or as input into another simulator.

The balance of the chapter is devoted to describing each of these steps in more detail.

2.3 GRID GENERATION
AND REFINEMENT PROCEDURES

The numerical solution of a PDE over some domain (i.e., the region chosen to represent the device geometry) requires that this domain be partitioned into a number of discrete subdomains. They should be small enough so that a sufficiently accurate approximation to the exact solution can be easily established over each subdomain. In the *finite difference* method, the simulation domain in two dimensions (typically a transistor cross section) is normally subdivided into regions defined by a *mesh* (or *grid*). In the simplest cases, this consists of a set of lines parallel to the coordinate axes. That is, in two-dimensions the simplest grid is a *rectangular grid*.* The PDEs are then solved only at specific, discrete locations (e.g., in two-dimensions only at the points where the lines meet), and these locations are referred to as the *nodes* (or *mesh points*).

For example, if we put NX lines parallel to the y-axis and NY lines parallel to the x-axis we get NX*NY intersection points in the domain on which an approximate solution of the PDEs is sought (e.g., if NX = 20 and NY = 30, we seek solutions at 600 points). The first and last lines in both the horizontal and vertical directions coincide with the boundaries. Figure 2-2 shows a uniform finite-difference mesh superimposed over a rectangular simulation domain. As we shall see the grid spacing may also be non-uniform in the x- and y-directions.

In the *finite element* method the domain is also subdivided into smaller regions, called *elements*. The elements need not be rectangular, and in fact the most common shape is the triangle. The unknown parameter is approximated in each finite element with a smoothly varying function, usually an interpolation polynomial.

To obtain accurate approximations using numerical analysis, the grid spacing (or finite element area) must by sufficiently small. However, if too small a grid spacing is used, computation time is unnecessarily increased. Because of the simplicity of the algorithms, many of the early simulation programs used *uniform* meshes (in which the

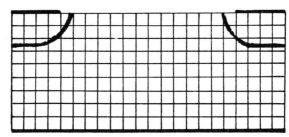

Fig. 2-2 (a) Uniform, rectangular, 2-D finite difference grid.

* The finite difference method is most easily applied to a rectangular grid, but can also be implemented on other (e.g., triangular) grids.

spacing is the same for all points). However, this benefit was gained at the expense of excessive computation time (because the smallest grid spacing needed in the entire domain had to be used everywhere). As a result, more sophisticated grid structures have been developed. The evolution of 2-D grid structures is depicted in Fig. 2-3.

The first improvement over the basic uniformly-spaced rectangular grid with a planar top surface (Fig. 2-3a) was the implementation of *variable* (or *nonuniform*) grid spacing. For example, when the potential in a MOSFET is found by solving the Poisson equation, it is observed that the variation of potential depends strongly on the local charge density. This implies that device regions where a large dopant-concentration gradient exists requires many grid points for accuracy. By using variable grid spacing many calculation points can be placed in regions of strongly varying doping concentrations (i.e., by employing a fine grid there). Conversely, fewer points can be used in less critical regions by specifying a coarse grid in such regions. A simple automatic grid generation scheme used in some second-generation MOSFET device simulators shows how non-uniform grid spacing can be exploited. That is, a fine grid is used at the silicon surface (with the minimum spacing being specified by the user) and the grid spacing is automatically increased geometrically toward the substrate. In the horizontal direction, fine grids are used in the channel and source/drain junction regions and a coarse grid in the middle of the channel (Fig. 2-3b).

The grid shown in Fig. 2-3b, however, does not permit simulation of the topology of the wafer surfaces found in VLSI devices because it assumes a *planar* surface. For example, LOCOS isolation structures and trenches cause the wafer surfaces in VLSI structures to be non-planar. To permit the effects of such non-planar structures to be simulated, a rectangular grid structure such as shown in Fig. 2-3c must be employed (together with numerical techniques that allow the PDEs to be solved on such a grid).

The incorporation of a non-planar surface does not yet produce a grid structure that is optimized for computation. That is, the disadvantage of the Cartesian grid is that when a finer mesh is needed in one region of the domain, this results in a finer mesh also being established in other parts where the extra refinement may not be necessary. On the other hand, a grid based on a triangular element shape (Fig. 2-3d) allows *local grid refinement*. That is, if a triangular grid is used, it is possible to achieve local refinement without adding unnecessary nodes in other parts of the device. Figure 2-4 illustrates how triangles which require refinement can be locally subdivided into four congruent subtriangles by joining the midpoints of the sides. These subtriangles may in turn be further refined. This permits the mesh to be refined adaptively as the computation progresses so as to limit the differences in the parameter being sought between any two mesh points to be less than a pre-specified limit. Adaptive meshes increase the complexity of the algorithm and may increase the solution time required, but provide a considerable improvement in accuracy and stability. Another advantage is that the triangular elements can work easily on arbitrary grid shapes (i.e., nonplanar device structures).

Three-dimensional device simulations require a 3-D grid. At present 3-D device simulators are actually based on 2-D device simulation programs which are applied to 3-D problems by replicating the 2-D model in the third dimension. Thus, the 3-D grid

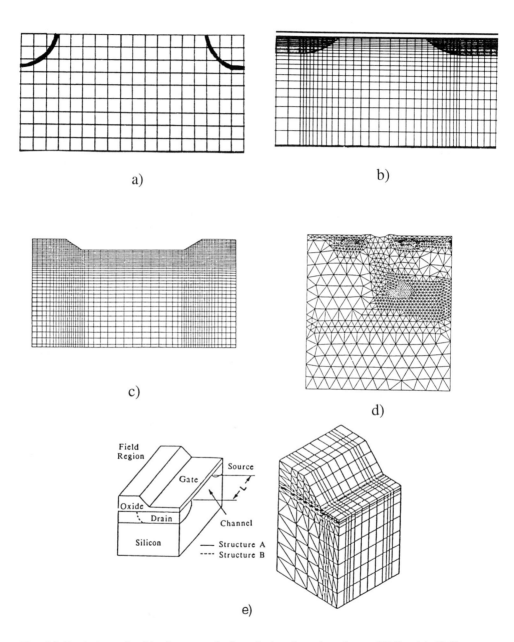

Fig. 2-3 Evolution of grids for numerical analysis of semiconductor PDEs. (a) Uniform rectangular (planar), 2-D grid. (b) Nonuniform rectangular (planar), 2-D grid. (c) Nonuniform rectangular non-planar 2-D grid. (d) Nonuniform triangular nonplanar 2-D grid. (e) Nonuniform triangular nonplanar 3-D grid.

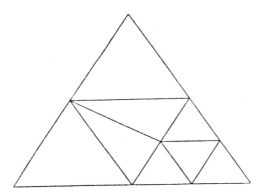

Fig. 2.4 How triangles which require refinement can be locally subdivided.

(Fig. 2-3e) is created by using a 2-D simulation program to create a 2-D triangular-based grid (as shown in Fig. 2-3d) in a single plane, and then this grid is replicated over many parallel planes to define the nodes in the third dimension. Several 3-D device simulators are commercially available, including DAVINCI™ (TMA Inc.), and HFIELDS-3D™ and THUNDER™ (Silvaco International).

The accuracy and efficiency of the discretization methods for solving PDEs can be significantly improved by using adaptive meshes. (An *adaptive mesh* is one that begins as a coarse mesh and is appropriately refined as the solution is evolved). An efficient way to implement adaptive meshes out is to provide a "self-generating" algorithm in the simulation software package. This algorithm automatically refines the grid on request by the user. The mesh is selected to minimize the discretization error and the number of mesh points required. Local refinement of the mesh may be based on the value of the truncation error or on changes in the doping concentration, potential, and carrier distributions (computed as the simulation progresses - that is, as the solution converges or as the distributions change with time). After the grid is adapted to the solution, the solution is computed again.

As an example, consider the adaptive triangular grid generator in PISCES II.[5] Starting with a list of boundary nodes specified by the user, a coarse grid is initially generated to cover the topology of the structure. This preliminary grid is then refined according to the doping profile before computing the equilibrium solution. The grid may be refined again at any time after this, using the variation of any physical variable to determine where the refinement is necessary. Note, however, that grid refinement is computationally expensive, and is thus usually updated only occasionally at the user's request. Otherwise it could completely dominate the solution time if it was invoked several times during each iteration

Figure 2-5a shows the cross-sectional geometry of an *n*-well CMOS device with trench isolation.[6] Figure 2-5b depicts the initial coarse triangular grid which was generated automatically by the device simulator Pisces-II. The formulation of the initial grid is based only on the device geometry. Using this initial grid, the triangles are refined based on the input doping profile, or later, on preliminary or intermediate solutions for the potential and carrier concentrations. Fig. 2-5c corresponds to a refined grid during the solution process, obtained after several refinements using criteria on doping and potential.

2.4 DISCRETIZATION OF DIFFERENTIAL EQUATIONS

As just discussed, the numerical solution of semiconductor process and device equations requires that the simulation domain (chosen to represent the device geometry) be partitioned into a number of discrete regions which are small enough to allow the numerical method to achieve the required level of precision. The model PDEs are then approximated in each of the subdivided regions by a set of algebraic equations which involve only values of the continuous dependent variables at discrete points in the domain. This latter process is known as *space discretization of the PDEs* and results (in general), in a large set of non-linear algebraic equations with unknowns comprised of approximations of the continuous dependent variables at discrete points.

The model PDEs can also be either *time independent* (*time invariant*) or *time dependent*. In the first case, $\partial/\partial t = 0$, and hence only space derivatives appear in the PDE. In the second case, $\partial/\partial t \neq 0$, and hence the PDEs contain time derivatives as well as space derivatives. In the latter case, the time interval being simulated must be divided into an appropriate number of time steps, and the time derivatives must be discretized. That is, the relevant PDEs must be fully discretized in both time and space. Algebraic techniques are then employed to solve the set of spatially discretized equations at each time step. The time is advanced after the spatial solution is found for a given time step, and that solution is used to the find the spatial solution at the next time step. We discuss the details of space discretization in sections 2.4.1, 2.4.2 and 2.4.3, and the aspects of time discretization in section 2.4.4.

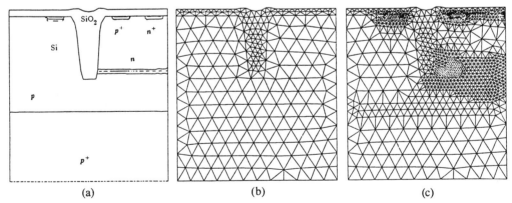

Fig. 2-5 (a) Cross-sectional geometry of an *n*-well CMOS device with trench isolation. (b) Initial coarse grid generated automatically by the device simulator PISCES. (c) Refined grid, based on either the input doping profile, or on preliminary solutions for the potential and carrier concentrations.[6] (© IEEE 1985).

2.4.1 Space Discretization

As noted earlier the continuous differential equations of IC process and device behavior must be transformed into discrete algebraic equations, so that they can be solved with numerical (i.e., algebraic) techniques. The two most important methods used for transforming these PDEs into discrete algebraic equations are the *finite difference method* and the *finite element method.* Either method can be used to discretize the *space derivatives* and they both have their advantages and drawbacks for this purpose. *Time derivatives*, however, are generally discretized using finite difference approximations.

Semiconductor simulation programs have been developed using both finite difference and finite element methods for space discretization. For example, in the process simulators SUPREM III, SUPREM IV and FINDPRO, finite differences are used to discretize the space derivatives of the diffusion equation. The device simulators GEMINI, MINIMOS, and PISCES-II also employ the finite difference method for space discretization. Programs using the finite element method for space discretization include FEDSS, FIELDAY, and some modules of SUPREM IV.

In our discussion we will provide more information on the finite difference method for space discretization. This is because the basis of finite difference schemes can be grasped in a rather straightforward manner, while the theory behind the finite element method is rather abstract (i.e., it is necessary to introduce concepts from functional analysis and variational methods in order to formulate the finite element algebraic equations). Since our intent is to introduce readers to the topics of numerical analysis (rather than to provide a rigorous treatment), we choose the simpler approaches to illustrate our examples whenever possible.

Nevertheless, it should be noted that the other numerical techniques being implemented in the latest simulation programs are also considerably more sophisticated than those used in the examples we present. Since the level of their mathematical complexity is far beyond the scope of our book, the ones we present allow the reader to gain a flavor of the techniques without being completely overwhelmed by the mathematics.

2.4.2. The Finite-Difference Method

There are also two ways in which the finite-difference technique is used to transform differential equations into their algebraic counterparts:

1. The *difference operator method*, in which the differential operators in the PDE are directly replaced by finite difference approximations.

2. The *box integration method*, in which the domain is divided into a set of subdomains, each one surrounding a node of the grid (see Appendix D). These subdomains partition the interior of the domain without overlap or exclusion. The finite difference approximation of the unknown (which in this case is the average value of the unknown over each subdomain) at each grid point (i.e., at each node) is obtained by integrating the PDE over the subdomain (i.e., the local area) surrounding the node. The integral for each node is then approximated to yield a discrete difference equation associated with each node.

We will provide more information on the *difference operator method* in this section because it is the simpler of the two. Nevertheless, finite-difference-based device simulators more often employ the *box integration method* (e.g., GEMINI and PISCES-II), primarily because it permits non-planar device structures to be handled more easily. In recognition of its importance, however, additional information on the box integration method is provided in Appendix D. This is intended as reference material for those who are interested the numerical procedures of box-integration-based device simulators.

In both methods, nevertheless, the resulting difference equations are applied at each node (except at the boundaries of the domain where boundary conditions specify the values of the unknowns at such boundary nodes), thereby relating the functional value at each node to those nearby. Consequently, a set of algebraic equations is developed which can be solved for the unknown functional values.

2.4.2.1 The Difference Operator Method.

As noted above, the approach of the *difference operator method* to solving differential equations is to replace the continuous space derivatives of the PDEs by discretized finite-difference approximations (difference expressions). This transforms the continuous PDE into an algebraic difference equation for the function at a given node. By relating the functional value of the unknown at each node to those nearby, and using these values in the finite-difference approximation expressions, a difference equation is constructed at each node of the finite difference mesh of the domain. In this fashion, a set of algebraic equations is developed which relates the value of the unknown at each node to the values at neighboring nodes. Upon applying the proper boundary and initial values, this set can then be solved using algebraic techniques for the unknown functional values at each node. By using a rectangular grid, this finite-difference method becomes particularly well-suited for treating simple device geometries.

2.4.2.2. Taylor Series.

The finite-difference expressions used to replace the differential operators in the course of discretizing a PDE can be derived from a truncated Taylor series. Since the Taylor series is also the basis of several other aspects of numerical analysis, we will briefly review the Taylor series and its properties here.

In general, the Taylor series is based on the assumption that any function can be expressed as a polynomial having an infinite number of terms. Consider the arbitrary function $f(x)$ given in Fig. 2-6. Assume also that $f(x)$ is a continuous, single-valued function of x with continuous derivatives, and has a known value $f(x_0)$ at $x = x_0$. If the functional value at a point $x = x_0 + \Delta x$ is derived, then we should be able to approximate $f(x_0 + \Delta x)$ by considering the slope of the function $df(x)/dx = f'(x)$ evaluated at $x = x_0$. Therefore the slope of the tangent line is easily evaluated in terms of the functional values $f(x_0)$ and $G(x_0 + \Delta x)$ to give

$$f'(x_0) = \frac{[G(x_0 + \Delta x) - f(x_0)]}{\Delta x}$$

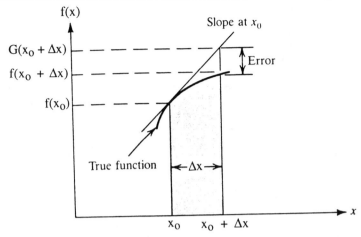

Fig. 2-6 Graphical illustration of functional approximation.

Solving for $G(x_0 + \Delta x)$ yields

$$G(x_0 + \Delta x) \;=\; \Delta x\, f'(x_0) + f(x_0). \qquad\qquad (2\text{-}3)$$

Obviously $G(x_0 + \Delta x)$ is not exactly equal to $f(x_0 + \Delta x)$: however, it can be used to approximate its value. That is,

$$f'(x_0 + \Delta x) \;=\; G(x_0 + \Delta x) \pm \text{ERROR} \qquad\qquad (2\text{-}4)$$

The reason that a $\pm$ sign is used is because if the true function is concave upward then the error is negative. Substituting Eq. 2-3 into Eq. 2-4 yields the following approximation:

$$f'(x_0 + \Delta x) \;=\; f(x_0) + \Delta x f'(x_0) \pm \text{ERROR} \qquad\qquad (2\text{-}5)$$

Note that here $f'(x_0)$ is the first derivative of the function evaluated at $x = x_0$.

The Taylor series simply states that $f(x_0 + \Delta x)$ is an infinite series containing higher derivative terms. That is, the error term can be reduced to zero if the second, third, and infinite derivatives are known at x_0. Hence

$$f(x_0 + \Delta x) = f(x_0) + \Delta x f'(x_0) + \frac{\Delta x^2}{2} f''(x_0) + \dots + \frac{\Delta x^n}{n!} f^n(x_0) + R_{n+1} \qquad (2\text{-}6)$$

where $f'(x_0)$ is the first derivative of the function evaluated at $x = x_0$, $f''(x_0)$ is the second derivative evaluated at $x = x_0$, and so on, and

$$R_{n+1} = \frac{\Delta x^{n+1}}{(n+1)!} f^{n+1}(s), \quad x_0 \le s \le x_0 + \Delta x \qquad\qquad (2\text{-}7)$$

Equation 2-6 is a Taylor series and Eq. 2-5 is then a truncated Taylor series. The term R_{n+1} is called the remainder term of the series.

2.4.2.3 One-Dimensional Finite Difference Approximations of Derivatives.

Assuming we are still dealing with the function $f(x)$ of the previous section, then $f(x_0 + \Delta x)$ can again be expressed using 2-6. The first-order discrete approximations of the first derivative $f'(x_0)$ can be found using Eq. 2-6 by truncating the series after the second term. That is, if the Taylor series is truncated after the second term, and the remaining expression is solved, for $f'(x_0)$, we get:*

$$f'(x_0) = \frac{f(x_0 + \Delta x) - f(x_0)}{\Delta x} \pm 0(\Delta x) \qquad (2-8)$$

where instead of using ERROR to denote the error term, we now use the symbol $0(\Delta x)$.**

If the Taylor series was expressed in terms of $f(x_0 - \Delta x)$, it would be written as

$$f(x_0 - \Delta x) = f(x_0) - \Delta x f'(x_0) + \frac{\Delta x^2}{2}f''(x_0) - ... - \frac{\Delta x^n}{n!}f^n(x_0) + R_{n+1} \qquad (2-9)$$

If $f'(x_0)$ was found in same manner by using Eq. 2-9 instead of Eq. 2-6, it would be expressed as

$$f'(x_0) = \frac{f(x_0 - \Delta x) - f(x_0)}{\Delta x} \pm 0(\Delta x) \qquad (2-10)$$

The symbol $0(\Delta x)$ indicates that as Δx approaches zero, the error term becomes proportional to Δx. This further implies that more accurate solutions are obtained for smaller values of Δx.

* Note that here $f'(x_0)$ is the first derivative of the function evaluated at $x = x_0$.

** If the entire Taylor series - which contains an infinite number of terms - was used to approximate a function, the error between the approximation function and the true function would be zero. However, for practical reasons (including the cost of computation), only a few terms - generally two or three - are used in the development of the derivative approximations. When the discrete approximation of a derivative is obtained from such a truncated Taylor series, the difference between the value of the true function at x_0 and that of the approximate function is known as the *error*. It is customary to express such errors in terms of the power of Δx. That is, in Eqs. 2-5 and 2-9 the error is assumed to be of the order of Δx, and is expressed as $0(\Delta x)$, whereas in Eqs. 2-11 and 2-12 the error is assumed to be of the order Δx^2 and is expressed as $0(\Delta x^2)$. This method of expressing the error allows the various forms of the difference formulas to be compared in terms of their order of error. That is, since it is almost always the case that $\Delta x \ll 1$, difference formulas having an error term of order $0(\Delta x^2)$ are more accurate than those having an error term of order $0(\Delta x)$.

The approximation to f '(x_0) given by Eq. 2-8 is called a *forward-difference approximation* because the derivative is approximated by relating the base point x_0 to a point x *forward* of it by Δx (x = x_0 + Δx). On the other hand, the right-hand side of Eq.2-10 is called a *backward-difference approximation* because the derivative is approximated by relating the base point x_0 to a point x *backward* of it by Δx (x = x_0 - Δx). Note that Eqs. 3-8 and 3-10 are both first-order approximations. For the purposes of finite difference approximations we will assume that Δx is the incremental distance between mesh points. In a uniform mesh this distance is constant, but in a non-uniform mesh, Δx varies throughout the mesh.

Second-order approximations of f '(x) and f "(x) can also be obtained from the Taylor series. Such an expression for f '(x) is found by truncating Eqs. 2-6 and 2-9 after the third term. Then the truncated version of Eq. 2-9 is subtracted from that of Eq. 2-6, and we solve the result to yield:

$$f'(x_0) = \frac{f(x_0 + \Delta x) - f(x_0 - \Delta x)}{2\Delta x} \pm 0(\Delta x^2) \qquad (2-11)$$

Likewise, the second-order expression for f "(x_0) is found by truncating Eqs. 2-6 and 2-9, then adding the two results, and finally solving the addend for f "(x_0):

$$f''(x_0) = \frac{f(x_0 + \Delta x) - 2f(x_0) + f(x_0 - \Delta x)}{\Delta x^2} \pm 0(\Delta x^2) \qquad (2-12)$$

These last two expressions are also known as the *central difference* approximations of the derivatives. Note that the error term for the central difference approximations implies that the error is proportional to Δx^2, while that of the forward- and backward-difference approximations is proportional to Δx. For $\Delta x \ll 1$, this indicates that the error of the central difference approximations is smaller than that of either the forward or backward difference approximations, which in turn implies the central-difference derivative expressions are of order of Δx more accurate than either of the other two. Since they are more accurate, the central difference approximations are almost always used for discretizing the space derivatives of PDEs, with Eq. 2-11 used to replace first derivatives, and Eq. 2-12 to replace second derivatives. For PDEs containing time derivatives, however, the forward and backward difference approximations are frequently used to discretize the time derivatives, as we shall see in section 2.4.4.

2.4.2.4. Two-Dimensional Space Discretization.
In a two-dimensional mesh, the distance between adjacent mesh points is often described using the following notation:

$$a_i = \Delta x = x_{i+1} - x_i \quad i = 0,1,2,3 \dots n \qquad (2-13a)$$

$$b_j = \Delta y = y_{j+1} - y_j \quad j = 0,1,2,3 \dots m \qquad (2-13b)$$

Using this notation for finite difference expressions in two dimensions, we get

$$f(x,y) = f_{i,j} \quad i = 0,1,2,3 \ldots n \quad j = 0,1,2,3 \ldots m \quad (2-14a)$$

$$f(x \pm \Delta x, y) = f_{i\pm1, j} \quad (2-14b)$$

$$f([x \pm \Delta x]/2, y) = f_{i\pm1/2, j} \quad (2-14c)$$

$$f(x, [y \pm \Delta y]) = f_{i, j\pm1} \quad (2-14d)$$

$$f(x, [y \pm \Delta y]/2) = f_{i, j\pm1/2} \quad (2-14e)$$

where the relative positions of the points i,j, etc are expressed in Cartesian co-ordinates. This notation is depicted in Fig. 2-7 where the mesh points and 'half-points' are shown. The mesh points shown in Fig. 2-7 constitute the *five point difference approximation*, includes the four neighbor nodes which are horizontally and vertically adjacent to the center node.

It is often assumed that the derivatives of potential (in the Poisson equation) or impurity flux (in Fick's 2nd Law equation) are constant between mesh points. In these circumstances the central difference first derivatives at the half points (e.g., at i + 1/2,j and i,j + 1/2) are

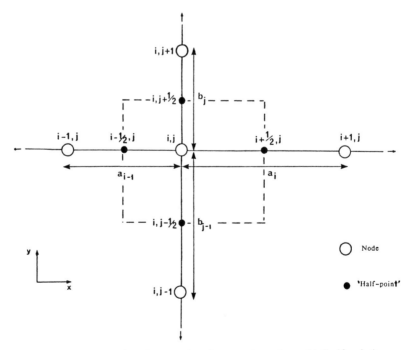

Fig. 2-7 Finite-difference mesh point notation for a rectangular grid (half-point).

$$\frac{\partial f}{\partial x}\bigg|_{@\, i+\frac{1}{2}j} = \frac{f_{i+1,j} - f_{i,j}}{a_i} + 0(a_i^2) \qquad (2\text{-}15a)$$

$$\frac{\partial f}{\partial y}\bigg|_{@\, i,j+\frac{1}{2}} = \frac{f_{i,j+1} - f_{i,j}}{b_j} + 0(b_j^2) \qquad (2\text{-}15b)$$

and the central difference second derivatives at these half points are

$$\frac{\partial^2 f}{\partial x^2}\bigg|_{@\, i+\frac{1}{2}j} = \frac{f_{i+1,j} - 2f_{i+\frac{1}{2}j} + f_{i,j}}{a_i^2} + 0(a_i^2) \qquad (2\text{-}15c)$$

$$\frac{\partial^2 f}{\partial y^2}\bigg|_{@\, i,j+\frac{1}{2}} = \frac{f_{i,j+1} - 2f_{i,j+\frac{1}{2}} + f_{i,j}}{b_j^2} + 0(b_j^2) \qquad (2\text{-}15d)$$

2.4.3 The Finite Element Method

The finite element method is the other most widely used spatial discretization procedure for numerically solving semiconductor differential equations. It is particularly useful for obtaining solutions for non-rectangular, irregularly shaped device geometries, where the inherent flexibility of the method can lead to a more efficient solution than can be obtained using finite difference methods. A major advantage of the finite element method is that there is no additional complexity introduced by using elements of different sizes. Another is that the domain can be subdivided in such a way as to increase the number of elements in regions where accurate results are desired and to reduce the overall number where the results are not so important. Hence, it is possible to reduce the total number of nodes needed for a given problem. The principal disadvantages of this method are: 1) initially more effort is required to implement the numerical algorithm; and 2) the stability and convergence criteria are not well understood at the present time.

A longer discussion of the finite element method applied to semiconductor simulation is given in Selberherr[2] and Snowden,[3] each of which devote a section 10-15 pages long to the subject. A introductory book on the application of the finite element method to electromagnetics is by Steele.[7] A more advanced and general treatment of the finite element method is given by Zienkiewicz.[8]

In the finite element method the spatial domain of interest is divided into small, basic elements. A physical object is thought of as composed of this finite number of pieces, each of which can be analyzed separately according to the laws of physics. Thus, each physical variable over the entire object can be expressed as a sum of finite elements, each element representing the contribution from one of the pieces. By combining the analyses of the separate pieces, a system of algebraic (usually linear) equations relating to the finite elements is deduced. Solution of this set of equations provides the desired approximate solution of the problem.

In IC simulation applications, the domain is the entire device geometry, and it is broken up into a mesh of fine pieces called *finite elements*, all having a standard shape (most often triangles). It is assumed that the exact solution of the differential equation in each region can be approximated by a simple, smoothly varying function over each element. Typically, interpolation polynomials (usually, first- to fourth-order polynomials) are selected to serve as the approximate solutions in each element. The approximate solutions in each element are also known as *partial solutions*. The total approximate solution for a parameter is given by the sum of the partial solutions over all the elements. For this to be possible, each approximation function is defined to be equal to zero for all finite elements except one. Therefore, when both sides of the differential equation are multiplied by the approximation functions, many matrix entries become equal to zero, allowing the resulting matrix to be solved efficiently. The accuracy of the method depends both on the complexity of the approximation functions used in each element and on the number of elements used to make the device geometry. A user may therefore increase the accuracy of the computation by using a greater number of finite elements or by using higher-order approximation functions.

The simplest, and most commonly used approximation function for a triangular element is a first-order polynomial, which, in Cartesian coordinates has the form

$$u_i^h (x,y) = Cx + By + A \qquad\qquad (2 - 16)$$

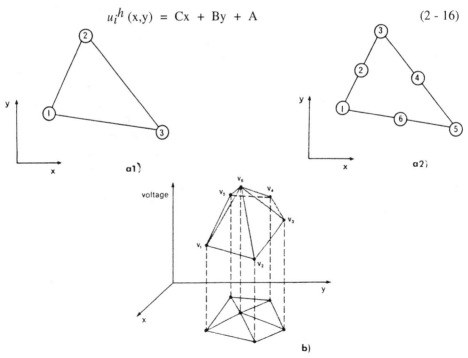

Fig. 2-8 Finite element discretization: (a) Triangular element of the finite-element grid [a1 - Linear approximation, a2 - Quadratic approximation]. (b) Solution is made continuous by setting the potential in common triangle vertices to be identical.

The coefficients of the polynomial are determined from three values of the approximate solution. In practice, these values are obtained at the nodes of the element for this linear approximation. For example, if the potential is defined over a first-order triangular finite element, the function has solution potential φ_1, φ_2, and φ_3 at the triangle vertices: the solution is interpolated linearly in between using the approximation polynomial (Fig. 2-8a). In other words, in this case the solution is approximated as a plane passing through the three nodal values of φ. As an example, in the solution surface over a mesh of five such first-order elements, the solution is made continuous by setting the potential in common triangle vertices to be identical (Fig. 2-8b).

A Galerkin matrix* is constructed for each finite element, and all these matrices are added together to create a single matrix equation for the entire device. Since the integral must be computed only over standard shapes, the computation of each separate Galerkin matrix becomes repetitive and is therefore greatly simplified. Similar types of matrix methods are used to solve the discretized equations generated using the finite element method as are used to solve the linearized equation sets resulting from the finite difference method (e.g., successive overrelaxation [SOR] methods).

2.4.4 Time Discretization

A PDE which has the time derivative on one and only one side of the equation is termed an *initial value problem*. The Fick's 2nd Law equation and the transient carrier-continuity equations (i.e., in which $\partial n / \partial t \neq 0$), are examples of such PDEs. To solve initial-value PDEs we begin by assuming that the solution is known at the starting time instant (i.e., the initial value is assumed known), and its evolution from that time on (i.e., the time derivative) can be obtained from the spatial variation.

To numerically solve such time-dependent PDEs, time derivatives must also be discretized. To do this, the total time interval of the process or device effect being simulated must first be divided up into an appropriate number of smaller time steps. The

---

* The *Galerkin method* is one of several methods for approximately solving differential equations based on the *calculus of variations* (others being: least squares, weighted residual, or Rayleigh-Ritz methods). When the Galerkin method is used to solve, for example the Poisson equation, the unknown potential distribution is approximated by writing it as a linear combination of known functions with unknown coefficients. This approximation is then substituted into the the original PDE, and both sides of the equation are multiplied by the full set of approximation functions. By integrating over the solution region a matrix equation is produced (a Galerkin matrix). Solving this matrix for the unknown coefficients provides the approximate potential. However, unless the solution domain is broken up into small finite elements, the Galerkin method as just described is not easy to solve with a computer solution. That is, the matrix entries are difficult to compute over regions of arbitrary shape and the matrix generated usually has no entries equal to zero. So, instead, the solution domain is subdivided into smaller regions of regular shape, and the Galerkin method is applied to each element. See Steele or Zienkiewicz or other books dealing with finite elements for more details on the Galerkin method.

solution of the variable is then found at each location for each time interval, with the solution of the PDE for the previous time step being used as the initial value for the next time step. After the unknowns are found for a given time step, time is advanced by an increment, and the solution is calculated again. This cycle is continued until the final specified time step is reached. Note that as these time-dependent equations are being solved it is assumed that the variables do not vary during the time interval over each individual subdomain; i.e., the concentrations of the various impurities present and the diffusivities in the Fick's 2nd Law equation, and φ, n, and p in the transient continuity equations keep their same values from the beginning to end of each time increment.

Solution of such time-dependent PDEs can be very CPU intensive because of the number of times the PDE must be solved. It is common for transient device analysis to require 100 to 1000 times the CPU time needed for a single dc analysis of the same device. (Note, however, that if the static I-V curve - for example of a MOSFET - is needed, the value of I_D must be calculated for the desired number of points of the I-V curve, see for example, Fig. 4-14. Thus, for many steady-state cases the PDE may also have to solved a number of times.)

2.4.4.1 Explicit Time Discretization. It is possible to discretize time derivatives in various ways, depending on the choice of time points at which the spatial variation of the unknown variable is evaluated.[9] The most straightforward technique computes the unknown at the present time and thus yields equations which can be solved explicitly for the values at the new time step. The simplest *explicit* time discretization method is called the *forward-difference* (or *forward-Euler*) time-discretization method. The single unknown variable at the next time step is found explicitly from the value of the variable at the present time step. For example, in a one-dimensional diffusion equation (in which for simplicity we assume D is a constant) the concentration of impurities at position m at time step t^{k+1} (C_m^{k+1}) can be found from

$$\frac{[C_m^{k+1} - C_m^k]}{\Delta t} = D \frac{\partial^2 C_m^k}{\partial x^2} \qquad (2 - 17)$$

If the central difference second derivative is used to discretize the spatial derivatives (right hand side), and the grid spacing is uniform, we get

$$C_m^{k+1} = \left\{ [\frac{D\Delta t}{\Delta x^2}]C_{m-1}^k - (1 - [\frac{2D\Delta t}{\Delta x^2}])C_m^k + [\frac{D\Delta t}{\Delta x^2}]C_{m+1}^k \right\} \qquad (2 - 18)$$

Now we can solve for C_m^{k+1} in terms of the known values of C_m^k from the previous (present) time step. In Fig. 2-9a, the reader can see that the forward Euler method connects mesh points C_{m-1}, C_m, and C_{m+1} at time step k to C_m at time step $k+1$.

The chief attraction of explicit time discretization is its simplicity. That is, at each time step neither a matrix solution nor a nonlinear iteration is needed to evaluate the unknown C_m^{k+1}. However, the approach is inherently unstable unless sufficiently small time steps are used. That is, the error caused by the discretization of the time

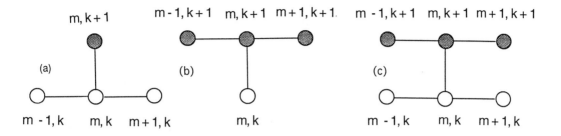

Fig. 2-9 Time discretization: (a) Forward-Euler (Explicit) Method; (b) Backward Euler (Implicit) Method; (c) Crank-Nicholson (Implicit) Method.

derivative can be cumulative in the forward Euler method, and is not bounded from one time step to the next. As a result, as time develops this accumulated error grows steadily and eventually yields a meaningless unphysical solution. In practice, to ensure sufficient accuracy while still guaranteeing stability with the forward-Euler method, unacceptably small time steps must be used to solve the diffusion equation and the current-continuity equations (e.g., of the order of 10^{-15} sec for doping concentrations of 10^{17} cm^{-3}). Use of such small time steps would entail the solution of the equations at an unnecessarily large number of time intervals to perform the simulation. As a result, the more complex (but also more stable) *implicit* time discretization methods are generally used instead.

2.4.4.2 Implicit Time Discretization. In *implicit time discretization* methods, the unknown parameters (e.g., the dopant concentrations at the next time step) are calculated using the values at the new time step as well as at previous time steps. In such methods, the discretization errors are partially canceled from one step to the next, and thus, accumulated errors can be limited to a certain, acceptably small value. Since the concentrations at the new time step are unknown, to find them requires the solution of a large system of equations at each time step, and may require large memory capacity. The long time needed to carry out the computations, however, is compensated by the greatly increased time step. Two of the most widely used implicit methods are the *backward Euler method* and the *Crank-Nicholson* method.

The first-order *backward-Euler method* is the most unconditionally stable of all the implicit methods. In the diffusion equation example above after time discretization using the backward-Euler method, the equation would be expressed as

$$C_m^{k+1} = C_m^k + \Delta t \left\{ \frac{\partial}{\partial x} D \left[\frac{\partial C_m^{k+1}}{\partial x} \right] \right\} \qquad (2\text{-}19)$$

or

$$C_m^{k+1} = C_m^k + \left\{ \left(\frac{D\Delta t}{\Delta x^2}\right)C_{m-1}^{k+1} - \left(\frac{2D\Delta t}{\Delta x^2}\right)C_m^{k+1} + \left(\frac{D\Delta t}{\Delta x^2}\right)C_{m+1}^{k+1} \right\} \qquad (2 - 19a)$$

In Fig. 2-9b, the reader can see that the backward-Euler method connects mesh point C_m at time step k to mesh points C_{m-1}, C_m, and C_{m+1} at time step $k+1$.

In the *Crank-Nicholson method* the time discretization is performed at the time step $k+1/2$ [i.e., the unknown variable is averaged between the value at previous time step (which is known) and the next time step (at which the value is unknown)]. The Crank-Nicholson method is attractive because it is second-order accurate in time, and also exhibits excellent stability. For example, if Eq. 2-17 was discretized using the Crank-Nicholson method, it would take the following form

$$C_m^{k+1} = C_m^k + \frac{1}{2}\left\{ \left(\frac{D\Delta t}{\Delta x^2}\right)C_{m-1}^k - \left(\frac{2D\Delta t}{\Delta x^2}\right)C_m^k + \left(\frac{D\Delta t}{\Delta x^2}\right)C_{m+1}^k \right.$$

$$\left. + \left(\frac{D\Delta t}{\Delta x^2}\right)C_{m-1}^{k+1} - \left(\frac{2D\Delta t}{\Delta x^2}\right)C_m^{k+1} + \left(\frac{D\Delta t}{\Delta x^2}\right)C_{m+1}^{k+1} \right\} \qquad (2 - 20)$$

In Fig. 2-9c, one can see that the Crank-Nicholson method connects mesh points C_{m-1}, C_m, and C_{m+1} at time step k to mesh points C_{m-1}, C_m, and C_{m+1} at time step $k+1$.

Another time discretization scheme that has been proposed is the *trapezoidal rule/backward difference-formula* (TR-BDF2). It is a composite method, i.e., it uses both implicit and explicit time discretization.[10]

2.5 ORDERING THE SET OF DISCRETIZED PDEs INTO APPROPRIATE MATRIX FORM

The set of discretized PDEs written for each node (using either the finite difference or finite element method) can be combined in matrix form so that a single matrix equation represents the entire system of equations. Matrix techniques can then be used to develop various solution techniques. For example, the discretized set of the Poisson equation may be more conveniently expressed in matrix form as

$$[B]\{\varphi\} = \{Q\} \qquad (2 - 21)$$

where $[B]$ - in the finite difference approach - is the coefficient matrix for the finite difference equations, and $\{\varphi\}$ and $\{Q\}$ are vectors consisting of the elements $\varphi_{i,j}$ and $Q_{i,j}$ for each node of the solution region where $\varphi_{i,j}$ is unknown. Equation 2-21 represents a system of m simultaneous equations, where m is the total number of elements in φ.

The matrix $[B]$ has a maximum of five-non-zero elements on any row of the matrix, and is therefore termed *sparse*. Sparse matrix solution techniques have been developed for such linear systems of equations which significantly reduce the cost of computation by exploiting the sparsity of the given system. A variety of sparse matrix solution software

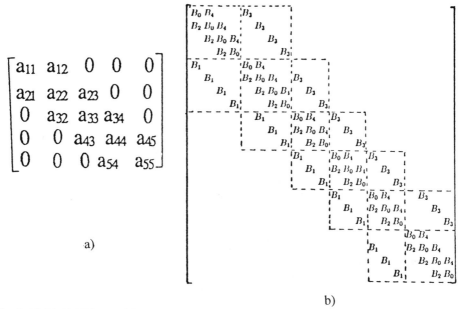

a)

b)

Fig. 2-10 (a) Tri-Diagonal Matrix; (b) Penta-Diagonal Matrix.

packages have been developed to solve such sparse matrix systems. However, the form of the coefficient matrix must be such as to allow the sparse matrix techniques to be used to best advantage. That is, the coefficient matrix should ideally be organized so that a tridiagonal matrix is obtained for one-dimensional PDEs (such as the 1-D Fick's Second Law equation, Fig. 2-10a), and pentadiagonal matrices are formed for two-dimensional PDEs (such as the 2-D Poisson equation, Fig. 2-10b).[*]

The form of [**B**], however, depends on the method of ordering the nodes within the solution region as well as on the equations associated with these nodes. The nodes can be sequenced in the order of i and j - i being held constant at each of its values while j takes on all values in its range. This is illustrated in Fig. 2-11 for a simple node structure where the numbers define the node ordering. The elements $\varphi_{i,j}$ and $Q_{i,j}$ are placed in $\{\varphi\}$ and $\{\mathbf{Q}\}$ using the same order as the node sequence. This type of node ordering scheme is called a *natural by columns* ordering method.

More sophisticated ordering sequences can be produced using one of several algorithms developed by various workers (to take advantage of the sparse nature of the coefficient matrices). One that is well established for ordering the nodes of sparse matrices which are to be solved using direct methods so that a minimum number of non-zero entries occur after factorization (see section 2.7) is by Cuthill and McKee.[11]

---

[*] A set of tridiagonal linear algebraic equations are characterized by the unique form of having nonzero elements on the diagonal and a maximum of one element to the left and the right of the diagonal. The rest of the elements are zeros. The tridiagonal matrix of the coefficients of such a set of equations is shown in Fig. 2-10a.

```
1    6   11   16   21
2    7   12   17   22
3    8   13   18   23
4    9   14   19   24
5   10   15   20   25
```

Fig. 2-11 *Natural by columns* node ordering scheme.

2.6 LINEARIZING NONLINEAR ALGEBRAIC EQUATIONS

The discretized, ordered algebraic equations representing the quantitative model for the unknown parameter in the device domain are generally *nonlinear* algebraic equations. [Nonlinear algebraic equations are defined as those which contain powers and/or transcendental functions of the unknown variable(s).] Nonlinear algebraic equations cannot be solved by conventional linear algebraic techniques. Instead, a method such as the *Newton-Raphson (NR) iteration method* must be used to linearize such equations, after which linear algebraic techniques can be applied to solve them. (*Iteration* is defined as a computational procedure in which the desired result is approached through a repeated cycle of operations, each of which more closely approximates the desired result.) In such iterative linearizing methods, the nonlinear terms are first linearized, and an initial estimate of the unknown being sought is chosen. This initial estimate is substituted into the resulting equations. Solving the linearized equations with an estimate of the unknown value yields a new estimate of the unknown. This new estimate is then compared to the previous estimate. If the difference between the two is too large, the procedure is repeated, using the new estimate as the known value in the linearized equation in the next iteration. The iteration procedure is halted when the difference between the new and the previous estimate (hopefully) becomes acceptably small. If this condition is reached, it is said that the iteration procedure has converged to the solution. However, if after a number of iterations the new estimate still does not approach the value of the previous estimate to within the desired limit, the iteration method might not converge at all. The maximum number of iterations is usually set by the user and is more or less arbitrary. The convergence of the NR method is chiefly dependent on how close the initial estimate is to the final solution.

In the NR iteration method, linearization is achieved by replacing the nonlinear terms of the unknown variable of the equations with a first order Taylor series expansion about the most recent estimate of the unknown variable, or

$$f(x_0 + \Delta x) = f(x_0) + f'(x_0)\,\Delta x \qquad (2 - 22)$$

The iteration is started by choosing an initial estimate of the unknown. For each iteration, the equation is linearized by this method, and a linear solution technique is then used to solve the equation. The iteration is stopped when adequate convergence is achieved, or after the number of iterations specified by the user are performed and convergence has not yet been reached.

As an example of the NR method, consider a simple circuit containing a dc voltage source of value V_A (in volts), a resistor of value R_A (in Ω), and a *pn* junction diode as shown in Fig. 2-12. Assume that the polarity of the voltage source is such that the diode is biased well into forward-bias operation, and the steady-state I-V relation for the diode is then

$$I = I_0 \exp(qV/kT) \qquad\qquad (2 - 23a)$$

where I_0 is the diode saturation current, and V is the voltage across the diode. The Kirchhoffs-Current-Law equation for node 2 of this circuit is

$$(V_A - v_2)/R_A - I_0\exp(qv_2/kT) = 0 \qquad\qquad (2 - 23b)$$

Since we have one nonlinear equation with one unknown (v_2) we can solve it using the NR iteration method. That is, we assume the initial value of v_2 is v_2^0 (e.g., $v_2^k @ k = 0 = v_2^0$ where here the superscript k denotes the number of the iteration). Then we apply a Taylor series expansion of the diode current I about this point, and retain only first-order terms. If in Eq. 2-22 I is $f(x_0 + \Delta x)$, and x_0 is now v_2^k and Δx is now $v_2^{k+1} - v_2^k$, $I = f(v_2^{k+1})$, and we get at the beginning of the first iteration,

$$I(v_2^1) = f(v_2^1) \sim f(v_2^0) - f'(v_2^0)(v_2^1 - v_2^0) \qquad\qquad (2 - 24a)$$

or

$$I \sim I_0\exp(qv_2^0/kT) + (dI/dV @ v_2^k = v_2^0)(v_2^1 - v_2^0) \qquad\qquad (2 - 24b)$$

$$\sim I_0\exp(qv_2^0/kT) + [q(v_2^1 - v_2^0)/kT]\, I_0\exp(qv_2^0/kT) \qquad\qquad (2 - 24c)$$

With this linearization the Kirchhoffs Current Law equation at node 2 becomes for the kth iteration

$$(V_A - v_2^{k+1})/R_A - I_0\exp(qv_2^k/kT) - [q(v_2^{k+1} - v_2^k)/kT]\, I_0\exp(qv_2^k/kT) = 0 \quad (2 - 25)$$

This equation is now linear in terms of the one unknown (v_2^{k+1}), and thus can be

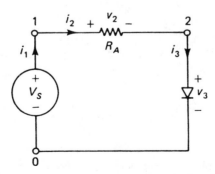

Fig. 2.12 Simple diode circuit to illustrate the method of nodal analysis when nonlinear elements are present.

solved to determine a new estimate for this voltage using linear algebraic techniques.

The NR iteration procedure can also be applied to a set of nonlinear algebraic equations expressed in matrix form. The first derivatives in the second term of the Taylor series are expressed in a matrix form known as the Jacobian matrix. That is, the *Jacobian* is a square matrix of partial derivatives, of the form

$$
\begin{bmatrix}
\dfrac{\partial Q_1}{\partial \varphi_1} & \dfrac{\partial Q_1}{\partial \varphi_2} & \cdots & \dfrac{\partial Q_1}{\partial \varphi_n} \\[2ex]
\dfrac{\partial Q_2}{\partial \varphi_1} & \dfrac{\partial Q_2}{\partial \varphi_2} & \cdots & \dfrac{\partial Q_2}{\partial \varphi_n} \\[2ex]
\dfrac{\partial Q_n}{\partial \varphi_1} & \dfrac{\partial Q_n}{\partial \varphi_2} & \cdots & \dfrac{\partial Q_n}{\partial \varphi_n}
\end{bmatrix}
\tag{2 - 26}
$$

Each of the terms of the Jacobian are evaluated at values of φ from the previous iteration.

If we use as an example the 2-D form of the Poisson equation, where φ is the unknown, the nonlinearized form of the matrix equation at the beginning of iteration k is

$$
[\mathbf{B}]\ \{\varphi^{k+1}\} \ = \ [\mathbf{Q}^{k+1}]
\tag{2 - 27}
$$

To linearize this equation using the NR iteration technique we replace $[\mathbf{Q}^{k+1}]$ (containing the nonlinear terms of φ) with

$$
[\mathbf{Q}^{k+1}] \ = \ [\mathbf{Q}^k] \ + \ [\mathbf{J}^k]\ \{\varphi^{k+1} - \varphi^k\}
\tag{2 - 28}
$$

so Eq. 2-27 becomes

$$
[\mathbf{B}]\ \{\varphi^{k+1}\} \ = \ [\mathbf{Q}^k] + [\mathbf{J}^k]\{\varphi^{k+1} - \varphi^k\}
\tag{2 - 29}
$$

where

$$
\mathbf{J}^k(p) = \partial[\mathbf{Q}](p)/\partial\varphi\ (p)\ @\{\varphi^k\}\quad p\ = 1,2,3, \ldots N
\tag{2 - 30}
$$

To express the matrix equation so that all the unknowns φ^{k+1} appear in the vector $\{\varphi^{k+1}\}$ we rearrange Eq. 2-29 to yield

$$
[\mathbf{B} - \mathbf{J}^k]\ \{\varphi^{k+1}\} \ = \ [\mathbf{Q}^k] \ - \ [\mathbf{J}^k]\{\varphi^k\}
\tag{2 - 31}
$$

Note that all of the terms in $\{\varphi^k\}$ are known, since they involve quantities calculated during the previous iteration. Thus, the set of nonlinear equations is linearized and a linear matrix solution technique can be used to find the values of $\{\varphi\}^{k+1}$. When this is found, the values of $\{\varphi\}^{k+1}$ are compared to those of the previous iteration according to

$$
|\{\varphi\}^{k+1} - \{\varphi\}^k /\{\varphi\}^{k+1}| < \delta_1
\tag{2 - 32}
$$

where δ_1 is a specified error bound. If the condition is met this indicates that the iteration has converged. If not, the iteration procedure is repeated until it is met (or until the maximum number of allowed iterations have been performed without convergence being reached). As noted earlier, the convergence of the NR method depends on how close the initial estimate is to the final solution. There are a number of ways for choosing a good initial guess to start the iteration, based either on physical reasoning (e.g., assuming that quasi-charge-neutrality exists at thermal equilibrium), or on some numerical techniques. Appendix A provides two worked out examples of the NR iteration method. An example of one of the equations of the matrix Eq. 2-31 is explicitly written out in Section 2.10.

2.7 MATRIX METHODS FOR SOLVING SIMULTANEOUS LINEAR ALGEBRAIC EQUATIONS

The solution of simultaneous linear algebraic equations is probably one of the most important procedures in modern engineering computations. For example, the finite element method and the finite difference method both involve the solution of systems of linear algebraic equations. Two classes of methods are available for solving a set of linear algebraic equations: *direct methods*, and *iterative methods*. Appendix A provides a basic introduction to both types of these methods, including simple worked examples for some of them.

The *direct methods* are based on the mathematical technique of matrix elimination. They include Cramer's Rule, Gauss elimination method, the Gauss-Jordan elimination method, and Cholesky's method (also called Crouts' method, or the *LU*-decomposition method). The most widely used direct method in process and device simulators is the latter, which is based on a symmetric variation of the Gaussian elimination technique. That is, in Cholesky's method *triangular factorization* is applied to the coefficient matrix e.g., [A] of the equation

$$[A]\{x\} = \{b\} \tag{2 - 33}$$

which yields

$$[A] = [L]\,[L^T] \tag{2 - 34}$$

where [L] is a *lower triangular matrix* and [L^T] is the transpose of the [L] matrix (and [L^T] is also an *upper triangular matrix* (see Appendix A for definitions of these terms). Using (2-34) in (2-33) we get

$$[L]\,[L^T]\,\{x\} = \{b\} \tag{2 - 35}$$

and by substituting $\{y\} = [L^T]\,\{x\}$, we can find $\{x\}$ by solving the triangular systems

$$[L]\{y\} = \{b\} \tag{2 - 36}$$

and

$$[L^T]\,\{x\} = \{y\} \tag{2 - 37}$$

However, upon factoring a sparse matrix using the Cholesky method, it suffers *fill-in* (i.e., [L] has nonzero entries in positions which are zero in the lower triangular part of [A]). By judicious reordering the equations of the set it is possible to end up with a triangular factor [l] which is just as sparse as the lower triangle of [A]. This will result in significant savings in computer execution time and storage (assuming of course that sparseness is exploited). Algorithms have been developed to automatically perform this reordering, one of the best established being by Cuthill and McKee.

An example of a worked problem using Cholesky's method is given in Appendix A, section A-4.1.5. A text which describes the direct solution methods of sparse linear matrix equations (emphasizing the Cholesky method) has been written by George and Liu.[12] It also provides information on SPARSPAK, a software package of direct linear matrix equation solvers.

The *iterative methods* include Jacobi's method, the Gauss-Seidel method, the successive-overrelaxation (SOR) method, the alternating-direction implicit (ADI), and Stone's strongly implicit method. Varga's text is a good introduction to iterative methods for solving linear matrix equations.[13] A good (but compressed) survey on the subject of the various matrix methods for solving sets of sparse matrix linear algebraic equations is by Duff.[14]

If an iterative method is used to solve the linearized matrix equation, it can be written as

$$[A]\{x\} = \{b\} \qquad (2 - 38)$$

where the elements of Eqs. 2-31 and 2-33a are related by

$$[A] = [B - J^k] \qquad (2 - 39a)$$
$$\{x\} = \{\varphi\}^{k+1} \qquad (2 - 39b)$$
$$\{b\} = \{Q^k\} - \{J^k \varphi^k\} \qquad (2 - 39c)$$

The iterative techniques use the notation $\{x\}^m$ to represent an approximation to $\{x\}$, where the superscript m indicates that x^m is obtained as a result of the mth linear iteration used to solve Eq. 2-38. The linear iteration procedure is started with $x^0 = \varphi^k$ as the initial selection of the approximation of the unknown vector, and is repeated until the approximation to x resulting from successive iterations satisfy the condition

$$|\{x_i\}^{m+1} - \{x_i\}^m / \{x_i\}^{m+1}| < \delta_2 \qquad (2 - 40)$$

The relative merits of direct and iterative methods often depend on the type of application. For systems of *moderate* size (e.g., the solution of the one-dimensional Fick's 2nd Law equation in SUPREM II), the use of direct methods is often advantageous. The large systems of simultaneous equations with sparse coefficient matrices obtained by finite-difference discretization are particularly well suited to solution by iterative methods. This is because iterative methods have smaller computer storage requirements, typically needing to store only $[A]$ $\{b\}$ and $\{x\}^k$. On the other hand, when $[A]$ is factored during a direct solution procedure, it typically suffers fill-in, so that the *filled matrix* must be stored. In addition, Gaussian elimination in its primary form requires more arithmetic operations than a single iteration cycle. Thus, if the matrix is large and the iteration converges to the desired accuracy in a small number of iterations, less storage is needed and considerable computing time can be saved by using an iterative method.

But, the newer direct methods require fewer operations since they take advantage of sparseness. Thus, a comparison of iterative versus direct methods of computation becomes quite complicated. In fact, unless the question of which class of method should be used is posed in a quite narrow and well-defined context, it is either very complicated or impossible to answer.[13]

2.8 VISUALIZATION OF THE RESULTS

To view 1-D or 2-D results from the data base, a postprocessor is needed to allow the calculated results to be presented in variety of formats at the user's option, including: linear, log-linear, contour, log-contour, or "bird's eye" (perspective). Here we will give some examples of the above formats. For a discussion of recent trends in scientific visualization for semiconductor technology simulation see ref. 15.

Figure 2-13a shows a entire MOSFET from a 3-D perspective. Next, in Fig. 2-13b we show the same device, also from 3-D perspective, but sliced down the middle of the

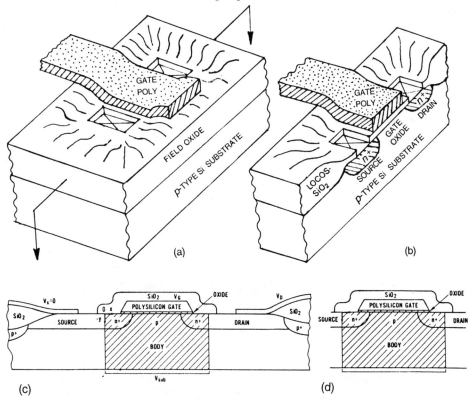

Fig. 2-13 (a) MOSFET structure from a 3-D perspective; (b) MOSFET from a 3-D perspective, but sliced down the middle of the channel so that a cross-section of the device is also visible; (c) 2-D cross-section of the MOSFET; (d) 2-D cross-section of the MOSFET showing only the active region.

channel so that a cross-section of the device along that direction is also visible. In Fig. 2-13c we show only this 2-D cross-section (including the surrounding field oxide region). Figure 2-13d shows the same cross-section, but excludes the field oxide region, so that only the active area of the device is depicted.

Next, we consider how the data obtained from a process or device simulation can be displayed. First we show a non-uniform mesh overlaying the device region (see Fig. 2-14a). We can display the simulated 2-D results of either doping concentration or the potential directly on the 2-D cross-section of the MOSFET active area using a contour plot format (Figs. 2-14b and 2-14c respectively). Note, however, that contour plots are somewhat cumbersome to interpret.

A graphical format that makes the 2-D variation easier to visualize is the 'bird's eye' (or *perspective*) surface plot. Note that this is still a plot of the 2-D dependence of the parameter of interest on position, but the third-dimension is used to allow the 2-D variation to be seen more vividly. We begin by taking the 2-D grid overlaying the active device region, and tilting it so it is lying flat (Fig. 2-14d). Next, we plot the value of the parameter being visualized as a point above the 2-D plane, with a height equal to the parameter value. When all these points are connected, a surface plot of the 2-D parametric variation is produced. We show such a surface plot of the doping concentration in the active region of a MOSFET in Fig. 2-14e1. (Here it is assumed that dopants have been placed under the oxide in the channel to adjust the threshold voltage, hence making the doping concentration in the channel near the surface higher than that deeper in the substrate.) In Fig. 2-14e2 we show a one-dimensional plot of doping in the channel at the center of the device as a function of depth below the oxide. Again, higher doping near the surface is due to the V_T-adjust implant. In Fig. 2-14f1 we show the 2-D variation of potential in this MOSFET (assuming both a gate and drain voltage have been applied), again using such a 'bird's eye' perspective plot. In Fig. 2-14f2 the 1-D potential variation as a function of depth beneath the gate oxide at the center of the channel is known. Note that the plots shown in Figs. 2-14e2 and 2-14f2 are but single examples of the many that can be extracted from the 2-D bird's eye plot.

If it is desired to show the doping variation in three-dimensions in a manner similar to the surface plot format, we could use color variation to represent change in doping concentration versus position, and this is one option being used in 3-D simulators.

2.9 DATA BASE OF THE SIMULATION PACKAGES

As we have noted, device and process simulation systems must operate on large volumes of data. This implies that large memory capacity must be available and that efficient data handling schemes must be established. Concerning the latter, a comprehensive, flexible data base is needed to keep from being overwhelmed by the mass of the simulation data. Included should be the capability for data storage and retrieval, and for pre- and post-processing of the data in an integrated, interactive environment. One manner of organizing such a data base is suggested by Cole et al.[15] In this suggested approach, the data is placed into five categories, or 'files':

1. A general *variable file* for parameters related to physical constants and coefficients needed by the models.

2. A *doping file* for impurity atom distribution (either a result of process simulation or created from a superposition of analytic functions).

3. A *geometry file* that contains the nodes & elements of the spatial discretization.

4. A *results file* that contains the discretized (nodal) values of such quantities as electronic potential, electron and hole concentrations, dopant atom concentrations, etc.

5. A *dictionary file* that provides a single indicator to any given simulation "run" and a cross-reference to data for that run contained in the other four data files mentioned above.

Other methods have also been proposed for handling the data. The most notable is that of Duvall, who proposed the Profile Interchange Format (PIF).[16] One of the objective of this data handling scheme is also to establish a standard protocol for exchanging data among simulation tools developed at different sites.

2.10 EXAMPLES OF THE PROCEDURES USED TO NUMERICALLY SOLVE THE MODEL PARTIAL-DIFFERENTIAL EQUATIONS OF MICROELECTRONICS

2.10.1 Outline of a Numerical Analysis Procedure for Solving the Two-Dimensional Poisson Equation to Simulate the Electrostatic Potential in a MOSFET

In this section we present an example of how the electrostatic potential as a function of position is simulated in an NMOSFET for a given set of bias conditions. This is done by solving the 2-D Poisson equation using numerical analysis techniques. We will assume that the geometry of the MOSFET in our example is as shown in Fig. 2-15. (Note that this device geometry is deliberately simplified to reduce the mathematical complexity of our example.) For the same reason, we also assume that $N_D = 0$. Finally, it is assumed the external dc biasing voltages (e.g., V_{GS} and V_{DS}) are restricted to values such that the MOSFET is operated only in the subthreshold region, and that these voltage values are given.

If the MOSFET is operated in subthreshold (see chap. 4), it can be assumed that the currents flowing in the device are small enough so that they do not change the electrostatic potential. Therefore, the solution of the Poisson equation alone yields an accurate simulation of the electrostatic potential in the silicon as a function of position $\varphi(x,y)$ in the device. To find $\varphi(x,y)$ we must set out to solve the Poisson equation in two dimensions.

Since analytic closed-form solutions of the 2-D Poisson equation are not known, numerical techniques must be used to obtain the solution. Here we outline the sequence of mathematical procedures based on the *difference operator finite-difference method* for doing this. The following steps must be taken:

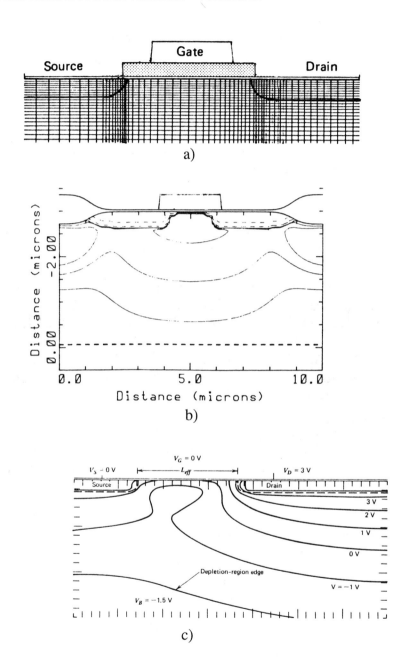

Fig. 2-14 (a) Non-uniform mesh overlaying the device region of the cross-section of a MOSFET. (b and c) Contour plot format of the doping concentration (b), and the potential of the MOSFET of part (a).

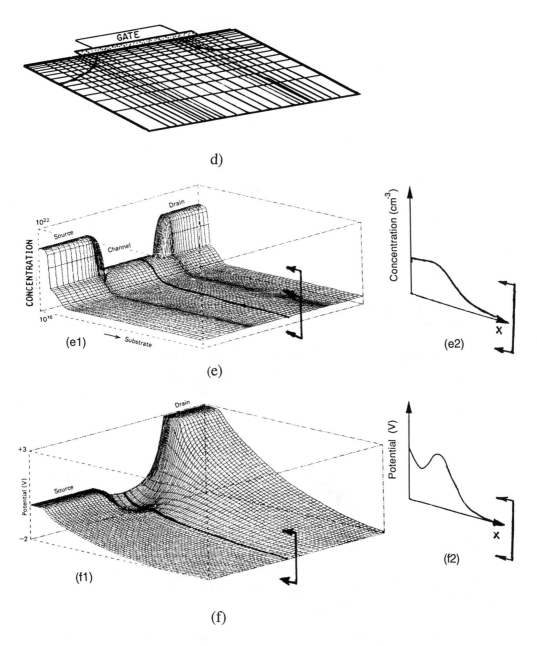

d)

(e1)

(e2)

(e)

(f1)

(f2)

(f)

Fig. 2-14 (cont.) (d) The mesh of part (a) lying on its back. (e and f) Perspective plot format used to depict the doping concentration (e1), and the potential (f1) of the same MOSFET of parts (b) and (c). Note That (e2) and (f2) show the 1-D variation of the doping concentration and potential versus depth (x) in the MOSFET at the center of the channel.

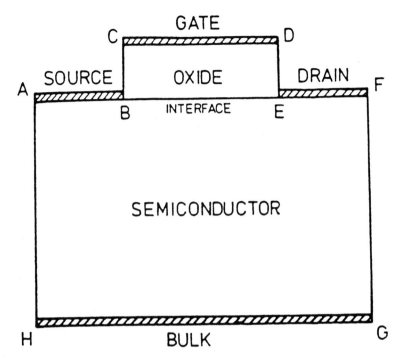

Fig. 2-15 The simulation geometry of the MOSFET for our example.

1. *State the Poisson equation in 2-D form for the Given Device Structure.* The Poisson equation in two dimensions for the silicon region of a MOSFET described above has the following form (i.e., assuming $N_D = 0$):

$$\frac{\partial^2 \varphi}{\partial x^2} + \frac{\partial^2 \varphi}{\partial y^2} = -\left(\frac{q}{\kappa_{Si}\varepsilon_o}\right)\left[-N_A + p_{po}\, e^{-q\varphi/kT} + N_D - n_{po}\, e^{q\varphi/kT}\right] \qquad (2-41)$$

where the right side expresses the charge in terms of the mobile charge concentrations (in terms of φ - assuming Boltzmann statistics), and the doping concentration N_A. The doping concentration as a function of position is assumed to be given. The Poisson equation is solved for the rectangular area A-F-G-H of the MOSFET in Fig. 2-15, which represents the silicon region. (In the area C-D-E-B, which represents the gate oxide, only the Laplace equation has to be solved - which is just the Poisson equation with the charge density equal to zero, $\partial^2 \varphi/\partial x^2 = 0$ - because we assume that no charge centers exist in an ideal oxide, and because $\partial^2 \varphi/\partial y^2 = 0$ [since there is no y- component of the oxide electric field in this structure].)

2. *Specify the Boundary Conditions.* In order to solve the 2-D PDE Poisson equation a set of spatial boundary conditions in φ is required. The boundary conditions for our example are assumed as follows: At the contacts (i.e., segment A-B: source contact, E-F: drain contact, and G-H substrate contact) a perfect ohmic contact is assumed to exist. The potential at each of these contact regions is thus kept fixed along the contact length at a value equal to the applied bias plus the built-in potential between the source/drain region and the substrate (e.g., if the source and substrate are both connected to ground, the potential at A-B is set at 0V + V_{bi}). Boundary conditions where the value of the dependent variable itself is specified are referred to as Dirichlet boundary conditions.

At the vertical boundaries (A-H, F-G) the derivative of the potential perpendicular to the boundary (i.e., the lateral electric field) is specified (that is, so-called Neumann boundary conditions are specified here). These values are set at zero in our example, which assumes that zero current flows across these boundaries.

The gate potential boundary condition is again of the Dirichlet type, with the voltage being fixed along the gate at a value of applied bias minus the flat-band voltage (to account for the work-function difference and any oxide charge at the Si-SiO_2 interface). At the Si-SiO_2 interface the potential must obey Gauss's law (see Eq. 3-15), so the boundary condition at the Si-SiO_2 interface is (since $\mathcal{E} = -\partial\varphi/\partial x$):

$$\kappa_{ox} \ (\partial\varphi/\partial x)_{ox} = \kappa_{si} \ (\partial\varphi/\partial x)_{si} \qquad (2 - 42)$$

The solution of the Poisson equation must also satisfy continuity equations internally. The continuity of the potential φ must be maintained everywhere to achieve the physically realistic condition of finite stored electrostatic field energy.

3. *Specify an appropriate grid.* The potential which solves the Poisson equation as defined by Eq. 2-41 is a continuous function of the spatial coordinates. The numerical solution of the Poisson equation requires that the potential and charge concentrations be represented by discrete values at a network of nodes within the solution regions. Hence, a 2-D rectangular grid (which defines the domain of the device geometry) must next be selected (Fig. 2-14a). To improve the solution accuracy, nonuniform grid spacing in the vertical and horizontal directions is usually chosen for this problem - being coarse in regions away from the silicon surface and closely spaced where the dopant concentration varies strongly with position. Each intersection of grid lines represents one of the nodes at which the potential will be determined. The discrete approximation to the continuous Poisson equation relates the potential value at a node to the value at neighboring nodes. The resulting nodes are also sequentially numbered so that when the discretized algebraic equations at each node are established, they will be ordered in a standard format that facilitates the solution of the matrix equation. An example of the sequential node ordering for a simple node structure is shown in Fig. 2-11. Generally, more sophisticated node-ordering algorithms are used.

4. *Discretize the Poisson equation Using the Finite-Difference Method.* Since the electrostatic (non time-varying) potential is being sought, time discretization is not necessary. Hence, only spatial discretization of the Poisson equation needs to be carried out. In this example the '5-point' finite difference approximation of Fig. 2-7 is used. This is the simplest approach for two-dimensional problems since it includes only the four nearest-neighbor nodes (i.e., those horizontally and vertically adjacent to the center node). The resulting equation associated with the center node (at position [i,j]) depends on the potential ($\varphi_{i,j}$) and charge values ($n_{i,j}$, $N_{Ai,j}$) at this node and its four neighbors.

In its simplest form, the finite-difference equation for the Poisson equation for a two-dimensional uniform mesh is (using the central difference approximations for the second derivatives)*

$$
\frac{\varphi_{i-1,j} - 2\varphi_{i,j} + \varphi_{i+1,j}}{\Delta x^2} + \frac{\varphi_{i,j-1} - 2\varphi_{i,j} + \varphi_{i,j+1}}{\Delta y^2}
$$

$$
= \left(\frac{-q}{\kappa_{Si}\,\varepsilon_0}\right)\left[-n_i e^{q(\varphi_{i,j} - \varphi_n)/kT} + n_i e^{q(\varphi_p - \varphi_{i,j})/kT}\ N_{A_{i,j}}\right]
\qquad (2-43)
$$

This is a nonlinear algebraic equation because φ appears on the right side in exponential form since $n_{i,j}$ and $p_{i,j}$ are expressed with Eqs. 1-6. The equation can nevertheless now be solved using algebraic techniques. Note that since the potential must be determined at each node, an equation at each node must be written (except for the nodes at which the potential is fixed by the externally applied voltage - i.e., the externally applied voltages become the boundary conditions at such nodes).

5. *Format the Set of Discretized Equations to Facilitate a Matrix Solution.* The result of the discretization procedure is a set of N simultaneous nonlinear algebraic equations, each having the form of Eq. 2-43. The solution of a large set of algebraic equations can be carried out using matrix methods. To implement this approach, the set of equations is represented as a single matrix equation, which can be written as

$$
[\mathbf{B}]\ \{\varphi\} = \{\mathbf{Q}\}
\qquad (2-44)
$$

where $[\mathbf{B}]$ is the coefficient matrix of the difference expressions, and the vector $\{\varphi\}$ consist of the elements $\varphi_{i,j}$ for each node in the solution, and the vector $\{\mathbf{Q}\}$ contains the terms on the right hand side of the equation. (We noted earlier that the nodes of the grid can be ordered so that three of the five nonzero values in each row occur along the principal diagonal and its two adjacent diagonals (Fig. 2-10). Thus, since most of the entries of $[\mathbf{B}]$ are zero, it is referred to as a *sparse matrix*. In addition, the elements $\varphi_{i,j}$ are placed in $\{\varphi\}$ using the same order as the node sequence, e.g. for the grid ordering scheme shown in Fig. 2-11, $\varphi_{3,4} = \varphi_{14}$ in $\{\varphi\}$.)

To put each equation into a format compatible with the matrix equation 2-44, we collect all the coefficients of the discrete dependent variables on the left-hand side of the

* In the case of a non-uniform mesh, the finite-difference representation of the 2-D Poisson equation is

$$
\{[(\varphi_{i+1,j} - \varphi_{i,j})/a_i] - [(\varphi_{i,j} - \varphi_{i-1,j})/a_{i-1}]\}/([a_i + a_{i-1}]/2)
$$

$$
+ \{[(\varphi_{i,j+1} - \varphi_{i,j})/b_j] - [(\varphi_{i,j+1} - \varphi_{i,j})]/b_{j-1}]/([b_j + b_{j-1}]/2)
$$

$$
= \left(\frac{-q}{\kappa_{Si}\,\varepsilon_0}\right)\left[-n_i e^{q(\varphi_{i,j} - \varphi_n)/kT} + n_i e^{q(\varphi_p - \varphi_{i,j})/kT} - N_{A_{i,j}}\right]
\qquad (2-45)
$$

equation. This puts the algebraic equation at each interior node (i,j) into the following form (for a uniform mesh)

$$\frac{\varphi_{i-1,j}}{\Delta x^2} + \frac{\varphi_{i,j-1}}{\Delta y^2} - \left(\frac{2}{\Delta x^2} + \frac{2}{\Delta y^2}\right)\varphi_{i,j} + \frac{\varphi_{i+1,j}}{\Delta x^2} + \frac{\varphi_{i,j+1}}{\Delta y^2}$$

$$= \left(\frac{-q}{\kappa_{Si}\varepsilon_o}\right)\left[-n_i e^{q(\varphi_{i,j} - \varphi_n)/kT} + n_i e^{q(\varphi_p - \varphi_{i,j})/kT} - N_{A_{i,j}}\right]$$

(2 - 46a)

For example, the equation for node (3,4) in such a uniform mesh would be,

$$\frac{\varphi_{2,4}}{\Delta x^2} + \frac{\varphi_{3,3}}{\Delta y^2} - \left(\frac{2}{\Delta x^2} + \frac{2}{\Delta y^2}\right)\varphi_{3,4} + \frac{\varphi_{4,4}}{\Delta x^2} + \frac{\varphi_{3,5}}{\Delta y^2}$$

$$= \left(\frac{-q}{\kappa_{Si}\varepsilon_o}\right)\left[-n_i e^{q(\varphi_{i,j} - \varphi_n)/kT} + n_i e^{q(\varphi_p - \varphi_{i,j})/kT} - N_{A_{i,j}}\right]$$

(2 - 46b)

and the coefficients of the terms on the left hand side would be placed in the coefficient matrix as shown below

Column	1	2	3	4	5
Row 1	B_{11}	:	0	0	0
2	0	B_{22}	B_{32}		0
3	0	B_{23}	$1/\Delta y^2$		
4	0	$1/\Delta x^2$	$-(2/\Delta x^2 + 2/\Delta y^2)$	$1/\Delta x^2$	0
5	0	0	$1/\Delta y^2$		
6	:	:	:		

If we filled the rest of the coefficient matrix [**B**] with the other terms from all the other equations we would see that it is tridiagonal matrix (although when boundary conditions are included it contains at most 5 nonzero entries per row).

6. *Linearize the Set of Discrete Equations.* Each of the individual algebraic equations (such as 2-46) are still non-linear (i.e., the mobile charge densities in the right hand side *n* and *p* depend exponentially on φ). Thus, the set of equations must be linearized before linear matrix solution techniques can be applied. As described in section 2.6, the Newton iteration method can be used to linearize the nonlinear terms in the equation about the most recent approximation to φ. For each iteration Eq. 2-44 is linearized by such a technique and then a linear matrix solution technique can be used to solve the resulting *linear* matrix equation of the new approximation to φ. It is desirable that the initial values of $\varphi_{i,j}$ (e.g., $\varphi_{i,j}{}^o$) be selected so that the iteration is initially numerically stable. In one approach, the vector elements $\{\varphi^o\}$ are chosen such that each element of

* Sparse-matrix ordering techniques must be used to ensure the optimum ordering of the matrices before setting out to solve the matrix equation. There are a variety of ordering algorithms available to deal with sparse matrices, as mentioned earlier.

the vector $\{\mathbf{Q}\} = 0$. This yields a condition of charge neutrality at each node within the region, guaranteeing numerical stability of the initial iteration. The iteration procedure is halted when adequate convergence is achieved (i.e., when the change in one value of φ from one iteration ($\varphi_{i,j}{}^{k}$) to the next ($\varphi_{i,j}{}^{k+1}$) is smaller than some specified error bound, δ_1, as given by Eq. 2-32.

In our example, the nonlinearized form of the matrix equation at the beginning of iteration $k+1$ is

$$[\mathbf{B}]\,\{\varphi^{k+1}\} = \{\mathbf{Q}^{k+1}\} \qquad\qquad (2\text{-}47)$$

To linearize this equation using the Newton iteration technique we replace $\{\mathbf{Q}^{k+1}\}$ (containing the nonlinear terms) with

$$\{\mathbf{Q}^{k+1}\} = \{\mathbf{Q}^{k}\} + [\mathbf{J}^{k}]\,\{\varphi^{k+1} - \varphi^{k}\} \qquad\qquad (2\text{-}48)$$

so Eq. 2-47 becomes

$$[\mathbf{B}]\{\varphi^{k+1}\} = \{\mathbf{Q}^{k}\} + [\mathbf{J}^{k}]\{\varphi^{k+1} - \varphi^{k}\} \qquad\qquad (2\text{-}49)$$

where the elements J^{k} of the Jacobian matrix $[\mathbf{J}^{k}]$ are

$$J^{k}(p,q) = \partial Q(p)/\partial \varphi(q)\,\big|_{\{\varphi k\}} \qquad p,q = 1,2,3, \dots N \qquad\qquad (2\text{-}50)$$

To express the matrix equation so that all the unknowns φ^{k+1} appear in the vector $\{\varphi^{k+1}\}$ we rearrange Eq. 2-49 to yield

$$[\mathbf{B} - \mathbf{J}^{k}]\,\{\varphi^{k+1}\} = \{\mathbf{Q}^{k}\} - [\mathbf{J}^{k}]\{\varphi^{k}\} \qquad\qquad (2\text{-}51)$$

Note that all of the terms in $\{\varphi^{k}\}$ are known, since they involve quantities calculated during the previous iteration.

For the single equation at node (3,4), since $Q_{i,j} = -N_{Ai,j} - n_i \exp\,[q(\varphi_{i,j} - \varphi_n)/kT$ and

$$J_{3,4}{}^{k} = \partial Q_{i,j}/\partial \varphi_{i,j}\,\big|_{\varphi 3,4}{}^{k} = (q/kT)\,n_i \exp\,[q\,(\varphi_{3,4}{}^{k} - \varphi_n)/kT] \qquad\qquad (2\text{-}52)$$

replacing $Q_{3,4}{}^{k+1}$ with $Q_{3,4}{}^{k} + [\partial Q_{i,j}/\partial \varphi_{i,j}\,|_{@\,\varphi 3,4}{}^{k}]\,[\varphi_{3,4}{}^{k+1} - \varphi_{3,4}{}^{k}]$, it becomes

$$\frac{\varphi_{2,4}^{k+1}}{\Delta x^2} + \frac{\varphi_{3,3}^{k+1}}{\Delta y^2} - \left(\frac{2}{\Delta x^2} + \frac{2}{\Delta x^2}\right)\varphi_{3,4}^{k+1} + \frac{\varphi_{4,4}^{k+1}}{\Delta x^2} + \frac{\varphi_{3,3}^{k+1}}{\Delta y^2}$$

$$= \left(\frac{-q}{\kappa_{Si}\varepsilon_o}\right)\left[\,-n_i e^{q(\varphi_{3,4}^{k}- \varphi_n)/kT} + n_i e^{q(\varphi_p - \varphi_{3,4}^{k})/kT}\,\right]$$

$$+ \left(\frac{-q}{\kappa_{Si}\varepsilon_o}\right)\left\{\,\left[\frac{q}{kT}\left(-n_i e^{q(\varphi_{3,4}^{k}- \varphi_n)/kT} + n_i e^{q(\varphi_p - \varphi_{3,4}^{k})/kT}\right]\right]\left[\varphi_{3,4}^{k+1} - \varphi_{3,4}^{k}\right] - N_{A3,4}\right\}$$

$$(2\text{-}53)$$

or

$$\frac{\varphi_{2,4}^{k+1}}{\Delta x^2} + \frac{\varphi_{3,3}^{k+1}}{\Delta y^2} - \left(\frac{2}{\Delta x^2} + \frac{2}{\Delta x^2} - \left[\frac{-q}{\kappa_{Si}\varepsilon_o}\right] \left[n_i e^{q(\varphi_{3,4}^k - \varphi_n)/kT} + n_i e^{q(\varphi_p - \varphi_{3,4}^k)/kT}\right]\right)\varphi_{3,4}^{k+1} + \frac{\varphi_{4,4}^{k+1}}{\Delta x^2} + \frac{\varphi_{3,3}^{k+1}}{\Delta y^2}$$

$$= \left(\frac{-q}{\kappa_{Si}\varepsilon_o}\right)\left[-n_i e^{q(\varphi_{3,4}^k - \varphi_n)/kT} + n_i e^{q(\varphi_p - \varphi_{3,4}^k)/kT}\right]$$

$$+ \left(\frac{-q}{\kappa_{Si}\varepsilon_o}\right)\left\{ \left[\frac{q}{kT}\left(-n_i e^{q(\varphi_{3,4}^k - \varphi_n)/kT} + n_i e^{q(\varphi_p - \varphi_{3,4}^k)/kT}\right)\right]\left[\varphi_{3,4}^k\right] - N_{A3,4}\right\}$$

(2 - 54)

Note that all of the terms on the right hand side of Eq. 2-54 involve φ at its previous iteration (φ^k) - which is known, while the terms on the left hand side involve φ^{k+1} - which is unknown.

Following this procedure at each node, the set of nonlinear equations for the unknown potential is thereby linearized. Linear matrix solution techniques can now be applied to the set to calculate φ^{k+1} at each node.

7. *Solve the Linear Matrix Equation.* As described in section 2.7 a number of matrix solution techniques have been developed to solve the resulting *linearized* (sparse) matrix equation. We also noted that such techniques can be grouped into two classes: direct methods and iterative methods. If a *direct* method is selected (e.g., Gaussian elimination, or some variation thereof), the solutions are checked against the previous nonlinear iteration estimate. If the solutions do not yet meet this convergence criterion, the nonlinear iteration procedure of step (5) is repeated until convergence is achieved. If an *iterative* technique is selected, the linear iteration is repeated until the iteration converges to a specified error bound δ_2, as given by Eq. 2-35. Then, the nonlinear convergence criterion is checked (Eq. 2-32), and if not met, another cycle through the linear iterative procedure is carried out. Thus, as shown in Fig. 2-18b, if an iterative technique is used to solve the linear matrix equation, this iteration is referred to as the *inner iteration* or *inner loop* of the algorithm, whereas the *non-linear iteration* is referred to as the *outer iteration* or *outer loop*.

8. *Display the Results in an Appropriate Graphical Format.* The values of φ computed for each of the grid points in the domain using this technique (the solution) can be represented in a number of ways. Since this example deals with a two-dimensional problem, the solution can be displayed in a number of ways, two of which are the *contour plot* (on which lines of equal potential are drawn through grid points of equal potential), and the *perspective graph* (in which the potential at each grid point is shown as height above that point on the grid, and the points are connected together to produce a surface in three dimensions, see Fig. 2-14).

2.10.1.1 Example of How Device Simulation Programs are Used to Obtain the Two-Dimensional Solution of the Poisson Equation in a MOSFET Structure Operating in Subthreshold.
Procedures for obtaining the solution of the 2-D Poisson equation by numerical analysis akin to the one described in the previous discussion are typically carried out with the aid of high-speed computers. The software programs that enable the numerical analysis procedures to be performed are part of such device-simulation packages such as GEMINI, PISCES, MINIMOS, MEDICI, etc. Here we present a brief synopsis of how such a simulation package is used to obtain such a solution.

Before we begin this synopsis it should again be pointed out that 2-D finite-difference-based device simulators (e.g., GEMINI and PISCES) typically use the box-integration discretization method rather than the difference-operator method described in the previous section. This permits non-planar device structures to be handled more easily. The form of the algebraic equations that approximate the 2-D Poisson equation is nevertheless essentially the same as that obtained using the difference-operator method. Hence, the matrix techniques for solving them are the same as those described earlier in the chapter. The derivation of the finite difference equations using the box-integration method with a five-point difference approximation is given in Appendix D. There we also demonstrate how the box-integration approach is exploited to facilitate the simulation of non-planar device structures.

Various quantities must be specified as input to the simulation program so that the solution of the Poisson equation for a particular MOSFET structure can be carried out. These include: (1) the material properties of each of the device regions, namely the semiconductor (e.g., silicon), the gate dielectric (e.g., SiO_2), and the gate material (e.g., Al or n^+ poly); (2) the dimensions of the MOSFET (e.g., the gate length, and the lengths of the source and drain); (3) the gate oxide thickness t_{ox}; (4) the operating temperature T; (5) the doping concentrations at each point in the structure being analyzed (normally provided to the device simulator in the form of doping profile data obtained from a 2-D process simulator); and (6) the values of the potential at the boundaries of the solution domain (i.e., at the boundaries of the device structure, including at the source and drain regions, at the gate, at the backside of the device [substrate contact], and at the vertical sides of the device).

Figure 2-16a shows the simulated doping profiles (in contour form) in an example MOSFET structure obtained from a 2-D process simulator.[19] In this case a parasitic MOSFET is analyzed. Such parasitic devices occur in the field regions of n-well CMOS structures, with the n^+ region being the source, the n-well being the drain, the field oxide being the gate oxide, and an aluminum line running over the field oxide being the gate, see also Fig. 2-16c. The channel is the p-substrate region between the n^+ diffusion and the n-well, here with a nominal length of 2.4 μm. Notice that in this structure boron ions are implanted under the field oxide to form a p-type channel stop between active NMOSFETs. The values of the potential at the boundaries in this example are V_{SS} and $V_{BS} = 0V$, and $V_{GS} = V_{DS} = V_{DD} = 5V$.

2-D device simulation programs (e.g., GEMINI, MINIMOS, or PISCES) are capable of using the doping profiles obtained from 2-D process simulators as their input.

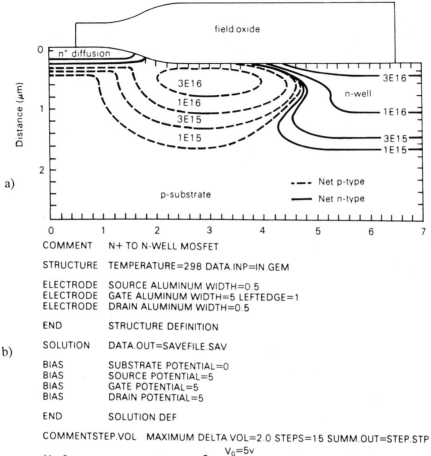

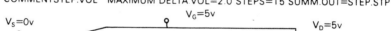

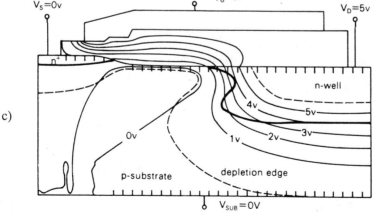

Fig. 2-16 Using GEMINI to analyze the potential in a parasitic MOSFET: (a) the simulated doping contours in an n^+ to n-well parasitic MOSFET; (b) the GEMINI input file; (c) the corresponding 2-D output potential plot as calculated with GEMINI.[19] (© 1986 IEEE).

Figure 2-16b lists the GEMINI input file for simulating the electrostatic potential as a function of distance (i.e., by solving the Poisson equation) for the device structure of Fig. 2-16a. Note that in the STRUCTURE statement of this file, the IN. GEM file used for DATA. INP in the GEMINI input file is from the file saved from running a 2-D process simulator. (That is, one of the last statements in the process simulator input file would be a SAVE statement instructing that the doping profile data is to be saved in the format of a file suitable as input to a particular device simulator - in this case to GEMINI). Also note that the dimensions and type of material of the electrodes at the source and drain contact and the gate are not specified by the process simulator input and hence must be defined. This is done using the three ELECTRODE statements in the example file given here.

Figure 2-16c depicts the output of the GEMINI program for the MOSFET structure of Fig. 2-16a. That is, here the form of the solution of the Poisson equation (the potential as a function of position in the MOSFET) is that of 2-D equipotential contours potential. The depletion region edge for the particular device structure and biasing is also shown (solid heavy black line).

2.10.2 Example of a Numerical Procedure for Solving the One-Dimensional Form of Fick's 2nd Law Equation as a Model for Impurity Diffusion in Silicon

In general, simulation of the redistribution of impurities in silicon under practical processing conditions involves the solution of the concentration-dependent nonlinear Fick's 2nd Law equation in a domain where one of the boundaries (the silicon-oxide interface) is continually and nonuniformly moving in space as a function of time. Analytical solutions of Fick's 2nd Law equation are only available for special, limited cases of process conditions (and usually only in one-dimension), and thus, this approach to obtain solutions of Fick's equation in the more general case equation is inadequate. For most practical process conditions, numerical analysis must be employed to obtain approximate solutions of the equation. Here we describe an example of a set of numerical procedures that can be used to solve the one-dimensional form of the equation.

We will follow the numerical analysis approach used in SUPREM II as described by Antoniadis.[17] In our example, however, the treatment is limited to the case of diffusion of boron or arsenic in silicon in an inert atmosphere. In this way we can maintain mathematical simplicity while still demonstrating the essential steps of the numerical analysis procedure.*

* If we treated the case of diffusion in an oxidizing ambient we would have had to include a boundary condition accounting for dopant segregation at the Si-SiO$_2$ interface, and would also have had to deal with the condition of a moving boundary (since Si is consumed during the diffusion process by the growth of an oxide on the Si surface). Even though we do not discuss these aspects of the simulation problem, they are, in fact, handled numerically in the SUPREM II and III simulators.

1. *State Fick's 2nd Law Equation in One-Dimensional Form.* The Fick's 2nd Law equation in its general three-dimensional form is

$$\partial C/\partial t = \text{div } F_D \qquad (2-55)$$

where the flux of impurities F_D according to Fick's first law is

$$F_D = -D \nabla C \qquad (2-56)$$

C is the concentration of dopants in the silicon, and D is the diffusion coefficient.
   In one-dimension, F_D is written as:

$$F_D(x) = -D(x) [dC(x)/dx] \qquad (2-57)$$

and the Fick's Second Law equation has the following form

$$\partial C/\partial t = \partial/\partial x \{-D(x) [\partial C(x)/\partial x]\} \qquad (2-58a)$$

or

$$\partial C/\partial t = \partial/\partial x \{F_D(x)\} \qquad (2-58b)$$

The boundary and initial conditions depend on the particular diffusion process being simulated. For example, the Si surface may have a constant doping concentration during the time of diffusion being analyzed (predeposition step), or a drive-in step may be carried out, either in an inert environment (in which case dopant may be evaporating from the surface during the process), or an oxide may be being grown (in which case, dopant segregation effects at the surface will cause the Si surface concentration to change). Finally, the initial doping profile might have been introduced with a previous ion implantation step, which again would impact the boundary and initial conditions.

2. *Specify the Grid in One-Dimension.* The one-dimensional domain over which Eq. 2-58 is to be solved is partitioned into discrete cells as function of depth beneath the silicon surface (see Fig. 2-17). In the latest versions of SUPREM III, these cells can

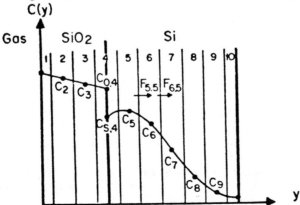

Fig. 2.17 Illustration of the partitioning of the simulation space into discrete cells with impurity fluxes across the cell boundaries.

have nonuniform sizes (specified by the user). The nodes at which the concentration C(x) is evaluated lie at the center of the cells, and these locations will be considered to be the points of the grid. The fluxes which give rise to the change in concentration in a cell, however, are evaluated across the cell boundaries (i.e., at the 'half-points' of the grid). The values of C and F_D are calculated using a discretized version of Eq. 2-58. For example, the concentration of impurities in some cell (say, cell 6, Fig. 2-17) is approximated by the concentration calculated at the grid point at x = 6. In the discretized equation, for purposes of calculation the concentration in each cell is also assumed to be constant throughout the cell. The change in number of impurities per unit area in a cell (ΔQ) from one time step to the next is found by computing the difference of the net fluxes of impurities crossing the cell boundaries (i.e., at x = 6.5 and x = 5.5) during that time interval (neglecting generation-loss terms). The change in the concentration is found by multiplying ΔQ by the width of the cell (e.g., $x_{6.5} - x_{5.5}$).

3. *Discretize the Fick's 2nd Law equation Using the Finite-Difference Method.* To approximate the change in concentration as a function of time we must discretize both the time and space derivatives in the Fick's 2nd Law equation. As discussed in section 2.4.4, time discretization can be done in a number of ways, using either *explicit* or *implicit* schemes. As was noted in section 2.4.4, however, the simple forward-Euler explicit time-discretization method is generally avoided because this approach can be unstable unless excessively small time steps are used.* Instead, the more complex, but also more stable and accurate, implicit time discretization methods are implemented in process (and device) simulators. In fact, the computation times for implicit methods are comparable to those when the explicit method is used, but accuracy in the former is better, and hence they are preferred.

In SUPREM II time-discretization is performed using the second-order implicit Crank-Nicholson technique. In this approach, the unknown parameter (e.g., C[x]) is averaged between its values at the previous step and the next time step. We will illustrate the Crank-Nicholson method for this equation after first describing the space discretization procedure.

To discretize the space derivatives of Eq. 2-58, we first deal with the outer partial derivative with respect to x in the right-hand side of Eq. 2-58b. That is, this operator is replaced with a first-order central difference approximation of the first derivative. Since we wish to evaluate the fluxes at the cell boundaries, we calculate their values at the half-points of the grid, e.g., a cell whose center is at x = i, has boundaries at i + 1/2 and i - 1/2. When this is done - for a cell whose midpoint is at x = i - the right-hand side of Eq. 2-58b becomes

$$\partial/\partial x \ \{F_D(x)\} \quad ----> \quad - \ [\ F_D(x_{i + 1/2}) - F_D(x_{i - 1/2})]/(x_{i + 1} - x_i) \qquad (2 - 59)$$

---

* Stability of the forward-Euler explicit method is guaranteed only if the dimensionless quantity $D\Delta t/(\Delta x)^2 = D\Delta t/[(x_{i + 1} - x_i)(x_{i + 1} - x_i)]$ in Eq. 2-59 does not exceed 0.5. This limit forces one to employ very small values of Δt, leading to very long computational times, since the equations must be solved at each time step.

For example, for cell 6, if the right-hand side of 2-59 is used in Eq. 2-58a, then 2-58b would be written as

$$dC(x = 6)/dt = -[F_D(x_{6.5}) - F_D(x_{5.5})]/(x_6 - x_5) \qquad (2 - 60)$$

where $F_D(x_{6.5})$ and $F_D(x_{5.5})$ are the impurity diffusive fluxes at the right and left-hand boundaries of cell 6, respectively. Next F_D is discretized and these discretized approximations of F_D are substituted into the right-hand side of 2-60. However, it should be noted that in SUPREM II a modified form of the Fick's First Law equation is actually discretized, and not Eq. 2-57. That is, Eq. 2-57 is modified before discretization by changing it to the following form:

$$F_D = -d/dx [D(x) C(x)] \qquad (2 - 61)$$

Note that this modification is valid for modeling boron and arsenic diffusion in silicon, and is used in SUPREM II for these dopants. For simulating phosphorus diffusion, however, this modification is not valid, and the correct (but more computationally lengthy) form (i.e., Eq. 2-57) should be used. This is done in SUPREM II when phosphorus diffusion is being simulated. For reasons of simplicity we nevertheless elect to use Eq. 2-61 in this example as the basis of the discretized forms of F_D.

According to the Crank-Nicholson method for time discretization, the value of F_D is calculated by taking the average of the first derivative approximations using $C(x)$ at the previous time step $(C[x]^k)$ and the next time step $(C[x]^{k+1})$. Hence, the appropriate discretized form of $F_D(x_{i+1/2})$ which is to be substituted in the right-hand side of 2-59 is

$$F_D\left(x_{i+\frac{1}{2}}\right) = -\frac{1}{2}\left[D(C_{i+\frac{1}{2}}^k)\frac{C_{i+1}^k - C_i^k}{x_{i+1} - x_i} + D(C_{i+\frac{1}{2}}^{k+1})\frac{C_{i+1}^{k+1} - C_i^{k+1}}{x_{i+1} - x_i}\right] \qquad (2 - 62)$$

Then, the fully discretized form of Eq. 2-53a is

$$\frac{C_i^{k+1} - C_i^k}{\Delta t} = -\left(\frac{F_D\left(x_{i+\frac{1}{2}}\right) - F_D\left(x_{i-\frac{1}{2}}\right)}{(x_{i+1} - x_i)}\right) \qquad (2 - 63)$$

or

$$C_i^{k+1} = C_i^k - \frac{\Delta t}{(x_{i+1} - x_i)}\left(F_D\left(x_{i+\frac{1}{2}}\right) - F_D\left(x_{i-\frac{1}{2}}\right)\right)$$

Substituting for $F_D(x_{i+1/2})$ and $F_D(x_{i-1/2})$ we get

$$C_i^{k+1} = C_i^k - \frac{\Delta t}{(x_{i+1} - x_i)}\left(-\frac{1}{2}\left[D(C_{i+\frac{1}{2}}^k)\frac{C_{i+1}^k - C_i^k}{x_{i+1} - x_i} + D(C_{i+\frac{1}{2}}^{k+1})\frac{C_{i+1}^{k+1} - C_i^{k+1}}{x_{i+1} - x_i}\right]\right.$$

$$\left. -\frac{1}{2}\left[D(C_{i-\frac{1}{2}}^k)\frac{C_i^k - C_{i-1}^k}{x_i - x_{i-1}} + D(C_{i-\frac{1}{2}}^{k+1})\frac{C_i^{k+1} - C_{i-1}^{k+1}}{x_i - x_{i-1}}\right]\right) \qquad (2 - 64)$$

4. (a) *Format the Set of Discretized Equations to Facilitate a Matrix Solution.* (b) *Linearize the Matrix Equation.* (c) *Solve Using an Appropriate Linear Matrix Solution Technique.* An equation like Eq. 2-64 is formulated for each node of the grid. Thus, we have a set of algebraic equations for our solution space at each time step. Note that the unknown at the next time step $(k+1)$ appears not only in the term describing the location of the cell of interest (e.g., for cell 6, i = 6 in the above equation), but also in the terms of the two neighboring cell concentrations (i - 1 and i + 1). Thus, when these unknowns are collected on the left-hand side of the equation, they will supply three coefficients to one of the rows of the coefficient matrix. The resulting equations are therefore mutually coupled and form a system of simultaneous algebraic equations. For each time step this set of equations must be solved. The result is a set of concentration values (one for each cell) for each time step. The final set of concentration values represents the approximate variation of doping concentration in one dimension after the completion of the diffusion process being simulated.

If the nodes are appropriately ordered, and the equation set is combined to form a matrix equation, the coefficient matrix [**A**] can be tridiagonal (sparse).

$$[\mathbf{A}] \, \{\mathbf{C}\}^{k+1} \;=\; \{\mathbf{M}\}^k \qquad\qquad (2\text{-}65)$$

where $\{\mathbf{M}\}^k$ is a vector containing concentration terms calculated from the previous time step, and hence are known. Now, matrix solution techniques, as described earlier, can be employed to efficiently solve Eq. 2-65. Note, however, that the diffusion coefficient D can also be a function of the impurity concentration; in that case, the system of equations becomes nonlinear. If the equation set is nonlinear, linearization techniques, such as the Newton iterative method described in section 2.6 must be used to linearize the set. Then, Newton iterations of the solution are performed until convergence of the results is achieved. In SUPREM II Antoniadis reports that a direct linear matrix solution technique (e.g., Gaussian elimination or variant thereof) is used to solve the linearized equation set.

5. *Display the results.* The results are a set of concentration values (one per cell) at each time step. Most commonly, these values are plotted (usually only the set of values at the last time step) versus distance in the silicon. An example of such a doping profile is shown in Fig. 2-18. Note that a 1-D doping profile like the one shown in Fig. 2-18 can also be extracted form a 2-D doping concentration surface plot (shown in Fig. 2-14e1).

2.11 SYSTEMS OF COUPLED EQUATIONS

We pointed out in chap. 1 that the quantitative model of semiconductor device operation is based on the set of coupled device PDEs (Eqs. 1-3 and 1-4). In addition, the modeling diffusion may also involve the solution of a set of coupled PDEs. Thus, we should briefly mention some of the issues involved in the solution of such coupled equations.

In general, two techniques were used in the 1970s to deal with a coupled set of PDEs. The algorithm flow diagram for these two techniques as applied to the coupled device

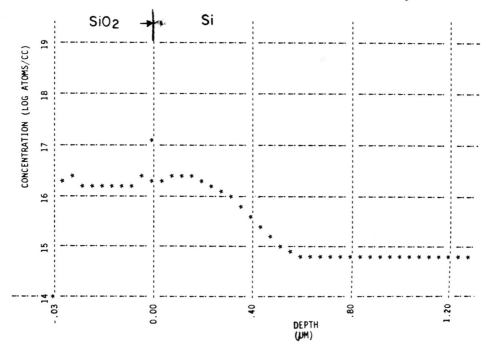

Fig. 2.18 SUPREM III output of boron distribution.

equations is shown in Fig. 2-19. These techniques are respectively: (1) *Gummel's iterative* (or *alternating*, or *decoupled*) method; and (2) *Newtons direct* method (also referred to as the *simultaneous*, or *coupled* method). The comparison between these two techniques is somewhat analogous to the comparison of direct versus iterative matrix solution methods for linear algebraic equations.

2.11.1 Gummel's Iterative Method

In *Gummel's method*, the equations are decoupled and solved sequentially and iteratively. As shown in Fig. 2-19b, Gummel's method begins with an initial guess of potentials and carrier concentrations. Then the Poisson equation is linearized and solved for the potential at each node of the mesh (e.g., using the Newton iteration method, or similar technique to linearize the discretized equations). The carrier concentrations are updated based on the new potentials and appropriate carrier statistics (Boltzmann or Fermi-Dirac), and the Poisson equation is solved again. This procedure is repeated until the potential is below some convergence criteria limit. This is the inner loop of the flow chart of Fig. 2-19b.

Next, the potentials obtained from the solution of the Poisson equation are applied to the current continuity equations. They are then solved for the carrier concentrations (keeping the potentials constant during this solution). The new carrier concentrations obtained require that the Poisson equation be solved again so that the algorithm loops back to the top of the flow chart (outer loop in Fig. 2-19b). Eventually, potentials and carrier concentrations converge and are consistent with both the Poisson and continuity equations. A direct (e.g., Gaussian elimination) method is often used for each decoupled linearized matrix equation in Gummel's method.

This method is preferred for zero/reverse bias and low-current conditions, in which the equations are loosely coupled (such as the subthreshold region of operation in MOSFETs). Because less work is expended on each pass through the outer loop than in the Newtons direct method, much less memory capacity is required and superior execution speed is obtained. However, the convergence rate of Gummel's method can be very slow if the Poisson equation and the continuity equations are strongly coupled, making the solutions under these conditions very costly. In addition, convergence is not even always guaranteed. As a result, in such cases, the device simulation software packages switches over solving the equations with the Newton method.

2.11.2 Newton's Direct Method

Newtons direct method for solving the device equations involves appending the three matrix equations (the Poisson equation and the two current continuity equations) together to form a matrix that is nine times as large as in the Gummel's method (because the coupling variables, arising from the partial derivatives of all combinations of potential and carrier concentrations for adjacent nodes must be included). Because the matrix becomes so large for grids of any practical size, inverting it requires a large

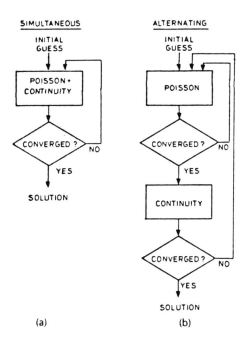

Fig. 2-19 Algorithm flow of simultaneous and alternating methods for solution of the coupled equations. (a) Simultaneous solutions. (b) Iterative solutions.[18] (© 1986 IEEE).

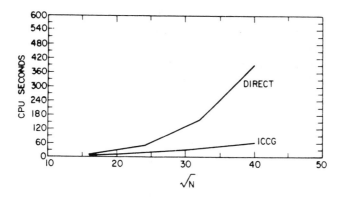

Fig. 2-20 Simulation speed comparison of direct and iterative solution versus square root of grid (VAX 11/780). (© 1986 IEEE).

memory capacity and much longer computing time than the Gummel's method. Hence, this method is results in more costly solutions at lower biases. However, it guarantees convergence at high bias levels. Consequently, it is invoked by the device simulation programs when device operating conditions are such that Gummel's method may not converge (i.e., when a MOSFET is in saturation), or when the equations are strongly coupled and convergence of Gummel's method is slow. The method is also needed for transient and ac analysis. Figure 2-20 illustrates the tradeoffs with number of grid points between direct and iterative solution methods (using an incomplete Cholesky conjugate gradient [ICCG] method as the iterative linear equation solution scheme).

Mixed mode methods for solving coupled systems of equations have also been investigated. Here, the tightly coupled equations are solved together and iterations are made between groups of loosely coupled equation solutions. Coupled PDEs also arise in simulating diffusion of impurities in silicon. Here, the diffusion equations for the impurities are coupled to those of the point defects. The same type of solution methods are applied to such coupled sets of PDEs as to the coupled device equations. A comparison of the estimated relative costs of simulating processing and device behavior using the numerical techniques described in this chapter are given in reference 18.

2.12 EVOLUTION OF DEVICE SIMULATORS

In Vol. 2, chap. 9 a synopsis of the evolution of process simulators is given. Here we trace the evolution of publicly (including commercially) available 2-D (and 3-D) MOSFET device simulators, as shown in Fig. 2-21. We will draw upon the material presented in the previous sections of this chapter as background material. Note that this discussion is not all inclusive. Specifically, a variety of other device simulators have been internally developed by large corporations and/or academic institutions, but since these are not available to the public either from academic or commercial vendors they are not described here.

2.12.1 CADDET. One of the first 2-D device simulators available to the public was CADDET. This simulator was developed by Hitachi and published in 1979.[21] It solves the Poisson equation and the continuity equation for electrons (single carrier analysis). Hence, it is suitable only for simulating FET devices. It uses a automatically generated, non-uniform rectangular grid, with a maximum of 2000 grid points. This early MOSFET simulator had many limitations, including the following: (1) the only doping profiles in the source/drain regions it could handle as input were uniform or Gaussian doping profiles (i.e., doping profiles generated by process simulators could not be used as input to CADDET); (2) only MOSFET structures with planar surface regions could be treated; (3) only single carrier analysis could be performed (i.e., could not simulate many bipolar device phenomena such as impact ionization or latch up, nor CMOS structures), and (4) only static (steady-state) device phenomena could be modeled.

2.12.2 MINIMOS. An improved 2-D FET simulator was introduced next called MINIMOS. It was published by Selberherr et al., at the Technical University of Vienna, in 1980.[22] MINIMOS solves the Poisson equation and both carrier continuity equations using a finite difference method. The program is easy to use and gained wide popularity. It can accept analytical doping profiles or doping profiles from SUPREM-III as input. It converts 1-D doping profiles to 2-D form suitable as input to the 2-D device simulation procedure. While it still finds much use and can be acquired from commercial vendors in its most recent version (MINIMOS4), it is slowly being replaced by more powerful device simulators such as PISCES-II because the following limitations make it less suitable for device structures of the 1990s: (1) MINIMOS can only handle MOSFET structures with planar surfaces; (2) it is a dc (steady-state) simulator, which means it cannot simulate transient MOSFET phenomena; (3) it uses a rectangular grid, which is not as computationally efficient as an irregular (e.g., triangular grid), as described in section 2.3; (4) because it is only a FET simulator, it cannot be used to simulate BiCMOS structures.

2.12.3 GEMINI. A 2-D Poisson solver, GEMINI, originally developed by Greenfield and Dutton at Stanford, was published in 1980.[23] As described earlier, GEMINI was the first 2-D device simulator developed to handle 2-D MOSFET structures with non-planar surfaces. That is, it solves the Poisson equation by using a box-discretization finite-difference method which permits non-planar surfaces to be treated. However, its simulations are valid only under a limited set of device operating conditions. That is, since it does not solve any of the carrier continuity equations, it must rely on analytical methods for calculating the drain current in MOSFETs from the solution that it generates of the Poisson equation. These analytical solution methods are only valid under operating conditions in low levels of current flow in the MOSFET.

The chief advantage that GEMINI offered for performing such device simulation was faster computation speeds than were possible from simulators that also had to solve the carrier continuity equations, and the ability to handle non-planar structures. Yet, advances in computing power has made the former advantage less important, and more powerful simulators such as PISCES-II also offered the ability to handle non-planar

Evolution of 2-D MOSFET Device Simulators

CADDET (1979)

* Solves Poisson Equation & One Carrier Continuity Equation
  These equations are solved Iteratively (Gummel iteration)
* Can Only Handle JFET and MOSFET Structures
* Non-Uniform, Planar Rectangular Grid
* Source/Drain Impurity Concentration Profiles
  must be Gaussian Doping Profiles
* Uses Finite Difference Discretization
* Primitive User Interface

MINIMOS (1980)

* Solves Poisson Equation and 2 Carrier Continuity Equations
* Non-uniform Rectangular Planar Grids (But Offers Adaptive Gridding)
* Can Accept Arbitrary Impurity Concentration Profiles
  from Process Simulators (SUPREM III) or Doping Profiles
  Described with Analytical Functions as Input
* Uses Finite-Difference Box-Integration Discretization
  Calculates Static-state solutions of I-V characteristics only
* User Friendly

GEMINI (1980)

* Solves Poisson Equation Only
  (i.e., Solves for Electrostatic potential $\varphi[x,y]$, then
  calculates $n[x,y]$ and $p[x,y]$ from $\varphi[x,y]$)
* Non-uniform, non-planar rectangular grid
  (Non-planar MOSFET structures can be handled)
* Uses Finite-Difference Box-Integration Discretization
  Calculates drain current from analytical expressions (dc values)
* Solutions it provides are only valid for low V_{DS} values in
  inversion or in subthreshold.

PISCES (1985)

* Solves Poisson Equation and 2 Carrier Continuity Equations
* Non-uniform Triangular Non-Planar Grids
  (Also permits Local Adaptive Refinement of Gridding)
* Can handle non-planar structures
* Can handle MOSFET and bipolar structures
* Can perform dc (static) and transient analysis
* Uses finite difference box-integration discretization scheme
* Commercial versions: MEDICI and S-PISCES-2B
* Can - Latchup in CMOS   - Hot-electron simulations
  simulate: - Substrate current in MOSFETs
  - Impact ionization   - Ionizing radiation effects

Other Device Simulators: FIELDAY (2-D Finite Element Device Analyzer)
DAVINCI (3-D Device Simulator - Commercial)
THUNDER (3-D Device Simulator - Commercial)

Fig. 2-21 Evolution of Device Simulators.

devices. Thus, GEMINI, like MINIMOS has largely been supplanted by such more powerful simulators. The limitations of GEMINI were the following: (1) it does not provide accurate simulation of MOSFETs when large currents flow in the MOSFET (e.g., when the MOSFET is in inversion and a large V_{DS} is applied). This means that the important saturation region of operation cannot be simulated by GEMINI; (2) GEMINI uses a rectangular grid, which is not as computationally efficient as a triangular grid, and; (3) it does not handle transient cases.

2.12.4. PISCES. A 2-D device simulator, named PISCES-II (**Poi**sson and **C**ontinuity **E**quation **S**olver) that is able to overcome the limitations of those just previously discussed, was published in 1984.[5,6] It was developed at Stanford by Pinto, Rafferty, and Dutton. PISCES-II solves both carrier continuity equations and the Poisson equation, and is capable of solving transient as well as steady-state problems. It accepts general doping profiles obtained from SUPREM-III, SUPREM-IV, or from analytic functions. It uses a box-discretization finite-difference, but with a non-uniform triangular grid. This permits non-planar device structures to be handled, and local adaptive gridding to be implemented. Unlike GEMINI, it can successfully simulate on-state MOSFETs in saturation. It also is capable of simulating bipolar transistor devices, allowing BiCMOS device structures to be simulated. Additionally, Fermi-Dirac statistics, incomplete impurity ionization, bandgap narrowing and Schottky barrier lowering are included. The recombination rate is modeled by both Shockley-Read-Hall and Auger band-to-band recombination. Mobility is modeled by Eq. 5-27 in chap. 5. Since it can handle transient problems, it can simulate such events as gate switching behavior, CMOS latchup, and single-event upset. (Note that comparably powerful 2-D device simulators based on finite-element discretization have been developed internally at IBM [FIELDAY],[24] the National Bureau of Standards [B2DE],[25] and other places.) An enhanced version of PISCES-II (dubbed MEDICI™) is now also commercially available from TMA Inc. PISCES-II is a more complex program than GEMINI or MINIMOS, but as computing power has continued to increase, results can now be obtained at reasonable cost with PISCES-II. Since PISCES is capable of performing the tasks of the earlier simulators and more, and the price and performance differential between them continue to decrease, it is increasingly replacing them.

2.12.5. Three-Dimensional Device Simulators. Several 3-D device simulators have been commercially released, including DAVINCI™ (TMA, Inc.), and THUNDER,™ and H-FIELDS-3D™ (Silvaco International). Triangular grids are created on a 2-D plane, and these grids are replicated many times in the third dimension to produce a 3-D grid structure. The program solves the semiconductor equations on each of the grids and assembles the solutions in a format that can be visualized in three dimensions.

REFERENCES

1. A.W. Al-Khafaji and J.R. Tooley, *Numerical Methods in Engineering Practice,* Holt, Rinehart and Winston, New York, 1986.
2. S. Selberherr, *Analysis and Simulation of Semiconductor Devices,* Springer-Verlag, Wien, New York, 1984.
3. C.M. Snowden, *Semiconductor Device Modelling,* Peter Peregrinus, London 1988.
4. P. Antognetti et al., Eds. *Process and Device Simulation for MOS-VLSI Circuits,* Martinus Nijhoff, Boston 1983.
5. M.R. Pinto, C.S. Rafferty, and R.W. Dutton, "PICSES II: Poisson and Continuity Equation Solver," Stanford University, Stanford CA 94305, September 1984.
6. C.S. Rafferty et al., "Iterative Methods in Semiconductor Device Simulation*," IEEE Trans. Electron Dev.* **ED-32**, October 1985, p. 2120.
7. C.W. Steele, *Numerical Computation of Electric and Magnetic Fields* (Van Nostrand Reinhold, New York, 1987.
8. O.C. Zienkiewicz, *The Finite Element Method,* McGraw-Hill, London 1977.
9. L. Lapidus and G.F. Pinder, *Numerical Solution of Partial Differential Equations in Science and Engineering,* John Wiley & Sons, New York, 1982.
10. R.E. Bank et al., "Transient Simulation of Silicon Devices and Circuits," *IEEE Trans. Electron Dev.* **ED-32**, October 1985, p. 1992.
11. E.H. Cuthill and J. McKee, "Reducing the bandwidth of sparse symmetric matrices," Proc. ACM Conference, 1969, p. 157.
12. A. George and J.W.H. Liu, *Computer Solution of Large Sparse Positive Definite Systems,* Prentice-Hall, Inc. Englewood Cliffs, N.J. (1981).
13. R.S. Varga, *Matrix Iterative Analysis*, Prentice-Hall, Englewood Cliffs, N.J., 1962.
14. I.A. Duff, "A Survey of Sparse Matrix Research," *Proc. IEEE* Vol. 65, p. 500 1977.
15. D.C. Cole et al., "The Use of Simulation in Semiconductor Technology Development," *Solid-State Electronics,* **33** No. 6, June 1990, p. 591.
16. S.G. Duvall, *IEEE Trans. on Computer-Aided Design,* vol. **CAD-7**, no. 7, July 1988, p. 741.
17. D.A. Antoniadis, "One Dimensional Simulation of IC Fabrication Processes," in *Process and Device Simulation for MOS-VLSI Circuits*, P. Antognetti et al., Eds., Martinus Nijhoff, the Hague, 1983, p. 226.
18. R. Dutton and M. R. Pinto, "The Use of Computer Aids in IC Technology Evolution," *IEEE Proceedings,* Vo. 74, No. 12, Dec. 1986, p. 1730.
19. A.G. Lewis, J.Y. Chen, R.A. Martin and T.Y. Huang, "Device Isolation in High-Density LOCOS-isolated CMOS," *IEEE Trans. Electron Dev.*, **ED-34**, p. 1337, 1987.
20. R.W. Dutton and A. Yu, *Technology CAD: Computer Simulation of IC Processes and Devices.,* Klewer Academic Publishers, Boston 1993.
21. T. Toyabe and S. Asai, "Analytical Models of Threshold Voltage and Breakdown Voltage of Short-Channel MOSFETs Derived from Two-Dimensional Analysis," *IEEE Trans. Electron Dev.,* **ED-26**, p. 453, April 1979.
22. S. Selberherr, A. Schutz, and H.W. Potzl, "MINIMOS - A Two-Dimensional MOS Transistor Analyser," *IEEE Trans. Electron Dev.,* **ED-27**, p. 1540, Aug. 1980.

23. J.A. Greenfield and R.W. Dutton, "Nonplanar VLSI Device Analysis Using the Solution of Poisson's Equation," *IEEE Trans. Electron Dev.*, **ED-27**, p. 1520, Aug. 1980.

24. E.M. Butturla et al., "Finite-Element Analysis of Semiconductor Devices: The FIELDAY Program," *IBM J. Res. Develop.*, vol. **25**, p. 218, July 1981.

25. J.L. Blue and C.L. Wilson, "Two-Dimensional Analysis of Semiconductor Devices Using General-Purpose Interactive PDE Software," *IEEE Trans. Electron Dev.*, **ED-30**, p. 1056, Sept. 1983.

PROBLEMS

1. Determine a root of the following equation using the Newton-Raphson iteration technique:

$$f(x) = x^3 - 3.5x^2 + 2x - 10$$

Note that since this method does not always converge to a root if the initial guess is not sufficiently close to the actual root, it may be necessary to use a graphical technique to get an estimate of the root that will be sufficiently close to the actual root that the numerical procedure will converge to the root.

2. Calculate the boron doping profile and junction depth resulting from a predeposition process performed at 950°C for 30 minutes in a nonoxidizing ambient using the analytical solution of Fick's 2nd Law. Assume the substrate is n-type with a background doping level of 1.5×10^{16} atoms/cm^3 and the boron surface concentration reaches solid solubility ($C_S = 1.8 \times 10^{20}$ atoms/cm^3.) Repeat the problem using the SUPREM III process simulator. Compare the results and comment on any differences between the two doping profiles.

3. Calculate the diffusion profile and junction depth after the predeposition of Problem 1 is subjected to a non-oxidizing ambient drive-in at 1050°C for 60 minutes, using the analytical solution of Fick's 2nd Law for this purpose. Repeat this procedure using the SUPREM III process simulator and compare the results with those obtained using the analytical solution. Comment on why the analytical and numerical results of Problem 3 are in better agreement than the results obtained in Problem 2.

4. Consider an n-channel MOSFET made with an n^+ polysilicon gate, a gate oxide thickness of 40 nm, and a substrate doping of $N_A = 9 \times 10^{14}$ cm^{-3}. Assume a threshold-adjust implant of 3.2×10^{12} cm^{-2} at 130 keV is also used. (a) Use SUPREM III to simulate the channel doping profile and save an "export" file for further use. (b) Use the "threshold" statement in SUPREM to extract and plot V_T versus V_{BS} for increments of V_{BS} of 0.25V between 0 and 5V. (c) Using the "export" file from SUPREM III, load the results into MINIMOS or PISCES and compute the surface-channel charge over the range of ±0.2V within the value of V_T computed in part (b), by sweeping V_{GS} in 0.02V increments over this range (and assume $V_{BS} = 0V$).

5. Starting with the contour plot of potential shown in Fig. 2-14c, create for yourself a perspective plot of the potential using the same positional grid.

CHAPTER 3

MOS TRANSISTOR DEVICE PHYSICS: PART 1

BASICS MOS PHYSICS

and

THE MOS CAPACITOR

A basic goal of IC manufacture is to produce circuits having the highest performance at lowest cost. For digital CMOS ICs (the largest category of silicon ICs in the mid-1990s), the main performance criteria are speed, power dissipation, and device packing density. Reduction in device size has been the chief vehicle for achieving these goals. Smaller devices also produce the twin benefits of decreased die size (more chips per wafer and higher fractional yield) which exert downward pressure on die cost. However, the mere reduction of all device dimensions by a constant factor, for example, without paying attention to other processing parameters can adversely impact IC performance. That is, power dissipation may worsen because of increased device leakage currents, or circuit speed may be degraded. Reliability problems which afflict submicron MOSFETs might also be exacerbated, including hot-carrier degradation, gate-oxide wearout, and electromigration. As a result, it is necessary to employ more sophisticated scaling guidelines for device design to ensure that the shrunken devices exhibit electrical behavior comparable to that of previous generations of larger devices. In the case of MOSFETs, the aim of such scaling guidelines is to provide a design path to *short-channel devices* which continue to exhibit the ideal characteristics of *long-channel devices*. (These terms are defined later in the chapter.)

Our purpose here is to present the issues of submicron MOS device design for semiconductor process engineers. An understanding of device physics has become even more important now that MOSFETs have crossed the long-channel frontier into the short-channel (submicron) realm. Device aspects which could once be ignored (because they cause only second-order effects in large MOS devices) are now significant - such as source/drain doping profiles, channel doping profiles, and the device geometry around the gate periphery. Furthermore, if the degree of process control is not increased, variations in these parameters will become larger (on a percentage basis) as the devices become even smaller. Since the uniformity of device characteristics will be adversely impacted, process control must be improved. In addition, better processes will need to be developed and devices will have to be designed with less process sensitivity. All of these issues can only be discussed in the context of short-channel MOSFET physics. By understanding the relationship between circuit behavior, device design, and process technology of submicron MOSFETs process engineers will be better able to contribute to the task of successfully designing and manufacturing submicron ICs.

The discussion of MOS device physics also serves to set the stage for some later topics of this book (and others of this series), namely the process technology developed to fabricate silicon ICs. To facilitate the understanding of the submicron MOSFET, we divide the topic of *MOS device physics* into three chapters. The first (chap. 3) deals with basic MOS theory and MOS capacitors The second (chap. 4) covers long-channel MOSFETs and the circuit models developed to predict the drain current characteristics of such devices. The last (chap. 5) describes short-channel (i.e., submicron) MOSFETs and issues of MOSFET device scaling.

In each of these chapters the following general approach is adopted. As each new topic is introduced it is first considered from a *qualitative* perspective, using visualization analogies whenever possible. This is intended to provide an intuitive, rudimentary grasp of the device phenomenon being presented. Then the same device effects are analyzed from a *quantitative* perspective, and mathematical relationships that describe the physical effects are developed. Where applicable, as a final task, quantitative models of the device behavior in terms of the terminal voltages and currents are derived. Where possible complicated mathematics and derivations are minimized to prevent them from standing in the way of conceptual explanations. Where such complications cannot be completely circumvented many of the intermediate steps are given. Hopefully this will make the material somewhat more digestible.

3.1 BASIC MOS THEORY and PHYSICS of IDEAL MOS CAPACITORS (MOS-C)

As noted in the introduction, the ultimate purpose of this and the next two chapters is to provide an understanding of short-channel MOSFET behavior (extending to devices with submicron channel lengths). Since the behavior of submicron MOSFETs is complex, the subject is best approached in a step-by-step fashion. That is, the device behavior of the simplest MOS structure (i.e., the two-terminal MOS capacitor, to be referred henceforth as the MOS-C) is considered first. The MOS-C exhibits behavior which is the foundation of both long- and short-channel MOSFET operation. Such behavior is easier to describe in the MOS-C since some of the device phenomena exhibited in more complex MOS structures (i.e., multi-dimensional electric fields and drain currents) are absent in the MOS-C. Once the reader acquires a good understanding of MOS-C behavior, these effects can be added, allowing a relatively straightforward explanation of long-channel MOSFET operation. Thereafter, submicron MOSFET behavior can be explored by showing how the long-channel MOSFET behavior is altered as the channel length is reduced. With this rationale in mind, we begin by describing the behavior of the MOS capacitor in this chapter - initially dealing with the *ideal* MOS capacitor, but later incorporating *nonideal* effects. We should also point out that the MOS-C itself is quite a complex and subtle structure. In fact, a lengthy and rigorous text that deals comprehensively with these subtleties has been written by Nicollian and Brews.[1]

3.1.1 The Structure of the MOS-C and the MOSFET

Although we begin by studying the MOS-C, it is useful to compare its structure with that of the MOSFET. To do this, an even-more-fundamental configuration, the generic MOS structure is first defined. The *MOS* or *metal-oxide-semiconductor* structure is a three-layered object. It consists of a conducting layer (referred to as the *gate*), atop an insulator layer (usually silicon dioxide), and a semiconductor substrate beneath the insulator (termed either the *substrate* or *body*). The substrate can be doped either *n*-type or *p*-type. Note that the acronym MOS stems from the early days of MOS fabrication when all gates were made of metal (aluminum). While heavily doped polysilicon has replaced aluminum as the standard gate material, the name MOS continues to be used.

The structure of the *MOS capacitor* (or *MOS-C*) is shown in Fig. 3-1a. It consists of the generic MOS structure with terminals G and B connected to the gate and substrate, respectively, making it a *two-terminal device*. An external bias can be applied across these terminals, called the *gate-substrate (or gate-body) voltage* V_{GB}. In Fig. 3-1a1 we show a perspective view of a MOS-C having a *p*-type Si substrate. Then in Fig. 3-1a2 we show the cross-section of this device cut along the middle of the gate. This cross-section is shown lying flat Fig. 3-1a3, and in Fig. 3-1a4 the same structure with only the Si beneath the oxide is shown.

The structure of the *MOS field-effect transistor* (or *MOSFET*) is given in Fig. 3-1b. It has two regions of doping opposite that of the substrate, one at each edge of the MOS structure. These regions are called the *source* and *drain*, and a *pn* junction exists between them and the substrate. When terminals are connected to all the various regions of the MOSFET a *four-terminal device* results, with the terminals designated as G (gate), S (source), D (drain), and B (substrate).

We next observe that since one of these terminals can be designated as the common (or reference) terminal, three independent terminal voltages can be applied to the MOSFET (e.g., if B is chosen as common we will have V_{GB}, V_{SB}, and V_{DB}). However, only one significant current exists in an ideal MOSFET. That is, we assume that the gate current is zero ($I_G = 0$), and that the source and drain junctions are always kept under reverse bias during normal MOSFET operation. Since reverse bias current in a *pn* junction can be considered negligible (and $I_G = 0$), substrate current will also be inconsequential ($I_{sub} \approx 0$).* Thus, only the drain current I_D which flows between the source and drain in the MOSFET needs to be considered. In summary, three independent terminal voltages and one current (i.e., I_D) are generally associated with the operation of the ideal MOSFET. In Fig. 3-1b1 we show the MOSFET in perspective, then in cross-section (Fig. 3-1b2), and finally (in Fig. 3-1b3), with the cross-section lying flat.

Figure 3-1 also defines the axes to be used in our discussion of both the MOS-C and the MOSFET structures. That is, the *x*-direction is perpendicular to the Si-SiO$_2$

---

* We'll remove these restrictions in chaps. 7 and 9.

interface (*vertical* direction), with $x = 0$ at the Si surface. The y-direction is parallel to the Si surface in the direction from source to drain (*lateral* or *longitudinal* direction). Since the source and drain are separated by a distance L (termed the *channel length*), we usually choose $y = 0$ at the source end of the channel, and $y = L$ at the drain end. The z-direction is the other direction parallel to the Si surface (perpendicular to the y-direction), and defines the channel width.

3.1.1.1. Comparison of MOS-Cs and Conventional Capacitor Structures.

It should be noted at the outset that the structure and behavior of the MOS-C differs from that of the more conventional metal-dielectric-metal capacitor structure. That is, in the latter structure both terminals are highly conductive, but in the MOS-C the semiconductor terminal is not of high conductivity. Consequently, if a potential difference is applied across the terminals of the conventional capacitor, an electric field arises within the dielectric, but is zero outside the dielectric. This implies that the "metal-dielectric-metal" capacitor stores all of the charge at the interfaces of the respective metal electrodes and the dielectric.

The situation is different in the MOS-C where one of the terminals of the capacitor is a semiconductor, not a metal. If we consider the case of a p-type semiconductor, then the application of a *negative* bias will induce a negative charge on the gate and a positive charge on the substrate. The high conductivity of the gate requires that the electric field within the dielectric again terminates at the gate-dielectric interface. Here, the charge on which the field lines terminate is the negative charge stored on the gate. At the substrate-dielectric interface, however, the semiconductor must supply positive charge to balance the gate's negative charge. This can readily occur because the majority mobile charge carriers in p-type Si are holes, implying that (1) they exist in great abundance and (2) that they are capable of moving to the interface in response to the negative bias on the gate. In this case, the p-type silicon MOS-C and the conventional capacitor structure behave identically. Furthermore, as we will describe in more detail in the next section, this bias condition is known as "accumulation" because it causes majority carriers to accumulate at the semiconductor surface.

On the other hand, if a *positive* gate bias is applied to this MOS-C, a somewhat different set of phenomena occur. That is, a positive gate potential produces a positive charge on the gate, and a negative charge must arise in the substrate to balance the gate charge. In this case, there are very few mobile negative charge carriers (electrons) in the p-substrate. Thus, their scarcity prevents them from supplying enough of the required negative charge, especially at small positive gate-bias values. Instead, the repulsion of holes (the majority carriers) by the positive bias drives the holes away from the substrate-dielectric interface. This forms a region depleted of mobile carriers (i.e., a *depletion region*) that penetrates from the surface into the substrate. The departure of holes from this surface region leaves it negatively charged because the immobile, ionized acceptor impurities remain within the region. This negative "background" charge thus becomes the negative charge induced by the positive gate potential. As a result, the electric field lines terminate on these negative charges. Unlike in the case of accumulation, however, the terminal charge of the MOS-C in the semiconductor is no

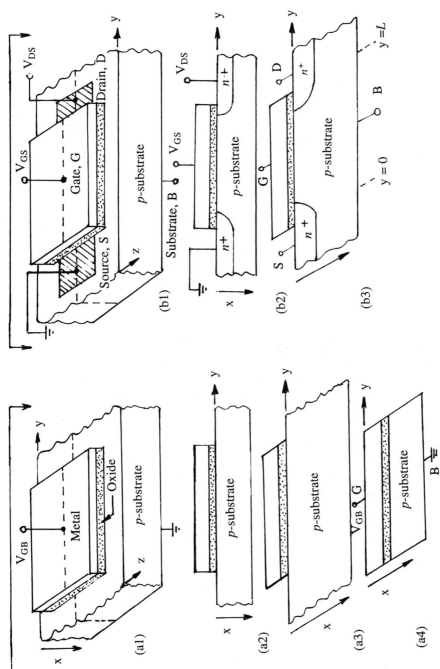

Fig. 3-1 (a1) Perspective view of the MOS-C, (a2) Cross-section of the MOS-C, (a3) Cross-section shown lying flat, (a4) Cross-section with only the Si beneath the oxide shown. (b1) Perspective view of the MOSFET structure, (b2) Cross-section of the MOSFET cut down the middle of the channel, (b3) Cross-section of the MOSFET cut along the middle of the structure, (a3) Cross-section of the MOSFET lying flat.

longer confined to the substrate-dielectric interface (i.e., to the Si surface). Instead, the charge is spread over some distance extending to the depth of the depletion region. This added distance increases the "effective" dielectric thickness and thus decreases the capacitance of the structure. Thus, unlike a conventional capacitor, whose capacitance is constant regardless of the applied bias, the capacitance of the MOS-C varies with the applied bias under some bias conditions.

Note, however, that if the value of the positive gate bias becomes sufficiently large, a large number of minority carrier electrons will be attracted to the surface. They will collect there and come to dominate the negative charge in the substrate. This induced charge due to the electrons at the surface is called an *inversion layer*. Note also that these phenomena will be described in more detail in the upcoming section, but the purpose of briefly introducing them here is to point out the fact that MOS-Cs indeed behave in a somewhat different fashion than conventional capacitor structures.

3.1.1.2 Why is the MOS-C Studied First? As illustrated above, the MOS-C forms the heart of the MOSFET. Yet it is a fundamental structure in its own right, just as the *pn* junction is a fundamental structure apart from the bipolar transistor. Yet, much in the same way that understanding *pn* junctions is central to understanding the operation of the bipolar transistor, an understanding of the MOS-C is central to understanding of MOSFETs. Hence, it seems logical that the behavior of MOS-Cs should be studied first, before considering the physics of the MOSFET.

We can see this by noting that the basis of MOSFET behavior essentially involves two phenomena: (1) the action of mobile carriers in the semiconductor in response to the application of a gate bias; and (2) the transport of these mobile carriers between the source and drain (in the form of a drain current, I_D) in response to the application of a drain bias. Therefore, to quantitatively describe MOSFET operation, initially we need to establish a quantitative model which allows the first of these two phenomena to be treated (i.e., we need to be able to determine the mobile charge distribution in a MOS structure for a given gate bias). Once this charge distribution is known, it can be used to develop a model for the relationship between I_D and the terminal voltages (i.e., the gate and drain biases). Such a model for mobile-charge versus gate-bias is most easily developed in MOS-C structures for the following reasons:

1. We noted that the MOS capacitor is a two-terminal device. If we assume the oxide is a perfect insulator, then the current through the oxide I_G is zero for dc biases between the gate and substrate. Since this is the only possible current in the MOS-C - and its value in ideal structures is zero - the redistribution of charges in the semiconductor with respect to changes in V_{GB} can be analyzed without the complication of current flow. Furthermore, since no current flows under dc bias, the behavior of MOS-Cs in such cases represents an electrostatic problem. Thus, only one of the five classical device equations introduced in chap. 1 needs to be solved (i.e., the Poisson equation) to completely characterize the potential and mobile charge distribution in the ideal MOS-C (i.e., even if $V_{GB} \neq 0$).

2. The electric field in the MOS-C is perpendicular to the silicon surface, making it essentially uni-directional (vertical). The electrostatic potential in the device can thus be found by solving the Poisson equation in its least complex (e.g., one-dimensional) form. On the other hand, if a bias is also applied between the source and drain of a MOSFET, the direction of the electric field in the semiconductor region of the MOSFET is no longer perpendicular to the silicon surface. That is, it generally contains components parallel as well as vertical to the silicon surface. Hence, to calculate the electrostatic potential in a MOSFET, it is in general necessary to solve the Poisson equation in its two- or three-dimensional form.

3. The absence of current flow in a MOS-C implies that equilibrium is maintained in the semiconductor region even if a dc V_{GB} is applied.* Thus, the equations used to calculate carrier concentrations in terms of equilibrium concepts (e.g., the Fermi level) can be used. This makes the solution of the Poisson equation simpler as well.

4. The MOS-C is widely used as the test structure for characterizing the reliability of the gate oxide film with respect to oxide breakdown and hot-electron degradation (as described in chaps. 7 and 9, respectively). Thus, the study of the MOS-C behavior is intrinsically useful for interpreting data obtained from such structures.

5. The quantitative relationships we develop for the mobile charge concentration in the channel region of the MOS-C under inversion are used in the I_D models of the long-channel MOSFET by invoking the *gradual-channel approximation.* This approximation will be examined in more detail in chap. 4.

3.2 QUALITATIVE DESCRIPTION OF MOS-C DEVICE BEHAVIOR

The behavior of the MOS-C from a qualitative perspective is considered first, namely a verbal description is given of how the mobile charge distribution in the semiconductor depends on the applied dc gate bias. To help visualize these phenomena we make use of energy-band and potential representations, as well as electric-field and charge distribution diagrams.

---

* The term *equilibrium* should be considered here to mean *thermal equilibrium,* as viewed from the microscopic perspective. That is, the net energy in the semiconductor is stored in the crystal-lattice vibrations (phonons) as well as by free carrier motion. Although external sources of energy (such as incident photoelectric radiation) may also excite a crystal, many situations exist where no such external forces act. In such cases, the total energy is a function of only the crystal temperature, and the semiconductor will spontaneously reach a state referred to as thermal equilibrium. In thermal equilibrium every process is exactly balanced by its inverse process. One such set of competing processes in a semiconductor involves carrier generation and recombination. At thermal equilibrium the rates of these two processes are equal (and are also assumed to be driven only by thermal processes). This makes it valid to use the equilibrium carrier concentration expressions (i.e., Eqs. 3-1a and 3-1b) to calculate the carrier concentrations in the MOS-C even when $V_{GB} \neq 0V$.

3.2.1 Energy-Band Diagram Representation of Semiconductor Devices

One of the most helpful tools for visualizing semiconductor phenomena is the *energy-band diagram*. In such diagrams, the vertical axis represents the energy possessed by electrons when they occupy energy levels at a given location in the device. (In one-dimensional representations, a location in the device is generally specified by a point x, which is designated as the distance along the horizontal axis of the diagram). Such one-dimensional representations are adequate for treating the MOS-C (with the *x*-direction representing the direction perpendicular to the silicon surface).

In the energy-band representation of a semiconductor (Fig. 3-2), E_c and E_v are the conduction and valence band edges, respectively. The intrinsic Fermi level E_i is at the middle of the band gap (i.e., $E_i \cong [E_c+E_v]/2$), corresponding to the Fermi-level of an intrinsic (undoped) semiconductor (Fig. 3-2a). In *n*-type doped silicon the Fermi level E_F is closer to E_c than to E_v (Fig. 3-2b), but in *p*-type it is closer to E_v (Fig. 3-2c) If an electron occupies a state at the bottom edge of the conduction band (E_c), its kinetic energy is defined to be zero (point A in Fig. 3-2d). As the kinetic energy of such an electron increases, it occupies energy levels higher in the conduction band (e.g., point B in Fig. 3-2d). If a semiconductor is in equilibrium, the Fermi level is invariant with position in the material, and this is depicted in a one-dimensional energy-band-versus-distance diagram as E_F being a straight, horizontal line (as in all of Fig. 3-2).

Assuming Maxwell-Boltzmann statistics, the electron and hole concentrations in a semiconductor at equilibrium (n_0 and p_0, respectively) can be expressed in terms of quantities found in the energy-band diagram (E_F, E_i), as well as T, and n_i (the intrinsic carrier concentration at T) according to the following expressions:

$$n_0 = n_i \exp (E_F - E_i)/kT \qquad (3-1a)$$

$$p_0 = n_i \exp (E_i - E_F)/kT \qquad (3-1b)$$

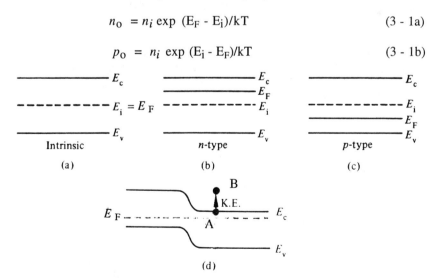

Intrinsic (a)   *n*-type (b)   *p*-type (c)

(d)

Fig. 3-2 Energy band representation of a semiconductor: (a) intrinsic; (b) *n*-type; (c) *p*-type; (d) Depicting the kinetic energy of an electron in the energy band diagram.

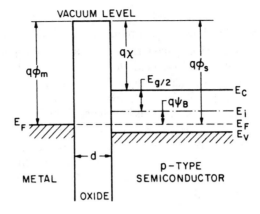

Fig. 3-3 Energy band diagram of an ideal MOS-C when V_{GB} = 0V (*flat-band condition*).

Note also that at equilibrium

$$n_0 \, p_0 \; = n_i^2 \qquad\qquad\qquad (3 - 1c)$$

3.2.2 Energy Band Diagram of the Ideal MOS Capacitor

Using the energy-band diagram representation we now consider the qualitative behavior of an *ideal* MOS-C subjected to dc bias. The following assumptions are assumed to be valid in an ideal MOS-C:

1. The energy difference between the work function of the gate material (metal), $q\varphi_m$ and that of the semiconductor, $q\varphi_s$ is zero (i.e., $q\varphi_{ms} = 0$);

2. No charges exist in the MOS-C under any biasing conditions, other than those existing in the semiconductor and those with equal but opposite sign on the gate, i.e., within the oxide there are no mobile charge carriers nor any charge centers;

3. No current can flow through the oxide under dc-biasing conditions ($I_G = 0$);

4. The semiconductor region is uniformly doped;

5. The gate layer is considered to be an equipotential region.

For our example we will consider an ideal MOS-C with a *p*-type semiconductor region.

First consider the case when no bias is applied ($V_{GB} = 0$V). The energy-band diagram for this case is shown in Fig. 3-3. We note that since equilibrium exists in the semiconductor and $q\varphi_{ms} = 0$ (Assumption #1), the Fermi level throughout the semiconductor must be invariant with position, and it must also line up with the Fermi level in the gate. This also implies that E_c, E_v, and E_i in the semiconductor are horizontal and straight (i.e., flat). An energy-band diagram in which E_c, E_v, and E_i are flat is said to be in a *flat-band condition*. *Thus, when $V_{GB} = 0$ in an ideal MOS capacitor, it's energy-band diagram is in a flat-band condition.* Note also that in *p*-type Si, E_F is below E_i, by an amount expressed as $|E_F - E_i|$.

Next let a dc bias be applied between the gate and substrate. Since $I_G = 0$ (Assumption #3), the silicon region remains in equilibrium, implying that E_F remains flat. This aspect of MOS-C behavior is unique, since the application of a dc bias across the electrodes of other semiconductor devices will cause at least some current to flow. Hence, MOS-C analysis remains simple under dc bias because the Fermi-level concept is still valid. Although the semiconductor region remains in equilibrium under dc bias (and E_F remains flat), the other bands are altered from that of the $V_{GB} = 0V$ case. This is seen in Fig. 3-4 where four different gate-bias conditions are depicted. Here in Fig. 3-4a we depict the MOS-C in cross-section, as was also shown in Fig. 3-1b2. This structure is then rotated as shown in Fig. 3-4b, and the energy-band and charge distribution versus x diagrams we show next refer to the MOS-C cross-section oriented in the manner of Fig. 3-4b.

3.2.2.1 Accumulation. In the first biasing case a *negative* bias is applied ($V_{GB}<0V$, Fig. 3-4c). The negative bias causes holes (the majority carriers in *p*-type Si) to be attracted to the silicon surface adjacent to the oxide. More holes accumulate near the Si surface than if $V_{GB} = 0V$. The effect of attracting additional majority carriers to the semiconductor surface is called *accumulation*. The conductivity of the region near the Si surface is increased by the presence of the extra holes.

Note that in the energy-band representation, extra holes at one location of a semiconductor (e.g., in this case, at the Si surface) implies that E_F must be closer to E_V than in a region containing fewer holes (e.g., the region deeper below the surface [bulk region]). However, since the *Fermi level* in the semiconductor must remain flat, the energy bands in the semiconductor (E_c, E_v, and E_i) near the surface must bend upward to reflect the presence of the extra holes at that location compared to the *bulk* (Fig. 3-4c1)

The applied gate bias also causes the Fermi levels in the gate and semiconductor regions to be separated by an amount equal to qV_{GB}, or

$$E_F(gate) - E_F(semiconductor) = -qV_{GB} \qquad (3 - 2)$$

Although the capacitance of the MOS-C varies with applied dc voltage under some bias conditions, in the accumulation mode it does not. That is, in this mode the capacitance per unit area remains constant as V_{GB} is changed, and is given by $C_{ox} = \kappa_{ox}\varepsilon_0/t_{ox}$, where κ_{ox} and t_{ox} are the dielectric constant and thickness of the oxide, and ε_0 is the permittivity of free space.

We now introduce the *charge-distribution versus distance* diagram as an additional visualization tool. This allows us to depict the approximate charge distribution inside the MOS structure. For the case of accumulation, applying a negative bias causes more electrons to move onto the gate. Holes are attracted toward the silicon surface in response. Thus, the charge inside the device as a function of position can be approximated as shown in Fig. 3-4c2. Note that a squared-off (or block) representation of the charge is used in this simple plot. Such block approximations are only intended to be a qualitative representation of the actual charge distribution, which, in general, is not distributed so simply. When interpreting the magnitude and spatial extent of the charge using such simplified diagrams this fact should be kept in mind.

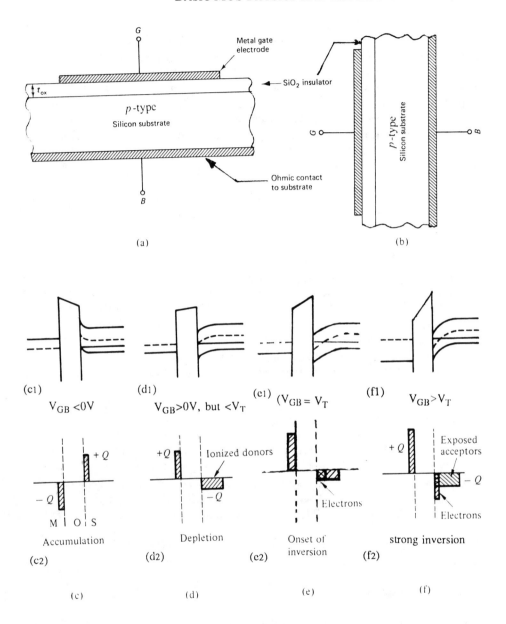

Fig. 3-4 (a) Cross-section of a MOS-C with p-substrate; (b) Cross-section of the same MOS-C, but rotated 90°; (c1) and (c2) Energy band and block charge diagrams when the MOS-C is biased to accumulation ($V_{GB}<0V$); (d1) and (d2) Same diagrams for depletion biasing ($V_{GB}>0V$, but $<V_T$); (e1) and (e2) Same diagrams at onset of inversion ($V_{GB} = V_T$); (f1) and (f2) Same diagrams at strong inversion ($V_{GB}>V_T$).

3.2.2.2 Depletion. In the second bias condition (Fig. 3-4d), a *small positive* voltage is applied to the gate of the *p*-type MOS capacitor. This causes holes in the semiconductor to be pushed away from the surface, creating a depletion region of width d, consisting primarily of negatively charged acceptor ions. In the energy-band representation of this phenomenon the bands bend downward near the surface (Fig. 3-4d1). In this mode of operation, known as *depletion,* the MOS capacitor exhibits two capacitances in series - the oxide capacitance per unit area C_{ox} and the depletion capacitance per unit area $C_d = \kappa_{si}\varepsilon_o/d$. While C_{ox} is constant, C_d is not. That is, C_d decreases as V_{GB} is made larger (more positive). The approximate charge distribution for this bias condition is shown in Fig. 3-4d2.

3.2.2.3 Inversion. If the positive voltage applied to the gate is increased, the bands are bent further downward, eventually causing E_F to cross over E_i and to be closer to E_c than to E_v at the surface. At this point the semiconductor surface is *inverted* (i.e., it has been changed from *p*-type to *n*-type) because there are now more electrons than holes at the surface.*

Another way to view this situation is to remember that the kinetic energy of an electron is zero when it occupies an energy state at the conduction band edge (corresponding to an energy E_c). Thus, under depletion or inversion biasing electrons near the Si surface having zero kinetic energy occupy energy states of lower *total* energy than electrons deeper in the Si having zero kinetic energy. Hence, when a positive bias is applied to the gate, electrons are more likely to fill such states near the surface. Consequently, electrons will be found at higher concentrations closer to the surface when $V_{GB}>0V$.

3.2.2.4 Strong Inversion. If V_{GB} is made even more positive, the bands will continue to bend further downward, until E_i at the surface is eventually below E_F by an energy equal to $|E_F - E_i|$. At this point the electron density per unit volume at the surface n_{surf} (located in a thin layer known as the *inversion layer*) is equal to the hole density in the bulk. This is known as the point of *onset of strong inversion,* and in this condition

$$E_i(bulk) - E_i(surface) = 2[E_i(bulk) - E_F] \qquad (3-3)$$

Solving this equation for E_i(surface), and using the result in Eq. 3-1a, the concentration of electrons at the Si surface at the onset of strong inversion, n_{surf}(inv) is

$$n_{surf}(inv) = n_i \exp[E_F - E_i(surface)]/kT = n_i \exp[E_i(bulk) - E_F]/kT = p_{obulk} \approx N_A \quad (3-4)$$

Figure 3-4e1 is the energy-band diagram depicting the condition of onset of strong

---

* The surface is actually inverted as soon as E_F crosses over E_i. However, the density of electrons at the surface remains small until E_F is considerably greater than E_i. The mode of operation when the electron density is smaller than the hole density in the substrate bulk is referred to as *weak inversion.* Weak inversion is important in submicron MOSFET behavior and will be discussed in detail in section 4.7.

inversion. In this diagram the width of the depletion region is denoted by d_{max}. The block charge diagram at the onset of strong inversion is shown in Fig. 3-4e2. Note that the voltage applied between the gate and substrate at the onset of strong inversion is known as the threshold voltage, V_T.

For further increases in positive bias, the electron concentration in the inversion layer at the surface exceeds the bulk equilibrium hole concentration, $p_0 = N_A$. This is referred to as *strong inversion*. The energy-band and block-charge diagrams depicting the strong inversion condition are shown in Figs. 3-4f1 and 3-4f2, respectively.

In general, the charges on the gate Q_G of a MOS-C must be balanced by the charges in the semiconductor Q_C

$$Q_G \ (C/cm^2) = -Q_C \ (C/cm^2) \qquad (3-5)$$

In strong inversion, the charge per unit area Q_C in a p-type semiconductor is the sum of the electrons in the inversion layer (Q_I) and the negative charges in the depletion region (Q_{Bmax}). Thus, in strong inversion

$$Q_G = -Q_C = -(Q_I + Q_{Bmax}) \qquad (3-6)$$

where $Q_{Bmax} = -qN_A d_{max}$. (Note that Q's in this chapter are expressed in units of charge/unit area - specifically, C/cm^2.) The total capacitance per unit area at strong inversion is the oxide capacitance C_{ox} in series with the depletion capacitance at the maximum depletion width in equilibrium $C_{dmax} = \kappa_{si}\varepsilon_0/d_{max}$. While the above discussion applies to a MOS-C with a p-type semiconductor, similar results can be obtained for an n-type semiconductor, with the polarity of the voltages and charges being reversed. A typical value of Q_I in a MOS-C or MOSFET in strong inversion is on the order of 10^{12} cm^{-2}.

3.2.2.5 Microscopic Perspective of the Mobile Charge Behavior in a MOS-C.
It is also useful to consider from a (qualitative) microscopic perspective the phenomena involving charge carriers near the silicon surface of the MOS-C under conditions of depletion and inversion biasing. That is, when the MOS-C is thus biased, a potential difference between the surface and the bulk exists, giving rise to a potential energy barrier (PEB) with respect to the majority carriers. The majority carriers (holes in our example) are thereby repelled from the surface, and minority carriers (i.e., electrons in this example) are attracted toward it. In either inversion or depletion a region largely devoid of carriers is established (depletion region), and in this region thermal generation of carriers continuously produces holes and electrons in an attempt to re-establish the mobile charge concentration values present in the charge-neutral regions at equilibrium. The holes so produced, however, are continuously repelled from the surface, while the generated electrons are likewise drifted toward the surface.

In a state of thermal equilibrium, some holes in the bulk nevertheless still possess sufficient energy to overcome the PEB at the surface, and they are able to penetrate the depletion region so that recombination with the electrons attracted to the surface can occur. At thermal equilibrium, the rate of such recombination at the surface exactly equals the rate of electron generation in the depletion region, and the electron and hole concentrations are thus maintained at a fixed, specific value, dependent on the temperature, doping concentration, and gate bias.

If the gate bias is instantaneously changed from one fixed value to another, the carrier concentrations must also change to reflect this new bias value. However, since an increase in the electron concentration relies essentially on their generation in the depletion region by thermal processes, some time must elapse before the new equilibrium electron concentration can be established. In fact, the response of a silicon MOS-C due to instantaneous changes in V_{GB} is relatively slow because thermal generation and recombination processes in the silicon substrate occur at low rates at room temperature. The situation that exists in a MOSFET, as we will describe in chap. 4, is quite different. That is, the presence of diffused regions of doping type opposite that of the substrate (i.e., the source/drain regions) permit electrons (under favorable bias conditions) to be injected into (or removed from) this surface region much more rapidly than if only thermal processes are responsible for contributing carriers (see section 4.2).

3.3 QUANTITATIVE DESCRIPTION OF MOS-C BEHAVIOR

We now consider the behavior of the ideal MOS-C from a quantitative perspective. Specifically, we seek to obtain mathematical relationships that permit us to calculate the following parameters in terms of the applied dc gate bias V_{GB}, the device structure parameters (i.e., t_{ox} and the doping concentration in the silicon), and the material parameters (i.e., ε_{si} and ε_{ox}):

1. The electrostatic potential as a function of position $\varphi(x)$;

2. The surface potential, φ_{surf}, which is the potential at $x = 0$, or $\varphi(0)$

3. The electric field as a function of position $\mathcal{E}(x)$;

4. The mobile charge concentrations $n(x)$ and $p(x)$ in the silicon;

5. The bulk charge per unit area Q_B in the silicon;

6. The inversion layer charge per unit area Q_I

Later, we will treat the nonideal MOS-C in which we will also include the effects due to the properties of the gate material and the charges in the oxide and at the Si-SiO$_2$ interface. We will also describe how to calculate the threshold voltage of MOS structures.

Three quantitative models of MOS-C behavior will be developed, differing in their complexity, accuracy, and generality. The simplest MOS-C model, based on the *depletion approximation* will be derived first. It is also the least general and least accurate of the three models, and provides accurate values of the mobile charge concentrations in the silicon only beyond strong inversion. Nevertheless, this model offers easy-to-interpret analytical expressions of MOS-C behavior, and is the model developed in most basic device physics texts. It is also the basis of the simpler long-channel MOSFET models described in chap. 4.

The second MOS-C model we derive is the most general and accurate model (in that it is valid for the accumulation, depletion, and inversion regimes of MOS-C operation), but it provides these benefits only at the expense of much greater mathematical complexity. That is, the second model does not provide analytical expressions for the quantities listed above, but requires numerical analysis for specific values to be obtained. Despite its mathematical complexity, this model is presented for several important reasons:

1. The MOS-C parameters listed above when calculated using this model are so accurate compared to experimental measurements that the model represents a benchmark to which the results of the other models can be compared to establish their accuracy.

2. It is the basis for the most general long-channel MOSFET model we present in chap. 4 (i.e., the Pao-Sah model).

3. It illustrates the principle that numerical analysis must be relied upon to obtain the most accurate quantitative representations even for the cases of the MOS-C and the long-channel MOSFET.

4. It implies that numerical analysis must certainly be employed to obtain accurate predictions of submicron MOSFET behavior.

However, the complexity of this model is such that it is not feasible to use it for constructing models of MOSFET circuit behavior, nor does it provide analytical expressions for the MOS-C quantities listed above. Thus, quantitative insights about MOS-C behavior are difficult to extract from this model, making it a poor tool for learning about MOS-C behavior. As a result, the previous simple model and a third model (which we describe last), find much wider use than this one.

The third MOS-C model is intermediate in accuracy, generality, and complexity between the other two models. It is referred to as the *charge sheet model,* and it calculates the characteristics of the MOS-C quite accurately over the entire range of inversion (i.e., from weak to strong inversion). It requires more computational effort than the simple model, but far less than the general model. Unlike the general model it provides analytical expressions for the mobile charge density which also extend beyond the operating regimes treated by the simple model. These expressions provide quantitative insight about the behavior of device operating regions that become more important in short-channel MOSFETs.

Note that we will designate the externally applied (i.e., terminal) voltages with the symbol V (e.g., V_{GB}), while the voltage drops internal to the MOS structure will be expressed with the symbol φ (e.g., the voltage drop across the oxide φ_{ox} and the voltage drop across the semiconductor from the Si surface to the bulk, φ_{surf}). Note, however, that both the external and internal voltage drops have units of volts.

3.3.1 The Electrostatic Potential in MOS Structures

Before setting out to derive the expressions listed above, let us make some introductory remarks about the *electrostatic potential* φ. First, we note that since the bias voltages applied to MOS devices are expressed in units of volts, it would be preferable if the quantitative MOS-C relationships we seek were also expressed in the same units (rather than in terms of units of energy, which would result if we used the energy-band representation of MOS behavior). In addition, one of the five classical semiconductor device equations is the Poisson equation, and its solution yields the electrostatic potential in the device. Hence, two of the relationships we obtain when solving the 1-D Poisson equation in the semiconductor region of a MOS-C involve the electrostatic potential, i.e.,

a. The relationship between V_{GB} and the *surface electrostatic potential* φ_{surf} (henceforth referred to as the *surface potential*), and;

b. An expression for the electrostatic potential versus position $\varphi(x)$ [which uses φ_{surf} obtained from **a** as one of the boundary values for calculating this function].

It turns out that the electrostatic potential at any location in a MOS device is related to the potential energy an electron possesses at that location. That is, the electrostatic potential-difference $\Delta\varphi$ observed in moving from one position to another in the semiconductor (assuming the kinetic energy of the electron is the same at both positions) can be computed (in terms of an electron) from

$$\Delta\varphi = \Delta E/(-q) \qquad (3 - 7)$$

where q is the magnitude of the electron's charge. It is evident from Eq. 3-7 that if an electron undergoes a *potential energy* decrease, it means that a *potential* increase exists between two locations, because of the algebraic sign of the electron charge. Thus, for the case of an electron, an energy-band diagram can be converted to a potential diagram by merely inverting one of the bands E_c, E_i, or E_v (as shown in Fig. 3-7, which depicts both representations).* Note that *downward* band bending while going, for example, from the bulk to the surface in a MOS structure, implies an *increase* in the electrostatic potential when moving between those same locations.

Since the potential is a relative quantity, the zero value of φ can be arbitrarily chosen. In our discussion we select the zero value as the electrostatic potential in the bulk (i.e., at x = ∞). We also choose the energy level of the intrinsic Fermi level E_i in the bulk [E_i(bulk)] to designate this level of zero on an energy-band diagram. Thus, elsewhere, the value of $\varphi(x)$ is measured with respect to E_i(bulk) according to

$$\varphi(x) = [E_i(bulk) - E_i(x)]/q \qquad (3 - 8)$$

---

* Note that since an electron at E_c will have the same kinetic energy (zero) at any location, the bending of the E_c band directly indicates the change in potential energy versus location.

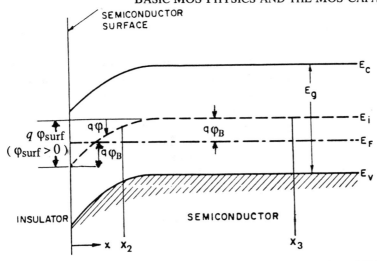

Fig. 3-5 The energy-band and potential diagram representations of the MOS-C (in this figure a MOS-C with a *p*-type substrate and biased to inversion is depicted).

as depicted in the figure. For example, in the bulk of the semiconductor (position x_3 in Fig. 3-5), $E_i(x_3) = E_i$(bulk). Hence, from Eq. 3-8 the potential at x_3 is 0. At x_2, however, $\varphi(x_2) \neq 0$, but instead is $\varphi(x_2) = [E_i(\text{bulk}) - E_i(x_2)]/q$.

Another consequence of choosing φ $(x = \infty) = 0$ is this: If we apply a bias to the gate of a MOS-C, part of the voltage will be dropped across the oxide φ_{ox} and part across the silicon φ_{si}, or,

$$V_{GB} = \varphi_{ox} + \varphi_{si} \qquad (3\text{-}9)$$

If $\varphi(x = \infty) = 0$, then the potential at the surface of the silicon (φ_{surf}) represents the voltage drop from the bulk ($x = \infty$) to the silicon surface ($x = 0$) in a MOS structure. In that case we can write Eq. 3-9 as

$$V_{GB} = \varphi_{ox} + \varphi_{surf} \qquad (3\text{-}10)$$

Now we see that if we can derive an expression for φ_{ox} in terms of φ_{surf}, an equation relating V_{GB} and φ_{surf} results. We show how this is done in the next section.

Let us also introduce another dimensionless parameter called the *doping parameter* φ_B which relates the potential of an electron at the Fermi level (in the bulk of the silicon in a MOS structure) to the doping concentration. The doping parameter is defined as

$$\varphi_B = [E_i(\text{bulk}) - E_F]/q \approx (kT/q)\ln(N_A/n_i)_{p\text{-type Si}} \approx (kT/q)\ln(n_i/N_D)_{n\text{-type Si}} \quad (3\text{-}11)$$

in the bulk region of the Si in the MOS capacitor, see Fig. 3-5). Note that $\varphi_B > 0$ for a *p*-type semiconductor and $\varphi_B < 0$ for an *n*-type semiconductor. For substrate doping concentrations usually encountered in MOSFETs (10^{14}-10^{17} cm^{-3}), the magnitude of φ_B is between $9kT/q$ and $16kT/q$ (where kT/q at 300K is ~0.025 V); that is, the magnitude of φ_B is between 225 and 400 mV at 300K for this range of doping concentrations.

Also, the value of the surface potential at the onset of weak and strong inversion can be expressed in terms of φ_B. That is, in section 3.2 we defined the onset of *weak inversion* as the condition when the electron concentration at the surface of *p*-type Si equals n_i. At that point, $\varphi_{surf} = \varphi_B$. Since the onset of *strong inversion* is the condition when the surface electron concentration equals N_A, at that point E_i (surf) - E_i (bulk) = 2 [E_F - E_i (bulk)]. By combining this fact with Eqs. 3-4 and 3-11, we see that the surface potential at the onset of strong inversion $\varphi_{surf}(inv) = 2\varphi_B$.

Note that it is also possible to express the equilibrium concentrations of electrons n_p (x) and p_p (x) in terms of $\varphi(x)$. That is, when the zero value of φ is defined as above

$$n_p \text{ (x)} = n_{po} \exp [q\varphi(x)/kT] \qquad (3 - 12a)$$

$$p_p \text{ (x)} = p_{po} \exp [-q\varphi(x)/kT] \qquad (3 - 12b)$$

where n_{po} and p_{po} are the equilibrium concentrations of electrons and holes in the bulk of the silicon (in this case in *p*-type Si). At the surface of the silicon, the concentrations n_{surf} and p_{surf} are given by

$$n_{surf} = n_{po} \exp (q\varphi_{surf}/kT) \qquad (3 - 13a)$$

$$p_{surf} = p_{po} \exp (-q\varphi_{surf}/kT) \qquad (3 - 13b)$$

Using Eq. 3-11 in Eq. 3-13a, we can express the electron concentration at the surface in terms of N_A and φ_B as:

$$n_{surf} = N_A \exp [q(\varphi_{surf} - 2\varphi_B)/kT] \qquad (3 - 13c)$$

This expression is plotted versus φ_{surf} in Fig. 3-6. This figure reiterates several aspects of MOS behavior established with the energy-band representation of MOS characteristics. First, using Eq. 3-11 we see that when $\varphi_{surf} = \varphi_B$, n_{surf} becomes equal to the intrinsic concentration, n_i. Thus, $\varphi_{surf} = \varphi_B$ is defined as the limit point between the regions of depletion and weak inversion. Second, as φ_{surf} increases above φ_B, n_{surf} grows very rapidly. Eventually, when $\varphi_{surf} = 2\varphi_B$, $n_{surf} = N_A$. This is commonly defined as the demarcation point between weak and strong inversion. Finally, beyond this point (i.e., $\varphi_{surf} > 2\varphi_B$), n_{surf} continues to increase rapidly, becoming much greater than N_A for small increases of φ_{surf} beyond $2\varphi_B$. This implies that in strong inversion the inversion layer charge density Q_I is generally much larger than the ionic charge density in the depletion region Q_B. An additional important point can also be inferred from this figure. That is, if the potential as a function of x is known we can calculate $n_p(x)$ from Eq. 3-12a.

3.3.2 General Approach to Deriving MOS-C Characteristics

Now we can set out to derive the expressions listed at the beginning of section 3.3. This can be done in four stages, assuming we are given V_{GB}, the oxide thickness t_{ox}, and the doping concentration N_A.

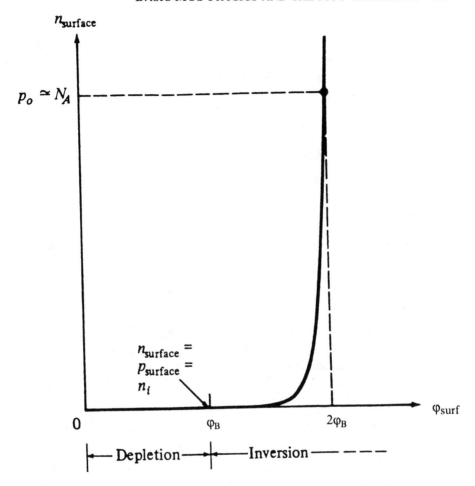

Fig. 3-6 Electron concentration at the surface of a MOS-C (with a p-type substrate) as a function of φ_{surf}.[6] Linear axes are used. Reprinted with permission of McGraw-Hill Book Co.

1. We first find a relationship between V_{GB} and φ_{surf} in the MOS structure. This is done by recalling that if we have an expression for φ_{ox} in terms of φ_{surf}, it can be substituted in Eq. 3-10 to yield an equation for φ_{surf} in terms of V_{GB}.

We begin the derivation of such an expression by noting that the oxide is considered to be an ideal insulator, with no mobile carriers or charge centers. Hence, the electric field in the oxide must be constant, or $\mathcal{E}_{ox} = -d\varphi_{ox}/dx =$ constant. Thus, the voltage across the oxide φ_{ox} is found from:

$$\varphi_{ox} = -\int_{-t_{ox}}^{0} \mathcal{E}_{ox}\, dx = t_{ox}\mathcal{E}_{ox} \qquad (3\text{ - }14)$$

The next step is to relate $\mathcal{E}_{ox}$ to the electric field in the semiconductor. Since the charge per unit area located at the Si-SiO$_2$ interface of an ideal MOS-C is assumed to be zero, the electric displacement, $D = \varepsilon \mathcal{E}$ perpendicular to the interface, is continuous [i.e., $D_{ox} = D_{si}(x = 0)$]. The field in the oxide is therefore related to the field at the surface of the silicon $\mathcal{E}_{si}$ (x = 0) by the equation

$$\mathcal{E}_{ox} = (\kappa_{si}/\kappa_{ox}) \, \mathcal{E}_{si} \, (x = 0) \qquad (3 \text{ - } 15)$$

Now, using Eq. 3-15 in Eq. 3-14 we can write φ_{ox} as

$$\varphi_{ox} = t_{ox} \, (\kappa_{si}/\kappa_{ox}) \, \mathcal{E}_{si} \, (x = 0) \qquad (3 \text{ - } 16)$$

and this result can be substituted for φ_{ox} in Eq. 3-10. In order to complete our goal of finding an expression for φ_{surf} in terms of V_{GB} we see that an expression for $\mathcal{E}_{si}$ (x = 0) in terms of φ_{surf} is needed. Since $\mathcal{E}(x) = - d\varphi/dx$, such expression can be obtained by integrating the one-dimensional form of the Poisson equation once, using the appropriate total charge density $\rho(x)$, and the boundary conditions $\mathcal{E}$ (x = ∞) = 0, and φ (x = 0) = φ_{surf}. We will carry out this integration for three cases in the upcoming sections.

2. We next solve the Poisson equation to find $\varphi(x)$. Since we have noted that the electric field is normal to the oxide surface in a MOS-C (neglecting fringing fields at the edges of the capacitor), we can consider the variation in electrostatic potential φ in a MOS-C to be one-dimensional (i.e., we assume $\partial\varphi/\partial y$ and $\partial\varphi/\partial z = 0$). Thus, it is only necessary to solve the Poisson equation in its one-dimensional form. We use the value of φ_{surf} from step **1** as one boundary condition [φ (x = 0) = φ_{surf}], and [φ (x = ∞) = 0] as the other, when we solve the Poisson equation to find φ (x).

3. To calculate the mobile charge concentrations $n_p(x)$ and $p_p(x)$, we can use the values of φ (x) found from step (2) in Eqs. 3-12.

4. To find expressions for Q_B and Q_I as a function of gate bias we proceed as follows:

a. First, we recall Gauss' law, which states that the charge contained in a volume equals the permittivity times the electric field emanating from the volume. Applying Gauss' law to a volume extending from the silicon surface to the field-free bulk region, which contains a total charge per unit area Q_C, we can write[*]

$$Q_C = - \kappa_{si}\varepsilon_o \, \mathcal{E}_{si} \, (x = 0) \qquad (3 \text{ - } 17)$$

[*] Note that only the $\mathcal{E}$-field at the Si-SiO$_2$ interface (which represents the top surface of the volume in which the charge in the semiconductor exists) must be included in Eq. 3-17 because the $\mathcal{E}$-field does not emanate from any other surfaces of the volume. This is because: (1) the $\mathcal{E}$-field emanating from the bottom of the volume under consideration (i.e., at x = d) is assumed to be zero, and; (2) since the $\mathcal{E}$-field in the MOS-C is assumed to be unidirectional, $\mathcal{E}_y = \mathcal{E}_z = 0$. Thus, the $\mathcal{E}$-field emanating from the sides of the volume is also zero.

We also note from Eq. 3-16 and from the fact that $C_{ox} = \kappa_{ox}\varepsilon_0/t_{ox}$ that

$$\varphi_{ox} = t_{ox} (\kappa_{si}/\kappa_{ox}) \, \mathcal{E}_{si} (x = 0) = \{\kappa_{si}\varepsilon_0 \, \mathcal{E}_{si} (x = 0)\}/C_{ox} \quad (3 - 18)$$

Thus, we can also write

$$Q_C = -\varphi_{ox} \, C_{ox} \quad (3 - 19)$$

b. Next, we note that the charge per unit area in the semiconductor Q_C is the sum of the inversion layer charge per unit area Q_I and the ionic charge per unit area Q_B. So we can write

$$Q_C = Q_I + Q_B \quad (3 - 20)$$

In general, Q_I can be found by calculating the total mobile charge in the inversion layer (in our example, the electrons). In other words, to get Q_I, we could integrate Eq. 3-12a from $x = 0$ to the depth x_c at which the electron concentration becomes negligible, or

$$Q_I(x) = -q \int_0^{x_c} n(x)\, dx \quad (3 - 21)$$

Then, Q_B could be found by subtracting Q_I from Q_C.

However, this approach to calculating Q_I and Q_B is quite complex, in fact, it requires that $\varphi(x)$ be computed first, and then this result be used to integrate $n(\varphi)$. Both of these calculations, in general, require numerical integration. Although we shall outline this approach in more detail, we will also illustrate simpler methods for calculating Q_I and Q_B which still provide values accurate enough for many applications.

3.3.3 Finding the Quantitative Characteristics of a MOS-C when the Depletion Approximation is Invoked

Let us derive the quantitative characteristics of the ideal MOS-C under some assumptions that simplify the mathematical treatment outlined above, but still provide expressions that are accurate enough for many applications. The simplest of such quantitative analyses assumes that we deal with the ideal uniformly doped MOS-C, and this analysis is also the one carried out in most basic device textbooks. Here we invoke the following approximations: (1) the *depletion approximation* is assumed to be valid; (2) the *one-sided abrupt junction approximation* is assumed; and (3) other simplifying approximations are assumed which allow the depletion region width d, the surface potential φ_{surf}, and the inversion layer charge Q_I to be simply computed beyond the point of strong inversion.

The *depletion approximation* invoked in this case is based on the following simplifying assumptions:

1. The mobile charges in the depletion region are totally absent in the depletion region for values of V_{GB} smaller than those needed to cause inversion (i.e., $n = p = 0$ in the depletion region over this range of gate-bias values).

2. For values of gate-bias voltages beyond inversion, the depletion region is still totally devoid of mobile carriers, except in the inversion layer, which is assumed to be a very thin layer near the silicon surface.

The *one-sided abrupt-junction approximation* assumes that the depletion region extends to a depth d, beyond which the silicon returns abruptly to a condition in which the mobile carrier densities are again equal to their equilibrium values [i.e., at $x = d$, $p = N_A = p_{po}$, and $n = n_{po}$].

The simplifying assumptions dealing with the d (depletion region width), φ_{surf} (surface potential), and Q_I (mobile charges in the inversion layer) are the following:

1. Beyond strong inversion, additional positive bias on the gate simply draws more electrons into the inversion layer. This negative electron charge balances the additional positive gate charge, and the depletion-region width d no longer increases. That is, d remains fixed at the value attained at the onset of strong inversion, and this value is denoted as d_{max}.

2. Since the depletion region no longer increases once the inversion layer is formed, the bands of the energy band diagram are not bent any further with increasing positive bias. Hence, φ_{surf} also remains fixed (or is *clamped*) at the value it has at the onset of inversion, namely at φ_{surf} (inv) $= 2\varphi_B$.

3. Beyond strong inversion, the ionic charge per unit area Q_B contained in the depletion region remains unchanged, since $d = d_{max}$. Hence, we can compute Q_B beyond inversion simply from a knowledge of N_A and d_{max}. Also if V_{GB} is given, and we know φ_{surf} beyond strong inversion, we can compute φ_{ox} from Eq. 3-10, and from this we can obtain Q_C. Then, Q_I can be found by subtracting Q_B from Q_C.

Using these assumptions, we set out to find the desired expressions. We initially solve the Poisson equation in the semiconductor region for $\varphi(x)$. That is, under depletion biasing conditions we have assumed $n = p = 0$, and so the charge density $\rho(x)$ is merely a constant term ($q N_A/\kappa_{si}\varepsilon_0$). In this case, the Poisson equation has the form:

$$d^2\varphi/dx^2 = q N_A/\kappa_{si}\varepsilon_0 \qquad 0 < x < d$$

$$= 0 \qquad x > d \qquad (3 - 22)$$

This is an ordinary, linear differential equation that can easily be integrated twice to yield a closed-form solution of $\varphi(x)$ in the semiconductor. That is, assuming the boundary conditions $\varphi(x = d) = 0$, and $\varphi(x = 0) = \varphi_{surf}$ we get,

$$\varphi(x) = \varphi_{surf}(1 - x/d)^2 \qquad (3 - 23)$$

where d is the depletion-region depth. The electric field $\mathcal{E}$ (x) is given by $-d\varphi/dx$ or

$$\mathcal{E} \ (x) = - d\varphi/dx \ = \ 2 \ \varphi_{surf} \ (1 - x/d)(-1/d) \qquad (3 - 24)$$

and

$$d^2\varphi/dx^2 \ = \ 2 \ \varphi_{surf}/d^2 \qquad \text{[from (3 - 23)]} \qquad (3 - 25)$$

$$= \ q \ N_A/\kappa_{si}\varepsilon_0 \qquad \text{[from (3 - 22)]} \qquad (3 - 26)$$

Then from (3 - 25) and (3 - 26) we can find d in terms of φ_{surf} and N_A

$$d \ = \ [\kappa_{si}\varepsilon_0(2\varphi_{surf})/qN_A]^{1/2}. \qquad (3 - 27)$$

Beyond the point of strong inversion $\varphi_{surf}(inv) = 2\varphi_B$, and so d_{max} is then

$$d_{max} \ = \ (4\kappa_{si}\varepsilon_0\varphi_B/qN_A)^{1/2} \qquad (3 - 28)$$

Next, we solve Eq. 3-10 for φ_{surf}. In this case, let us initially assume that the MOS-C is biased into depletion, but below inversion. In that case, no inversion layer exists ($Q_I = 0$), thus, $Q_C = Q_B$ and Q_B is given by

$$Q_B \ = \ q \ N_A \ d \qquad (3 - 29)$$

Since $\varphi_{ox} = - Q_C/C_{ox} \ = -Q_B/C_{ox}$, by using Eq. 3-29 in this result, we get

$$\varphi_{ox} = -q \ N_A \ d/C_{ox} = \{[\kappa_{si}\varepsilon_0(2\varphi_{surf})qN_A]^{1/2}\}/C_{ox} \qquad (3 - 30)$$

Now if we let $\eta = \{[2\kappa_{si}\varepsilon_0qN_A]^{1/2}\}/C_{ox}$, we can write $\varphi_{ox} = \eta\sqrt{\varphi_{surf}}$. Substituting this into Eq. 3-10 we get

$$V_{GB} \ = \ \varphi_{surf} + \eta\sqrt{\varphi_{surf}} \qquad (3 - 31)$$

If we let $\alpha = \sqrt{\varphi_{surf}}$, we can write Eq. 3-31 as a quadratic equation

$$0 \ = \ \alpha^2 + \eta\alpha - V_{GB} \qquad (3 - 32)$$

We can now easily solve this for α, using the quadratic formula. Once we have α we can find φ_{surf}, since $\varphi_{surf} = \alpha^2$.

Now that φ_{surf} has been obtained, we can find Q_B (from Eq. 3-29) and $\varphi(x)$ (from Eq. 3-23). Below inversion we do not need to find n (x) and p (x), since for this case we have assumed them to be zero for x<d.

Beyond inversion we can calculate d_{max} from Eq. 3-28, and Q_{Bmax} from Eq. 3-29, (using $d = d_{max}$). Then, since $\varphi_{ox} = V_{GB} - 2\varphi_B$, we can find Q_C from

$$Q_C = - (V_{GB} - 2\varphi_B) \ C_{ox} \qquad (3 - 33)$$

Now, since $Q_I = Q_C - Q_{Bmax}$

$$Q_I = - [(V_{GB} - 2\varphi_B) \ C_{ox}] - q \ N_A \ d_{max} \qquad (3 - 34)$$

$$Q_I = -[(V_{GB} - 2\varphi_B) C_{ox}] + \overline{\sqrt{4\kappa_{si}\epsilon_0\varphi_B q N_A}} \qquad (3-35)$$

The results of this analysis are summarized in Fig. 3-7. Here the energy band diagrams of an ideal MOS capacitor (*p*-type Si substrate) are shown for the case of $V_{GB} = 0V$ (Fig. 3-7a). In Fig. 3-7b the case when sufficient gate voltage is applied to strongly invert the silicon surface is shown. Also depicted in these figures are the charge (Fig. 3-7c), $\mathcal{E}$-field (Fig. 3-7d) and electrostatic potential versus distance diagrams (Fig. 3-7e) for these two conditions. We note that since there are no charges in the oxide, the electric field is constant in the oxide, and that the slope of φ is thus constant in the oxide. In Fig. 3-7f we show the electrostatic potential versus distance diagram for an ideal MOS-C with an *n*-type substrate biased into strong inversion. It is useful to note that since a positive bias is needed to invert the *p*-type MOS-C, the φ versus x diagram curves upward, with the maximum value of φ at the surface. However, for the *n*-type MOS-C a negative gate bias is needed. Thus, in such cases the φ versus x diagram curves downward, with its minimum at the surface.

Another important point to which we will refer when discussing the so-called *gradual-channel approximation* (GCA) involves the gradient of the vertical electric field in the silicon, i.e., $\partial\mathcal{E}/\partial x$. In strong inversion $\partial\mathcal{E}/\partial x$ in the silicon is greatest in the inversion layer thickness, since $Q_I >> Q_B$ in strong inversion and the inversion layer is quite thin (~30-300Å thick). Hence, $\partial\mathcal{E}/\partial x$ can be estimated by approximating the vertical electric field value to be zero at the bottom edge of the inversion layer thickness t_{inv}. Then, $\partial\mathcal{E}/\partial x \sim [\mathcal{E}_{si}(x=0) - 0]/t_{inv} = \mathcal{E}_{si}(x=0)/t_{inv}$. We will make use of this result when examining the GCA in chap. 4.

3.3.4 More Accurate and General Model for MOS-C Behavior

The assumption that no mobile charges exist in the depletion region of the MOS-C (depletion approximation) does not accurately reflect the actual charge distribution condition in the silicon, especially below inversion. Thus, the expressions for $\varphi(x)$, φ_{surf}, $\mathcal{E}(x)$, and Q_I, obtained using this assumption are not accurate. In order to obtain a more accurate quantitative model of the MOS-C, we need to use the Poisson equation in which p and n have non-zero values. This will allow us to obtain more accurate expressions of the above quantities. As noted in the introduction of this section, this analysis is complicated. The complexity arises in part because it provides a model that is valid in all regimes (accumulation, depletion, and all ranges of inversion). Although the accumulation and depletion regions are not very important regimes of operation in most MOSFET applications, we nevertheless present this complex MOS-C model here for the several reasons listed in the introduction.

In this more accurate and general representation of the MOS-C, we treat the Poisson equation in the following form:

$$\frac{d^2\phi}{dx^2} = -\left(\frac{q}{\kappa_{Si}\epsilon_0}\right)[-N_A + N_D + p - n] \qquad (3-36)$$

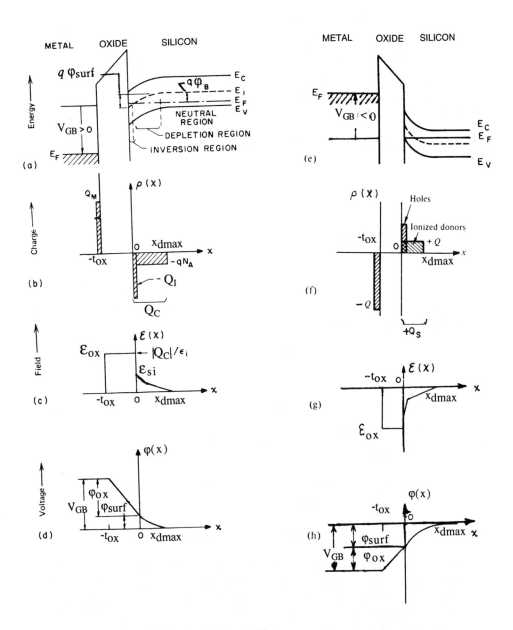

Fig. 3-7 Ideal p-type Si MOS-C when biased into inversion [$V_{GB}>V_T$]: (a) Energy-band diagram; (b) Charge distribution; (c) Electric field; and (d) Potential distribution; (e) - (h) Comparable diagrams for an ideal n-type Si MOS-C.

Equations 3-12a and 3-12b for $n(\varphi)$ and $p(\varphi)$ are substituted for n and p to give

$$\frac{d^2\phi}{dx^2} = -\left(\frac{q}{\kappa_{Si}\varepsilon_o}\right)\left[-N_A + p_{po}\,e^{-q\varphi/kT} + N_D - n_{po}\,e^{q\varphi/kT}\right] \qquad (3-37)$$

In general, Eq. 3-37 can be integrated once to give an analytic expression for the electric field, $\varepsilon = -d\varphi/dx$. This is accomplished by first multiplying both sides of Eq. 3-37 by $2(d\varphi/dx)$. The left-hand side is then recognized as $(d/dx)(d\varphi/dx)^2$, and we can write the result as

$$\frac{1}{2}\frac{d}{dx}\left(\frac{d\phi}{dx}\right)^2 = -\left(\frac{q}{\kappa_{Si}\varepsilon_o}\right)\left[-N_A + p_{po}\,e^{-q\varphi/kT} + N_D - n_{po}\,e^{q\varphi/kT}\right]\left(\frac{d\phi}{dx}\right) \qquad (3-38)$$

Integrating this expression from the bulk ($x = \infty$, where $\varphi = 0$) to an arbitrary point x, we get

$$\left(\frac{d\phi}{dx}\right)^2_\infty - \left(\frac{d\phi}{dx}\right)^2_x = -\left(\frac{2q}{\kappa_{Si}\varepsilon_o}\right)\int_0^\varphi\left[-N_A + p_{po}\,e^{-q\varphi/kT} + N_D - n_{po}\,e^{q\varphi/kT}\right]d\varphi \qquad (3-39)$$

If we note that $p_{po} \approx N_A$, then $n_{po} = n_i^2/N_A$. In addition, since $\varphi_t = q/kT$, and $\varepsilon = -d\varphi/dx$, and $\varepsilon_{si}(x = \infty) = 0$, the first term on the left hand side of Eq. 3-39 is zero. Thus, after integrating the right-hand side we get

$$-\frac{d\varphi}{dx} = \varepsilon_{si}(x) = \sqrt{\frac{2q\,N_A}{\kappa_{Si}\varepsilon_o}}\sqrt{\varphi_t e^{-\varphi/\varphi_t} + \varphi - \varphi_t + e^{-2\varphi_B/\varphi_t}\left(\varphi_t e^{-\varphi/\varphi_t} - \varphi - \varphi_t\right)} \qquad (3-40)$$

This result allows us to obtain the electric field at the surface ($x = 0$) if φ_{surf} is known

$$\varepsilon_{si}(x = 0) = \sqrt{\frac{2q\,N_A}{\kappa_{Si}\varepsilon_o}}\sqrt{\varphi_t e^{-\varphi_{surf}/\varphi_t} + \varphi_{surf} - \varphi_t + e^{-2\varphi_B/\varphi_t}\left(\varphi_t e^{-\varphi_{surf}/\varphi_t} - \varphi_{surf} - \varphi_t\right)} \qquad (3-41)$$

In addition, by applying Gauss' law we can use Eq. 3-41 to find Q_C - i.e., from Eq. 3-17 $[Q_C = -\kappa_{Si}\varepsilon_o\varepsilon_{si}(x = 0)]$ we get:

$$Q_C = \sqrt{2q\,N_A\kappa_{Si}\varepsilon_o}\sqrt{\varphi_t e^{-\varphi_{surf}/\varphi_t} + \varphi_{surf} - \varphi_t + e^{-2\varphi_B/\varphi_t}\left(\varphi_t e^{-\varphi_{surf}/\varphi_t} - \varphi_{surf} - \varphi_t\right)} \qquad (3-42)$$

This equation is valid for all regimes (accumulation, depletion, and inversion). Figure 3-8 depicts the variation of total charge concentration Q_C with φ_{surf} as calculated using Eq. 3-42.[6] It provides a quantitative representation of the total charge dependence on φ_{surf} that was qualitatively described in section 3.2.* We see that for negative values of φ_{surf}, Q_C is positive, corresponding to the accumulation regime. For $\varphi_{surf} = 0$, we

* Note that in section 3.3.1 we also examined the variation of the mobile charge concentration at the silicon surface n_{surf} versus φ_{surf} for depletion and inversion ($\varphi_{surf} > 0V$).

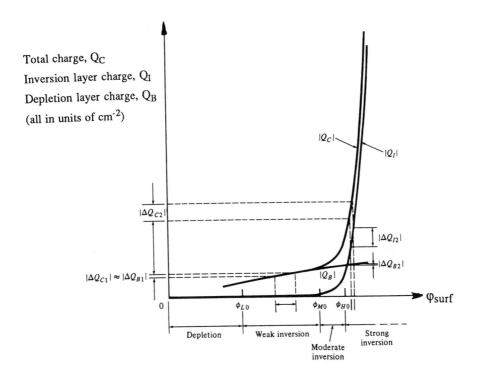

Fig. 3-8 Magnitude of inversion layer charge, depletion layer charge, and their sum (all per unit area) versus φ_{surf}.[6] Reprinted with permission of McGraw-Hill Book Company.

have the flat-band condition, in which $Q_C = 0$. When φ_{surf} is positive, and its value lies between 0 and $2\varphi_B$, Q_C is negative and is $\sim\sqrt{\varphi_{surf}}$. This means that in depletion and weak inversion the mobile charge density is much smaller than the ionic charge density. For $\varphi_{surf} > 2\varphi_B$, strong inversion occurs, and $Q_C \cong -\exp(q\varphi_{surf}/2kT$, indicating that the mobile charge density is now much greater than the ionic charge density.

To calculate φ_{surf}, assuming we are given V_{GB}, C_{ox} and N_A, we use

$$V_{GB} = \varphi_{ox} + \varphi_{surf} \tag{3-43}$$

and

$$\varphi_{ox} = \{\kappa_{si}\varepsilon_0 \, \mathcal{E}_{si} \, (x = 0)\}/C_{ox} \tag{3-44}$$

$$V_{GB} = \varphi_{surf} + \frac{\sqrt{2q \, N_A\kappa_{si}\varepsilon_0}}{C_{ox}}\sqrt{\varphi_t e^{-\varphi_{surf}/\varphi_t} + \varphi_{surf} - \varphi_t + e^{-2\varphi_B/\varphi_t}\left(\varphi_t e^{-\varphi_{surf}/\varphi_t} - \varphi_{surf} - \varphi_t\right)}$$

$$\tag{3-45}$$

* (cont.) The conclusions we drew concerning the mobile charge concentration in the silicon in that case for these regions are reiterated here. However, in Fig. 3-8 the contribution of Q_B to the change in Q_C as φ_{surf} is varied is also included.

Note that to find φ_{surf} from this equation we must perform a numerical iteration.

To calculate Q_I accurately we must follow the procedure outlined in section 3.3.2. That is, we must use Eq. 3-21. Here we also change the variable of integration to φ

$$Q_I = -q \int_0^{x_c} n(x)\, dx = -q \int_{\varphi_{surf}}^{\varphi_c} \frac{n(\varphi)\, d\varphi}{d\varphi/dx} \qquad (3\text{-}46)$$

By using Eqs. 3-12a and 3-40 in Eq. 3-46 (since $\mathcal{E} = -d\varphi/dx$), we get

$$Q_I = q \int_{\varphi_{surf}}^{\varphi_c} \frac{n_{po}\, e^{\varphi/\varphi_t}}{\sqrt{\dfrac{2q\,N_A}{\kappa_{Si}\varepsilon_o}}\sqrt{\varphi_t e^{-\varphi/\varphi_t} + \varphi - \varphi_t + e^{-2\varphi_B/\varphi_t}\left(\varphi_t e^{-\varphi/\varphi_t} - \varphi - \varphi_t\right)}}\, d\varphi \qquad (3\text{-}47)$$

A similar procedure gives Q_B (consisting of ionized acceptor atoms and holes)

$$Q_B = q\, p_{po} \int_{\varphi_{surf}}^{\varphi_c} \frac{e^{-\varphi/\varphi_t} - 1}{\sqrt{\dfrac{2q\,N_A}{\kappa_{Si}\varepsilon_o}}\sqrt{\varphi_t e^{-\varphi/\varphi_t} + \varphi - \varphi_t + e^{-2\varphi_B/\varphi_t}\left(\varphi_t e^{-\varphi/\varphi_t} - \varphi - \varphi_t\right)}}\, d\varphi \qquad (3\text{-}48)$$

To get $\varphi(x)$ we must integrate the Poisson equation a second time. That is, to find φ at some point x we start with Eq. 3-40, separate variables and integrate from x to 0 on the right hand side, and from φ to φ_{surf} on the left:

$$-\int_{\varphi}^{\varphi_{surf}} \frac{d\varphi}{\sqrt{\dfrac{2q\,N_A}{\kappa_{Si}\varepsilon_o}}\sqrt{\varphi_t e^{-\varphi/\varphi_t} + \varphi - \varphi_t + e^{-2\varphi_B/\varphi_t}\left(\varphi_t e^{-\varphi/\varphi_t} - \varphi - \varphi_t\right)}} = x \qquad (3\text{-}49)$$

However, unlike the first integration which yielded the analytical expression for $\mathcal{E}(x)$ given by Eq. 3-40, this second integration cannot be carried out analytically. That is, we must use numerical procedures to calculate $\varphi(x)$ in this case. This was first done by Young in 1961.[2] Numerical integration must also be used to find the electron and hole densities using Eqs. 3-12 a and 3-12b. Sample plots of $[\rho/qN_A]$ versus x and $\varphi(x)$ versus x calculated using such numerical analysis techniques are shown for accumulation (Fig. 3-9a), depletion (Fig. 3-9b), onset of strong inversion, $\varphi_{surf} = 2\varphi_B$ (Fig. 3-9c), and strong inversion, $\varphi_{surf} = 2\varphi_B + 0.15V$ (Fig. 3-9d) for a MOS-C with $\varphi_B = 0.3V$.[3]

We observe from these curves that: (1) the mobile charge in the inversion layer is confined to a very thin layer near the surface; and (2) the depletion-region edge is fairly abrupt, with the charge concentration dropping to negligible values over a distance of ~0.5 μm. The first observation supports the use of the following two approximations

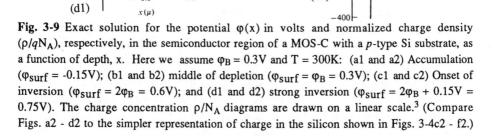

Fig. 3-9 Exact solution for the potential $\varphi(x)$ in volts and normalized charge density (ρ/qN_A), respectively, in the semiconductor region of a MOS-C with a p-type Si substrate, as a function of depth, x. Here we assume $\varphi_B = 0.3V$ and T = 300K: (a1 and a2) Accumulation $(\varphi_{surf} = -0.15V)$; (b1 and b2) middle of depletion $(\varphi_{surf} = \varphi_B = 0.3V)$; (c1 and c2) Onset of inversion $(\varphi_{surf} = 2\varphi_B = 0.6V)$; and (d1 and d2) strong inversion $(\varphi_{surf} = 2\varphi_B + 0.15V = 0.75V)$. The charge concentration ρ/N_A diagrams are drawn on a linear scale.[3] (Compare Figs. a2 - d2 to the simpler representation of charge in the silicon shown in Figs. 3-4c2 - f2.)

invoked in both the simplified and charge sheet models of the MOS-C: (a) the inversion layer can be treated as an infinitesimally-thin sheet of charge at the interface; and (b) the presence of mobile charge in the depletion region can be ignored (the depletion approximation). The second observation indicates it is reasonable to assume that transition from the bulk to the depletion region occurs abruptly.

In summary, the complicated procedure outlined above involves the following steps to get exact values of MOS-C parameters. For an ideal, uniformly doped p-type MOS-C, if we are given N_A, t_{ox}, and V_{GB}

    1. Calculate φ_{surf} using Eq. 3-45.

    2. With this value of φ_{surf} we can get Q_I from Eq. 3-47, $\mathcal{E}(x)$ from Eq. 3-40, and $\varphi(x)$ from Eq. 3-49.

    3. Once $\varphi(x)$ is known we can calculate $n(x)$ and $p(x)$ using Eqs. 3-12a and b.

From the sample plots of the charge distribution we see that in accumulation and inversion the mobile charge resides in an extremely narrow portion of the semiconductor immediately adjacent to the oxide-semiconductor surface. This substantiates the validity of the assumption used in the depletion approximation analysis that the inversion layer charge is confined to a very thin layer near the silicon surface. Thus, a third model based on this approximation (that is intermediate in complexity between the two models just described) has been developed by Baccarani et al.,[4] and Brews.[5] It is called the *charge-sheet model* and will be presented next.

3.3.5 Charge-Sheet Model for Determining the Characteristics of the Ideal MOS-C

The third quantitative model of the MOS-C is the *charge-sheet model*. It is more accurate than the simple depletion approximation model, but does not require the numerical analysis of the general model to obtain Q_I. Since it includes mobile charge carriers in the Poisson equation it provides information about the charge distribution in the MOS-C below strong inversion (unlike the depletion approximation model, which assumes that no mobile charges are present below strong inversion). Since the charge-sheet model assumes that the mobile charge concentrations are zero in the depletion region outside of the thin layer at the surface (that would contain the inversion layer - see assumption 2 below), this model is not as accurate for characterizing the MOS-C in depletion or accumulation as the general model. However, since inversion is responsible for current conduction in MOSFETs, accurate quantitative characteristics of the depletion and accumulation regimes in MOS-Cs and MOSFETs are usually not of much concern. Hence, this does not represent a significant limitation for most applications.

To begin the derivation, we list the assumptions upon which the charge-sheet model is based:

    1. Mobile charge can exist in the silicon beyond the onset of *weak* inversion i.e., when $\varphi_{surf} > \varphi_B$ (unlike the previous model that assumed that no mobile charge exists in the channel until strong inversion, i.e., until $\varphi_{surf} > 2\varphi_B$);

2. All this mobile charge is confined to a negligibly thin inversion layer at the silicon surface, so that the remainder of the depletion region contains no mobile charges ($n = p = 0$, for $0 < x \leq d$);

3. The depletion region is defined by a sharp boundary at a depth d (i.e., an abrupt transition between the depletion region and the bulk exists), in the same manner as was invoked the depletion approximation model;

4. The voltage drop across the inversion layer in the x-direction is zero, hence V_{GB} (in an ideal MOS-C) is still the sum of φ_{surf} and φ_{ox};

5. The value of φ_{surf} beyond strong inversion is not clamped at exactly $2\varphi_B$. Instead its exact value can be calculated from the model equations;

6. The depletion width at strong inversion is calculated using Eq. 3-28, so that the ionic charge in the depletion region can be calculated using Eq. 3-29;

7. The value of Q_I can be found by subtracting Q_B from Q_C.

Since both holes and electrons are included in the charge density term of the Poisson equation, we start the development of the charge sheet model again with Eq. 3-37. The first integration of the Poisson equation is also carried out in the same way as in the general model analysis, yielding the identical value for $\varepsilon_{si}(x = 0)$. Q_C is also expressed by Eq. 3-42. However, since the goal of the charge sheet model is to provide accurate MOS-C expressions only for the case of inversion (including weak inversion), Q_C can be simplified for this operating range. That is, if $\varphi_{surf} \geq \varphi_B$ (where, as we noted in section 3.3.1, φ_B is $9\varphi_t$ to $16\varphi_t$ for the range of doping concentrations used in MOSFETs), several terms in Eq. 3-42 become insignificant and can be dropped, yielding

$$Q_C \approx \sqrt{2q\,N_A\kappa_S\varepsilon_o}\sqrt{\varphi_{surf} \; + \; \varphi_t\,e^{(\varphi_{surf} - 2\varphi_B)/\varphi_t}} \qquad (3-50)$$

Now, since we assume that in the depletion region there are no mobile charges present (i.e., all the mobile charge is in the inversion layer, which is infinitesimally thin), the depth of the depletion region is again given by Eq. 3-27

$$d \; = \; [\kappa_{si}\varepsilon_o(2\varphi_{surf})/qN_A]^{1/2} \qquad (3-51)$$

Then, Q_B will consist only of the uncovered acceptor atoms in the depletion region, and can again be expressed by Eq. 3-29, repeated here:

$$Q_B \; = \; q\,N_A\,d \; = \; (2\kappa_{si}\varepsilon_o q N_A \varphi_{surf})^{1/2} \qquad (3-52)$$

To get Q_I we can now subtract Q_B from Q_C as given by Eq. 3-50 to get

$$Q_I = \sqrt{2q\,N_A\kappa_S\varepsilon_o}\left(\sqrt{\varphi_{surf} \; + \; \varphi_t\,e^{(\varphi_{surf} - 2\varphi_B)/\varphi_t}} \; - \; \sqrt{\varphi_{surf}}\,\right) \qquad (3-53)$$

Also note that if we use Eq. 3-50 to approximate Q_C in Eq. 3-19 for φ_{ox}, and insert this into Eq. 3-10, the expression relating φ_{surf} and V_{GB} is now

or

$$V_{GB} = \varphi_{surf} - Q_C/C_{ox} \qquad (3\text{-}54)$$

$$V_{GB} = \varphi_{surf} + \frac{\sqrt{2q\,N_A\kappa_S\varepsilon_0}}{C_{ox}}\sqrt{\varphi_{surf} + \varphi_t\,e^{(\varphi_{surf}-2\varphi_B)/\varphi_t}} \qquad (3\text{-}55)$$

We note, however, that this equation cannot be solved explicitly for φ_{surf}, but requires a numerical iteration approach to solve for φ_{surf}.

Nevertheless, the charge sheet model provides analytical expressions for Q_I and Q_B in a MOS-C that are quite accurate over the entire range of inversion (i.e., $\varphi_{surf} > \varphi_B$). This makes it more useful in many applications than the more general MOS-C model.

It should also be noted that when the equation for Q_I from the charge sheet model is plotted versus the surface potential (i.e., using a log-linear plot, as shown in Fig. 3-10),[6] two inversion regimes can be identified: (1) weak inversion; and (2) strong inversion. In each of these regimes we can simplify the expression for Q_I given by Eq. 3-53.

3.3.5.1 Approximation of Q_I in Weak Inversion.
First, we recall from section 3.3.4 that Q_I is much smaller than Q_B in weak inversion. Therefore, we can simplify Q_I by treating the term $\varphi_t \exp(\varphi_{surf} - 2\varphi_B)/\varphi_t$ in Eq. 3-53 as small compared to

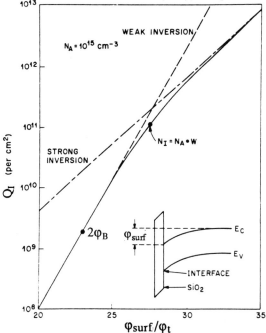

Fig. 3-10 Inversion layer carrier density per unit area versus φ_{surf}/φ_t as computed from Eq. 3-53 and from approximations to this equation for the case of weak inversion (Eq. 3-58), and strong inversion (Eq. 3-62). [5] (© IEEE 1978).

the term φ_{surf}. Then, if we let

$$\zeta = \varphi_t \exp(\varphi_{surf} - 2\varphi_B)/\varphi_t \qquad (3-56)$$

the first square root term in the parentheses in Eq. 3-53 becomes $\sqrt{\varphi_{surf}} + \zeta$. Since ζ is smaller than φ_{surf}, we can approximate the function $\sqrt{\varphi_{surf}} + \zeta$ by the first two terms of its Taylor expansion about $\zeta = 0$:

$$\sqrt{\varphi_{surf} + \xi} \approx \sqrt{\varphi_{surf}} + \frac{1}{2\sqrt{\varphi_{surf}}}\xi \qquad (3-57)$$

Using Eq. 3-56 and Eq. 3-57 in Eq. 3-53 we get

$$Q_I \text{ (weak inv)} \approx \frac{\sqrt{2q\,N_A\kappa_S\varepsilon_0}}{2\sqrt{\varphi_{surf}}}\varphi_t\, e^{(\varphi_{surf} - 2\varphi_B)/\varphi_t} \qquad (3-58)$$

This expression implies that in weak inversion the inversion layer charge is essentially an exponential function of φ_{surf}. Note from Fig. 3-10 that the weak inversion approximation of Q_I from Eq. 3-53 is quite accurate up to $2\varphi_B$, but becomes increasingly inaccurate beyond strong inversion.

   We can easily solve for φ_{surf} in weak inversion as well. That is, since $Q_I \ll Q_B$, we can write Eq. 3-10 as

$$V_{GB} = \varphi_{surf} - Q_B/C_{ox} \qquad (3-59)$$

or using Eq. 3-52

$$V_{GB} = \varphi_{surf} + [(\sqrt{2\kappa_{si}\varepsilon_0 qN_A})/C_{ox}]\sqrt{\varphi_{surf}} \qquad (3-60)$$

$$= \varphi_{surf} + \gamma\sqrt{\varphi_{surf}} \qquad (3-60a)$$

where $\gamma = (\sqrt{2\kappa_{si}\varepsilon_0 qN_A})/C_{ox}$. Equation 3-60a can be solved for φ_{surf} to yield

$$\varphi_{surf} = \left[-\frac{\gamma}{2} + \left(\frac{\gamma^2}{4} + V_{GB}\right)^{1/2}\right]^2 \qquad (3-61)$$

To relate Q_I to V_{GB}, we can substitute the value of φ_{surf} from Eq. 3-61 into Eq. 3-58.

3.3.5.2 Approximation of Q_I in Strong Inversion.   In strong inversion $Q_I \gg Q_B$. As a result, the exponential term in Eq. 3-53 is the only significant term within the parentheses. Thus, Q_I in strong inversion can be well approximated as

$$Q_I \text{ (strong inv)} \approx (\sqrt{2\kappa_{si}\varepsilon_0 q}\, n_i \exp{(\varphi_{surf}/2\varphi_t)} \qquad (3-62)$$

The inversion-layer charge in strong inversion is thus seen to be an exponential function of the surface potential with a slope of $1/(2\varphi_t)$. Therefore, a small increase in the surface potential induces a large change in Q_I (strong inv). This implies that φ_{surf} will remain almost unchanged even in the face of a large increase in V_{GB} or Q_I beyond strong inversion. The approximation that φ_{surf} (inv) is clamped at $2\varphi_B$ made in the depletion approximation model is thus seen to be reasonably accurate for actual MOSFETs. If the gate voltage corresponding to value needed to produce φ_{surf}(inv) is

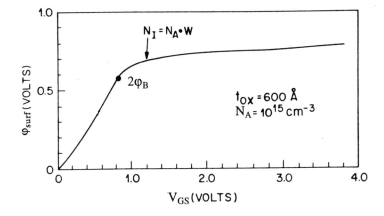

Fig. 3-11 φ_{surf} versus V_{GB} calculated from the charge sheet model for an oxide thickness of 60 nm, and a substrate doping level of $N_A = 10^{15}$ cm^{-3}. The dot indicates $\varphi_{surf} = 2\varphi_B$.[5] (© IEEE 1978).

termed the threshold voltage V_T (see next section for how to compute this value), then the Q_I (strong inv) dependence on V_{GB} can be approximated by

$$Q_I \approx - C_{ox} (V_{GB} - V_T) \qquad (3 - 63)$$

We should mention that φ_{surf}(inv) does change slightly as V_{GB} is increased beyond strong inversion, as shown in Fig. 3-11, where φ_{surf} from Eq. 3-55 is plotted versus V_{GB}. We see that φ_{surf} in strong inversion actually increases beyond $2\varphi_B$ by ~150 mV before leveling off. Thus, models of Q_I that use φ_{surf}(inv) $= 2\varphi_B$ underestimate the actual value. This has an impact on the accuracy of predicted drain current values in MOSFET circuit models based on this approximation. We will discuss this further in chap. 4.

3.4 THRESHOLD VOLTAGE of IDEAL MOS CAPACITORS

Strong inversion in MOSFETs occurs in essentially the same manner as in MOS-Cs. In fact, one of the most important parameters of a MOSFET is the gate voltage at the onset of strong inversion. This parameter is known as the *threshold voltage* V_T. We can obtain an expression for V_T using an ideal MOS-C in which we assume the depletion approximation is valid. Then we follow the same analysis as in section 3.3.3.

---

* Note that a third inversion regime, intermediate to the two mentioned above, namely *moderate inversion*, has been defined by Tsividis (see Fig. 3-6).[6] This allows an even more careful representation of MOS behavior to be developed. Interested readers can consult ref. 6 for more details.

That is, we begin with Eq. 3-10:

$$V_{GB} = \varphi_{ox} + \varphi_{surf} \qquad (3 - 64)$$

At the *onset* of strong inversion (i.e., implying that the inversion layer is just at the verge of forming, so Q_I is still zero), the magnitude of the charge on the gate is balanced by just the charge in depletion region of the semiconductor Q_B due to the ionized dopants, or:

$$Q_G = -Q_B = q\, N_{SUB}\, d_{max} \qquad (3-65)$$

where N_{SUB} is the substrate doping (i.e., N_A in *p*-type and N_D in *n*-type substrates), respectively. Then, φ_{surf} at the onset of inversion $= 2\varphi_B$. It can also be expressed in terms of d_{max} using Eq. 3-27. Setting these two equal, we have for a *p*-type substrate

$$\varphi_{surf}(inv) = 2\varphi_B = qN_A\,(d_{max})^2\,/2\kappa_{si}\varepsilon_o) \qquad (3-66)$$

Solving this for d_{max}, and substituting into Eq. 3-65 we get Q_B in terms of N_A and φ_B. Finally, using this expression for Q_B in Eqs. 3-19 and 3-20 ($\varphi_{ox} = -Q_B/C_{ox}$), and putting this into Eq. 3-64 we obtain the gate voltage value at the onset of strong inversion in an ideal MOS capacitor (V_T) expressed as a single equation in terms of t_{ox}, T, n_i, and N_A:

$$V_T \text{ (of an ideal MOS capacitor)} = 2\sqrt{\kappa_{si}\varepsilon_oqN_A\varphi_B}/C_{ox} + 2\varphi_B \quad (3-67)$$

3.5   PHYSICS OF NON-IDEAL MOS CAPACITORS (n^+-PolySi-SiO$_2$-Si MOS Capacitors)

Although the ideal MOS capacitor is a useful structure for introducing MOS behavior, from the perspective of this text the most important MOS capacitor structure is the metal (Al, or heavily-doped polysilicon)-SiO$_2$-Si structure. In the metal-SiO$_2$-Si structure (and other "real" MOS capacitors), the work function difference φ_{ms} is virtually never zero, and various charges are also always present inside the oxide or at the Si-SiO$_2$ interface. These phenomena exhibited by "real" MOS capacitors significantly alter ideal MOS behavior. They are also inherent in "real" MOSFETs, and must therefore be included to accurately describe actual device behavior.

3.5.1 Workfunction Difference Between Gate and Semiconductor

We noted earlier that the energy-band diagram of an *ideal* MOS capacitor is in a flat band condition when $V_{GB} = 0$. In real MOS capacitors, however, a flat band condition with $V_{GB} = 0$ is essentially never observed. Instead, when $V_{GB} = 0$ the bands are almost always bent as a result of the work function difference between the gate and semi-conductor regions, as well as the charges that exist in the MOS capacitor.

The *work function* of a material is defined as the minimum energy required to bring an electron from the Fermi level to the vacuum level. In MOS structures, however, it is more useful to deal with the *modified* work function. This is defined as the minimum energy required to bring an electron from the Fermi level in the gate E_{Fm} or the semiconductor E_{FS} to the oxide conduction-band edge ($q\varphi_m'$ or $q\varphi_s'$, respectively), as shown in Fig. 3-12. Note also that $q\varphi_s' = q[\chi' + (E_c - E_F)_\infty] = q(\chi' + E_G/2 + \varphi_B)$ for a *p*-type semiconductor, where χ' is the *modified electron affinity* (defined as the energy difference between the conduction band edges of the semiconductor and the oxide). In the Si-SiO₂ case, $q\chi' = 3.23$ eV.

Figure 3-12a shows the energy-band diagram for an Al-SiO₂-*p*-type-Si structure before contact. For Al-SiO₂, $q\varphi_m' = 3.2$ eV, while for *p*-type Si-SiO₂ $q\varphi_s' = (3.23 + 0.55 + q\varphi_B) \sim 4.1$ eV. Obviously, $q\varphi_m'$ and $q\varphi_s'$ are not equal. Hence, if a MOS structure could be formed by bringing the 2 regions in contact, the effect of this difference on the energy-band diagram of the MOS capacitor would be as shown in Fig. 3-12b. That is, if such a MOS capacitor was unbiased ($V_{GB} = 0$), the Fermi levels would have to "line up" (be at the same energy level) everywhere in the capacitor, Fig.

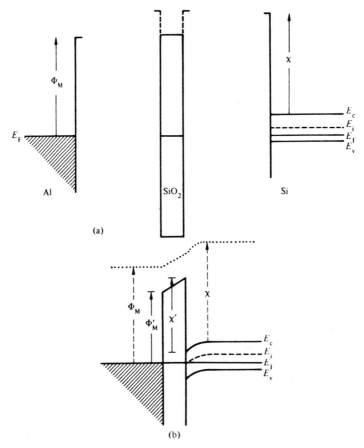

Fig. 3-12 The MOS capacitor structure and idealized energy-band diagram (a) before contact and (b) after contact.[12] Reprinted with permission of Addison-Wesley.

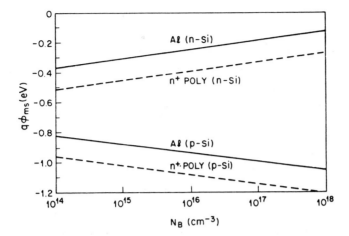

Fig. 3-13 Work-function difference ϕ_{ms} (V) versus doping for n^+ and p^+ polysilicon, and Al gate electrodes.[7] Reprinted with permission of Solid-State Electronics.

3-12). Since the modified work functions in this structure are different, the E_c, E_i, and E_v bands would be bent downward when $V_{GB} = 0$ to satisfy the requirement of a constant Fermi level. To achieve a flat-band condition in this structure, a negative voltage [equal to $(\varphi_m - \varphi_s)$], would have to be applied to the gate (in this example $\cong -0.9$ V).

In submicron ICs, however, the gate material is normally heavily-doped polysilicon. The Fermi level in heavily doped n-type polysilicon resides at the conduction band edge (and in heavily doped p-type poly, at the valence band edge). Hence, for an n-channel device with n^+ poly on a p-type substrate $\varphi_{ms}(n\text{-ch}) = (\varphi_m - \varphi_s) = (-E_G/2q) - \varphi_B$ (with its value between -0.9 to -0.95V for 10^{16} cm^{-3}<N_A<10^{17} cm^{-3} - the appropriate doping range for submicron technologies if L>0.5 μm). Likewise, the p-channel φ_{ms} for an n^+ poly on an n-type substrate is $\varphi_{ms}(p\text{-ch}) = (\varphi_m - \varphi_s) = (-E_G/2q) + |\varphi_B|$, with its value between -0.15 to -0.2V for the same doping range. Finally, for a p-channel device having a p^+ poly on an n-substrate, $\varphi_{ms}(p\text{-ch}) = (\varphi_m - \varphi_s) = (E_G/2q) + |\varphi_B|$. Figure 3-13 shows the value of φ_{ms} for various substrate-doping values if an aluminum, n^+-poly, or p^+-poly gate electrode is used.

3.5.2 Oxide Charges and Traps

Four different types of charges are associated with the oxide and Si-SiO$_2$ interface as shown schematically in Fig. 3-14. The effective net (i.e., total) charge per unit area at the Si-SiO$_2$ interface (in C/cm^2) is denoted by the symbol Q_{tot}, whereas the net (total) number of charges per unit area (Q_{tot}/q) is given by N_{tot}. The standardized terminology and symbols used to differentiate the various individual charge types are as follows:

1. Mobile ionic charge per unit area Q_m (C/cm^2), and N_m (no. of mobile charges/cm^2);

2. Fixed oxide charge per unit area Q_f (C/cm^2), and N_f (no. of fixed oxide charges/cm^2);

3. Interface trap charge per unit area Q_{it} (C/cm^2), and N_{it} (no. of interface trapped charges/cm^2); D_{it} - number of interface trapped charges per unit area *and* energy (no. of interface trapped charges/cm^2-eV);

4. Oxide trapped charge Q_{ot} (C/cm^2), and N_{ot} (no. of oxide trapped charges/cm^2).

Since issues relating to the reliability of submicron MOSFETs also involve these charges, a brief review concerning the origin of the charges, their effect on device behavior, and techniques to minimize their presence is given here. A more detailed description of their characteristics can be found in Vol. 1 and refs. 1 and 7.

3.5.2.1 Mobile Ionic Charges. Mobile ionic charges Q_m in the oxide layer arise mostly from the presence of sodium or potassium ions, which have very high diffusivities in the oxide (even at temperatures of less than 200°C). Their presence leads to threshold instabilities and to a deterioration of the oxide reliability. After it was confirmed that sodium in even very small concentrations is ruinous to MOSFET operation, stringent procedures were developed to keep the level below $N_m = 10^9$ cm^{-2}. At such levels, the instabilities in V_T are negligibly small. Procedures to counteract Na contamination include: using clean processing techniques; employing gettering techniques; neutralization of the sodium in the oxide by growing the oxide in ambients containing chlorine compounds; and using SiN (or oxynitride) passivation films. (Such films are impervious to the transport of Na.) Tests for Na contamination are also routinely performed (using MOS-C monitor structures) to detect any accidental contamination. Steps can then be taken to find and eliminate the contamination source. More information on the details of these techniques can be found in Vol. 1, Chap. 7.

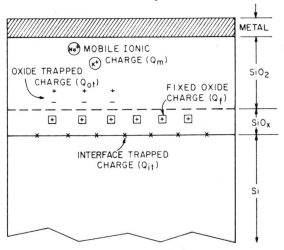

Fig. 3-14 Standardized terminology for oxide charges associated with thermally oxidized silicon.[13] (© IEEE 1980).

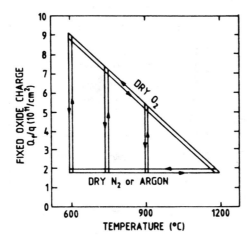

Fig. 3-15 The *Deal triangle,* which specifies the expected Q_f/q after dry O_2 oxidation and after inert ambient annealing.[9] Reprinted by permission of the publisher, The Electrochemical Society, Inc.

3.5.2.2 Fixed Oxide Charge. The fixed oxide charge Q_f (usually positive) is located in the oxide within approximately 30Å of the Si-SiO$_2$ interface. Since its density does not vary with surface potential (unlike interface trapped charge Q_{it}), it is termed *fixed* oxide charge. It is generally accepted that Q_f is associated with the structure of the interfacial transition region between the silicon and SiO$_2$. One hypothesis is that Q_f is due to *excess ionic silicon* which has broken away from the silicon proper and is waiting to react in the vicinity of the Si-SiO$_2$ interface when the oxidation process is abruptly terminated.

Regardless of the origin, it has been experimentally confirmed that the magnitude of Q_f is influenced by substrate orientation, oxidation temperature, and anneal conditions after oxide growth. These factors were carefully studied by Deal et al., and their results are summarized by the well-known "Deal-triangle" shown in Fig. 3-15. In this figure N_f (Q_f/q) is plotted for (111) Si against final oxidation or anneal temperature. It can be seen that the minimum N_f value for (111) material is $\sim 2 \times 10^{11}$ cm^{-2}. The time required to reach a minimum value of N_f is less than 5 min at 1200°C and about an hour at 550°C. In addition, after an oxide growth step, wafers are annealed in an inert ambient (part of the annealing step occurring during the slow withdrawal from the furnace). It should be noted, however, that continued annealing in inert ambients (e.g., N$_2$) at high temperatures leads to a marked increase of N_f. Fig. 3-16 shows how N_f changes as a function of time during a nitrogen anneal at 950, 1100 or 1200°C.

The value of N_f also depends on the orientation of the Si surface, and is lowest on (100) orientations (in which the minimum N_f value is $\sim 1.1 \times 10^{10}$ cm^{-2}). As the lowest values of N_f are desired, (100) material is used to build MOS ICs.

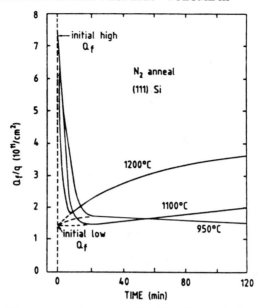

Fig. 3-16 Variation of fixed oxide charge as a function of time during nitrogen anneal at 950, 1100 or 1200°C.[10] Reprinted by permission of the publisher, The Electrochemical Society, Inc.

Since Q_f is located at the Si-SiO$_2$ interface, the change in V_T that it causes (ΔV_T) is simply calculated as the shift in V_T that would be produced by a sheet of positive charge placed at the interface, or

$$\Delta V_T = -Q_f/C_{ox} = q\, N_f\, /C_{ox} \qquad (3-68)$$

3.5.2.3 Interface Trapped Charge. Interface trapped charge Q_{it} arises from allowed energy states (also referred to as *surface states, interface states,* or *interface traps*) that somehow exist in the forbidden gap of the Si in the region very close to the Si-SiO$_2$ interface. Although models exist that detail the *electrical* behavior of interface traps, their *physical origin* has not been totally clarified. The weight of experimental evidence supports the view that the interface traps arise primarily from unsatisfied chemical bonds or so-called "dangling bonds" at the surface of the semiconductor. When a silicon lattice is abruptly terminated along a given plane to form a surface, one of the four surface-atom bonds will be left dangling as pictured in Fig. 3-17. It seems plausible that most, but maybe not all, of such Si-surface bonds would be tied up as a result of thermally growing an SiO$_2$ layer (Fig. 3-17b). The remaining dangling bonds might become interfacial traps. Other possible interfacial trap-formation effects include Si-Si bond stretching - due to the absence of an oxygen atom (Fig. 3-17c), Si-O bond stretching (Fig. 3-17d), and the presence of a metallic impurity at the Si surface (Fig. 3-17e).[11] These interface traps are also considered further in chaps. 7 and 8.

Based on the wide-ranging and degrading effects they cause in the operational behavior of MOSFETs (and the fact that Q_m and Q_f can generally be acceptably minimized), interface trapped charges must be considered to be the most perfidious of the oxide charges. Because they are not usually caused by the presence of foreign impurities, but instead are due to a disruption of the periodicity of the crystal lattice, they are not associated with well-defined energy levels. Instead, interface trapped charges are distributed throughout the entire band gap at closely spaced levels. (Interface levels

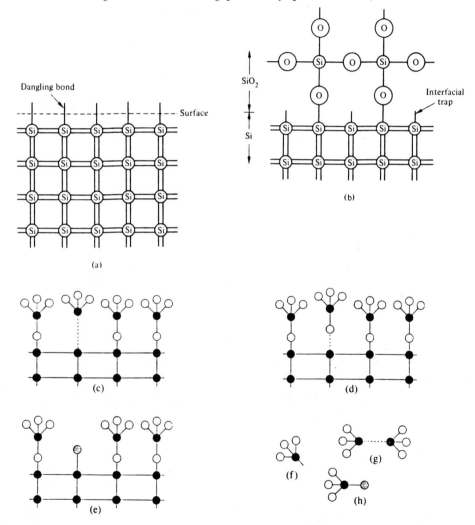

Fig. 3-17 Physical model for the interfacial traps. (a) "Dangling bonds" which occur when the Si lattice is abruptly terminated along a given plane to form a surface. (b) Post oxidation dangling bonds (relative number greatly exaggerated) that become the interfacial traps. (c) Si-Si bond stretching. (d) Si-O bond stretching. (e) presence of a metallic impurity at the Si surface. (f) - (h) possible defects in the SiO_2 bulk that may give rise to oxide trapped charge.

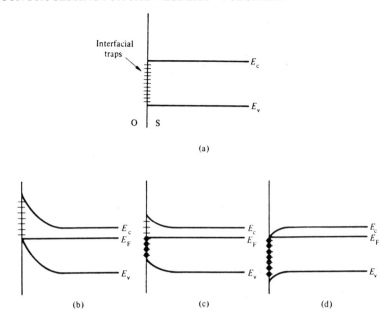

Fig. 3-18 (a) Electrical modeling of interfacial traps as allowed electronic levels localized in space at the oxide-semiconductor interface. (b) - (d) Filling of the interface levels under (b) inversion, (c) depletion, and (d) accumulation biasing in an n-type device. From R.F. Pierret, *Modular Series on Solid-State Devices; Vol. IV - Field Effect Devices.* Copyright, 1983, Addison-Wesley. Reprinted with permission.

can also occur at energies greater than E_c or less than E_v, but such levels are usually obscured by the much larger density of conduction- or valence-band states.) By using an energy-band diagram to show how these energy levels are distributed throughout the forbidden gap (Fig. 3-18a), we can more easily visualize their impact on a MOS-C.

That is, if an n-doped Si MOSFET (PMOS) is biased into inversion (Fig. 3-18b), the Fermi level at the surface will be close to E_v. In this case, the interfacial traps will mostly be empty, as they lie in energies above E_F. Furthermore, if these empty trap sites are assumed to be donorlike (that is, positively charged when empty and neutral when filled with an electron), the net charge per unit area associated with the interfacial traps (Q_{it}) will be positive. Changing the gate bias to achieve depletion conditions (Fig. 3-18c) positions E_F near the middle of the band gap at the surface. Since the interface levels always remain fixed in energy relative to E_c and E_v at the surface, depletion biasing obviously draws electrons into the lower interface state levels, and Q_{it} reflects the added negative charge. If the MOS capacitor is biased into the accumulation mode, most of the traps will be filled with electrons (Fig. 3-18d), and Q_{it} will approach its minimum value. The purpose of the above discussion is to show that the interface traps charge and discharge as a function of bias, thereby affecting the charge distribution inside the device, as well as the device characteristics in a complex but somewhat predictable manner.

Once again, however, since Q_{it} is located at the Si-SiO$_2$ interface, the change in V_T due to Q_{it} can be simply calculated from

$$\Delta V_T = -Q_{it} \, (\varphi_{surf}) \, / C_{ox} \tag{3-69}$$

Since Eq. 3-69 shows that Q_{it} depends upon the bias condition (and is therefore a function of φ_{surf}), its value will change as V_{GB} changes. Under conditions of inversion Q_{it} takes on its largest positive value, and decreases as the bias progresses from depletion to accumulation. The distribution of trap levels as a function of energy in the band gap has a U-shaped distribution (see Fig. 3-19). The minimum level of D_{it} at midgap is usually the density used to characterize their presence.

The overall value of Q_{it}, as well as the precise density of states as a function of energy, makes the value of D_{it} sensitive to a variety of process conditions used to fabricate the MOSFET. Nevertheless, certain definite trends concerning these values have been uncovered. First, Q_{it}, like Q_f, is greatest on (111) surfaces, and smallest on (100) surfaces, and the ratio of midgap-D_{it} values on the two surfaces is ~3:1. Second,

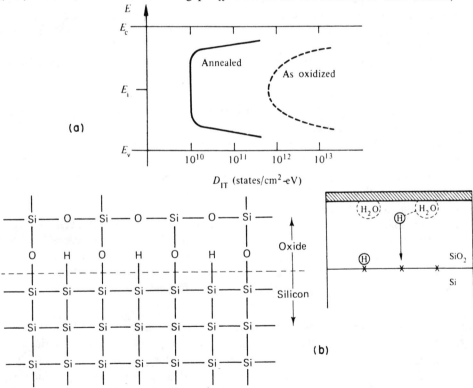

Fig. 3-19 (a) Energy distribution of interface states within the band gap. General form and magnitude of the interfacial trap density observed before and after interface state anneal. (b) Conceptual picture of how hydrogen is thought to passivate dangling bonds.

after oxidation in a dry O_2 ambient, the midgap value of D_{it} is relatively high ($\sim 10^{11}$-10^{12} states/cm²-eV), with the values decreasing as the oxide temperature is increased (this is also the case with Q_f). However, annealing at lower temperatures in inert ambients *does not* reduce the value of D_{it}. Instead, annealing in the presence of hydrogen at relatively low temperatures ($\leq 500°C$) for 5-10 minutes minimizes D_{it}. D_{it} at midgap under an optimum set of processing conditions is $\sim 10^{10}$/cm²-eV. See Fig. 3-19b for a conceptual picture of how hydrogen is thought to passivate the dangling bonds at the silicon surface and how this thus reduces the interface trap density.

3.5.2.4 Oxide Trapped Charge. The oxide trapped charge Q_{ot} is due to holes or electrons trapped in the *bulk* of the oxide, and hence can be positive or negative. Q_{ot} is associated with defects in the SiO_2, which may arise from ionizing radiation, hot carrier injection, or high currents through the oxide (e.g., due to Fowler-Nordheim tunneling - as described in chap. 7), or other reactions which either tend to break Si-O bonds in the oxide or otherwise lead to carrier trapping on sites or traps somehow already present in the oxide. Figure 3-17 f - h shows possible defects in the SiO_2 bulk that may give rise to such traps. For example, a trivalent Si atom in the SiO_2 will introduce a deep trap level in the SiO_2 bandgap ($.Si \equiv O_3$), and stretched Si-O or Si-Si bonds (in the latter a missing bridging oxygen atom leads to a defect, $(O_3 \equiv Si.. S \equiv O_3)$ introduce a continuum of shallow or deep trap levels in the SiO_2 bandgap when located in the bulk of the SiO_2.

Q_{ot} can be annealed out by low-temperature treatments (450-550°C) although some neutral traps may remain. Therefore, oxide trapped charge has been considered relatively less important than the other oxide charges in just-completed MOSFETs. In early generations of MOSFET ICs, exposure of the devices to ionizing radiation encountered in space flights was the main concern involving Q_{ot}. However, more recently-introduced processing techniques such as ion-implantation, electron-beam evaporation of metal films, reactive-ion etching, and x-ray lithography are all potential sources for creating charged and neutral traps in the gate dielectric (all of which may not be completely annealed out at the end of the fabrication process). This may result in long-term reliability problems, especially if hot carriers are injected in these oxides and get trapped (see chap. 9). Another reliability concern involves gate oxide degradation due to high oxide electric fields (and subsequent Fowler-Nordheim tunneling currents in the oxide). This has become more of a concern as oxide thickness has been scaled down.

3.5.2.5 Combined Effect of Oxide Charges on V_T of Submicron MOSFETs. It is now possible to control the level of Q_m in modern IC fabrication processes so that it has an insignificant effect on V_T stability. Thus, Q_f and Q_{it} are the remaining important charges that must be controlled during fabrication. For this discussion, let the sum of Q_f and $Q_{it} = Q_{tot}$. Then, combining Eqs. 3-68 and 3-69,

$$\Delta V_T = -Q_{tot}/C_{ox} = -(Q_f + Q_{it})/C_{ox}. \qquad (3-70)$$

If $N_{tot} = Q_{tot}/q$ is maintained at $<5 \times 10^{10}$/cm², for oxides <200Å thick:

$$\Delta V_T \;=\; Q_{tot}/C_{ox} = q N_{tot} \, t_{ox}/3.9 \, \varepsilon_o$$

$$= \; (1.6 \times 10^{-19} \text{ C})(5 \times 10^{10} \text{ cm}^{-2})(2 \times 10^{-6} \text{ cm}) \, /(3.5 \times 10^{-13} \text{ F/cm})$$

$$= \; 0.05 \text{ V}$$

Thus, for routine submicron process technology, it may seem that these charges are no longer a major problem. However, this is not true as far as the problems of gate oxide reliability and MOSFET degradation due to hot-carrier injection effects are concerned. That is, due the high electric fields present in submicron MOSFETs, phenomena occur that give rise to the generation of additional Q_{ot} and Q_{it} during normal device operation. Thus, the value of these charges can rise during the lifetime of the device, and cause performance degradation or failure. This topic will be revisited in more detail in chaps. 7 and 9.

3.6 THE THRESHOLD VOLTAGE EQUATION OF Si-SiO$_2$ MOS CAPACITORS

To obtain a flat-band condition in a real (non-ideal) MOS capacitor, a voltage must be applied to the gate to overcome the effects of $\varphi_{ms} \neq 0$ and $Q_{tot} \neq 0$. The total voltage needed to offset these effects is referred to as the *flat-band voltage* V_{FB} and is given as

$$V_{FB} \;=\; \varphi_{ms} - Q_{tot}/C_{ox} \tag{3-71}$$

The gate voltage that must then be applied to a real MOS capacitor structure to achieve the onset of strong inversion (i.e., threshold voltage, V_T) must include the flat band voltage as well. Thus, the V_T equation for real MOS capacitors (and long-channel MOSFETs when the source-to-substrate voltage $V_{SB} = 0$V) is given as

$$V_{T \text{ (uniform doping, long-channel)}} = V_{T(ud,lc)} = V_{FB} + 2\sqrt{\kappa_{si}\varepsilon_o q N_{sub}\varphi_B}/C_{ox} + 2\varphi_B$$

$$= \; \varphi_{ms} - Q_{tot}/C_{ox} + 2\sqrt{\kappa_{si}\varepsilon_o q N_{sub}\varphi_B}/C_{ox} + 2\varphi_B \tag{3-72}$$

Figure 3-20 plots Eq. 3-72 for n^+ silicon-gate MOSFETs (both PMOS and NMOS) versus substrate doping concentration for several values of t_{ox} (i.e., 65, 25, and 15 nm thick) as the parameter, and assuming also that $Q_{tot} = 0$.

Note that Eq. 3-72 also assumes that the Si substrate is uniformly doped. In practical MOSFETs, however, V_T is normally adjusted by implanting a thin layer of impurity atoms (boron or arsenic) at the Si surface. Thus, the substrate becomes non-uniformly doped, and the V_T equation must be modified to take this into account. To a first order this is done by treating the implanted impurity atoms as if they are an additional layer of charge very close to the Si-SiO$_2$ interface. Their presence is accounted for by adding a term to the V_T equation similar to the term used to describe

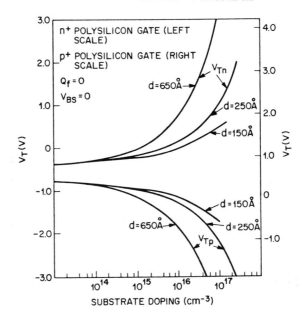

Fig. 3-20 Calculated threshold voltages of *n*-channel (V_{Tn}) and *p*-channel (V_{Tp}) transistors as a function of their substrate's doping, assuming n^+ polysilicon gate (left scale) and p^+ polysilicon gate (right scale). Curves for gate oxide thicknesses *d* of 150 Å, 250 Å, and 650Å are shown. From S.M. Sze Ed. *VLSI Technology,* 2nd Ed., Chap. 11, "VLSI Process Integration." Copyright, 1988 Bell Telephone Laboratories. Reprinted with permission.

the presence of oxide charge Q_{tot}. Details of V_T adjustment and the term used to modify Eq. 3-72 are discussed in chap. 4.

Example 3-1: Find $V_{T(ud,lc)}$ of an ideal MOS-C ($\varphi_{ms} = 0V$, $Q_{tot} = 0$) with a uniform substrate doping $N_A = 10^{15}/cm^2$. The gate-oxide thickness is $t_{ox} = 15$ nm.

Solution: φ_B (sub) $= (E_i - E_F)/q = 0.29$ V

$$\varepsilon_{ox} = 3.9\varepsilon_0 = 3.5 \times 10^{-13} \text{ F/cm}; \quad C_{ox} = \varepsilon_{ox}/1.5 \times 10^{-6} = 2.3 \times 10^{-7} \text{ F/cm}^2$$

$$2\sqrt{\kappa_{si}\varepsilon_0 q N_A \varphi_B} = 2 \, [1.02 \times 10^{-12} \times 1.6 \times 10^{-19} \times 10^{15} \times 0.29]^{1/2} = 1.4 \times 10^{-8} \text{ C/cm}^2$$

$$2\sqrt{\kappa_{si}\varepsilon_0 q N_A \varphi_B} / C_{ox} = 1.4 \times 10^{-8} /2.3 \times 10^{-7} = 0.06 \text{ V}$$

$$V_{T(ud,lc, ideal)} = 0.58V + 0.06V = 0.64 \text{ V}$$

Example 3-2: Find $V_{T(ud,lc)}$ of a 'real' MOS-C just like the one of Example 3-1, except that it has a heavily-doped silicon gate (doped to $N_D = 10^{20}/cm^3$), and $Q_{tot} = q \, (5 \times 10^{10} /cm^2)$.

Solution: According to Eq. 3-72, the threshold voltage of the 'real' MOS-C is shifted from that of the 'ideal' MOS-C by the value of V_{FB}. This term is the sum of φ_{ms} + Q_{tot}/C_{ox}. Thus, since

$$\varphi_{ms} \text{ (from Fig. 3-13)} = -1.02 \text{ V}$$

and

$$Q_{tot}/C_{ox} = -1.6 \times 10^{-19} \times 2 \times 10^{10} / 2.3 \times 10^{-7} = -0.01 \text{ V}$$

$$V_{T(ud,lc)} = V_{T(ud,lc, ideal)} + V_{FB}$$

$$= 0.64V + (-1.03V) = -0.39 \text{ V}$$

Note that a negative value of $V_{T(ud,lc)}$ is yielded, implying that this MOSFET would be ON at $V_{GB} = 0V$ (and would therefore behave as a depletion-mode device). The parameters used in this calculation of $V_{T(ud,lc)}$ are typical of the NMOS device parameters encountered in the early days of MOS ICs. Hence, at that time it was not possible to easily and/or reliably fabricate enhancement-mode NMOS transistors. In chap. 4 we shall show how this problem was overcome by the development of ion implantation. With this process it became possible to introduce dopants into the channel region near the silicon surface, such that the threshold voltage is shifted from the value it has in the case of a uniformly doped substrate, to the desired value. This enabled enhancement-mode NMOSFETs to be manufactured with appropriate threshold voltage values.

The typical value of V_T in NMOSFETs is 0.7V. This means that V_T of the MOS-C structure of Example 3-2 must be shifted by 1.11V. Equation 4-73 indicates that a shallow implant with a dose of ~1.6×10^{12} boron ions/cm^2 will produce such a V_T shift in the MOSFET of Example 3-2.

3.7 VISUALIZATION OF MOS-C AND MOSFET PHENOMENA USING POTENTIAL VERSUS POSITION DIAGRAMS

Many aspects of the behavior of the MOS-C and the MOSFET are described in terms of the variation of the electrostatic potential in the silicon as a function of position. By plotting such relationships in a graphical format, a visual model is obtained which helps to portray many of the phenomena associated with MOS-C and MOSFET behavior.

When describing the MOS-C most graphical representations are one-dimensional, reflecting the one-dimensional nature of the behavior of such structures [i.e., usually $\varphi(x)$ versus x plots are presented]. However, when the potential in the MOSFET is being depicted, a two-dimensional representation is needed to appropriately depict the MOSFET behavior. Thus, we have decided to illustrate the potential versus position in the MOS-C using both the 2-D plot (as is needed for the MOSFET), as well as the 1-D potential plots more usually encountered when MOS-C behavior is being studied. This is done in Fig. 3-21, in which both 1-D and 2-D potential plots for a MOS-C cross-section are depicted. We note that $\varphi_{surf} = \varphi(x = 0)$ is constant versus y in the MOS-C, and thus the 1-D representation of the potential in the MOS-C would be adequate. However, when the 2-D potential versus position diagrams of the MOSFET are presented (i.e., in chaps. 4 and 5), it will be easier to interpret their details by comparing them to the simpler 2-D cases introduced here.

In Fig. 3-21a we show the 2-D cross-section of a *p*-substrate MOS-C, with a bias V_{GB} connected between the gate and body. In Fig. 3-21b we show the case of the *ideal* MOS-C described in Example 3-1. We observe that when $V_{GB} = 0$ (Fig. 3-21b1), $\varphi(x,y) = 0$ everywhere, corresponding to the flat-band condition in the energy-band representation. In Fig. 3-21b2 we portray the case of $V_{GB} = V_T = 0.64V$ for the MOS-C of Example 3-1. Here we note that $\varphi_{surf} = 2\varphi_B = 0.58V$, with the variation of $\varphi(x)$ expressed by Eq. 3-23.

In Fig. 3-21c we note that the *real* MOSFET of Example 3-2 is depicted for the bias condition of $V_{GB} = 0V$. Since we noted that $V_T = -0.39V$, implying that a negative voltage of -0.39V must be applied to cause a condition of $\varphi_{surf} = 2\varphi_B = 0.58V$, which corresponds to the onset of strong inversion. Thus, when $V_{GB} = 0V$, $\varphi_{surf} = 0.97V$, which is larger than $2\varphi_B$, as shown in Fig. 3-21c1.

In order for this MOS-C to exhibit a value of $V_T = 0.7V$, we indicated in the previous section that a dose of 1.6×10^{12} boron ions/cm^2 must be implanted into the channel region. If this is done, when $V_{GB} = 0V$, φ_{surf} will then equal -0.05V, and the potential versus position diagram will as shown in Fig. 3-21d1. Note that when $V_{GB} = 0.7V$, $\varphi_{surf} = 0.58V$, but the potential versus x variation is different from that of the uniformly doped case of Fig. 3-21b. The effect of the implant dose on the depletion region width of the channel and other MOSFET phenomena are discussed in chap. 4.

REFERENCES

1. E.H. Nicollian and J.R. Brews, *MOS Physics and Technology,* Wiley-Interscience, New York, 1982.
2. C.E. Young, "Extended Curves of the Space Charge, Electric Field, and Electrostatic Potential Inside a Semiconductor," *J. Appl. Phys.,* **32**, p. 329, (1961).
3. R.F. Pierret and J.A. Shields, "Simplified long-channel MOSFET theory," *Solid-State Electronics,* vol. 26, p. 143, 1983.
4. G. Baccarani et al., "Analytical i.g.f.e.t.model including drift and diffusion currents," *IEE Journal on Solid-State and Electron Devices,* vol. 2, p. 62, March 1978.
5. J.R. Brews, "A Charge-Sheet Model of the MOSFET," *Solid-State Electronics,* vol. 21, p. 345, 1978.
6. Y.P. Tsividis, *Operation and Modeling of the MOS Transistor,* McGraw-Hill, New York, 1987.
7. W.M. Werner, "The Work Function Difference of the MOS-System with Aluminum Field Plates and Polysilicon Field Plates," *Solid-State Electronics,* **17**, 769 (1974).
8. P. Balk Ed., *The Si-SiO$_2$ System,* Elsevier, New York, 1988.
9. B.E. Deal et al., "Characteristics of the Surface State Charge of Thermally Oxidized Silicon," *J. Electrochem. Soc.,* **114**, p. 266 (1967).
10. B.E. Deal et al., *J. Electrochem. Soc.,* **121**, p. 198C (1974).

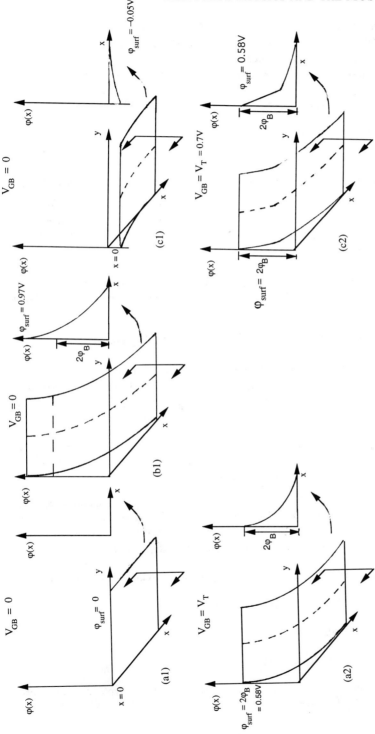

Fig. 3-21 Visualization of the electrostatic potential in *p*-type MOS-Cs with $N_A = 10^{15}$ cm^{-3}, and $t_{ox} = 150$Å. (a1) $\varphi(x,y)$ in an *ideal* MOS-C ($\varphi_{ms} = 0$ and $Q_{tot} = 0$) when $V_{GB} = 0$V (flatband condition); and (a2) when $V_{GB} = V_T$. (b1) $\varphi(x,y)$ in *real* MOSFET with uniformly doped substrate and n^+ polysilicon gate ($\varphi_{ms} = 1.02$V), when $V_{GB} = 0$V. (c1) $\varphi(x,y)$ in *real* MOSFET with n^+ polysilicon gate and V_T-adjust implant into substrate such that $V_T = 0.7$V, when $V_{GB} = 0$V. (c2) $\varphi(x,y)$ when $V_{GB} = V_T$.

11. P. Roblin, S. Samman, and S. Bibyk, "Simulation of Hot-Electron Trapping and Aging in nMOSFETs," *IEEE Trans. Electron Dev.*, **ED-35**, December 1988, p. 2229.

12. R.F. Pierret, *Modular Series on Solid-State Devices; Vol. IV - Field Effect Devices.*, R.F. Pierret and G.W. Neudeck, Eds., Addison-Wesley Publ. Co., Reading MA, 1983.

13. B.E. Deal, "Standardized Terminology for Oxide Charges Associated with Thermally Oxidized Silicon," *IEEE Trans. Electron Dev.*, **ED-27**, p. 606, (1980).

PROBLEMS

1. Explain why it is useful to study the behavior of the MOS-C prior to studying the behavior of the MOSFET.

2. Sketch the energy-band diagrams of a MOS-C with a heavily-doped n-polysilicon gate when (a) $V_{GB} = 0$, and (b) in the flat band condition when the Si substrate: (1) 1-Ω-cm n-type, and (2) 1-Ω-cm, p-type.

3. For an ideal MOS-C with $t_{ox} = 30$ nm and $N_A = 5 \times 10^{15}$ cm^{-3}, find the applied voltage and electric field at the interface needed to: (a) make the silicon surface intrinsic; and (b) to bring about strong inversion.

4. Using Eq. 3-13c prove that for $n_{surf} = 10 N_A$, φ_{surf} is only 58 mV greater than $2\varphi_B$.

5. Calculate the flatband voltage and the threshold voltage (a) in 1 Ω-cm p-type silicon and (b) in 1 Ω-cm p-type silicon. The MOS-Cs for each case have : (i) aluminum gate for which $q\varphi_m = 4.3$ eV, (ii) $t_{ox} = 100$ nm; and (iii) the oxide is free of charge except for a surface density of $Q_f = 5 \times 10^{10}$ cm^{-2}. The electron affinity of silicon is 4.05 eV.

6. Use the "threshold" statement in SUPREM III to extract and plot V_T vs. V_{SB} for increments of 0.25V between 0 and 5V for the device specified in Prob. 4. Compare the zero bias ($V_{BS} = 0$V) value with the two corresponding values of V_T found in Prob. 4.

7. Consider Poisson's equation in the substrate of a MOS-C. Using the condition that there is charge neutrality in the substrate, show that the impurity doping terms $N_D - N_A$ can be written as $n_i (\exp(u_B) - \exp(-u_B)] = 2 n_i \sinh u_B$, where u represents the potential normalized to (kT/q) and u_B is the substrate potential ($u_B = -q\varphi_B/kT$) in a p-type substrate.

8. Using the form derived in Problem 6, show that the Poisson equation can be written in terms of u as:
$$d^2u/dx^2 = (1/L_{Di})^2 [\sinh(u) - \sinh(u_B)]$$

where L_{Di} is the intrinsic Debye length

$$L_{Di} = (\varepsilon_{si} k T/2q^2 n_i)^{1/2}$$

9. Calculate the maximum depletion layer depth in a MOS-C with a p-type substrate doped uniformly at 2×10^{15} cm^{-3} if T = 77K and 300K.

10. Consider the establishment of a p-type inversion layer in a MOS-C. Show that for a nondegenerate n-type semiconductor, the surface charge density Q_C needed to make $p_{surf} = n_o$ (the equilibrium electron concentration in the bulk) is given by

$$Q_C = \sqrt{2\varepsilon_{si}\, q\, N_D\, (\varphi_B)}.$$

CHAPTER 4

MOS TRANSISTOR DEVICE PHYSICS: PART 2

LONG-CHANNEL MOSFETS

A description of the physics of the MOS capacitor (MOS-C, chap. 3) provides a solid foundation for analyzing the behavior of the MOSFET. Hence, in this chapter the device physics of long-channel MOSFETs is undertaken. In chap. 5 we examine the behavior of short-channel (i.e., submicron) MOSFETs.

Long-channel MOSFETs are discussed first for the following reasons:

1. The derivation of accurate long-channel-MOSFET drain-current models can be achieved by solving both the *Poisson equation* and the *drift-diffusion current density equations* in one-dimensional form, whereas accurate modeling of short-channel MOSFET behavior requires the solution of these equations in two (or even three) dimensions. Thus, it is logical to undertake the simpler analysis first.

2. The long-channel drain-current MOSFET models derived from the solution of the 1-D device equations can be expressed in analytical form. Hence, these models are widely used in circuit-design applications. In addition, quantitative insight about the device physics of MOSFET operation can also be obtained by examining these models. On the other hand, physically based analytical models of short-channel MOSFET behavior do not arise from the solution of the two-dimensional device equations, and thus it is harder to gain quantitative insight into MOSFET operation from them.

3. The analytical expressions for I_D from two of the four long-channel MOSFET models derived in this chapter are the I_D expressions used in SPICE for simulating MOSFET behavior in IC circuit design applications.

4. As MOSFETs are scaled down, they eventually become prone to 'short-channel' effects. In most cases, however, these effects are considered detrimental. That is, it is the task of the device designer to suppress them when scaling-down MOSFET structures. The goal is to produce 'short-channel' MOSFETs with 'long-channel' behavior. Thus, it is important to define long-channel behavior and to describe the physics that produce such characteristics in MOSFETs. This understanding provides insight into the measures that must be employed to suppress unwanted short-channel effects.

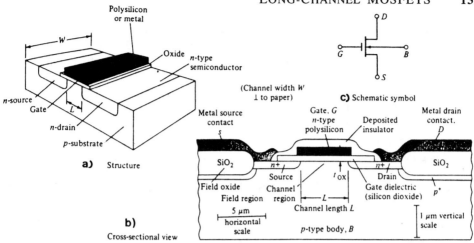

Fig. 4-1 (a) Structure of an MOS device. (b) Cross sectional view. (c) Schematic symbol.[1] From D. A. Hodges and H. G. Jackson, Analysis and Design of Digital Integrated Circuits, Copyright, 1983 McGraw-Hill Book Co. Reprinted with permission.

In this chapter the following topics dealing with MOSFETs are covered:

a. Introduction to the terminology of MOSFETs and their behavior

b. Effect of Applying a Bias to the Inversion Layer of the MOS-C

c. Definition of the Long-Channel MOSFET and the Gradual-Channel Approximation

d. Qualitative Description of Long-Channel MOSFETs

e. Quantitative Models of dc Long-Channel MOSFET Behavior

  i. Pao-Sah Model
  ii. Charge-Sheet Model
  iii. Variable-Depletion-Charge Model
  iv. Square-Law Model

f. Threshold-Voltage Control in Long-Channel MOSFETs

  i. Body Effect
  ii. Threshold-voltage adjustment by ion-implantation

g. Subthreshold behavior of Long-Channel MOSFETs

  i. Physics and modeling of subthreshold current flow
  ii. Subthreshold swing
  iii. Gate-induced leakage current (GIDL)

4.1 TERMINOLOGY OF MOSFET DEVICE STRUCTURES

Figure 4-1 shows the cross-section of the MOSFET, as introduced in chap. 3. The important difference between the MOS-C and the MOSFET is that in the latter a *pn* junction exists at each side of the MOS-C channel region. Each of these junctions are also close enough to make contact with the inversion layer. By making external connections to each of these edge junctions, the MOSFET becomes a four-terminal device (with the terminals designated respectively as the *gate* G, *body* B, *source* S, and *drain* D). The MOS-C, on the other hand, remains a two terminal device (*gate* and *body*). The source and drain terminals of the MOSFET allow a bias V_{DS} to be applied across the ends of the channel region, giving rise to a *drain current* I_D.

As described in chap. 3, the inversion layer can be established by applying an appropriate bias to the gate. For the device shown in Fig. 4-1a, the induced charge in the channel inversion layer is *n*-type, and the device is known as an *n*-channel MOSFET (or simply an NMOS transistor). A *p*-channel MOSFET (or PMOS) is obtained by interchanging the *n* and *p* regions. Just as in the ideal MOS-C it is assumed that current in the gate oxide (*gate current,* I_G) is negligible. We also assume that the MOSFET is a symmetrical device, insofar as connecting the two junction terminals to a circuit (i.e., the drain current should remain the same if the two terminals are interchanged). Regardless of the way a MOSFET is connected, the terminal tied to the more positive voltage (in NMOS circuits) is defined to be the *drain*, and the other is the *source*.

4.1.1 Basics of MOSFET Operation

In simplest terms, the operation of a MOS transistor involves the application of an input voltage to the gate electrode. This establishes an electric field perpendicular (or transverse) to the Si-SiO$_2$ interface in the channel region of the device (Fig. 4-2a). The conductance of the channel region (in which the device output current I_D flows) can be modulated by varying this electric field. Since an electric field is responsible for controlling the output current flow, such devices are termed *field-effect transistors* (FETs).

If no gate bias is applied, however, the circuit path between source and drain consists of two back-to-back *pn* junctions in series. In this case, if V_{DS} is applied (such that the drain and source *pn* junctions are reverse biased), I_D will consist of only the reverse-bias diode leakage current, which is normally negligible.

When positive bias is applied to an NMOS transistor gate, however, electrons will be attracted to the channel region and holes will be repelled (as is the case in the MOS-C). Once the positive gate voltage becomes strong enough to form an inversion layer, an *n*-type channel is formed that connects the source and drain regions (Fig. 4-2a). A drain current I_D can then flow if a voltage V_{DS} is applied between the source and drain terminals. In the simplest analysis we assume that the voltage-induced *n*-type channel does not form unless the voltage applied to the gate exceeds the threshold voltage V_T.

MOS devices such as those just described (in which no conducting channel exists when $V_{GS} = 0$), are referred to as *enhancement-mode* (or *normally OFF*) transistors (see Fig. 4-2b). With NMOS enhancement-mode transistors, a positive gate voltage, V_{GS}, greater than V_T must be applied to create the channel (or to turn them ON), while to turn ON PMOS enhancement-mode devices, a negative gate voltage (whose magnitude is $>V_T$) must be applied. Note that in NMOS transistors a positive voltage must also

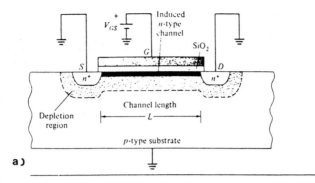

a)

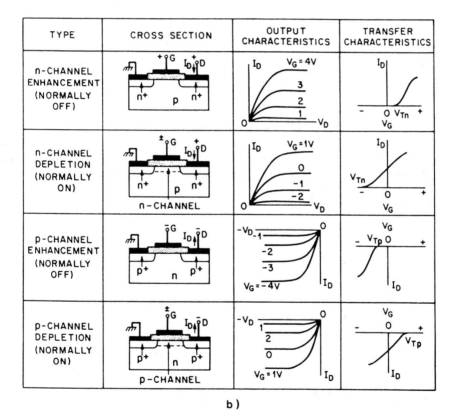

b)

Fig. 4-2 (a) Idealized NMOS cross section with positive V_{GS} applied showing depletion regions and induced channel. From D. A. Hodges and H. G. Jackson, Analysis and Design of Digital Integrated Circuits, Copyright, 1983 McGraw-Hill Book Co. Reprinted with permission.   (b) Cross sections and output and transfer characteristics of four types of MOSFETs. From S.M.Sze, Semiconductor Devices - Physics and Technology, 1985, John Wiley & Sons. Reprinted with permission.

be applied to the drain to keep the drain-substrate reverse-biased, while in PMOS devices this voltage must be negative.

On the other hand, it is also possible to build MOS devices in which a conducting channel region exists when $V_{GS} = 0V$ (see also Fig. 4-2b), and such MOS devices are described as being *normally ON*. Since a bias voltage to the gate electrode is needed to deplete the channel region of majority carriers, and thus turn them OFF, such devices are also commonly called *depletion-mode MOSFETs*. NMOS depletion-mode devices require a negative gate voltage to be turned OFF, while corresponding PMOS devices require positive gate voltages.

4.2 BIASING THE INVERSION LAYER (BODY EFFECT)

Before undertaking a detailed discussion of MOSFET behavior, we first study the consequences of *applying a dc bias to the inversion layer of a MOS-structure*. This topic is actually an extension of the subject of MOS-C behavior, but also serves as an important prelude to the discussion of MOSFET operation. Consequently, when we discuss the operation of the MOSFET we will refer back to the results developed in this section.

We examine the effect of biasing the inversion layer from both the qualitative and quantitative perspectives. In the latter we will show how the expressions for the mobile charge concentrations in the inversion layer of the MOS structure are altered when a such bias is applied, as well as how the application of a bias to the inversion layer modifies the threshold voltage equation derived for the MOS-C.

Biasing the inversion layer is accomplished by the application of a dc voltage between the substrate and a diffused region adjacent to, and in contact with, the inversion layer. This implies that a modified MOS-C structure must be used. Specifically, a diffused region must be added to the edge of the MOS-C channel region (see Fig. 4-3a), and a terminal must be connected to this region (designated by the letter C). The result, as shown, is the *three-terminal MOS device* depicted in Fig. 4-3a.

If we choose the substrate (body or B) terminal as the reference, the voltage applied between terminal C and the substrate (body) is denoted by V_{CB}, and the voltage between the gate (terminal G) and substrate by V_{GB} (see Fig. 4-3a).* For simplicity we also assume an ideal *p*-type Si-substrate MOS structure (i.e., $\varphi_{ms} = 0$ and $Q_{tot} = 0$).

4.2.1 Qualitative Discussion of the Effect of Applying a Bias to the Inversion Layer of a MOS Structure

If a MOS-C with a *p*-type substrate is biased into inversion by a gate voltage V_{GB}, a *pn* junction exists between the surface and the bulk of the silicon (as a result of the region near the silicon surface having been inverted to *n*-type). If there is an adjacent *n-doped* region in contact with the *induced n*-type inversion layer, it is possible to apply a bias to the induced junction by applying a bias V_{CB} between terminal C and B (the substrate)

---

* As elsewhere, we use the convention that the second letter of the voltage subscript designates the reference terminal.

as shown in Fig. 4-3a. (Note that here we have a MOS structure in which the induced junction is contacted only at one end of the channel.*) We also assume that the polarity of V_{CB} is such that the induced *pn* junction is either unbiased or under reverse bias (i.e., V_{CB} in Fig. 4-3a is $\geq$0V). We will refer to V_{CB} as the *channel voltage*.

Before presenting the equations relevant to this structure, let us first consider the qualitative effect of applying various V_{CB} bias values.

4.2.1.1 Case When Both V_{GB} and V_{CB} = 0V.

In Fig. 4-3b we show the two-dimensional potential φ versus position diagram for the three-terminal MOS structure when both V_{GB} and V_{CB} = 0V. We note that the channel region is in a flat-band condition and that a built-in voltage φ_{bi} exists across the n^+p (doped) junction. We also recall that even if $V_{GB} \neq$ 0V, as long as V_{CB} remains at 0V, the structure is still in equilibrium, because I_G is assumed to be zero and there is no current in the n^+p junction if V_{CB} = 0V. Hence, this implies that when V_{CB} = 0V the channel region of this structure exhibits the same behavior as that of the MOS-C described in chap. 3.

4.2.1.2 Case When $V_{GB} \geq V_T$ and V_{CB} = 0V.

If we now consider the case where V_{CB} = 0V, but $V_{GB} \geq V_T$, we encounter a situation as shown in Fig. 4-3c. That is, the channel region is now inverted, and a *field-induced junction* now exists between the *n*-type inversion layer and the underlying *p*-type substrate. Since a bias is not applied across the field-induced junction, it is in equilibrium and is again characterized by the same Fermi level as in the diffused junction. The surface depletion region in the field-induced junction under these conditions is also described by the equilibrium theory presented in chap. 3.

Note, however, that the potential difference between the inversion layer and the n^+ region is now much smaller than in the case when V_{GB} = 0V. Specifically, this potential difference is now ~$(\varphi_{bi} - 2\varphi_B)$. This implies that the inversion layer is in "communication" with the n^+ region adjacent to it. The term "communication" means that once the inversion layer is formed and a bias V_{CB} is applied between terminals C and B, this bias will appear across the entire length of the field-induced junction (i.e., no longer just across the doped n^+p junction at the edge of the channel). Thus, *if an inversion layer exists in the channel, then V_{CB} does have an influence on φ_{surf}.*

For example, if V_{CB} is suddenly allowed to increase from 0V to some non-zero value (while V_{GB} is held fixed), electrons will be observed to flow out of the inversion layer through the C terminal. Why this happens, and what the effects are on the behavior of the MOS structure are described next.

4.2.1.3 Case When V_{GB} = 0V, But V_{CB}>0V.

If we next apply a non-zero V_{CB} bias while keeping V_{GB} = 0V, equilibrium will cease to exist in the three-terminal structure. This is because V_{CB} causes a small reverse-bias leakage current to flow in the n^+p junction. (Although this reverse-bias leakage current is extremely small, its

---

* However, in a MOSFET, contact to the inversion layer can be made at both ends of the induced junction since a diffused region exists at each end of the channel. In the MOSFET these two regions are called the source and drain, and the terminals are designated by the abbreviations S and D.

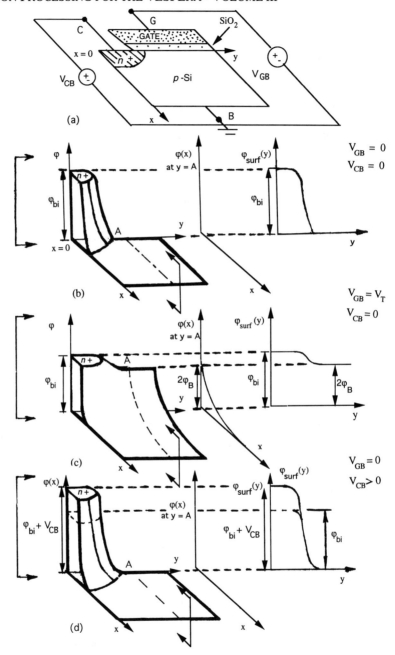

Fig. 4-3 (a) Applying a bias V_{CB} to an induced channel beneath the gate oxide by applying this bias V_{CB} between terminal C and the substrate of a three-terminal MOS structure. Two-dimensional potential φ versus position diagrams in the three terminal MOS structure when: (b) both V_{GB} and $V_{CB} = 0$; (c) $V_{GB} > V_T$ and $V_{CB} = 0V$; (d) $V_{GB} = 0V$ and $V_{CB} > 0V$.

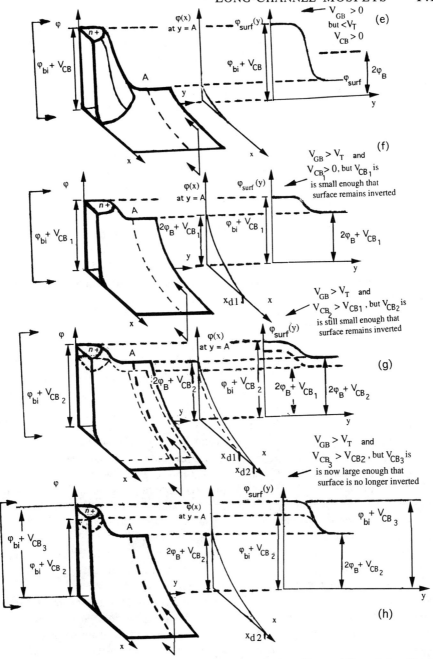

Fig. 4-3 (cont.) (e) $V_{GB} > 0$, but is $< V_T$, and $V_{CB} > 0$; (f) $V_{GB} > V_T$ and $V_{CB} > 0$, but $V_{CB} = V_{CB1}$, which we assume is small enough so that inversion still exists. (g) V_{GB} is the same as in part (f), but $V_{CB} = V_{CB2}$, where $V_{CB2} > V_{CB1}$, but V_{CB2} is still small enough to keep surface inverted. (g) $V_{GB} = V_T$, $V_{CB} = V_{CB3}$ (large enough to suppress the channel inversion layer).

existence implies that the MOS structure is no longer in equilibrium because some of the carrier energy now depends on an externally applied force, namely the extra electric field created in the depletion region by V_{CB}.) However, if V_{GB} remains fixed at 0V, V_{CB} is dropped entirely across the n^+p junction. Hence, the surface potential along the channel is not altered from when $V_{CB} = 0V$. Instead, only the potential difference between the n^+ and p (substrate) regions is increased by V_{CB} (as shown in Fig. 4-3d), leaving the channel region to the right of the n^+p junction in a flat-band state. In addition, Fig. 4-3d indicates that *if no inversion layer is present, changing V_{CB} has negligible impact on the surface potential φ_{surf} along the channel.* This last statement also applies to the case illustrated in Fig. 4-3e (i.e., $V_{GB} > 0V$, but is less than V_T, and V_{CB} is increased from 0V to some value greater than 0V). Here we observe that there is still no impact on φ_{surf} as long as no inversion layer is present in the channel.

4.2.1.4 Case When $V_{GB} \geq V_T$ and $V_{CB} > 0V$. Let us now consider the case when $V_{GB} > V_T$ and a reverse-bias voltage V_{CB} is applied to the induced *pn* junction (such that the surface remains inverted even after V_{CB} is applied). Since the surface is inverted, the potential in the inversion region is very close to the potential value in the diffused region, as shown in Fig. 4-3f (and as exists in the case shown in Fig. 4-3c). That is, a point at the surface is at about the same potential (with respect to the substrate deep in the bulk) as a point in the n^+ region. Therefore, the surface is about as "attractive" for electrons as is the n^+ region. Consequently, electrons have no reason to prefer only the n^+ region as opposed to the "surface" at the right. As a result, the n^+ region can "communicate" with the inversion layer (implying that a bias applied to the n^+ region is also applied to the inversion layer). In addition, just as in the case of a MOS-C, the value of the surface potential φ_{surf} remains clamped at the value it has at the onset of strong inversion (i.e., for the case of Fig. 4-3f, at a value of $\varphi_{surf} \sim 2\varphi_B + V_{CB1}$). That is, as V_{GB} is increased beyond V_T, φ_{surf} remains unchanged, but the mobile charge concentration in the inversion layer continues to increase.

We also recall from *pn* junction theory that if a reverse-bias voltage is applied to a previously unbiased *pn* junction, the junction depletion-region width will increase. Thus, the depletion region on the *p*-side of the induced junction will also increase if a reverse-bias is applied between terminals C and B. However, if V_{GB} is kept fixed (such that $V_{GS} \geq V_T$) as the reverse-bias voltage V_{CB} is increased (see Fig. 4-3g), the charge on the gate terminal will remain the same as when $V_{CB} = 0V$. Therefore, the *total* charge in the semiconductor must also remain unchanged to maintain balance with the unchanged value of charge on the gate. However, since the application of V_{CB} widens the depletion region (thereby uncovering more charge in this region of the induced junction), fewer electrons are needed in the inversion layer to balance the unchanged gate charge. Consequently, electrons must exit the inversion layer, resulting in a lower level of inversion. (Looking at it in another way, the increased positive potential at terminal C will attract electrons from the inversion layer, which will start flowing toward the n^+ region, and from it into the top terminal of the voltage source.) However, if a sufficiently large value of V_{CB} is applied (while holding V_{GB} fixed), this effect can entirely extinguish the charge in the inversion layer. In other words, a gate voltage capable of causing inversion in the three-terminal MOS structure when $V_{CB} = 0V$ may no longer be able to sustain inversion if a non-zero value of V_{CB} is applied.

As also shown in Figs. 4-3f and g, as long as the surface remains in inversion as V_{CB} is increased, the depletion region under the field induced junction increases (from x_{d1} in Fig. 4-3f to x_{d2} in Fig. 4-3g). This means that the bands are bent more, and thus φ_{surf} also increases. This supports the statement that as V_{CB} increases, the n^+ region communicates this change in V_{CB} to the field-induced junction. However, once a sufficiently large number of electrons depart from the inversion layer so that it essentially disappears, further increases in V_{CB} no longer influence the channel region, and the depletion region no longer widens (as shown in Fig. 4-3h), and remains fixed at a value dependent on V_{CB} (e.g., at x_{d2}, see Figs. 4-3g and h) as expressed by Eq. 4-8.

If a non-zero V_{CB} is applied and it is desired to re-establish inversion, φ_{surf} must be increased to a value larger than that needed when $V_{CB} = 0$. Specifically, at the onset of inversion, it is necessary to increase V_{GB} so that $q\varphi_{surf} \sim q(V_{CB} + 2\varphi_B)$. Note that the effect just described can also be exploited as a technique for raising the threshold voltage of a MOSFET, as will be discussed in section 4.6.2.

4.2.1.5 Summary of the Behavior of the Three-Terminal MOS Structure and the Significance of Such Behavior on the Operation of the MOSFET.

In summary, it is possible to establish "communication" with the channel region (i.e., an external bias voltage can be applied to the channel region of a MOS structure) if an inversion layer has been induced there. On the other hand, if the channel region is not inverted, the application of a bias voltage to a diffused region adjacent to the channel region will have no effect on the surface potential in the channel. Such "communication" (or lack of) has the following impact on the behavior of a MOSFET:

1. If the gate voltage applied to a MOSFET is less than the threshold voltage, the device is said to be operating in the subthreshold regime. From our discussion, this means that if a bias is applied to the drain (V_{DS}) of a MOSFET being operated in subthreshold, this voltage will be dropped entirely across the diffused n^+p junction (i.e., the drain-substrate junction), and it will have no impact on φ_{surf}. Hence, φ_{surf} will be determined by the gate potential, which is constant everywhere on the gate. Consequently, the potential drop along the y direction at the surface of the channel will be essentially zero. We will use this information when we discuss subthreshold current flow in MOSFETs in section 4.7.

2. If the channel is inverted, and V_{CB} is increased (and the channel remains in inversion for the range of applied V_{CB} values), the depletion region of the field-induced channel increases. If V_{GB} is held fixed, the number of electrons in the inversion layer will decrease as V_{CB} is increased. At some value of V_{CB} the inversion layer charge will entirely disappear. These effects occur when a drain bias V_{DS} is applied to a MOSFET. That is, for a fixed gate voltage (greater than the threshold voltage value), as V_{DS} is increased, the depletion region of

will correspondingly decrease, making it less inverted. Thus, in a MOSFET operating in inversion and with $V_{DS}>0$, the depletion region near the drain will be wider than at the source (i.e., assuming the source is the common terminal).

3. "Communication" with the channel also permits the diffused region to become an additional source (or sink) of mobile carriers to the channel (i.e., in addition to the carriers thermally generated in the depletion regions). As noted, two such diffused regions exist in a MOSFET, one which supplies mobile carriers (the source), and the other which removes them (the drain). Specifically, if a drain bias is applied to a MOSFET in inversion, the channel carriers will be attracted to and move into the drain. These are replenished by carriers entering the channel from the source. The resultant flow of charge in the channel constitutes a current in the drain terminal I_D. Since the channel is not a perfect conductor, this current also gives rise to a potential drop along the direction of the channel.

4.2.1.6 Body Effect. Until now we have chosen the substrate to be the reference terminal in the three-terminal MOS structure. However, when MOSFETs are used in circuits, the source terminal S (corresponding here to terminal C), is normally chosen to be the reference. Hence, *body effect* is the term used to describe the increase in the threshold voltage of a MOSFET (with reference to the source) upon the application of a reverse bias to the inversion layer. If, as shown in Fig. 4-4b, we choose terminal C to be the reference terminal (instead of the body terminal), the bias voltages are now applied between the gate and C (V_{GC}), and between the body and C (V_{BC}). In this case, for a given value of V_{BC}, a value of V_{GC} greater than that needed when $V_{BC} = 0V$ must be applied to the MOS structure to establish strong inversion. In section 4.2.2.2 we will derive an expression that determines the increase in V_T as a function of V_{BC}.

4.2.2 Quantitative Description of Effects of Biasing the Inversion Layer of MOS Structures

For the three-terminal MOS structure introduced above, it is possible to develop the quantitative relationships in a general manner for all cases of inversion. However, these can also be simplified somewhat for the more limited (but still most widely used form) of the strong inversion case. Note that in deriving these expressions we also include V_{FB}, which accounts for the work-function difference and oxide charge that can exist in 'real' MOS structures.

4.2.2.1 General Inversion Case. In the general inversion case (which covers weak as well as strong inversion), five equations characterize the phenomena in the channel region (i.e., the Si region in the vicinity of the Si-SiO$_2$ interface to the right of the n^+ junction in Fig. 4-3a) of three-terminal MOS structure (as they do for the MOS-C). If we invoke the charge-sheet and depletion approximations, four of these equations are identical to those for the expressions derived for the charge-sheet model of the MOS-C, and are repeated here for the readers convenience:

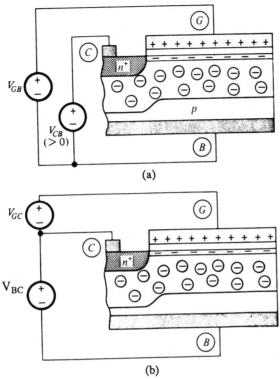

Fig. 4-4 Bias notation when: (a) terminal B is the reference terminal; (b) terminal C as the reference terminal instead of terminal B.[5] Reprinted with permission of McGraw-Hill Co.

$$V_{GB} = \varphi_{surf} + V_{FB} + \varphi_{ox} \qquad (3\text{-}10) \qquad (4\text{-}1a)$$

$$Q_C = Q_I + Q_B \qquad (3\text{-}20) \qquad (4\text{-}1b)$$

$$Q_C = -C_{ox}\varphi_{ox} \qquad (3\text{-}19) \qquad (4\text{-}1c)$$

$$Q_B = -\gamma C_{ox}\sqrt{\varphi_{surf}} \qquad (3\text{-}29) \qquad (4\text{-}1d1)$$

$$= [2qN_A\kappa_{si}\varepsilon_o(\varphi_{surf})]^{1/2} \qquad (4\text{-}1d2)$$

The fifth equation is a modified form of Eq. 3-53, in which we replace $2\varphi_B$ by $(2\varphi_B + V_{CB})$ to get

$$Q_I = \sqrt{2q\,N_A\kappa_{si}\varepsilon_o}\left(\sqrt{\varphi_{surf} + \varphi_t e^{(\varphi_{surf} - 2\varphi_B - V_{CB})/\varphi_t}} - \sqrt{\varphi_{surf}}\right) \qquad (4\text{-}2)$$

Then, combining Eqs. 4-1a, 4-1c, and 4-1b we get

$$V_{GB} = \varphi_{surf} + V_{FB} - [Q_I(\varphi_{surf}) + Q_B(\varphi_{surf})]/C_{ox} \qquad (4\text{-}3)$$

Next, using Eqs. 4-1d1 and 4-2 in Eq. 4-3, V_{GB} can be written as

$$V_{GB} = \varphi_{surf} + V_{FB} + \gamma \sqrt{\varphi_{surf} + \varphi_t e^{(\varphi_{surf} - 2\varphi_B - V_{CB})/\varphi_t}} \qquad (4-4)$$

Now, if V_{GB} and V_{CB} are given, Eq. 4-4 can be solved iteratively for φ_{surf}. This value can then be inserted into Eq. 4-2 to calculate Q_I, or into Eq. 4-1d2 to calculate Q_B.

An expression for Q_I in terms of φ_{surf} and V_{GB} can also be derived from the above equations. That is, by inserting Eqs. 4-1c and 4-1d1 into Eq. 4-1b above, we get

$$- C_{ox}\varphi_{ox} = Q_I + \gamma C_{ox}\sqrt{\varphi_{surf}} \qquad (4-5)$$

Then, solving for φ_{ox}, and substituting the result into Eq. 4-1a, we obtain

$$Q_I = - C_{ox} (V_{GB} - V_{FB} - \varphi_{surf} - \gamma \sqrt{\varphi_{surf}}) \qquad (4-6)$$

4.2.2.2 Strong Inversion Case. For the three-terminal structure biased to strong inversion, the above general analysis can be simplified. That is, with $V_{CB} = 0V$, φ_{surf} of the three-terminal MOS structure at the onset of inversion is $2\varphi_B$. With a reverse bias applied to the induced junction, the surface potential at the onset of strong inversion becomes

$$\varphi_{surf}(inv) \approx 2\varphi_B + V_{CB} \qquad (4-7)$$

Since the applied V_{CB} extends the range of gate voltages under which the surface region remains in depletion, d_{max} is now larger. The expression for d_{max} for the case of an applied V_{CB} is (assuming the depletion approximation):

$$d_{max} = [2\kappa_{si}\varepsilon_0(2\varphi_B + V_{CB})/qN_A]^{1/2} \qquad (4-8)$$

and the depletion layer charge (per unit area), Q_{Bmax}, when $d = d_{max}$ is expressed as

$$Q_{Bmax} = [2q\kappa_{si}\varepsilon_0 N_A (2\varphi_B + V_{CB})]^{1/2} \qquad (4-9)$$

The expression for the inversion layer charge per unit area Q_I in strong inversion in terms of V_{GB} and V_{CB} is

$$Q_I = - C_{ox} [V_{GB} - V_{FB} - 2\varphi_B - V_{CB} - \gamma (2\varphi_B + V_{CB})^{1/2}] \qquad (4-10)$$

Assuming again that Q_I is negligible at the onset of inversion, the total charge per unit area in the semiconductor is given by Q_B. Hence, the gate-substrate bias at the onset of strong inversion is

$$V_{GB} = V_{FB} + \varphi_{surf} + \varphi_{ox} = V_{FB} + (2\varphi_B + V_{CB}) + \gamma (2\varphi_B + V_{CB})^{1/2} \qquad (4-11)$$

Noting that $V_{GC} = V_{GB} - V_{CB}$, the threshold voltage, referenced to terminal C, is given by the expression

$$V_T \text{ (with ref. to term C)} = V_{T(ud,lc)} = V_{FB} + 2\varphi_B + \gamma (2\varphi_B + V_{CB})^{1/2} \quad (4 - 12)$$

Note that the term γ, which was defined in Eq. 3-60a as $[\sqrt{2qN_A\kappa_{si}\varepsilon_0}]/C_{ox} = [\sqrt{2qN_A\kappa_{si}\varepsilon_0}]t_{ox}/\varepsilon_{ox}$ is a factor which determines how much V_T will increase when V_{CB} is increased. Hence, γ has been given the name *body effect coefficient*. By inspecting the expression for γ we note that it predicts the body effect is stronger for heavier substrate dopings and/or thicker gate oxides. Conversely, the body effect can be made smaller by using lower doping concentrations and/or thinner gate oxides. Figure 4-5 shows the threshold voltage shift versus substrate bias for various γ values.[26]

4.3 DEFINITION OF TERM: LONG-CHANNEL MOSFET

It is appropriate at this point to provide a detailed definition of the term *long-channel MOSFET*. From a qualitative perspective, long-channel MOSFETs are assumed to have channel regions sufficiently long and wide so that "edge" effects along the four sides of the channel can be neglected. Insofar as the channel length is concerned, we assume the channel length L is much longer than the sum of the source and drain

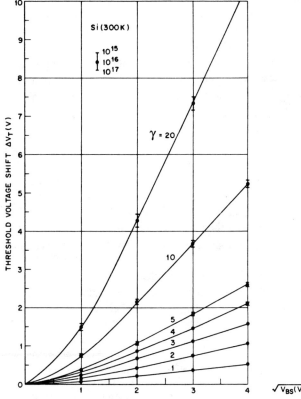

Fig. 4-5 Threshold voltage shift versus substrate reverse bias for various γ values.[2] Reprinted with permission of John Wiley & Sons.

depletion-region widths, or $L\!>\!>\!(d_{source} + d_{drain})$. The channel width, on the other hand is assumed to be much greater than the gate depletion-region depth, d (or Z>>d).

Even when the above criteria are well-satisfied, however, it is apparent that the electric fields and potential in the MOSFET still vary in at least two dimensions.* It seems that to accurately model device characteristics, the semiconductor device equations in their two-, or even three-dimensional forms must be solved. But in modeling long-channel MOSFET behavior this complexity can in fact be circumvented. That is, in such structures the solutions of the semiconductor device equations in their one-dimensional form yield drain-current device characteristics that are quite close to those obtained from measurements of actual long-channel MOSFETs.

Why is it possible to treat long-channel MOSFET behavior as a one-dimensional problem and still obtain relationships that give accurate estimates of I_D as a function of the applied the terminal voltages? First, consider the case of the MOSFET in which no drain bias is applied, and V_{GB} is the only external bias. We know that V_{GB} produces an electric field perpendicular to the device surface. Now, if $L\!>\!>\!(d_{source} + d_{drain})$ the junctions extend over such a small fraction of L that the $\mathcal{E}$-fields of these junctions have negligible impact on the $\mathcal{E}$-field due to the gate. Likewise, insofar as the channel width is concerned, if Z >>d the extension of the gate depletion region beyond the sides of the channel along which there is no source or drain hardly alters the total ionic charge uncovered by the gate voltage. Thus, the fringing field effect in the z direction can also be ignored. If both of these conditions are met, we can approximate the $\mathcal{E}$-field in a long-channel MOSFET when $V_{DS} = 0V$ as being perpendicular to the surface everywhere along the channel. In this case, the one-dimensional analysis we applied to the MOS-C can also be used to determine Q_I, $\mathcal{E}$, φ and V_T in a long-channel MOSFET.

Next, if a drain bias V_{DS} is simultaneously applied, we assume that in long-channel MOSFETs the *gradual-channel approximation* is valid. This approximation assumes that the two aspects of drain current flow can be treated as strictly one-dimensional, independent problems. The two aspects are: (1) that the gate field acts approximately vertically to induce the channel (i.e., the mobile charge concentration that participates in I_D), and; (2) that the drain-to-source voltage acts approximately horizontally to move these mobile charges, and thus to drive the current I_D in the channel. The assumption that these two one-dimensional effects are independent of one another permits the results of the MOS-C analysis (shown to be valid in the case of a MOSFET with no drain bias), to also be applied when deriving the I_D-V_{DS} relationship of the MOSFET. Since the gradual-channel approximation is such a key simplification invoked when developing the models of long-channel MOSFET behavior, we need to examine it more rigorously.

---

* This is the case whether or not a drain current flows in the MOSFET. That is, if a gate bias is applied, but $I_D = 0$, there will still be electric fields arising from the source and drain junctions at the edges of the channel. If a drain current flows, it is obvious that there must be a component of the electric field along the y-direction. In fact, each of these cases should be examined separately when considering our definition in detail.

4.3.1 The Gradual Channel Approximation (GCA)

If a drain bias V_{DS} is applied to a MOSFET in inversion, drain current I_D flows. Owing to the channel's finite resistance and the passage of current, a potential variation occurs along the channel length (i.e., if the source is grounded, the channel potential near the source is close to ground, whereas near the drain it is close to V_{DS}). This causes the inversion-layer (mobile) charge density to decrease with position toward the drain because the gate is assumed to be an equipotential region (i.e., the voltage along the gate is invariant with position y along the channel), making the gate-to-channel voltage decrease with position toward the drain. Since I_D must remain constant at all points in the channel under dc biasing conditions, the electric field parallel to the flow of I_D ($\mathcal{E}_y$) must increase toward the drain to offset the decrease in mobile charge density. Thus, a gradient in the $\mathcal{E}_y$ value must exist in the channel (i.e., $\partial\mathcal{E}_y/\partial y \neq 0$). The *gradual-channel approximation* (GCA), however, assumes that this gradient $\partial\mathcal{E}_y/\partial y$ is much smaller than the $\mathcal{E}$-field gradient in the x-direction, $\partial\mathcal{E}_x/\partial x$ (i.e., $\partial\mathcal{E}_x/\partial x >> \partial\mathcal{E}_y/\partial y$).

The two-dimensional form of the Poisson equation with $\partial^2\varphi/\partial x^2$ and $\partial^2\varphi/\partial y^2$ replaced respectively by $-\partial\mathcal{E}(x,y)/\partial x$ and $-\partial\mathcal{E}(x,y)/\partial y$ can be written as:

$$\frac{\partial\mathcal{E}(x,y)}{\partial x} + \frac{\partial\mathcal{E}(x,y)}{\partial y} = \frac{\rho(x,y)}{\kappa_{si}\,\varepsilon_o} \tag{4-13}$$

If the GCA approximation is valid, the $\partial\mathcal{E}(x,y)/\partial y$ term in Eq. 4-13 can be neglected. Then, Eq. 4-13 can be approximated as a one dimensional differential equation with the form:

$$\frac{d\mathcal{E}_x(x)}{dx} \approx \frac{\rho(x,y)}{\kappa_{si}\,\varepsilon_o} \tag{4-13a}$$

The GCA is generally valid when the channel of the MOSFET is long enough (e.g., L ~2 μm or longer), in which case the electric field strength along the y-direction $\mathcal{E}_y$ changes gradually from a small value near the source to values of the order of V_{DS}/L near the drain. Thus, neglecting the $\partial\mathcal{E}(x,y)/\partial y$ term in such devices is appropriate, and the one-dimensional form of the Poisson equation is sufficiently accurate for calculating Q_I used in the expressions for I_D. However, at large drain biases, the GCA always becomes invalid (even in long-channel MOSFETs), at least in a certain section of the channel near the drain where the gradient of the longitudinal field $\mathcal{E}_y$ becomes comparable to or larger than the gradient of the transverse field $\mathcal{E}_x$. In such cases, as will be described later, the drain current then becomes nearly independent of drain bias, and the MOSFET is said to be in *saturation*. This implies that under conditions of bias that cause saturation, the I_D behavior of long-channel MOSFETs can no longer be adequately modeled by invoking the GCA along the entire length of the channel. Instead, modifications to the long-channel models must be made (as described in chap. 5).

The importance of being able to invoke the gradual channel approximation should be emphasized, as this is the basis of the derivation of the long-channel MOSFET I_D-V_{DS} models. That is, by invoking the GCA, the problem of having to treat the semiconductor equations in their two-dimensional form to calculate I_D in a MOSFET is avoided. Instead, the task is broken down into two one-dimensional analyses, each independent of the other. As a result, I_D is determined by the superposition of two one-dimensional solutions. Namely, by assuming that the *gradient* of the "horizontal" field in the channel is negligible, the one-dimensional *Poisson equation* can be solved to get the total charge in the silicon at each point y along the channel (i.e., the sum of the inversion layer charge Q_I [see Fig. 3-8] and the ionic charge Q_B in the depletion region). This means that the same formulas derived for the MOS-C are also applicable for calculating the local values of $Q_I(y)$ and $Q_B(y)$ in the long-channel MOSFET (provided, of course, that the effect of the channel voltage caused by the drain-source bias is also included in the MOS-C formulas). Then we note that within the conducting channel of a MOSFET the current flows almost exclusively in the y-direction. Thus, we can ignore the fact that there must be a slight x-component in the "horizontal" $\mathcal{E}$-field. This allows us to solve the one-dimensional *drift-diffusion current-density equation* in the y direction for I_D as a function of the terminal voltages [using the local $Q(y)$ values obtained from the solution of the Poisson equation in this current-density equation].

Note, however, that if the GCA is not valid, but it is still invoked in order to enable one-dimensional analysis to be used for calculating Q_I, it is unlikely that accurate values of I_D will be yielded This is the situation that arises in so-called short-channel devices (as described in chap. 5). In such cases, to obtain good agreement between calculated and measured values of I_D, the two-dimensional forms of the semiconductor equations must be solved (usually numerically).

4.3.1.1 Verifying the Validity of the GCA as a Function of the Geometrical Factors of the MOSFET Device Structure and Bias Conditions. The validity of the GCA for a particular MOSFET structure can be checked by making rough estimates of $\partial\mathcal{E}_x/\partial x$ and $\partial\mathcal{E}_y/\partial y$ values under given bias conditions. Since we are most interested in I_D when the MOSFET is in strong inversion, we will establish expressions that allow the GCA to be tested if the MOSFET is being operated in strong inversion.*

We begin this derivation by recalling that under strong inversion the inversion layer charge density Q_I is much larger than the ionic charge density Q_B in the depletion region (see section 3.3.3), and that the inversion layer is very thin (~30-300Å). Thus, in strong inversion $\partial\mathcal{E}_x/\partial x$ in the silicon is greatest in the inversion layer region (see Fig. 4-6). Now $\partial\mathcal{E}_x/\partial x$ can be estimated by approximating the vertical electric field value at the bottom edge of the inversion layer as zero. Using this assumption implies that $\partial\mathcal{E}_x/\partial x \sim [\mathcal{E}_{si}(x=0) - 0]/t_{inv} = [\mathcal{E}_{si}(x=0)]/t_{inv}$, where t_{inv} is the effective inversion layer

---

* Note that in weak inversion the surface potential $\varphi_{surf}(y)$ along the channel in long-channel MOSFETs is almost constant (see section 4.7). Thus, $\partial\mathcal{E}_y/\partial y$ is very small, implying that $\partial\mathcal{E}_x/\partial x >> \partial\mathcal{E}_y/\partial y$, because $\mathcal{E}_x$ drops from its value at $x = 0$ to zero at the bottom edge of the channel depletion region, which is a relatively small distance. Thus, in long-channel MOSFETs the GCA is also valid in weak inversion. However, in short-channel MOSFETs, this will no longer necessarily be the case, as we shall see in chap. 5.

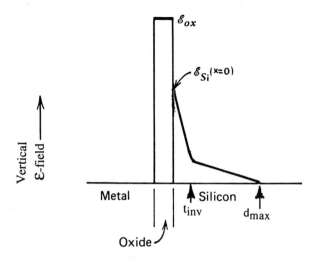

Fig. 4-6 The vertical electric field in a MOS-C (or MOSFET channel) when a large enough gate bias to cause inversion is applied. Note that since $Q_I > Q_B$ in inversion, that the gradient of the $\mathcal{E}$-field over the inversion layer thickness t_{inv} is larger than that over the depletion region width d_{max}, and we can therefore approximate the $\mathcal{E}$-field value at the bottom of the inversion layer thickness as being equal to zero for the purposes of estimating t_{inv}.

thickness. From Eq. 3-15, $\mathcal{E}_{si}(x=0) = \varepsilon_{ox}\mathcal{E}_{ox}/\kappa_{si}\varepsilon_o$, and from Eq. 3-14, $\mathcal{E}_{ox}$ is ~$(V_{GS} - V_T)/t_{ox}$. Thus,

$$\frac{\partial \mathcal{E}_x}{\partial x} \approx \left(\frac{\varepsilon_{ox}}{\kappa_{si}\varepsilon_o t_{inv}}\right)\frac{(V_{GS} - V_T)}{t_{ox}} \qquad (4 - 14a)$$

Now, according to Eq. 3-12a, the concentration of electrons at some point in the semiconductor at equilibrium is exponentially dependent on the potential, with the exponential constant being $1/\varphi_t = kT/q$. This implies that the majority of the charges is contained within a distance from the surface over which φ drops by kT/q (i.e., since Eq. 3-12a predicts that if the electron concentration at the surface [x = 0] is n_{surf}, then at the point where the potential drops below φ_{surf} by an amount kT/q, n_{surf} will have dropped to a value $1/e$ of its value at x = 0, or to $0.37 n_{surf}$). Thus, we assume that t_{inv} is roughly equal to that distance below x = 0. If we also assume that the vertical electric field $\mathcal{E}_x$ in the inversion layer is roughly the potential difference across the inversion layer $\Delta\varphi_{inv}$ divided by its thickness t_{inv} ($\mathcal{E}_x \sim \Delta\varphi_{inv}/t_{inv}$) we get $t_{inv} \sim (kT/q)/\mathcal{E}_{si}(x=0)$. Thus, substituting this expression for t_{inv} into Eq. 4-14a we finally obtain the following expression for roughly estimating $\partial\mathcal{E}_x/\partial x$:

$$\frac{\partial \mathcal{E}_x}{\partial x} \approx \left(\frac{\varepsilon_{ox}}{\kappa_{si}\varepsilon_o}\right)^2 \frac{q(V_{GS} - V_T)^2}{kT\,t_{ox}^2} \qquad (4 - 14b)$$

If we also assume that the value of $\mathcal{E}_y$ varies gradually from a small value near the source to values of the order of V_{DS}/L near the drain, $\partial\mathcal{E}_y/\partial y$ can be roughly estimated as $\partial\mathcal{E}_y/\partial y \sim V_{DS}/L^2$. Thus, if we assume that the GCA is valid when the ratio $(\partial\mathcal{E}_x/\partial x)/\partial\mathcal{E}_y/\partial y$ is large, then it is also valid if the following inequality is large

$$\frac{\partial\mathcal{E}_x/\partial x}{\partial\mathcal{E}_y/\partial y} = \left(\frac{\varepsilon_{ox}\,L}{\kappa_{si}\varepsilon_0}\right)^2 \frac{q\,(V_{GS} - V_T)^2}{kT\,t_{ox}^2\,V_{DS}} \gg 1 \qquad (4 - 15)$$

For a MOSFET at 300K with $L = 1.0\ \mu m$, $t_{ox} = 300\text{Å}$, $V_{GS} - V_T = 0.5V$, and $V_{DS} = 0.5V$, the left-hand side of the inequality (4-15) is ~2300, indicating that the GCA is a very good approximation for such a MOSFET. This also implies that the GCA can be valid even in submicron MOSFETs, provided that $V_{GS} - V_T$ is not too small.

However, as we will see in chap. 5, $\mathcal{E}_y$ is quite non-uniform along the length of the channel at high values of V_{DS}, becoming much stronger near the drain. Furthermore, from Eq. 4-10 we note that the inversion layer charge density can be approximated as $Q_I \sim [V_{GS} - V_T - V(y)]$, if we replace V_{GB} with V_{GS}, and V_{CB} with $V(y)$ [where $V(y)$ is the channel voltage induced by V_{DS}]. However, this approximation is only valid when Q_I is positive, i.e., when $V_{GS} - V_T > V(y)$. Thus, if V_{DS} exceeds $V_{GS} - V_T$ (i.e., the condition which occurs in the region of the channel near the drain when the MOSFET is operated in saturation), the GCA becomes invalid in this region of the channel. [Because, when $V(y)$ is greater than $V_{GS} - V_T$, this implies that $\mathcal{E}_y > \mathcal{E}_x$, and that $\partial\mathcal{E}_y/\partial y$ is therefore at least comparable to, if not greater than, $\partial\mathcal{E}_x/\partial x$].

In summary, the GCA appears to be valid for MOSFETs operated in strong inversion even if the channel length is shorter than 1 μm - provided that V_{DS} is small enough that the MOSFET is not being operated in saturation (i.e., $V_{DS} \leq V_{DSsat}$, where V_{DSsat} is the voltage at the onset of saturation). On the other hand, if the MOSFET is operated in saturation, use of the GCA to calculate I_D will not yield accurate results, and alternative approximations (as described in chap. 5) must be employed to get good agreement with experimental I_D-V_{DS} characteristics.

4.3.2 Circuit Characteristics of Long-Channel MOSFETs

From the perspective of the MOSFET as a circuit component, long-channel behavior has been specified in a number of ways. A list of device parameters from a circuit perspective deemed to be characteristic of long-channel MOSFETs include the following:

1. The threshold voltage V_T is independent of channel length L.

2. The threshold voltage V_T is independent of drain bias voltage, V_{DS}.

3. The drain current in saturation I_{Dsat} is independent of V_{DS}.

4. The drain current has a linear dependence on $1/L$ (i.e., one quantitative criterion is that there should be no more than a 10% departure from linearity as the channel length is decreased).

5. The subthreshold current I_{Dst} is independent of drain bias.

6. The subthreshold swing S_t is independent of gate length.

As the behavior of the MOSFET is described later in this chapter, the terms associated with these device characteristics will be defined and discussed in more detail.

4.4 QUALITATIVE DESCRIPTION OF MOSFET OPERATION

The operation of the MOSFET is first described from a qualitative perspective. Specifically, our goal is to qualitatively explain the so-called *static characteristics* of the MOSFET; i.e., the drain current characteristics of the MOSFET as a function of the applied dc terminal voltages V_{GS} and V_{DS}. This behavior is normally depicted using an I_D-V_{DS} plot, with V_{GS} as the parameter.

For simplicity we consider an ideal (i.e., $V_{FB} = 0$) long-channel NMOSFET (*p*-type substrate) as our example device structure, with the source being chosen as the reference terminal (Fig. 4-4b). We also assume that the source-substrate and drain-substrate junctions are always kept under reverse bias and that the resulting reverse-bias leakage currents are negligible (this is valid as long as the bias voltage is kept smaller than the junction breakdown voltage), and that $V_{SB} = 0V$. We also use energy-band versus position and potential versus position diagrams to help depict the qualitative MOSFET behavior. Note that in the case of the MOS-C one-dimensional diagrams were adequate. Here, however, two-dimensional energy-band and potential diagrams must be used. Axes and terminal voltage designations are the same as in Fig. 4-2a.

4.4.1 MOSFET Behavior in Response to Gate Bias Alone

We begin by describing how a MOSFET behaves in response to a gate bias V_{GS} alone. In this case, the region under the oxide responds in the same way as does an ideal MOS-C. However, because the source and drain regions are present in a MOSFET the overall device behavior differs from that of a MOS-C with a V_{GB} applied.

To analyze the MOSFET behavior, let us assume that all three bias voltages are initially set to zero (i.e., $V_{GS} = V_{DS} = V_{BS} = 0V$). In this case a flat band condition in exists in the gated region of the MOSFET (as is also observed when $V_{GB} = 0V$ in an ideal MOS-C). The two-dimensional energy-band diagram corresponding to this condition is shown in Fig. 4-7b. We observe that E_c in the *x*-direction at the cut A-A is indeed flat. (The potential versus position diagram in the MOSFET for this bias condition is also shown in Fig. 4-8b). Assuming that $\varphi(x = \infty) = 0$, in this case $\varphi_{surf} = 0$ as well.)

At the surface ($x = 0$), however, a potential energy barrier of value qV_{bi} exists between the *p* region and each of the n^+ regions (where V_{bi} is the built-in potential of the *doped pn$^+$* junction). This is shown in the E_c versus *y* direction plot for $x = 0$ in Fig. 4-7b. For this case (and for cases of when a reverse bias exists across the doped junctions) only the very small leakage current of a reverse-biased *pn* junction flows.

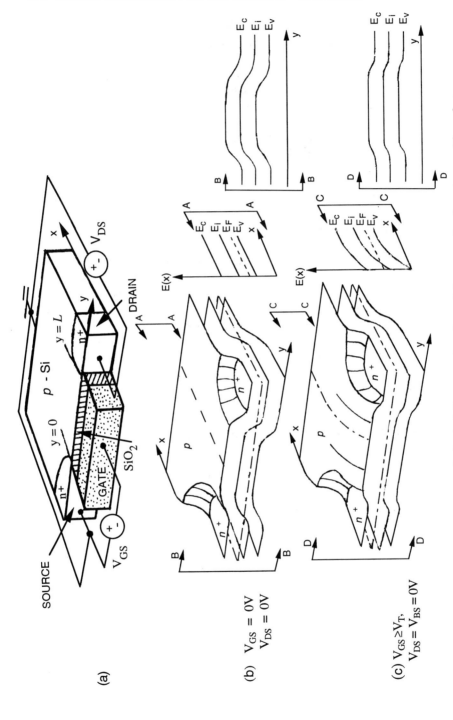

Fig. 4-7 (a) Cross section of an NMOS device. (b & c) 2-D perspective plots of the energy bands versus position of an ideal long-channel NMOS device when (b) $V_{GS} = 0V$ (flat-band condition), and (c) $V_{GS} > V_T$, $V_{DS} = V_{BS} = 0V$.

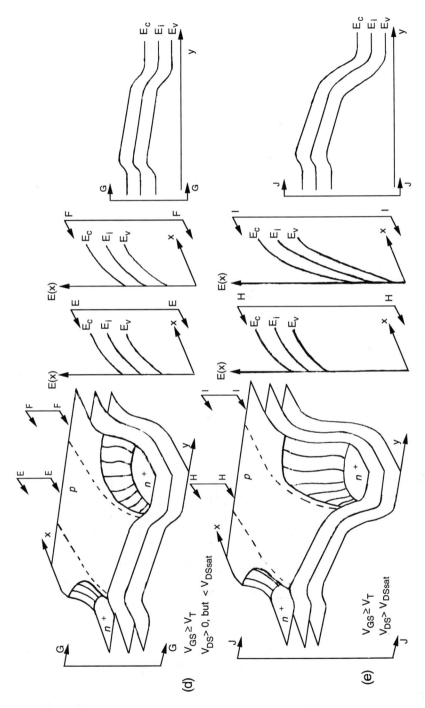

Fig. 4-8 (cont.) (d & e) 2-D perspective plots of the energy bands as a function of position an ideal long-channel NMOS device when: (d) $V_{GS} \geq V_T$ and V_{DS} is small (i.e., $< V_{DSsat}$); and (e) $V_{GS} \geq V_T$ and $V_{DS} > V_{DSsat}$. $V_{BS} = 0$ in both cases.

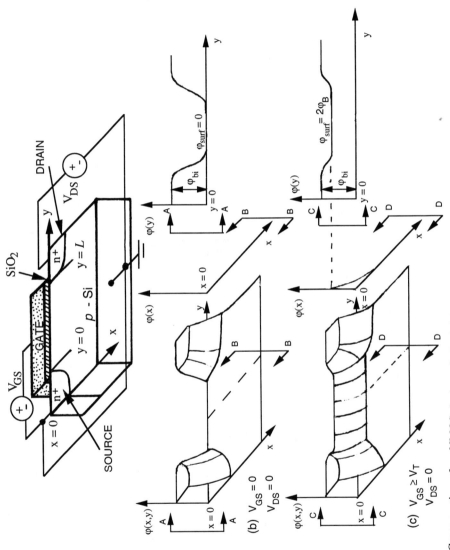

Fig. 4-8 (a) Cross section of an NMOS device. (b & c) 2-D perspective potential versus distance diagrams of an ideal NMOS device when: (b) $V_{GS} = 0V$ (flat-band condition), and $V_{DS} = 0V$; and (c) $V_{GS} \geq V_T$, $V_{DS} = V_{BS} = 0V$.

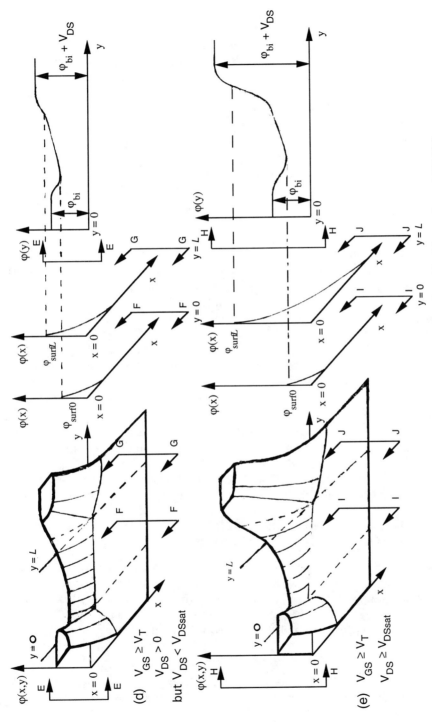

Fig. 4-8 (cont.) (d & e) 2-D perspective potential versus distance diagrams of an ideal long-channel NMOS device when (d) $V_{GS} \geq V_T$ and $V_{DS} > 0V$, but $< V_T$; and (e) $V_{GS} > V_T$, and $V_{DS} > V_{DSsat} \sim V_{GS} - V_T$.

Thus, the circuit path between the n^+ source and drain regions effectively appears as an open circuit. This means that even if a voltage is applied between the source and drain ($V_{DS} \neq 0V$), essentially no drain current will flow. Moreover, if we apply either a negative V_{GS} (or a positive V_{GS} such that $V_{GS} < V_T$,) the gated region contains either an excess of holes (*accumulation*, when $V_{GS} < 0V$) or a deficit of holes and very few electrons (*depletion*, when $V_{GS} < V_T$). In this case, the circuit path between source and drain still appears essentially as an open circuit. That is, no current flows in the drain terminal even if a drain voltage is applied. For all of these conditions, the MOSFET is said to be in an "OFF" state.

If a positive V_{GS} is applied such that $V_{GS} > V_T$, an inversion layer containing mobile electrons is formed adjacent to the Si surface throughout the entire gated region between the source and drain (here we still assume that $V_{DS} = V_{BS} = 0V$). Thus, the circuit path between source and drain now contains an induced "n-type" region (the inversion layer), as shown in Fig. 4-9. This means that a conducting path or *channel* exists between the source and drain. (However, if $V_{DS} = 0V$, no drain current will yet flow.) Now, if a drain voltage is applied (i.e., $V_{DS} > 0V$), drain current will flow. The device in this state is said to be "ON." Obviously, the larger the value of gate voltage (V_{GS}), the more electrons pile up at the Si surface, and the greater the conductance of this channel. This demonstrates that the input voltage to the MOSFET can induce a source-to-drain channel and will determine the maximum conductance of the channel.*

Figure 4-7c shows the energy band diagram of the MOSFET when $V_{GS} > V_T$ and $V_{DS} = V_{BS} = 0V$, and Fig 4-8c also shows the potential diagram for this case. Note that the bands along the x-direction in the gated region are no longer flat (see section B-B) and that $\varphi_{surf} > 2\varphi_B$ everywhere along the channel. The potential-energy barrier between the n^+ and p regions is also reduced (see the E_c versus y plot in Fig. 4-7c). Hence, only a very low barrier to current injection exists between the source and the channel. The barrier height is smallest at the surface with its value controlled by the bias on the gate. At strong inversion and beyond, the barrier height is assumed to be remain constant at $\sim q(V_{bi} - 2\varphi_B)$, because φ_{surf} is assumed to be clamped at $2\varphi_B$ in strong inversion. However, as V_{GS} is increased, the inversion charge density continues to increase, increasing the conductance of the channel

4.4.2 Qualitative MOSFET Behavior when both Gate and Drain Bias are Applied

We now consider the variation of I_D with V_{DS}. At first we assume that V_{GS} is kept fixed at a single value while V_{DS} is varied, and $V_{BS} = 0V$. Later we show how varying the value of V_{GS} impacts the I_D-V_{DS} characteristic. In this section we also assume that

---

* Note that when V_{GS} is positive but smaller than V_T, the gated region can be in state of weak inversion. In weak inversion only small, so-called *subthreshold currents* are able to flow between the drain and source. These subthreshold currents are not large enough to be useful as driving currents for most applications, but they are sufficiently large to cause troublesome leakage - which can complicate the design of some circuits. We will describe subthreshold currents in more detail in section 4.7 and in chap. 5, as part of discussion on the quantitative behavior of the long-channel MOSFET and the submicron MOSFET.

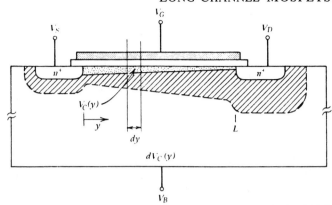

Fig. 4-9 Depletion region width variation from source to drain end of a MOSFET when $V_{DS} > 0V$.

sufficient gate bias is applied to ensure that the MOSFET is being operated in inversion (i.e., $V_{GS} > V_T$). We then describe what happens as a dc V_{DS} is applied, with its value being increased in small steps, starting from $V_{DS} = 0V$.

As noted earlier, when $V_{DS} = 0V$, $I_D = 0$, even if $V_{GS} > V_T$ (see Fig. 4-10b). However, when V_{DS} is increased slightly, I_D starts to flow. When V_{DS} is small (i.e., a few tenths of a volt or less), the surface channel behaves like a simple resistor (Fig. 4-10c). That is, an I_D proportional to V_{DS} flows into the drain. If a plot of I_D versus V_{DS} is used to demonstrate the I_D-V_{DS} behavior, the response to small values of V_{DS} is shown as the line from the point 0 to the point A in Fig. 4-10a.

When V_{DS} is increased beyond a few tenths of a volt, the MOSFET exhibits a new phase of behavior. That is, current flowing in the channel gives rise to a significant voltage drop in the channel (unlike the case in the three-terminal structure introduced in section 4.2.1, where the channel voltage is constant along the entire channel length because essentially no current flows along it). Specifically, the *channel voltage* (introduced in section 4.2.1) is V_{DB}, at the drain end and V_{SB} at the source end. If $V_{SB} = 0V$, the channel voltage at the source end will equal zero. But even with $V_{SB} = 0V$, the channel voltage at the drain end will not be zero, since we assume $V_{DS} > 0V$. As shown in Fig. 4-9 such a non-zero V_{DB} causes the depletion region under the gate to widen toward the drain end of the channel. As described in section 4.2.1, this implies that the mobile charge concentration in the inversion layer simultaneously decreases. The smaller number of carriers causes the channel conductance to decrease, which in turn is manifested as a smaller slope in the I_D-V_{DS} characteristic as V_{DS} is increased. As the drain voltage is further increased, the depletion region continues to widen and the slope of the I-V characteristic continues to decrease (see Figs. 4-10a and 4-10c).

The energy-band and potential diagrams of the MOSFET when both a small V_{DS} and a $V_{GS} > V_T$ are applied are shown in Figs. 4-7d and 4-8d, respectively. Even if the drain voltage is small enough so that the entire surface region remains in inversion, we see that near the drain the band bending is larger than at the source (see the E_c vs. y diagram in Fig. 4-7d). This implies that the depletion region under the gate is wider there. Since the gate-to-body voltage is constant across the entire gated region, less voltage is

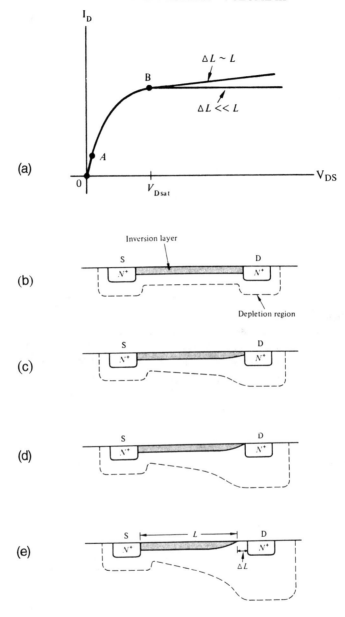

Fig. 4-10 (a) I_D-V_{DS} characteristic of a MOSFET being operated at a fixed V_{GS}, with V_{GS}>V_T. (b -e) Visualization of the various phases of V_{GS}>V_T MOSFET operation: (b) V_{DS} = 0V; (c) channel (inversion layer) narrowing under moderate V_{DS} biasing; (d) pinchoff; and (e) post pinchoff (V_{DS}>V_{DSsat}).[30] Reprinted with permission of Addison-Wesley Pub. Co.

available near the drain to establish the inversion layer charge. Hence, inversion is less strong in the channel near the drain.

Eventually, if V_{DS} is sufficiently increased such that $V_{DS}>(V_{GS} - V_T)$, the inversion layer ceases to exist near the vicinity of the drain. The disappearance of the inversion layer due to an increase in V_{DS} is termed *pinch-off* (see Fig. 4-10d). The pinch-off point on the I_D-V_{DS} characteristic is shown as point B in Fig. 4-10a. We see that the slope of the I_D curve here has become approximately zero. Note, however, that pinch-off does *not* mean that I_D vanishes as V_{DS} exceeds the pinch-off voltage. In fact, it is the *gradual channel approximation* that is no longer valid in the region of the device in which pinch-off exists. That is, mobile charges still move through the depleted region near the drain, and drain current continues to flow. However, the equations for the charge distribution derived from the one-dimensional solution of the Poisson equation (which are valid for the case of the MOS-C) predict that no mobile charge exists in the pinch-off region. But in the depleted pinched-off region the one-dimensional Poisson equation is no longer valid. Instead, a two-dimensional numerical analysis (or an analytical expression based on a modified 1-D form of the Poisson equation - see section 5.4.3.3) must be used to calculate the potential and carrier concentrations in the pinched-off device region. A detailed numerical analysis of the saturation range has been carried out using the two-dimensional device simulator MINIMOS.[3] This work showed that for voltages greater than V_{DSsat} the current stream of the carriers moving into the pinched off region is no longer confined to the inversion layer region near the surface, but begins to move away from the surface and into the bulk. Note that this physical picture is plausible because once V_{DS} becomes larger than $(V_{GS} - V_T)$ the polarity of the vertical electric field in the pinched-off region is reversed. This tends to push any mobile carriers flowing in the channel *away* from the surface. Thus, in the region of the channel where $V_{DS}>(V_{GS} - V_T)$ the mobile carriers flow toward the drain *beneath* the surface.

Nevertheless, as the drain voltage increases beyond the pinch-off voltage V_{DSsat} the pinched-off section of the channel widens from just a point into a segment ΔL in length (see Fig. 4-10e). Most of the voltage drop in excess of V_{DSsat} is dropped across this pinched-off section ΔL. I_D remains approximately constant (*saturated*) for drain voltages greater then V_{DSsat} so long as $\Delta L<<L$. If ΔL becomes comparable to L (which is a condition that may occur in short-channel MOSFETs), the same voltage drop appears across a shorter channel $(L - \Delta L)$, and the post-pinch-off current I_{Dsat} in such devices will increase somewhat as V_{DS} is increased further beyond V_{DSsat}. Figures 4-7e and 4-8e show the energy-band diagrams and potential diagrams, respectively, for a long-channel MOSFET biased into pinch-off.

The response of the long-channel MOSFET to separate manipulation of gate and drain dc biases has been qualitatively described up to this point. This has allowed us to visualize the general variation of I_D with V_{DS} for a fixed value of $V_{GS} >V_T$. To allow the complete set of I_D versus V_{DS} characteristics to be obtained, we need to combine the results from the individual cases. These are as follows:

For $V_{GS} <V_T$, no channel exists and $I_D \approx 0$ for all drain biases below junction breakdown. For each value of $V_{GS} >V_T$, a characteristic of the form shown in

Fig. 4-10a will be observed. Since the conductance of the channel will increase as V_{GS} is made larger, the initial slope of I_D will also become steeper with increasing V_{GS}. Furthermore, since the inversion layer contains more electrons, a larger value of V_{DS} is needed to produce pinch-off (V_{DSsat} increases for increasing V_{GS}.). Based on these phenomena, the static I_D-V_{DS} characteristics assume the form shown in Fig. 4-11.

Let us next consider quantitative models which allow these static (i.e., dc) I_D-V_{DS} characteristics to be accurately simulated.

4.5 QUANTITATIVE BEHAVIOR OF MOSFETS: DC CIRCUIT MODELS OF LONG-CHANNEL MOSFETS

Although the discussion in the previous section provides a qualitative picture of how a MOSFET operates, we need to express this behavior in quantitative form. Specifically, to design circuits with MOSFETs we must be able to calculate how much current is carried in the "ON" state of a MOSFET and how much leakage current flows in the "OFF" state. In short, we need the current-voltage characteristics of the MOSFET, specifically the quantitative relationship between the drain current and terminal voltages.

In this section our goal is to derive relationships that allow the dc drain current I_D of long-channel MOSFETs to be quantitatively predicted. Such I_D-V_{DS} relationships are referred to as the *static (dc) circuit models* of the MOSFET. As is the case for the MOS-C, there exists a hierarchy of such long-channel MOSFET I_D-V_{DS} models in terms of their generality, accuracy, and complexity. Our discussion in this section will derive four of these models, using as our foundation two of the five classical semiconductor equations introduced in chap. 2: the one-dimensional Poisson equation, and the one-dimensional drift-diffusion current density equation (as well as the three models of the MOS-C derived in chap. 3).

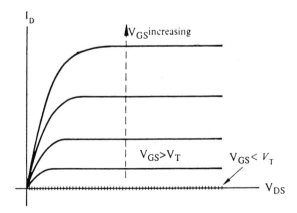

Fig. 4-11 General form of the I_D-V_{DS} characteristics expected from a long-channel MOSFET.

The first of these models is the *Pao-Sah* model, which is the most general and accurate of our four dc I_D long-channel MOSFET models. Like the general MOS-C model, it also the most computationally complex (in that it requires numerical analysis techniques to calculate I_D for a given set of terminal voltages). The three less-computationally complex long-channel models are derived from the Pao-Sah model by making suitable simplifying approximations. The first of these that we will study is the *charge-sheet MOSFET* model. It is based on the same assumptions used in the MOS-C charge-sheet model introduced in chap. 3. Unlike the Pao-Sah model, it provides an analytical expression for I_D in terms of V_{GB} and φ_{surf}, and thus involves much less computational effort. Nevertheless, it is only slightly less accurate than the Pao-Sah model provided the MOSFET is operated in inversion (i.e., this model is valid from weak through strong inversion). However, while this model provides an analytical expression for I_D, it still requires a numerical procedure to obtain the values of the surface potential needed to evaluate the I_D expression. That is, I_D is not explicitly stated in terms of the terminal voltages. (The terminal voltage values are used to first calculate φ_{surf}, which is then used to compute I_D.) Thus, the charge-sheet model is still too cumbersome to serve as a MOSFET model for most circuit-simulation applications.

By making suitable approximations that are valid over a more limited range of operation (namely, the strong inversion regime), two simpler long-channel MOSFET models have been derived that are extensively used in circuit analysis and design. They are the *variable depletion-charge* and the *square-law* models. These provide analytical expressions which give I_D explicitly in terms of the terminal voltages. We show how they can be derived from the charge-sheet model by making additional simplifying assumptions. At the end of the section we compare these four models in more detail.

4.5.1 General Approach to Deriving the DC Drain-Current Relationships in Long-Channel MOSFETs

The derivation of the dc drain current relationship recognizes that, in general, the current in the channel of a MOSFET can be caused by both drift and diffusion current. In an NMOSFET we can accurately assume that only electrons contribute to the drain current. Thus, we only need to use Eq. 1-5a to describe the drain current density J_D

$$J_D = J_n = q\ \mu_n\ n\ \mathcal{E}\ +\ q\ D_n\ \nabla n \qquad (4\text{-}16)$$

Within the conducting channel of a MOSFET the current flows almost exclusively in the y-direction, thus Eq. 4-14 can be simplified to the following one-dimensional form:

$$J_D \approx J_{ny} = q\ \mu_n\ n\ \mathcal{E}_y + q\ D_n\ dn/dy\ =\ -q\ \mu_n\ n\ d\varphi/dy + q\ D_n\ dn/dy \quad (4\text{-}16a)$$

Since we also assume there are no current sources or sinks inside the device, the current flowing through any cross-sectional plane within the channel must be constant, having some value I_D. We also assume that the current density is constant in the z-direction, but not necessarily in the x-direction. Hence, if J_{ny} is integrated over Z we get

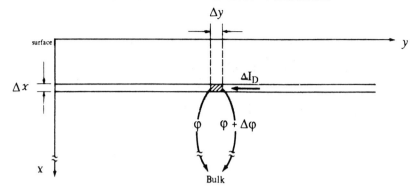

Fig. 4-12 The drain current I_D in a MOSFET can be modeled as the sum of currents in slices ΔI_D each having a thickness Δx and a width Z. These slices exist from the surface to the depth at which the electron concentration becomes negligible.[5] Reprinted with permission of McGraw-Hill Book Co.

$$I_D = -\int\int J_{ny}\ dx\ dz = -Z\int_0^{x_c(y)} J_{ny}\ dx \qquad (4\text{-}17)$$

If the flow of electrons can be considered to be laminar, we can assume that the total current I_D is the sum of elemental currents ΔI, each flowing horizontally in an inversion layer slice parallel to the surface, having width Z and depth Δx, as shown in Fig. 4-12. If we allow Δx to become a differential, the current in each slice dI_D is

$$dI_D = dI_{Ddrift}\ (x,y) + dI_{Ddiff}\ (x,y) \qquad (4\text{-}18a)$$

Since $\mathcal{E}(y) = -d\varphi/dy$, the drift component of Eq. 4-18a can be written as

$$dI_{Ddrift}\ (x,\ y)\ = q\ \mu_n\ Z\ n\ (x,\ y)\ \partial\varphi(x,\ y)/\partial y \qquad (4\text{-}18b)$$

The diffusion component of Eq. 4-18b can also be rewritten as,

$$dI_{Ddiff}\ (x,\ y)\ = -Z\ q\ D_n\ \partial n(x,\ y)/\partial y = -Z\ \mu_n\ kT\ \partial n(x,\ y)/\partial y \qquad (4\text{-}18c)$$

since $D_n/\mu_n = kT/q$.

An expression for the total drain current for each of these components can be obtained by integrating each expression over the depth from $x = 0$ to a point below the surface at which the electron concentration is negligible, x_c or

$$I_{Ddrift}\ = q\ \mu\ Z\ \frac{d\varphi}{dy}\int_0^{x_c(y)} n\ (x,y)\ dx \qquad (4\text{-}19)$$

$$I_{Ddiff} = - \mu Z kT \frac{d}{dy} \left[\int_0^{x_c(y)} n(x,y) \, dx \right] \qquad (4-20)$$

Since the charge per unit area due to carriers in the inversion layer, Q_I is given by

$$Q_I(y) = -q \int_0^{x_c(y)} n(x,y) \, dx \qquad (4-21)$$

Thus, Eqs. 4-19 and 4-20 can be written as

$$I_{Ddrift} = \mu Z (-Q_I) \frac{d\varphi}{dy} \qquad (4-22)$$

and

$$I_{Ddiff} = \mu Z \frac{kT}{q} \frac{dQ_I}{dy} \qquad (4-23)$$

Our goal is to derive a model in which I_D is expressed in terms of the terminal voltages V_{GS} and V_{DS}. To do this we must integrate the sum of Eqs. 4-22 and 4-23. The integration is carried out by changing the variables of integration by multiplying both sides of Eqs. 4-22 and 4-23 by (dy). Since we recognize that I_D is constant along the length of the channel, when we integrate the left hand side of the sum of Eqs. 4-22 and 4-23 (namely I_D[dy] from 0 to L) we get

$$I_D L = \int_0^L I_D \, dy \qquad (4-24)$$

Then we can write the total drain current I_D as

$$I_D = \frac{\mu Z}{L} \int_{\varphi_{surf0}}^{\varphi_{surfL}} (-Q_I) \, d\varphi + \frac{\mu ZkT}{Lq} \int_{Q_{I,source}}^{Q_{I,drain}} dQ_I \qquad (4-25)$$

We see that the first term on the right hand side of Eq. 4-25 is no longer integrated with respect to position, but with respect to voltage. (In the *variable-depletion charge model* [section 4.5.4, Eq. 4-58], and the *square-law model* [section 4.5.5, Eq. 4-62], we assume that only the drift current term is needed to describe I_D. Hence, only this integral needs to be carried out to calculate I_D. By changing the variable of integration from position to voltage this integration becomes easy to perform, yielding Eqs. 4-58 and 4-62.) The limits of integration of the first term of Eq. 4-25 are the value of the surface potential at the source end φ_{surf0} (which is usually set equal to zero), and the surface potential value at the drain end φ_{surfL} (which is usually set to V_{DS}). The limits of the integration of the second term are the value of the mobile charge density at the source end of the channel $Q_{Isource}$, and the value at the drain end Q_{Idrain}.

4.5.2 Pao-Sah Model

The *Pao-Sah* model,[4] published in 1966, was the first advanced long-channel MOSFET model to be developed. While it retained the gradual-channel approximation, it did not invoke the depletion approximation and permitted carrier transport in the channel by both drift and diffusion current. The formulation of the I_D equation it develops is therefore quite general, but as a result requires numerical integrations in two dimensions. Such numerical complexity has limited the role of this model to theoretical analyses of the MOSFET. Other simpler models of the MOSFET have been developed for use in IC circuit design applications.

The Pao-Sah model follows the approach outlined in the previous section for deriving the I_D relationship from the semiconductor device equations. However, the derivation is usually carried out using a more compact formulation, in which the drift and diffusion current expression are combined into a single equation. When we derive the charge-sheet MOSFET model we will return to calculating both current components separately, as this results in a simpler derivation. Here, the opposite is true, and so we also elect the single equation approach to deriving the Pao-Sah model. Note that the presentation of the derivation in this section, and the next, closely mimics the method proposed by Tsividis.[5]

We begin by noting that the Pao-Sah approach invokes the gradual channel approximation (like all long-channel MOSFET models), and assumes that μ is constant along the channel. In our derivation we also assume that the substrate doping is uniform and that an *n*-channel MOSFET is being treated.

To simplify the expression for I_D so that it consists of one instead of two terms on the right hand side of Eq. 4-16, we start by noting that at the source end of the channel in the MOSFET (where $y = 0$), n can be expressed in terms of φ by

$$n\,(x, 0) = n_{po} \exp q[\varphi\,(x, 0) - V_{SB}]/kT \qquad (4\text{-}26)$$

and at the drain end by

$$n\,(x, L) = n_{po} \exp q[\varphi\,(x, L) - V_{DB}]/kT \qquad (4\text{-}27)$$

For an arbitrary position y along the channel, n is given by

$$n\,(x, y) = n_{po} \exp q[\varphi\,(x, y) - V_{ChB}(y)]/kT \qquad (4\text{-}28)$$

where $V_{ChB}\,(0) = V_{SB}$ and $V_{ChB}\,(L) = V_{DB}$. In Eq. 4-28, V_{ChB} represents the potential corresponding to the difference between the quasi-Fermi level of the electrons in the inversion layer and the quasi-Fermi level of holes in the bulk, as shown in Fig. 4-13. That is, because the source and drain will in general be biased with respect to the substrate, the channel is also at some potential $V_{ChB}\,(y)$ relative to the substrate. Clearly this voltage is a function of position y along the channel if $V_{DS} \neq 0$, because at the source end we have $V_{ChB}\,(0) = V_{SB}$ and at the drain end $V_{ChB}\,(L) = V_{DB}$.

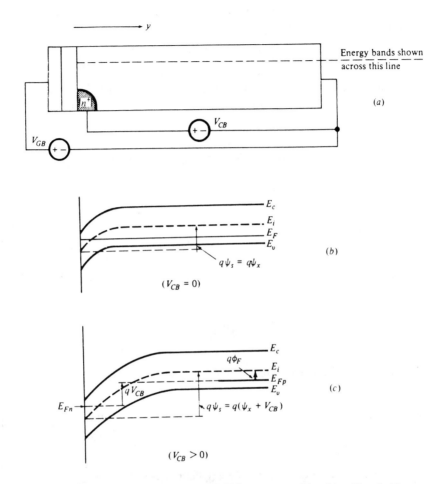

Fig. 4-13 Energy-band diagram of a three-terminal MOS structure with a bias V_{CB} (= V_{ChB} in a MOSFET) showing how the applied bias V_{CB} is related to the difference between the quasi-Fermi levels of the electrons in the inversion layer E_{Fn} and that of the holes E_{Fp}.[5] Reprinted with permission of McGraw-Hill Book Co.

If Eq. 4-28 is differentiated with respect to y we get

$$\frac{\partial n(x, y)}{\partial y} = \frac{q n(x, y)}{kT}\left[\frac{\partial \varphi(x, y)}{\partial y} - \frac{\partial V_{ChB}(y)}{\partial y}\right] \qquad (4\text{-}29)$$

Using Eq. 4-29 in Eq. 4-18 we obtain

$$d\,I_{Ddiff}(x, y) = -(Z\,dx)\,q\,\mu\,n(x, y)\left[\frac{\partial \varphi(x, y)}{\partial y} - \frac{\partial V_{ChB}(y)}{\partial y}\right] \qquad (4\text{-}30)$$

If Eq. 4-30 is inserted together with Eq. 4-17 into Eq. 4-16 it is seen that the $\partial\varphi/\partial x$ terms cancel out, leaving

$$d\, I_D\,(x,\,y)\ =\ (Z\,dx)\,q\ \mu\,n\,(x,\,y)\,\frac{dV_{ChB}\,(y)}{dy} \qquad (4\text{ - }31)$$

As was done above for Eqs. 4-19 and 4-20, I_D from Eq. 4-31 can be obtained by integrating from the surface to a depth $x = x_c$ beneath which the electron concentration is negligibly small

$$I_D\ =\ \mu\,Z\,\frac{dV\,(y)}{dy}\,q\int_0^{x_c(y)} n\,(x,\,y)\,dx \qquad (4\text{ - }32)$$

From Eq. 4-21 we can write Eq. 4-32 as

$$I_D\ =\ \mu\,Z\,(\,\text{-}Q_I\,)\,\frac{dV\,(y)}{dy} \qquad (4\text{ - }33)$$

Now, integrating over the channel length and using Eq. 4-24, we get

$$I_D\ =\ \frac{\mu\,Z}{L}\int_{V_{SB}}^{V_{DB}}(\,\text{-}Q_I\,)\,dV \qquad (4\text{ - }34)$$

We can now rewrite the expression for Q_I given by Eq. 4-21 as

$$Q_I\ =\ q\int_0^{x_c} n\,(x,\,y)\,dx\ =\ q\int_{\varphi_{surf}}^{\varphi_c}\frac{n\,(\varphi)\,d\varphi}{d\varphi/dx} \qquad (4\text{ - }35)$$

If we define $\varphi_t = kT/q$ we can write $n\,(\varphi)$ in Eq. 4-35 as

$$n\,(\varphi) = N_A\,\exp\,[\varphi\,(x,y) - 2\varphi_B - V_{ChB}(y)]/\varphi_t \qquad (4\text{ - }36)$$

because $p_{po} \approx N_A$, and $n_{po} = n_i^2/N_A$, and $\varphi_B = kT/q\ \ln\,(N_A/n_i)$. Thus,

$$(N_A/n_i)^2\ =\ \exp\,(2\varphi_B)/\varphi_t \qquad (4\text{ - }37)$$

Solving Eq. 4-37 for n_i^2 and substituting the result for n_i^2 into $n_{po} = n_i^2/N_A$, we get

$$n_{po}\ =\ N_A\,\exp\,(\text{-}2\varphi_B/\varphi_t). \qquad (4\text{ - }38)$$

In addition, we recall that $\mathcal{E}(x) = -\,d\varphi/dx$. In chap. 3 we derived an expression for $\mathcal{E}(x)$ in a MOS-C in which both electrons and holes were allowed in the depletion region of the semiconductor. This expression, with φ being replaced by $\varphi \longrightarrow \varphi + V_{ChB}$, is the expression we use for $d\varphi/dx$ in the denominator of Eq. 4-35. That is, $\mathcal{E}(x)$ is now

$$-\frac{d\varphi}{dx} = \mathcal{E}\,(\varphi) = \sqrt{\frac{2q\,N_A}{\kappa_{Si}\varepsilon_o}}\sqrt{\varphi_t e^{-(\varphi + V_{ChB})/\varphi_t} + \varphi - \varphi_t + e^{-2\varphi_B/\varphi_t}\left(\varphi_t e^{-(\varphi + V_{ChB})/\varphi_t} - \varphi - \varphi_t\right)}$$

$$(4 - 39)$$

Then substituting Eqs. 4-36 and 4-39 into Eq. 4-35 we obtain the *Pao-Sah* I_D *expression* *

$$I_D = \frac{q\,\mu\,Z\,N_A}{L} \int_{V_{SB}}^{V_{DB}} \int_{\varphi_{surf}}^{0} [\{e^{(\varphi - 2\varphi_B - V_{ChB})/\varphi_t}\}/\,\mathcal{E}\,(\varphi)] \; d\varphi \, dV \qquad (4 - 40)$$

In this equation, we must first calculate the limit of integration φ_{surf} by using

$$V_{GB} = V_{FB} + \varphi_{surf} \qquad (4 - 41)$$

$$+ \; \gamma\sqrt{\varphi_t e^{-(\varphi_{surf} + V_{SB})/\varphi_t} + \varphi_{surf} - \varphi_t + e^{-2\varphi_B/\varphi_t}\left(\varphi_t e^{-(\varphi_{surf} + V_{SB})/\varphi_t} - \varphi_{surf} - \varphi_t\right)}$$

where $\gamma = \sqrt{2\kappa_{Si}\varepsilon_o N_A}/C_{ox}$. Note that this equation must be solved iteratively for φ_{surf}.

To solve for I_D once φ_{surf} is obtained, Eq. 4-40 must be solved numerically. This involves numerically evaluating the double integral in Eq. 4-40. This is a computationally lengthy procedure. Nevertheless, the Pao-Sah model has been found to accurately predict the I_D in long-channel MOSFETs.

Figure 4-14 is an example of the I_D-V_{DS} characteristics of a long-channel MOSFET

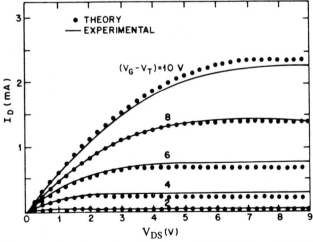

Fig. 4-14. Drain current in a long-channel *p*-channel MOSFET as calculated with the Pao-Sah model (dots) and as measured (solid lines).[4] Reprinted with permission of Solid-State Electronics.

* If $V_{BS} = 0V$, the limits of the voltage integral become 0 and V_{DS}, respectively.

calculated with the Pao-Sah model, together with experimentally measured results. We see that the agreement between measured and predicted I_D values is excellent.

The computational complexity of the Pao-Sah model, however, makes it impractical for use as a MOSFET model in circuit simulation applications. Thus, we show how simpler analytical models can be developed by limiting the validity of the model to reduced regimes of operation. We also mention that an approach has been proposed to reduce Eq. 4-40 to a single-integral formula (which, however, must still be evaluated numerically).[6] However, we do not discuss this approach here.

4.5.3 The Charge Sheet Model

The limited practical utility of the Pao-Sah model motivated a search for an approximate advanced analytical model that still was accurate over a wider range of operating conditions than the earlier *variable depletion-charge* (introduced in 1964) and *square law* models, which are only valid if the MOSFET is operated in strong inversion. The charge-sheet MOSFET, introduced separately by Bacarani[7] and Brews[8] in 1978, has become the most widely adopted long-channel MOSFET model that is accurate over the entire range of inversion.

The charge-sheet model of the long-channel MOSFET makes some simplifying assumptions so the numerical analysis needed in the Pao-Sah model to calculate I_D can be avoided. By doing so, it develops an analytical closed-form expression for I_D in terms of V_{GB} and the surface potential at the drain and source ends of the channel.* It is somewhat less general than the Pao-Sah model in that it is not valid if the MOSFET is operated in depletion or accumulation. However, it is only slightly less accurate than the Pao-Sah model if the MOSFET is being operated in inversion. Hence, by using this model it is possible to get quite accurate predictions of I_D in these regimes without having to resort to the complex numerical analysis required by the Pao-Sah model.

We introduced the charge-sheet approximation for the MOS-C in chap. 3. The MOSFET model is based on essentially the same approximations, with a few more added to account for the current flow behavior of the MOSFET. That is, the charge-sheet approximation basically assumes that the inversion layer (both in weak and strong inversion) can be treated as an infinitesimally thin sheet of charge at the Si surface, and that the depletion approximation is valid for the depletion region below the inversion layer. As such, the inversion-layer charge density Q_I can be found by subtracting the ionic charge in the depletion region Q_B from the total charge in the semiconductor Q_C.

The other assumptions of the charge-sheet model of the MOSFET are the following:

    1. The gradual channel approximation applies to the MOSFETs being treated by this model.

    2. The drain current consists of both drift and diffusion components.

    3. The mobility μ in the channel is proportional to the electric field and is constant with position along the channel.

---

* Although, as we shall see, a numerical iteration procedure must be used to determine these surface potential values from the terminal voltages.

We begin the derivation of the charge-sheet I_D model by assuming that I_D consists of both drift and diffusion current components. Since we also assume that the mobile charge is located in a very thin region near the surface, all the current is located at one depth (i.e., there is no x-dependence of current). Hence, Eq. 4-16 can be expressed as

$$I_D(y) = I_{Ddrift}(y) + I_{Ddiff}(y) \qquad (4-42)$$

Now, we consider each of these terms separately. To express I_{Ddrift}, we treat a small element of the inversion layer between y and Δy, as depicted in Fig. 4-15. The potential difference across this element is given by the difference of φ_{surf} at the points y and $y + \Delta y$, or $\varphi_{surf}(y + \Delta y) - \varphi_{surf}(y)$. Hence we can write an expression for the drift current using Eq. 4-22 with $\Delta\varphi(y)$ replaced by $\Delta\varphi_{surf}(y)$. In addition, we can express this equation in terms of the mobile charge density per unit area Q_I instead of in terms of n by multiplying the mobile charge density in the channel (qn) by the inversion layer thickness t_{inv}, or $Q_I = -q\, n\, t_{inv}$. Since $I_{Ddrift}(y) = A\, J_{drift} = Z\, t_{inv}\, J_{drift}$, $I_{Ddrift}(y)$ becomes

$$I_{Ddrift}(y) = \mu\, Z\, (-Q_I)\, \Delta\varphi_{surf}(y)\, /\Delta y \qquad (4-43)$$

If we allow Δy to approach zero we get

$$I_{Ddrift}(y) = \mu\, Z\, (-Q_I)\, d\varphi_{surf}\, /dy \qquad (4-44)$$

The diffusion component of Eq. 4-42 can likewise be rewritten as

$$I_{D\,diff}(y) = Z\, D\, dQ_I/dy = Z\, \mu\, (kT/q)\, dQ_I/dy \qquad (4-45)$$

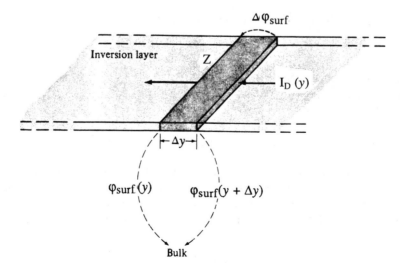

Fig. 4-15 Small element of the inversion layer in a long-channel MOSFET.[5] Reprinted with permission of McGraw-Hill Book Co.

In the case of dc biasing, the total current in the channel must be constant for all points in the y-direction. Thus, Eq. 4-42 can be written as

$$I_D(y) = \mu Z (-Q_I) d\varphi_{surf}/dy + Z\mu (kT/q) dQ_I/dy \qquad (4-46)$$

If we designate φ_{surf} at the source end of the channel ($y = 0$) by φ_{surf0}, and Q_I there by $Q_{Isource}$, and the corresponding quantities at the drain end of the channel ($y = L$) by φ_{surfL} and Q_{Idrain}, then by integrating from $y = 0$ to $y = L$ we get

$$\int_0^L I_D \, dy = \mu Z \int_{\varphi_{surf0}}^{\varphi_{surfL}} (-Q_I) \, d\varphi_{surf} + \frac{\mu Z kT}{q} \int_{Q_{I,source}}^{Q_{I,drain}} dQ_I \qquad (4-47)$$

or

$$I_D = \frac{\mu Z}{L} \int_{\varphi_{surf0}}^{\varphi_{surfL}} (-Q_I) \, d\varphi_{surf} + \frac{\mu Z kT}{Lq} \int_{Q_{I,source}}^{Q_{I,drain}} dQ_I \qquad (4-48)$$

To perform the integrals in Eq. 4-47 and 4-48 we require an expression relating Q_I and φ_{surf}. Equation 4-6 derived in section 4.2.2.1 is the appropriate expression we seek, and is repeated here

$$Q_I = -C_{ox}(V_{GB} - V_{FB} - \varphi_{surf} - \gamma \sqrt{\varphi_{surf}}) \qquad (4-49)$$

Using this in Eq. 4-48 for the drift current component of the drain current, performing the integration from φ_{surf0} to φ_{surfL}, we get the following expression for I_{Ddrift}

$$I_{Ddrift} = (\mu C_{ox} Z/L) [(V_{GB} - V_{FB})(\varphi_{surfL} - \varphi_{surf0}) - (1/2)(\varphi_{surfL}^2 - \varphi_{surf0}^2)$$

$$- (2/3) \gamma (\varphi_{surfL}^{3/2} - \varphi_{surf0}^{3/2}) \qquad (4-50)$$

Using Eq. 4-49 for Q_I (in which we let $\varphi_{surf} = \varphi_{surf0}$ at the source and φ_{surfL} at the drain when we compute the values of Q_I at the limits of integration), in the term of Eq. 4-48 for I_{Ddiff}, we get

$$I_{Ddiff} = (\mu C_{ox} Z/L)(kT/q)(\varphi_{surfL} - \varphi_{surf0}) + (kT/q) \gamma (\varphi^{1/2}_{surfL} - \varphi^{1/2}_{surf0}) \qquad (4-51)$$

The last step needed when computing I_D with this model is to determine φ_{surf0} and φ_{surfL} from the terminal voltages V_{GB}, V_{SB}, and V_{DB}. It turns out that Eq. 4-4 is the appropriate expression for this task if φ_{surf} and V_{CB} are replaced with φ_{surf0} and V_{SB} at the source end of the channel, and with φ_{surfL} and V_{DB} at the drain end. Then we get

$$\varphi_{surf0} = V_{GB} - V_{FB} - \gamma\sqrt{\varphi_{surf0} + \varphi_t \, e^{(\varphi_{surf0} - 2\varphi_B - V_{SB})/\varphi_t}} \qquad (4-52a)$$

$$\varphi_{surfL} = V_{GB} - V_{FB} - \gamma\sqrt{\varphi_{surfL} + \varphi_t \, e^{(\varphi_{surfL} - 2\varphi_B - V_{DB})/\varphi_t}} \qquad (4-52b)$$

These equations for φ_{surf0} and φ_{surfL} however, are relatively complex transcendental equations which must be solved by iterative techniques to find φ_{surf0} and φ_{surfL}.

Now, I_D predicted by the charge-sheet model is a single expression given by the sum of Eqs. 4-50 and 4-51.

$$I_D \text{(charge sheet)} = I_{Ddrift} \text{ (Eq. 4-50)} + I_{Ddiff} \text{ (Eq. 4-51)} \qquad (4-53)$$

Experimental MOSFET characteristics are observed to agree very well with such predictions.

4.5.4 Variable Depletion-Charge (or Bulk-Charge) Model

As just described, the charge-sheet model for I_D in its full form includes drift and diffusion current components, making it accurate over the MOSFET operating regimes from weak to strong inversion. However, the fact that neither Eq. 4-50 nor 4-51 is explicitly expressed in terms of the terminal voltages makes the full charge-sheet formulation too cumbersome for use in circuit design applications.

Nevertheless, it is possible to simplify the charge-sheet model formulation to obtain analytical expressions that explicitly give I_D in terms of the terminal voltages. The price for such simplicity (while maintaining adequate accuracy) is that the resulting equations are only accurate over a limited operating range. Specifically, instead of being required to evaluate I_D from Eq. 4-53 (which is a single, relatively complex equation, valid from weak to strong inversion), we develop two less complex approximations to Eq. 4-53, one which is only valid over the weak inversion regime (subthreshold), and the other only over the strong inversion regime. In this section we derive the strong-inversion approximation to Eq. 4-53, which is termed the *variable-depletion-charge* or *bulk-charge* model, and was developed in 1964.[9] In section 4.7 we develop the simplified I_D equation valid for weak inversion. Note that in both of these models the charge-sheet and depletion approximations are still invoked.

We begin the derivation of the strong-inversion model by recalling that once a MOSFET is biased beyond the point of strong inversion, the diffusion current component of I_D is negligible compared to the drift current component; thus we can approximate I_D with only the drift current term of Eq. 4-53. In addition, we assume that beyond the onset of strong inversion φ_{surf} remains fixed. That is, the surface potential at the source and drain ends of the channel in strong inversion is assumed to be clamped at the value possessed at the onset of strong inversion. In that case, φ_{surf} can be approximated as

$$\varphi_{surf0} \approx 2\varphi_B + V_{SB} \qquad (4-54a)$$

and

$$\varphi_{surfL} \approx 2\varphi_B + V_{DB} \qquad (4-54b)$$

The final approximation we use to derive the variable-depletion-charge model is that if V_{GS} is biased below strong inversion (i.e., $V_{GS} < V_T$), I_D is assumed to be zero.

Invoking these approximations, I_D in a MOSFET can now be approximated by Eq. 4-50, with the values of φ_{surfo} and φ_{surfL} in this equation given by Eqs. 4-54a and 4-54b. Thus, by substituting these into Eq. 4-50 we get

$$I_D = \frac{\mu\, C_{ox}\, Z}{L}(V_{GB} - V_{FB})(V_{DB} - V_{SB}) - \frac{1}{2}[(V_{DB} + 2\varphi_B)^2 - (V_{SB} + 2\varphi_B)^2]$$

$$- \frac{2}{3}\gamma[(V_{DB} + 2\varphi_B)^{3/2} - (V_{SB} + 2\varphi_B)^{3/2}] \qquad (4-55)$$

By rearranging terms, this equation becomes

$$I_D = \frac{\mu\, C_{ox}\, Z}{L}(V_{GB} - V_{FB} - 2\varphi_B)(V_{DB} - V_{SB}) - \frac{1}{2}[(V_{DB}^2 - V_{SB}^2)$$

$$- \frac{2}{3}\gamma[(V_{DB} + 2\varphi_B)^{3/2} - (V_{SB} + 2\varphi_B)^{3/2}] \qquad (4-56)$$

We observe that I_D is now explicitly expressed in terms of the terminal voltages V_{GB}, V_{DB}, and V_{SB}. To put Eq. 4-56 into a form in terms of V_{GS}, V_{DS}, and V_{BS}, we recall that $V_{GB} = V_{GS} + V_{BS}$ and $V_{DB} = V_{DS} + V_{BS}$. This allows us to rewrite Eq. 4-56 as

$$I_D = \frac{\mu\, C_{ox}\, Z}{L}(V_{GS} - V_{FB} - 2\varphi_B)V_{DS} - \frac{1}{2}V_{DS}^2$$

$$- \frac{2}{3}\gamma\,[(V_{DS} + V_{BS} + 2\varphi_B)^{3/2} - (V_{BS} + 2\varphi_B)^{3/2}] \qquad (4-57)$$

If $V_{BS} = 0V$, Eq. 4-57 becomes

$$I_D = \frac{\mu\, C_{ox}\, Z}{L}(V_{GS} - V_{FB} - 2\varphi_B)V_{DS} - \frac{1}{2}V_{DS}^2 - \frac{2}{3}\gamma(2\varphi_B + V_{DS})^{3/2} - (2\varphi_B)^{3/2} \qquad (4-58)$$

Equation 4-57 (and 4-58) is sometimes referred to as the *Ihantola and Moll model*, since it was initially developed by them in 1964.[9] The name *variable-depletion charge model* signifies that the model computes Q_I as the difference between Q_C and Q_B (*bulk* charge), taking into account the variation of the depletion region width along the channel to compute Q_B. We will see that the square-law model assumes the depletion region width is constant from source to drain.

Equation 4-57 predicts that for a given V_{GS} the drain current first increases linearly with V_{DS} (the *linear* regime), then gradually levels off, approaching a saturated value (the *saturation* regime). Thus, it behaves quantitatively as depicted by the basic output characteristic of the idealized MOSFET of Fig. 4-11.

We noted in section 4.4.2 that as V_{DS} is increased, the output characteristic levels off. This leveling off occurs because as V_{DS} increases, the channel near the drain is driven toward pinch off. In terms of the gradual channel approximation, pinch off is the point at which Q_I drops to zero. (In fact, once Q_I gets very small, the gradual channel approximation breaks down and Eq. 4-57 no longer applies.) When the V_{DS} reaches the value at which pinch off has been reached, the measured I_D value in long-channel MOSFETs *saturates*. That is, it becomes essentially constant as V_{DS} is increased further. The I_D value at that point is denoted as I_{Dsat}. Although Eq. 4-57 is no longer valid for this regime, we use the maximum value of I_D found using Eq. 4-57 as I_{Dsat}. We denote the V_{DS} value to just reach this condition as $V_{DS,sat}$.

Since $V_{DS,sat}$ is the V_{DS} value when I_D reaches its maximum, such a maximum can be found by setting $dI_D/dV_{DS} = 0$ from Eq. 4-57 and solving for $V_{DS} = V_{DS,sat}$

$$V_{DSsat} = V_{GS} - V_{FB} - 2\varphi_B + \frac{\gamma^2}{2} - \gamma\sqrt{V_{GS} - V_{FB} + V_{BS} + \frac{\gamma^2}{4}} \qquad (4 - 59)$$

The value of $V_{DS,sat}$ obtained from Eq. 4-59 is used in Eq. 4-57 to calculate I_{Dsat}.

Note that the linear and saturation regimes of MOSFET operation have been defined. Since we also assume in this model that $I_D = 0$ for $V_{GS} < V_T$, we define this bias range as the *cutoff* regime. In fact, a small but nonzero drain current exists even when $V_{GS} < V_T$, so it is more appropriate to refer to this regime as the *subthreshold* regime. Further details on this regime are given in section 4.7.

4.5.5 Square-Law Model

Equation 4-57 predicts I_D values in long-channel MOSFETs (operated in strong inversion) quite accurately. However, even this formulation is mathematically too complex for use in hand calculations. Furthermore, when it is necessary to simulate the circuit behavior of digital IC circuits containing a large number of MOSFETs, using Eq. 4-57 in SPICE significantly slows the simulation time. For such applications, a simplified version of Eq. 4-57 could be useful, even at the expense of somewhat less accuracy. This can be obtained if $2\varphi_B + V_{BS} >> V_{DS}$. In this case, we can use the binomial expansion to get

$$(2\varphi_B + V_{SB} + V_{DS})^{3/2} = (2\varphi_B + V_{SB})^{3/2} \left(1 + \frac{V_{DS}}{2\varphi_B + V_{SB}}\right)^{1/2} \qquad (4 - 60)$$

$$\approx (2\varphi_B + V_{SB})^{3/2} + \frac{3}{2}(2\varphi_B + V_{SB})^{1/2} V_{DS} \qquad (4 - 61)$$

Thus,

$$I_D = \frac{\mu C_{ox} Z}{L}\left(V_{GB} - V_{FB} - 2\varphi_B - [2\kappa_{si}\varepsilon_0 N_A (2\varphi_B + V_{BS})/C_{ox}]^{1/2} - V_{DS}/2\right)V_{DS} \qquad (4 - 62)$$

which can be written more succinctly as

$$I_D = [\mu C_{ox} Z/L] (V_{GB} - V_T - V_{DS}/2)V_{DS} \qquad V_{GS} \geq V_T \qquad (4 - 63a)$$

$$V_{DS} \leq (V_{GS} - V_T)$$

since $V_T = V_{FB} + 2\varphi_B + [2\kappa_{si}\varepsilon_0 N_A(2\varphi_B + V_{BS})/C_{ox}]^{1/2}$. Or, Eq. 4-63a can be written in an even more compact way (again assuming that $V_{BS} = 0$, in which case $V_{GB} = V_{GS}$), as

$$I_D = k [(V_{GS} - V_T)V_{DS} - V_{DS}^2/2] \qquad (4 - 63b)$$

where k (the so-called device transconductance parameter) is defined as

$$k = \mu C_{ox} Z/L \qquad (4 - 64)$$

For very small V_{DS} values, Eq. 4-63 can be further approximated as

$$I_D = k (V_{GS} - V_T) V_{DS} \qquad (4 - 65)$$

For $2\varphi_B + V_{SB} >> V_{DS}$, the condition for saturation becomes

$$- C_{ox} (V_{GS} - V_{FB} - 2\varphi_B - V_{DS,sat}) + (2\kappa_{si}\varepsilon_0 qN_A[2\varphi_B + V_{BS}])^{1/2} = 0 \qquad (4 - 66)$$

so

$$V_{DS,sat} \approx V_{GS} - V_T \qquad (4 - 67)$$

In saturation, I_D in this model is given by Eq. 4-62 evaluated at $V_{DS} = V_{DS,sat}$; that is

$$I_{Dsat} = k/2 (V_{GS} - V_T)^2 \qquad V_{GS} \geq V_T: \qquad (4 - 68)$$

$$V_{DS} > (V_{GS} - V_T)$$

Since Eq. 4-68 predicts that I_{Dsat} will vary as the square of the gate voltage above threshold, Eq. 4-62 is termed the *square-law model*.

Equation 4-68 is often used as the basis for measuring V_T. In this technique, the gate and drain of the transistor are tied together as shown in Fig. 4-16, and then the drain current is measured as a function of applied drain voltage. Because V_{DS} is set equal to V_{GS} in this circuit, the transistor is in the saturated region of operation. Now a plot of

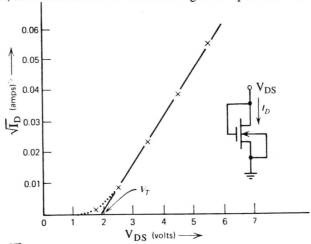

Fig. 4-16 Plot of $\sqrt{I_D}$ versus V_{DS} for n-channel MOSFET in saturation. Inset shows the circuit arrangement. The threshold voltage is indicated by the intercept of the straight line with the voltage axis.

$\sqrt{I_D}$ versus V_{GS} should be a straight line with a voltage axis intercept equal to V_T. In fact, plotting $\sqrt{I_D}$ versus V_{GS} is the most widely used method of determining V_T, yielding as will be discussed in section 4.6, the so-called *extrapolated threshold voltage* value.

From a physical perspective the square-law model can be derived by approximating that the channel depletion region has a constant width along the entire length of the channel (with a value equal to that near the source), even under $V_{DS} \neq 0$ biasing. This approximation is somewhat reasonable in strong inversion since the last term in the strong-inversion form of Q_I (Eq. 4-10), namely $[\sqrt{2\kappa_{si}\varepsilon_0 q N_A}\ (2\varphi_B + V_{ChB})]$, is small compared to the other terms. Since it is the only term that depends on the depletion-region charge, and this charge is much smaller than the mobile charge concentration under strong inversion, the variation of this term will not change the value of Q_I much. That is, as long as the channel region remains inverted, Q_I does not vary much from the source to the drain ends of the channel. Hence, approximating this term by a constant value (namely with the charge that would exist if the depletion region had a constant width, equal to the value it at has at the source end) does not change the value of Q_I significantly. Yet it results in a much simpler form of the I_D model.

At the source the depletion region width is d_{max}(source), which can be calculated from Eq. 4-8

$$d_{max}\ (source) = \ [2\kappa_{si}\varepsilon_0(2\varphi_B + V_{BS})/qN_A]^{1/2} \qquad (4\text{-}69)$$

Then

$$Q_B \ = \ [2\kappa_{si}\varepsilon_0 N_A(2\varphi_B + V_{SB}]^{1/2} \qquad (4\text{-}70)$$

and using Eq. 4-10

$$Q_I \ = \ - C_{ox}[V_{GB} - V_{FB} - 2\varphi_B - V_{ChB} - \gamma(2\varphi_B + V_{BS})^{1/2}]$$

$$= \ - C_{ox}[V_{GB} - V_T \ - V_{ChB}) \qquad (4\text{-}71)$$

Thus,

$$I_D \ = \ \frac{\mu\ C_{ox}\ Z}{L} \int_{V_{SB}}^{V_{SB} + V_{DS}} (V_{GB} - V_T - V_{ChB})\ dV_{ChB} \qquad (4\text{-}72)$$

Integrating 4-72 from source to drain gives 4-62.

4.5.6 Comparison of the Four MOSFET Circuit Models

Let us summarize the characteristics of the four long-channel MOSFET dc circuit models just described, and make some further comparisons about their relative accuracies and utility. Recall first off that all are based on the long-channel (GCA) approximation.

The most general and accurate of the models is the *Pao-Sah* model. While it retains the gradual-channel approximation, it does not invoke the depletion approximation and permits carrier transport in the channel by both drift and diffusion current. The formulation of the I_D equation it develops is therefore quite general, but also requires numerical integrations in two dimensions. Such numerical complexity has limited the role of this model role to theoretical analyses of the MOSFET. As a result the other three MOSFET models are more frequently used to calculate the I_D-V_{DS} characteristics.

The *charge sheet* model allows I_D to be calculated with much less computational effort than that of the Pao-Sah model and yet provides I_D values very close to those predicted by the more complex model over the regime of inversion (both weak and strong). The accuracy of the charge-sheet model when compared to measured dc I_D-V_{DS} characteristics of a MOSFET in inversion is about 1% or better. This model calculates the surface potential by solving the Poisson equation assuming the depletion approximation and the charge-sheet approximation. It also assumes that both drift and diffusion current can contribute to I_D. While not applicable to the depletion and accumulation regimes of operation, it is valid over all regimes of inversion. Although it accurately predicts I_D over these regions of operation, it requires values of the surface potential to be calculated at the source and drain ends of the channel. These equations for φ_{surf} are complex transcendental equations that require iterative techniques to solve them. As a result, the computational effort for determining I_D is still too great for most circuit simulation applications, and thus the charge sheet model has not been incorporated into such popular circuit simulation programs as SPICE.*

Since the charge-sheet model is too complex to be used in most circuit simulation applications, the simpler bulk-charge and square law models are used instead. They both assume that the MOSFET is biased to strong inversion, and that only drift current contributes to I_D. As long as the MOSFET is biased into strong inversion (V_H in Fig. 4-17) the results of the bulk-charge I_D equation agree very well with the charge-sheet model results. That is, to allow the simpler analytical expressions of the bulk-charge (Eqs. 4-57 and 4-59) and square-law models (Eqs. 4-63 and 4-68) to be used to accurately calculate I_D, the allowable regime of operation must be reduced to the strong-inversion regime. If the MOSFET is operated in weak inversion, an alternate analytical expression (as derived in section 4.7) must be used to get an accurate value of I_D in long-channel MOSFETs.

When comparing the utility of the *bulk-charge* and *square-law* models, the primary asset of the square-law model is its simplicity. It provides good insight into the device operation and is useful for obtaining first-order design data without an excessive amount of mathematical entanglement, particularly for the case of digital circuits. Most hand calculations for circuit design with MOSFETs therefore make use of the square-law model. It is also the model used for the simplest (Level-1) analyses of circuits containing MOSFETs in the SPICE program. The apparently arbitrary adjustment of k

---

* Note that the bulk-charge and square-law MOSFET models assume that the surface potential at inversion is fixed at $2\varphi_B + V_{CB}$. In reality this is the value of φ_{surf} at which the surface just enters strong inversion. If the electron charge in the channel is substantial, the surface potential must be greater than this value (but not much more than a few kT above $2\varphi_B + V_{CB}$). Nevertheless, both these models must therefore consistently underestimate the φ_{surf}.

Now, if φ_{surf} is underestimated, so is the magnitude of the depletion region charge Q_B. If Q_B is underestimated, then from Eq. 4-1b Q_I must be overestimated. The bulk charge model therefore consistently overestimates the amount of mobile electron charge in the channel, and thus overestimates the drain current - fortunately by less than 10 percent in most cases.

The charge sheet model, on the other hand does not make the above assumption, but instead calculates φ_{surf}. Hence, this error is avoided in the charge-sheet model approach.

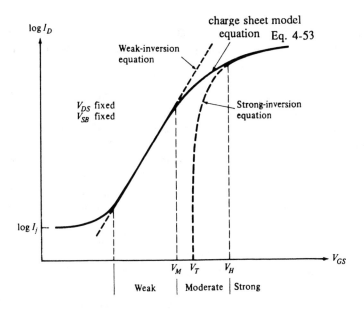

Fig. 4-17 Log I_D versus V_{GS} for fixed V_{DS} and V_{BS}, and comparison to weak- and strong-inversion equations.[5] Reprinted with permission of McGraw-Hill Book Co.

mentioned above is also not a practical problem since MOS processing procedures do not allow for the precise control of μ_n, and the parameter must be extracted from measurements.

There are many cases of circuit design for which the increased accuracy of the bulk-charge model is not necessarily an advantage when computational complexity is considered. Often, for example, the designer is interested only in MOSFET operation in the saturated region (i.e., only the value of I_{Dsat} is needed). To obtain I_{Dsat} from the bulk-charge model, it is first necessary to calculate V_{DSsat} from Eq. 4-59 and then use this voltage value in Eq. 4-58 to calculate I_{Dsat}. This lengthy process is greatly simplified in the square-law model in which I_{Dsat} is calculated directly from Eq. 4-68.

The bulk-charge model is used when more accurate modeling of circuit behavior is needed. Measurements of I_D versus V_{DS} characteristics of long-channel MOSFETs are in reasonable agreement with the predictions of this model (i.e., usually within 10% of the measured data). However, the computational complexity is considerably increased, and hence it is typically implemented only in computer analyses. This model is available as the Level-2 model of the MOSFET in SPICE. Note that when comparing Eqs. 4-57 and 4-59 with 4-63 and 4-68, the added terms in the bulk-charge model equations are always negative and act primarily to reduce I_D and V_{DSsat} for a given set of operational conditions.

A plot of I_D versus V_{DS} (with V_{GS} as a parameter) for a long-channel NMOS transistor calculated using both models is shown in Fig. 4-18. As can be seen the square-law model predicts larger values of I_{Dsat} and V_{DSsat} for each value of gate voltage. The general behavior of both sets of curves is, however, similar. Note especially that in the linear region of operation both models give the same results, but that in saturation - for the same value of k in both models - the bulk-charge model predicts a smaller value of I_{Dsat}.

4.5.6.1 MOSFET Models of the SPICE Circuit Simulator.

The SPICE circuit simulator contains four MOSFET models which differ in the way they formulate the I-V characteristic. The simplest is the Level-1 model which is based on the rudimentary square-law model (Equations 4-63 and 4-68), with empirical adjustment. The most important adjustment it employs is the use of a coefficient in these equations to bring I_{Dsat} into congruence with experiment and the more accurate models. That is, to obtain satisfactory results in circuit analysis and design using this model, measured data on samples of MOSFETs must be obtained. Measured data is fitted to the threshold voltage equation and Eqs. 4-63 and 4-65. Specifically V_T and k are determined from data obtained as shown in Fig. 4-16. Note that the extrapolated threshold voltage value V_{T0} is used in SPICE because it is obtained by extrapolating the experimental curve of $\sqrt{I_D}$ versus V_{DS} (with $V_{DS} = V_{GS}$) to zero drain current. The subscript "0" in the V_{T0} symbol signifies that this is the extrapolated threshold voltage when $V_{BS} = 0V$.

The more-accurate Level-2 SPICE MOSFET model is based on the bulk-charge model equations (Eqs. 4-57 and 4-59). The Level-2 model also incorporates an approximate[*]

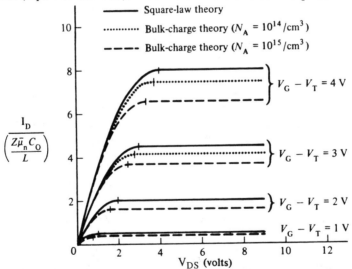

Fig. 4-18 Theoretical predictions of I_D versus V_{DS} using the bulk-charge model equations (solid lines) and the square-law model equations (dashed lines). I_D is taken to be equal to I_{Dsat} for $V_{DS} > V_{DSsat}$.[30] Reprinted with permission of Addison-Wesley.

---

[*] For example, in the Level-2 MOSFET model, the carrier mobility is not treated as a constant. Instead, the mobility is modeled as being impacted by the gate-induced electric field (see chap. 5). The value used in the Level-2 model μ_{eff} is found using the expression Eq. 5-26.

treatment of some of the short-channel effects discussed in chap. 5 and is capable of computing the subthreshold current (in the manner as described in section 4.7).

The basic device structure parameters required to describe a MOSFET when using either the Level-1 or Level-2 model are the substrate doping, the gate oxide thickness, and the channel length and width. SPICE computes the threshold voltage from N_A (NSUB in SPICE) and t_{ox} using Eq. 4-12 (assuming $V_{FB} = 0$). Alternatively, the threshold voltage (for the case of $V_{SB} = 0$) can be input directly by supplying a value to the model parameter V_{T0}, in which case the internally computed threshold voltage is overridden.

The Level-2 SPICE MOSFET model, being based on the bulk-charge MOSFET model, has a three-halves-power dependence of I_D, rather than the square-law dependence of the Level-1 SPICE MOSFET model. Because the numerical handling of a fractional power requires significantly more computation time than if a power in integer form must be computed, circuit designers sought a model that was more accurate than the Level-1 model, but was faster to execute than the Level-2 model. Hence, the Level-3 model was developed and incorporated into SPICE.[*]

The Level-3 model not only removed the computational shortcoming of the Level-2 model, but was formulated to deal empirically with many other effects as well, including short-channel and narrow-channel effects. In fact, the Level-3 model represents an attempt to pursue a semi-empirical modeling approach, i.e., which only approximates device physics and relies on the proper choice of the empirical parameters to accurately reproduce device characteristics. As a result, a more physically based short-channel MOSFET model has also been developed for SPICE, known as the Berkeley Short-channel IGFET Model (BSIM). It has been implemented into the SPICE program as the Level-4 MOSFET model. We will describe BSIM in more detail in chap. 5.

4.5.6.2 SPICE Models of the MOSFET Operated in Saturation. As

we noted in section 4.4.2, the value of I_D may increase as V_{DS} exceeds the pinchoff voltage value V_{DSsat}. This was modeled by assuming that the pinched-off region with a length ΔL makes the channel length appear shorter (i.e., $L - \Delta L$). To predict I_D as V_{DS} exceeds V_{DSsat} the value of ΔL is needed. In the Level-1 and Level-2 MOSFET models

---

[*] The I_D equation that constitutes the dc long-channel Level-3 model of the MOSFET[10] in the SPICE program is derived from Eq. 4-57 by employing a three-term binomial-series expansion for the second term in Eq. 4-57. This yields the Level-3 MOSFET equation for I_D in the form:

$$I_D = \frac{\mu\, C_{ox} Z}{L} \left[(V_{GS} - V_T) V_{DS} - \left(\frac{1}{2} + \frac{\sqrt{\varepsilon_0 q\, N_A / (-\varphi_B)}}{4\, C_{ox}} \right) V_{DS}^2 \right]$$

Notice by comparing it to the Level-1 expression, Eq. 4-63, that it differs only in the last term, a change that accounts for the ionic-charge variations that were ignored in the Level-1 model. Here, however, the square root term is only dependent on device structure parameters and not on V_{DS}, and hence this square-root term only needs to be evaluated once when calculating the I_D-V_{DS} characteristics.

SPICE offers two possible approaches to calculating ΔL. The first allows the *channel-length modulation parameter*, λ (LAMBDA) to be specified, in which case ΔL is obtained from the simple empirical expression $\Delta L = $ LAMBDA $\cdot$ V_{DS}. LAMBDA can be used in either the Level-1 or Level-2 model. The value of LAMBDA is typically in the range of 0.1 to 0.01 V^{-1}. Empirical values of $1/\lambda$ can be obtained by finding an approximate intercept with the V_{DS} axis of tangents to the I_D curves beyond V_{DSsat} in measured I_D-V_{DS} curves.

If the value of LAMBDA is not specified in the Level-2 model, however, then ΔL is computed by using Eq. 5-47, which is based on the 1-D Reddi-Sah model of the MOSFET operated in saturation (see chap. 5, section 5.4.3.1).

4.6 THRESHOLD-VOLTAGE CONTROL IN MOSFETS

4.6.1 Measuring Threshold Voltage

Equation 4-1 calculates V_T of real MOSFETs based on various device parameters. Yet, when devices are fabricated, they must be tested to ensure that the desired characteristics have been produced. Two approaches are used to obtain the V_T values of MOSFETs from measurements. The first yields an *extrapolated-V_T* value, and the second, a *constant-current-V_T* value.

As described in section 4.5.5, the extrapolated V_T is determined by connecting the drain and gate of a MOSFET together and measuring the drain current as a function of gate voltage (Fig. 4-16). Equation 4-68 predicts that a plot of $\sqrt{I_D}$ (with a linear I_D axis) versus V_{GS} should be linear. If $\sqrt{I_D}$ is plotted vs. V_{GS}, and the linear portion of the curve is extrapolated to intercept the voltage axis (corresponding to the condition that $V_{GS} = V_T$ in Eq. 4-68) the extrapolated-V_T value is yielded. (Note that the dotted section of the curve in Fig. 4-16 results from currents that flow below the threshold voltage. Such *subthreshold currents* are discussed in section 4.7.)

The constant-current-V_T is obtained by measuring the gate voltage at which a specific small drain current flows and this gate voltage is defined as V_T. For active MOSFETs, the gate voltage at which 1 μA of drain current flows per μm of drain width for $V_{DS} = $ 0.5V is the most common criterion applied when specifying constant-current-V_T. The constant-current-V_T is generally measured in the IC production environment, while the extrapolated V_T is preferred when the threshold voltage parameter is needed for circuit simulation (e.g., in a SPICE analysis). Note also that the extrapolated V_T is typically 100 mV larger than the 1 $\mu A/\mu m$ constant-current V_T.

4.6.2 Adjusting Threshold Voltage

As pointed out earlier, in many MOS IC applications it is critical to be able to establish and maintain a uniform and stable V_T. The factors that impact V_T are given in Eq. 3-72. An examination of each term will reveal the device parameters that can be adjusted to provide practical control of V_T.

The φ_{ms} term depends on the work-function difference between the gate, $q\varphi_m$(gate), and the semiconductor, $q\varphi_B$ (sub). While $q\varphi_m$(gate) for metal and heavily doped silicon gates is constant, the parameter ϕ_B (sub) depends on the substrate doping - but only in a logarithmic manner. Hence, each factor-of-10 increase in substrate doping will change the ϕ_{ms} term by only 2.3 kT/q, or ~0.06 V (kT/q = 0.026 V at 300K). Thus, changes in the substrate-doping concentration produce changes in V_T through the ϕ_{ms} term which are too small to provide the required degree of threshold-voltage control. The next term ($2\phi_B$) also changes only slightly as a result of changes in the substrate doping concentration (for the same reason given for the ϕ_{ms} term); thus, the $2\phi_B$ term is also ineffective for controlling V_T.

Since every attempt is made to keep Q_{tot} as low as possible through various processing procedures, and C_{ox} is relatively large (since t_{ox} is very thin in submicron MOSFETs), the Q_{tot}/C_{ox} term is also very small in modern MOSFETs. Hence, this term must also be ruled out as a candidate for controlling V_T.

While is true that C_{ox} could be varied (primarily by changing t_{ox}), this is not a practical approach to controlling V_T in active devices, since t_{ox} is normally made as thin as possible to maximize I_D. (In the field regions, however, large V_{TF} values are needed to prevent inversion under the field oxide. A thick field oxide makes C_{ox} small, allowing V_{TF} to be increased Thus, C_{ox} is one of the parameters normally used to control V_{TF} in the field regions of the circuits.)

This leaves the $2\sqrt{\kappa_{si}\varepsilon_0 q N_{sub}\phi_B}/C_{ox}$ term as the remaining candidate for controlling V_T in active devices. Since the change of V_T in this term depends on $\sqrt{N_{sub}}$, it indicates that V_T control is possible by exploiting this effect. In fact, Eq. 3-72 indicates that increasing the substrate doping (i.e., N_A in n-channel devices, and N_D in p-channel devices) will increase V_T. Figure 4-19 shows how V_T varies in MOSFETs (both PMOS and NMOS) with substrate doping concentration (assuming the substrate is uniformly doped - i.e., no threshold adjust implant is used - and that $Q_{tot} = 0$), for various gate-oxide thicknesses.

Merely increasing the substrate doping, however, is not desirable since it will adversely impact other MOSFET characteristics, such as lower junction-breakdown voltages, larger junction capacitances, and lower carrier mobilities. Yet, prior to the development of ion implantation in the early 1970s, adjustment of substrate doping was the only practical *processing* approach for significantly controlling V_T in active devices.

We showed earlier that a *circuit* approach based on applying a bias between the source and body (and hence known as body biasing) can also control V_T (section 4.2.2.2, Eq. 4-12). Generally, an increase in V_{BS} will raise V_T. Figure 4-20 gives an example of how the application of V_{BS} can change the V_T value in an NMOS device. The intercept of the channel conductance and the V_{GS} axis when $V_{BS} = 0$ in this example is +0.99V. As V_{BS} is increased from 0V to -5V, V_T increases up to +2.3V. However, body biasing is an added complication, and is now avoided whenever possible as a technique for adjusting V_T, in favor of the ion implantation V_T-adjust method.

4.6.3 Ion Implantation for Adjusting Threshold Voltage

The development of ion implantation for V_T adjustment removed the last obstacle to reliable production of n-channel devices for MOS ICs, as this procedure made it possible to select the substrate-doping value without having to consider its impact on V_T. That

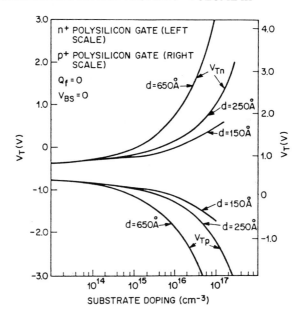

Fig. 4-19 Calculated threshold voltages of n-channel (V_{Tn}) and p-channel (V_{Tp}) transistors as a function of their substrate's doping, assuming n^+ polysilicon gate (left scale) and p^+ polysilicon (right scale). Curves for gate oxide thicknesses t_{ox} of 150 Å, 250 Å, and 650 Å are shown. From S. M. Sze, Ed., VLSI Technology, 2nd. Ed., Chap. 11, "VLSI Process Integration." Copyright, 1988 Bell Telephone Laboratories. Reprinted with permission of McGraw-Hill.

is, implantation can be used either to increase or to decrease (by compensation) the net dopant concentration at the silicon surface. As a result, substrate doping can be selected strictly on the basis of optimum device performance since V_T can now be set by the V_T-

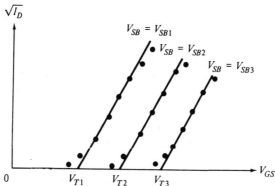

Fig. 4-20 Plot of $\sqrt{I_D}$ vs. V_{DS} for an NMOSFET showing the effects of a bias V_{BS} between the source and the substrate. The observed shift in the threshold is predicted by Eq. 3-71.[16] Reprinted with permission of John Wiley & Sons.

adjust implant process. In addition, since dopants can be selectively implanted into the *field regions*, high-performance NMOS circuits can be fabricated on lightly doped substrates, without the possibility of inadvertent inversion of the surrounding field regions.

As mentioned earlier, the V_T-adjust-implant technique involves implantation of boron, phosphorus, or arsenic ions into the regions under the gate oxide of a MOSFET. Boron implantation produces a positive shift in V_T, while phosphorus or arsenic implantation causes a negative shift. For shallow implants, the procedure has essentially the same effect as placing an additional sheet of "fixed" charge at the SiO_2-Si interface.

To first order, if the implant and substrate are of the same type (e.g., boron into a *p*-substrate), and the effective depth of the implant x_i (see Fig. 4-21) is less than d_{max}, the threshold-voltage change (ΔV_T) can be reasonably well estimated from[11]

$$\Delta V_T \text{ (II)} = q \, D_I / C_{ox} \qquad (4 - 73)$$

Example 4-1: If the V_T of a uniformly doped NMOS transistor is -0.41V and it is to be used in an application that requires a $V_T = 1.0V$, calculate the B dose (to first order) needed to adjust $V_{T(nud,lc)}$ to this value.

Solution: The $V_{T(ud,lc)}$ of the device is -0.41 V. We wish to have a V_T of 1.0 V. Thus, the threshold voltage must be shifted (ΔV_T) by +1.41 V. Using Eq. 4-73, we see that the boron dose needed to cause this ΔV_T is

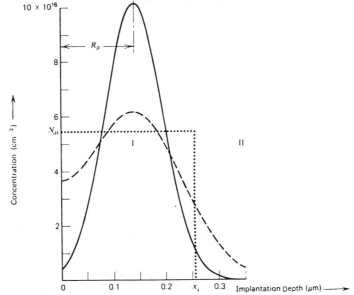

Fig. 4-21 Distribution of the implanted dopant (solid curve) as-implanted, and after activating anneal and diffusions (dashed curve). The dotted "box" curve shows the distribution used to calculate the threshold voltage. (After Rideout, Gaensllen & LeBlanc in ref. 27.)

$$D_I = \Delta V_T(II) \, C_{ox}/q = [1.41V \times 2.3 \times 10^{-7} \, F/cm^2]/1.6 \times 10^{-19} \, C$$

$$= 2.1 \times 10^{12} \text{ boron atoms } /cm^2.$$

where D_I is the dose of the implanted ions (atoms/cm^2) which penetrate into the silicon. For example, Eq. 4-73 predicts that when $D_I = 5 \times 10^{11}$ ions/cm^2 and $t_{ox} = 25$ nm, a shift in V_T of 0.58 V will be produced. Thus, Eq. 3-72 must be modified to account for threshold-adjust implants, as (where *nud* stands for non-uniformly doped)

$$V_{T(nud,lc)} = V_{T(ud,lc)} + \Delta V_T(II) \tag{4-74}$$

A more exact formula for calculating for V_T in this case (assuming $V_{BS} = 0$) is[12,13,14]

$$V_{T(nud,lc)} = V_{FB} + 2\varphi_B + qD_I/C_{ox} + \gamma_2 (\sqrt{2\varphi_B + qD_I x_i /2\kappa_{si}\varepsilon_0}) \tag{4-75}$$

where

$$\gamma_2 = (\sqrt{2q\kappa_{si}\varepsilon_0 N_A})/C_{ox} \tag{4-76}$$

The V_T-adjust implant is often done through an oxide layer.* The implant energy is selected to place the peak of the implant slightly below the oxide-silicon interface (Fig. 4-21). After the implant-activating anneal, the implanted distribution is broader than the as-implanted profile.

Calculating the effect of the implant on V_T is greatly simplified by approximating the actual distribution via a "box" distribution, as is also shown in Fig. 4-21 (in which the implanted dopant is assumed to have a constant density N_A' from the surface to the depth x_i.) Figure 4-22 plots V_T vs. effective implant depth x_i, and we can see that V_T does not change much as x_i is varied. Since the second term under the square root in Eq. 4-75 is the only one that depends on x_i, if we ignore it when calculating V_T the results are still adequate for many applications. Thus, the first-order approximation of ΔV_T given by Eq. 4-73 is useful for hand calculations of $V_{T(nud,lc)}$.

Another slightly more complicated approach to calculating V_T for this case is to solve the Poisson equation using a high-low step doping profile, which results in an effective concentration N_{eff} given by[28]

$$N_{eff} = N_A' \frac{\varphi_s}{\varphi_i} \left[1 - \frac{N_A}{N_A'} + \frac{N_A'}{N_A} \sqrt{1 + \frac{N_A}{N_A'} \left(\frac{\varphi_s}{\varphi_i} - 1 \right)} \right]^2 \tag{4-77}$$

where $\varphi_s = kT/q \, [\ln (N_A'N_A/n_i^2)]$ and $\varphi_i = qN_A'x_i^2/2\kappa_{si}\varepsilon_0$. Here φ_i is the potential corresponding to x_i of the step profile. N_{eff} is then substituted for N_A in the body effect coefficient term γ of Eq. 4-12, and then Eq. 4-12 with this value of N_{eff} is used to calculate the value of V_T in MOSFETs with implanted channels. This method for calculating V_T in MOSFETs with non-uniformly doped channel regions is often called the *doping transformation procedure,* and reportedly gives excellent results.

Ion implantation can also be used to fabricate depletion-mode MOSFETs. Depletion-mode NMOS devices (i.e., in which $V_T < 0V$) are commonly used in NMOS logic circuits. In order for the required negative threshold voltage for a depletion-mode NMOS device to be produced, n-type impurities are implanted into the p-type substrate to form a built-in channel between the source and drain. The dose required to shift the threshold voltage by the desired value may also be estimated using Eqs. 3-72 and 4-73.[*]

4.6.3.1 Impact of the V_T-adjust Implant on the Body Effect. The implanted layer also impacts the variation of V_T with V_{SB}. This is shown in Fig. 4-23. We observe that for uniformly doped substrates [curves (a) and (b)] the variation of V_T with V_{SB} follows the data shown in Fig. 4-20. For shallow implants [curve (c)], the V_T vs. V_{SB} behavior approaches that for a delta function dose at the surface. That is, V_T is observed to be merely shifted by qD_I/C_{ox} from the V_T values given by curve (a), and thus curve (c) is parallel with curve (a). However, for a deeper implant [curve (d)], the initial variation in V_T with V_{SB} is comparable to that for a uniformly doped region of concentration N_A' [i.e., curve (b)]. However, as V_{SB} is increased, the channel depletion region width d approaches and soon exceeds x_j, and the variation of V_T with V_{SB} thereafter behaves as if the substrate is doped with the bulk concentration N_A [like curve (c)]. Since it is generally desirable to have V_T exhibit a low substrate bias sensitivity

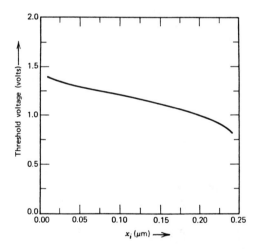

Fig. 4-22 Dependence of the threshold voltage on the effective implantation depth x_j as predicted by Eq. 4-75 for a MOSFET with an 87 nm-thick gate oxide, $Q_f/q = 10^{11}$ cm^{-2}, $D_I = 3.5 \times 10^{11}$ cm^{-2}, and $N_A = 2 \times 10^{15}$ cm^{-3}. Both the substrate and source terminal are assumed be grounded.[11] Reprinted with permission of John Wiley & Sons.

---

[*] Note that if x_j is greater than d_{max}, $V_{T(nud,lc)}$ can be calculated using Eq. 3-72, with N_A replaced by $N_A' = N_A + D_I/x_j$. However, this condition is generally avoided when choosing the V_T-adjust implant parameters, since the increased doping near the substrate edge of the source and drain junctions leads to higher junction capacitance, lower breakdown voltage, and a larger body effect.

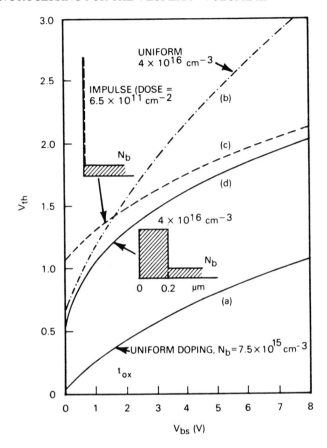

Fig. 4-23 Calculated substrate sensitivity for various doping profiles. (After Rideout, Gaensllen and LeBlanc in ref. 27.)

(i.e., small body effect), Fig. 4-23 also demonstrates that a shallow implant with an appropriate dose can raise V_T while maintaining a small body effect.

4.6.4 Impact of V_T-Adjust Implant on Other MOSFET Characteristics

By implanting ions near the Si surface, a nonuniformly doped channel region is produced. Besides shifting V_T, this alters the MOSFET behavior in several ways compared to devices having uniformly doped channels. First, the V_T-adjust implant introduces extra ions into the channel depletion region, causing its width to be modified. This effect is discussed here. In addition, the non-uniform doping profile changes the long-channel subthreshold characteristics (i.e., the slope of the log I_D vs. V_{GS} curves) as well as the punchthrough behavior of short-channel devices. These two latter effects will be discussed later, in chap. 5.

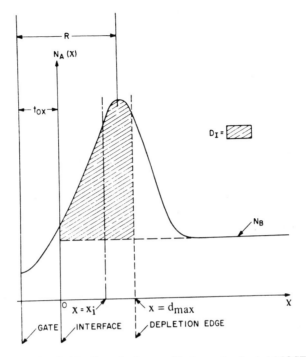

Fig. 4-24 Schematic of the threshold adjust doping profile in an implanted MOSFET. The shaded portion of the profile is the portion of the implanted dose in the depletion region, whose depth extends to d_{max}. The effective depth of the implant (or centroid) is labeled x_i.[8,15] Reprinted with permission of Solid-State Electronics.

However, all of the above effects depend only upon the so-called *exposed dose* D_I (i.e., the portion of the implant dose that ends up in the depletion region), and upon the *centroid x_d* of the exposed dose. That is, those implanted ions which do not penetrate the screening oxide or which penetrate beyond the edge of the channel depletion region have no impact. Thus, these terms must be defined. D_I (the shaded portion in Fig. 4-24), and x_d are given in terms $N_{sub'}(x)$ and N_{sub} by[15]

$$D_I \text{ (cm}^{-2}) = \int_0^d [N_{sub'}(x) - N_{sub}] \, dx \qquad (4\text{-}78)$$

and

$$x_d = \frac{1}{D_I} \int_0^d [N_{sub'}(x) - N_{sub}] \, x \, dx \qquad (4\text{-}79)$$

where $N_{sub'}(x)$ is the true channel profile, including the implanted ions, and N_{sub} is the uniform background doping of the substrate, as depicted in Fig. 4-24.

The change in width of the channel depletion region is most easily illustrated by replacing the actual implant profile shown in Fig. 4-24 with a simpler delta-function equivalent implant. That is, the equivalent doping profile $N_{sub'}(x)$ is given by

$$N_{sub'} (x) = N_{sub} + D_I \delta(x - x_d) \tag{4 - 80}$$

Using such a delta-function replacement for the actual profile, the effects of the V_T-implant are illustrated in Fig. 4-25. Figure 4-25a shows a potential versus distance diagram [$\varphi(x)$ versus x] of a long-channel MOSFET with a non-implanted (i.e., uniformly doped) channel region. The channel depletion region width is d and the band bending is φ_{surf}. In Fig. 4-25b, the effect of varying the *dose* D_I on the same depletion region is shown. The presence of D_I at x_d causes a larger voltage drop to occur between x_d and the surface, leaving a smaller portion of φ_{surf} to deplete the region behind the implant. Hence, the total width is reduced to $d_I = d_{DI}$. Doubling D_I further reduces the width (in Fig. 4-25b to d_{2DI}). Eventually, for a value of dose termed the *effective* dose, D_{eff}, d_I is reduced to a point $d_I = x_d$. Any increase of dose beyond D_{eff} simply is neutralized in the bulk, and the condition of $d_I = x_d$ is maintained. In other words, D_{eff} is the minimum dose needed to bring the depletion edge to that depth, making $d_I = x_d$.

Fig. 4-25c depicts the result of increasing implant *depth*. In this case, increasing x_d also increases the voltage drop between x_d and the surface, again reducing the width to a

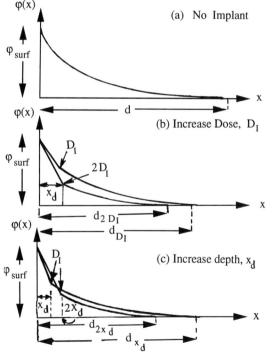

Fig. 4-25 The effects of a delta function implant upon the depletion width. (a) Unimplanted, (b) Effects of changing dose, and (c) Effect of changing depth.[13] (© IEEE 1978)

smaller d_I. As a deeper x_d is used, d_I moves toward the implant. For example, in Fig. 4-25c, we see that for an implant with depth x_d, $d_I = d_{xd}$. This is deeper than d_I due to a an implant with a depth $2x_d$ (here $d_I = d_{2xd}$). Ultimately, $d_I = x_d$, and $D_I = D_{eff}$, corresponding to this depth. Any further increase in x_d carries the depletion region edge with the implant. The depletion region edge becomes *clamped* to the implant.

The quantitative variation of d_I can also be simply expressed by again assuming a delta-function implant. That is, the depletion-region width in the presence of a V_T-adjust implant d_I is calculated from

$$d_I = \sqrt{2}\, L_D\, [\varphi_{surf}/\varphi_t - D_I x_d/(N_{sub}L_D{}^2) - 1]^{1/2} \qquad (4 - 81)$$

where L_D is the Debye length $\{[\kappa_{si}\varepsilon_o\varphi_t/qN_{sub}]^{1/2}\}$. Eq. 4-81 shows that the implant reduces the width, since in a uniformly doped channel the width d is given by

$$d = \sqrt{2}L_D\, [\varphi_{surf}/\varphi_t - 1]^{1/2} \qquad (4 - 82)$$

Likewise, D_{eff} is given by

$$D_{eff} = N_{sub}\, (d^2 - x_d{}^2)/2x_d. \qquad (4 - 83)$$

4.7 SUBTHRESHOLD CURRENTS IN LONG-CHANNEL MOSFETs (I_{Dst} when $V_{GS} < |V_T|$)

The small drain current which flows in the MOSFET channel below threshold (i.e., in weak inversion) is called *subthreshold current*, I_{Dst}. In most applications I_{Dst} is far too small to be useful as a drive current. However, it can represent an unwanted leakage current, especially in ICs designed for low-power applications. It can also give rise to premature discharging of memory-cell capacitors or dynamic-logic circuit nodes, preventing these circuits from operating properly. The issues involving leakage currents in MOSFETs will become even more important with the proliferation of battery-powered (i.e., portable) electronic systems. The common range of V_T in submicron digital CMOS ICs is 0.6-0.8V. Thus, when $V_{GS} = 0$V the MOSFETs in these circuits may be close to weak inversion. Consequently, for many applications (especially those requiring low standby-power dissipation), subthreshold leakage must be well characterized so that the total IC leakage current of the chip can be predicted during the design phase of the product.

In actual MOSFETs, when $V_{GS}<V_T$ the minority carrier concentration in the channel (e.g., n_{ps}) is small (but not zero). That is, as V_{GS} is increased from 0V and approaches V_T, the mobile charge concentration due to n_{ps} remains smaller than the ionic charge of the bulk doping concentration, but continues to increase as V_{GS} rises. In section 3.3.5 we defined *weak inversion* in terms of φ_{surf}, namely as $\varphi_B<\varphi_{surf}<2\varphi_B$.

The bulk-charge and square-law models of I_D are not suitable for treating subthreshold behavior because they were developed to describe MOSFET behavior only in strong inversion. That is, both models assume that $I_D = 0$ if $V_{GS}< |V_T|$. While the Pao-Sah model can provide accurate predictions of I_{Dst}, it requires too much computation to be practical for circuit simulation applications. Thus, the charge-sheet model becomes the candidate for characterizing I_{Dst}. We noted in section 4.5.3, however, that the I_D expression of the charge-sheet model in its full form is also still too cumbersome for most circuit-design simulation tasks. Fortunately, by making some appropriate simplifying approximations, the general form of the charge-sheet model I_D equation can be reduced to a less complex formulation that still provides accurate predictions of I_{Dst} in long-channel MOSFETs.

Consider the case of a long-channel NMOSFET in which: (1) the source is grounded; (2) V_{GS} approaches (but remains less than) V_T, and; (3) $|V_{DS}| \geq 0.1V$. Now recall that in inversion (i.e., when $V_{GS} > |V_T|$), the free-carrier concentration n_{ps} in the channel is large (e.g., $n_{ps} \geq N_A$), and I_D in this case is dominated by drift current. However, when $V_{GS} < |V_T|$, n_{ps} is much smaller than N_A, but is not zero In addition, in weak inversion the drain voltage V_{DS} drops almost entirely across the reverse-biased drain-substrate depletion region.

Figure 4-26a illustrates the variation of inversion-layer charge concentration versus channel position in a long-channel NMOSFET in weak inversion. Figures 4-26b and c depict $\varphi_{surf}(y)$ and a 2-D perspective plot of the potential $\varphi(x,y)$ diagrams in weak inversion, respectively. We see that the band bending in the x-direction is too small to establish a strongly inverted channel [i.e., $\varphi_B < \varphi_{surf} < 2\varphi_B$], thus the channel mobile charge density Q_I is very small. In the y-direction most of the band bending occurs at the drain junction. Since the value of φ_{surf} along the y-direction remains essentially constant over most of the length of the channel, the $\mathcal{E}$-field along the y-direction is also very small [i.e., $\mathcal{E}(y) = -\partial\varphi_{surf}/\partial y$ is very small]. The combination of a small lateral $\mathcal{E}$-field acting on a relatively small number of free carriers implies that the drift component of I_{Dst} is negligibly small in weak inversion. In addition, in long-channel MOSFETs, the *gradient* of the $\mathcal{E}$-field in the y-direction along most of the channel length must also be very small. This means it is valid to apply the GCA when calculating I_{Dst} in such devices. In short-channel MOSFETs, however, the gradient of $\mathcal{E}(y)$ can no longer be neglected, even in weak inversion, and thus the long-channel formulation of I_{Dst} given here may not yield accurate estimates of I_{Dst} in short-channel MOSFETs.

On the other hand, we shall show that the *gradient of the free carriers* along the y-direction in the channel in weak inversion can be relatively large. Since diffusion current is proportional to the carrier-density gradient, in such cases carrier diffusion can produce a significant I_{Dst}. In fact, diffusion is the dominant mechanism that establishes subthreshold current flow in long-channel devices. The expression for the diffusion current component is given by:

$$I_{diff} = A\, J_{diff} = A\, [q\, D_n\, dn\, (y)/dy] = Z\, t_{inv}\, [\, q\, D_n\, dn\, (y)/dy\,] \qquad (4-84)$$

where D_n is the electron diffusion constant, A is the cross-sectional area of the electron flow, and t_{inv} is the inversion layer thickness (or $A = Z\, t_{inv}$). We can express this equation in terms of the mobile charge density per unit area Q_I instead of in terms of n by multiplying the mobile charge density in the channel (qn) by the inversion layer thickness t_{inv}. As shown in section 4.3.1.1, t_{inv} can be approximated as $(kT/q)\mathcal{E}_{si}$ (x = 0), where $\mathcal{E}_{si}$ (x = 0) is given by $\sqrt{2qN_A\varphi_{surf}/\kappa_{si}\varepsilon_o}$, so

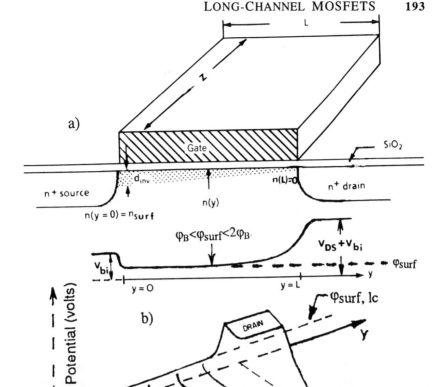

Fig. 4-26 (a) Cross-sectional area of an NMOSFET in weak inversion showing the variation of inversion layer charge concentration versus position along the channel; (b) Plot of $\varphi_{surf}(y)$ versus y for the device of part (a); (c) 2-D perspective plot of potential versus position in a long-channel NMOSFET in weak inversion.

$$t_{inv} \approx \frac{kT}{q} \frac{\sqrt{\kappa_{si}\varepsilon_0}}{\sqrt{2q N_A \varphi_{surf}}} \qquad (4\text{-}85)$$

In addition, the carrier concentration in the inversion layer can be found using Eq. 3-13 (with $n_{po} = n_i^2/N_A$), or $n = (n_i^2/N_A) \exp(q\varphi_{surf}/kT)$. Using these relationships, $Q_I(y)$ can be expressed as

$$Q_I = q\, t_{inv}\, n(y) \approx q \frac{kT}{q} \frac{\sqrt{\kappa_{si}\varepsilon_0}}{\sqrt{2q N_A \varphi_{surf}}} \frac{n_i^2}{N_A} \exp\left(\frac{q\,\varphi_{surf}}{kT}\right) \qquad (4\text{-}86a)$$

By some algebraic manipulation this expression for Q_I can be shown to be identical to the equation for the mobile charge density per unit area Q_I in a MOS-C under weak inversion given in chap. 3 (i.e., Eq. 3-58, which we repeat here)

$$Q_I \text{ (weak inv)} \approx \frac{\sqrt{2q\,N_A\kappa_S\varepsilon_0}}{2\sqrt{\varphi_{surf}}}\,\varphi_t\,e^{[\varphi_{surf}(GB) - 2\varphi_B]/\varphi_t} \qquad (4 - 86b)$$

where the surface potential in the MOS-C is established just by the gate-body bias V_{GB} (and $\varphi_t = kT/q$). We can include the effect of a bias between the channel and substrate in Eq. 4-85. That is, with the source grounded (i.e., $V_{BS} = 0V$, implying that $V_{DB} = V_{DS}$), Q_I at the source and drain ends of the channel in a MOSFET under weak inversion, can be written using Eq. 4-86a as follows:

$$Q_{I,source} \approx q\,\frac{kT}{q}\,\frac{\sqrt{\kappa_{si}\varepsilon_0}}{\sqrt{2\,q\,N_A\,\varphi_{surf}(source)}}\,\frac{n_i^2}{N_A}\,\exp\left(\frac{q\,\varphi_{surf}(source) - 2\varphi_B}{kT}\right) \quad (4 - 87a)$$

$$Q_{I,drain} \approx q\,\frac{kT}{q}\,\frac{\sqrt{\kappa_{si}\varepsilon_0}}{\sqrt{2\,q\,N_A\,\varphi_{surf}(source)}}\,\frac{n_i^2}{N_A}\,\exp\left\{\frac{q\,[\varphi_{surf}(source) - 2\varphi_B - V_{DS}]}{kT}\right\} \quad (4 - 87b)$$

where $\varphi_{surf}(GB) = \varphi_{surf}(source)$ in this case, as $V_{BS} = 0V$. Since the diffusion current is constant along the channel, the gradient of Q_I (i.e., dQ_I/dy) is also constant and can be approximated by the following expression, using Eqs. 4-87a and b:

$$\frac{dQ_I}{dy} = \frac{Q_{I,source} - Q_{I,drain}}{L} \approx \frac{Q_{I,source}}{L}\left[1 - \exp\left(\frac{-q\,V_{DS}}{kT}\right)\right] \qquad (4 - 88)$$

Then the expression for the diffusion component of the drain current in weak inversion I_{Dst} can be written as

$$I_{Dst} = D_n\,Z\,\frac{dQ_I}{dy} = \frac{D_n\,Z\,Q_{I,source}}{L}\left[1 - \exp\left(\frac{-q\,V_{DS}}{kT}\right)\right] \qquad (4 - 89)$$

Now, if $|V_{DS}| \geq 0.1V$, at room temperature the term $\exp(-qV_{DS}/kT)$ in Eq. 4-88 is smaller than e^{-4}. Hence, this term in Eq. 4-89 will be much smaller than 1. As a result, if V_{DS} exceeds a few φ_t (i.e., a few kT/q, or at 300K, $\geq 0.1V$), we can consider $Q_{I,drain}$ to be negligibly small compared to $Q_{L,source}$.

In such cases, the expression for I_{Dst} in long-channel MOSFETs can be approximated as $I_{Dst} \sim D_n Z Q_{Isource}/L$, or, in expanded form:

$$I_{Dst} \approx q\,D_n\,\frac{Z}{L}\,\frac{kT}{q}\,\frac{\sqrt{\kappa_{si}\varepsilon_0}}{\sqrt{2\,q\,N_A\,\varphi_{surf}(source)}}\,\frac{n_i^2}{N_A}\,\exp\left(\frac{q\,\varphi_{surf}(source)}{kT}\right) \qquad (4 - 90)$$

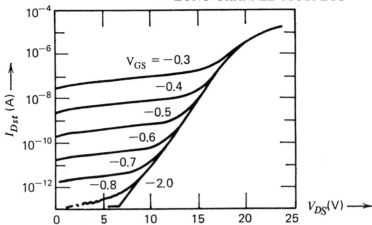

Fig. 4-27 Experimental low-current characteristics for a MOSFET with $L = 2.1\ \mu m$, with the source and substrate both tied to ground. For lower values of V_{DS}, I_{Dst} is reduced by roughly one order of magnitude for each 0.1V reduction in V_{GS} below the threshold value. At higher values of V_{DS}, a subsurface current flows that is independent of V_{GS}.[24] (© IEEE 1974).

Since φ_{surf}(source) is roughly proportional to V_{GS} in the subthreshold region,[16] Eqs. 4-87 and 4-90 imply that $Q_{I,source}$ and I_{Dst}, respectively, are both exponentially dependent on V_{GS}.

In summary, Eq. 4-90 predicts that in long-channel MOSFETs I_{Dst} will exponentially increase with V_{GS} but will remain substantially independent of V_{DS}. Figure 4-27 illustrates this subthreshold behavior in a MOSFET with $L = 2.1\ \mu m$. For values of V_{DS} smaller than the punchthrough voltage (i.e., roughly the V_{DS} value where the I_D curves intercept the more steeply rising portion of the curve in Fig. 4-27), I_{Dst} is seen to be essentially independent of V_{DS} and increases exponentially with V_{GS}.

It turns out, however, that devices with gate lengths of ~2 μm are at the transition between long-channel and short-channel device behavior. That is, when V_{DS} is sufficiently increased in MOSFETs with $L{\leq}2\ \mu m$, the source and drain depletion regions merge, and at that point I_{Dst} starts to become dependent on V_{DS} (as is also illustrated in Fig. 4-27 in the right side of the characteristics, where I_{Dst} no longer depends on V_{GS}). This short-channel effect, known as *punchthrough*, is discussed in chap. 5. In general, however, punchthrough must be prevented from occurring in normal device operation, even in short-channel devices. That is, at the maximum operating V_{DS} value the punchthrough current should be kept smaller than the long-channel I_{Dst} value. One simple rule of thumb to accomplish this in a MOSFET that employs a V_T-adjust implant is to set the substrate doping concentration N_{sub} at $>0.1N_I$, where $N_I = D_I/x_d$, and D_I and x_d are the threshold-adjust implant dose and the effective implant depth (or centroid), respectively.

It should also be noted that the V_T-adjust implant generally increases the subthreshold swing S_t, and this is one reason that S_t in real devices is larger (~100 mV/dec) than the theoretically predicted value of ~60 mV/dec at 300K. A more complete discussion of S_t is given in the upcoming section.

4.7.1 Subthreshold Swing S_t

Another important device characteristic in the subthreshold regime is the slope of log I_D versus V_{GS}. This characteristic indicates how effectively a MOSFET can be turned OFF as V_{GS} is decreased below V_T. The inverse of the slope is defined as the subthreshold swing S_t.[17] As voltage levels are reduced in an effort to save power and to use smaller devices, this characteristic becomes a limitation on how small a power-supply voltage can be used. In MOSFETs with uniformly doped substrates, S_t is calculated from

$$S_t = \ln 10 (d\ln I_D / dV_{GS})^{-1} = 2.3 \, (kT/q) \, (1 + C_d/C_{ox}) \qquad (4-91a)$$

$$= 2.3 \, (kT/q) \, [1 + \kappa_{si} t_{ox}/\kappa_{ox} d)] \qquad (4-91b)$$

S_t is expressed in units of mV per decade. (The factor 2.3 comes from the conversion of $\ln(x)$ to $2.3 \log_{10}[x]$). Let us consider the S_t parameter in more detail.

Ideally, an abrupt change in I_D should occur as V_{GS} passes through V_T. If a MOSFET exhibits a steep decline in I_D as V_{GS} is decreased below V_T, its S_t value will be small. Conversely, if a MOSFET structure is known to possess a small S_t, the implication is that only a small reduction of V_{GS} below V_T will effectively turn off the device; whereas if the device exhibits a large S_t value (meaning a gradual slope in log I_D vs V_{GS}) a significantly large I_{Dst} may still flow in the OFF state (e.g., when $V_{GS} = 0$).

According to Eq. 4-91b, at 300K in the ideal limit of $t_{ox} \rightarrow 0$, $S_t = (2.3kT/q)$ ~60 mV/dec. However, any nonidealities in an actual device (e.g., the presence of interface states, or a nonzero value of t_{ox}) cause S_t to become larger than the 60 mV/dec value (also, note that if T increases, so does the value of S_t). The S_t value of typical submicron NMOSFETs operating at 300K is ~100 mV/decade, and in such devices I_D will drop from 1 μA to 1 pA for a 0.6V decrease in V_{GS}. Thus, if a MOSFET exhibits a *constant-current-V_T* of 0.6V (i.e., $I_D = 1 \, \mu A/\mu m$ when $V_{GS} = V_T = 0.6V$), when $V_{GS} = 0V$, I_D will be reduced to 1 pA/μm. Thus, if S_t is known, Eq. 4-91a can be used to estimate I_{Dst} in long-channel MOSFETs in subthreshold operation (Fig. 4-28).[18] That is, circuit designers can readily calculate the gate bias required to keep the subthreshold leakage current below its specified maximum. Typically, to ensure that I_{Dst} will be negligibly small, the maximum bias applied to the gate when the device is in the OFF state should be kept at least 0.5 V below V_T.

Equation 4-91 also indicates that S_t can be made smaller by using a thinner t_{ox} or a lower substrate doping concentration (which will make the channel depletion-region width d larger). In addition, Eq. 4-91 implies that S_t increases with temperature (for example, at 100°C, the minimum theoretical value of S_t is increased to ~100 mV/dec).*

---

* Note that in a non-uniformly doped channel (e.g., one which uses a V_T-adjust implant), the expression for S_t is modified to

$$S_t = (kT/q) \ln 10 \, [\, 1 + C_d/C_{ox}]/\{1 - [(\kappa_{si}/\kappa_{ox})(t_{ox}/L_D)]^2 [C_d/C_{ox}]^2\} \qquad (4-92)$$

Basically, this equation indicates that the V_T-adjust implant causes S_t to be somewhat increased (since the additional dopant in the channel reduces the depletion-region width, thus making C_d in Eq. 4-91 larger). However, if the implant is deep enough, the depletion region

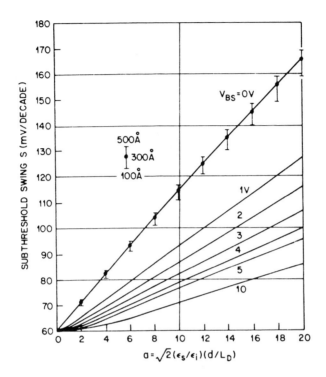

Fig. 4-28 Subthreshold gate swing S_t required to reduce the subthreshold current one decade versus the parameter $a = [\sqrt{2}\, t_{ox}/\kappa_{ox}q)][\kappa_{si}kT/\varepsilon_0 N_A)^{1/2}$. Vertical bars indicate the variation in S_t at constant a when the oxide thickness is varied from 500 to 100 Å, and doping level and mobility adjusted accordingly. $V_{DS} \gg kT/q$.[13] (© IEEE 1979).

Finally, it should be noted that because the depletion width increases when a substrate bias is applied, the subthreshold swing decreases according to Eq. 4-91b. This effect is shown in Fig. 4-29.[17,24]

Note that when the channel length gets small, the values of I_{Dst} are larger than those predicted by the above model. This is due to so-called short-channel effects (discussed in chap. 5). As a result, measurements of S_t versus channel length are used to detect the onset of these short-channel effects (punchthrough and surface drain-induced barrier lowering). Since the measurable I_{Dst} is the sum of both the normal subthreshold and short-channel-induced components, an increase in the value of S_t will signal the onset of the latter.

* (cont.) width will eventually be equal to that of the unimplanted device, and S_t returns to the value exhibited by a device with no V_T-adjust implant. Nevertheless, the general dependences of S_t on t_{ox}, T, and channel substrate doping exhibited in devices with uniformly doped channels still apply.

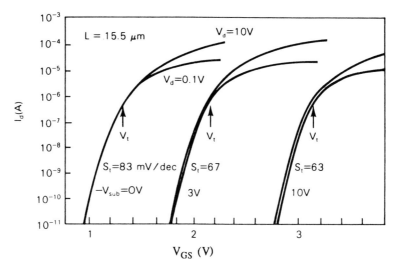

Fig. 4-29 Experimental subthreshold characteristics for a long-channel device (L = 15.5 μm).[24] (© IEEE 1974).

4.7.2   Gate-Induced Drain Leakage (GIDL)

Another form of leakage current observed in OFF-state MOSFETs is *gate-induced drain leakage (GIDL)*.[19] The carriers responsible for GIDL originate in the region of the drain that is overlapped by the gate, and GIDL is occurs when the gate is grounded and the drain is at V_{DD}. A large electric field then exists across the oxide (ε_{ox}), which must be supported by charge in the drain region. This charge is provided by the formation of a depletion region in the drain as shown in Fig. 4-30a. If ε_{ox} becomes sufficiently large, in addition to the depletion region, an inversion layer will attempt to form at the silicon surface of the drain. However, as the minority carriers arrive at the surface to form the inversion layer, they are immediately swept laterally to the substrate (which is a region of lower potential for the minority carriers). Hence, in this case, the depletion region under the oxide in the drain instead becomes a *deep depletion layer*.* The zone near the surface where an inversion layer should be formed is referred to as an "incipient inversion layer." The current that flows as a result of the carriers being swept from this

---

* *Deep depletion* is a non-equilibrium condition where there are fewer minority carriers in a depletion region than would exist in equilibrium. Consider the case of an n^+MOS structure (i.e., the condition that exists in an NMOS drain region), that is biased so that an inversion layer of holes should exist at the surface (and a depletion layer exists below it). Under equilibrium conditions, this condition can persist indefinitely under appropriate dc bias. In the structure described above, a dc bias is applied that attempts to establish such an inversion layer of holes at the surface of the n^+drain. However, the potential of the substrate is lower for holes than the surface potential of the drain, and thus any holes arriving at the drain surface move laterally to the substrate region. Thus, the depletion region under the overlap area becomes a zone of deep depletion.

incipient inversion layer constitute the GIDL current.

The magnitude of GIDL current is independent of temperature, and hence it is believed that thermal generation of carriers in the incipient inversion region plays only a minor role in GIDL. Instead, it is proposed that when $\mathcal{E}_{ox}$ becomes large enough, the voltage drop in the deep-depletion layer becomes so large that various trap-assisted carrier-generation events become possible (Fig. 4-30b).[20] These include thermal emission of an electron from the valence band to a trap site (expressed as a vertical transition in the diagram) and then tunneling to the conduction band (horizontal transition), and trap-assisted tunneling from valence band to conduction band. For even larger fields (a few MV/cm), trap-free band-to-band tunneling may also occur (see also Fig. 4-30b).

Like other forms of leakage current, GIDL will contribute to standby power, giving rise to the previously mentioned problems of excessive heat dissipation at large device counts and heavy current drain in portable systems. Hence, GIDL must be controlled so that it does not exceed some specified maximum value (typically, ≤ 10 pA/μm).

In order to control GIDL, the most important mechanisms that may cause it need to be identified. This allows processes involving these mechanisms to be avoided or modified to minimize GIDL. For example, it has been observed that shallow junction

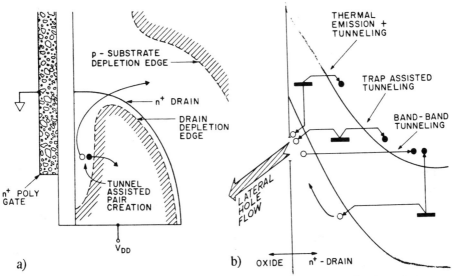

Fig. 4-30 (a) Gate induced drain leakage in the MOSFET. A schematic view of the gate-drain overlap region for a grounded gate and the drain biased at V_{DD}. Tunneling created pairs lead to a lateral hole flow in the n^+ drain. This flow prevents formation of an inversion layer inside the drain. (b) Various mechanisms that can contribute to gate-induced drain leakage. Vertical transitions are thermal-emission processes. Horizontal transitions are tunneling processes. Holes are prevented from forming an inversion layer by lateral transport to the substrate. This flow is normal to the plane of the diagram, as indicated by the slanted arrow, lateral hole flow.[20] From J.R. Brews, "The Submicron MOSFET," Chap. 3, in *High-Speed Semiconductor Devices*, Ed. Sze. Copyright 1990, John Wiley & Sons. Reprinted with permission.

fabrication using Ge preamorphization introduces bulk midgap traps that increase GIDL.[21] Other reports indicate that interface traps caused by hot carrier injection,[22] or Fowler-Nordheim tunneling[23] increase GIDL by stimulating additional tunneling.

There are several general procedures that appear to be effective in reducing GIDL. First, the oxide thickness can be increased to reduce ε_{ox} for a given voltage. But this is usually not implemented, since a thicker gate oxide will adversely impact other device characteristics. Second, the trap density in the near-surface area can be reduced, but such trap elimination generally requires a carefully controlled fabrication sequence. Third, the doping in the drain can be increased, as this will decrease the depletion region width and the tunneling volume. Unfortunately, the latter approach favors abrupt junctions, because graded or lightly-doped-drain (LDD) structures will lead to a significant lateral extension of the drain within which the doping is lighter, inviting greater GIDL. Tradeoffs of field reduction against GIDL may need to be considered. On the other hand, it has also been reported that LDD devices can suppress GIDL by suppressing the lateral field.

Nevertheless, it has been reported that GIDL sets a limit on the power supply voltage V_{DD} of an LDD MOSFET of[25,29]

$$V_{DD} = 4 \times 10^6 \text{ V/cm} \times t_{ox} + 1.2V - V_{FB} \qquad (4 - 93)$$

A non-LDD MOSFET would have a much higher GIDL current. This implies that suppression of GIDL may be a strong reason to retain the LDD structure in MOSFETs even after V_{DD} is reduced to suppress hot-carrier effects. (Note that in Eq. 4-93 V_{FB} is ~0V for an n^+ polysilicon gate on an n^+ drain and about 1.1V for an n^+ polysilicon gate over a p^+ drain.)

4.8 SUMMARY OF LONG-CHANNEL MOSFET BEHAVIOR

The behavior of the long-channel as detailed in this chapter can be summarized by examining the I-V characteristics of the long-channel MOSFET in strong inversion (Fig. 4-31a), and in the subthreshold region of operation (weak inversion, see Fig. 4-31b).

In strong inversion we plot the output characteristics of the MOSFET (I_D versus V_{DS} with V_{GS} as the parameter) on an axis with linear I_D and V_{DS} scales. We see that for a fixed value of $V_{GS} > V_T$, the drain current first increases linearly with V_{DS}. Eventually, as shown in Fig. 4-31a, the drain current saturates. Beyond the value of saturation voltage (i.e., when $V_{DS} > V_{DSsat}$), I_D remains constant with increasing V_{DS}. The value of I_{Dsat} is also proportional to $(V_{GS} - V_T)^2$ - as predicted by charge-control model. The values of I_D versus V_{DS} and V_{GS} in the linear region, as well as the values of I_{Dsat} and V_{DSsat} can be calculated using any one of the four long-channel MOSFET models given in section 4.5, depending on the accuracy desired.

In the subthreshold region of operation, the behavior is described by plotting I_D (with a logarithmic scale) versus V_{GS} (with a linear scale). As shown in Fig. 4-31b, in long-channel MOSFETs the drain current I_D drops exponentially once V_{GS} becomes ~0.2V below V_T. Furthermore, in long-channel MOSFETs the slope of this log I_D-V_{GS}

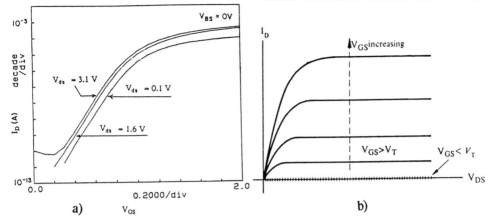

Fig. 4-31 (a) I_D versus V_{DS} characteristics of long-channel MOSFETs beyond strong inversion. (b) I_D versus V_{GS} characteristics of a long-channel MOSFET below threshold (weak inversion).

characteristic does not change with increasing V_{DS}, nor does the value of I_D increase at a fixed value of V_{GS} as V_{DS} is increased.

Finally, the threshold voltage of the long-channel MOSFET does not vary as L is decreased, nor does it change with increasing V_{DS}, although this V_T behavior is not indicated by either Fig. 4-31a or Fig. 4-31b.

REFERENCES

1. D. A. Hodges and H. G. Jackson, *Analysis and Design of Digital Integrated Circuits,* McGraw-Hill Book Co., New York, 1983.
2. S. M. Sze, *Semiconductor Devices - Physics and Technology*, John Wiley & Sons, New York, 1985, p. 444.
3. S. Selberherr, A. Schutz, and H.W. Potzl, "MINIMOS-A two dimensional MOS analyzer," *IEEE Trans. Electron Dev.,* **ED-27**, p. 1540, 1980.
4. H.C. Pao and C.T. Sah, "Effects of Diffusion Current on Characteristics of Metal-Oxide (Insulator)-Semiconductor Transistors," *Solid-State Electron.* 9, 927, (1966).
5. Y.P. Tsividis, *Operation and Modeling of the MOS Transistor,"* McGraw-Hill, New York, 1987.
6. R.F. Pierret and J.A. Shields, "Simplified long-channel MOSFET Theory," *Solid-State Electronics,* vol. 26, p. 143, 1983.
7. G. Baccarani et al., "Analytical i.g.f.e.t.model including drift and diffusion currents," *IEE Journal on Solid-State and Electron Devices,* vol. 2, p. 62, March 1978.
8. J.R. Brews, "A Charge-Sheet Model of the MOSFET," *Solid-State Electronics,* vol. 21, p. 345, 1978.
9. H.K. Ihantola and J.L Moll, "Design Theory of a Surface Field-Effect Transistor," *Solid-State Electronics* 7, 423 (1964).

10. A. Vladimirescu, A.R. Newton, and D.O. Pederson, *SPICE Version 2G.2 Users Guide,* Electronics Research Laboratory, University of California, Berkeley.
11. R.S. Muller and T.I. Kamins, *Device Electronics for Integrated Circuits,* 2nd. Ed., New York, John Wiley & Sons, 1986.
12. V.L. Rideout, F.H. Gaensslen, and A. LeBlanc, "Device Design Consideration for Ion-implanted *n*-Channel MOSFETs," *IBM J. Res. Dev.,* p. 50, (1975).
13. J.R. Brews *IEEE Trans. Electron Dev.,* **ED-26(11)**, 1696 (1979),
14. D. Antoniadis "Calculation of threshold voltage in nonuniformly doped MOSFETs," *IEEE Trans. Electron Dev.,* **ED-31,** p. 303, March 1984.
15. J.R. Brews, "The Physics of the MOS Transistor," in *Silicon Integrated Circuits*, Part A, Ed. D. Kahng, New York, Academic Press, 1981.
16. S. M. Sze, *Semiconductor Devices: Physics and Technology,,* John Wiley & Sons, New York, p. 213, 1985.
17. J.R. Brews, J. "Subthreshold Behavior of Uniformly and Nonuniformly Doped Long-Channel MOSFET," *IEEE Trans. Electron Dev.,* **ED-26** (9) p. 1282, Sept. 1979.
18. *ibid.* , (**16**), p. 470.
19. T. Y. Chan et al., 1987 IEDM Tech. Digest, p. 718.
20. J.R. Brews, "The Submicron MOSFET," chap. 3 in *High-Speed Semiconductor Devices,* S.M. Sze Ed., Wiley- Interscience, New York, 1990.
21. D.-S. Wen et al., "Tunneling Leakage in Ge-PreAmorphized Shallow Junctions," *IEEE Trans. Electron Dev.,* **ED-35** (7), 1107 (1988).
22. C. Duvvury et al., "Leakage Current Degradation in *n*-MOSFETs Due to Hot-Electron Stress," *IEEE Electron Dev. Lett.* **EDL-9** (11), 579 (1988).
23. I. C. Chen et al., "Interface-Trap Enhanced Gate-Induced Leakage Current in MOSFET," *IEEE* Electron Dev. Lett., **EDL-10**, (5), 216 (1989).
24. R.R. Troutman, "Subthreshold Design Considerations for IGFETs," *IEEE J. Solid-State Circuits,* **SC-9**, p. 55, (1974).
25. S. Parke et al., "Design for suppression of gate-induced leakage in LDD MOSFETs."
26. *ibid.,* reference **16** p. 444.
27. V.L. Rideout, F.H. Gaensslen, and A. LeBlanc, *IBM J. Res. Dev.,* **19**, p. 50, (1975).
28. N.D. Arora, *Solid-State Electronics*, **30**, p. 559, (1987).
29. H.-J Wann, P.K. Ko, and C. Hu, "Gate-Induced Band-to-Band Tunneling Leakage Current in LDD MOSFETs," *Tech. Dig. IEDM,* 1992, p. 147.
30. R.F. Pierret, *Field Effect Devices*, Vol. IV Modular Series on Solid-State Devices, Addison-Wesley Publishing Co. Reading, MA., 1983.

PROBLEMS

1. Another way to model the drain current in a MOSFET is to note that it can be represented as mobile charge induced in the channel divided by the *transit time* (or average time required for an electron to move from the source to drain). For an n-channel MOSFET with a 250Å oxide, 1 μm channel length, 10 μm channel width, and $V_T = 1$V, operated at $V_{GS} = 5$V and $V_{DS} = 0.1$V, calculate the total electron charges in the channel and the electron transit time. Then, show that this charge divided by the transit time is equal to the current calculated at the linear region as given by Eq. 4-65.

2. Evaluate the coefficient k of Eq. 4-64 for a MOSFET in which $\mu_n = 580$ cm^2/V sec, Z/L = 1 and (a) $t_{ox} = 50$ nm, and (b) $t_{ox} = 10$ nm.

3. Account qualitatively for the differing drain current I_D predictions of the bulk-charge and square-law models of the long-channel MOSFET.

4. Describe how the saturation voltage V_{DSsat} is defined and derive $V_{DSsat} \sim V_{GS} - V_T$ as a first order expression.

5. The sheet resistances of the source (R_S) and the drain (R_D) are both parasitic resistances (see Appendix B). Discuss why R_S decreases I_D more than does R_D in the saturation region of operation. Also, derive an analytic expression of g_m in the linear region as a function of R_S and R_D.

6. If a circuit designer wants to ensure that a MOSFET exhibits no more than no more than 1 pA of leakage current in the off state, and also wants $V_T = 0.9$V (where V_T is defined as the gate voltage that causes 1 μA current), what maximum S_t value must the device exhibit.

7. Verify that the expression for the capacitance of the surface space-charge region C_d in Eq. 4-91 is correct (i.e., that $C_d = \kappa_{si}\varepsilon_o/d$).

8. The I_D-V_{GS} characteristics for a long n-channel MOSFET are shown in Fig. 4P-1. Using the square-law model and information available from the graph, compute the drain current I_D when $V_{GS} = 3$V and $V_{DS} = 5$V.

9. A MOSFET has been fabricated on a p-type substrate with doping concentration $N_A = 4\times10^{15}$ cm^{-3}. The gate oxide thickness is 50 nm, the gate is n^+ polysilicon, the oxide charge is $Q_{tot} = 2\times10^{10}$ cm^{-2}, and V_T-adjust implant of 2×10^{12} boron atoms/cm^2 is performed through the gate oxide. Assume that Z/L = 1 and $\mu_n = 800$ cm^2/V sec, and $V_{BS} = 0$V. (a) Calculate the threshold voltage of the device; and (b) Calculate V_{DSsat} and I_{Dsat} for the MOSFET using: (i) the bulk-charge model and; (ii) the square-law model. Take $V_{GS} = 5$V. Comment on the accuracy of the square-law model.

10. Explain why we can approximate the thickness of the inversion layer as the depth beneath x = 0 at which $\varphi(x)$ has dropped to a value of $0.38\varphi_{surf}$.

11. Explain why I_D does not become zero if $V_{GS} > V_T$ and $V_{DS} > V_{DSsat}$, as might be the conclusion based on the long-channel approximation used to calculated I_D.

12. Derive the I-V characteristics of a MOSFET with the drain and gate connected together and the source and substrate grounded. Can one obtain the threshold voltage from these characteristics?

13. An NMOSFET with $Z/L = 15$, $t_{ox} = 80$ nm and $\mu_n = 600$ cm^2/V sec is to be used as a controlled resistor: (a) What charge density is required for the device to exhibit a dc resistance of 3.5 kΩ between the source and drain in the saturation region? (b) What value of $(V_{GS} - V_T)$ is needed to obtain the desired resistance?

14. An Al gate enhancement-type NMOSFET has a substrate doping of $N_A = 6 \times 10^{15}$ cm^{-3} and a gate oxide thickness of 100 nm, and $Q_{tot} = 5 \times 10^{10}$ cm^{-2}. Determine V_T of this device. When the device is operated in the linear region with $V_{DS} = 0.5$V, calculate the gate voltage needed to obtain a drain current of 2 mA. Assume $L = 10$ μm, $Z = 100L$, and $\mu_n = 500$ cm^2/V sec.

CHAPTER 5

MOS TRANSISTOR DEVICE PHYSICS: PART 3

THE SUBMICRON MOSFET

The two major goals of MOSFET scaling are to increase the *density* and *speed* of the digital ICs in which such scaled-down devices are used. Increasing *density* obviously means using smaller channel lengths and widths. To increase the *speed* of digital ICs, the MOSFET saturation drain current I_{Dsat} must be increased (i.e., to allow faster charging and discharging of parasitic capacitances). From the long-channel MOSFET models given in chap. 4, a decrease in either the channel length L or gate oxide thickness t_{ox} will lead to an increase in I_{Dsat}. In fact, the long-channel MOSFET models predict that I_{Dsat} should continue to increase indefinitely as L and t_{ox} are decreased, seeming to imply that only the limitations of process technology (and not device effects) prevent the manufacture of even smaller, higher-performing MOSFETs. In addition, the MOSFET models of chap. 4 also accurately describe many other device characteristics of long-channel MOSFETs, including threshold voltage, subthreshold current, and the I_D-V_{DS} characteristics in strong inversion.

However, as process technology improved to the point where devices could be fabricated with gate lengths smaller than ~2 μm, it turned out that MOSFETs began to exhibit phenomena not predicted by the long-channel MOSFET models. Such phenomena were thus termed *short-channel effects.* One of the more surprising of such short-channel effects (which becomes especially pronounced as L decreases below 0.5 μm) is that the drain current in saturation I_{Dsat} shows far less increase as L is decreased than is predicted by the long-channel models (see Fig. 5-1).[1,47] In fact, in the simple model to be presented in section 5.4, I_{Dsat} is predicted to become independent of L in extremely small MOSFETs, approaching instead, a constant value given by $Q_I v_{sat} Z$ (where v_{sat} is the saturation velocity of the carriers, as described in section 5.4.1.2). In contrast, reducing t_{ox} (which has the effect of increasing the oxide field, and in turn causes Q_I to increase), yields a considerably greater increase in I_{Dsat}. Furthermore, as shown in Fig. 5-1 I_{Dsat} will also increase more rapidly as L is decreased if the MOSFET has a thinner gate oxide. This benefit provides even a greater impetus for making t_{ox} as thin as possible as gate lengths are decreased further in the drive for higher density.

Since the quest for higher density still requires L (and Z) to be further reduced, it will nevertheless be necessary to confront the other short-channel effects (besides the

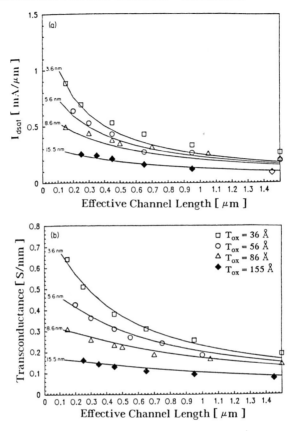

Fig. 5-1 Measured and calculated I_{Dsat} for an array of deep submicron NMOS transistors with four different gate-oxide thicknesses.[47] (© 1987 IEEE).

one of the I_{Dsat} dependence on L mentioned above). These other short-channel effects can be classified into two groups: (1) increased leakage current when the MOSFET is "off," and; (2) reliability problems associated with short-channel device structures.

Increased "off-state" leakage in short-channel MOSFETs is due to several phenomena, including: (a) lowering of the threshold voltage V_T as L is decreased and/or V_{DS} is increased; (b) the onset of punchthrough at smaller drain biases as L is decreased, and; (c) an increase in isolation leakage current as the isolation spacing is decreased. We will discuss V_T lowering and punchthrough in this chapter, and isolation leakage phenomena in chap. 6.

The reliability problems that arise in short-channel MOSFETs include: (a) thin gate-oxide breakdown (to be discussed in chap. 7); (b) device degradation due to hot-carrier effects (to be discussed in chap. 9); and (c) reliability problems associated with the interconnects between MOSFETs (e.g., electromigration failures in the metal lines). The latter problem is treated in Vol. 2, chaps. 3 and 4.

Table 5-1. Comparison of Long-Channel and Short-Channel MOSFET Characteristics

Long-Channel MOSFET Behavior	Short-Channel MOSFET Behavior
1. The threshold voltage V_T is independent of channel length L and width Z.	1. V_T decreases as L is decreased. V_T may also be impacted by changes in Z.
2. V_T is independent of drain bias voltage.	2. V_T decreases with increasing V_{DS}.
3. V_T depends on V_{BS} according to Eq. 4-12 (with V_{BC} in Eq. 4-12 replaced by V_{BS}).	3. V_T increases less rapidly with V_{BS} than predicted by Eq. 4-12.
4. The subthreshold current I_{Dst} increases linearly as L decreases.	4. I_{Dst} increases more rapidly than linearly as L decreases.
5. I_{Dst} is independent of drain bias.	5. I_{Dst} increases with increasing V_{DS}.
6. The subthreshold swing S_t is independent of gate length.	6. S_t increases with decreasing L.
7. The drain current in saturation I_{Dsat} is independent of V_{DS}.	7. I_{Dsat} increases as V_{DS} increases.
8. I_{Dsat} is proportional to $(V_{GS} - V_T)^2$	8. I_{Dsat} is proportional to $(V_{GS} - V_T)$.
9. I_{Dsat} is proportional to $1/L$.	9. As $L \to 0$, I_{Dsat} becomes independent of L.

In this chapter we will also cover several device design scenarios developed to keep leakage currents sufficiently small as the MOSFET is scaled down. In addition, we describe the issues related to submicron PMOSFET design.

5.1 DEVICE CHARACTERISTICS OF LONG-CHANNEL VERSUS SHORT-CHANNEL MOSFETS

From the perspective of MOSFETs as circuit components, long-channel behavior has been specified in a number of ways. As a result, short-channel device effects can be so designated when a deviation from long-channel MOSFET behavior can be correlated with a reduction in the gate length (and/or gate width) dimension. Table 5-1 gives a list of long-channel device characteristics that undergo variation as the gate dimensions are decreased. As the behavior of the short-channel MOSFET is described later in this chapter, the terms associated with these characteristics will be defined and discussed in more detail.

From Table 5-1 we can see that the short-channel effects can be divided into the following categories: (a) those that impact V_T (Items 1-3): (b) those that impact subthreshold currents (Items 4-6); and (c) those that impact I_D when the MOSFET is operated in saturation [i.e., $V_{DS} > (V_{GS} - V_T)$], namely Items 7-9. In this chapter we discuss these effects in detail, as well as measures that can be adopted to minimize their impact on MOSFET behavior.

5.2 EFFECT OF GATE DIMENSIONS ON THRESHOLD VOLTAGE

In this section we will describe three short-channel effects on the threshold voltage of MOSFETs, namely: (1) the short-channel threshold-voltage shift; (2) Narrow gate width effects on threshold voltage; and (3) the reverse short-channel threshold voltage shift.

5.2.1 Short-Channel Threshold-Voltage Shift

Experimentally, it is observed that as the dimensions of the gate are reduced, the threshold voltage of MOSFETs become less well predicted by the long-channel V_T equation (Eq. 4-74). The error becomes significant as the *channel length dimension L* is reduced to less than 2 μm. Usually, V_T decreases as L is reduced.* In addition, in short-channel MOSFETs V_T also decreases as V_{DS} is increased. To get good agreement with measured data, a term ΔV_{TSC} must be subtracted from the value of V_T obtained from Eq. 4-74. (In n-channel enhancement-mode MOSFETs the measured value of V_T becomes less positive than that predicted by Eq. 4-74, while in p-channel enhancement-mode MOSFETs, V_T becomes less negative.)

The decrease of V_T with L and V_{DS} in short-channel devices is crucial because enhancement-mode FETs in CMOS are generally designed to operate with V_T magnitudes of 0.6-0.8V. If the magnitude of V_T drops even slightly below its designed value, the device may exhibit excessive drain leakage current when $V_{GS} = 0V$. As discussed earlier, V_T values of 0.6-0.8V in long-channel NMOS devices with lightly doped substrates can only achieved by increasing the doping concentration at the surface of the channel (i.e., with a V_T-adjust implant). If short-channel effects reduce V_T below the long-channel values, the channel doping concentration must be increased even more to re-establish the desired V_T. Higher channel doping, however, generally degrades other device characteristics, such as carrier mobility and off-current. Thus, it is important to be able to model ΔV_{TSC} to facilitate reliable tradeoffs between process and electrical parameters and leakage current levels.

The failure of Eq. 4-74 to give good agreement with measured V_T values in short-channel MOSFETs arises because this equation was derived assuming one-dimensional theory. That is, Eq. 4-74 assumes the space charge under the gate is controlled only by the vertical $\mathcal{E}$-field, $\mathcal{E}_x$. In that case, the channel depletion region charge will be influenced only by the charge on the gate. When the channel of a MOSFET is long, this is a reasonable assumption, as the influence of the drain and source junctions (and the influence of V_{DS}) on the quantity of channel charge can be neglected (Figs. 5-2a and b).

---

* In section 5.2.3, however, we will see that V_T may initially increase as L shrinks, before ultimately decreasing as described here. This unexpected effect is referred to as a *reverse short-channel effect* (RSCE), and will be described in section 5.2.3.

However, as L approaches the dimensions of the source/drain junction depletion-region widths, a greater part of the channel-depletion region begins to consist of the space charge in the junction depletion regions (Fig. 5-2c and d). Hence, less gate charge (and a smaller vertical $\mathcal{E}$-field) is needed to cause inversion in short-channel MOSFETs than in long-channel MOSFETs (assuming each has the same substrate doping). This makes it appear that a smaller V_T is needed to turn on a short-channel device. Furthermore, as the reverse bias applied to the drain (V_{DS}) is increased, the drain depletion region grows wider, leaving even less charge under the control of the gate.

There are four approaches that have been taken to establish quantitative values of ΔV_{TSC}. They are the following:

1. *Numerical analysis* is used to find solutions of the two-dimensional Poisson equation for calculating the electric field and potential in the channel region.

2. Analytical expressions for ΔV_{TSC} are derived using the *charge sharing model.*

3. Analytical expressions for ΔV_{TSC} are derived using the drain-induced barrier lowering model, in which the 2-D Poisson equation is simplified to a one-dimensional form, making it solvable with analytical functions.

4. Analytical expressions for ΔV_{TSC} are derived using the drain-induced barrier lowering model in which a *quasi 2-D* approach is employed to analytically solve the Poisson equation.

While the numerical solution approach is the most accurate, this technique is not feasible for circuit simulation and statistical modeling. As a result, substantial effort has been expended to develop analytical models which provide rapid, inexpensive, and sufficiently accurate simulation of ΔV_{TSC}. Hence, we devote most of our discussion to the latter three approaches.

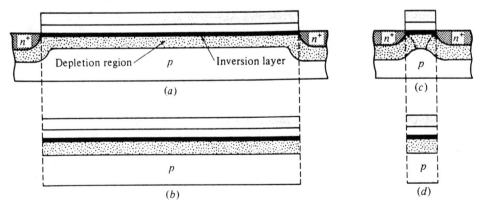

Fig. 5-2 (a) Long-channel transistor; (b) the channel of (a) with edge effects neglected; (c) a short-channel transistor; (d) the channel of (c) with edge effects neglected. From Y.P Tsividis, *Operation and Modeling of the MOS Transistor*, McGraw-Hill, New York, 1987. Reprinted with permission.

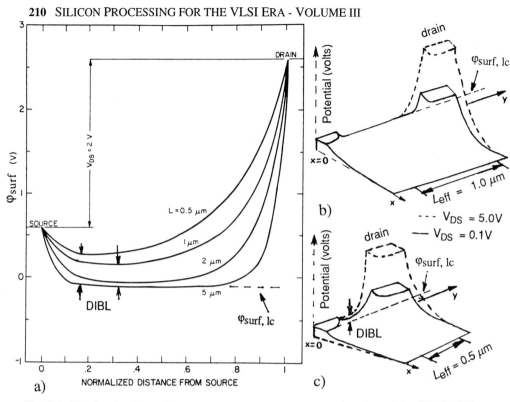

Fig. 5-3 Simulated values of the surface potential φ_{surf} along the channel for NMOSFETs with different channel lengths (note channel length is normalized). $N_A = 10^{15}$ cm^{-3}, $t_{ox} = 500$Å, $r_j = 0.33\mu m$, $V_{GS} = 0V$, $V_{DS} = 2.0V$, $V_{BS} = 0V$.[109] (© 1979 IEEE). (b & c) 2-D potential variation for NMOSFETs with (b) $L_{eff} = 1.0$ μm, and (c) $L_{eff} = 0.5$ μm (see also Fig. 5-5). Solid line, $V_{DS} = 0.1V$ and dashed line, $V_{DS} = 5.0V$.

5.2.1.1 Numerical Solution of the 2-D Poisson Equation for Calculating ΔV_{TSC}.
The most accurate method for simulating this effect is to solve the 2-D Poisson equation (i.e., as given here)

$$\frac{\partial^2 \varphi\,(x,\,y)}{\partial y^2} + \frac{\partial^2 \varphi\,(x,\,y)}{\partial x^2} = -\frac{\rho\,(x,\,y)}{\kappa_{si}\,\varepsilon_0} \qquad (5\text{-}1)$$

for the electrostatic-potential φ and the electric-field $\mathcal{E}$ in the channel region. While exact analytical solutions of the 2-D Poisson equation are not possible, numerical methods can be used to obtain solutions of Eq. 5-1. As noted in chap. 2, several software programs have been developed which allow these methods to be implemented.[2,21] Specifically, such numerical Poisson solvers are available in device simulators (e.g., GEMINI, MINIMOS, and PISCES-II). However, numerical solutions of 2-D partial differential equations are computationally intensive (and hence time-consuming and expensive), and therefore as noted, are not suitable for use in circuit simulation applications in which the electrical behavior of large circuits must be simulated. Nevertheless, they serve as accurate benchmarks of ΔV_{TSC} against which the values derived from the analytical models can be compared. Thus, they are a valuable tool for helping to develop more accurate analytical ΔV_{Tsc} models. Figure 5-3 shows such numerically calculated values of φ_{surf} versus y in NMOSFETs operated in subthreshold as L is decreased from 5.0 μm to 0.5 μm.

5.2.1.2 Charge-Sharing Models.

The *charge-sharing* perspective assumes that not all of the electric-field lines emanating from the charge under the gate terminate on the gate charge. Instead, some terminate on space charge in the source and drain depletion regions. The depletion charge under the gate is thus fractionally established by the source and drain (and in this sense, the channel charge is considered to be "shared" among the gate, source, and drain charge, see Fig. 5-4). Hence, less gate charge is required to cause inversion, making V_T appear smaller. The fraction of the charge induced by the source and drain becomes significant as the channel length is of the order of the junction depletion region widths. Charge-sharing models seek to quantitatively determine the fractional charge induced by the gate.

In 1974, Yau proposed a simple, widely used analytical model based on the *charge-sharing* perspective.[3] This model assumes that the charge controlled by the gate is

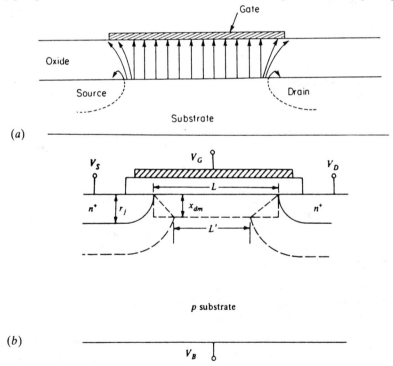

Fig. 5-4 (a) Schematic showing perturbation of the electric field lines in the oxide near the source and the drain.[5] (© 1985 IEEE). (b) Yau's model of charge sharing.[3] Reprinted with permission of Solid-State Electronics.

reduced to the charge in the trapezoidal region of the channel shown in Fig. 5-4b. The resulting analytical expression based on this assumption allows the value of ΔV_{Tsc} to be calculated in devices with uniformly doped channels:

$$\Delta V_{Tsc} = \frac{q\,N_{SUB}\,d_{max}\,r_j \left(\sqrt{\left\{1 + \frac{2\,d_{max}}{r_j}\right\}} - 1\right)}{C_{ox}\,L} \qquad (5\text{-}2)$$

where d_{max} is the maximum width of the depletion region in the channel, and r_j is the junction depth of the source/drain regions. According to Eq. 5-2, as L decreases, ΔV_{Tsc} increases. Eq. 5-2 also implies that to keep ΔV_{Tsc} as small as possible, shallow source/drain junctions and thin gate oxides should be used ($C_{ox} = \varepsilon_{ox}/t_{ox}$). In addition, the channel depletion-region width should also be as small as possible. Although it will be seen that some of the assumptions used in Yau's model are generally invalid, the qualitative guidelines it yields for minimizing ΔV_{Tsc} appear to be correct as channel lengths are shrunk, regardless of the model employed for predicting ΔV_{Tsc}. Yau's model also permits qualitative insight of V_T lowering with decreasing L to be gained, even if the quantitative ΔV_{Tsc} values do not accurately reflect experimental observations.

By modifying Eq. 5-2, Yau's model can also be used to estimate the effect of drain voltage on ΔV_{Tsc}. That is, in Eq. 5-2 it is assumed that the width of the source, drain, and channel depletion regions are equal. However, under drain bias the drain depletion region grows wider. Thus these three depletion regions no longer have equal widths. To reflect the effect of drain-width variation on ΔV_{Tsc}, Eq. 5-2 is reformulated as follows:[4]

$$\Delta V_{Tsc} = \frac{q\,N_{sub}\,d_{max}\,r_j \left(\left[\sqrt{\left\{1 + \frac{2\,W_S}{r_j}\right\}} - 1\right] + \left[\sqrt{\left\{1 + \frac{2\,W_D}{r_j}\right\}} - 1\right]\right)}{2\,C_{ox}\,L} \qquad (5\text{-}3)$$

Despite the appealing simplicity of the charge-sharing models, they fail to give good quantitative agreement with measured V_T values in devices with very short channels (e.g., < 1 μm) or under large drain voltages. This apparently occurs because several of the assumptions used to derive the model are not valid, especially under short-channel and large V_{DS} conditions. These include the following:

1. In Yau's model the induced charge is arbitrarily apportioned among the gate, source, and drain, whereas an accurate apportionment can only be accomplished by numerical integration of Poisson's equation and graphical analysis.

2. In the long-channel MOSFET model we assume that in subthreshold operation the entire V_{DS} is dropped across the drain depletion region. Thus, the channel potential in the rest of the channel region is essentially independent of V_{DS} and depends only on the gate bias. This also implies φ_{surf} in this region is independent of position (i.e., its value is constant with position along the channel). However, as we shall see this assumption breaks down in the case of short-channel MOSFETs (and as is evident from the data shown in Fig. 5-3). Yau's model, however, continues to assume that the potential in the channel region is constant with position. The portion of the charge that is shared is assumed to be distributed evenly under the gate to uniformly reduce the depletion charge density in the gate area. Obviously, this is not what actually happens physically.

These and other questionable assumptions of Yau's model are examined in ref. 5.

Nevertheless, despite the fact that charge-sharing models generally do not provide accurate quantitative results, they are still useful for providing first-order estimates of ΔV_{TSC}, as well as for helping to intuitively visualize the physical basis of changes in V_T as L is decreased.

5.2.1.3 Barrier-Lowering Models and DIBL.

The *barrier-lowering* perspective introduced by Troutman in 1979, provides a more rigorous foundation for deriving analytical models of ΔV_{TSC}.[6] It seeks to determine the change in the potential energy barrier between the source and channel at the Si interface caused by the junction depletion region charges (which in turn arise from both the built-in *pn* junction $\mathcal{E}$-field and the reverse-bias drain voltage) as well as the gate charge.

Troutman made measurements of DIBL,[6] and he and others[1,2,6] performed numerical analysis of the Poisson equation (Eq. 5-1) to match experimental and theoretical results. As noted earlier, numerical analysis is necessary to obtain more accurate results. However, because of the extensive computational procedures required, this solution approach is not appropriate for applications involving computer-aided circuit design. As a result, other workers sought to develop approximate analytical solutions of Eq. 5-1 which would be suitable for such applications.

This is done by finding analytical models of the surface potential φ_{surf} which relate it to the MOSFET structural parameters (e.g., t_{ox}, r_j, L), substrate doping levels, and applied biases. The value of φ_{surf} from these models is used in the threshold voltage equation to calculate the modified V_T value. The mathematical approach is to try and discover approximate analytical solutions to the 2-D Poisson equation, generally by converting it to a form that contains a differential term in only one dimension. This approach may be fruitful in this case, since we are only interested in finding the minimum value of φ at the surface (i.e., of φ_{surf}) along the y-direction from source to drain, i.e., we want to determine $[\varphi_{surf}(y)]_{min}$. In most cases analytical solutions with approximate boundary conditions are proposed as the model. The accuracy depends on the degree of approximation in the boundary conditions.

Many DIBL-based analytical models have been developed. In general, they are more complex than the charge-sharing models. One of the simplest and most widely adopted is that of Hsu et al.[7] In this model, the 2-D Poisson equation is reduced to a 1-D equation by essentially approximating the $(\partial^2 \varphi / \partial x^2)$ term of the 2-D equation as a constant. With the Poisson equation thereby converted into a 1-D form, it becomes possible to find an analytical solution, and Hsu's solution becomes the model for calculating ΔV_{TSC}. Jain and Balk extend this model to include the effect of non-uniform channel width.[8] They also point out that both the Hsu model and their extension are expected to be accurate only for small values of DIBL (i.e., for devices having channels that are not too short and in which V_{DS} is not too large). In addition, these models were derived for MOSFET structures with uniformly doped channel regions.

More recently, Skotnicki et al., reported another approach which allows the 2-D Poisson equation to be reduced to a 1-D equation using a so-called *voltage-doping transformation*. Using this technique they derived an analytical barrier-lowering model that is applicable to MOSFETs with non-uniformly doped channels.[9] Good agreement with measured data is also reported for devices with L as small as 0.8 μm (and in which V_{DS} values are as large as 3V). A final approach, as described in the next section, also provides good agreement with measured data over the ranges of voltages studied.

Nevertheless, the accuracy of the barrier-lowering-based analytical models has not yet been confirmed for predicting the value of ΔV_{TSC} in all device structures. As a result, it may still be prudent to use empirical measurements and/or numerical analysis to obtain accurate estimates of barrier lowering in specific device structures.

5.2.1.4 Quasi-Two-Dimensional Analytical Solution for ΔV_{TSC}.

By using a quasi-2-D approach to solve the 2-D Poisson equation in the channel of the MOSFET, an analytical model has been derived that reportedly predicts ΔV_{TSC} accurately, even for devices with channel lengths below 0.5 μm.[22] It begins by approximating the 2-D Poisson equation in the channel with the expression:

$$\frac{\varepsilon_{si} \, d_{max}}{\eta} \frac{d\mathcal{E}_y \, (y)}{dy} + \varepsilon_{ox} \frac{[V_T - V_{FB} - \varphi_{surf}(y)]}{t_{ox}} = q \, N_{sub} \, d_{max} \qquad (5-4a)$$

or

$$\frac{\varepsilon_{si} \, d_{max}}{\eta} \frac{d^2\varphi_{surf} \, (y)}{dy^2} + \varepsilon_{ox} \frac{[V_T - V_{FB} - \varphi_{surf}(y)]}{t_{ox}} = q \, N_{sub} \, d_{max} \qquad (5-4b)$$

where the parameters of this equation have been defined previously (except for η, which is a fitting parameter). The second term on the left-hand side is an approximation of the term $\partial \mathcal{E}_x / \partial x$ in the 2-D form of the Poisson equation. This quasi-2-D approach is also used in deriving a model for I_{Dsat} and thus, the details involved in transforming Eq. 5-1 into a form akin to Eq. 5-4 are given in section 5.4.3.

The solution to Eq. 5-4, namely $\varphi_{surf}(y)$, under the boundary conditions $\varphi_{surf}(0) = V_{bi}$ and $\varphi_{surf}(L) = V_{DS} + V_{bi}$ is:

$$\varphi_{surf}(y) = V_{sL} + (V_{bi} + V_{DS} - V_{sL}) \frac{\sinh \, (y/l)}{\sinh \, (L/l)} + (V_{bi} - V_{sL}) \frac{\sinh \, (L - y)/l)}{\sinh \, (L/l)} \qquad (5-5)$$

In Eq. 5-5 $V_{sL} = V_{GS} - V_T$, V_{bi} is the built-in potential between the source-substrate and drain-substrate junctions, and l is the characteristic length defined as

$$l = \sqrt{\frac{\varepsilon_{si} \, t_{ox} \, d_{max}}{\varepsilon_{ox} \, \eta}} \qquad (5-6)$$

Equation 5-5 can now be plotted for a sufficient number of points between $y = 0$ and $y = L$ (e.g., 10 or more). From such plotted data, and a fitted curve, the minimum value of $\varphi_{surf}(y)$ can be found. By subtracting the long-channel value of φ_{surf} at V_T from $\varphi_{surf}(y)_{min}$, we can find ΔV_{TSC}. Figure 5-5 plots Eq. 5-5 for φ_{surf} at a given V_{GS}, and for two values of V_{DS} [i.e., $V_{DS} = 0.05V$ (dashed lines) and $V_{DS} = 1.5V$ (solid lines)] for

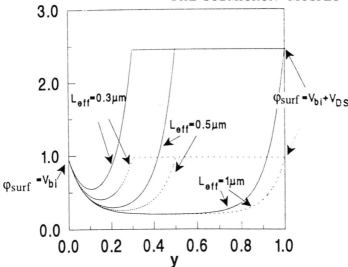

Fig. 5-5 (a) Calculated surface potential along channel for different channel lengths using Eq. 5-5. The device parameters are t_{ox} = 100Å, N_{sub} = N_A = 10^{16} cm^{-3}, n^+ = 10^{20} cm^{-3}, and η = 1, i.e., l = 0.1 μm.[22] (© IEEE 1993).

MOSFETs with different channel lengths. In this example, the device with L_{eff} = 1 μm has a region where φ_{surf} is constant as a function of position along a large fraction of the channel length (i.e., at a value of φ_{surf} ~0.2V in this figure), and this value is determined merely by the gate bias (and not V_{DS}). A constant value of φ_{surf} versus y is indicative of long-channel behavior and V_T in this device can thus be accurately found using Eq. 4-74.

In Fig. 5-5, devices with channel lengths 0.5 μm or smaller have a minimum value of φ_{surf} greater than the long-channel φ_{surf} value (i.e., $|2\varphi_B|$), and no region of constant φ_{surf} (y) is evident, even for small values of V_{DS}. (This is different than the charge sharing approach, in which a region of constant [but somewhat larger] φ_{surf} versus distance is assumed to exist even in very short length devices.) The results of Fig. 5-5 have been verified by 2D numerical simulation using such programs as MINIMOS and PISCES (e.g., as shown in plots of φ_{surf} versus y for various L values, see Fig. 5-3).

The minimum value of $\varphi_{surf}(y)$ is also seen in Fig. 5-5 to increase (i.e., the potential energy barrier for electron flow between source and drain will decrease) with decreasing channel length and increasing V_{DS}. If the minimum long-channel value of φ_{surf} is subtracted from the minimum value calculated from Eq. 5-5 we get an expression for ΔV_{Tsc}. When V_{DS} is small, this expression can be approximated as

$$\Delta V_{Tsc} = [2 (V_{bi} - 2\varphi_B) + V_{DS}] (e^{-L/2l} + 2e^{-L/l}) \qquad (5-7)$$

Figure 5-6a shows the value of ΔV_{Tsc} versus L as calculated with Eq. 5-7 as well as with 2D numerical simulation. Agreement with the numerical simulation results is seen to be very good. It should also be noted that if $L > 5l$, then this equation reduces to a single exponential term, much like the one derived from the simpler barrier-lowering models described in the previous section.* For most technologies l is about 0.1-0.15 μm, hence these simple models give accurate results for ΔV_{TSC} only if the channel length exceeds 0.5-0.8 μm.

When V_{DS} is not small, the expression for ΔV_{TSC} from this model is more complex, with its value when $L > 5l$ given approximately as

$$\Delta V_{TSC} = 3(V_{bi} - 2\varphi_B) + V_{DS}) e^{-L/l} + 2\sqrt{(V_{bi} - 2\varphi_B)(V_{bi} - 2\varphi_B + V_{DS})}e^{-L/2l} \quad (5-8)$$

Eq. 5-8 reduces to Eq. 5-7 for large L/l and small V_{DS} as expected. Figure 5-6b shows the results of calculating V_T versus V_{DS} for $L_{eff} = 0.3$ μm with Eqs. 5-7 and 5-8 as well as with 2D numerical simulation. Eq. 5-8 is seen to compare well with the 2D numerical simulation results, but Eq. 5-7 overestimates ΔV_{TSC} at high V_{DS}. In Fig. 5-7 the value of V_T is calculated versus L using the charge sharing model, 2D numerical simulation, and Eq. 5-8. The results using Eq. 5-8 and numerical simulation are comparable. Finally, Fig. 5-8 compares the values of V_T versus L (with V_{BS} as the parameter) calculated with Eq. 5-8 and with measured V_T values in non-LDD

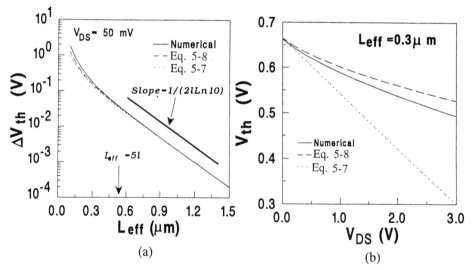

(a)

(b)

Fig. 5-6 (a) The calculated ΔV_T shifts versus channel length at $V_{DS} = 0.005$V. Note that the values obtained from the simple analytical models agree well with the numerical solution. The device parameters are the same as those in Fig. 5-5. Note that when $L > 5l$, all the curves have the same slope of l ($2l$ in Eq. 5-8). (b) Comparison between simple analytical solutions and numerical solution of threshold voltage versus drain voltage. The solution based on $y_0 = L/2$ (Eq. 5-7) overestimates the variation in threshold voltage.[22] (© 1993 IEEE).

* If $L = 5l$ then the first exponential term in Eq. 5-7 is $e^{-2.5}$ while the second term is e^{-5}, which is much smaller than $e^{-2.5}$. Thus, for $L > 5l$, the second exponential term in Eq. 5-7 can be neglected, leaving an expression with only one exponential term. For cases where L is smaller than $\sim 5l$, the second exponential term cannot be neglected, and the full Eq. 5-7 must be used to get accurate values of ΔV_{TSC} when V_{DS} is small.

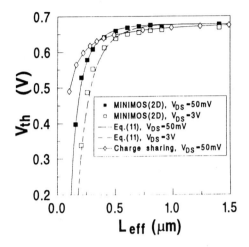

Fig. 5-7 Comparison of the V_T calculated using the charge sharing model, the two-dimensional numerical simulation (using MINIMOS), and the model of ref. 22. The device parameters are the same as those used in Fig. 5-5.[22] (© 1993 IEEE).

MOSFETs. Again, agreement is very good. The report describing this model also describes its application to LDD MOSFETs.

The characteristic length l defined in Eq. 5-6 needs to be more exactly determined in order for this model to give accurate values of ΔV_{TSC}. That is, due to the fitting parameter η in Eq. 5-6, the value of l from Eq. 5-6 only gives its correct order of magnitude. The exact value of l needs to be extracted from V_T data taken from actual MOSFETs.

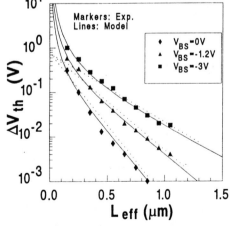

Fig. 5-8 ΔV_T versus L_{eff} at $V_{DS} = 0.005V$ and different V_{BS} values for an non-LDD device. The solid lines are calculated results and the dashed lines are lines best fitting the experimental data of $L_{eff} >> 5l$.[22] (© 1993 IEEE).

An alternative form to Eq. 5-6 for expressing l which allows its exact value to be empirically extracted is based on the empirical expression of Brews et al[23] for the minimum channel length L_{min} a MOSFET must have in order to exhibit acceptable subthreshold behavior (see section 5.6.1.2 for more details on this expression):

$$L_{min} = 0.41 (r_j \ t_{ox} \ d_{max}^2)^{1/3} \qquad (5 - 9)$$

If we assume L_{min} is about $4l$, using Eq. 5-9 yields an empirical expression for l as

$$l = 0.1 (r_j \ t_{ox} \ d_{max}^2)^{1/3} \qquad (5 - 10)$$

According to this model, for an n-channel MOSFET with an n^+ poly gate, it can be shown that in order to maintain V_T at 0.7V, i.e.,

$$V_T = 0.7V = V_{FB} + 2\varphi_B + \frac{t_{ox}}{\varepsilon_{ox}} \frac{4 \ \varepsilon_{si} \ \varphi_B}{d_{max}} \qquad (5 - 11)$$

it is necessary that

$$d_{max} = \frac{t_{ox}}{\varepsilon_{ox}} \frac{4 \ \varepsilon_{si} \ \varphi_B}{(V_T - V_{FB} - 2\varphi_B)} \approx \frac{2 \ \varepsilon_{si}}{\varepsilon_{ox}} \ t_{ox} \qquad (5 - 12)$$

By substituting Eq. 5-12 into Eq. 5-10, l can be rewritten as

$$l = 0.0007 \ r_j^{1/3} \ t_{ox} \qquad (5 - 13)$$

where r_j and l are in μm and t_{ox} is in Å. On the other hand, for an n-channel MOSFET with a p^+ poly gate,

$$d_{max} = 4 \ (\varepsilon_{si}/\varepsilon_{ox}) \ t_{ox} \qquad (5 - 14)$$

(assuming $V_T = 1.2V$). Therefore one has $l \sim 0.0011 \ r_j^{1/3} t_{ox}$. This helps explain why buried-channel devices, either NMOSFETs or PMOSFETs generally have worse short-channel effects than comparable surface-channel N- or PMOSFETs.

5.2.1.5 Measuring Surface-DIBL Effects.

Surface-DIBL in MOSFET structures with a fixed L can be empirically characterized by measuring and plotting a set of log I_{Dst} versus V_{GS} curves with increasing values V_{DS} as the parameter (as shown in Fig. 5-9). When analyzing such a set of curves, it must first be ascertained that subsurface-punchthrough current is not flowing (see section 5.3 for a discussion on punchthrough). For example, in Fig. 5-9 there is no indication that such punchthrough current occurs over the applied V_{DS} range, since S_t remains constant as V_{DS} is increased.*

Once it is verified that punchthrough current is not significant, a quantitative estimate of surface-DIBL can be extracted from the shift in gate voltage ΔV_{GS} at a fixed drain current (typically 0.1 $\mu A/\mu m$) as the drain-source voltage is increased. That is, the

---

* If a device exhibits punchthrough current within the normal operating V_{DS} range, the structure must be redesigned to eliminate this behavior. Devices exhibiting punchthrough will exhibit excessive leakage current at $V_{GS} = 0V$ (i.e., when the device is nominally OFF).

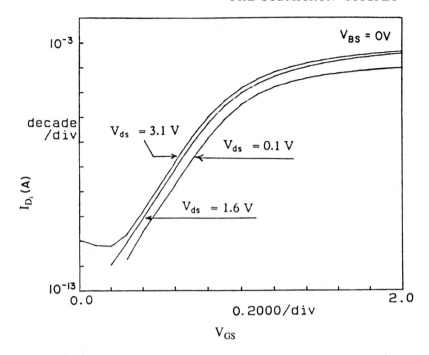

Fig. 5-9 Plot of log I_D versus V_{GS} for an NMOSFET operated below threshold, with V_{DS} as the parameter. The value of $\Delta V_{GS}/\Delta V_{DS}$ for a fixed value of I_D (e.g., 1×10^{-7} A/μm) is used to characterize DIBL.

ΔV_{GS} value represents a good first-order estimate of the expected shift in V_T as a function of drain bias. The shift in V_{GS} is normally expressed in normalized form as $\Delta V_{GS}/\Delta V_{DS}$. An acceptable value of $\Delta V_{GS}/\Delta V_{DS}$ is ~25 mV/V, depending on the circuit application and specific leakage requirements. $\Delta V_{GS}/\Delta V_{DS}$ is a strong function of channel length (Fig. 5-10) and must be guaranteed to at least 3-σ below the target channel length.

An alternative method of evaluating DIBL is to measure the change in drain current as V_{DS} is increased at some fixed gate voltage below V_T (e.g., the change ΔI_D in Fig. 5-10 when V_{DS} is increased from 0.1 [solid line in Fig. 5-10] to 5.0V [dashed line]). Because of its simplicity, this measurement is easily implemented on automated test equipment.

Another perspective on this last technique for measuring surface-DIBL is that such barrier lowering raises the electron density at the surface in subthreshold operation. That is, the electron density at the source end of the channel n_s(source) - where the surface potential is at a minimum - is increased due to surface-DIBL from its long-channel device value $n_s = (n_i^2/N_A) \exp(q\varphi_{surf}/kT)$ to

$$n_{sDIBL} = (\frac{n_i^2}{N_A}) e^{q\varphi_{surf}/kT} e^{q\Delta V_{Tsc}/kT} \qquad (5-15)$$

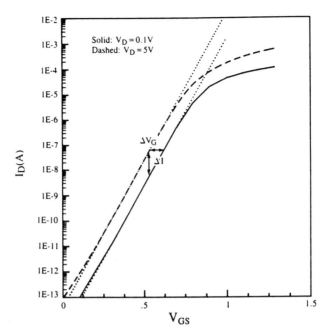

Fig. 5-10 Simulated values of I_D versus V_{GS} for two values of V_{DS} (0.1V and 5V) in a MOSFET with L_{eff} = 0.7V. From J. Teplik, Chap. 2, "Device Design," in *BiCMOS Technology and Applications*, A. Alvarez Ed., Klewer Academic Publishers, Boston MA, 1989. Reprinted with permission.

where ΔV_{TSC} will become larger as V_{DS} is increased. This also implies that surface-DIBL will cause I_{Dst} at a fixed value of V_{GS} and L to increase - by a factor of $\exp(q\Delta V_{TSC}/kT)$ - above that expected in a long-channel device.[*] Experimental data can be plotted to depict this effect in the following way: As shown in Fig. 5-11, log I_D is plotted versus V_{DS} with V_{GS} as the parameter. Figure 5-11a shows such characteristic curves for an NMOS device with L = 2.1 μm and Fig. 5-11b for a device with L = 0.8 μm. In both figures the curves exhibit two distinct regions. At low values of V_{DS}, I_D depends primarily on V_{GS} and increases only slightly with V_{DS} (*but it is this change in I_D that represents surface-DIBL*).[**] Eventually the I_D curves intercept a more steeply

[*] Note, however, that as V_{GS} is decreased, the value of n_s at the source will decrease as quickly with decreasing V_{GS} as in a long-channel device, because, the gate still has control of the charge giving rise to I_D. So, S_t will not change, even though V_T is smaller. But, when the device is in punchthrough, the gate no longer has the same control of charge flow as V_{GS} is reduced. Hence, drain current doesn't decrease as quickly with shrinking V_{GS}, or S_t gets larger in punchthrough.

[**] Note that according to the model of subthreshold behavior in long-channel MOSFETs at a fixed value of V_{GS}, I_{Dst} is independent of the drain voltage V_{DS} for V_{DS}>0.1V (see Eq. 4-90). But because of surface-DIBL, for a fixed value of L and V_{DS}, I_{Dst} increases as V_{DS} increases, as described in earlier sections.

rising curve, and for V_{DS} values beyond this point I_D is no longer influenced by V_{GS}, but instead rises quickly as V_{DS} is increased. The I_D behavior in this latter region is indicative that subsurface-DIBL (punchthrough) has set in, as discussed in section 5.3.

5.2.1.6 Dependence of V_T on V_{BS} in Short-Channel MOSFETs.

In long-channel, uniformly doped MOSFETs the threshold voltage depends on the body-substrate voltage V_{BS} as given by Eq. 4-12 (repeated here for convenience)

$$V_T = V_{FB} + 2\varphi_B + \gamma (2\varphi_B + V_{BS})^{1/2} \qquad (5 - 16)$$

In short-channel MOSFETs, however, the effect on V_T when a substrate bias V_{BS} is applied is not well modeled by this expression. That is, as shown in Fig. 5-12, at shorter channels or higher drain biases, V_T is less sensitive to V_{BS} than predicted by Eq. 5-16. For example, in the case of $L = 1.5$ μm and $V_{DS} = 8V$ shown in Fig. 5-12, V_T becomes almost independent of V_{BS} at larger values of V_{BS}. In addition, for the case of $L = 0.7$ μm, V_T becomes independent of V_{BS} for all values of V_{BS}.[10] This implies that the substrate tends to lose control of the channel (just as does the gate itself), at shorter channel lengths. The break in the slope of the $L = 1.5$ μm curves in Fig. 5-12 occurs with punchthrough of the depletion regions of the source and drain (see sec. 5.3 for details on punchthrough). This is because punchthrough decouples the edge of the depletion region from the gate, thereby decoupling the channel from the substrate.

The data shown in Fig. 5-12 also implies that this effect can be modeled numerically by using a smaller body effect coefficient γ (defined in Eq. 4-8a as $\gamma = [\kappa_{si}\varepsilon_o/qN_A]^{1/2}$)

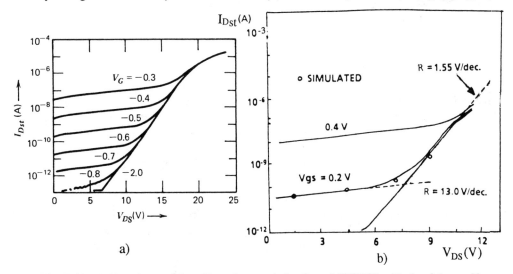

Fig. 5-11 (a) Experimental I_{Dst}-V_{DS} characteristics for a MOSFET with $L = 2.1$ μm, $V_S = V_B = 0V$. For smaller values of V_{DS}, I_{Dst} is reduced by roughly one order of magnitude for each 0.1V decrease in V_{GS} below V_T. At higher values of V_{DS}, a subsurface punchthrough current flows that is independent of V_{GS}.[111] (© 1974 IEEE). (b) Experimental and simulated values of I_{Dst} versus V_{DS} for a 0.8 μm NMOSFET with Z = 20 μm.[74] (© 1988 IEEE).

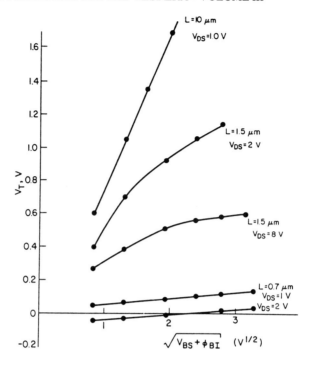

Fig. 5-12 Variation of V_T versus V_{BS} for three different channel lengths: $L = 10$ μm (long channel); $L = 1.5$ μm (short channel); $L = 0.7$ μm (punched through at $V_{BS} = 0V$). $N_A = 10^{15}$ cm^{-3}, $t_{ox} = 1000$Å, $r_j = 1$ μm.[10] Reprinted with permission of *Solid-State Electronics*.

in the threshold voltage equation. Similar results have been obtained by Sheu et al.[11] They, however, elected to model this effect in the short-channel MOSFET SPICE model (BSIM, see section 5.5) by including another empirical term in the V_T equation (i.e., this new term is $P_2[2\varphi_B - V_{BS}]$, see Eq. 5-75). The coefficient P_2 of this term is empirically determined from measurements, and has a value of 0.8634 in BSIM.

5.2.2 Narrow Gate-Width Effects on Threshold Voltage

As device *widths* shrink, three additional effects begin to modify the expected V_T behavior of such *narrow-channel* MOSFETs. Although these effects are less critical than short-channel effects, they cannot be ignored. The first two cause measured values of V_T to *increase* above those calculated by Eq. 5-16 as the width is decreased (making the MOSFET appear narrower than its geometrical width).[12] The third causes V_T to *decrease*, in effect making the device appear wider. The first two effects are exhibited by MOSFETs fabricated with either raised field-oxide isolation structures (in which the field oxide is grown and then etched to expose the active device regions, Fig. 5-13a) or with semi-recessed LOCOS isolation structures (see chap. 6) as shown in Fig. 5-13b.

The third effect occurs in devices which use fully-recessed-LOCOS or trench-isolation structures (in which the trench is filled with an insulator).

The first effect is the opposite of the short-channel V_T shift effect. That is, at the source and drain ends of the channel (i.e., along the length dimension L), a depletion region exists at each pn junction (even at V_{FB}), requiring less voltage to be applied to invert the channel. As just mentioned, this leads to a *decrease* in V_T in *short-channel* MOSFETs. However, at the ends of the channel perpendicular to the drain current flow, no pn junction exists (i.e., along the edges of the device in the *width* dimension). Hence, a gate bias that repels majority carriers must not only deplete such carriers in the channel in the vertical direction, but also in the lateral direction beyond the thin gate oxide. Because the lateral depletion region width in this region extends beyond the gate, an effective bulk charge width larger than the actual width is apparently present. If the width Z is small, these side regions represent a large percentage of the depleted volume. Hence, a larger V_{GS} must be applied to invert the channel than if these edge regions did not have to be depleted. This leads to an *increase* in V_T.

The second effect arises from the encroachment of the channel-stop dopants under the edges of the sides of the gate. (In the case of NMOSFETs boron channel-stop dopants

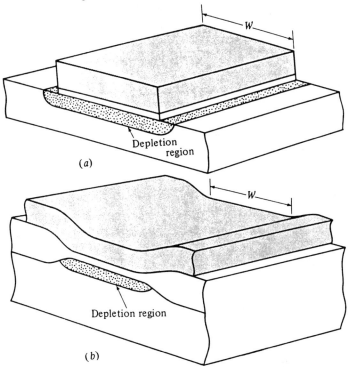

(a)

(b)

Fig. 5-13 Effect of fringing field on spreading the depletion region sideways. (a) In MOSFET with field oxide grown and then etched to expose the active region. (b) In MOSFET having a semirecessed LOCOS field oxide. From Y.P Tsividis, *Operation and Modeling of the MOS Transistor*, McGraw-Hill, New York, 1987, p. 192. Reprinted with permission.

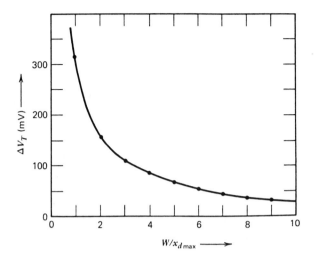

5-14 Threshold voltage shift ΔV_T caused by this narrow-channel effect for a MOSFET with $N_A = 10^{15}$ cm^{-3}, and $t_{ox} = 50$ nm.[12] From G. Merkel, *Process and Device Modeling for IC Design,* (F. Van de Wield, Ed.), Noordhoff, Leyden, (1977). Reprinted with permission.

encroach under the gate edges. In the case of PMOSFETs, where a channel-stop implant may not be used, phosphorus pileup at the silicon surface during field oxidation produces *n*-type channel stop dopants at higher concentrations in the field regions. This also gives rise to subsequent encroachment into the active regions.) This has the effect of doping the channel at the edges along the width dimension more heavily than at the center (see Fig. 6-10). Again, a larger voltage must be applied to the gate to completely invert the channel than if the additional doping at the edges was not present (Fig. 5-14). From another perspective, the channel at the edges will be less turned on than the channel at the center. Thus, for the same ($V_{GS} - V_T$), significantly less current may be conducted in a narrow-channel MOSFET with channel-stop dopant encroachment than in one without such encroachment.

In practice, the latter (encroachment-related) effect is more severe than the edge-depletion-region effect, especially in devices with heavy channel-stop implants. An analytical expression that models both effects in semirecessed MOSFETs is given in ref. 13. For more precise calculations, however, numerical analyses are required.[14] Several methods are described in chap. 6 for reducing the channel-stop encroachment and thus reducing this narrow-width effect.

Because the third effect *decreases* V_T, is often called the *inverse narrow-width effect*. As pointed out earlier, the effect occurs in MOSFETs with trench or fully recessed LOCOS isolation structures, as shown in Fig. 5-15. (Note that the narrow width effects described earlier does not occur in trench isolation structures. Since there is no semiconductor region beyond the edges of the gate in the width dimension, there is no region that is subject to depletion.)

Figure 5-15a depicts the edge of the channel, the trench field-oxide, and the gate (which always overlaps the channel to some degree). When the gate is biased, the field lines from the overlapping region are focused by the edge geometry of the channel. Thus, at the edges of the channel, an inversion layer is formed at lower voltages than at the center. As a result, *less* bias overall must be applied to the gate to invert the channel across its full width. From another perspective, a *corner parasitic MOSFET* in parallel with the main device is established. The parasitic device turns on at voltages lower that the main channel, resulting in a "hump" in the drain current versus gate voltage curves (Fig. 5-15b).[15] Thus, the parasitic device increases the subthreshold leakage current of the active device.

An analytical expression that simulates the narrow-width effect in an ideal isolation trench structure is given in ref. 16. A more general analysis of the narrow width effect that covers both the first and third effects is carried out in ref. 17. An even more recent model of the inverse-narrow-width effect in trench isolated submicron MOSFETs, including the impact of non-uniformly doped channels was proposed by Chung and Li.[18]

However, the inverse-width effect is also sensitive to several other factors,[19] including:

1. The *doping concentration in the sidewalls of the silicon*, which can be impacted by channel-stop dopant redistribution, dopant segregation during field-oxide growth, or intentional doping of the sidewalls by such processes as large-tilt-angle implantation.

2. The trench isolation spacing.

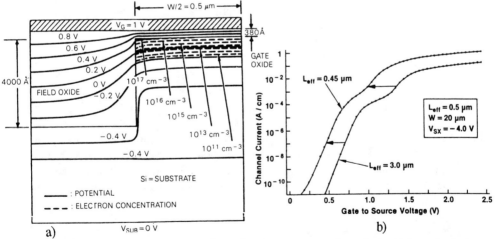

a)

b)

Fig. 5-15 (a) Structure and two dimensional contours of equipotentials and electron concentrations for a MOSFET employing a trench or fully-recessed oxide isolation structure. [112] (© 1979 IEEE). (b) "Hump" in subthreshold I_D-V_{GS} curve due to the inverse narrow width effect in trench isolated MOSFETs.[15] This paper was originally presented at the Fall 1988 Meeting of the Electrochemical Society held in Chicago IL.

3. The shape of the corner region at the edge of the gate. (If the top surface of the field oxide is depressed below the gate-oxide surface, the effect will be more severe than if the field oxide surface is raised above the gate oxide surface.)

Thus, if trench isolation is used, the planarization technology that determines the final wafer topology at the conclusion of the isolation structure fabrication will have to be tightly controlled to maintain precise control of V_T (see also chap. 6).

5.2.2.1 Devices Exhibiting Both Short- and Narrow-Width Effects. In devices in which both effects are capable of causing a shift in V_T, neither the short-channel nor the narrow-channel models alone suffice to accurately predict the resultant V_T. Some simplified analytical expressions employing a three-dimensional approximation of the depletion regions have been developed,[20] but for cases involving various device voltages and non-uniform channel doping concentrations, numerical analyses are necessary.

5.2.3 Reverse Short-Channel Effects on Threshold Voltage (RSCE)

In the previous sections it was implied that the V_T of a MOSFET decreases monotonically with decreasing channel length. This was explained by two-dimensional electrostatic field considerations, and various models for predicting such effects were described. However, in some situations it has been found that V_T initially *increases* with decreasing channel length (beginning when L ~2-3 μm), contrary to what is normally expected.[91,92] This phenomenon has been termed *reverse short channel effect (RSCE)*, V_T *roll-up*, or *anomalous threshold behavior*. After V_T reaches a maximum value due to RSCE (at ~0.7 μm), it then declines as channel lengths are further decreased (V_T *roll off*). Apparently the two-dimensional effects that are responsible for V_T roll-off eventually compete with the effects causing V_T roll-up and the former come to dominate at the shortest channel lengths. (In fact, the ultimate rate of V_T roll-off with L_{eff} is reported to be much faster than can be explained by conventional models of laterally uniform channel doping). The combined RSCE and V_T roll-off effects result in a "hump" in the V_T versus L characteristics (Fig. 5-16). The initial rate of enhancement of V_T with decreasing L is also maximum at zero bias and decreases with increasing bias. As will be described in the next sections, different explanations have been given for the V_T roll-up effect. However, while several models which seem to provide good quantitative agreement with experimental observations of RSCE have been developed, a consensus has not yet been reached as to which physical mechanism(s) are responsible for the effect.

5.2.3.1 Model which Proposes RSCE is Due to Lateral Dopant Nonuniformity at the Channel Si-SiO$_2$ Interface (Arising from Enhanced Diffusion of Channel Dopants Caused by Interstitial Injection During Poly Reox, Salicide Formation, or Implant Damage). The first explanation of RSCE is based on the fact that this effect was initially observed in NMOSFETs fabricated with two boron channel implants (i.e., a

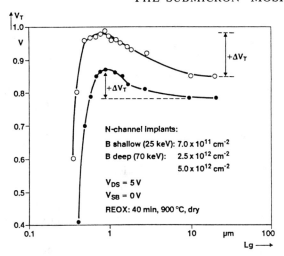

Fig. 5-16 Experimental *n*-channel threshold voltage versus channel length.[92] (© 1987 IEEE).

shallow boron implant for adjustment of the threshold voltage, as described in chap. 4, and a deeper boron implant for suppression of punchthrough, as described in section 5.3).[92] The doping profile as a function of x in the channel beneath the gate oxide resulting from these two implants is qualitatively depicted in Fig. 5-17a.

After the polysilicon gate is defined by etching and the source/drain regions are implanted, a thermal oxidation step (referred to as *reoxidation* or *re-ox*) is performed (see also chap. 9, sec. 9.7.1.4). This oxidation serves several purposes, including: (1) to re-oxidize the source/drain regions. (The source/drain implant is carried out with the gate oxide intact over these regions. The heavy implant is likely to damage and contaminate this oxide, and so it is stripped after the implant. The reoxidation step regrows a fresh oxide over the source/drain regions, as well as on and around the poly gate); (2) the thermal oxide on the poly serves as a diffusion mask which prevents boron dopants from the BPSG interlevel dielectric from diffusing into the n^+ poly during the BPSG flow and reflow processes; (3) to reduce the MOSFET gate-to-drain overlap capacitance and strengthen the gate oxide at the poly gate edge. The latter benefits are obtained because oxidation-induced encroachment gives rise to a so-called *gate bird's beak* - or *graded gate oxide* [GGO] - under the polysilicon edge, as shown in Fig. 5-17b. The thicker oxide due to GGO at the gate edge reduces the gate-to-drain overlap capacitance and relieves the electric-field intensity at the corner of the gate structure, thus enhancing the gate oxide integrity at its edge. However, the reoxidation step can also detrimentally impact the characteristics of MOSFETs which employ lightly-doped drains (LDD), and thus the re-ox step must be optimized for this type of device, as is described in more detail in chap. 9. Here only the proposed impact on V_T due to the re-ox step is considered.

As described in chap. 7. vol. 1, the injection of interstitials which accompanies thermal oxidation causes oxidation-enhanced-diffusion (OED) of dopants in the vicinity of the growing oxide (see Fig. 5-17b). In the re-ox step, the diffusion of dopants is enhanced not only under the oxidizing (i.e., source/drain) regions but also in the adjacent channel region (due to lateral diffusion of the injected Si self-interstitials into the channel region). The OED causes boron to diffuse more rapidly. This brings more boron from the deep buried peak to the surface near the edges of the channel (because the injected interstitial concentration is highest near the channel edges). As a result, the boron surface concentration becomes larger at the channel edges than if diffusion of the implanted boron profile had not been enhanced (see Fig. 5-18). The increased concentration of the boron in these regions gives rise to an overall increase in V_T if L becomes small enough to make these regions a significant fraction of the channel length.

The V_T roll-up has also been observed in MOSFETs in which a salicide is fabricated[93] (i.e., a *salicide* is a self-aligned silicide formed on the source/drain regions to reduce the sheet resistance of the source and drain, see chap. 3, Vol. 2). Lu and Sung propose that during silicide formation vacancies are injected and these enhance the dopant diffusion of the boron in the dual-implant profile, again giving rise to a lateral nonuniform lateral distribution of boron along the channel surface. As in the OED model, this gives rise to an enhancement of V_T as the MOSFET channel length is decreased.

An analytical model of RSCE based on nonuniform lateral boron surface concentrations arising from either (or both) of the above effects has been developed by Arora and Sharma,[94] although they model the RSCE as being due to a nonuniform buildup of oxide charge along the Si-SiO$_2$ interface (see also section 5.2.3.4).

5.2.3.2 Model Which Proposes RSCE Arises from Boron Segregation to Implant Damaged Regions at the Edge of the Channel. Although the above models appear plausible, V_T roll-up has also been

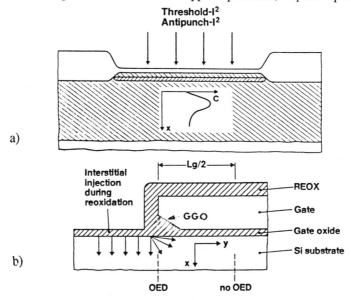

Fig. 5-17 (a) Vertical doping profile in an NMOSFET channel which uses a punchthrough implant. (b) Conceptual diagram of local interstitial injection during reox.[92] (© 1987 IEEE).

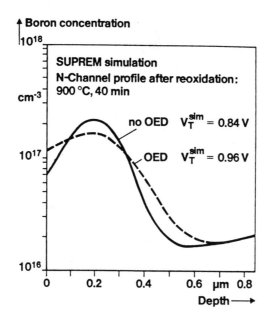

Fig. 5-18 Simulated vertical *n*-channel profiles at x = 0 and x = *L*/2 with and without oxidation-enhanced diffusion (OED).[92] (© 1987 IEEE).

observed in MOSFETs with uniformly doped channel regions (Fig. 5-19). In such MOSFETs the above models would predict that boron surface concentrations would *decrease* near the edges of the channels. (That is, boron would segregate into the growing oxide, and then boron from the center of the channel would diffuse into these depleted regions, resulting in a loss of boron from the channel region). Thus, the model of section 5.2.3.1 predicts that V_T would *decrease monotonically* with decreasing channel length in MOSFETs with nonimplanted (i.e., uniform) channel regions. Furthermore, when the channels get very short, (i.e., ≤0.3 μm) the observed V_T *roll-off* is more rapid than that predicted by the 2-D DIBL numerical analyses assuming a laterally uniform channel doping. As a result, another phenomenon has been suggested as being responsible for the RSCE (including both the initial V_T roll-up and the subsequent enhanced roll-off effects as the channel length is decreased), namely the depletion of boron from the channel region by strong segregation of the boron into the adjacent source and drain regions during the source/drain implant-activation anneal.[95, 96]

This segregation is thought to occur as a result of the presence of crystal defects caused by the source/drain implant step. (Such defects have, in fact, been detected using TEM micrographs of the source/drain regions after the source/drain implant step.) The boron is theorized to have a higher local solubility in the defective regions, and thus will diffuse to them during the anneal steps performed after the source/drain implant. Figure 5-19 shows the measured and calculated V_T versus *L* curves. The triangular data points in this figure are calculated using a 2-D device simulator assuming a uniform lateral doping profile in the channel, and these show the conventional roll-off versus L as described in section 5.2.1. The data points indicated by the squares and filled circles show the V_T versus L values calculated using the same device simulator, but with nonuniform lateral boron channel doping (see Fig. 5-20). The open-circle data points are the experimental data.

The V_T roll-up is well predicted by this model, as is the enhanced V_T roll-off for channel lengths shorter than about 0.3 μm. (This model also gives good agreement with RSCE in PMOSFETs.) For MOSFETs in which $L \leq 0.3$ μm the center of the channel is so small that the channel region depleted of boron extends across the entire channel length (see, for example, case where $L = 0.2$ μm in Fig. 5-20), and there is not sufficient dopant present in this region to cause the peaks of the boron concentration at the channel edges to rise to a degree that would offset the enhanced V_T decrease due to the depletion effect.

The defects that give rise to the lateral dopant redistribution are observed to be eventually extinguished by a higher temperature anneal step (e.g., 900°C in N_2 for 5 min). Thus, it has been suggested that recrystallization of the defective regions using RTP could be carried out, such that the anneal would take place over a sufficiently short time as not to permit lateral dopant redistribution to occur.[95] If this is possible MOSFETs could be fabricated which would exhibit neither the V_T roll-up nor enhanced roll-off effects. Another suggestion to alleviate the enhanced roll-off effect is to use a halo implant to increase the boron dopant concentration near the source and drain such that the B depletion would be counteracted.[96]

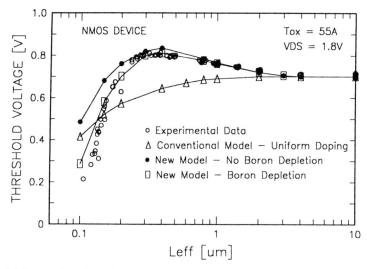

Fig. 5-19 Measured and modeled V_T versus L curves. The conventional model results assume laterally uniform channel doping. The new model results assume box approximations for the lateral channel doping profile shown in Fig. 5-20. The boron depletion case assumes that the bulk doping is depleted into the source and drain regions within 0.1 mm of their edges.[95] (© 1993 IEEE).

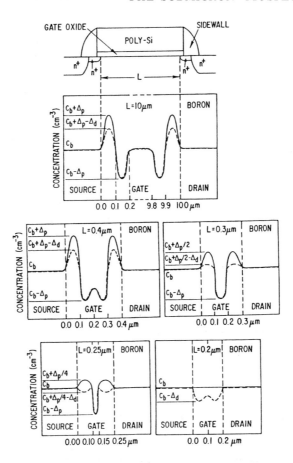

Fig. 5-20 Conceptual schematic of the lateral channel doping profile of the present model for different channel lengths. The solid lines represent the case of no bulk depletion while the dotted lines represent the case of bulk depletion.[95] (© 1993 IEEE).

5.2.3.3 Model Which Attributes RSCE to Transient Enhanced Diffusion of Channel Dopants to the Silicon Surface Arising from Implant Damage.

Another model that explains the occurrence of RSCE in MOSFETs with uniformly doped channel regions was developed by Rafferty et al.[98] In this model, it is proposed that the effect is associated with damage from the LDD implant. That is, point defects (interstitials) are assumed to be created by the LDD implant. They diffuse laterally into the channel region during the relatively low-temperature step used to deposit the CVD interlevel dielectric layer (needed to create the gate-sidewall spacers). As these point defects are primarily created at a depth corresponding to the end-of-range damage, the interstitial concentration peak exists beneath the surface. Thus, a retrograde profile of interstitials in the channel will arise. Since the dopant diffusivity is proportional to the interstitial concentration, the retrograde interstitial concentration profile will cause a net boron diffusion flux toward the surface (i.e., during the source/drain activation anneal) even if a flat boron dopant profile exists in the vertical direction. As a result, boron piles up at the surface, leading to an increase in V_T. Experimental confirmation of such an impurity pile-up is found in SIMS analysis of flat profiles subjected to silicon damage and subsequent anneal.[99] The diffusion of boron toward the channel surface from this effect is a transient phenomenon because the interstitials are eventually annihilated during the anneal. Good agreement between this model and experimental data is also reported if the transient diffusion is modeled using a coupled impurity/point defect simulator.

5.2.3.4 Model which Attributes RSCE to Silicon Interstitial Capture in the Gate Oxide. Jacobs et al. note that V_T can also be shifted by a change in fixed oxide charges Q_f at the Si-SiO$_2$ interface.[97] Thus, they propose that RSCE in the absence of a vertical gradient in the channel dopant profile can be explained by the trapping of injected silicon interstitials by the gate oxide. These captured interstitials introduce the negatively charged complex in the oxide required for the observed V_T roll-up). The oxide surface is known to be an effective sink for interstitials, and the process steps which supply the excess interstitials can be those mentioned above. The result is a position-dependent oxide charge distribution along the Si-SiO$_2$ interface, similar to the assumption of an exponentially decaying fixed charge variation made by Arora when deriving the analytical model of RSCE mentioned in section 5.3.2.1.[94]

5.3 PUNCHTHROUGH (Subsurface-DIBL) IN SHORT-CHANNEL MOSFETS

In chap. 4, section 4.7 we described the nature of subthreshold current in long-channel MOSFETs. We noted that in weak inversion I_{Dst} flows at the surface of the channel region, and its value is calculated from Eq. 4-89. We also saw that the subthreshold-swing parameter (S_t) is an important characteristic of subthreshold behavior, and in long-channel, uniformly-doped-substrate devices it can be modeled using Eq. 4-91.

In short-channel MOSFETs, however, if V_{GS} is fixed while V_{DS} is increased, larger values of I_{Dst} values than are predicted by the long-channel device equations are observed. This larger subthreshold current is due in part to increased I_{Dst} flowing at the surface as a result of surface-drain-induced barrier lowering (DIBL), as described in section 5.2). If only surface DIBL is occurring in a MOSFET, S_t values are observed to remain unchanged. However, another short-channel effect known as *subsurface punchthrough* can also give rise to an increase in I_{Dst}, and one manifestation of this effect is an increase in the measured value of S_t. That is, the gate has less control of the subsurface punchthrough current than it has over the surface subthreshold current. Thus, once a MOSFET enters subsurface punchthrough and such current starts to flow, the S_t value of the MOSFET becomes larger than if only normal subthreshold current is flowing. Since the measurable drain current is the sum of both current components,

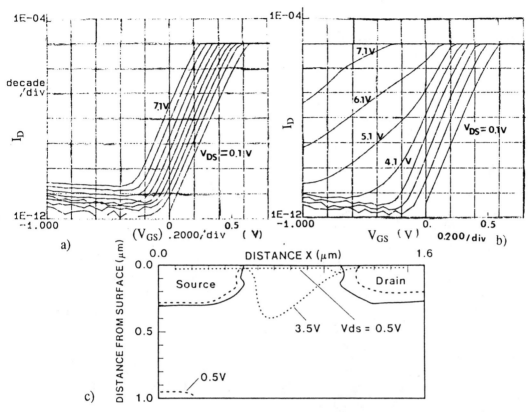

Fig. 5-21 Two sets of log I_D versus V_{GS} curves for MOSFETs, with V_{DS} varying in 1V increments. (a) No indication of punchthrough is observed, as S_t remains constant for all values of V_{DS}. (b) Onset of punchthrough occurs as V_{DS} reaches ~6V, as evidenced by an increase in S_t that point. (c) Punchthrough current paths (dotted) in a surface-channel NMOSFET with V_{DS} = 0.5 and 3.5V. Solid line shows the depletion region edge. The current path transfers from the surface to bulk as V_{DS} is increased.[74] (© 1988 IEEE).

one technique for detecting the onset of punchthrough in a MOSFET is to monitor S_t as V_{DS} is increased. .

For example, in Fig. 5-21 two sets of I_{Dst} versus V_{GS} curves with V_{DS} as the parameter are shown. In the MOSFET characterized by Fig. 5-21a S_t remains constant as V_{DS} is increased, indicating that no punchthrough is observed up to the maximum applied V_{DS}. In Fig. 5-21b S_t increases as V_{DS} is increased beyond ~4V, indicating that punchthrough sets in at about this value.

Punchthrough is a phenomenon associated with the merging of the source and drain depletion regions in the MOSFET. That is, as the channel gets shorter, these depletion region edges get closer (assuming that the channel-region doping is kept constant as L is decreased). When the channel length is decreased to roughly the sum of the two junction depletion widths, punchthrough is established. (Note that punchthrough may even exist in a short-channel device at $V_{DS} = 0$, depending on L and the substrate doping.) Nevertheless, since the depletion regions of a *pn*-junction widen as reverse-bias is increased, all MOSFETs would eventually enter punchthrough if a high enough V_{DS} could be applied. However, in MOSFETs with $L>2.0$ μm, breakdown of the drain-substrate junction generally sets in before this punchthrough voltage is reached. As a result, in practice, punchthrough is not a limiting factor in long-channel digital MOSFET design. In shorter-channel devices (i.e., $L\leq2.0$ μm), however, punchthrough does represent a serious limitation.

Another factor also impacts punchthrough behavior in *n*-channel MOSFETs. That is, in submicron NMOSFETs a V_T-adjust implant is used to raise the doping of the surface-channel region above the doping of the substrate. (This can also be viewed as an increase in the electrostatic potential at that point near the source.) Thus, the source/drain depletion-region widening is greater beneath the surface due to the lighter doping there. A punchthrough condition would therefore be first established below the surface in such devices, and hence this effect is referred to as *subsurface punchthrough* (see Figs. 5-22 and 5-23). Note that in PMOSFETs fabricated with n^+ polysilicon gates the punchthrough problem occurs in a somewhat different manner, which we will describe in a later section dealing with this issue (i.e., section 5.8.2.3).

Once subsurface punchthrough occurs, any increase in the applied reverse-bias drain voltage (beyond that required to establish punchthrough) will lower the potential energy barrier for majority carriers in the source.[6] With a diminished barrier height, a larger number of source-region majority carriers (e.g., electrons in an NMOSFET) have enough energy to be injected from source to substrate. Some of these injected electrons are collected by the drain, causing I_{Dst} to increase. The component of I_{Dst} which flows as a result of subsurface punchthrough is known as *punchthrough current*. When designing MOSFETs one criterion of a successful device design is that the punchthrough current should be insignificant under normal bias conditions. That is, if sufficient punchthrough current is observed, the device structure must be redesigned to effectively suppress such current.

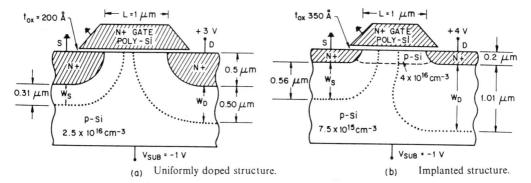

(a) Uniformly doped structure.   (b) Implanted structure.

Fig. 5-22 (a) NMOSFET without V_T-adjust implant. (b) NMOSFET with V_T-adjust implant, showing the bulging of the drain depletion region beneath the surface as V_{DS} is increased, due to the lower doping concentration in the substrate below the depth of the V_T-adjust implant.

Two-dimensional simulations of the potential in the channel regions of short channel NMOSFETs with V_T-adjust implants support the view that depletion-region widening is greater beneath the surface. In addition, they indicate that the point of maximum source-substrate potential energy barrier lowering is also beneath the Si-SiO$_2$ interface (generally at approximately the same depth as the source/drain junction depths). Figures 5-23a, c, e and g show a "bird's eye" or perspective view of the electrostatic potential variation in a short-channel MOSFET computed using such 2-D numerical analyses, as V_{DS} is increased from V_{DS} = 3V to V_{DS} = 9V. Figures 5-23b, d, f and h show contour plots of these same results. We can see that when the device enters punch-through the location of the electrostatic potential saddle point is beneath the surface, and the value of the potential at this saddle point may be higher than the potential minimum at the surface. Since electrons follow the potential peak (see Figs. 5-23g and i), in such cases the component of current due to subsurface punchthrough will be larger than the channel-current component, and the subsurface current will flow along the path indicated by the subsurface potential ridge connecting the source and drain. Figure 5-21c shows a simulation of the subthreshold current paths in an NMOSFET with L = 0.6 μm for surface-DIBL (i.e., V_{DS} = 0.5V) and for subsurface-DIBL (punchthrough, V_{DS} = 3.5V). This shows that the subthreshold current path transfers from the surface to the bulk as V_{DS} increases, which supports the view that at low V_{DS} surface-DIBL is responsible for the increase in I_{Dst} in short-channel NMOSFETs, but that at high V_{DS} punchthrough becomes the primary cause of subthreshold leakage.

Subsurface punchthrough exerts the biggest impact on circuit operation when the MOSFET is OFF, since a tiny punchthrough current in this case can still represent intolerable leakage. However, the device parameter most commonly used to characterize punchthrough behavior is the *punchthrough voltage* V_{PT} defined as the value of V_{DS} at which I_{Dst} reaches some specific magnitude (e.g., 1 nA/μm) when V_{GS} = 0. The goal in designing a MOSFET is to have V_{PT} exceed any possible operating V_{DS}. Thus, V_{PT} is measured when the device is in subthreshold, as will be discussed in upcoming paragraphs. Note that V_{PT} can be roughly estimated by determining the value of V_{DS} at which the sum of the depletion widths W_S under the source and W_D under the drain (using the value of the doping concentration in the substrate as N_{SUB}) equals the channel length L, or from the expression[24]

$$V_{PT} \propto N_{SUB} (L - r_j)^3 \qquad (5 - 17)$$

Nevertheless, no accurate analytical model exists for estimating V_{PT} as a function of implant dose and depth. A full numerical solution of the 2-D Poisson equation must thus be obtained to predict the variation of V_{PT} for each device structure.

Several measures can be taken to prevent short-channel MOSFETs from entering subsurface punchthrough. First, the substrate doping can be increased to decrease the depletion-layer widths. A simple rule-of-thumb proposed by Klaasen[25] is to select a minimum substrate doping value according to $N_{SUB} > N_{ch}/10$, where N_{SUB} is the uniform bulk-substrate doping/cm^3 and N_{ch} is the average doping/cm^3 in the implanted region of the channel (e.g., D_I/x_c). This approach, together with a single V_T-adjust implant can produce appropriate threshold and punchthrough voltages for NMOSFETs

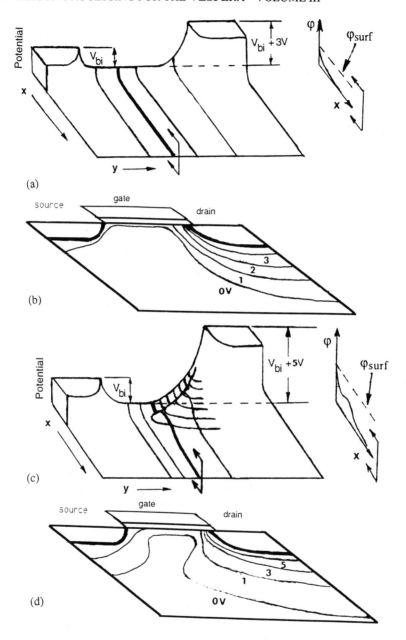

Fig. 5-23 (a and c) 2-D perspective plots of the potential in an *n*-channel MOSFET with a drain bias of (a) 3 V and (c) 5 V, respectively. Channel length = 1 μm. (b and d) 2-D contour plots of the same cases. From K. M. Cham, et al., *Computer Aided Design & VLSI Device Development.* Copyright 1986 Kluwer Academic Publishers. Reprinted with permission.

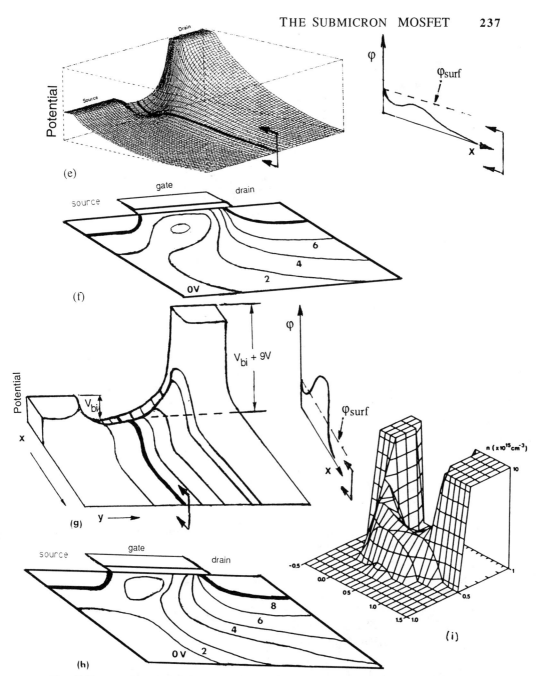

Fig. 5-23 cont. (e and g) 2-D perspective plots of the potential in an *n*-channel MOSFET with a drain bias of (e) 7 V and (g) 9 V, respectively. Channel length = 1 *μ*m. (f and h) 2-D contour plots of the same cases. From K. M. Cham, et al., *Computer Aided Design & VLSI Device Development.* Copyright 1986 Kluwer Academic Publishers. Reprinted with permission. (i) Electron concentration of the MOSFET in punchthrough, i.e., case g & h.

with drawn gate lengths of 1.3 μm nominally operated at 2.5V power supply (e.g., a single 20 keV B$^+$ implant at ~9×10^{11} cm^{-2}). A similar process has also been applied to 1.25 μm CMOS devices using a 5V supply. Although some short-channel effects are observed, V_T and V_{PT} voltages are reasonable. However, for devices with drawn gate lengths of ~1 μm (L_{eff} ~0.55 μm), a single V_T/punchthrough implant cannot adequately satisfy all requirements, especially if high resistivity (>10 Ω-cm) substrates are used.

As a result, another approach using an additional implant known as a *punchthrough stopper implant* (or *punchthrough implant,* PTI) must be employed. The second implant peak concentration is located at a depth near the bottom of the source-drain regions. Fig. 5-24a qualitatively depicts such a MOSFET structure. The additional doping introduced by such an implant (e.g., boron in NMOSFETs) reduces the lateral widening of the drain-depletion region below the surface without increasing the doping under the junction regions. With such implants, the component of the punchthrough current can be suppressed to well below the long-channel I_{Dst} value in MOSFETs down to 0.5 μm, while still maintaining a lower value of N_{SUB} (for reduced values of C_j). However, precise control of the placement and dose of this implant within the channel region is required to achieve the intended enhancements. For example, Fig. 5-24b shows the as-implanted doping profile of the channel with (dashed line) and without (solid line) a punchthrough implant (i.e., prior to annealing the implants). In addition, it is important to keep the punchthrough implant profiles from spreading out appreciably during annealing (see Fig. 5-24c), since the additional doping above the well's value adds to the source/drain-to-well capacitance and the transistor's threshold voltage sensitivity to back biasing of the *p*-well. Thus, the post channel implant thermal cycles should be kept to a minimum. An example of such a punchthrough implant for a 1 μm NMOSFETs is a 70 keV B$^+$ implant at 6×10^{11} cm^{-2}.

A third technique is to locally implant *p*-type dopants (in NMOSFETs) under the lightly doped tip region of the LDD as shown in Fig. 5-25a, and such implants have been termed a "halo" implants. (The use of halo implants as punchthrough stoppers in PMOSFETs is discussed in section 5.8.1.1.) Because the implanted dopant raises the doping concentration only on the inside walls of the source/drain junctions, the channel length can be decreased without needing to use a higher-doped substrate. That is, punchthrough does not set in until a shorter channel length because of the "halo." A penalty in increased sidewall junction capacitance is paid, but this cost is smaller than that incurred should the bottom area of the junctions lie above heavily doped substrate material. The maximum halo doping is determined by the onset of low-level avalanche breakdown of the pn^+ junction as is shown in Fig. 5-25b.

A halo NMOSFET with $L = 0.35$ μm, $t_{ox} = 15$ nm, and operated at 3V has been reported.[26] The junction depth r_j and *p*-halo peak doping were ~0.14 μm and ~3×10^{17} cm^{-3}, respectively. A more recent report applied a large-angle tilt (LAT) implant of boron ions in NMOS and phosphorus in PMOS (Fig. 5-25c) to form a halo-like structure in each device (called a *self-aligned pocket implantation*). A tilt angle of 25-30° was used to implant the pocket dopants after gate formation, so that the gate structure acted as a self-aligned implant mask. Devices with channel lengths as small as 0.2 μm that still exhibited long-channel subthreshold V_T behavior were fabricated.[27]

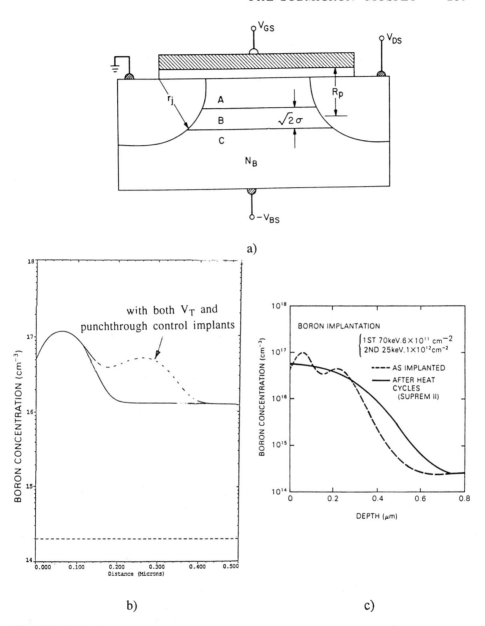

Fig. 5-24 (a) An implanted NMOS structure with three regions of different doping. Level A contains the dopant from the V_T implant. Level B contains the dopant from the punchthrough control implant, considered to be a Gaussian centered at a distance R_p from the gate, with a straggle σ. Level C is the original substrate. (b) As-implanted channel doping profiles with (dashed line) and without (solid line) punchthrough implant. (c) Example of simulated channel impurity profile of an NMOSFET with both V_T and punchthrough control implants - as-implanted (dashed lines), and after anneal (solid line).[113]   (© 1982 IEEE).

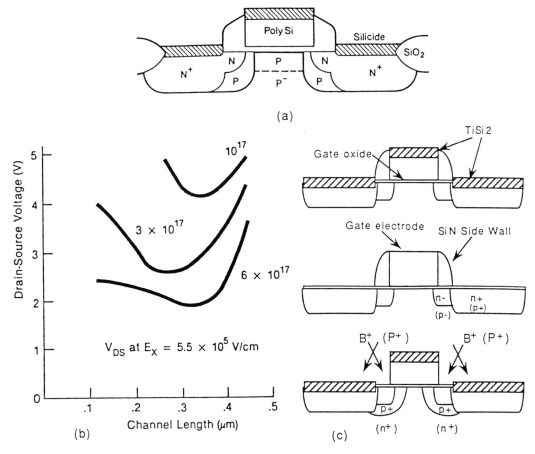

Fig. 5-25 (a) "Halo" NMOS structure.[26] (© 1985 IEEE). (b) V_{DSmax} limited by avalanche breakdown versus channel length for various peak halo doses.[26] (© 1985 IEEE). Process for producing "halo" NMOS structure using a Self-Aligned Pocket Implantation [SPI] technology is shown.[27] (© 1991 IEEE).

5.3.1 Experimentally Characterizing Punchthrough

The onset of punchthrough in a device can be measured in several ways. As mentioned at the outset of the discussion, for a specific device (i.e., one that has a single, specific channel length and channel doping profile), the onset of punchthrough over the operating range of V_{DS} can be monitored by measuring log I_{Dst} vs. V_{GS} for different V_{DS} values (Figs. 5-21a and b). If the curves look like those of Fig. 5-21a, the device does not exhibit subsurface punchthrough up to the maximum V_{DS} applied (since the slope of the log I_{Dst} curves remain constant as V_{DS} is increased). The curves of Fig. 5-21b however, indicate that punchthrough is setting in, with its onset marked by the V_{DS}-curve having a larger S_t value than that exhibited at small V_{DS}. (Note that since punchthrough current flows in parallel with ordinary I_{Dst}, S_t will noticeably increase

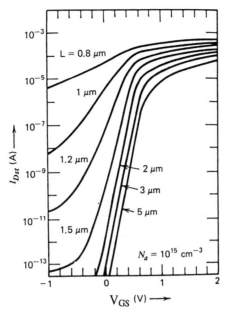

Fig. 5-26 Simulated behavior of I_{Dst} versus V_{GS} for various channel lengths, $r_j = 0.33$ μm, $t_{ox} = 500$Å, $V_{DS} = 2$V, and $V_{BS} = 0$V.[109] Reprinted with permission of *Solid State Electronics*.

once punchthrough current exceeds a small fraction of the long-channel I_{Dst} value.) Punchthrough voltage V_{PT} (as defined earlier) can also be extracted with this procedure by continuing to increase V_{DS} until the specified I_{Dst} is reached at $V_{GS} = 0$.

One way to detect the onset of punchthrough in a family of devices with varying channel lengths is to plot log I_{Dst} vs. V_{GS} for a fixed V_{DS} for the devices of different channel lengths on a single graph (Fig. 5-26). A second method is to measure S_t at a fixed V_{DS} for devices with different channel lengths, and then to plot these values as shown in Fig. 5-27. Here the impact of a punchthrough implant on S_t versus channel length is depicted. A third way is to measure I_D vs V_{DS} at $V_{GS} = 0$, and to pick off the V_{DS} value when I_{Dst} reaches the specified value (e.g., 0.1 μA/μm).

An example of the impact of a punchthrough implant (as well as the impact of depth and dose) is shown in Fig. 5-28. Here a 1.2-μm MOSFET with a substrate doping of 1.9×10^{15} cm^{-3} (but without a punchthrough-stopping implant) shows a very large S_t value (and hence a large I_{Dst} when $V_{GS} = 0$ V - curve A). The large I_{Dst} at V_{GS} = 0V indicates that the device is in punchthrough even when $V_{DS} = 0$V.[28] Implants of boron with a dose of 8×10^{11} atoms/cm^2 and different energies are then performed in an attempt to produce a V_T and an S_t equal to the values exhibited by a long-channel (7.8 μm) device (curve B). If the punchthrough implant is too shallow, it has the effect of increasing the V_T of the device to well beyond the desired value (curve C). When the energy is increased so that the implant is sufficiently deep, S_t drops to a value comparable to that exhibited by the long-channel device (curves D and E). At the same time, the surface concentration remains essentially unchanged, so that V_T is not

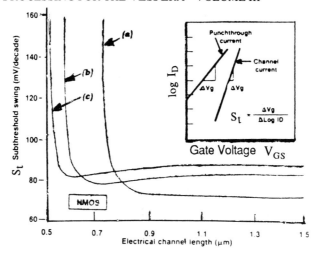

Fig. 5-27 Subthreshold slope versus electrical channel length for NMOS devices $V_T = 0.7V$, having a common threshold adjustment implant and punchthrough implant doses of: (a) zero; (b) 2×10^{11} cm^{-2}; (c) 3×10^{11} cm^{-2}.[29] Reprinted with permission of Semiconductor International.

appreciably shifted. Note, however, that S_t in the punchthrough implanted device is somewhat larger than that of the long-channel device.

In another example, the S_t of a device without a punchthrough-prevention implant is measured as its length is varied (Fig. 5-27).[29] At an L_{eff} of ~0.85 μm the S_t starts to increase, indicating that punchthrough current begins to dominate I_{Dst}. By adding an implant that places boron atoms in subsurface region below the V_T-adjust implant, the punchthrough component of I_{Dst} is suppressed so that it is not observed until L_{eff} becomes nearly as small as 0.5 μm. Again, the price of an increased punchthrough implant dose is an increase in S_t. This tradeoff is discussed in more detail in the section on device scaling based on I_{off} (that is, on I_{Dst} at $V_{GS} = 0$).

5.3.2 Modeling Punchthrough

As discussed in the previous sections, punchthrough behavior can be measured in a number of ways, including measurements which determine V_{PT}. It is also often convenient to use punchthrough voltage (V_{PT}) as a device parameter during the tasks of device scaling and device design. Unfortunately, the amount of drain current used to define V_{PT} is not universally standardized. Depending on the particular circuit application, this current level may vary from 1 pA for a DRAM to 1 nA for a static logic circuit. As a result, it would instead be useful to be able to predict the actual value of subthreshold surface-DIBL or punchthrough current in a MOSFET from the design parameters of the device prior to its fabrication. This, in fact, can be accomplished by using a 2-D device simulator which numerically solves both the Poisson equation and the carrier continuity equations to find φ, n, and p, and then uses these values to calculate the currents using the drift-diffusion current equations. Such an entirely numerical approach, however, does not offer quantitative insight into the phenomenon of punchthrough, nor does it provide any information on trends in the device behavior as the terminal voltages are varied. However, a popular, hybrid approach that first employs a numerical method to calculate φ and then uses this solution in an analytical expression to calculate I_{Dst} (instead of first solving the carrier continuity equations) has been implemented. This technique has been widely adopted for analyzing subthreshold behavior in MOSFETs because it offers some insight into the device physics, gives accurate results (provided its use is restricted to low-current operating conditions), offers a very computationally efficient approach to device analysis, and can handle both surface-DIBL and subsurface-DIBL (punchthrough) effects in MOSFETs.

This method uses the numerical techniques described in chap. 2 (with the aid of a computer and a 2-D Poisson solver software program), to find the solution of the 2-D Poisson equation. The electrostatic potential found in this manner is used in an analytical expression to calculate the value of I_{Dst}. That is, the value of the electrostatic potential at its minimum point, together with its variation in the vicinity of this minimum point, is used in the calculation of I_{Dst}, as described below. This technique was implemented in the device simulation program called GEMINI. The program has been used to analyze many aspects of MOSFET IC behavior including many of the

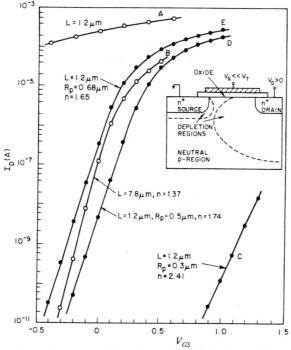

Fig. 5-28 Drain current versus gate voltage for n-channel devices with a substrate doping of 1.9×10^{15} atoms/cm^3, source/drain junctions are 0.47 μm deep, t_{ox} = 575Å, and V_{DS} = 5V, and V_{BS} = 0V. Devices A and B have no channel implant, and devices C and E have a boron channel implant of 8×10^{11} atoms/cm^2 at various energies.[28] (© 1978 IEEE).

topics discussed in this chapter and elsewhere in the book.[2,5,74,114,115,116]
   The analytical expression for I_{Dst} used in this approach is

$$I_{Dst} = -q \, D_n \, Z \frac{t^*}{L^*} \frac{n_i^2}{N_A} \exp\left[\frac{q}{kT}(\varphi^* - V_S)\right] \left\{1 - \exp\left(\frac{-qV_{DS}}{kT}\right)\right\} \qquad (5 - 18a)$$

Note that this equation has the same basic form as the general expression derived for
I_{Dst} in long-channel MOSFETs in chap. 4 (i.e. Eq. 4-89). When $V_{DS} \geq 0.1V$ (the only
operating condition of practical interest), Eq. 5-18a reduces to the following expression,
which now has a form similar to that of Eq. 4-90 (but with some important differences):

$$I_{Dst} = -q \, D_n \, Z \frac{t^*}{L^*} \frac{n_i^2}{N_A} \exp\left[\frac{q}{kT}(\varphi^* - V_S)\right] \qquad (5 - 18b)$$

That is, in Eq. 5-18, φ^* is the value of the potential at the point P between the source
and drain where it has its minimum value (i.e., along the surface when surface-DIBL
dominates I_{Dst}, or at the saddlepoint in the bulk region when subsurface-DIBL
[punchthrough] dominates I_{Dst}), and V_S is the source potential. At P the lateral electric
field (i.e., the direction of the field along the direction of current flow) becomes zero,
and any current at that point must thus be due entirely to carrier diffusion. Point P is
taken as the origin of a coordinate system (r,θ) with the r axis oriented along the current
path and the θ axis oriented in the orthogonal direction at P (see Fig. 5-29). The

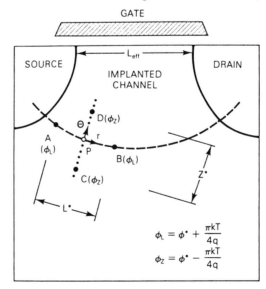

Fig. 5-29 Cross-section of a MOSFET with a bulk current path showing the two axes (r and
θ) used to calculate the current. The points defining the approximate effective length L^* and
effective thickness t* are shown.[2] (© 1980 IEEE).

electrostatic potential φ^* at P corresponds to a potential minimum along the r axis and to a potential maximum along the θ axis. The value of φ^* used in Eq. 5-18b is determined by numerically solving the 2-D form of the Poisson equation in the device region. The functional variation of the electrostatic potential at some point (r,θ) in the vicinity of point P with respect to the value φ^* is $h\ (r,\theta)$. Hence, the electrostatic potential at point (r,θ) can be written as $\varphi(r,\theta) = \varphi^* + h\ (r,\theta)$.

In addition, the inversion layer thickness t_{inv} used in Eq. 4-90, is replaced in Eq. 5-18 by t^*, and the channel length L with L^*. These two terms represent, respectively, the *effective length* and *effective thickness* of the electron path near the point P, which controls the current transport. Note that when Eq. 5-18 is used to model surface-DIBL, the values of t^* and L^* are the same as in Eq. 4-90 (i.e., t^* and L^* in Eq. 5-18 in this case become t_{inv} and L). Hence, the only difference between 5-18 when it is modeling surface-DIBL-induced I_{Dst} and Eq. 4-90 is the use of φ^* instead of φ_{surf} (which was calculated using the analytical solution of the 1-D form of the Poisson equation).

On the other hand, when Eq, 5-18b is used to model punchthrough, t^* and L^* take on somewhat different meanings. Although the detailed derivations of their expressions is given in ref. 2, as shown in Figs. 5-29a and b, L^* is the distance along the r axis between points A and B where $\varphi = \varphi^* + \pi kT/4q$, and t^* is the distance along the θ axis between C and D where $\varphi = \varphi^* - \pi kT/4q$. The functional variation of φ about point P found from the 2-D solution of the Poisson equation is used calculate t^* and L^*.

Results obtained with this approach have been compared to solutions found from solving the carrier continuity equations as well as the Poisson equation, and with experimental data. Generally, good agreement has been found, if the operational limits of the approach are respected.[2,115]

5.3.3 Modeling the Simultaneous Occurrence of Surface-DIBL and Subsurface-DIBL

As a final note, we should recognize that up to now surface-DIBL and subsurface-punchthrough effects have been treated as separate, unconnected phenomena. However, when a device exhibits severe short-channel behavior, both phenomena are likely to be occurring simultaneously (see, for example, Figs. 5-23e & f), and the effects may be coupled. It may not even be possible to distinguish which one is dominant, either from a model or from measurements. In fact, the concepts of V_T and ΔV_{TSC} break down in devices that exhibit severe DIBL (surface and/or subsurface), because the log I_D vs. V_{GS} plots depend sensitively on the value of V_{DS}. That, is if a V_T is defined as the V_{GS} at which a specific I_D flows, in severe short-channel-effect devices this will not be a unique value because the same specified current will be obtained at different gate voltages if V_{DS} is changed. It is for this reason that a major goal of submicron MOSFET design is to produce devices without severe subthreshold short-channel behavior, and instead exhibit subthreshold behavior comparable to that of long-channel MOSFETs.

Nevertheless, it would still be highly useful to predict the degree to which each of these effects is occurring in a MOSFET, because each surface and bulk mechanism needs a different strategy for its suppression. One paper by Skotnicki et al. offers an analytical model that allows both surface and bulk punchthrough currents to be calcu-

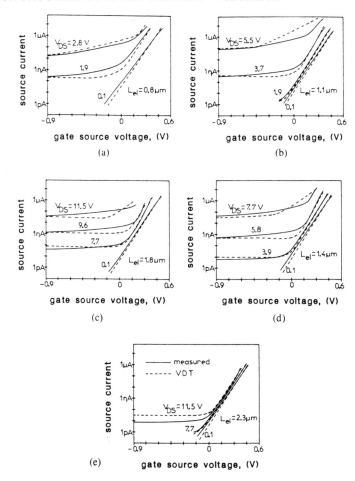

Fig. 5-30 Measured (solid line) and analytically calculated (dashed lines) I_{Dst} versus V_{GS} characteristics at $V_{BS} = 0V$ and various V_{DS} values for a series of MOSFETs with electrical channel lengths from 0.8 to 2.3 μm. The parameters in the VDT calculations are $r_j = 0.27$ μm, $t_{ox} = 280$Å, and $Z = 50$ μm.[30] (© 1988 IEEE).

lated simultaneously.[30] The same voltage-doping transformation (VDT) method introduced in ref. 9 is used to reduce the 2-D Poisson equation to a 1-D form. Using the VDT-method, the actual barrier heights at the surface and in the bulk can be calculated as a function of the applied voltages and channel length using the long-channel expressions where the doping concentrations in the channel N_{ch} and N_{SUB} are replaced by reduced values N_{ch}^* and N_{SUB}^*. With the barrier heights known, the surface and bulk punchthrough currents can be determined. (This model is also valid in MOSFETs with non-uniformly doped channels.) Results reported show that good agreement with measured subthreshold currents is obtained for devices with gate lengths as small as 0. 8 μm and with V_{DS} as large as 5.5V (see Fig. 5-30).

5.4 SHORT-CHANNEL EFFECTS ON THE I-V CHARACTERISTICS OF MOSFETS OPERATED IN THE STRONG INVERSION REGIME

Short-channel effects significantly alter the dc I_D-V_{DS} characteristics of long-channel MOSFETs being operated in strong inversion in three ways. First, the combined effects of reduced gate length and gate width produce a change in V_T. Second, the mobility of the carriers in the channel is reduced by two effects, which in turn reduces I_D. These two effects are the *mobility-degradation factor* (due to the gate field), and the *velocity-saturation factor* (due to the lateral [channel] field). Third, the channel length is modulated by the drain voltage when the device is in saturation (i.e., when $V_{DS} > [V_{GS} - V_T]$), causing an increase in I_{Dsat} with increasing V_{DS} (*channel-modulation* effect). Figure 5-31 shows the I-V characteristics of an MOS device.[31] The curves in Fig. 5-31a are those of an ideal long-channel MOS device, while those in Fig. 5-31b show the effect of adding the channel modulation factor. Figure 5-31c shows the effect of adding the velocity saturation factor to the curves of Fig. 5-31b.

Here we describe some relatively simple models which allow an analytical dc model of the I_D-V_{DS} characteristics of short-channel MOSFETs to be obtained. These analytical models allow circuit designers to estimate such dc parameters as I_D and g_m for various bias conditions using only hand calculations. They also allow an intuitive understanding of the short-channel electrical behavior to be developed, making such models useful for

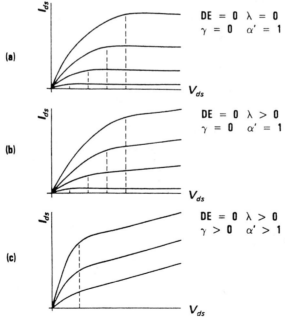

Fig. 5-31 The I-V curves of an MOS device showing the effects of progressively increasing short-channel behavior on the operation of the device in inversion. (a) Long-channel behavior; (b) with channel-length modulation; (c) addition of velocity saturation.[31] (© 1986 IEEE).

device designers and process engineers who need to relate device and process parameters to circuit parameters. Finally, they allow I_D to be calculated merely from a knowledge of device width Z, channel length L, the device threshold voltage V_T, the gate oxide thickness t_{ox}, the source/drain junction depth r_j, and with $(V_{GS} - V_T)$ as the independent terminal voltage parameter. On the other hand, to use the elaborate models provided in circuit simulators (such as BSIM the short-channel MOSFET model in SPICE, see the next section), it is necessary to determine a large number of model parameters. These model parameters must be derived from device measurements, often with the help of automated parameter extraction tools.

5.4.1 Impact of the MOSFET Electric Fields on Mobility

In deriving the long-channel dc MOSFET models (chap. 4) we assumed that the channel mobility was constant as a function of position along the channel. We also ignored any effect on the mobility due to the transverse and longitudinal electric fields acting on the carriers. In fact, both the gate-induced electric field (i.e., also called the vertical, normal, or transverse electric field), and the drain-induced electric field (i.e., referred to also as either the lateral, horizontal, or longitudinal electric field) influence the velocity of the moving carriers in the inversion layer of the channel. Since each effect can be modeled separately, this is done first. Later we show how both effects can be incorporated into the MOSFET models, allowing their impact on the I_D-V_{DS} curves to be calculated. Before discussing how these electric fields alter the velocity of channel carriers, let us briefly review the concept of carrier mobility in a semiconductor.

The electron and hole mobilities (μ_n and μ_p, respectively), are a measure of the ease of carrier motion in a semiconductor crystal. In the semiconductor bulk (i.e., at a point far away from the semiconductor surface), the carrier mobilities are typically determined by the amount of lattice scattering and ionized impurity scattering taking place inside the material. For a given temperature and semiconductor doping, these bulk mobilities are well-defined and documented material constants. (In lightly doped silicon at 300K, μ_n and μ_p are ~1350 cm^2/V sec and ~500 cm^2/V sec, respectively.)

Carrier transport in the MOSFET, however, primarily occurs in the surface inversion layer. The lateral electric field due to V_{DS} acts to accelerate the carriers parallel to the Si-SiO$_2$ interface, whereupon they suffer scattering much as in the bulk. The transverse field, however, also causes the carriers to be accelerated toward the Si-SiO$_2$ surface. Thus, the carriers near the surface experience additional motion-impeding collisions with the silicon surface (see Fig. 5-32). As a result, the carrier mobilities at the surface are observed to be lower than in the bulk. (In the substrate doping range N_A, $N_D < 10^{17}$ cm^{-3}, the mobilities of electrons and holes in the inversion layer at $V_{GS} = V_T$ are μ_{no} ~670 cm^2/V sec and μ_{po} ~160 cm^2/V sec, respectively.) The surface-scattering mechanisms include phonons, coulombic scattering sites, and surface roughness (see chap. 7). For a good quality Si-SiO$_2$ interface in strong inversion, phonon scattering is generally accepted to be the dominant scattering mechanism.

At low electric fields, the drift velocity of carriers in the bulk of a semiconductor is proportional to the electric field. The mobility is the proportionality constant in the

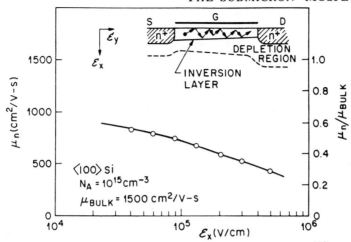

Fig. 5-32 Visualization of surface scattering at the Si-SiO$_2$ interface.[119] Reprinted with permission of the American Physical Society.

equation which relates the drift-velocity to the electric field (at low $\mathcal{E}$–field values). However, experimental data indicate that if the electric fields get too large (i.e., $>\sim 3\times 10^3$ V/cm in the bulk), the drift velocity no longer increases linearly with increasing field. In fact, at sufficiently high fields, the drift velocities approach a saturation velocity ($\sim 10^7$ cm/sec for electrons in bulk Si).

Electrons and holes drifting in the channel also reach a saturation velocity if the lateral electric fields are high enough. In fact, in MOSFETs operating in the saturation regime, carriers moving in the pinched off region of the channel travel at this saturation velocity. The surface saturation velocity of electrons is estimated to be between 6×10^6 to 1×10^7 cm/sec, while that of holes is between 4-to-8x10^6 cm/sec.[32] These saturation velocities also appear to be relatively independent of the gate (transverse) field. In the next sections we discuss the quantitative models of both mobility degradation due to gate-induced field and the velocity-lateral field relationship (velocity saturation).

5.4.1.1 Models of Mobility Degradation Due to Gate-Induced Electric Fields.
As the gate bias is increased, more carriers are drawn closer to the oxide-semiconductor interface. In addition, the stronger transverse (vertical) electric field acts on these carriers. This combination of effects is thought to enhance the phonon scattering of the carriers near the surface, which thereby lowers the average carrier mobility. According to Eq. 4-65 when V_{DS} is small, i.e., $V_{DS}<<(V_{GS} - V_T)$, we can determine the mobility of the electrons in the MOSFET channel by measuring the slope of the I_D-V_{DS} characteristic at fixed V_{DS}. When this is done, a reduction in the mobility of carriers near the surface is observed (compared to that in the bulk). Not only is the surface electron mobility under low lateral electric fields (μ_{no}) found to be only one-half to two-thirds that of the low-field bulk electron mobility, but μ_n is also observed to decrease as the transverse field is increased.

An early, widely used empirical model introduced by Crawford for calculating the degree of degradation due to the transverse field (i.e., yielding an effective mobility μ_{eff})

is[33]

$$\mu_{eff} = \mu_0 / [1 + \theta \, \mathcal{E}_x] \tag{5 - 18}$$

$$= \mu_0 / [1 + \theta \, C_{ox} (V_{GS} - V_T) / \kappa_{si}\varepsilon_0] \tag{5 - 19}$$

where μ_0 is μ_{no} for electrons and μ_{po} for holes, $\mathcal{E}_x$ is the transverse field in the silicon at the Si-SiO$_2$ interface, and θ is an empirical parameter found to be technologically and substrate-bias dependent. While it is difficult to assign a coherent physical interpretation to θ, it's value has been empirically determined to be 10^{-7}-10^{-6} cm/V.

To improve the agreement between calculated and experimental values, an alternative empirical expression to that of Eq. 5-18 for the effective mobility was proposed, namely[34]

$$\mu_{eff} = \mu_0 \, (\mathcal{E}_{crit}/\mathcal{E}_{eff})^{UEXP} \tag{5 - 20}$$

where $\mathcal{E}_{crit}$ and UEXP are empirically determined constants. This expression was used together with the results of Sabnis and Clemens,[35] who showed in 1978 that the channel carrier mobility on the (100) surface of silicon is a unique function of the *effective transverse field*, $\mathcal{E}_{eff}$ (which is defined as the field averaged over the electron distribution in the inversion layer). The expression of Sabnis and Clemens for $\mathcal{E}_{eff}$ is given by

$$\mathcal{E}_{eff} = [Q_B + (Q_I/2)] / \kappa_{si}\varepsilon_0 \tag{5 - 21}$$

Equation 5-21 can be understood as follows: The electric field at the Si-SiO$_2$ interface $\mathcal{E}_{si}$ (x = 0) can be written in terms of the total charge per unit area in the Si

$$\mathcal{E}_{si} (x = 0) = Q_C / \kappa_{si}\varepsilon_0 \quad \text{(Eq. 3-17)} \tag{5 - 22}$$

If an inversion layer exists, $Q_C = Q_B + Q_I$. If no inversion layer exists, $Q_C = Q_B$. Thus, $\mathcal{E}_{si1}(x = 0) = (Q_B + Q_I)/\kappa_{si}\varepsilon_0$ and $\mathcal{E}_{si2} (x = 0) = Q_B /\kappa_{si}\varepsilon_0$ when an inversion layer is present, or not, respectively. Also, if an inversion layer exists, the electric field at the boundary of the inversion layer x_i and the depletion region is the same as at x = 0 if no inversion layer exists, or $\mathcal{E}_{si} (x = x_i) = Q_B /\kappa_{si}\varepsilon_0$. Thus, the effective transverse electric field within the channel can be approximated as the average of $\mathcal{E}_{si1}(x = 0)$ and $\mathcal{E}_{si} (x = x_i)$, or

$$\mathcal{E}_{eff} = [\mathcal{E}_{si1}(x = 0) + \mathcal{E}_{si} (x = x_i)] /2 \tag{5 - 23}$$

If we express Eq. 5-23 in terms of Q_I and Q_B we get

$$\mathcal{E}_{eff} = [Q_B + Q_I + Q_B] / 2\kappa_{si}\varepsilon_0 = [Q_B + (Q_I/2)] /\kappa_{si}\varepsilon_0 \tag{5 - 24}$$

Eq. 5-24 can be approximated as

$$\mathcal{E}_{eff} \cong C_{ox} [V_{GS} - V_T] / (2\kappa_{si}\varepsilon_o) \qquad (5\text{-}25)$$

Then, if Eq. 5-25 is substituted into Eq. 5-20 the following expression is obtained

$$\mu_{eff} = \mu_o \{ \kappa_{si}\varepsilon_o U_{crit} / (C_{ox} (V_{GS} - V_T))\}^{UEXP} \qquad (5\text{-}26)$$

where U_{crit} is $2\mathcal{E}_{crit}$. Equation 5-26 is the model used to calculate μ_{eff} in the Level-2 MOSFET model in SPICE.*

In 1986 Liang et al[36] developed a modified form of the model of Eq. 5-26 for μ_{eff} also based on the concept of $\mathcal{E}_{eff}$. Their equation has the form:

$$\mu_{eff} = \mu_o / \{1 + (\mathcal{E}_{eff}/\mathcal{E}_{crit}]^v \} \qquad (5\text{-}27)$$

where $\mathcal{E}_{crit}$ and v are empirically determined constants. Values for these parameters are shown in Table 5-2. Universal curves for μ_{eff} for electrons and holes at room temperature as a function of $\mathcal{E}_{eff}$ calculated using Eq. 5-27 are shown in Fig. 5-33.

Eq. 5-27 can also be expressed in a more useful form that explicitly relates $\mathcal{E}_{eff}$ to the device parameters and terminal voltages:

$$\mathcal{E}_{eff} \cong [(V_{GS} - V_T) / 6t_{ox}] + [(V_T + V_a) / 3t_{ox}] \qquad (5\text{-}28)$$

where it has been semi-empirically determined that $V_a \cong 0.5V$ in typical n^+ polysilicon gate MOSFETs (e.g., for NMOS and PMOS devices in an n^+ polysilicon gate CMOS technology with $V_{Tn} = 0.7V$ and $V_{Tp} = -0.7V$).[37] Note that in this equation it is assumed that $Q_I = C_{ox} (V_{GS} - V_T)$. Since this assumption overestimates Q_I at low $(V_{GS} - V_T)$,[38] the $\mathcal{E}_{eff}$ according to Eq. 5-28 would be higher than its actual value. But, the error is small for $(V_{GS} - V_T) > 1V$.

Using Eq. 5-27 and the parameter values in Table 5-2, the carrier mobilities for NMOS and PMOS devices are plotted in Fig. 5-34 for several gate oxide thicknesses as a function of $(V_{GS} - V_T)$. These curves are useful for rough estimates of device performance or as first-order calibrators in process monitoring and control. A theoretical explanation of the electron and hole mobility dependencies on the transverse electric field has been developed by Lee et al.[39]

5.4.1.2 Models of the Carrier-Velocity Dependence on Drain Electric Field (Velocity Saturation).

As we noted earlier, the carrier velocities (v) near the Si-SiO$_2$ interface tend to saturate at high lateral electric fields, in a manner qualitatively similar to velocity saturation in the bulk. There have been

---

* In the Level-1 MOSFET model, however, the effective electron mobility is not explicitly expressed in terms of the field, but is treated as a fixed value.

Table 5-2. **Parameters for the Effective Mobility Models for Electrons and Holes[36]**

	Electron (surface)	Hole (surface)	Hole (buried channel)
μ_0 (cm²/ V sec)	670	160	290
$\mathcal{E}_0$ (MV/cm)	0.67	0.7	0.35
v	1.6	1	1

several empirical models developed to describe the dependence of the carrier velocity on lateral field (v-$\mathcal{E}_y$).[40,41,42] Two of the most widely used are

Model I $$v = \mu_{eff} \mathcal{E} \ / \{1 + (\mathcal{E} /\mathcal{E}_{sat})^\alpha \}^{1/\alpha} \qquad (5 - 29)$$

where $\mathcal{E}_{sat}$ and α are empirically determined parameters (i.e., $\alpha = 2$ for electrons and $\alpha < 2$ for holes). In Model II, the α term in Model I is taken to be unity, allowing Eq. 5-29 to become

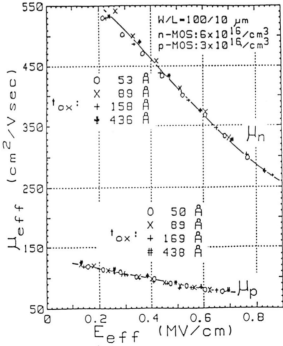

Fig. 5-33 Measured universal μ_{eff} versus $\mathcal{E}_{eff}$ curves for electrons and holes in the inversion layer.[36] (© 1986 IEEE).

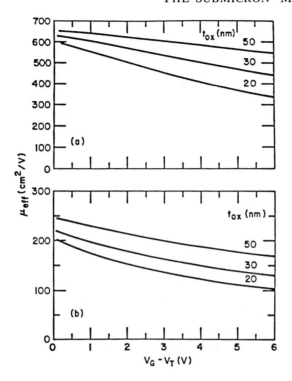

Fig. 5-34 Calculated μ_{eff} of current carrier versus $(V_{GS} - V_T)$ for three different values of t_{ox}: (a) NMOS device and (b) PMOS devices. The "buried-channel" parameters in Table 5-2 are used for PMOS. (From [36] © 1986 IEEE) and[46] © 1988 IEEE).

Model II $v = \mu_{eff} \mathcal{E} \,/\, \{1 + (\mathcal{E}/\mathcal{E}_{sat})\}$ (5 - 30)

A comparison of these two models with experimental data for electrons is shown in Fig. 5-35.[43] It is seen that Model I fits the measured data quite well, while Model II significantly underestimates the velocity at moderate fields (the same value of saturation velocity is used in both models plotted in Fig. 5-35). On this basis Model I would be preferred for estimating v. However, if Model I was inserted into an expression to calculate I_D, a solution could only be obtained by carrying out a prohibitively complex calculation.[44] Thus, to improve the accuracy of the carrier velocity model without incurring the complexity of Model I, a third, simpler, two-region piecewise model can be used. This model is defined by

Model III $v = \mu_{eff} \mathcal{E} \,/\, \{1 + (\mathcal{E}/\mathcal{E}_{sat})\}$ $\mathcal{E} < \mathcal{E}_{sat}$ (5 - 31a)

                $= v_{sat}$ $\mathcal{E} > \mathcal{E}_{sat}$ (5 - 31b)

By using this model in the expression which calculates I_D a closed-form solution of the I_D-V_{DS} characteristics of the MOSFET is obtained. In addition, the carrier velocity saturates at ε_{sat}. ε_{sat} can be expressed in terms of v_{sat} and μ_{eff} by matching the carrier velocities given by Eqs. 5-31a and 5-31b at $\varepsilon = \varepsilon_{sat}$. Therefore,

$$v_{sat} = \mu_{eff}\,\varepsilon_{sat} / [1 + (\varepsilon_{sat}/\varepsilon_{sat})] \qquad (5\text{-}32)$$

or

$$\varepsilon_{sat} = 2\,v_{sat} / \mu_{eff}. \qquad (5\text{-}33)$$

This model is also plotted in Fig. 5-35 over a wide range of electric fields. Note that it slightly overestimates the carrier velocity near ε_{sat}.

5.4.2 A Simple, Analytic DC Circuit Model of the Short-Channel MOSFET in Strong Inversion

Now that we have described the influence of the transverse and lateral fields on the velocity of the channel carriers, we can use the models of these effects to modify the dc circuit models of the MOSFET operating beyond threshold. In this way we develop a simple analytical dc circuit model that is valid for short-channel MOSFETs beyond threshold, and which can be used for first-order, hand calculations of I_D-V_{DS} and g_m for devices with channel lengths down to ~1 μm.[45,46]

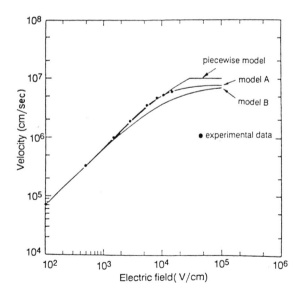

Fig. 5-35 Comparison of velocity-field models: models A and B as given in Eqs. 5-29 and 5-30, respectively. The piecewise model is given in Eq. 5-31, and $\mu_o = 710$ cm²/V-sec, $v_{sat} = 1\times10^7$ cm/sec.[38] Reprinted with permission of *Solid State Electronics*.

We first note that the factors resulting from both mobility degradation due to transverse fields and velocity saturation effects are outside of the integral in the equations used to calculate I_D (see Eqs. 4-16 and 4-19). Hence, they merely serve as multiplicative factors if incorporated into any of the long-channel dc models described in chap. 4. This means that any one of the long-channel models could be used to demonstrate the impact of these mobility effects the I_D-V_{DS} characteristics. Here, for mathematical simplicity, we elect to use the square-law model of section 4.5.5 for this purpose. To complete the dc short-channel MOSFET model, however, we will later still need to add some discussion of the short-channel effects that occur when the MOSFET is operated in saturation (i.e., the effects of channel-length modulation).

5.4.2.1 DC Circuit Model of the Short-Channel MOSFET in the Linear Regime.

As noted above, all of the long-channel MOSFET dc model equations can be modified in the same manner to take into account both effects described above. For simplicity, the square-law long-channel model is chosen to be modified. In the linear-region, the modified (i.e., short-channel) version of dc I_D-V_{DS} equation of the square-law model (Eq. 4-68) is

$$I_D = \frac{\mu_{eff} \, C_{ox} \dfrac{Z}{L}}{(1 + \dfrac{V_{DS}}{\mathcal{E}_{sat}L})} \left[(V_{GS} - V_T)V_{DS} - \frac{V_{DS}^2}{2} \right] \qquad (5\text{-}34)$$

Taking the ratio of the two currents given by Eqs. 5-22 and 4-68, we get

$$I_D \,(5\text{-}34)/I_D \,(4\text{-}68) = (\mu_{eff} / \mu_n) \left[1/\{1 + (V_{DS}/\mathcal{E}_{sat}L)\} \right] \qquad (5\text{-}35)$$

Note that since $\mathcal{E}_{sat}$ and L appear as a product term in both Eqs. 5-22 and 5-23, a MOSFET is "long-channel-like" if either $\mathcal{E}_{sat}$ or L is large. Therefore, a MOSFET with a thinner gate oxide is more "long-channel-like" because the thinner oxide will produce a larger transverse field, making the carrier mobility lower so that $\mathcal{E}_{sat}$ is high.

The saturation drain voltage V_{DSsat} can next be calculated by equating the current at the drain to the current given by Eq. 5-34 when $V_{DS} = V_{DSsat}$. The current at the drain is given by the product of the carrier density and the drift velocity. The charge density at the drain, assuming that the GCA is still valid, is $ZQ_I = C_{ox}(V_{GS} - V_T - V_{DSsat})$ and the drift velocity is v_{sat}. Therefore the current is

$$I_D = Z \, v_{sat} \, C_{ox} \, [V_{GS} - V_T - V_{DSsat}] \qquad (5\text{-}36a)$$

$$= \frac{Z}{L \, \mu_{eff} \, C_{ox}} [V_{GS} - V_T - (V_{DSsat}/2)] \, V_{DSsat} \left[\frac{1}{1 + (V_{DS}/\mathcal{E}_{sat} L)} \right] \qquad (5\text{-}36b)$$

After some algebra, an expression for V_{DSsat} is obtained

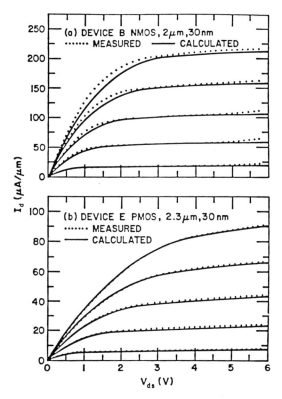

Fig. 5-36 Measured and calculated I-V characteristics for a (a) NMOS device and (b) a PMOS device.[46] (© 1988 IEEE).

$$V_{DSsat} = \frac{\mathcal{E}_{sat}L\,[V_{GS}-V_T]}{(V_{GS}-V_T)\,+\,\mathcal{E}_{sat}L} \qquad (5-37)$$

where $\mathcal{E}_{sat}$ is the critical field for velocity saturation ($\sim 4 \times 10^4$ V/cm).

The saturation drain current can be determined by substituting Eq. 5-37 into Eq. 5-36a to get

$$I_{Dsat} = Z\,v_{sat}\,C_{ox}\,\frac{[V_{GS}-V_T]^2}{(V_{GS}-V_T)\,+\,\mathcal{E}_{sat}L} \qquad (5-38)$$

The small-signal saturation transconductance g_{msat} can be found by differentiating Eq. 5-36a with respect to V_{GS}:

$$g_{msat} = Z\,v_{sat}\,C_{ox}\,[1\,-\,(\partial V_{DSsat}\,/\,\partial V_{GS})] \qquad (5-39)$$

Equations 5-36, 5-38, and 5-39 form the core equations of this simple model for calculating the dc drain characteristics for short-channel MOSFETs. Some modeling results using these equations are shown in Figs. 5-36a and b.[46] (Note that the I_D values for $V_{DS} > V_{DSsat}$ in these curves are calculated using a saturation region model to be described in the next section.) Good agreement with measured data is seen in these figures, and other work has shown good agreement for devices with channel lengths as small as 0.2 μm.[47] For example, agreement between calculated and measured values of g_m is better than ±6 percent over most of the gate voltage range for channel lengths from 3 μm down to 1 μm.

Equation 5-37 indicates that as the channel length is decreased, the channel field at the drain end will reach $\mathcal{E}_{sat}$ at a lower value of V_{DS}. Thus, V_{DSsat} is predicted to decrease with decreasing L as well. When the gate oxide thickness is made smaller, μ_{eff} decreases because $\mathcal{E}_{eff}$ is larger (see Eq. 5-27). Consequently, $\mathcal{E}_{sat}$ will increase, and so will V_{DSsat}. MOSFETs with thin gate oxides thus appear more "long-channel-like," as was discussed earlier.

The short-channel dc model of the MOSFET given by Eq. 5-36 also predicts four effects that impact the value of I_{Dsat} in short-channel devices not addressed by the long-channel dc models. First, mobility degradation reduces I_{Dsat} in short-channel devices by a factor (μ_{eff}/μ_0). Since the effective mobility decreases as V_{GS} increases, this indicates that I_{Dsat} can be significantly reduced for large gate voltages. Second, I_{Dsat} is also reduced by velocity saturation effects - to a value equivalent to the one predicted by the long-channel models (which assume a constant value of mobility, e.g., 4-68), except that the channel length appears longer than L by the factor $V_{DS}/\mathcal{E}_{sat}$.

Third, Eq. 5-36 indicates that if the product $\mathcal{E}_{sat}L$ is large compared to ($V_{GS} - V_T$), then I_{Dsat} varies quadratically with ($V_{GS} - V_T$). On the other hand, if ($V_{GS} - V_T$)$\gg \mathcal{E}_{sat}L$ then I_{Dsat} becomes linearly proportional to ($V_{GS} - V_T$). Since one of the criteria in Table 5-1 for long-channel behavior is that $I_{Dsat} \propto (V_{GS} - V_T)^2$, long-channel behavior will be exhibited by devices in which either L or $\mathcal{E}_{sat}$ is large. On the other hand, if L or $\mathcal{E}_{sat}$ are both small, such that $\mathcal{E}_{sat}L \ll (V_{GS} - V_T)$, the saturation regime behavior of the MOSFET will be "short-channel-like." Note that even a very short-channel device will exhibit some long-channel behavior if ($V_{GS} - V_T$) is small enough. The drain current under this situation is given by

$$I_{Dsat} = [\mu_{eff} \, Z \, C_{ox} / 2 \, L] \, (V_{GS} - V_T)^2 \quad \text{if } \mathcal{E}_{sat}L \gg (V_{GS} - V_T) \quad (5\text{-}40)$$

In shorter channel MOSFETs there is an observable trend toward a linear variation of I_{Dsat} with ($V_{GS} - V_T$) instead of the quadratic dependence, as is predicted without velocity saturation. This behavior is illustrated in Fig. 5-37a.

The fourth effect predicted by Eq. 5-36 (as noted in the introduction of this chapter) is observed in the limit of very strong velocity saturation (i.e., when the channel length is very short, such that V_{DSsat} approaches zero). In such cases, Eq. 5-36 indicates that the drain current is independent of L, and I_{Dsat} is given by

$$I_{Dsat} = [v_{sat} \, Z \, C_{ox}] \, (V_{GS} - V_T) \quad (5\text{-}41a)$$

Under this condition, even the carriers at the source [whose density is given by $C_{ox}(V_{GS} - V_T)$] are velocity saturated.

However, I_{Dsat} of a device with practical geometries is always lower than the maximum predicted by Eq. 5-41b. As a result, an ideality factor K has been defined as a useful figure of merit which indicates how close I_{Dsat} in a real device comes to that in an ideal device. This factor is inserted in Eq. 5-41b to yield

$$I_{Dsat} = K \, [v_{sat} \, Z \, C_{ox}] \, (V_{GS} - V_T) \quad \text{where } K < 1 \qquad (5 - 41b)$$

Then if we compare Eqs. 5-36 and 5-41b, we obtain a definition of as

$$K = (V_{GS} - V_T - V_{DSsat})/(V_{GS} - V_T) \qquad (5 - 41c)$$

This factor is a very handy parameter for device performance evaluation. That is, if an NMOS device with $t_{ox} = 60$ nm and $L = 1$ μm saturates at a V_{DS} of 1.3V when $(V_{GS} - V_T) = 4.3$, the value of K is $(4.3 - 1.3)/4.3 = 0.72$. This implies that shrinking the device would improve its driving current by no more than 30%. The K factor given by Eq. 5-41c is plotted against L for two different oxide thicknesses in Fig. 5-37c. The

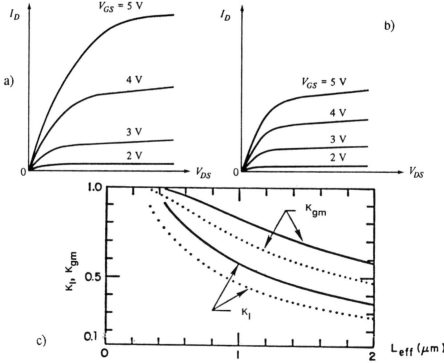

Fig. 5-37 Device characteristics (a) in the absence and (b) in the presence of velocity saturation effects. From Y.P Tsividis, *Operation and Modeling of the MOS Transistor*, McGraw-Hill, New York, 1987, p. 180. Reprinted with permission. (c) The calculated drain current ideality factor K_1 versus L for different gate-oxide thicknesses. Solid lines: $t_{ox} = 250$Å; dotted lines $t_{ox} = 100$Å.[46] (© 1988 IEEE).

K of the thicker oxide device saturates at longer channel lengths. As a result, decreasing the channel length of a thick oxide MOSFET cannot significantly improve the current drive. On the other hand, as L becomes very short (e.g., of the order of 0.25 μm), K approaches unity independent of t_{ox}. Thus, I_{Dsat} becomes proportional to C_{ox}. Since, in MOSFETs with very short channels, I_{Dsat} becomes independent of channel length, the chief means of increasing I_{Dsat} will be to make t_{ox} as thin as possible (i.e., the device driving current will increase linearly with C_{ox}). Data and numerical simulation results support this argument.

  As a last comment, note that because the value of v_{sat} for electrons and holes is comparable, n-channel and p-channel MOSFETs tend to perform similarly under velocity saturation, other things being equal. This is not the case under normal operation. That is, because I_D is proportional to μ_0 in normal operation, and in this case the value of μ_0 for holes in p-channel devices is one-half to one-fourth the corresponding value of μ_0 for n-channel devices.

5.4.2.2 Effects of Scaling on g_{msat}. From Eq. 5-39 the maximum available value of g_{msat} for a given t_{ox} is given by

$$g_{msat} = Z \, v_{sat} \, C_{ox} \qquad\qquad (5 - 42)$$

This is the ultimate relationship for very-short-channel MOSFETs. However, the g_{msat} of a device with practical geometries with finite channel length is always lower than this maximum. In general,

$$g_{msat} = K_{gm} \, Z \, v_{sat} \, C_{ox}, \qquad \text{where } K_{gm} < 1 \qquad (5 - 43)$$

Compared to Eq. 5-39, K_{gm} can be written as

$$K_{gm} = [1 - (\partial V_{DSsat} / \partial V_{GS})] \qquad\qquad (5 - 44)$$

It is observed that g_{msat} of a short-channel device often peaks at some moderate gate bias, beyond which it appears to either remain flat or sometimes decrease slightly, as shown in Fig. 5-38. This is a consequence of the term $\partial V_{DSsat}/\partial V_{GS}$ in Eq. 5-44, which becomes almost constant beyond a gate bias roughly equal to $\mathcal{E}_{sat}L$.

5.4.2.3 Comparing the Values of I_D Calculated with the Long- and Short-Channel MOSFET Models as a Function of Channel Length. The values of I_{Dsat} as the channel length is reduced from 5 μm to 0.3 μm as calculated both by the charge-control dc circuit model of the long-channel MOSFET (Eq. 4-68), and the short channel dc circuit model (Eq. 5-38, whose basis is also the charge-control model) are given in Table 5-3. We observe that Eq. 4-68 predicts larger values of I_{Dsat} than those calculated with Eq. 5-38 (and these in turn are much closer to the measured values). This reiterates the importance of choosing the correct device model when performing technology scaling studies.

Table 5-3   Comparison of Drive Current Values versus Gate Length with the Long-Channel (Eq.4-68) and Short-Channel MOSFET Models.

Technology/Gate Length (μm)	5	3	2	1	0.5	0.3
Gate Oxide (nm)	100	60	40	20	12.5	7.5
Calaculated I_{Dsat} @ $V_{GS} = 5V$ Long-channel Model (μA/μm)	1	2.61	6.25	20	99.3	206
Calaculated I_{Dsat} @ $V_{GS} = 5V$ Short-Channel Model (μA/μm)	1	2.18	4.12	10.5	19.9	30

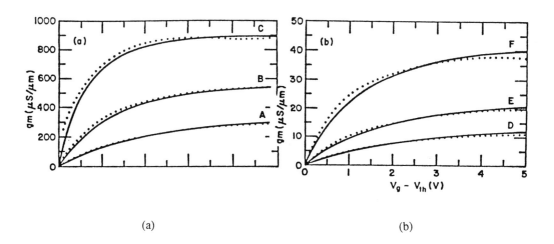

(a)

(b)

Fig. 5-38 Measured and calculated g_m vs (V_{GS} - V_T) @ V_{DS} = 5V for (a) NMOS; & (b) PMOS devices with L = 3 μm (A & D); L = 2 μm (B & E); and L = 1 μm (D & F).[46] (© 1988 IEEE).

5.4.3 Modeling the Saturation Region of Operation in Short-Channel MOSFETs

For drain voltages in excess of the pinch-off voltage (V_{DSsat}) the gate-to-drain voltage drops below the voltage value needed to establish an inversion layer (i.e., it becomes smaller than the threshold voltage). Hence, long-channel MOSFET theory implies that the inversion layer no longer exists in this case, and that there are no longer any mobile carriers present in the channel at such locations. The portion of the channel extending back from the drain over which the inversion layer is extinguished is called the *pinched-off region*. The length of the pinched off region is ΔL, and its length increases as V_{DS} grows beyond V_{DSsat} (see Fig. 5-39). In addition, in saturation most of the drain voltage in excess of V_{DSsat} is dropped across this region. From a modeling perspective this makes it appear as if the normal channel length (in which the GCA is still applicable, and in which mobile charges still exist) is growing shorter. The apparent shrinkage in channel length from this effect is known as *channel-length modulation*.

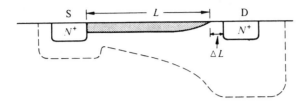

Fig. 5-39 Visualization of the velocity saturation region in a MOSFET, having a length ΔL.

In long-channel MOSFETs the length of the pinched-off region is much smaller than the original channel length (i.e. $\Delta L \ll L$), even at large values of V_{DS}. Thus, I_D remains approximately constant for drain voltages in excess of V_{DSsat}. In short-channel MOSFETs, however, ΔL can be comparable to L. Thus, the same voltage drop (V_{DSsat}) will appear across a substantially shorter channel ($L - \Delta L$). Hence, when $V_{DS} > V_{DSsat}$ in short-channel MOSFETs, I_D can increase significantly with increasing V_{DS} (as is seen in Fig. 5-31b). Since I_{Dsat} is proportional to $1/L$, the equation of drain current I_D in saturation has the general form of

$$I_D \ (V_D > V_{DSsat}) \ = \ I_{Dsat} \ [L \ /(L - \Delta L)] \tag{5-45}$$

To be able to predict the increase in I_D in short-channel MOSFETs, the value of ΔL as a function of the terminal voltages is needed. The most general approach to calculate ΔL, however, is to simultaneously solve the current transport equation (Eq. 1-4), and the two-dimensional form of the Poisson equation (Eq. 1-3) in the pinch-off region. Unfortunately, this general approach requires numerical solution of these equations, using such 2-D device simulators as MINIMOS or PISCES (see chaps. 1 and 2). To obtain an analytical expression for ΔL some approximations must be made to reduce the 2-D Poisson equation to a 1-D form. Analytical solutions of the Poisson equation can then be found, and these solutions can be used to derive analytical expressions for ΔL. The analysis used to derive models for ΔL will also yield expressions that calculate the value of the channel electric field. These can be employed to find the magnitude of the maximum channel $\mathcal{E}$-field strength $\mathcal{E}_{ymax}$, a quantity that is needed when the subject of hot-carrier effects in MOSFETs is considered (see chap. 9).

For the purposes of modeling the MOSFET in saturation, the most common approach for reducing the 2-D Poisson equation to a 1-D form *assumes that $\partial \mathcal{E}/\partial x$ (i.e., the gradient of the electric field in the vertical (x) direction) is much smaller than $\partial \mathcal{E}/\partial y$*. In such cases, the $\partial \mathcal{E}/\partial x$ term in the 2-D Poisson equation can be dropped, turning a 2-D partial differential equation into the form of a one-dimensional (ordinary) differential equation. We note that this approach is opposite to the one taken in the GCA approximation. Namely, in the GCA approach the $\partial \mathcal{E}/\partial y$ term is considered to be much smaller than the $\partial \mathcal{E}/\partial x$ term, and thus it is the term dropped from the Poisson equation. Here we will derive three analytical models for ΔL. The simplification of dropping $\partial \mathcal{E}/\partial x$ entirely from the 2-D Poisson equation is used in the first two.

5.4.3.1 Modeling MOSFET Saturation Behavior Using the Abrupt Junction and Depletion Approximations.
The first and simplest approach to modeling saturation behavior in MOSFETs divides the MOSFET channel into two regions: one in which the long-channel I_D models are still assumed to be valid, and the pinched-off region. This simple model also invokes three approximations in the pinched-off region, which are:

a. Only the drain field is assumed to be responsible for determining the current flow in the pinched-off region. (That is, the vertical field due to the gate is ignored.) In addition, the drain field is assumed to have only a horizontal component, $\mathcal{E}_y(y)$. Furthermore, its magnitude is assumed to be constant as a function of x. The map of the drain field in the pinched-off region is thus qualitatively depicted in Fig. 5-40. The strength of the field is indicated by the length of the arrows, and the field direction at each point by the direction of the arrow.

b. No mobile charge is present in the pinched-off region. That is, only the ionic charge [uniformly distributed with a concentration $\rho(x,y) = -qN_A$] is assumed to be present (i.e., the depletion approximation described in section 3.2.3 is once again invoked here).

c. The abrupt junction approximation is also invoked. This implies that $\mathcal{E}_y = 0$ at the leading edge of the pinched-off region $y = (L - \Delta L)_+$ (because the electric field at the edge of the depletion region in any abrupt junction is assumed to be zero).

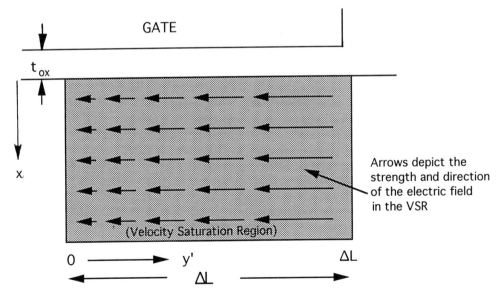

Fig. 5-40 Map of the drain field in the VSR region.

Using these approximations the Poisson equation is reduced to the form:

$$\frac{d\mathcal{E}_y(y)}{dy} = \frac{q\,N_A}{\kappa_{si}\,\varepsilon_0}$$

(5 - 46)

The expression for calculating the channel length modulation is found from Eq. 5-46 to be

$$\Delta L = \sqrt{\frac{2\varepsilon_{si}}{q\,N_A}(V_{DS} - V_{DSsat})}$$

(5 - 47)

This equation for calculating ΔL was introduced by Reddi and Sah in 1965.[48]

Using this method to estimate ΔL, however, leads to some physical inconsistencies in the value of $\mathcal{E}_y(y)$ as well as yielding values of ΔL that substantially overestimate its length (i.e., it predicts that ΔL can be larger than L, even in 2 μm MOSFETs under normal operating conditions). A more complex model must therefore be invoked to reconcile these apparently unphysical results, as well as to improve the predictive capability of the ΔL model. Before we describe such more-complex models let us first discuss the shortcomings of the Reddi-Sah ΔL model in more detail.

The variation of the channel electric field when the device is saturated provides some insight into the shortcoming of this ΔL model. We calculate the channel field using the approximations that led to the charge-control long-channel dc MOSFET model (adopted here again for the sake of mathematical simplicity). The channel field $\mathcal{E}_y(y)$ for $y < L - \Delta L$ can be found by substituting Eq. 4-63 into Eq. 4-22. Combining with the pinchoff conditions that led to Eq. 5-47, we get

$$\mathcal{E}_y(y) = \frac{V_{GS} - V_T}{2\,(L - \Delta L)}\,\frac{1}{1 - [y\,/(L - \Delta L)\,]} \qquad \text{for } y < L - \Delta L \qquad (5 - 48)$$

$$= \frac{q\,N_A}{\varepsilon_{si}}\,[\,y - (L - \Delta L)] \qquad \text{for } y > L - \Delta L \qquad (5 - 49)$$

These two equations for $\mathcal{E}_y$ are plotted as a function of y in Fig. 5-41. Note from Eq. 5-49 that $\mathcal{E}_y$ increases linearly with y in the pinched-off region. In addition, from Eq. 5-48 we see that the model predicts $\mathcal{E}_y$ goes to infinity at $y = L - \Delta L$. This occurs because at the point where the pinched-off begins (i.e., $y = L - \Delta L$), the inversion-layer charge concentration Q_I becomes zero, as required by the pinchoff (and depletion-approximation) condition. To maintain current continuity when the mobile-charge concentration approaches zero, the electric field must approach infinity. In addition, Fig. 5-41 shows that $\mathcal{E}_y$ is discontinuous at $y = L - \Delta L$ (i.e., $\mathcal{E}_y$ is infinite at $[L - \Delta L]_-$, and is zero at $[L - \Delta L]_+$). Both of these predictions are, of course, unphysical. The problem lies with the pinchoff condition. That is, the concentration of mobile charges in the pinched-off region never actually becomes zero because of carrier velocity saturation. As a result, to derive a more accurate and physically correct model of the

MOSFET in saturation, a somewhat more complex formulation of the Poisson equation than Eq. 5-46 must be employed.

It should be noted that a completely empirical approach based on the Reddi-Sah model of ΔL was developed by Frohman-Bentchkowsky and Grove.[49] In this approach, Eq. 5-47 is still used, but two terms - each containing an empirically determined constant - are added as corrections to this equation to improve the accuracy with which it predicts the value of ΔL. One of the correction terms is attributed to the fringing field between the gate and sidewall of the drain and the other to the fringing field between the gate and the end of the channel. These effects are not considered in the basic model represented by Eq. 5-47. Agreement with experiment is good for channel lengths from 2 to 4 μm and $N_{SUB} \sim 10^{15} - 10^{16}$ cm^{-3}.

5.4.3.2 Constant-Field-Gradient Model. The prediction of an infinite electric field strength at $y = L - \Delta L$ arises from the assumption that no mobile charge exists in the depletion region. If we remove this assumption (approximations **b** of the Reddi-Sah model), and also approximation **c** (which leads to the nonphysical discontinuity in the $\mathcal{E}$-field value at the leading edge of the pinched-off region), but retain approximation **a**, the formulation of the second of the three saturation models is obtained. That is, we now assume that a uniform mobile charge concentration (with a density N_m) exists to a depth r_j in the pinched-off region, and also that these carriers are velocity saturated. Hence, it is appropriate to rename the pinched-off region as the *velocity saturation region* (VSR). Now, the mobile charge density in the VSR can be expressed in the following form[50] *

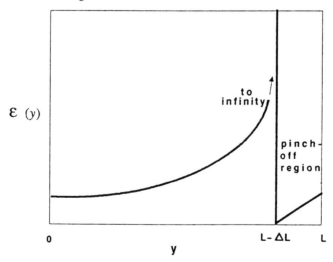

Fig. 5-41 General behavior of $\mathcal{E}(y)$, the channel field, for a device in saturation according to the long-channel model.[45] Reprinted with permission of Academic Press.

* Note that Eq. 5-50 is similar to the more familiar drift current expression $I_{drift} = J_{drift} A = q$ $n <v> A$, where N_m corresponds to n, v_{sat} to $<v>$, and $r_j Z$ to A.

$$q\,N_m = (A_{ph}\,I_D)\,/\,v_{sat}\,r_j\,Z \qquad (5\text{-}50)$$

where I_D in this region is assumed to consist of velocity saturated carriers distributed uniformly into the bulk to a depth equal to the source/drain junction depths r_j, and A_{ph} is a fitting parameter. With the total charge in the VSR now expressed as the sum of the ionic and mobile charges, the one-dimensional form of the Poisson equation (Eq. 5-46) becomes

$$\frac{d\mathcal{E}_y\,(y)}{dy} = \frac{q\,N_A}{\kappa_{si}\,\varepsilon_0} + A_{ph}\,\frac{I_D}{\kappa_{si}\,\varepsilon_0\,r_j\,v_{sat}\,Z} \qquad (5\text{-}51)$$

Using this equation, we can solve for the value of $\mathcal{E}_y(y)$ in the VSR. When removing approximation **c** we instead apply the boundary condition that $\mathcal{E}_y(0) = \mathcal{E}_{sat}$ at the leading edge of the VSR (instead of the boundary condition that $\mathcal{E}_y = 0$ at $[L - \Delta L]_+$, as is done in the Reddi-Sah model).

Since the terms on the right hand side of Eq. 5-51 are constant as a function of y, this model indicates that the gradient of the channel electric field in the y-direction in the VSR, $d\mathcal{E}_y(y)/dy$, is also a constant (hence the name, the *constant-field-gradient model*). As a result, $\mathcal{E}_y(y)$ is predicted by this model to increase linearly with y in the VSR (as is also predicted by Reddi-Sah model). Since more charge is now assumed to exist in the VSR, however, the magnitude of the linear gradient in this model is larger. We plot this result over the channel position ΔL as the dotted line in Fig. 5-42.[54]

The channel field $\mathcal{E}_y(y)$ as calculated from a numerical solution of the two-dimensional form of the Poisson equation is also plotted in Fig. 5-42.[55] The numerical simulation predicts that $\mathcal{E}_y(y)$ exhibits a near-exponential-dependent rise towards the drain, implying that the constant-field-gradient model significantly underestimates the peak channel electric field. Because hot-carrier effects are extremely sensitive to the magnitude of the peak channel field, it has been concluded that this model is not sufficiently accurate for use in analyzing hot-carrier problems. Consequently, a more accurate analytical model of the saturation region is still needed.

5.4.3.3 Pseudo-Two-Dimensional Model of the MOSFET Operating in Saturation.

The chief reason the constant-field-gradient model underestimates the maximum value of $\mathcal{E}_y$ in the VSR is that it ignores the effect of the gate field in the analysis. A pseudo-two-dimensional approach, which includes the effect of this field, has therefore been developed to obtain a more accurate analytical model of ΔL and $\mathcal{E}_y$ in the VSR. From these relationships a model for I_{Dsat} as a function of V_{DS} can also be obtained. The original pseudo-2-D model was introduced by Elmansy and Boothroyd in 1977.[51] Later, Ko et al. developed an enhanced version[52,53] that has also been applied to modeling hot-carrier effects and subthreshold MOSFET behavior (as outlined in section 5.2.1.4). Here we present a simplified version of this model, adapted from the description by Ko in references 52 and 53.

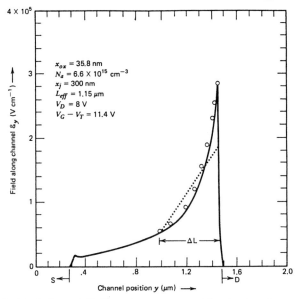

Fig. 5-42 Calculated channel field region versus position in the channel near the drain end for three models (t_{ox} =358Å, N_A = 6.6x10^{15} cm^{-3}, r_j = 0.3 μm, L_{eff} = 1.15 μm, V_{DS} = 8V, (V_{GS} - V_T) = 1.14V. Electrons in the channel have saturated velocities over the region ΔL which extends from the channel pinch-off point to the drain. From R.S. Muller and T.I. Kamins, *Device Electronics for Integrated Circuits*, 2nd Ed. Copyright John Wiley & Sons, New York, 1986. p. 491, Reprinted with permission.

In this approach we again remove approximations **b** and **c**, but also modify approximation **a** of the Reddi-Sah model. In Fig. 5-43a a schematic diagram of the VSR is shown. As in the previous approach the mobile carriers in this region are assumed to be velocity saturated and are uniformly distributed in the VSR to the depth of the source and drain junctions r_j (with a concentration N_m). The VSR is thus approximated as a box bounded on the sides by ABCD. This box encloses all of the VSR mobile charges and most of the ionic charges of interest. The electric field and voltage at the leading edge of the VSR (point A) are assumed to have a values $\mathcal{E}_{sat}$ and V_{DSsat}, respectively. Since in steady-state the total number of mobile charges in the VSR is constant with time the phenomenon being analyzed is essentially an electrostatic problem, solvable using the Poisson equation.

Approximation **a** is modified as follows: First, let the coordinate system be selected such that $y = 0$ at A and $y = \Delta L$ at D. Next, we see that the charge enclosed in the VSR is the sum of the mobile charge and ionic charge concentrations, qN_A and qN_m, respectively, or:

$$\rho \ (x,y) = qN_A + qN_m \qquad (5 - 53)$$

The drain $\mathcal{E}$-field is still assumed to have only a horizontal component $\mathcal{E}_y$ that varies with position y, but not with position x. The map of the drain field component in the

VSR bounded by ABCD is shown in Fig. 5-43b. The effect of the field due to the gate charge, however, is now also included in the Poisson equation. This field is assumed to have only a vertical component $\mathcal{E}_x$ which varies with position y (i.e., $\mathcal{E}_x$ gets weaker as the drain is approached). $\mathcal{E}_x$ has a value at the Si-SiO$_2$ interface given by $\mathcal{E}_x(0,y)$ and is assumed to be zero at the bottom edge of the depletion region [$\mathcal{E}_x(d_{max},y) = 0$]. The value of $\mathcal{E}_x(r_j,y)$ is also assumed to be close to zero, even though r_j is not as deep as d_{max}. (This latter assumption is plausible since the MOSFET is biased into strong inversion, making qN_m in the VSR larger than qN_A. Thus, most of the total charge in the VSR region of the channel [i.e., from $y = 0$ to $y = \Delta L$], is confined within the depth from $x = 0$ to $x = r_j$). *It is now assumed that the value of $\partial \mathcal{E}_x / \partial x$ at each point y can be replaced by the average value of $\partial \mathcal{E}_x / \partial x$ from $x = 0$ to $x = r_j$.* This average value is given by [$\mathcal{E}_x(0,y) - \mathcal{E}_x(r_j,y)/r_j$]. Since $\mathcal{E}_x(r_j,y)/r_j \sim 0$, the average value of $\partial \mathcal{E} / \partial x$ can be approximated as just $\mathcal{E}_x(0,y)/r_j$.

The above modifications to approximation **a** result in the following important conclusion: *The term $\partial \mathcal{E} / \partial x$ in the Poisson equation can be approximated as $\mathcal{E}_x(0,y)/r_j$.* With this approximation, the 2-D Poisson equation which governs the relation between the electric-field and the charge density in the VSR, can be expressed as follows (with $\mathcal{E}_x(0,y)$ being written as $\mathcal{E}_{si}(0,y)$:

$$\frac{d\mathcal{E}_y(y)}{dy} + \frac{\mathcal{E}_{si}(0,y)}{r_j} = \frac{q\,N_A}{\kappa_{si}\,\varepsilon_0} + \frac{q\,N_m}{\kappa_{si}\,\varepsilon_0} \qquad (5\text{-}54)$$

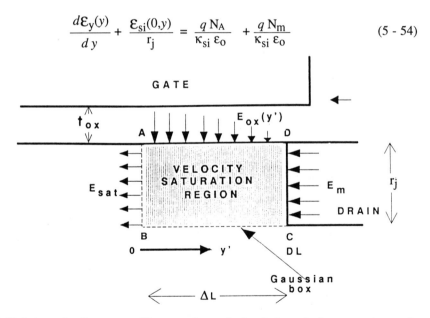

Fig. 5-43 Schematic diagram to illustrate the analysis of the velocity saturation region (VSR). From P.K. Ko, "Approaches to Scaling," Chap. 1, in *Advanced MOS Device Physics*, N.G. Einspruch and G. Gildenblatt, Eds., Vol. 18 VLSI Electronics. Academic Press 1989. Reprinted with permission.

Thus, by using this modified approximation, not only is the Poisson equation reduced to a 1-D form (i.e., dependent only on y), but in addition, the effects of the both the vertical (gate) and the horizontal (drain) fields in the VSR are included. Consequently, the name chosen for this model (i.e., the *pseudo-2-D model*) is appropriate.

Now, we can further simplify Eq. 5-54 by noting that $\mathcal{E}_{si}(0,y)$ can be described in terms of $\mathcal{E}_{ox}$ (according to Eq. 3-15) as

$$\mathcal{E}_{si}(0,y) = (\varepsilon_{ox}/\kappa_{si}\varepsilon_0)\, \mathcal{E}_{ox}(0,y) \tag{5-55}$$

Substituting the right hand side of Eq. 5-55 into Eq. 5-54 for $\mathcal{E}_{si}$, and then recalling that we since we can express $\mathcal{E}_{ox}(0,y)$ as

$$\mathcal{E}_{ox}(0, y) = [V_{GS} - V_{FB} - 2\varphi_B - V(y)]/t_{ox} \tag{5-56}$$

[see Eq. 3-14, with $\varphi_{ox} = V_{GS} - V_{FB} - 2\varphi_B - V(y)$], we can make these both of changes in Eq. 5-54 to get

$$\frac{d\mathcal{E}_y(y)}{dy} + \frac{\varepsilon_{ox}}{\kappa_{si}\varepsilon_0}\frac{1}{t_{ox}}\frac{[V_{GS} - V_{FB} - 2\varphi_B - V(y)]}{r_j} = \frac{q\,N_A}{\kappa_{si}\varepsilon_0} + \frac{q\,N_m}{\kappa_{si}\varepsilon_0} \tag{5-57}$$

Since $V(y=0) = V_{DSsat}$ we can use Eq. 5-56 to write

$$\mathcal{E}_{ox}(y=0) = \frac{1}{t_{ox}}[V_{GS} - V_{FB} - 2\varphi_B - V_{DSsat}] \tag{5-58}$$

In addition, since the GCA approximation is still valid at the leading edge of the VSR ($y = 0$), the total charge in the silicon (Q_C) at that point can still be calculated by Eq. 4-1c ($Q_C = \varphi_{ox}C_{ox}$), where $C_{ox} = \varepsilon_{ox}/t_{ox}$ and $\mathcal{E}_{ox} = \varphi_{ox}/t_{ox}$. Thus, since Q_C (cm^{-2}) is ($qN_Ar_j + qN_mr_j$), and $Q_C = \mathcal{E}_{ox}\varepsilon_{ox}$, we can also write

$$\mathcal{E}_{ox}(y=0) = (q\,N_A\,r_j + q\,N_m\,r_j)/\varepsilon_{ox} \tag{5-59}$$

Hence,

$$\frac{\varepsilon_{ox}}{\kappa_{si}\varepsilon_0}\frac{1}{t_{ox}}[V_{GS} - V_{FB} - 2\varphi_B - V_{DSsat}] = \frac{q\,N_A}{\kappa_{si}\varepsilon_0}r_j + \frac{q\,N_m}{\kappa_{si}\varepsilon_0}r_j \tag{5-60}$$

Now we can substitute $(\varepsilon_{ox}/\kappa_{si}\varepsilon_0 t_{ox}r_j)[V_{GS} - V_{FB} - 2\varphi_B - V_{DSsat}]$ for the right hand side of Eq. 5-57, allowing Eq. 5-57 to be simplified to

$$\frac{d\mathcal{E}_y(y)}{dy} = \frac{\varepsilon_{ox}}{\kappa_{si}\varepsilon_0 t_{ox}r_j}[V(y) - V_{DSsat}] \tag{5-61}$$

or

$$\frac{d\mathcal{E}_y(y)}{dy} = \frac{[V(y) - V_{DSsat}]}{l^2} \qquad \text{where } l^2 = \frac{\kappa_{si}\varepsilon_0}{\varepsilon_{ox}}t_{ox}\,r_j \tag{5-62}$$

or

$$\frac{d^2[V(y) - V_{DSsat}]}{dy^2} = \frac{[V(y) - V_{DSsat}]}{l^2}$$ (5 - 63)

where the parameter l is the effective length of the VSR.

A qualitative physical interpretation of equations 5-62 and 5-63 can be given as follows: At $y = 0$, where $V(0) = V_{DSsat}$, the charge in the VSR is still controlled entirely by the vertical field ($\mathcal{E}_x$). Since, for conditions of dc current flow the total charge density (i.e., the sum of the mobile and ionic charge densities) must remain constant along the VSR toward the drain, the total electric field at each point y must also remain constant. However, the voltage $V(y)$ increases toward the drain. Thus, from Eqs. 5-55 and 5-56, we see that $\mathcal{E}_x$ must decrease toward the drain, and so must the amount of charge in the VSR controlled by it. According to the Poisson equation, this charge must be taken up by the gradient of $\mathcal{E}_y$. Thus, the gradient of $\mathcal{E}_y$ must increase toward the drain. In Eq. 5-62, the RHS is the amount of charge released by $\mathcal{E}_x$ as a result of the rise in the channel voltage [equal to $V(y) - V_{DSsat}$], while the LHS is the corresponding increase of the gradient in $\mathcal{E}_y$ in order to support these charges.

The general solution of Eq. 5-63 is:

$$[V(y) - V_{DSsat}] = A\, e^{y/l} + B\, e^{-y/l}$$ (5 - 64)

By applying the boundary conditions: $V(0) = V_{DSsat}$, and $\mathcal{E}_y(0) = [\partial V(y)/\partial y]@_{y=0} = \mathcal{E}_{ysat}$, the coefficients in Eq. 5-64 are found to be $A = l\mathcal{E}_{sat}/2$ and $B = -l\mathcal{E}_{sat}/2$. Thus, we can write the expressions for $V(y)$ and $\mathcal{E}_y(y)$ in the VSR as

$$V(y) = V_{DSsat} + l\,\mathcal{E}_{sat}\, \sinh(y/l)$$ (5 - 65a)

and

$$\mathcal{E}_y(y) = dV/dy = \mathcal{E}_{sat} \cosh(y/l)$$ (5 - 66a)

Note that near the drain end of the VSR

$$V(y) \approx V_{DSsat} + l\,\mathcal{E}_{sat}\, \exp(y/l)$$ (5 - 65b)

and

$$\mathcal{E}_y(y) \approx [(l\mathcal{E}_{sat})/l]\, \exp(y/l)$$ (5 - 66b)

At the drain end of the channel $V(y)$ and $\mathcal{E}_y$ have their maximum values V_{DSmax} and $\mathcal{E}_{ymax}$, as given by

$$V_{DSmax} = V_{DSsat} + l\,\mathcal{E}_{sat}\, \sinh(\Delta L/l)$$ (5 - 67)

and

$$\mathcal{E}_{ymax} = \mathcal{E}(y = \Delta L) = \mathcal{E}_{sat} \cosh(\Delta L/l)$$ (5 - 68)

Equations 5-67 and 5-68 can be combined to yield an expression for ΔL

$$\Delta L = l \ln \frac{\{[V(y) - V_{DSsat}]/l\} + \varepsilon_{ymax}}{\varepsilon_{sat}} \qquad (5 - 69)$$

and

$$\varepsilon_{ymax} = \left[\frac{[V_{DS} - V_{DSsat}]^2}{l^2} + \varepsilon^2_{sat} \right]^{1/2} \qquad (5 - 70a)$$

Equations 5-66 to 5-70 describe important aspects of the behavior of the MOSFET in saturation. First, Eq. 5-66b indicates that ε_y grows almost exponentially towards the drain, as was predicted by 2-D numerical simulation. In Fig. 5-42, Eq. 5-66a is plotted along with the results of the 2-D numerical simulation. Close agreement is observed. However, the parameter l must be adjusted to give approximately the same peak channel field. We indicate below how this has been done using both experimental data and numerical simulation.

From Eq. 5-70, ε_{ymax} is seen to depend explicitly on $[V(y) - V_{DSsat}]$, but the channel length L only influences ε_{ymax} indirectly. Furthermore, if V_{DS} is more than about 2V greater than V_{DSsat}, $(V_{DS} - V_{DSsat})/l >> \varepsilon_{sat}$. In this case Eq. 5-70a for ε_{ymax} is simplified to

$$\varepsilon_{ymax} \approx [V_{DS} - V_{DSsat}]/l \qquad (5 - 70b)$$

From experimental data and 2-D device simulations using MINIMOS the following expressions for l that appear valid over a wide range of t_{ox}, N_A, and r_j have been deduced:[1]

$$l \approx 0.22 \, t_{ox}^{1/3} \, r_{j}^{1/3} \qquad \text{if} \quad t_{ox} \geq 15 \text{ nm} \qquad (5 - 70c1)$$

and

$$l \approx 1.7 \times 10^{-2} \, t_{ox}^{1/8} \, r_{j}^{1/3} \qquad \text{if} \quad t_{ox} < 15 \text{ nm} \qquad (5 - 70c2)$$

where l, r_j and t_{ox} are in centimeters.

By substituting Eq. 5-70c1 into Eq. 5-70b a simple, explicit expression for the maximum channel electric field is obtained

$$\varepsilon_{ymax} \approx [V_{DS} - V_{DSsat}]/0.22 \, r_j^{1/3} \, t_{ox}^{1/3} \qquad (5 - 71)$$

where V_{DSsat} is found using Eq. 5-37 and ε_{sat} in that equation is taken to be the critical field for velocity saturation ($\sim 5 \times 10^4$ V/cm). Equations. 5-71 and 5-37 can thus be used to estimate the peak channel electric field ε_{ymax} as a function of device dimensions and bias voltages in conventional (i.e., non-graded drain) MOSFETs.

For example, by substituting some realistic values of t_{ox} and r_j into Eq. 5-71 (i.e., using values typical of 1-μm CMOS technology, namely, $t_{ox} = 250$Å and $r_j = 0.2$ μm), we get $l = 135$ nm, and $1/l = 7.5 \times 10^4$ cm^{-1}. At low $(V_{GS} - V_T)$ values, $V_{DSsat} \sim 0$. Using $\varepsilon_{sat} = 5 \times 10^4$ V/cm and $V_{DS} = 5$V, from Eq. 5-71 we get $\varepsilon_{ymax} = 3.85 \times 10^5$ V/cm. Since ε_{ymax} is proportional to $(1/r_j^{1/3} \, t_{ox}^{1/3})$, it is apparent that device scaling will magnify the high-field problems unless the power-supply voltage is also correspondingly reduced, or the MOSFET device structure is modified to reduce ε_{ymax}.

With an expression for ΔL also in hand (Eq. 5-69), a relationship for the drain current in saturation based on the pseudo-2D saturation model can now be derived, namely for $V_{DS} > V_{DSsat}$:

$$I_D (\Delta L) = I_{Dsat} \left[\frac{L}{L - \Delta L}\right]\left[\frac{V_{DSsat} + \mathcal{E}_{sat} L}{V_{DSsat} + \mathcal{E}_{sat} (L - \Delta L)}\right] \qquad (5 - 72)$$

5.5. SHORT-CHANNEL MOSFET MODELS USED IN THE *SPICE* CIRCUIT SIMULATOR

The simple, analytical short-channel MOSFET model described in section 5.4 is adequate for hand calculations. However, for computer-aided circuit analysis and design a more accurate model is needed, which also retains the benefit of simplicity to allow rapid circuit-simulation execution times. The Level-1 and Level-2 MOSFET models in SPICE are not suitable since they do not work well for small geometry transistors. Likewise, the Level-3 model relies too heavily on a semi-empirical approach. Thus, a simple and accurate, physically based, short-channel MOSFET model suitable for circuit simulation programs was needed.

Such a model has been developed and is incorporated in the circuit simulator SPICE. This model, named BSIM (Berkeley Short-channel IgFET Model), was introduced in 1987.[56] It is a modified version of the Bell Labs model CSIM with substantial enhancements (Compact Short-Channel IgFET Model).[57] BSIM is the Level-4 MOSFET model in SPICE, and BSIM2 (introduced in 1990) is the Level-5 MOSFET model.[58] By 1993, BSIM3 was developed and incorporated into SPICE.

BSIM is capable of simulating the drain current in short channel MOSFETs in both the strong-inversion and weak inversion regimes. It can model such short-channel effects as channel-length shortening, channel narrowing, mobility degradation, drain-induced barrier lowering, nonuniform channel doping for ion-implanted devices, subthreshold slope, and geometric dependencies. Terms with strong physical meaning are employed to model the fundamental physical effects while empirically derived parameters are judiciously used to embrace less-well-understood (and generally subtle) device characteristics. This approach is well-suited for circuit-analysis purposes, especially as two- and three dimensional small geometry effects become more important.

BSIM2 is an extension of the original BSIM model, but BSIM3 is essentially a new model. That is, while BSIM has about 60 parameters (17 for modeling the dc characteristics) and BSIM2 about 120, BSIM3 has 38 (the Level-1 and Level-2 SPICE models described in chap. 4 each have a total of about 15). It is generally conceded that while the Level-1 and Level-2 models had too few parameters, BSIM and BSIM2 had too many. BSIM3 is a compromise that seeks to use just the right number. In addition, many BSIM and BSIM2 parameters were put into the model strictly for curve fitting and did not have much physical basis. This makes it difficult to generate fast and slow models using BSIM or BSIM2. For the most part, the BSIM3 parameters are based on reasonable physical assumptions, and almost all have some connection with the real world, making the results of BSIM3 easier to interpret.

BSIM also includes a dedicated parameter extraction program, which together with the parameter-extraction system hardware (consisting of three major elements: a desktop computer, an H-P 4145 semiconductor parameter analyzer, and a probe station) allows the BSIM model parameters for a family of devices to be automatically extracted from measurements of actual test devices.

5.5.1 BSIM Model Equations

The formulation of BSIM can be broken down into the following aspects: (1) an equation for the threshold voltage V_T of the short-channel MOSFET; (2) equations for the operation of the short-channel MOSFET in strong inversion; and (3) equations for the operation in weak inversion (subthreshold regime).

5.5.1.1 BSIM Threshold Voltage Equation. The equation used to model V_T in long-channel MOSFETs (i.e., Eq. 4-12, with V_{BC} replaced with V_{BS}), is modified in BSIM to allow the threshold lowering effect observed in short-channel MOSFETs to be modeled. The BSIM V_T equation is

$$V_T = V_{FB} + 2\varphi_B + \gamma (2\varphi_B + V_{BS})^{1/2} - K_T (2\varphi_B - V_{BS}) - \eta V_{DS} \qquad (5-73)$$

We observe that in addition to the three parameters V_{FB}, φ_B, and γ, Eq. 5-73 contains two more for modeling V_T, namely K_T and η. K_T is the source and drain depletion charge sharing coefficient, and η is the drain-induced barrier lowering coefficient (which is roughly inversely proportional to the channel length L). Together, K_T and η model the threshold lowering effect.

5.5.1.2 BSIM Equations for I_D when the MOSFET is Operated in Strong Inversion. The BSIM I_D equations contain three additional parameters to allow the mobility degradation and velocity saturation effects to be modeled. These are the vertical field mobility degradation coefficient U_0, the velocity saturation coefficient U_1, and the carrier mobility μ_0. (Note that μ_0 in BSIM is a function of the substrate and drain biases.) In order to speed up the circuit simulation time, instead of using I_D in the form of the ionic charge model (i.e., of the form of Eq. 4-57 - which has a 3/2 power dependence of the drain current on the drain and substrate bias), a numerical approximation to the terms of Eq. 4-57 that contain V_{BS} is used. The resulting BSIM equations for I_D in the linear and saturation regions are:

Linear Region: [$V_{GS} > V_T$), and $0 < V_{DS} < V_{DSsat}$]

$$I_D = \frac{\mu_0}{[1 + U_0(V_{GS} - V_T)]} \frac{C_{ox}\frac{Z}{L}}{(1 + \frac{U_1}{L}V_{DS})} \left(V_{GS} - V_T\right)V_{DS} - \frac{aV_{DS}^2}{2}) \qquad (5-74)$$

where

$$a = 1 + \frac{\gamma}{2\sqrt{2\varphi_B - V_{BS}}} \left[1 - \frac{1}{1.744 + 0.8364 (2\varphi_B - V_{BS})} \right] \qquad (5\text{-}75)$$

If we compare Eq. 5-74 with the linear I_D equation of the square-law model (Eq. 4-63b), we see that Eq. 5-74 is similar but that it also has some extra terms. The first fractional term of Eq. 5-74 models the vertical field mobility degradation effect, and has the same form as Crawford's mobility expression (Eq. 5-18). The denominator of the second fractional term models the velocity saturation effects. The last term of Eq. 5-74 is like the last term of Eq. 4-63b except that it also contains the empirical parameter 'a.' This formulation allows the terms of Eq. 4-57 containing V_{BS} to be handled via a numerical approximation, rather than by having to compute terms to the 3/2 power (as would have to be done if Eq. 4-63 was used here instead to compute I_D). The values of I_D computed with this approximation are quite close to the values that would be computed if the Eq. 4-57 was used instead (over a reasonable range of V_{BS} and V_{DS}). See Appendix C to see how this approximation is derived, starting from Eq. 4-57.

Saturation Region: [$V_{GS} > V_T$), and $V_{DS} \geq V_{DSsat}$]

$$I_D = \frac{\mu_0}{[1 + U_0(V_{GS} - V_T)]} \frac{C_{ox} \frac{Z}{L} (V_{GS} - V_T)^2}{2aV} \qquad (5\text{-}76)$$

where

$$V = \frac{1 + v_c + \sqrt{1 + 2 v_c}}{2} \quad \text{and} \quad v_c = U_1 (V_{GS} - V_T)/a \qquad (5\text{-}77)$$

and

$$V_{DSsat} = (V_{GS} - V_T)/aV \qquad (5\text{-}78)$$

5.5.1.3 BSIM Equations for I_D when the MOSFET is Operated in Weak Inversion (Subthreshold Regime).

In BSIM the total drain current is modeled as the linear sum of the strong and weak inversion drain current components ($I_{D,S}$ and $I_{D,W}$, respectively) to allow proper matching of these two components at a transition point close to the threshold voltage. The weak inversion component is expressed as

$$I_{D,W} = (I_{exp} I_{limit})/(I_{exp} + I_{limit}) \qquad (5\text{-}79)$$

where

$$I_{exp} = \frac{\mu_0 C_{ox} Z}{L} \left(\frac{kT}{q}\right)^2 e^{1.8} e^{(q/kT)(V_{GS} - V_T)/\eta} [1 - e^{-V_{DS}(q/kT)}] \qquad (5\text{-}80)$$

and

$$I_{limit} = \frac{\mu_0 C_{ox} Z}{L} \left(3 \frac{kT}{q}\right)^2 \qquad (5\text{-}81)$$

The factor $e^{1.8}$ is empirically chosen to achieve best fits in the subthreshold characteristics with minimum effect on the strong-inversion characteristics. The subthreshold parameters η_0, η_B, and η_D are used to model the subthreshold slope coefficient η, as:[59]

$$\eta = \eta_0 + \eta_B V_{BS} + \eta_D V_{DS} \qquad (5-82)$$

The subthreshold swing S_t is expressed as (Eq. 4-91)

$$S_t = (2.3kT/q)\,\eta = (2.3kT/q)\,(1 + C_d/C_{ox}) \qquad (5-83)$$

where η is the subthreshold slope coefficient calculated from Eq. 3-82. As discussed in chap. 4 and earlier in this chapter, the subthreshold swing is a function of both substrate and drain biases, and this bias dependence is modeled in BSIM by the linear relation given by Eq. 5-82.

5.6 MOSFET SCALING

A roadmap of the scaling of MOSFET devices was proposed by Hu in 1993.[24] He assumed that a new generation of technology will continue to be developed every three years, with perhaps a slow-down to four years beyond the 0.35 μm generation. His proposal for MOSFET scaling is outlined as follows, with the result summarized in Table 5-4.

1. The IC industry/market will agree on the next power-supply voltage standard V_{cc} several years in advance of introducing a technology/product using that voltage.

2. For a given V_{cc}, the thinnest gate oxide (i.e., from manufacturability, reliability and GIDL considerations) will be used to get maximum I_D.

3. Junction depths will be scaled aggressively to keep the short-channel effects (i.e., subthreshold leakage current) within a desired limit.

4. V_T of general purpose technology will remain basically unchanged. A significant reduction in V_T is unacceptable for channel subthreshold leakage.

5. The well doping concentration or punchthrough implant dose will be increased, and the gate length may be chosen to be larger than the minimum feature size in order to achieve acceptable leakage and standby current.

6. Drain engineered structures will be used as necessary to meet the constraints of hot-carrier reliability, breakdown voltage, and GIDL.

5.6.1 Design of Submicron MOSFETs: Scaling Guidelines

The fundamental issue of downsizing MOSFETs is to preserve long-channel characteristics after miniaturization. Several approaches have been proposed as roadmaps for designing submicron MOSFETs ($L<1$ μm) so that they exhibit such behavior.

Table 5-4   MOSFET Technology Projection[24] (High-Speed Scenario)

Minimum Feature Size (μm)	0.5	0.35	0.25	0.18	0.13	0.09
Year of Introduction	1991	1994	1997	2001	2005	2009
SRAM Density	4M	16M	64M	256M	1G	4G
V_{CC} (V) (+10% for max V_{CC})	5	3.3	3.3	3.3	2.2	2.2
MOSFET Gate Oxide (nm)	13.5	9	8	7	4.5	4
Junction Depth (μm)	0.15	0.15	0.1	0.08	0.08	0.07
Effective Channel Length (μm)	0.40	0.30	0.25	0.2	0.15	0.13
Threshold Voltage (V)	0.7	0.7	0.7	0.7	0.7	0.7
NMOS I_{Dsat} @ $V_{GS} = V_{CC}$ (mA/μm)	0.64	0.48	0.55	0.65	0.51	0.57
PMOS I_{Dsat} @ $V_{GS} = V_{CC}$ (mA/μm)	0.31	0.22	0.26	0.32	0.24	0.28

Three of the most important scaling methodologies are the following: (1) constant electric-field scaling and its derivatives (constant voltage and constant electrostatic scaling); (2) scaling based on subthreshold behavior; (3) scaling to achieve a desired value of subthreshold current, I_{off}. Because subthreshold conduction is the dominant short-channel performance issue that limits MOSFET scaling,[60] the latter two have more applicability, but for completeness we also include a brief discussion of approach #1.

5.6.1.1 Constant Electric-Field, Constant Voltage & Electrostatic Scaling.
The method of *constant electric-field scaling* for designing submicron MOSFETs was proposed by Dennard et al. in 1974.[61] In this approach, a successful larger device structure is selected (e.g., from the previous generation of ICs) and all its dimensions and voltages are reduced by a constant scaling factor λ (>1). The new device dimensions are then $L' = L/\lambda$, $t_{ox}' = t_{ox}/\lambda$, and $W' = W/\lambda$, while the operating voltages are $V' = V/\lambda$. With this approach, operating speed increases, component density increases, and power density remains constant. Unfortunately, current density also increases by the scaling factor (a condition that aggravates electromigration failure in metal interconnect lines). In addition, the threshold voltage V_T' is reduced to V_T/λ, which makes the subthreshold current larger at $V_{GS} = 0$. The worst shortcoming, however, is that the power-supply voltage must be reduced by the same factor as the channel length. This is not compatible with circuit requirements such as noise margin, current driving capability, and power-supply voltage compatibility from one generation to the next. Thus, this method has not been adopted in its original form.

Indeed, scaling of the power-supply voltage has not been implemented in digital ICs down to device dimensions of 0.8 μm. Instead, it has been maintained at 5.0 V, primarily to permit the next generation of semiconductor products to "plug in" to existing systems. Only for devices with smaller dimensions has a reduced power-supply voltage been implemented (3.3V). This has led to the consideration of *constant-voltage scaling* as a miniaturization alternative. In this approach, device dimensions are scaled by the same factor λ as in constant-$\mathcal{E}$-field scaling, but the applied voltages remain constant. While this solves the circuit incompatibility problems, it leads to higher electric fields inside the device. These high fields cause mobility degradation, hot-carrier effects, oxide tunneling, and other reliability problems.

A compromise approach named *constant-electrostatic scaling* (or *quasi-constant voltage scaling*) was thus proposed by Bacarani et al.[62] Dimensions are still scaled by λ but the potentials are allowed to be scaled by a separate factor κ (e.g., $\kappa = \sqrt{\lambda}$). The operating voltages can then correspondingly decrease to $V' = V/\kappa$. This has allowed suitable fabrication parameters for MOSFETs to be derived for devices down to channel lengths of 0.25 μm (some degree of power supply voltage reduction is used).

However, even with the latter method, the depletion regions of the source and drain junctions scale by a factor less than λ, and hence devices specified according to this approach are subject to such two-dimensional problems as punchthrough and DIBL. In addition, subthreshold turn-off does not scale because it is dominated by the exponential dependence on potential of the carrier density (and the subthreshold current is dominated by a diffusion rather than a drift component). Thus, the subthreshold current does not scale with field. Consequently, the scaled down device fails to turn off at $V_{GS} = 0$ (because the voltage swing needed to drive the device "off" - which is in the range of 0.5-0.8V - cannot be scaled because the subthreshold portion of this swing $\{\Delta I_{Dst}/\Delta V_{GS}\}$ is invariant). As a result, the target V_T value of a new, reduced-design-rule process will not decrease with the other physical parameters relative to an existing, larger-design-rule process. Hence, for ICs in which subthreshold leakage currents must be minimized, even this scaling method is not adequate.

5.6.1.2 Subthreshold Scaling. Another approach to scaling which overcomes the above difficulty was proposed by Brews et al.[63] They introduced an empirical formula which determines the minimum gate length a MOSFET can have so that its subthreshold behavior remains insensitive to drain bias. That is, by using this formula, a constraint upon each single combination of device parameters is identified, such that if this constraint is satisfied with this combination of parameter values, the resulting device exhibits long-channel subthreshold behavior.

We recall that when long-channel devices are operated in subthreshold, I_{Dst} is independent of drain-to-source voltage once V_{DS} exceeds a few kT/q (see Eqs. 4-87 and 4-89). Thus, the criterion selected to represent acceptable long-channel behavior was that no more than a 10% change in drain current could occur for a 0.5V change in V_{DS} (e.g., I_{Dst} should not vary more than 10% as V_{DS} is increased from 0.5 to 1.0V).

Brews et al. found empirically that such subthreshold long-channel behavior will be preserved provided the channel length L exceeds a minimum value L_{min}

$$L \geq L_{min} = A \, [r_j \, t_{ox} \, (W_S + W_D)^2 \,]^{1/3} \tag{5 - 84}$$

where, r_j is the junction depth, t_{ox} is the oxide thickness, W_S and W_D are the depletion widths of the source and drain (in a one-dimensional, abrupt junction for uniform doping). With r_j, W_S, and W_D in microns, and t_{ox} in angstroms, the fitting parameter is $A = 0.41 \, Å^{-1/3}$. The substrate doping dependence is contained in the depletion-width equations, inasmuch as W_S and W_D (e.g., in an NMOSFET) are given by

$$W_S = \sqrt{2\kappa_{si}\varepsilon_o V_{bi}/qN_A} \tag{5 - 85}$$

$$W_D = \sqrt{2\kappa_{si}\varepsilon_o(V_{bi} + V_{DS})]/qN_A} \tag{5 - 86}$$

According to Eq. 5-84, miniaturization requires shallower junctions (r_j), thinner oxides (t_{ox}), lower voltages, or heavier doping in the channel region (i.e, this will reduce $W_S + W_D$).

A set of experimental and computer-generated points were fitted to Eq. 5-84. The validity of the equation was established for gate lengths as small as 0.3 μm and for device parameters in the ranges of $100Å \leq t_{ox} \leq 1000Å$, $10^{14} \, cm^{-3} \leq N_A \leq 10^{17} \, cm^{-3}$, $0.18 \, \mu m \leq r_j \leq 1.5 \, \mu m$, and for drain voltages up to 5V. Figure 5-44 shows a plot of Eq. 5-84 for L_{min} (solid line) compared with experimental measurements and computer simulations. For the ranges of device parameters examined, Fig. 5-44 indicates that Eq. 5-84 provides a reliable guideline for scaling MOSFET gate lengths down to 0.3 μm.

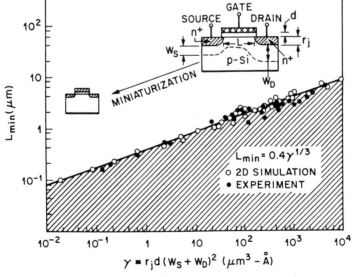

Fig. 5-44 Equation 5-84 for L_{min} compared with experimental measurements and computer simulations. The criterion for L_{min} is that for $L = L_{min}$ a 10% variation in drain current occurs as V_{DD} varies from 0.5 to 1.0V in the subthreshold regime of gate biases. The units of the abscissa reflect the choice of units: d in $Å$, the other variables in μm.[63] (© 1980 IEEE).

This approach is also more flexible than the earlier ones because not all device parameters need to be scaled by the same factor λ. Instead, various device parameters can be adjusted independently as long as the value of L_{min} remains the same. This is shown in Fig. 5-44, which also plots L_{min} versus γ [where $\gamma = r_j \, t_{ox}(W_S + W_D)^2$]. All devices with channel lengths lying above the line exhibit long-channel subthreshold behavior, while those below the line (crosshatched area) exhibit short-channel subthreshold behavior.

As an example, this figure shows that in order to design a MOSFET with L_{min} = 0.5 μm, γ should be 2. Once γ is determined, r_j, t_{ox}, W_S, and W_D can be chosen so that the resulting γ does not exceed 2. Unlike electrostatic scaling, it is not necessary to start with an optimal large device and then scale it down by a single constant factor. Rather, any device that fits the criterion will be suitable. In addition, it allows voltages to be kept fixed or only reduced modestly, provided the other factors are changed to compensate.

To some degree Eq. 5-84 appears plausible. For example, it seems reasonable that L_{min} should increase if the depletion widths increase, because such an increase enlarges the two-dimensional regions controlled by the source and drain at the expense of the region controlled by the gate. Similarly, increased junction depth increases the influence of source and drain regions, so we expect that shorter-channel devices will require smaller values of r_j (i.e., shallower junctions). Finally, as t_{ox} is increased, the screening effect of the gate is reduced, and the field lines emanating from the source and drain penetrate further into the channel region, and fewer of them terminate on the gate, causing L_{min} to increase. However, while these simple ideas appear to support the validity of Eq. 5-84, the authors of this approach in fact admit that they do not know why it works.[65] In addition, Eq. 5-84 is known to be valid only over the fitted range, and has not been tested below 0.3 μm.

Nevertheless, Eq. 5-84 is useful in keeping DIBL under control. On the other hand, this approach still does not incorporate all of the necessary tradeoffs to handle such problems as hot-carrier degradation, or circuit-related constraints such as noise margin or off-current requirements. Consequently, the reduced devices designed with this criterion still need adjustments, especially as L gets deeper below 1 μm.

Note as well, that in modern MOSFETs the substrate doping is not uniform. That is, ion implantation is used to increase the doping in the region between the source drain so that the doping there is heavier than in the substrate region beneath the source and drain. This allows a shorter source-to-drain spacing. With many MOSFET designs this surface doping is nearly uniform out to the junction depth. Thus, in Eq. 5-84 it is this doping concentration (i.e., N_A in Eqs. 5-85 and 86) that must be used to calculate W_D and W_S.

In addition, another aspect of modern NMOSFETs is the formation of shallow junction extensions by implantation using the gate as a mask (the LDD structure). It is the depth of this shallow junction extension that is used in Eq. 5-84. (The entire length of the junction is not made shallow, to avoid junction series resistance and junction leakage problems.)

Finally, Eq. 5-84 does not take into account the lateral ballooning of the drain depletion region in the lightly doped substrate beneath the source and drain regions. That is, this effect may allow bulk (subsurface) punchthrough to occur between drain and source. To prevent such subsurface punchthrough the substrate doping cannot be made as low as one would like in an attempt to reduce junction capacitance and threshold variation under source-to-substrate bias. A rough guideline for selecting the minimum value of substrate doping to avoid subsurface punchthrough has been suggested by Klaassen[64] to be

$$N_{SUB} \geq N_{ch}/10 \qquad\qquad (5\text{-}87)$$

where N_{SUB} is the substrate doping and N_{ch} is the doping in the region between the source and drain. Equation 5-87 sets a lower bound on the junction-to-substrate capacitance.

5.6.1.3 Off-Current Scaling Approach.
Another scaling approach employing a more flexible criterion for acceptable "off"-state behavior (but which is also somewhat more complex than the previous subthreshold approach), has been recently proposed.[66] We will provide a brief outline of this method in this section. The crux of the procedure involves finding a channel doping profile which yields an acceptable combination of off-current I_{off} (I_D when $V_{GS} = 0V$) and V_T in a device with as small an L as possible. The following three parameters are varied to arrive at the appropriate channel doping profile: the exposed dose D_I and centroid x_c of the V_T implant, and the substrate doping N_{SUB}. The profile is initially determined assuming that the device exhibits long-channel behavior (i.e., no significant punchthrough should be observed in the subthreshold operating region). However, the acceptable value of "off"-current in the long-channel device ($I_{off,lc}$) is deliberately picked to be smaller than I_{off} in the short-channel device being designed - in anticipation of the increase in I_{off} due to surface-DIBL in the shrunken device. The estimate of the increase in $I_{off,lc}$ due to surface-DIBL depends on the DIBL model chosen by the designer. To ensure that the subthreshold punchthrough current remains insignificant at maximum V_{DS}, a minimum N_{SUB} is identified. Finally, in the process of selecting appropriate values of D_I and x_c, the criterion that the channel depletion-region width d should be a minimum is applied (to keep ΔV_{TSC} as small as possible when L is shrunk, as suggested by either Eq. 5-2 or barrier-lowering analysis).

In the report that describes this scaling strategy, the example to which it is applied is a symmetrical CMOS process (i.e., in which NMOSFETs are built with n^+-poly gates and PMOSFETs with p^+ poly gates), a technological approach that is gaining more popularity as L is decreased to 0.5 μm or smaller. Let us now also consider this scaling strategy as applied to a symmetrical CMOS process in more detail.

First, the approach assumes that the following parameters are set by system and processing constraints: V_{DD}; the type of gate material (e.g., heavily doped poly); and minimum values of t_{ox} and r_j. The minimum manufacturable L is also limited by the lithographic process. However, I_{off}, V_T, and the actual value of L are left as parameters that can be traded off later, based on the specific circuit or system application requirements. The tradeoffs between V_T and long-channel I_{off} ($I_{off,lc}$) values are carried out with the aid of families of curves that relate V_T and $I_{off,lc}$ for a fixed t_{ox} (with N_{SUB} as a parameter). Figure 5-45 is an example of one such family of curves, in which t_{ox} = 100Å. Notice that the x-axis is expressed in $N_{off,lc}/N_{mg}$ instead of $I_{off,lc}$. However, since $I_{off,lc}$ is directly proportional to $N_{off,lc}$ (the latter being defined as the free-carrier density in the channel per unit area - e.g., per cm^{-2} - when V_{GS} = 0V) according to

$$I_{off,lc} = \mu \ (Z/L)(kT/q)qN_{off,lc} \tag{5 - 88}$$

$I_{off,lc}$ is implicitly expressed in these curves. In Eq. 5-88, Z and L are the device width and length, respectively. In addition, N_{mg} is the free-carrier concentration per unit area in the channel at midgap,* and this value can be found from

$$N_{mg} \ (cm^{-2}) = \ n_i \ (\kappa_{si} / \kappa_{ox})(2kT/E_g) \ t_{ox} \tag{5 - 89}$$

N_{mg} is therefore the free-carrier density in the channel at the point when the surface is undergoing its field-induced reversal of polarity (e.g., from p-type to n-type). Thus, N_{mg} represents the smallest free-carrier concentration in the channel in weak inversion. As is also indicated by Eq. 5-89, N_{mg} is independent of N_{SUB}. In an Si-SiO$_2$ MOS device at 300K, Eq. 5-89 can be written to explicitly express the relation between N_{mg} and t_{ox} as

$$N_{mg} \ (@ \ 300K, \ in \ cm^{-2}) = 10^{10}(cm^{-3})(11.8/3.9) \ 22.4 \ t_{ox}(cm) = 1.33 \times 10^9 \ t_{ox}(cm).$$

Thus, for a MOSFET with t_{ox} = 15 nm = 1.5×10^{-6} cm

$$N_{mg} \sim 2 \times 10^3 \ cm^{-2}.$$

Thus, if $I_{off,lc}$ is given, and it is desired to relate this value to a point on a curve in which one axis is expressed in terms of $N_{off,lc}/N_{mg}$ (such as Fig. 5-45), it can be done as follows:

Example 5-1: If a maximum off-current $I_{off,lc}$ at 300K of 10 pA is required in an NMOSFET with L = 3 μm, Z = 6 μm, t_{ox} = 15 nm, and μ_n = 400 cm^2/Vsec, find the value of $N_{off,lc}/N_{mg}$ that corresponds to this $I_{off,lc}$ value.

Solution: Since $N_{off,lc} = I_{off,lc}/[\mu_n \ (Z/L) \ (kT/q)q]$

$$= 1 \times 10^{-11} \ A \ / \ [400 \ cm^2/Vsec \ (6/3) \ (0.025V) \ 1.6 \times 10^{-19}C]$$

$$= 3.1 \times 10^7 \ carriers/cm^2$$

* *Midgap* is the state of a MOSFET in which band bending is causing E_F at the Si surface to co-incide with the energy level at the middle of the bandgap (which is also where E_i resides). Also at midgap, $\varphi_{surf}/\varphi_t = \ln(N_{SUB}/n_i)$ as shown in Fig. 5-46. In the special case of midgap occurring at V_{GS} =0V, N_{mg} is the free-carrier concentration (cm^{-2}) in the channel for that condition.

and since N_{mg} (300K, t_{ox} = 15 nm) = 2×10^3 cm^{-2},

$$N_{off,lc}/N_{mg} = 1.5 \times 10^4$$

To arrive at the V_T values exhibited in a family of curves such as those in Fig. 5-45, we follow the general procedure given in section 4.6.3. That is, the value of $V_{Tud,lc}$ (assuming a uniformly doped channel region with a doping of N_{SUB}) is calculated using Eq. 3-71, and this is added to $\Delta V_T(II)$ using Eq. 4-73, to get $V_{Tnud,lc}$ (Eq. 4-74 or Eq. 4-75) However, to accurately determine $\Delta V_T(II)$ the value of both D_I and x_c must be specified. In addition, the impact of N_{SUB} must included.

That is, in the simple long-channel analysis of a MOSFET in section it was assumed that $V_{Tud,lc}$ can be shifted by choosing D_I and x_c independent of N_{SUB}.

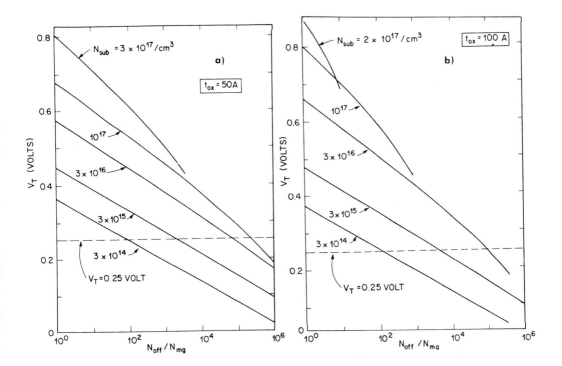

Fig. 5-45 Threshold voltage for implanted structures with the indicated substrate doping as a function of N_{off}/N_{mg}. The dose and centroid of the implants are chosen for minimum depletion width. (a) t_{ox} = 50Å; (b) t_{ox} = 100Å. From J.R. Brews, K.K. Ng, and R.K. Watts, Chap. 1, "The Submicrometer Silicon MOSFET," in *Submicron Integrated Circuits*, R.K. Watts, Ed., Wiley-Interscience, New York, Copyright 1989 p. 34. Reprinted with permission.

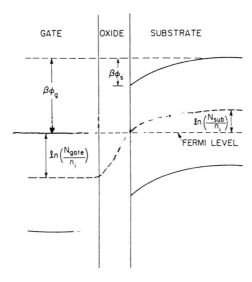

Fig. 5-46 An MOS structure at zero gate bias with midgap level and the Fermi level at the surface being equal at zero bias (*midgap* occurs).

However, for the following reasons N_{SUB} cannot be ignored, especially when designing short-channel devices: First, a minimum N_{SUB} must be identified to prevent subsurface punchthrough, e.g., $N_{SUB} \geq N_{ch}/10$. (Note that in this analysis, the effect of a punchthrough implant is not considered, and hence only the substrate doping plays a role in preventing subsurface punchthrough.)   Second, the choice of N_{SUB} impacts d_I (the channel depletion region width in the presence of an V_T implant) in that larger values of N_{SUB} will cause d_I to decrease (see Eq. 4-80). To make d_I smaller (i.e., to keep ΔV_{TSC} as small as possible, as described earlier), larger N_{SUB} values are needed.*   Third, N_{SUB} impacts $N_{off,lc}$, because S_t depends on d (see Eq. 4-91b). In general, increasing the value of N_{SUB} will cause the value of S_t to increase. If V_T remains the same, the consequence of an increase in S_t is a larger $N_{off,lc}$ (as is also evident in Fig. 5-45). Obviously, the first two issues call for large N_{SUB} values, while the third calls for smaller values. Hence, tradeoffs may be necessary.

Values for the exposed dose D_I and the centroid x_c that will produce a minimum value of d are plotted versus $N_{off,lc}/N_{mg}$ with N_{SUB} as a parameter, and $t_{ox} = 50\text{Å}$ in Fig. 5-47. The value of D_I is obtained from the following equation:

* The equations used to generate the V_T versus $N_{off,lc}/N_{mg}$ curves are derived by invoking the constraint that the channel depletion width in weak inversion (d) must be a minimum. This constraint is derived from Eq. 5-2, and the fact that we want ΔV_{TSC} to be as small as possible. Since it is assumed that the device will employ the smallest t_{ox} and r_j values allowed by process technology, the last parameter in Eq. 5-2 that can reduce ΔV_{TSC} when the device is shrunk to its minimum L, is d_{max}.

$$qD_I = (Q/Q_{mg})(\kappa_{ox}\varepsilon_0/t_{ox})(kT/q)(\beta E_g/2q) \qquad (5\text{-}90)$$

The value of Q/Q_{mg} is found in terms of $N_{off,lc}/N_{mg}$ with the aid of Fig. 5-48.* (It turns out that for most cases of interest the substrate doping independence of D_I assumed in section does in fact continue to hold to larger values of N_{SUB} when the devices have thin oxides. Thus, Eq. 5-90, which is independent of N_{SUB}, continues to be valid for such cases). Once D_I is known, its value is used to find x_c from

$$x_c/d = -D_I/(N_{SUB}d) + \{(D/N_{SUB}d)^2 + 1\}^{1/2} \qquad (5\text{-}91)$$

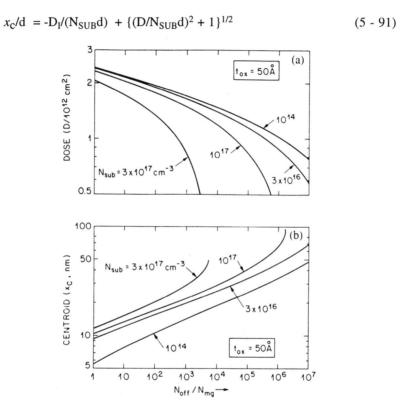

Fig. 5-47 (a) Dose in units of $10^{12}/cm^2$ as a function of N_{off}/N_{mg} with substrate doping as parameter. (b) Centroid or depletion layer width $x_c = w$ in nanometers versus N_{off}/N_{mg}. In both figures $t_{ox} = 50\text{Å}$. From J.R. Brews, K.K. Ng, and R.K. Watts, Chap. 1, "The Submicrometer Silicon MOSFET," in *Submicron Integrated Circuits*, R.K. Watts, Ed., Wiley-Interscience, New York. Copyright 1989 p. 28. Reprinted with permission.

* Note that Q here is a dimensionless surface charge defined as by

$$Q = (D_I/N_{SUB}L_D) + (N_{off,lc}/N_{sub}L_D) + (d/L_D) \qquad (5\text{-}92)$$

where L_D is the Debye length, and $Q_{mg} = (\kappa_{ox}L_D E_g/2kT\kappa_s t_{ox})$. But for the purposes of our abbreviated description of this scaling strategy (described more completely in ref. 65), it suffices to note that Q/Q_{mg} can be determined in terms of $N_{off,lc}/N_{mg}$ by using Fig. 5-48.

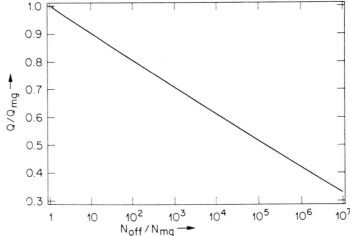

Fig. 5-48 The normalized field parameter Q/Q_{mg} of Eq. 5-90 as a function of zero-bias carrier density to midgap carrier density ratio N_{off}/N_{mg}. From J.R. Brews, K.K. Ng, and R.K. Watts, Chap. 1, "The Submicrometer Silicon MOSFET," in *Submicron Integrated Circuits*, R.K. Watts, Ed., Wiley-Interscience, New York, Copyright 1989 p. 28. Reprinted with permission.

Once V_T is determined for an acceptable value of $N_{off,lc}$, a check is made to ensure that the chosen N_{SUB} value exceeds the minimum substrate concentration identified as being able to provide adequate subsurface punchthrough protection. If N_{SUB} is found to be large enough to prevent punchthrough, the design process can proceed to the next step - barrier-lowering analysis. (However, if the chosen value of N_{SUB} cannot prevent punchthrough, a larger N_{SUB} value may need to be accepted, which in turn may possibly require an adjustment of the maximum acceptable I_{off}.)

The barrier-lowering analysis examines the effect of shrinking L to the minimum value that can be fabricated with the best lithographic process at hand. At that length the value of ΔV_{Tsc} is calculated, using the DIBL model of choice. The value of the long-channel off current $I_{off,lc}$ in the device designed using the strategy outlined above now becomes the basis for determining the short-channel device I_{off}, according to

$$I_{off} = I_{off,lc} \, exp \, (q\Delta V_{Tsc}/kT) \tag{5 - 93}$$

If I_{off} is less than or equal to the target value, the device with that value of L will succeed in meeting the circuit requirements and is deemed nominally manufacturable. If I_{off} is too high, either the channel length will need to be increased, or a larger value of I_{off} will need to be accommodated by changing the circuit design.

The term *nominally manufacturable* is used, because as the channel length is reduced, the sensitivity of V_T to channel length variations increases. As already noted, the impact of channel length variation is to require a more conservative setting of nominal-I_{off} so that devices with smaller than nominal V_T values will still have acceptable off-currents. As the channel length is reduced, at some point this lowered I_{off} estimate will encounter the same punchthrough limit already discussed. If channel length is under very tight control, then V_T variations from length variation remains small, and only variation due to changes in V_{DS} will matter. However, it is more common that channel length variations will dominate the choice of L_{min} as illustrated in the next section.

5.6.2 Manufacturing Considerations in Submicron MOSFET Device Design

As noted above, the "off"-current value in submicron MOSFETs must be maintained over the range of manufacturing tolerances. For example, assume that a typical 0.8 μm NMOS transistor (i.e., the drawn channel length L is 0.8 μm) has an L_{eff} of 0.7 μm and a 3-sigma manufacturing tolerance on patterned gate length of ±0.12 μm. Hence, the shortest L_{eff} in a device that still meets the manufacturing tolerance (i.e., patterned gate length is 0.68 μm) will be 0.58 μm. At this gate length, the CMOS devices will still have to possess sufficient V_T control, satisfactory hot-carrier reliability, and acceptable punchthrough characteristics. To enable a MOSFET to meet these requirements, N_{SUB} will need to be raised to a value higher than that needed for the nominal device length. As a result, the performance of the nominal gate length device ($L = 0.8$ μm) will be degraded through increased source/drain junction capacitance and subthreshold turnoff.

The importance of manufacturing control on patterned gate length is illustrated in Fig. 5-49.[67] This figure plots the NMOS and PMOS device leakage in the "off" state

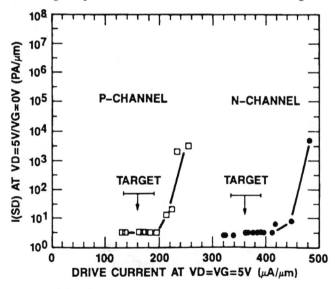

Fig. 5-49 NMOS and PMOS drive current, defined as the drain current for 5V applied to the gate and drain, versus leakage in the off state with 0V on the gate and 5V on the drain. The parameter is gate length, with a target value of 0.8 μm. From R.A. Haken et al., "BiCMOS Process Technology," Chap. 3, p. 85, in *BiCMOS Technology and Applications,* A. Alvarez Ed. Klewer, Norwell MA, Copyright 1989. Reprinted with permission.

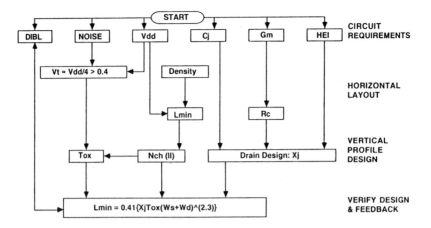

Fig. 5-50 First order MOS device design methodology. Horizontal design generally precedes the vertical profile design. The horizontal design is set to optimize intrinsic device delay (L_{eff}, R_{SD}). Vertical profile design is set to minimize short-channel effects.[68] (© 1988 IEEE).

(in this figure I_{SD} with 0V on the gate and 5V on the drain), versus drive current, defined as I_D when $V_{DS} = V_{GS} = 5V$. Although I_D is the x-axis variable, the actual parameter being varied is L, since I_D is inversely proportional to L. In this example, for the n-channel device, when $L = 0.8$ μm ($L_{eff} = 0.7$ μm), I_D is 400 μA/μm. The device design has been optimized for a patterned gate length of 0.8 μm with a manufacturing 3-σ control on L of ±0.12 μm. According to Fig. 5-49, as the 3-σ manufacturing control limit is reached, the device leakage current increases to ~10^4 pA/μm (i.e., from Fig. 5-49 the leakage starts to rapidly rise when $I_D = 480$ μA/μm, which means it is occurring when $L = 0.68$ μm, or $L_{eff} = 0.58$ μm). Such high levels of device leakage might cause circuits to become nonfunctional, or could cause them to fail a particular circuit specification, such as maximum standby power.

5.7 DESIGN OF SUBMICRON NMOSFETS

We outline two approaches for the design of submicron NMOSFETs that have appeared in the literature. The first is fundamentally based on Eq. 5-87, while the second relies on the off-current scaling approach.

5.7.1 Design Methodology Based on the Subthreshold Scaling Equation

Figure 5-50 shows a flow-chart of the steps taken in the subthreshold-scaling approach to designing submicron MOSFETs in CMOS.[68] It assumes that the following circuit constraints on the device are defined (as dictated by the application being served): the power-supply voltage V_{DD}, the required drive current I_D in μA/μm (or transconductance,

g_m), the required noise margin, the minimum intrinsic gate delay, and the maximum allowed device degradation (long-term) due to hot-carrier effects (HEI in the diagram).

The given V_{DD} and noise-margin constraint determine the choice of V_T. V_{DD} and the lithographic-processing capability limit the minimum channel length L_{min}. By thinning t_{ox}, I_D can be increased, but minimum t_{ox} is set by V_{DD} and processing constraints.

The maximum allowed parasitic resistance R_S depends on g_m (which is really the inverse of R_{ch}). For example, R_S may need to be kept smaller than 10% of R_{ch}. This may then dictate the minimum horizontal dimensions of the drain and source regions, and also the depth r_j of the source and drain junctions. The required R_S value may also determine the doping profile of the tip region of the LDD structure and may dictate whether or not salicided source/drains are necessary. The minimum gate delay τ_d will be impacted by the intrinsic device characteristics (i.e., I_D through L_{min}, and C_L through C_{gate} and C_j). By minimizing gate area and source/drain junction areas, smaller C_{gate} and C_j can be realized. Lower substrate doping also decreases C_j.

The selection of the channel doping concentration (N_{ch}) will be impacted by the substrate concentration and the V_T-adjust implant. V_T and N_A will determine the V_T adjust implant dose. The drain design (e.g., an LDD) is impacted by the desire to keep hot-carrier degradation to an acceptable value (see chap. 9). The depletion region widths of the source and drain junctions - W_S and W_D - are determined by N_{ch} and the drain structure design.

Once the values of t_{ox}, r_j, and W_S and W_D are determined, they are inserted into Eq. 5-84. If the right hand side of the equation is a number smaller than L_{min} with this group of parameters, then according to past experience it is likely that a MOSFET with this L_{min} can be successfully fabricated (i.e., the device should satisfy the subthreshold leakage current criterion given in section 5.6.1.2). Hence, if some acceptable combination of manufacturable parameters meeting this criterion can be found, fabrication success is likely. If not, a larger value of L_{min} may have to be accepted.

5.7.2 Design Methodology Based on Required Off-Current Value

The flow chart of the I_{off} design strategy of submicron MOSFETs is shown in Fig. 5-51.[69] In summary, a MOSFET is designed by selecting what appears to be an appropriate set of V_T and I_{off} values, applying the principles of long-channel MOSFET physics to derive the channel doping profile. Then the device length is shortened and punchthrough analysis and barrier-lowering analysis is performed on the shortened device to ensure that the I_{off} circuit specification is still met. If not, the design procedure must be repeated, trading off V_T and I_{off} against channel length until the best set of parameters for the application at hand is achieved. Details of the various steps in the flow chart were described in section 5.7.1.

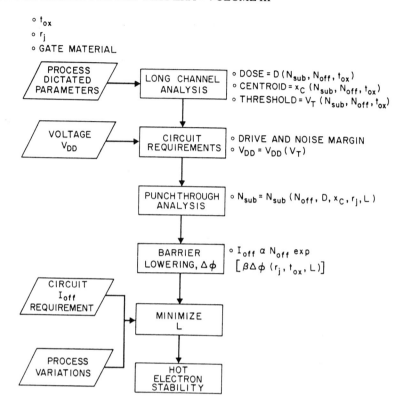

Fig. 5-51 A flow chart of the I_{OFF} strategy. From J.R. Brews, K.K. Ng, and R.K. Watts, Chap. 1, "The Submicrometer Silicon MOSFET," in *Submicron Integrated Circuits*, R.K. Watts, Ed., Wiley-Interscience, New York, Copyright 1989, p. 24. Reprinted with permission.

5.8 SHORT-CHANNEL PMOS DEVICES IN CMOS

Early MOS ICs were built using PMOS technology, primarily because enhancement-mode MOSFETs with suitable V_T values could only be fabricated as *p*-channel devices using aluminum or n^+-doped polysilicon gates and uniform lightly doped *n*-substrates. That is, at that time it was not possible to produce enhancement-mode *n*-channel MOSFETs using n^+-poly or Al gates on a uniform, lightly doped *p*-substrate because such structures exhibit a negative threshold voltage (see Fig. 3-20). However, with the advent of ion implantation it became possible to build NMOSFETs with positive V_Ts by adjusting channel doping profiles. Thus, enhancement-mode and depletion-mode NMOSFETs could then be fabricated with little extra difficulty. Since *n*-channel transistors have greater drive current (and hence speed), NMOS naturally replaced PMOS as the dominant digital IC technology. During this era of NMOS dominance, interest in

p-channel MOSFETs languished. However, when CMOS arose to become the main technology for VLSI in the late 1980s, the need for enhancement-mode p-channel MOSFETs returned.

The fabrication of p-channel devices with short channels in CMOS, however, presents some unique problems which arise from having to build both NMOS and PMOS devices on the same chip. The problems revolve around the choice of a doping type for the polysilicon gate electrode and the impact that this choice has on the threshold voltage and other characteristics of PMOS devices.

5.8.1 PMOS Devices with n^+-Polysilicon Gates

To achieve high drive current it is necessary to make the threshold voltage of a MOSFET as close to 0V as possible (with the minimum value limited by noise margin and subthreshold-leakage considerations). When MOS IC technologies were initially being developed V_T values with a magnitude of ~1V were acceptable. In early PMOS (and early p-well CMOS) it was relatively straightforward to build p-channel devices with $V_T = -1$V since the doping in the n-substrates was in the range of 1-3x10^{15} cm^{-3}. As seen in Fig. 3-20, V_{Tp} of PMOS devices made on such substrates is -0.8V to -1.0V, which is well within the acceptable V_T range.

However, in n-well CMOS (which was developed after p-well CMOS), as well as in twin-well CMOS, the situation changes. That is, in n-well CMOS the doping in the well is about 10x the doping in the substrate, making it at least 1x10^{16} cm^{-3}. Twin-well CMOS becomes the well-architecture of choice as the gate lengths decrease below about 1 μm. For 1 μm MOS devices (both p- and n-channel) the substrate doping density must be 2-3x10^{16} cm^{-3}. Thus, as shown in Fig. 3-20, the V_T values of PMOS devices made with n^+-poly gates in either n-well or twin-well CMOS will be at least -1.5V, whose magnitude is too large. To make matters worse, in PMOSFETs with $L \leq 1$ μm, punchthrough effects are more severe than in comparably sized NMOSFETs (primarily due to the inability to make p^+ source/drain junctions as shallow as n^+ junctions, as will be described later). To suppress such punchthrough current it is necessary to increase the n-doping in the substrate (i.e., by an extra deep phosphorus implant into the channel of PMOS devices). The resultant increase in channel doping makes short-channel PMOS devices even more strongly enhancement mode (i.e., V_T is increased even more).

For optimal logic-gate performance the threshold voltages of the n- and p-channel devices in CMOS circuits should also have comparable magnitudes. In addition, to allow for maximum current-driving capability, they should also be as small as possible. Thus, for 5V CMOS technologies, desirable threshold voltages are 0.6 to 0.8V for V_{Tn} and -0.6 to -0.8V for V_{Tp}. Furthermore, as mentioned above, the most common choice for the gate material has historically been heavily doped n-type polysilicon. The work function of n^+ polysilicon is ideal for n-channel devices since these yield threshold voltages of less than 0.7 V for reasonable values of channel doping and oxide thicknesses.*

Figure 3-20 plots V_T for long-channel, uniformly doped MOSFETs with n^+ poly gates (left scale)[70] as a function of p-substrate doping (assuming the substrate is uniformly doped and that $Q_{tot} = 0$). The value of V_{Tn} is less than 1.0V for gate-oxide thicknesses of 25 nm or less and substrate dopings of less than 10^{17} cm^{-3}. Thus, V_{Tn} can easily be adjusted to the desired values by implanting boron into the channel.

However, when n^+ poly is the gate electrode of a PMOS device, adjustment of V_{Tp} to -0.7 V is not as simple, especially as the PMOS channel lengths shrink below about 2 μm. First, as we noted above, the magnitude of V_T of PMOS devices when the substrate doping exceeds 2×10^{16} cm^{-3} is significantly greater than -0.8V (e.g., -1.4V or larger). Even higher values of substrate doping will be needed as the channel lengths are decreased below 1 μm, implying that V_T would be even larger in submicron PMOS devices with uniformly doped substrates. In addition, such short-channel PMOSFETs are more prone to punchthrough than NMOSFETs of the same channel length. This means that the substrate doping concentration will need to be increased even further in submicron PMOS devices to suppress these effects (e.g., by performing an additional deep n-type [phosphorus] implant into the channel region).

The increased susceptibility to punchthrough of scaled-down PMOS devices with uniformly doped channels is caused in part by the dopant used to form the source and drain regions of the PMOS device, i.e., boron. Boron diffuses much more quickly than the dopant used to form the source and drain junctions in NMOSFETs (arsenic). As a result, the junction depths of the p^+ regions in 1 μm PMOS are ~0.35 μm, whereas the n^+ regions in 1 μm NMOS are shallower (typically only ~0.2 μm deep). The deeper junctions accentuate the punchthrough susceptibility. The extra n-implant used to suppress punchthrough mentioned above must also place the additional doping at a depth below the source and drain depths to be effective (e.g., with a peak at ~0.15 μm and increased doping above the background level to a depth of ~0.5 μm). This extra implant, however, not only increases the V_T value to about -2V, but also increases the source/drain-to-substrate capacitance.

In any case, it is obvious that the magnitude of V_T in short-channel PMOS devices of advanced CMOS technologies needs to be reduced. However, implanting the n-doped substrate with more n-type dopant would only *increase* the magnitude of V_{Tp}, rather than bringing its value closer to the desired -0.7V. To reduce the magnitude of V_{Tp} when an n^+ poly gate is used, a thin sheet of *negative* charges must therefore be placed at the Si-SiO$_2$ interface. This is accomplished by implanting a shallow layer of boron atoms, which as we know become negatively charged acceptor ions in the Si lattice. The boron dose must be heavy enough to overcompensate the n-surface so that a p-region (depleted of holes at $V_{GS} = 0V$) is formed. This shifts V_{Tp} toward more positive values. In practice, the boron dose depends on the substrate doping, as shown

---

* Note that the polysilicon layer may be combined with a layer of silicide for sheet resistance reduction; since the polysilicon remains as the underlayer of the polycide, the work function of the gate electrode will not be changed.

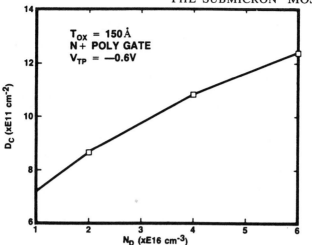

Fig. 5-52 Simulation of the counter-doping dose versus *n*-type substrate concentration for a fixed *p*-channel threshold voltage of -0.6V.[115] (© 1984 IEEE).

in Fig. 5-52 for devices with t_{ox} = 15 nm in which a V_{Tp} = -0.6V is desired. Typical doses of such implanted layers are of the order of 5×10^{11} cm^{-2} at 25 keV.

The fact that boron is implanted to adjust both V_{Tn} and V_{Tp} in CMOS circuits with n^+ poly gates suggests that a single implant could be used instead of two separate implants. Figure 5-53 shows that this can be accomplished if the appropriate background dopings are chosen for the substrate and the well.[71] On the other hand, it may be decided to use two separate implants in order to achieve better short-channel behavior through individual optimization of the *n*- and *p*-channel devices. In the latter case, if the boron dose needed to adjust V_{Tp} is smaller than the dose needed to adjust V_{Tn}, the former implant can be made into both the *p*- and *n*-channel regions without use of a mask. Then the second implant for adjusting V_{Tn} is done with a mask that protects the *n*-well region. (A third boron implant may also be performed at that time to suppress punchthrough in the *n*-channel devices.) In other processes, however, it may be necessary to use a separate mask for both the V_{Tp}- and V_{Tn}-adjust implants.

5.8.2 Why PMOS Devices with n^+ Poly Gates and Implanted *p*-Surface Layers Exhibit Enhanced Susceptibility to Short-Channel Effects

The result of implanting boron atoms to adjust V_T is that such PMOS devices exhibit worse short-channel effects than NMOSFETs with the same *L*. This susceptibility arises mainly because the implanted boron layer has a finite thickness (i.e., instead of being an infinitely-thin sheet of charge at the surface, as would exist in the ideal case). Figure 5-54 illustrates this fact, in which the channel doping profile of a PMOS device with such a boron implant is seen to extend well below the channel surface. The penetration of the *p*-layer into the *n*-substrate gives rise to two phenomena not observed in surface-channel NMOSFETs: (1) a *pn* junction is formed beneath the gate oxide in the channel, extending to a depth Y_j (as can also be seen in Fig. 5-54); and (2) the potential minimum is moved away from the surface. The latter effect gives rise to important device-behavior effects that differ from those of surface-channel MOSFETs. We explain this behavior by first comparing the location of the potential minimum in such boron-implanted-layer PMOSFETs to its location in surface-channel MOSFETs.

Figure 5-55 shows the one-dimensional potential diagrams of two PMOS devices, one with a p^+-polysilicon gate and a uniformly doped *n*-substrate (3.4×10^{16} cm^{-3}), and the other with a n^+-polysilicon gate and a shallow boron V_T-adjust implant. In both devices $V_{GS} = 0V$, and $V_{DS} = -5V$. The potential profile is taken at the point along the channel at which the longitudinal field vanishes (to match the fact that in a MOS-C there is also no longitudinal electric field). In the p^+-poly gate device the potential minimum is located at the surface, implying that such a device will operate much like the surface-channel NMOSFETs described in chap. 4. In the PMOS structure with the n^+-poly gate and boron V_T-adjust implant, however, we see that the potential minimum is away from the Si surface. The mobile carriers (holes) will thus be found at highest density near the location of the potential minimum. This implies that, unlike in the

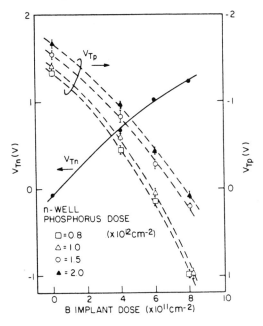

Fig. 5-53 Threshold voltages of *n*-channel (V_{Tn}) and *p*-channel (V_{Tp}) transistors as a function of boron threshold-adjustment dose. The CMOS structure uses an *n*-well implanted into a *p*-substrate (whose doping level is 6×10^{14} atoms/cm^3). V_{Tp} results are shown for various implant doses of the *n*-well.[71] (© 1980 IEEE).

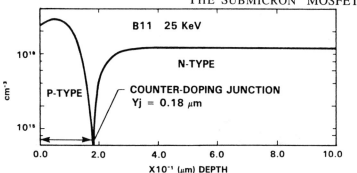

Fig. 5-54 Simulated channel profile for a *p*-channel MOSFET with an implanted B dose at the channel surface.[115] (© 1984 IEEE).

case of conventional surface-channel devices, more current will flow in a channel *beneath* the surface of the device than at the surface.[72] Such PMOS devices are therefore referred to as *buried-channel* (BC) transistors. As also seen in Fig. 5-56 (which gives the calculated variation of the potential as a function of distance below the surface as the channel *pn* junction depth is varied), the potential minimum moves further into the substrate as the thickness of the implanted *p*-layer is increased. The mobility of carriers in the buried channel is ~15% higher than carriers at the surface, and thus BC MOSFETs exhibit a somewhat larger drive current than comparable surface channel FETs. While this is an advantage, it is outweighed by several other disadvantages exhibited by BC FETs. Let us examine how the presence of the channel junction and

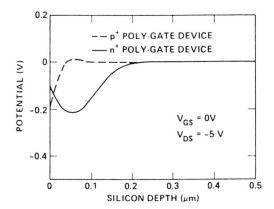

Fig. 5-55 Simulations of the electrical potential perpendicular to the surface in the channel region of two long-channel PMOS devices using GEMINI and SUPREM III simulations of devices with *n*+ polysilicon and *p*+ polysilicon gates with effective gate lengths of 20 μm.[114] (© 1985 IEEE).

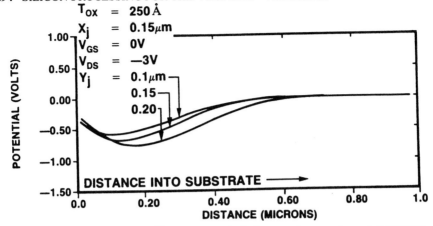

Fig. 5-56 Channel potential profile versus vertical distance for a *p*-channel MOSFET with $Y_j = 0.1, 0.15$, and $0.2~\mu$m, and $V_{DS} = -3$V and $V_{GS} = 0$V.[115] (© 1984 IEEE).

the shifting of the potential minimum beneath the Si surface worsen the susceptibility of the PMOS device to short-channel effects.

5.8.2.1 Threshold-Voltage Roll-Off in Buried-Channel PMOS.
As the channel length of MOSFETs is decreased, the threshold voltage decreases from the value it exhibits in long-channel devices. This effect, as described in section 5.2.2, is referred to as V_T-*roll-off*. The V_T-roll-off effect is more severe in BC PMOS devices than in surface channel FETs (Fig. 5-57a).[114] This is due to an effect in BC FETs that does not occur in surface-channel FETs. That is, the implanted *p*-layer is a lightly doped *p*-region that extends entirely between the p^+ source and drain regions of the device. Holes diffuse from the regions of high concentration into the lightly doped layer as depicted in Fig. 5-57b.[106] The diffusion length d_p is given by[107]

$$d_p = L_D \tan^{-1}[(N_p^+/N_p^-)^{1/2}] \qquad (5-94)$$

where

$$L_D = [(2~\kappa_{si}\varepsilon_0~kT)/(q^2~N_p^-)]^{1/2} \qquad (5-95)$$

and N_p^+ and N_p^- are the doping levels in the p^+-source/drain and *p*-layer regions, respectively. If the diffusion length is smaller than half the channel length, the net effect of this hole diffusion is to increase the effective positive charge in the channel, thus making its threshold voltage smaller in magnitude. As the channel length is decreased, the proportionate contribution of the diffused mobile charge to the total channel charge increases, and as a result, the threshold is shifted to smaller values. Eventually, at short enough channel lengths, the diffused hole distribution from the source meets that from the drain.[108] When that occurs, the potential barrier between the source and drain is reduced, giving rise to poor subthreshold characteristics.

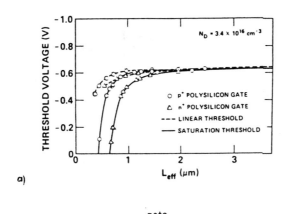

a)

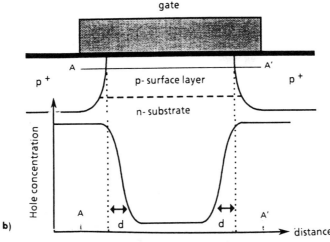

b)

Fig. 5-57 (a) Threshold voltage variation as a function of channel length L_{eff} in surface-channel (p^+-poly gate) and buried-channel (n^+-poly gate) PMOSFETs.[114] (© 1985 IEEE). (b) The origin of short-channel threshold shifts in buried-channel PMOS transistors. From A.G. Lewis and J.Y. Chen, "Current Trends in MOS Process Integration," in N.G. Einspruch and G. Gildenblatt, Eds. *Advanced MOS Device Physics,* Academic Press, San Diego CA, 1989, p. 58. Reprinted with Permission.

Experimental values of V_T in BC PMOS devices with a gate oxide thickness of 15 nm versus channel length are shown in Fig. 5-58a. As in Fig. 5-57a we see that the magnitude of V_T decreases as L is reduced. Simulation studies indicate that the severity of the V_T roll-off is increased as Y_j is made deeper (see Fig. 5-58b). This is due to the fact that more holes are able to diffuse into the thicker p-layer of the channel region from the source/drain regions as Y_j is made deeper, accentuating the roll-off effect. As in surface channel devices, V_T roll-off is decreased as t_{ox} is made smaller (Fig. 5-58c). Thus, we conclude that smaller Y_j and t_{ox} values are needed to mitigate the V_T-roll-off effect in BC PMOS.

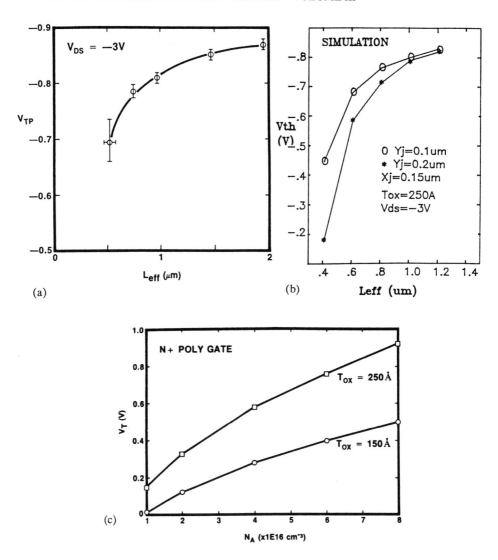

Fig. 5-58 (a) Experimental data of *p*-channel threshold voltage versus L_{eff} for gate oxide thickness of 15 nm. (b) Simulation of threshold voltage versus L_{eff} for *p*-channel MOSFETs with different Y_j. (c) Simulated *p*-channel threshold voltage versus L_{eff} for two different gate oxide thicknesses. From K. M. Cham, et al., *Computer Aided Design and VLSI Device Development.* p. 187-8, Copyright 1986 Kluwer Academic Publishers. Reprinted with permission.

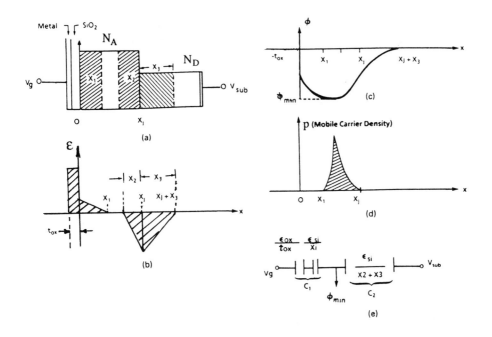

Fig. 5-59 Buried-channel PMOSFET when biased to inversion: (a) Doping profile and depletion regions; (b) electric field; (c) electron potential; (d) mobile carriers; and (e) equivalent capacitances in sub-pinchoff condition.[120] (© IEEE 1978).

5.8.2.2 Subthreshold Swing (S_t) in Buried-Channel PMOS.

The PMOSFETs used in CMOS must be enhancement-mode devices; i.e., they need to be OFF when $V_{GS} = 0V$. If such PMOSFETs are buried-channel devices, the entire implanted p-layer in the BC PMOS devices must be depleted of holes when $V_{GS} = 0V$. On the other hand, upon applying a gate voltage equal to the threshold voltage, the p-layer of such devices is no longer depleted. That is, holes will have returned to the layer, forming a p-type conducting channel between the source and drain. But this channel will exist beneath instead of at the surface. Thus, for gate voltages greater than V_T, two depletion regions will be present in this p-layer; one that is formed between the surface and the buried channel (to a depth x_1) and the other due to the channel pn junction, as is shown in Fig. 5-59a. The BC MOSFETs thus have two capacitances in addition to the oxide capacitance $\kappa_{ox}\varepsilon_0/t_{ox}$; namely the depletion capacitance from the surface ($\kappa_{si}\varepsilon_0/x_1$), and the depletion capacitance from the pn junction ($C_2 = \kappa_{si}\varepsilon_0/[x_2 + x_3] \sim \kappa_{si}\varepsilon_0/x_3$). The potential minimum is located in the position between these two capacitors, as shown in Fig. 5-59e. As also noted earlier, the location of the potential minimum causes most of the free carriers to appear in the bulk Si rather than at the Si-SiO$_2$ interface. It is expected that since the free carriers are now farther away from the surface they will be harder to modulate by the gate voltage. (In the same way that carriers in a surface-channel MOSFET with a thicker gate oxide are harder to modulate - because of reduced gate-to-channel capacitive coupling - than in one with a thinner gate oxide.) Hence, to achieve the same degree of turn-off, the gate voltage will need to be reduced more than in the case of a surface-channel device. Thus, we expect that the turn-off characteristic will be less sharp, which means that S_t will be larger.

Quantitatively the buried channel turn-off characteristic can be modeled by an expression that gives the subthreshold swing S_t in a structure with two such depletion regions, i.e.,

$$S_t = 2.3 \ (kT/q) \ (1 + C_2/C_1) \tag{5 - 96}$$

$$= 2.3 \ (kT/q) \ [1 + (\kappa_{ox}\varepsilon_0 x_1 + \kappa_{si}\varepsilon_0 t_{ox})/(\kappa_{ox}\varepsilon_0 x_2 + \kappa_{ox}\varepsilon_0 x_3)] \tag{5 - 97}$$

where C_1 is the oxide capacitance (C_{ox}) in series with the depletion capacitance from the surface ($\kappa_{si}\varepsilon_0/x_1$), and C_2 is defined above. Let us compare Eq. 5-96 with Eq. 4-91 (which gives S_t for the case of surface-channel MOSFETs, and is repeated here for convenience).

$$S_t = \ln10(d\ln I_D/dV_{GS})^{-1} = 2.3 \ (kT/q) \ (1 + C_d/C_{ox}) \tag{5 - 98}$$

By noting that C_1 is smaller than C_{ox}, and C_2 is typically comparable in value to C_d, we see that S_t is expected to be larger in BC devices. Experimental results confirm that S_t is worse (i.e., larger) in buried channel devices, especially in short-channel PMOSFETs. That is, S_t values in buried-channel PMOSFETs range from 0.5 to 1.5 V/decade, compared to the 70-120 mV/decade S_t values observed in active NMOSFET devices. Figure 5-60 compares the subthreshold behavior of the two 0.8 μm BC PMOS

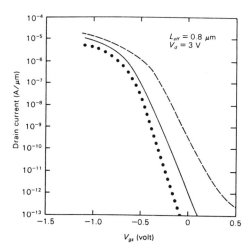

Fig. 5-60 Subthreshold I-V curves in PMOS device in CMOS. Dashed lines: buried channel PMOS in a lightly doped substrate. Solid lines: buried-channel PMOS in a retrograde *n*-well. Dotted lines: surface channel NMOS drawn for comparison.[72] (© IEEE 1982).

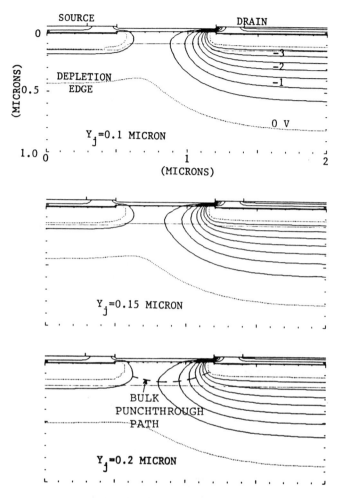

Fig. 5-61 Simulated 2-D potential profile for *p*-channel MOSFET with Y_j = 0.1, 0.15, and 0.2 μm. V_{GS} = 0V and V_{DS} = - 3V. [115] (© 1984 IEEE).

devices with that of a comparable surface-channel NMOSFET. (Note that the V_{GS} scale for the NMOSFET should be +1.5V to -1.5V from left to right.) It indicates that S_t is larger for the BC PMOS devices.

The effect on S_t of the depths of the channel and source/drain junctions Y_j and r_j, respectively, and of the gate-oxide thickness t_{ox} has also been investigated with simulation studies. Figure 5-61 illustrates the 2-D simulated potential profiles for a 0.5 μm *p*-channel MOSFET as Y_j is increased from 0.1 to 0.2 μm. It is observed that as Y_j is increased the potential contours spread more from drain to source, and the bulk punchthrough path passes through the depletion region near the *pn* junction. Figure 5-62 shows the calculated values of S_t for three Y_j values (i.e., 0.1, 0.15, and 0.2 μm), as r_j is varied in a BC PMOS device with an L_{eff} = 0.5 μm, a t_{ox} = 25 nm, bulk punchthrough path passes through the depletion region near the *pn* junction. Figure 5-62 shows the calculated values of S_t for three Y_j values (i.e., 0.1, 0.15, and 0.2 μm), as r_j is varied in a BC PMOS device with an $L_{eff} = 0.5$ μm, a $t_{ox} = 25$ nm, and $V_{DS} = -3V$. Each curve corresponds to a fixed value of Y_j. The threshold voltage [defined as the gate voltage at which the drain current is 100 nA*(Z/L)] is specified at each point. The data shows that S_t is strongly dependent on Y_j and r_j. That is, as Y_j is increased for a fixed value of r_j, S_t increases. For a fixed value of Y_j, S_t also increases as r_j is increased. In Fig. 5-63 the simulated value of S_t for two different gate oxide thicknesses is shown as Y_j is varied. It is seen that S_t improves for thinner gate oxides, but the dependence of S_t on Y_j is only slightly reduced. The overall conclusion from these studies is that small values of Y_j, r_j, and t_{ox} are also needed to realize small values of S_t in submicron BC PMOS devices.

5.8.2.3 Punchthrough Susceptibility of Buried-Channel PMOS.

The larger S_t values exhibited by BC PMOS devices implies that they are susceptible to larger leakage currents in the OFF state. In fact, such relatively large leakage currents are commonly observed in short PMOSFETs, especially at high drain bias. For example, it has been shown that in submicron PMOS transistors ($L_{eff} = 0.8$ μm), I_{Dst} will increase by two orders of magnitude if V_{DS} is increased from -1V to -10V.[74] In this case, if I_{Dst} was 1 nA at -1V, it would increase to 0.1 μA if V_{DS} was raised to -10V. It would be useful to be able to predict the value of I_{Dst} prior to fabricating the device.

As described in section 5.3.1 an increase in S_t has been correlated to the onset of subsurface punchthrough in surface-channel MOSFETs. The increase in S_t in BC PMOS devices as a result of various device parameters (i.e., L, Y_j, r_j) discussed in the previous section can also be considered from the perspective of the phenomenon of punchthrough (subsurface-DIBL), which was introduced in section 5.3. However, we will see that the subthreshold leakage behavior in BC PMOSFETs differs from that observed in surface-channel FETs. To help explain this difference, we will once again

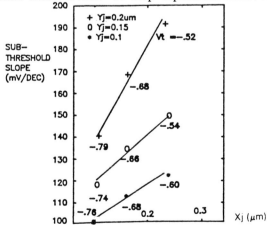

Fig. 5-62 Simulated subthreshold slope versus r_j and Y_j for *p*-channel MOSFETs in which $L_{eff} = 0.5$ μm, $t_{ox} = 250$Å, and $V_{DS} = -3V$. V_T is the threshold voltage.[115] (© 1984 IEEE).

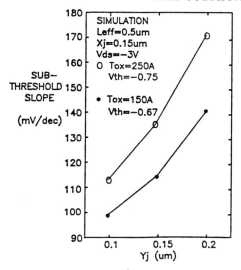

Fig. 5-63 Simulated subthreshold slope versus Y_j and t_{ox}.[115] (© 1984 IEEE).

employ the punchthrough modeling technique described in section 5.3.2, but here it will be applied to quantitatively model I_{Dst} in BC PMOSFETs. The results of this analysis will permit us to compare the subthreshold leakage behavior of surface-channel and buried channel MOSFETs.

We recall that punchthrough current is determined by carrier injection over the potential energy barrier at the saddle point of the electrostatic potential in the bulk (see Fig. 5-64).[117] Therefore, analysis of the channel potential, especially the change of the potential at the saddle point P of the BC PMOS device with V_{DS} is necessary. This analysis can be performed with the aid of 2-D device simulators,** and here we present the results of one report that performed such a study using the device simulator GEMINI.[74] The simulated potential along the direction from source to drain of a BC PMOSFET in an n-well with $L_{eff} = 0.55$ μm as V_{DS} is increased is shown in Fig. 5-65. It is observed that the magnitude of φ^* (the potential at the saddle point P), begins to drop as soon as V_{DS} is increased above 0V. This is due to the fact that there is no pn junction along the channel region in a p-channel BC MOSFET. (Conversely, in the case of short, surface-channel MOSFETs, at low drain-bias values the V_{DS} drop occurs almost entirely across the drain-channel junction, and the barrier at the source does not decrease as long as V_{DS} remains small. Only when V_{DS} becomes large enough to cause subsurface-DIBL does the barrier begin to drop as V_{DS} exceeds this value.) The decrease of the potential barrier height $(\varphi^* - V_S)$ in a BC PMOSFET as V_{DS} is increased is plotted in Fig. 5-66. Here we see that $(\varphi^* - V_S)$ is linearly proportional to the increase in drain voltage, even at low values of V_{DS}.

** Note that an entirely analytic model of punchthrough in PMOSFETs has also been published by Skotnicki et al.[117]

Once $(\varphi^* - V_S)$ is found for a given value of V_{DS}, it can be used to calculate I_{Dst} with the aid of an analytic expression (Eq. 5-18b) as discussed in section 5.3. This expression for I_{Dst} is repeated here for the case of a PMOS device:

$$I_{Dst} = -q \, D_p \, Z \frac{t^*}{L^*} \frac{n_i^2}{N_D} \exp[\frac{q}{kT}(V_S - \varphi^*)] \qquad (5-99)$$

To exploit the results plotted in Fig. 5-66, we express Eq. 5-99 in logarithmic form as

$$\log(I_{Dst}) = \{\log[-q \, D_p \, Z \, (t^*/L^*) \, (n_i^2/N_D)]\} - q(\varphi^* - V_S)/k \qquad (5-100)$$

or

$$\log(I_{Dst}) = A - q\varphi_b/kT \qquad (5-101)$$

where $A = \log[-q \, D_p \, Z \, (t^*/L^*) \, (n_i^2/N_A)]$, and $\varphi_b = (\varphi^* - V_S)$. Now, Fig. 5-66 shows that the decrease in φ_b is linearly proportional to V_{DS}, i.e.,

$$\varphi_b = (\varphi_{bo} - b \, |V_{DS}|) \qquad (5-102)$$

where φ_{bo} is the barrier height at $V_{DS} = 0V$, and b represents the slope of the curve of Fig. 5-66 (i.e., $d\varphi_b/dV_{DS}$). We also note that the values of both φ_{bo} and b can be determined from Fig. 5-66. Then we can write Eq. 5-101 as

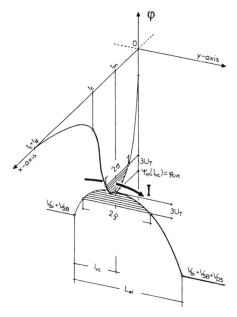

Fig. 5-64 Perspective view of the electrical potential distribution in two perpendicular cross sections of the channel of a buried-channel PMOSFET. Shadowed regions are those corresponding to t* and L^* in Eq. 5-99.[117] (© 1989 IEEE).

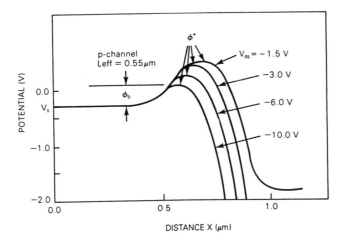

Fig. 5-65 Simulated potential distributions along the buried channel of a PMOSFET for various drain voltages.[74] (© 1988 IEEE).

$$\log (I_{Dst}) = A - q(\varphi_{bo} - b\,|V_{DS}|)/kT \qquad (5\text{-}103)$$

or

$$= A' + V_{DS}/R \qquad (5\text{-}104)$$

where $A' = A - q\varphi_{bo}/kT$ and $R = kT/bq$. The parameter R is the incremental voltage that the drain can sustain before I_{Dst} increases by another order of magnitude ($R = \partial V_{DS}/\partial\log I_{Dst}$). The larger the value of R, the lower the DIBL rate, hence the better the MOSFET is able to maintain low subthreshold leakage as the drain bias rises.

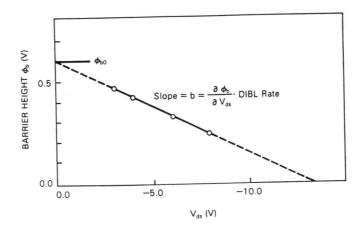

Fig. 5-66 Potential barrier height as a function of drain voltage.[74] (© 1988 IEEE).

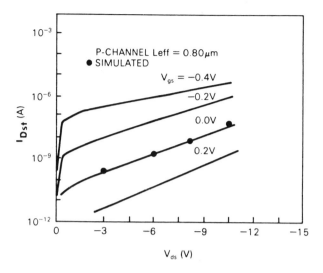

Fig. 5-67 Subthreshold I_{Dst}-V_{DS} characteristics for a submicron PMOSFET.[74] (© 1988 IEEE).

Equation 5-104 implies that the relationship between log I_{Dst} and V_{DS} should be linear in BC PMOSFETs operating in subthreshold. Figure 5-67 shows the measured log I_{Dst}-V_{DS} curves for a 0.8 μm BC PMOSFET, together with some simulated I_{Dst} values at $V_{GS} = 0V$. The agreement between the experimental and simulated data is good. We also see that R in this device is about -4.4V/decade for $V_{GS} = 0V$. This means that if I_{Dst} is 10 pA at $V_{DS} = -1V$, it will increase to 10 nA at $V_{DS} = -10V$.

Now we can compare the I_{Dst} behavior of SC and BC MOSFETs with respect externally applied biases. We note that in the case of surface channel MOSFETs two regions of different slope are observed in the log I_{Dst} versus V_{DS} curves (see Fig. 5-11). At low values of V_{DS} the value of R is large (e.g., in Fig. 5-11b R = 12.6V/decade when V_{DS} <6.0V), but when V_{DS} exceeds about 8.0V, the value of R drops to about 1.0V/decade. This change implies that in surface-channel MOSFETs there is a transfer from surface-DIBL to subsurface-DIBL (punchthrough) - e.g., in the device of Fig. 5-11b at about 6.0V. Also, up to some value of V_{DS} (e.g., V_{PT}), the drain bias has little effect on I_{Dst}. In BC PMOSFETs, however, the value of R is relatively constant (e.g., it has a magnitude of R = 4.4V/decade for all values of V_{DS} in the case of the device characterized in Fig. 5-67). This implies that the nature of subthreshold leakage current in BC PMOSFETs does *not* undergo a change from surface- to subsurface-DIBL, but instead the DIBL phenomenon in a BC device is a combination of both effects. Furthermore, the intermediate value of R also supports the view that *both* the gate and the drain voltages affect the potential of the p-type layer, and thus both can impact I_{Dst} at all values. Finally, this indicates that the measured slope of log I_{Dst} versus V_{DS} (defined as $1/R$), reflects the effect of V_{DS} on φ_b through DIBL, and permits a comparison of the subthreshold leakage behavior of various PMOS device structures.

5.8.3 Techniques Used to Suppress Short-Channel Effects in Buried-Channel PMOS

5.8.3.1 Techniques Used to Keep the Implanted *p*-Layer as Thin as Possible.
The most obvious solution to suppressing short-channel effects in PMOS devices is to increase the PMOS device channel length. This is done in many CMOS technologies, and it is the reason that the minimum channel lengths of PMOS devices are often larger than those of the NMOS devices on the same chip. But we also noted that to achieve small values of S_t, less V_T-roll-off, and larger punchthrough voltages in BC PMOS devices, the *p*-buried layer depth Y_j must be as shallow as possible. That is, the thinner the *p*-layer, the more the device resembles a surface channel FET. Several methods have been reported to realize shallow *p*-layer implant profiles, including the following:

1. Using the lowest practical implant energy, which in ordinary medium-current implanters is typically 20-25 keV.

2. Implanting BF_2^+ (which produces shallower boron layers than implantation with elemental boron, see Vol. 1, chap. 9).

3. Using a high-energy *n*-implant (e.g., P^+ at 400 keV) to form a retrograde *n*-well in the regions where the PMOS devices are formed. This places more *n*-type dopant atoms beneath the channel *pn* junctions, and the more heavily doped regions absorb the drain voltage in a shorter distance, while simultaneously squeezing the channel *pn* junction toward the surface, as shown in Fig. 5-68.

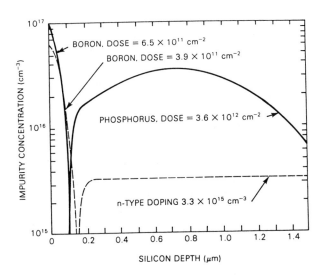

Fig. 5-68 Simulated doping profiles in PMOS channel regions: dashed lines lightly doped substrate; solid lines, retrograde *n*-well.[72] (© 1982 IEEE).

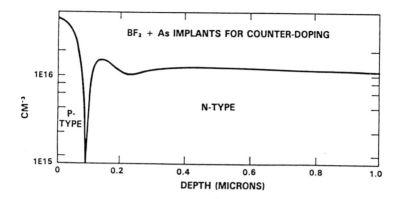

Fig. 5-69 (a) Simulated channel profile for *p*-channel with BF$_2$ and As counterdoping.[115] (© 1984 IEEE).

4. An extra *n*-type implant (typically arsenic) can be performed into a conventional *n*-well or *n*-substrate, with it's peak located below the *p*-layer immediately following the BF$_2^+$ implant (Fig. 5-69a). The *n*-doping under the *p*-layer is thus raised, making the junction depth lie further up the tail of the boron distribution (and thereby making it shallower). The arsenic diffuses relatively slowly, and thus will largely remain in the vicinity of where it was implanted. This forms a steep profile at the counter-doping junction, and maintains a shallow junction depth. The simulation shown in Fig. 5-69a indicates that Y$_j$ with such an arsenic implant is ~0.09 μm. Such an extra implant can also be used with a retrograde *n*-well.

Two drawbacks of this technique are that since the boron channel implant is compensated by an arsenic implant very good process control must be maintained for it to be successful, and it also requires an extra masking step to prevent the arsenic implant from entering the *n*-channel transistor regions.

To prevent a shallow implanted-boron layer from growing thicker, it is necessary to use a reduced thermal budget in order to restrict boron diffusion following the implant. Specific steps for restricting boron redistribution include the following:[76]

1. Implanting the boron through the gate oxide. This avoids the oxidation-enhanced diffusion of boron that would occur during the growth of the gate oxide if the implant were performed first. In this case, it is necessary to prevent the gate oxide from becoming contaminated during implant, either by material sputtered by the beam line or by vaporized resist material used as a mask against the implant. To prevent such contamination, a thin layer of polysilicon may be deposited on the gate oxide prior to the implant (in fact, immediately after the oxide is grown).[77]

2. After the implant has been performed, the remainder of the polysilicon film is deposited. In order to avoid the 900°C thermal cycle that would have to be used if the poly were doped following deposition, this polysilicon is doped *in situ* at ~600°C with phosphorus.

3. A BPSG glass layer is used as the dielectric between the gate and the first level of metal. A significantly lower temperature can be used to flow BPSG than PSG (e.g., 900°C versus 1000°C). A lower temperature cycle can thus be used to smooth the surface topography (flow step) and gently taper the contact holes after etch (reflow step).

5.8.3.2 Shallow p^+ Source/Drain Junctions to Suppress Punchthrough in PMOSFETs.

As noted in our discussion of MOSFET scaling in section 5.6.1.2, reducing the source/drain junction depths also decreases the susceptibility to short-channel effects. By reducing the vertical depth of the source/drain junctions the lateral spread of the dopants in these regions beneath the gate also becomes smaller. Hence, a longer effective channel length is possible for a fixed drawn gate length. In addition, the lateral spread of source and drain depletion regions below the surface layer makes a MOSFET more prone to punchthrough. Consequently, shallow source and drains effectively suppress subsurface punchthrough paths.

In NMOSFETs, it is easier to fabricate shallow n^+ source/drain regions (i.e., ≤ 0.2 μm in depth) because dopants with heavy ionic masses (usually arsenic) are implanted to form these regions. They yield implant profiles with small projected ranges and little channeling. Furthermore arsenic has a low diffusivity, so that little redistribution occurs during postimplant annealing. In PMOSFETs, however, the only practical *p*-type dopant for forming the p^+ regions is boron, and junctions formed with boron are much deeper than those formed with arsenic for several reasons. First, the projected range of the low-mass boron is relatively larger, even at low implantation energies. Ion channeling also causes the implanted boron profile to have a long tail, even if the target wafers are tilted to minimize this effect. Thus, the minimum junction depth which results when boron is implanted into a lightly doped *n*-type crystalline silicon wafer is about 0.35 μm.

The high diffusivity of boron compounds the problem. That is, in CMOS processes both the *n*- and *p*-implants that form the NMOS and PMOS source and drain regions, respectively, must be annealed. The anneal used for the arsenic implant will cause significant (>0.1 μm) redistribution of the boron implant. In CMOS technologies with channel lengths of 2 μm or longer, this issue does not arise because the boron can be implanted after the arsenic implantation and anneal steps (i.e., allowing the boron to be annealed only for the minimum time and temperature needed for full activation). Thus, boron redistribution after implantation can be minimized. However, in submicron CMOS processes it is generally not possible to perform the boron implant after the n^+ arsenic implant. This is because submicron NMOS devices usually use LDD structures, in which the arsenic implant is performed after spacers have been formed. The boron p^+ implant, however, must be carried out before the spacers are formed for two reasons. First, this ensures that the boron implant sufficiently counterdopes the n^- implant (used to form the LDD tip region) everywhere in the areas of the PMOS source and drain (i.e., the n^- implant is typically done unmasked to maintain process simplicity). Second, this also guarantees that the p^+ doping will extend under the gate. Thus, in CMOS processes that use LDDs in the NMOS devices the p^+ regions must experience the same anneal cycle as the n^+ regions. Alternative approaches have been proposed to avoid subjecting the implanted boron to the n^+ anneal, as will be described below.

Techniques to decrease the p^+ junction depths fall into two groups: (1) those which set out to reduce the junction depth of the implanted boron profile; and (2) those which attempt to reduce the diffusion of the boron during the post-implantation anneals.

The approaches mentioned earlier when discussing techniques to reduce the depth of the as-implanted boron region in the channel of PMOS devices also apply to reducing the source/drain junction depths. These include use of BF_2^+ instead of atomic boron as the implant species, and implanting through a screen oxide. Pre-amorphizing the wafer surface region into which the junction dopants will be implanted to a depth of several tenths of a micron (with an earlier implant of silicon or germanium) has also been investigated (see Vol. 2, chap. 3). The amorphous layer effectively prevents channeling, and subsequent annealing at a low temperature is sufficient to achieve recrystallization by solid-phase epitaxy. Use of very-low-energy ion implanters (<5 keV) for implanting the boron has also been studied, as have techniques for implanting the boron into silicide layers formed above the source/drain regions and then diffusing the boron into the substrate from these silicide layers.

Several techniques to limit the redistribution of boron after implant have also been suggested. The first involves use of rapid thermal processing instead of a conventional furnace treatment following the implant. Relatively high temperatures are employed to realize adequate dopant activation, while keeping the times short enough so that boron redistribution is minimized. The second makes use of lower temperature flow and reflow steps by employing BPSG as the interlevel dielectric material instead of PSG. The third modifies the process sequence so that the boron implant is done after the arsenic implant. If the spacers required for NMOS LDD formation are in place, the boron implant must be sufficiently redistributed to ensure that the p-regions extend under the p-channel gates.[105] On the other hand, some process sequences have been reported in which the spacers are removed prior to implanting the boron. Other materials than SiO_2 must be used for such removable spacers (e.g., silicon nitride,[102] TiN,[103] or polysilicon[104]) since removing SiO_2 spacers would significantly thin the field oxide. Concerns about damaging the gate oxide at the gate edge have been raised if dry etching is used for such spacer removal. In the reports describing silicon nitride and TiN removable spacers, wet etching is used to remove them.

5.8.3.3 LDD Structures in PMOS to Limit Punchthrough.   Another way to achieve a shallow junction in a PMOS device is to use an LDD structure. The junction depth of the lightly-doped LDD tip region is shallower than the heavily doped

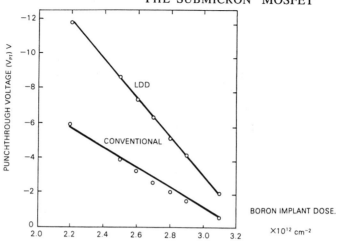

Fig. 5-70 Punchthrough voltage as a function of boron implant dose for a 0.4 μm PMOSFET with and without LDD structure.[75] (© 1986 IEEE).

p^+ source/drain junction depth implanted at the same energy. Figure 5-70 indicates that the punchthrough voltage V_{PT} is increased by 2-3V when an LDD is incorporated into a PMOS device. (The LDD structure, of course, may also be used to increase the hot-carrier resistance of the PMOS devices, especially as the channel length is decreased below about 0.8 μm.) The LDD, however, will generally reduce I_D due to a rise in the series resistance of the drain region. Thus, a tradeoff analysis between an increase in V_{PT} and a decrease in the drain current must be made.

Adding an LDD structure to a PMOS device in CMOS involves relatively straight-forward changes to the process sequence. The gate sidewall spacers are already available from the creation of NMOS LDDs, but there is some increase in process complexity, (especially if the former process used a maskless n^- implant to form the tip regions of the NMOS LDD). That is, to form both PMOS and NMOS LDDs four masking steps are generally needed (n^-, p^-, n^+, p^+), rather than just two. However, a two-mask process, which employs removable polysilicon spacers, has also been reported.[104]

5.8.3.4 New PMOS Device Structures Designed to Suppress Punchthrough.
New PMOS device structures have also been proposed to minimize punchthrough current. For example, a small segment of an n-type region can be created by ion implantation between the p-type S/D and the channel as a punchthrough stopper (refer to Fig. 5-71). This structure has been termed a double-implanted or *halo structure*. One report of such a halo device with $L = 0.5$ μm used a phosphorus implant dose of 1×10^{12} cm^{-2} at 130 keV.[78] A sidewall spacer was used to form the lateral offset of the n-type region in this device. However, since the p^+ source/drain is offset from the gate by the sidewall spacer, this method of forming the local n-regions degrades the drive current and impairs hot-electron immunity.[79] Furthermore, as this technique also places a highly doped n-region adjacent to a highly doped p-region, the maximum halo doping

is determined by the onset of low-level avalanche at the chosen supply voltage and channel length.

A large-tilt-angle implant can be used to fabricate halo-type structures without a sidewall spacer, thereby gaining the benefits while avoiding the problems of the structure of Fig. 5-71.[79] The dopant is placed precisely between the p^+ source and the buried p-channel junction. The lateral penetration and depth of the n-type region are controlled by the implant energy and tilt-angle. The peak concentration is set by the dose. A typical implant sequence to form such a *large-angle tilt implanted punchthrough stopper* (LATIPS) structure as shown in Fig. 5-72 is: (1) implant phosphorus at 90 keV with a dose of 2×10^{13} cm^{-2} at 25° tilt, in two segments, with the target rotated 180° between segments; then (2) implant BF_2^+ (source/drain) at 40 keV (no tilt) to a dose of 3×10^{15} cm^{-2}. [80]

Devices fabricated using the LATIPS process were compared to conventional PMOSFETs. LATIPS devices showed dramatically improved punchthrough characteristics for physical gate lengths as small as 0.5 microns. As an example, the OFF-state leakage current was eight orders of magnitude smaller (at -3V drain bias) than that of a conventional control device fabricated without the LATIPS structure. This dramatic improvement in punchthrough resistance was achieved without extreme scaling of the source/drain junction depth or the n-well background doping. That is, the p^+ source/drain junction depth was about 0.2 μm and the n-well concentration was 1×10^{16} cm^{-3}. Furthermore, the benefits were obtained without significant degradation of device performance. That is, no gate-oxide degradation was observed as a result of using BF_2^+ source/drain implants at 8 keV, even at doses of 5×10^{15} cm^{-2}. Better high-current drive capability than conventional devices was also exhibited, as well as a smaller body (back-gate bias) effect.

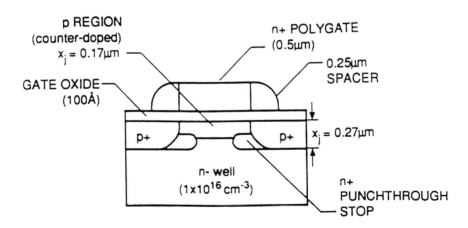

Fig. 5-71 PMOS Punchthrough-stop structure.[78] (© 1985 IEEE).

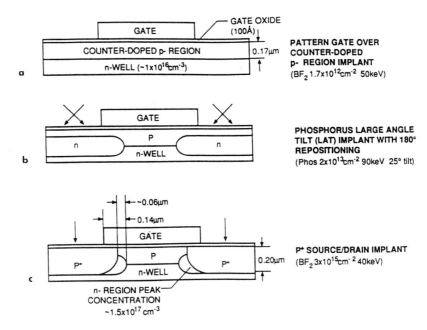

Fig. 5-72 LATIPS process sequence for PMOSFET: (a) Pattern gate over an n-well region that has been conterdoped with a p-type implant (BF$_2$); (b) Large angle tilt implant with phosphorus; (c) p^+ Source/Drain implant (BF$_2$).[79] (© 1988 IEEE).

5.8.4 PMOS Devices with p^+-Polysilicon Gates

The use of a boron implant to adjust V_{Tp} becomes less feasible as devices use even thinner gate oxides, since larger doses of boron are needed. Y_j thus becomes deeper, and the punchthrough problem worsens. In addition, buried channel devices are subject to more process variability stemming from the difficulty of controlling the compensating implant. Solutions involving the use of gate electrodes other than n^+ polysilicon must therefore be explored. One alternative is to use p^+ polysilicon for PMOS devices. This approach appears to become necessary for CMOS and BiCMOS once L becomes smaller than 0.5 μm.

When p^+ polysilicon is used for the gate material, V_{Tp} is shifted from the values that occur when n^+ polysilicon is used. Figure 3-20 also plots V_{Tp} as a function of substrate doping when p^+ polysilicon is employed (using the scale on the right side of the figure). V_{Tp} can be seen to be less negative than -0.7 V over the substrate doping range of 10^{15}-10^{17} cm^{-3}. Thus, V_{Tp} can easily be made more negative through the implantation of phosphorus or arsenic into the channel. If p^+ polysilicon is used throughout the circuit, however, the NMOS device then has to be overcompensated in order for V_{Tn} to be reduced to sufficiently small values. (Note that some reports have been published on the use of p^+ polysilicon alone.[81,82]) This implies it would be ideal to use both n^+ and p^+ poly gates on the same chip (with n^+ poly for NMOS devices, and p^+ poly for PMOS devices).[83]

Such a dual-doped poly approach, however, adds process complexity, and also introduces other problems. One drawback of is that the sheet resistance of p^+ poly is ~3x higher than that of an n^+ poly film of the same thickness, because the mobility of holes is ~3x smaller than that of electrons in Si. A second problem arises from the need to connect the two types of poly (e.g., at the input of an inverter). Such problems occur when a silicide overlayer (or strap) is used to make the connection between n^+ and p^+ poly (as a method to avoid a separate, space-consuming metal contact). Because the silicide strap provides a very rapid diffusion path for boron and arsenic, one type of poly can be counterdoped by the other when the device is subjected to high-temperature excursions. This counterdoping can occur to the degree that a region of poly can change doping types (i.e., from n^+ to p^+). In such cases, the threshold voltage of devices with counterdoped poly will be shifted from their designed value.

If the processing temperature is limited to 800°C after the two types of poly have been connected by the silicide, such lateral diffusion does not produce significant shifts in V_T.[84] On the other hand, temperatures of 900°C will produce sufficient counter-doping to significantly shift V_T. Since one of the last high temperature steps in CMOS is activation of the source/drain implants, this would mean either using a lower-temperature activation step, or performing the step prior to formation of the silicide layer.

Another approach is to form a polysilicon electrode with an overlying conductor layer that suppresses such counterdoping. One such structure is a W-TiN-poly electrode structure.[85] The thin (30-nm) TiN film acts as a diffusion barrier to the dopants in the poly and also prevents reaction between the poly and the W. Very little of the dopant present in the poly is found to diffuse into the W, even following an anneal at 900°C for 1 hour.

Another problem encountered with p^+ poly gates when a thin gate oxide is used is poor V_T process control in the PMOS devices, due to penetration of the boron into the oxide (or further, into the silicon). It is reported that boron will penetrate gate oxides that are ≤12.5 nm thick during a 900°C 30-minute post-implant anneal in N_2.[86] This implies that if p^+ poly gates are used, a lower processing temperature may be needed. If too low a temperature is used, however, the boron implanted into the polysilicon will not be sufficiently redistributed. The polysilicon dopant concentration at the polysilicon-gate oxide interface could thus end up being less than the mid-10^{19}/cm^3. This would make the work function of the polysilicon different from the desired degenerately doped value, creating V_T control problems in the MOS devices.

It has also been found that the presence of fluorine in the gate oxide worsens the boron penetration problem (Fig. 5-73).[87,88] Such fluorine can be introduced into the gate oxide if the PMOS source drain regions are implanted using BF_2^+. Elemental boron is therefore considered inherently superior to BF_2^+ as the implant species for surface-channel PMOS devices in CMOS technologies that use p-doped polysilicon. A

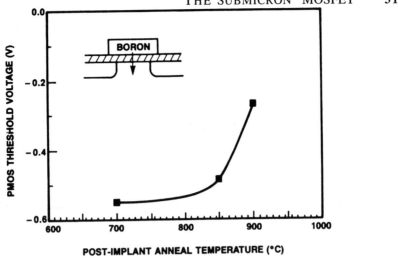

Fig. 5-73 Boron penetration through the gate oxide causes V_T in BF_2 implanted PMOSFETs to shift positive at anneal temperatures above ~800 °C.[87] (© IEEE 1989).

study of enhanced boron diffusion through thin SiO_2 layers in a wet oxygen atmosphere is also reported in reference 89.

It also appears that nitrided oxides and reoxidized nitrided oxides (see chap. 9) are effective in blocking boron diffusion.[90] For this, and other reasons, they are being extensively studied for use as candidates to replace SiO_2 as the gate insulators in dual-gate CMOS processes. An alternative approach to introducing nitrogen into the gate oxide to block boron penetration is through ion implantation. Recently, ion implantation of nitrogen into the gate p- and n-doped poly electrodes of a 0.25 μm CMOS process has been reported. The heavy nitrogen dose (1×10^{15} cm^{-2}) resulted in the gate oxide incorporating high concentrations of nitrogen. This had the effect of suppressing boron penetration of the gate oxide.[110]

Hot carrier effects in p^+-poly 0.5-μm PMOSFETs have also been examined. Stress experiments showed significantly more electron trapping in short stress times than is observed in NMOSFETs. The device degradation due such trapping can be severe enough that it may pose a problem in such devices.[118]

REFERENCES

1. J.E. Chung et al., "Performance and Reliability Design Issues of Deep Submicron MOSFETs," *IEEE Trans. Electron Devices* **ED-38**, March 1991, p. 545.
2. J. Greenfield and R. Dutton, "Nonplanar VLSI Device Analysis Using the Solution of Poisson's Equation," *IEEE Trans. Electron Dev.*, **ED-27**, p. 1520 (1980).
3. L..D. Yau, "A Simple Theory to Predict the Threshold Voltage in Short-Channel IGFETs," *Solid-State Electronics,* **17**, p. 1059, (1974).

4. W. Fichtner and H.W. Poetzl, "MOS Modelling by Analytical Approximations - Subthreshold Current and Subthreshold Voltage," *Int. J. Electronics*, **46**, p. 33, Jan. 1979.

5. C.R. Viswanathan, B.C. Burkery, G. Lubberts, and T.J. Treadwell, *IEEE Trans. Electron Dev.*, **ED-32**, p. 932, (1985).

6. R.R. Troutman, "VLSI Limitations from Drain-Induced Barrier Lowering," *IEEE Trans. Electron Dev.*, **ED-26**, p. 461, (1979).

7. F.-C. Hsu et al., *IEEE Trans Electron Dev.*, **ED-30**, p. 571 (1983).

8. S.C. Jain and P. Balk, "A Unified Analytical Model for DIBL ... in Short-Channel MOSFETs," *Solid-State Electronics*, 30 (5), p. 503, May 1987.

9. T. Skotnicki et al., *IEEE Electron Dev. Letts.*, **EDL-9**, p. 109, March 1988.

10. G.W. Taylor, *Solid-State Electronics*, **22**, p. 701, (1979).

11. B.J. Sheu, D.L. Scharfetter, P.K. Ko, and M.-C. Jeng, "BSIM: Berkeley Short-Channel IGFET Model for MOS Transistors," *IEEE J. of Solid State Circuits*, August 1987, p. 558.

12. G. Merkel, *Process and Device Modeling for IC Design*, (F. Van de Wield et al., Eds.), Noordhoff, Leyden, (1977), p. 705.

13. L. A. Akers et al., "A Model of a Narrow-Width MOSFET including Tapered Oxide and Doping Encroachment," *IEEE Trans. Electron Dev.* **ED-28**, p. 1490, 1981.

14. C.R. Ji and C.T. Sah, "Two-Dimensional Analysis of the Narrow-Gate Effect in MOSFET," *IEEE Trans. Electron Dev.*, **ED-30**, P. 635, June 1983.

15. T. Furukawa and J.A. Mandelman, "Process and Device Simulation of Trench Isolation Corner Parasitic Device," *Ext Abs. Mtg. Electrochem. Soc.*, Fall 1988, p. 329.

16. L. A. Akers, "The Inverse Narrow-Width Effect," *IEEE Electron Dev. Letts.*, **EDL-7** (7), p. 419, July 1986.

17. E.H. Li et al., "The Narrow-Channel Effect in MOSFETs with Semi-Recessed Oxide Structures," *IEEE Trans. Electron Dev.*, **ED-37** (3) p. 692, March 1990.

18. S. S. Chung and T.-C. Li, "An Analytical Threshold-Voltage Model of Trench-Isolated MOS Devices with Nonuniformly Doped Substrates," *IEEE Trans. on Electron Dev.*, March 1992, p. 614.

19. K. Ohe et al., "Narrow-Width Effects of Shallow Trench-Isolated CMOS with n^+-Polysilicon Gate," *IEEE Trans. Electron Dev.*, **ED-36** (6), p. 1110, June 1989.

20. G. Merkel, "A Simple Model of the Threshold Voltage of Short and Narrow Channel MOSFETs," *Solid-State Electronics.*, **23**, p. 1207, December 1983.

21. S. Selberherr et al., "MINIMOS - A Two-Dimensional MOS Transistor Analyzer," *IEEE J. Solid State Circuits*, **SC-15**, p. 605 (1980).

22. Z.-H. Liu et al., "Threshold Voltage Model for Deep-Submicrometer MOSFETs," *IEEE Trans. Electron Dev.*, **ED-40**, January 1993, p. 86.

23. J.R. Brews, W. Fichtner, E.H. Nicollian, and S.M. Sze, "Generalized Guide for MOSFET Miniaturization," *IEEE Electron Dev. Letts.*, **EDL-1**, p. 2, 1980.

24. C. Hu, "Future CMOS Scaling and Reliability," *Proceedings of the IEEE*, **81**, p.682, May 1993.

25. F.M. Klaasen, "Design and Performance of Micron-Sized Devices," *Solid-State Electron.*, **21**(3), p. 565 (1978).

26. C.F. Codella and S. Ogura, "Halo Doping Effects in Submicron DI-LDD Device Design," *Tech. Dig. IEDM*, p. 230, 1985.

27. A. Hori et al., "A Self-Aligned Pocket Implantation (SPI) Technology for 0.2 μm-Dual Gate CMOS," *Tech. Dig. IEDM,* p. 641, 1991.

28. H. Nihara et al., "Anomalous Drain Current in NMOS and its Suppression by Deep Ion Implantation," *Tech. Dig. IEDM,* p. 487 (1978).

29. L.C. Parrillo, "CMOS Active and Field Device Fabrication," *Semicond. International,* April 1988, p. 64.

30. T. Skotnicki, G. Merkel, and T. Pedron, "A New Punchthrough Current Model Based on the Voltage-Doping Transformation," *IEEE Trans. on Electron Dev.,* **ED-35**, July 1988, p. 1076.

31. C. Duvvury, "A Guide to Short-Channel Effects in MOSFETs," *IEEE Circuits and Systems Magazine,* November 1986, p. 6.

32. J. A. Cooper and D.F. Nelson, "Measurement of the high-field drift velocity of electrons in the inversion layer in silicon," *IEEE Electron Dev. Lett.,* **EDL-2**, July 1983, p. 169.

33. R.H. Crawford. *MOSFETs in Circuit Design*, McGraw-Hill, New York, 1967.

34. D. Frohman-Bentchkowsky, "On the effect of mobility in inversion and accumulation layers on thermally oxidized silicon surfaces," *Proc. IEEE,* **vol. 56**, p. 217, 1968.)

35. A.G. Sabnis and J.T. Clemens, "Characterization of Electron Velocity in the Inverted <100> Si Surface," *Tech. Dig. - IEDM,* p. 19, 1979.

36. M.S. Liang et al., "Inversion layer capacitance and mobility of very thin gate oxide MOSFETs," *IEEE Trans. Electron Dev.,* **ED-33**, March 1986, p. 409.

37. K.K Hung, *Electrical characterization of the Si-SiO$_2$ interface for thin oxides,* Doctoral Thesis, Hong Kong University, (1987).

38. C.G. Sodini, T. Ekstedt, and J. Moll, "Charge Accumulation and Mobility in Thin Dielectric MOS Transistors," *Solid-State Electronics,* **25**, p. 833, (1982).

39. K. Lee et al., "Physical Understanding of Low Field Carrier Mobility in Silicon Inversion Layer," *IEEE Trans. Electron Devices,* **ED-38**, August 1991, p. 1905.

40. S.R. Hofstein and G. Warfield, "Carrier mobility and current saturation in the MOS transistor," *IEEE Trans. Electron Dev.,* **ED-12**, p. 129, (1965).

41. F.N. Trofimenkoff, "Field-dependent mobility analysis of the field-effect transistor," *Proc. IEEE,* **53**, p. 1765, (1965).

42. D.M. Caughey and R.E. Thomas, "Carrier mobilities in silicon empirically related to doping and field," *Proc. IEEE,* **55**, p. 2192 (1967).

43. C.G. Sodini, P.K. Ko, and J.L. Moll, "The effect of high fields on MOS device and circuit performance," *IEEE Trans. Electron Dev.,* **ED-31**, October 1984, p. 1386.

44. E.A. Talkhan, I.R. Mansour, and A.I. Barboor, "Investigation of the effect of drift-field-dependent mobility on MOSFET characteristics," Parts I and II. *IEEE Trans. Electron Dev.* **ED-19**, August 1972, p. 899.

45. P.K. Ko, "Approaches to Scaling," Ch. 1, in *Advanced MOS Device Physics,* N.G. Einspruch and G. Gildenblatt, Eds. Academic Press, Orlando, FL., 1989, p. 1

46. K.Y. Toh, P.K. Ko, and R.G. Meyer, "An engineering model for short-channel MOS devices," *IEEE J. Solid-State Circuits,* August 1988, p. 950.

47. M.C. Jeng et al., "Performance and reliability of deep-submicron MOSFETs," *Tech. Dig. IEDM,* 1987, p. 710.

48. V.G. Reddi and C.T. Sah, "Source to Drain Resistance Beyond Pinchoff in Metal-Oxide-Semiconductor Transistor (MOST," *IEEE Trans. Electron Dev.,* **ED-12**, p. 108, (1969).

49. D. Frohman-Bentchkowsky and A.S. Grove, *IEEE Trans. Electron Devices* **ED-16**, p. 108, (1969).

50. G. Baum and H. Beneking, "Drift Velocity Saturation in MOS Transistors," *IEEE Trans. Electron Devices*, **ED-17**, June 1972, p. 481.

51. Y.A. Elmansy and A.R. Boothroyd, "A simple two-dimensional model for IGFET operation in the saturation region," *IEEE Trans. Electron Dev.,* **ED-24**(3), p. 254-62, (1977).

52. P.K. Ko, R.S. Muller, and C. Hu, "A Unified Model for Hot-Electron Currents in MOSFETs," *Tech. Dig. IEDM,* p. 600, 1981.

53. P.K. Ko, *Hot-electron effects in MOSFETs,"* Doctoral Thesis, University of California, Berkeley, (1982).

54. R.S. Muller and T.I Kamins, *Device Electronics for Integrated Circuits,* John Wiley & Sons, New York, 1986, p. 491.

55. T.Y. Chan, P.K. Ko, and C. Hu, "Dependence of Channel Electrical Field on Device Scaling," *IEEE Electron Dev. Lett.,* **EDL-6**, October, 1985, p. 531.

56. B. J. Sheu et al., "BSIM: Berkeley Short-Channel IGFET Model for MOS Transistors," *IEEE J. Solid-State Circuits,* Aug. 1987, p. 558.

57. B. J. Sheu, D. L. Scharfetter, and H. C. Poon, "Compact short-channel IGFET Model," Univ. of Calif., Berkeley, CA Memo. UCB/ERL M84/20, March 1984.

58. M.-C. Jeng, *Design and Modeling of Deep-Submicron MOSFETs,* ERL Memo No. ERL M90/90, Electronics Research Laboratory, University of California, Berkeley, October 1990.

59. A.H.-C. Fung, "A Subthreshold Conduction Model for BSIM," Univ. of Calif., Berkeley, Memo, UCB/ERL M65/22, March 1985.

60. B. Eitan and D. Frohman-Bentchkowsky, "Surface Conduction in short-channel MOS Devices as a limitation to VLSI scaling," *IEEE Trans. Electron Dev.* vol. ED-29, p. 254, Feb. 1982.

61. R. H. Dennard, et al., "Design of II MOSFETs with Very Small Physical Dimensions," *IEEE J. Solid-State Circuits,* **SC-9** (5), 256, (1974).

62. G. Bacarani, M. R. Wordeman, and R. H. Dennard, "Generalized Scaling Theory and its Application to a 0.25 μm MOSFET Design," *IEEE Trans. Electron Dev.,* **ED-31**(4), 452 (1984).

63. J.R. Brews et al., "Generalized Guide to MOSFET Miniaturization," *IEEE Electron Dev. Letts.,* **EDL-1**, January 1980, p. 2.

64. F.M. Klaassen, "Design and Performance of Micron-Size Devices," *Solid-State Electronics,* **21,** March 1978, p. 565.

65. J.R. Brews, K.K. Ng, and R.K. Watts, in "The Submicron Silicon MOSFET," Ch. 1, p. 19, *Submicron Integrated Circuits,* Ed. R.K. Watts, Wiley Interscience, New York, 1989.

66. *ibid.* pp. 23- 37.

67. R.A. Haken et al., "BiCMOS Process Technology," Chap. 3, p. 85, in *BiCMOS Technology and Applications,* A. Alvarez Ed. Klewer, Norwell MA, 1989.

68. A. Alvarez et al., "Application of Statistical Design and Response Surface Methods to Computer-Aided VLSI Device Design," *IEEE Trans. Computer-Aided Design,* **CAD-7**, February 1988, p. 272.

69. *ibid.* ref. 65, p. 24.

70. S.M. Sze, Ed. *VLSI Technology,* 2nd edition, chap. 11, McGraw-Hill, New York, 1988.

71. T. Ohzone et al., *IEEE Trans. Electron Dev.,* **ED-32**, 1789, (1980).

72. G.J. Hu et al., *Tech. Dig. IEDM,* 1982, p. 710.

73. K.M. Cham et al., *Computer-Aided Design and VLSI Device Development,* Boston, Klewer Academic Publishers, 1986, p. 182.

74. J. Zhu, R.A. Martin, and J.Y. Chen,, "Punchthrough Current for Submicrometer MOSFETs in CMOS VLSI," *IEEE Trans. Electron Dev.,* February 1988, p. 145.

75. A. Schmitz and J. Y. Chen, "Design, Modelling, and Fabrication of Submicron CMOS Transistors," *IEEE Trans. Electron Dev.,* **ED-33**, p. 148, (1986).

76. L.C. Parrillo, "CMOS Active and Field Device Fabrication," *Semicond. Internat.,* April 1988, p. 64.

77. R. A. Chapman et al., "A 0.8 μm CMOS Technology," *Tech. Dig. IEDM,* 1987, p. 362.

78. S. Odanaka et al., "A New Half-Micron P-Channel MOSFET with Efficient Punchthrough Stops," *1985 Symp.VLSI Tech., Digest of Tech. Papers,* p. 62.

79. T. Hori et al., "A New P-Channel MOSFET with Large Tilt Angle Implanted Punch-through Stopper (LATIPS)," *IEEE Electron Dev. Letts.,* **EDL-9,** Dec. 1988, p. 641.

80. M. Stinson et al., "Effects of Ion Implantation on Deep-Submicrometer Drain-engineered MOSFET Technologies," *IEEE Trans. Electron Dev.,* **ED-38,** March 1991, p. 487.

81. L. C. Parrillo et al., *Tech Dig. IEDM,* 1984, p. 418.

82. K. M. Cham et al., *IEEE Electron Dev. Lett.,* January 1986, p. 49.

83. C.Y. Wong et al., *Tech. Dig. IEDM,* 1988, p. 238.

84. S. J. Hillenius et al., "A Symmetric Submicron CMOS Technology," Tech. Dig. IEDM, 1986, p. 252.

85. P.-H. Pan, J.G. Ryan, and M.A. Lavoie, *Ext. Abs. of the Electrochem. Soc. Meeting,* Spring 1989, Abs. 138, p. 193.

86. M.L. Chen et al., "Constraints in *p*-Channel Device Engineering for Submicron CMOS Technologies," *Tech. Dig. IEDM,* 1988, p. 390.

87. F.K. Baker, et al., *Tech. Dig. IEDM,* 1989, p. 443.

88. J.M. Sung, *Tech. Dig. IEDM,* 1989, p. 447.

89. Y. Sato, K. Ehara, and K. Saito, *J. Electrochem. Soc.,* June 1989, p. 1777.

90. H. Fang et al., "Low-Temperature Furnace-Grown Reoxidized Nitrided Gate Dielectrics as a Barrier to Boron Penetration," *IEEE Electron Dev. Letts.,* **EDL-13** (4) p. 217 April 1992.

91. M. Nishida and H. Onodera, "An anomalous increase of threshold voltages with shortening of the channel lengths fro deeply boron-implanted *n*-channel MOSFETs," *IEEE Trans. Electron Dev.,* **ED-28**, p. 1101, 1981.

92. M. Orlowski, C. Mazure, and F. Lau, "Submicron short-channel effects due to gate re-oxidation induced lateral diffusion," *IEDM Tech. Dig.* 1987, p. 632.

93. C.Y. Lu and J.M. Sung, "Reverse Short-Channel Effects on Threshold Voltage in Submicron Salicide Devices," *IEEE Electron Dev. Lett.,* **EDL-10**, p. 446, October, 1989.

94. N.D. Arora and M.S. Sharma, "Modeling the Anomalous Threshold Voltage Behavior of Submicrometer MOSFETs," *IEEE Electron Dev. Lett.,* **EDL-13**, p. 92, February 1992.

95. H. Hanafi et al., "A Model for Anomalous Short-Channel Behavior in MOSFETs," *IEEE Electron Dev. Lett.,* **EDL-14**, p. 575, December 1993.

96. D. Sadana et al., "Enhanced Short-Channel Effects in NMOSFETs due to Boron Redistribution Induced by Arsenic Source and Drain Implant," *IEDM Tech. Dig.* 1992, p. 849.

97. H. Jacobs et al., "MOSFET Reverse Short Channel Effect Due to Silicon Interstitial Capture in Gate Oxide," *IEDM Tech. Dig.* 1993, p. 307.

98. C.S. Rafferty et al., "Explanation of Reverse Short Channel Effect by Defect Gradients," *IEDM Tech. Dig. 1993,* p. 311.

99. M.D. Giles, *Appl. Phys. Lett.,* **62(2)**, p. 1940, (1993).

100. J.Y. Chen, "An *n*-well CMOS with self-aligned channel stops," *Tech. Dig. IEDM* 1983, p. 526.

101. T.M. Liu and W.G. Oldham, *IEEE Electron Dev. Letts.,* **EDL-5**, 299 (1984).

102. J.R. Pfiester et al., "A Poly-Framed LDD Sub-half-Micrometer CMOS Technology," *IEEE Electron Dev. Letts.* **EDL-11,** November 1990, p. 529.

103. J.R. Pfiester et al., "An Integrated 0.5 μm CMOS Disposable TiN LDD/Salicide Spacer Technology," *Tech. Dig. IEDM,* 1989, p. 781.

104. L.C. Parrillo, "CMOS Active and Field Device Fabrication," *Semiconductor International,* April 1988, p. 64.

105. S. Meguro et al., *Tech. Dig. IEDM, 1984,* p. 59.

106. J.S.T. Huang, J.W. Schrankler, and J.S. Kueng, *IEEE Trans. Electron Dev.,* **ED-31**, 1889, (1984).

107. S. Ogura et al., *IEEE Trans. Electron Dev.,* **ED-27**, 1359 (1980).

108. Y. Omura and K. Ohwada, *Solid-State Electronics,* **24**, 301 (1981).

109. N. Kotani and S. Kawazu, *Solid-State Electronics,* **22**, p. 63, (1979).

110. T. Kuroi et al., "Novel NICE (Nitrogen Implantation into CMOS Gate Electrode and Source-Drain) Structure for High Reliability and High Performance 0.25 μm Dual Gate CMOS," *Tech. Dig. IEDM, 1993,* p. 325.

111. R.R. Troutman, *IEEE J. Solid-State Circuits,* **SC-9,** p. 55 (April 1974).

112. J.Y. Chen et al., "A Fully Recessed Field Isolation Technology Using Photo-CVD Oxide," *Tech. Dig. IEDM,* 1982, p. 233.

113. T. Shibata et al., "An optimally designed process for submicrometer MOSFETs," *IEEE Trans. Electron Dev.* **ED-29**, p. 531, (1982).

114. G.J. Hu and R.H. Bruce, "Design Tradeoffs Between Surface and Buried-Channel FETs," *IEEE Trans. Electron Dev.,* **ED-32**, March 1985, p. 584.

115. K.M. Cham and S.Y. Chiang, "Device design for the Submicrometer *p*-channel FET with n^+ polysilicon gate," *IEEE Trans. Electron Dev.,* **ED-31**, p. 964 (1984).

116. K.M. Cham et al., "Characterization and modeling of the trnch surface inversion problem for the trench isolated CMOS technology," in *IEDM Tech. Dig.,* p. 23, 1983.

117. T. Skotnicki, G. Merckel, and T. Pedron, "Analytical Study of Punchthrough in Buried-Channel PMOSFETs," *IEEE Trans. E.ectron Dev.,* April 1989, p. 690.

118. Y. Hiruta et al., "Impact of Hot Electron Trapping of Half-Micron PMOSFETs with p^+ Poly -Si Gate," *Tech. Dig. IEDM,* 1986, p. 718.

119. J. Cooper and D. Nelson, "High-Field Drift Velocity of Electrons at the Si-SiO$_2$ Interface as Determined by the Time-of-Flight Technique," *J. Appl. Phys.* **54**, 1445 (1983).

120. T.E. Hendrikson, "A Simplified Model for Subpinchoff Condition in Depletion Mode IGFETs," *IEEE Trans. Electron Dev.*, **ED-25**, p. 435 (1978).

PROBLEMS

1. Calculate the threshold voltage (a) in 1 Ω-cm p-type silicon and (b) in 1 Ω-cm p-type silicon. The MOS devices for each case have : (i) n^+-polysilicon gate; (ii) t_{ox} = 100 nm; and (iii) the oxide is free of charge except for a surface density of $Q_f = 5 \times 10^{10}$ cm^{-2}.

2. For exercise **1**, what are the threshold voltages if p^+ polysilicon is used for both the n- and p-channel devices.

3. Describe punchthrough current and subthreshold current and explain the difference between them.

4. An n-channel MOSFET has a tox of 20 nm, an L_{eff} = 1 μm, r_j = 0.2 μm, and V_T = 0.6V. If the device is biased at V_{GS} = 3V and V_{DS} = 5V, calculate the saturation voltage V_{DSsat} and the maximum electric field.

5. Use one-dimensional junction theory to estimate the punchthrough voltage of a MOSFET with a channel length of 1 μm. Assume a substrate doping of 3×10^{16}/cm^3, a substrate bias of 0V, and a uniformly doped substrate (no V_T-adjust implant).

6. Using Eq. 5-97, calculate the buried-channel S_t value for x_1 = 500Å, t_{ox} = 250Å, $x_2 \ll x_3$ = 3000Å and compare it with the S_t value calculated for a surface-channel MOSFET with the same t_{ox} and a channel depletion width of $d = x_3$.

7. How does a MOSFET's threshold change when constant field scaling rules are applied? Does it scale proportionately?

8. Consider a long-channel MOSFET with L = 3 μm, Z = 21 μm, N_A = 5×10^{15} cm^{-3}, C_{ox} = 1.5×10^{-7} F/cm^2, and V_T = 1.5V. Calculate V_{DSsat} for the case when V_{GS} = 4V. If a constant scaling factor is used to reduce the channel length to 1 μm, find the following scaled-down parameters: Z, C_{ox}, and I_{Dsat}.

9. A MOSFET with gate oxide thickness of 20 nm is to be fabricated on a p-type substrate of doping $N_A = 10^{16}$ cm^{-3}. The source/drain regions have a depth of 0.2 μm and $N_D = 10^{19}$ cm^{-3}. The device is to be operated with V_{BS} = 0V, but V_{DS} could be as large as 3V. From Eq. 5-84 estimate the minimum channel length this MOSFET can have while still exhibiting electrically long-channel behavior. (The gate length is the channel length plus twice the junction depth.) A smaller value of minimum channel length could be obtained if a larger N_A was used. Suggest some undesirable side effects that such a choice could produce.

10. Qualitatively describe the differences between a surface-channel and a buried-channel MOSFET.

11. We have stated in this chapter that the saturation of electron velocity can limit the drain current in a MOSFET with a channel length of 1 μm or less operating from a 5-V supply. Examine this effect by using SPICE to generate the I_D-V_{DS} characteristic of an NMOSFET with L = 1 μm formed on a substrate of doping $N_A = 10^{16}$ cm^{-3} with a 50 nm thick gate oxide. Set V_{GS} = 5V and sweep V_{DS} from 0 to 5V using the Level 2 model. First run a simulation in which VMAX is not specified, and then repeat the simulation with VMAX = 8×10^6 cm sec^{-1}, which corresponds roughly to the scatter-limited velocity of electrons in a MOSFET channel.

12. Qualitatively summarize why a surface channel NMOSFET is prone to suffering punchthrough only after the punchthrough voltage is exceeded, but that a buried-channel PMOSFET exhibits punchthrough current behavior even when drain voltages are very small.

13. Why does the subthreshold slope of the I_D-V_{GS} curve appear to increase at the onset of subsurface punchthrough?

CHAPTER 6

ISOLATION STRUCTURES IN
SUBMICRON CMOS ICs

Implementing electric circuits involves connecting isolated devices through specific conducting paths. Thus, to fabricate monolithic-silicon ICs, devices isolated from one another must first be created in the silicon substrate. Only later are they interconnected to form the desired circuit function. Isolation of devices in the substrate of an IC is also important for other reasons. For example, the state (*ON* or *OFF*) and conductance of individual MOSFETs can only be controlled if proper isolation exists among devices. If not, leakage currents may occur, causing dc power dissipation, noise-margin degradation, and voltage shift on dynamic nodes. Crosstalk among transistors can also destroy the logic state of a gate. In CMOS circuits, leakage current in the isolation region can escalate latchup. From these perspectives, it is evident that device isolation technology is one of the critical aspects of IC fabrication.

Establishing effective isolation in submicron ICs in the face of increased transistor counts and decreased isolation space is a challenging task. In ULSI chips, a tiny amount of leakage per device can induce significant power dissipation for the entire circuit. As an example, if a chip has ten million transistors, and each device exhibits leakage current in the 10-20 nA range, the total power dissipation for the entire chip is increased by several tenths of a watt. Ensuring that isolation leakage currents in submicron ICs are limited to much smaller values (e.g., ≤ 10 pA/μm) is major challenge.

Besides negligibly small leakage currents, the other desired characteristics of IC isolation schemes include: (1) the spacing between active areas should be as small as possible; (2) the process of fabricating the isolation structure should not adversely impact the characteristics of the active devices; (3) the isolation structure should produce as planar a surface topography as possible; and (4) the overall process sequence used to fabricate the isolation structures should be simple to implement and control.

A variety of techniques have been developed to isolate devices in integrated circuits. One reason for such diversity is that different IC types (e.g., NMOS, CMOS, and bipolar) have somewhat different isolation requirements. Furthermore, the various isolation technologies exhibit differing characteristics with respect to minimum isolation spacing, surface planarity, process complexity, and density of defects generated during fabrication of the isolation structure. Tradeoffs can be made among these attributes when choosing an isolation technology for a particular circuit application. A survey of the evolution of isolation technologies from the early 1960's down to those used in 1.0 μm IC generations is provided in Vol. 2, chap. 2. In this chapter we limit the discussion to the chief isolation technologies adopted for submicron CMOS and BiCMOS ICs (1.0 μm to 0.5 μm). The problem of *latchup* (which represents a form of isolation breakdown between the power and ground rails in CMOS and BiCMOS ICs) is not discussed here, but is covered instead in Vol. 2, chap. 6.

We begin with a description of how isolation in MOS ICs is characterized, including some test structures used for this purpose. The less difficult problem of isolation among devices having identical polarity (i.e., among devices which are exclusively PMOS or NMOS) is treated first. The additional problems arising when isolation must be established among devices having different polarities - e.g., between PMOS and NMOS devices - are considered later as part of the CMOS isolation discussion.

Next, the basic *LOCOS isolation* technique (for LOCal Oxidation of Silicon) is reviewed, including the reasons why basic LOCOS becomes inadequate for submicron MOSFETs. This sets the stage for the discussion of the two most widely used isolation structures used to replace basic LOCOS: (1) *polybuffered LOCOS*; and (2) *shallow-trench and refill isolation*. These are examined in depth. Although *deep-trench isolation* is also important, it is more commonly used in bipolar ICs, and thus the discussion of this approach (as well as that of silicon-on-insulator [SOI] isolation techniques), is left to Vol. 2, chap. 2.

6.1 CHARACTERIZING MOS ISOLATION

MOS transistors are self-isolated as long as: (1) the source-substrate and drain-substrate *pn* junctions are held at reverse bias, and (2) spurious channels are prevented from forming among adjacent devices. Since the reverse-bias current of properly-fabricated Si *pn* junctions at 300K is negligibly small, the component of drain current due to reverse-bias drain-substrate leakage should also be insignificantly small. In addition, in the *OFF* state, very little drain-source current should flow (it is also assumed that such mechanisms as punchthrough and GIDL do not produce any significant leakage). Thus, only if the device is turned *ON* by the establishment of a channel under the gate should a significant drain current exist. Similarly, leakage currents between *adjacent* MOS devices should also be negligible provided spurious channels are prevented from forming between them (Fig. 6-1).* *The primary task of isolation in MOS ICs is therefore to ensure that spurious channels do not arise among the MOSFETs in the IC.*

Having stated that spurious channels between MOS devices must be prevented, let us first identify the source of their origin - namely, parasitic MOS structures. Such parasitic devices arise in planar ICs because wiring paths are established with metal or

---

* Such MOS self-isolation also implies that the buried *pn* junction needed to isolate bipolar transistors is unnecessary in MOS ICs. This represents a substantial area savings for NMOS (and PMOS) circuits as compared to junction-isolated bipolar circuits, allowing much higher density MOS circuits to be fabricated.

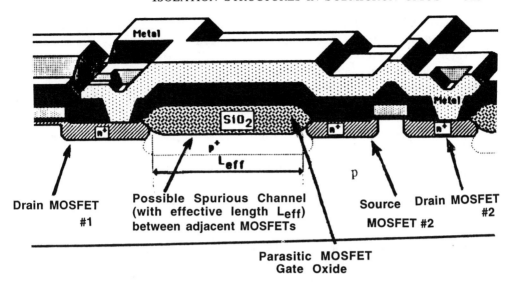

Fig. 6-1 No current should flow between source and drain regions of adjacent MOSFETs. This figure shows the parasitic field transistor with a possible channel under the field oxide if the substrate under this oxide is inverted. From W. Maly, *Atlas of IC Technologies,* Copyright 1987 by the Benjamin/Cummings Publishing Co. Reprinted with permission.

poly-silicon lines adherent to the oxide in the field regions (Fig. 6-1). These conducting lines behave as the gate electrodes of the parasitic MOSFETs, with the field oxide beneath them acting as the gate oxide, and the diffused regions (Drain MOSFET #1 and Source MOSFET #2) in Fig. 6-1 serving as the parasitic MOSFET source and drain, respectively. The channel region of such parasitic devices exists between the source and drain as is also shown in Fig. 6-1. If a voltage exceeding the threshold voltage of the parasitic MOSFET is applied to these conducting lines, inversion of this parasitic channel region occurs, establishing a leakage current path between adjacent devices. Consequently, to avoid the loss of isolation among neighboring MOS devices, the threshold voltage of such parasitic field transistors (V_{TF}) must be greater than any possible operating voltage.

Two methods for increasing V_{TF} are: (1) making the field-oxide thicker, and; (2) increasing the doping beneath the field oxide. V_{TF} could be made adequately high by forming a sufficiently thick oxide on the wafer surface, but the large resulting oxide steps would give rise to severe step-coverage problems.(Note that thick field oxides were used as the isolation structures in early MOSFETs. Such grow-field-oxide-and-etch structures are illustrated in Figs. 6-6b and 6-40a.)Thus, practical approaches generally combine a more moderate increase in field oxide thickness with an increase in doping under the field oxide.

The field oxide is nevertheless much thicker than the gate oxide in the active regions. The thicker oxide (typically 0.5 to 1.0 μm thick) reduces the parasitic capacitance between the interconnect runners and the substrate, which also improves the speed characteristics of the circuits. Normally, ion implantation is used to increase the doping under the field oxide, and the procedure is called a *channel-stop implant*. The combination of thick oxide and channel-stop implant can provide adequate isolation for PMOS and NMOS (and for oxide-isolated bipolar) ICs. Additional isolation issues, however, arise in CMOS circuits, as will be discussed in later sections.

As mentioned in the introduction, the maximum allowable leakage current between neighboring devices is extremely small in many IC applications (e.g., ≤ 10 pA/μm). In practice, the *nominal* V_{TF} needs to be 8-10V above the supply voltage (V_{DD}) to ensure that less than 1 pA/μm of current flows between isolated MOS devices when V_{DD} is applied to the parasitic gate electrode.[1] This is because the *nominal* constant-current-V_{TF} is typically specified in the same way as the constant-current-V_T of active MOSFETs (i.e., nominal V_{TF} is typically defined as the gate voltage that must be applied to cause a drain current of 1 μA per micron of device width [$I_D = 1$ μA/μm] in the parasitic MOSFET). Hence, for 5V circuit operation, *nominal* V_{TF} values usually exceed 15V, at least an order of magnitude higher than V_T's of active MOSFETs.

Operationally, parasitic field-oxide MOSFETs must exhibit such large *nominal* V_{TF} values for several reasons. First, allowance must be made for supply voltage fluctuations (normally 10% of the specified value), as well as for possible conditions of overshoot on interconnect lines. Second, as the operating temperature of a MOSFET rises, the threshold voltage decreases (mainly due to changes in φ_B and φ_{ms}). Reductions of as much as 2V in V_{TF} values have been observed as the temperature is increased from 25°C to 125°C.[2] Finally, the thick field-oxide and relatively heavy channel-stop doping result in (parasitic) devices with very poor subthreshold swing S_t, and S_t increases even more as T is raised (e.g., by ~40% at T = 100°C - see section 4.71 for a background discussion of S_t). Because the S_t effects have the largest impact on isolation leakage (and hence, on the nominal V_{TF} required), we examine them more thoroughly for the case of parasitic field MOSFETs.

In an *ideal* MOSFET, I_D exhibits an abrupt drop for small decreases in V_{GS} below V_T, implying that S_t in such devices is also very small. Therefore, in an *actual* MOSFET, the smaller the S_t value, the more closely it approaches ideal behavior. Now, as discussed in chap. 4, section 4.7.1, if a MOSFET exhibits an S_t value of ~0.1 V/dec - typical of S_t an ordinary active MOSFET - the value of I_{Dst} will drop from 1 μA/μm to 1 pA/μm for a 0.6V decrease in V_{GS} below V_T. But, the S_t values of parasitic field-MOSFETs is much larger (in the range of 0.5-1.5 V/dec), due to their much greater gate-oxide thickness. (Equation 4-91 indicates that S_t will increase if t_{ox} is increased.) Hence, a significant current still flows in the parasitic MOSFET if V_{GS} is decreased by only 0.6 V below the nominal V_{TF}. Thus, to keep the isolation leakage current acceptably small (e.g. ≤ 10 pA/μm) when $V_{GS} = V_{DD} = 5$V, it is necessary to ensure that the nominal V_{TF} is least 5 or 6 V above the worst-case parasitic gate bias. In fact, the minimum nominal V_{TF} of 15V is arrived at by assuming a maximum operating temperature of 100°C, and then allowing for the 2V drop in nominal V_{TF} at the elevated temperature, and for the increase in S_t with increasing T (from 0.6V/dec at 25°C to ~1.0V/dec at 100°C). With such a nominal V_{TF}, I_D will remain <10 pA/μm when $V_{DD} = 5$V at 100°C.

If the circuits are to be operated in a radiation environment, an additional threshold-voltage margin must be allowed. That is, radiation-induced oxide charges will produce a threshold-voltage shift, and the shift will be proportional to the gate oxide thickness to a power of between 2 and 3. For such rad-hard circuits, the nominal V_{TFS} of the parasitic field-oxide MOSFETs may thus be specified at ~20V.

6.1.1 Test Structures for NMOS Isolation Structures

As noted in the previous section, the traditional method for determining the *nominal* V_{TF} value has been to measure V_{GS} when $I_D = 1$ μA per μm of device width, and then call this the nominal V_{TF}. However, since 1 μA/μm would generally represent unacceptably high leakage in parasitic field-oxide MOS transistors, a more appropriate way to characterize isolation structures would be to measure the gate voltage V_{TFiso} at much smaller drain currents (e.g. at 1 pA-1 nA) *and* at drain voltage equal to the power supply voltage, e.g., at $V_{DD} = 5$V, and this approach is now being used more frequently. (V_{TFiso} is measured at $V_{DS} = V_{DD}$ because this represents the worst-case DIBL-induced-leakage condition in a short-channel device.) Furthermore, when it is necessary to fully characterize the efficacy of isolation in a PMOS or NMOS process, V_{TFiso} versus n^+ to n^+ (or p^+ to p^+) spacing is typically measured over some range of drain current values. From such data it can be determined whether V_{TF} exceeds V_{DD} at the maximum acceptable leakage current (e.g., 1 or 10 pA/μm) and at the minimum isolation spacing. This section describes the isolation test structures used to obtain such data. The gate voltage at which the maximum-allowed leakage current arises in the isolation test structure is defined as V_{TFiso} for that value of I_{Dst}.

Figure 6-2 shows a layout (top-view) and cross-sectional view of test structures used to measure the leakage current between adjacent NMOS devices.[1] Figs. 6-2a and 6-2b de-pict an IC structure with an aluminum interconnect line running between two active n-channel MOSFETs, and Figs. 6-2c and 6-2d show the case of a polysilicon line running between two active n-channel MOSFETs. This allows testing of both types of field transistor types: those in which the aluminum   line acts   a gate on the thick field oxide, and those in which polysilicon acts as the gate (the two n^+ diffusions adjacent to the respective gate film act as source and drain, forming the parasitic FET). Since the source and drain in both of these types of parasitic FETs are identical, they are referred to as symmetric parasitic FETs. In Fig. 6-3 we depict two layouts: in Fig. 6-3a two poly-gate FETs with a poly interconnect line running between them are shown, and in Fig. 6-3b with a poly line serving as both the gate and the common interconnect line between them. Both conditions occur in actual ICs, and the test structure of Figs. 6-2c and d is used to characterize the isolation behavior of both of these layouts.

Notice a subtle but important difference between the two test structures of Fig. 6-2. In the latter structure (the poly gate FET) the n^+ regions adjacent to the polysilicon gate do not abut the field oxide. This exact structure may not exist in an actual IC layout because polysilicon lines normally do not extend over the active (thin oxide) area (but instead are layed out as shown in Fig. 6-3a) unless they are also used as the gate electrode of active transistors (see Fig. 6-3b, in which the polysilicon line serves as a gate electrode as well as the interconnect between the two electrodes). In Figs. 6-2c and d the silicon surface under the thin oxide regions is normally inverted at a very low gate voltage (<1V), resulting in ultra shallow "n^+"

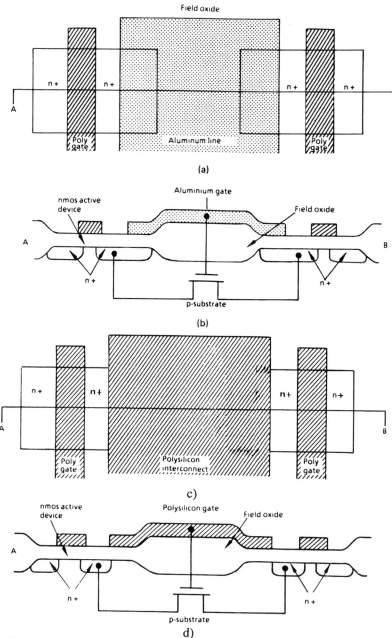

Fig. 6-2 (a) Layout of aluminum-gate parasitic MOSFET between two active devices in NMOS technology; (b) Cross-sectional view of (a); (c) Layout of polysilicon-gate parasitic MOSFET between two active devices in NMOS technology; (d) Cross-sectional view of (c).[1] From J.Y. Chen, *CMOS Devices and Technology for VLSI*, p. 235-6, Copyright Prentice-Hall, 1990. Reprinted with permission.

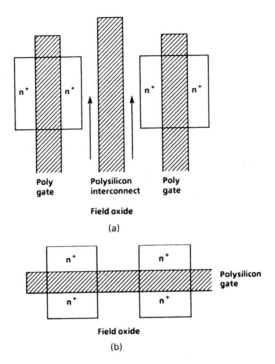

Poly
gate

Polysilicon
interconnect

Poly
gate

Field oxide

(a)

Polysilicon
gate

Field oxide

(b)

Fig. 6-3 (a) Layout of polysilicon lines as transistor gate in real NMOS IC; (b) Layout of interconnect in real NMOS ICs.[1] From J.Y. Chen, *CMOS Devices and Technology for VLSI*, p. 237, Copyright Prentice-Hall, 1990. Reprinted with permission.

regions, which then abut the field oxide. If the silicon surface under the field oxide is then also inverted, the two transistors are basically shorted and isolation between the two transistors is completely broken down. Thus, the test structure shown in Figs. 6-2c and 6-2d is a good test vehicle for the case shown in Fig. 6-3b, because leakage current measured from the parasitic FET indicates the onset of surface inversion under the field oxide.

The test structure of Figs. 6-2c and d also represents a stringent test structure for the layout shown in Fig. 6-3a (which is often seen in a real circuits). That is, since polysilicon in the test structure completely overlaps the field oxide, this structure tests the worst-case condition of the layout of Fig. 6-3a, in which the poly does not completely overlap the field oxide. (That is, it is harder to cause inversion beneath regions of field oxide that are not covered with a poly line, namely the areas pinpointed by arrows in Fig. 6-3a). The configuration in Fig. 6-3a is thus unlikely to exhibit isolation problems if the test structure of Figs. 6-2c and d passes the isolation test.

Another difference between the aluminum and polysilicon gate parasitic FETs is that there is a thicker oxide in the former devices due to an additional oxide layer deposited to separate polysilicon and aluminum interconnects. The total oxide under the aluminum is typically 1-2 μm, while in the polysilicon device the gate oxide is composed of thermally grown oxide only, which is about 0.5 - 1.0 μm thick. In both cases, the thick field oxide and the doped silicon surface underneath inhibit surface inversion unless the gate voltage is raised several volts above the 5V supply.

Figure 6-4 shows the V_{TFiso} values measured at drain currents of 10 pA, 1 nA, and 0.1 μA in a 20 μm wide n-channel FET, using the test structures shown in Figs. 6-2a & b, and 6-2c & d.[3] The LOCOS field-oxide thicknesses for polysilicon- and aluminum-gate FETs are about 0.5 and 1.0 μm, respectively in this example. A boron field implant of 4×10^{13} cm^{-2} at 25 keV is used for the channel-stop formation before the field oxide growth. The higher current curves (0.1-1.0 μA) corresponds to a threshold similar to the threshold defined at the onset of strong inversion. As noted earlier, this definition is suitable for the active MOS transistors but not particularly useful for

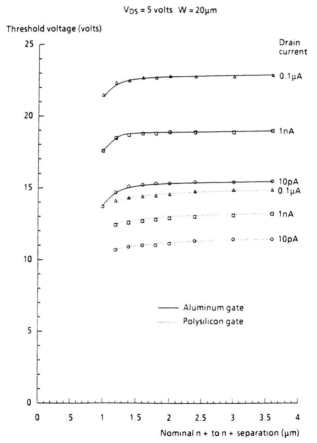

Fig. 6-4 n-Channel field threshold voltages V_{TFiso} for symmetrical parasitic MOSFETs between two active devices.[1] From J.Y. Chen, *CMOS Devices and Technology for VLSI*, p. 253, Copyright Prentice-Hall, 1990. Reprinted with permission.

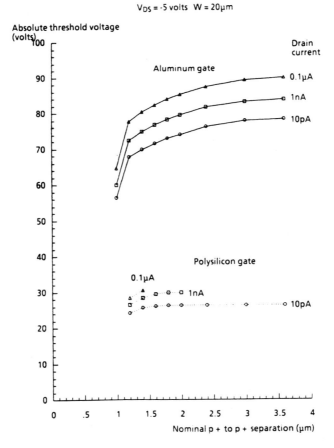

Fig. 6-5 *p*-Channel field threshold voltages V$_{TFiso}$ for symmetrical parasitic MOSFETs between active devices.[1] From J.Y. Chen, *CMOS Devices and Technology for VLSI*, p. 254, Copyright Prentice-Hall, 1990. Reprinted with permission.

parasitic FETS in which only very low level of leakage currents (10 pA - 1 nA) can be tolerated.

Notice that the V$_{TFiso}$s are higher for the aluminum gate because of the associated thicker field oxide. The thicker oxide also gives poorer subthreshold slope, causing V$_{TFiso}$ curves to separate further. The V$_{TFiso}$ decreases as the channel length (n^+-to-n^+ separation) is reduced in a way that is analogous to the short-channel effect commonly observed in active MOSFETs. The effect is less significant in the polysilicon gate structure because the short-channel effect is smaller in device with thinner gate oxides and shallower S/D junctions. (The S/D junction in the poly-gate parasitic structure is the "n^+" [inversion layer charge]/substrate junction.) This effect should be taken into account when setting n^+-to-n^+ layout design rules. For the example shown in Fig. 6-4, V$_{TFiso}$ values are 10 V or above even at 1 μm separation between two *n*-channel active devices. Leakage is also possible in the parasitic FETs if punchthrough between n^+ regions occurs. Due to the relatively high doping concentration in the field region, punchthrough usually does not take place unless the n^+-to-n^+ separation is scaled below 1 μm.

Parasitic FETs among p-channel active devices are identical to those shown in Figs. 6-2a, 6-2b, 6-2c, and 6-2d except that the doping types are reversed. Symmetric parasitic PMOSFETs are, in general, harder to turn on because the net oxide charge density is commonly positive, making the V_{TF} even more negative. As shown in Fig. 6-5, the absolute V_{TFiso} values are well above 5 V.[3] The test devices used here are fabricated from the same CMOS process which made the devices used for obtaining the data in Fig. 6-4. The channel stop is formed by a shallow phosphorus implant inside the n-well. The very high V_{TFiso} values in the polysilicon gate devices are not always measurable due to dielectric breakdown in the thin oxide region between the polysilicon gate and the source. Notice that the aluminum gate devices exhibit greater short-channel V_T roll-off effects, due to the thicker oxide. But, in summary, isolation among p-channel active devices is normally not a problem.

6.1.2 Punchthrough Prevention between Adjacent Devices in MOS Circuits

Parasitic conduction between adjacent devices due to punchthrough (Fig. 6-1) must also be prevented (see chap. 5 for additional information on punchthrough). In MOS circuits, the source and drain regions of each transistor must be kept far enough from the source and drain regions of any neighboring devices so that the depletion regions do not merge (i.e., this distance must be roughly greater than twice the maximum depletion-region width). Substrate doping and channel-stop doping concentrations must also be considered, because lighter substrate doping allows wider depletion-region widths, and punchthrough is more likely to occur at lower voltages in lightly doped regions. It is reported that at isolation spacings of <0.8 μm even advanced LOCOS processes begin to exhibit excessive leakage due to punchthrough.[4]

6.2 THE BASIC LOCOS ISOLATION PROCESS

The most widely used method for creating isolation in NMOS and PMOS ICs is the basic LOCOS structure (*LOC*al *O*xidation of *S*ilicon), introduced by Appels and Kooi in 1970.[5,21] (Note that Kooi has also recently written a book *The Invention of LOCOS* giving a first hand description of the development of LOCOS.[6]) In the LOCOS approach, the oxide is selectively grown over the field regions of the IC. This is done by covering the active regions with a thin layer of silicon nitride. When the field oxide is grown, the active regions remain covered by nitride, which prevents oxidation of the silicon beneath. In the field regions the surface of the Si substrate is exposed prior to field oxidation by etching away the nitride layer in these areas. In addition, the silicon in the field regions is also selectively implanted at this point with the channel-stop dopant. Thus, the channel-stop regions become self-aligned to the field oxide.

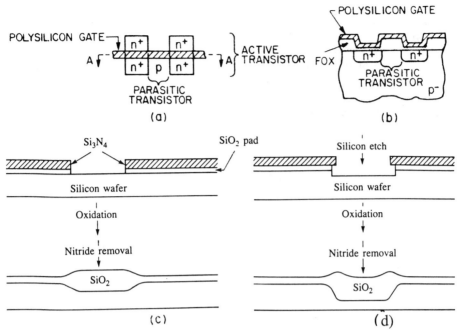

Fig. 6-6 MOSFET isolation. (a) Top view of adjacent MOS transistors with common polysilicon gate illustrating active and parasitic transistor conduction paths. Cross section through A - A for: (b) Grow-oxide-and-etch isolation structure; (c) Semirecessed LOCOS isolation structure; and (d) Fully recessed LOCOS structure.

If the field oxide is selectively grown without etching the silicon (Fig. 6-6c) the resulting field oxide will be *partially (or semi) recessed*. On the other hand, if the silicon is etched (to a depth of about half the desired field oxide thickness) after the oxide-preventing layer is patterned (Fig. 6-6d), the field oxide can be grown until it forms a planar surface with the silicon substrate. (Note that this occurs because the growing oxide film is about twice as thick as the silicon layer it consumes; see Vol. 1, chap. 6). This is known as a *fully recessed isolation oxide process*. In the semirecessed process, the height of the oxide protruding above the level of the active region surface is larger than in the fully recessed process, but it is smaller than in the grow-oxide-and-etch process. In addition, the semirecessed oxide step has a gentle slope that is more easily covered by subsequent polysilicon and metal layers.

The semirecessed LOCOS structure has become the workhorse isolation technology for MOS devices down to about 1.5-μm geometries. The advantages of semirecessed LOCOS over fully recessed LOCOS are that fabrication is less complex and fewer process-induced defects are created in the silicon substrate. Fully recessed LOCOS is primarily used for isolating digital bipolar ICs, where a thicker field oxide is needed than in MOS. A semirecessed oxide with such a larger thickness would produce intolerably high oxide steps, while the use of the fully recessed approach mitigates this problem. Details describing fully recessed LOCOS are given in Vol. 2, chap. 2.

6.2.1 Details of the Basic Semi-recessed LOCOS Process

Details of each of the steps used to fabricate the basic, conventional semirecessed LOCOS structures are presented in this section (Fig. 6-7).

6.2.1.1 Pad-Oxide Layer. A wafer with a bare silicon surface is cleaned, and a 40-50 nm SiO_2 layer (called a *pad* or *buffer* oxide) is thermally grown on the surface. Its function is to cushion the transition of stresses between the silicon substrate and the subsequently deposited nitride. For example, assume that a nitride film is deposited directly on a silicon wafer. When the field oxide is subsequently grown, stresses occur in the nitride due to various effects, including: (1) mismatch between the thermal coefficient expansion of the nitride film and the silicon substrate; (2) a tendency of the

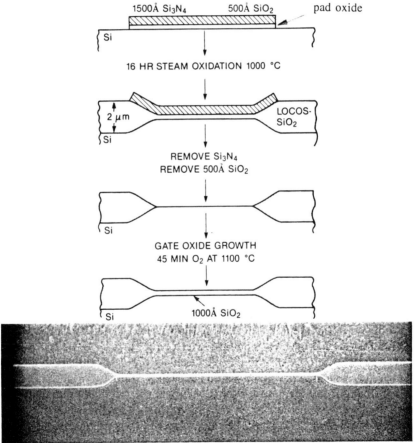

Fig. 6-7 Cross section depicting process sequence for semirecessed oxidations of silicon.[21] This paper was originally presented at the Spring 1973 Meeting of the Electrochemical Society. Reprinted with permission.

Fig. 6-8 Severe corner cracks in a nitride oxidation mask on silicon. The cracks occurred at concave corners. LOCOS thickness is 2-μm.[6] (© 1991 IEEE).

growing field oxide to lift the edges of the nitride. In some locations (e.g., 270° corners in the nitride film - see Fig. 6-8), the stresses in the brittle nitride film cause it to crack, defeating the purpose of the nitride to act as an oxidation barrier. The pad oxide flows during the field-oxide growth process in such a way that the stresses in the nitride can be kept small enough to prevent cracking. Stresses are also transmitted from the nitride to the silicon, and these can produce defects in the silicon crystal as well. The pad oxide also serves to prevent these defects. In general, the thicker the pad oxide, the fewer the defects in both the nitride films and the silicon substrate. However, a thick pad-oxide layer will render the nitride layer ineffective as an oxidation mask by allowing lateral oxidation to take place. Hence, the thinnest pad oxide that will serve as an effective stress relief layer is employed. Typically, pad oxide layers are 50 nm thick.

6.2.1.2 CVD of Silicon Nitride Layer. Next, a 100-200 nm thick layer of CVD silicon nitride which functions as an oxidation mask is deposited. Silicon nitride is effective in this role because oxygen and water vapor diffuse very slowly through it, preventing oxidizing species from reaching the silicon surface under the nitride. In addition, the nitride itself oxidizes very slowly as the field oxide is grown (typically, only a few tens of nm of nitride are converted to SiO_2 during the field-oxide growth process). Thus, the nitride behaves as an integral oxidation-barrier layer during the entire field-oxide-growth step. Figure 6-9 compares the oxidation rate of silicon and silicon nitride, and shows that silicon oxidizes approximately 25 times faster than silicon nitride.[9] One criterion for selecting the nitride thickness is that it should be greater than the thickness that will be converted to SiO_2 during the subsequent field oxidation step.

Silicon-nitride films, however, have the well-known drawback of exhibiting a very high tensile stress when deposited by CVD on silicon (on the order of 10^{10} dynes/cm^2). The termination of intrinsic stresses at the edge of a nitride film gives rise to a horizontal force that acts on the substrate. Under some circumstances, this stress can exceed the critical stress for dislocation generation in silicon, thus becoming a source of fabrication-induced defects. The pad oxide, as described in the previous section, is used to combat these stresses and avoid dislocation generation.

6.2.1.3 Mask and Etch Pad-Oxide/Nitride Layer to Define Active Regions.
The active regions are now defined with a photolithographic step. A resist pattern is normally used to protect all areas on which active devices will later be formed. The nitride layer is then dry etched, and the pad oxide may be etched by means of either a dry- or wet-chemical process. In many cases, however, it is desirable to retain some of the pad oxide after the nitride etch. In this case, the dry nitride-etch process must be optimized to prevent all the pad oxide from being removed during the nitride overetch

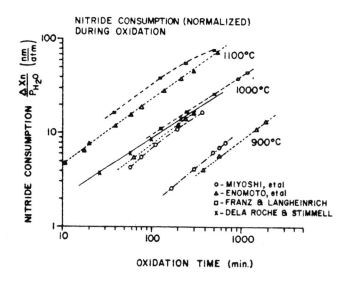

Fig. 6-9 Nitride consumption during oxidation.[9] Reprinted with permission of Semiconductor International.

that the resist is left in place to serve as a masking layer during the channel-stop-implant step, and must be stripped prior to the field-oxide growth step.

6.2.1.4 Channel-Stop Implant. An implant is performed in the field regions to create a channel-stop doping layer under the field oxide. In NMOS circuits, a *p* implant of boron is used, while in PMOS (and in the *n*-tubs of CMOS circuits) an *n* implant of arsenic is utilized. Although this normally requires two masking steps in CMOS circuits, a single mask process for implanting both *p* and *n* channel stops has been reported.[11] After the implant has been completed, the masking resist is stripped.

6.2.1.5 Problems Arising from the Channel-Stop Implants. During field oxidation, the channel-stop boron experiences both segregation and oxidation-enhanced diffusion. Thus, relatively high boron doses are needed (5×10^{12}-5×10^{13} atoms/cm^2) in order for acceptable field threshold voltages to be achieved. This also implies that the peak of the boron implant must be deep enough that it is not absorbed by the growing field-oxide interface (implant energies in the 60-100 keV range are typical). If the channel-stop doping is too heavy, it will cause high source/drain-to-substrate capacitances and reduce source/drain-to-substrate *pn* junction breakdown voltages.

The lateral diffusion of the boron also causes it to encroach into the NMOS active areas (Fig. 6-10). Such redistribution raises the boron surface concentration in the active regions near the edge of the field oxide, causing V_T to increase in that region of the active device. As a result, the edges of the channel will not conduct as much current as the central portion, making I_D smaller (narrow-width effect). This effect is also enhanced as the dose of the channel-stop implant is increased.

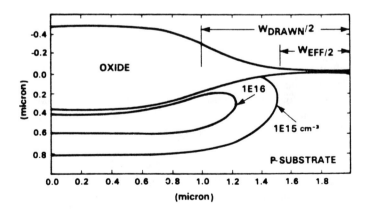

Fig. 6-10 Field oxide and boron encroachment in LOCOS.[10] From K. M. Cham et al., *Computer-Aided Design and VLSI Device Development.* Copyright 1986, Kluwer Academic Publishers. Reprinted with permission.

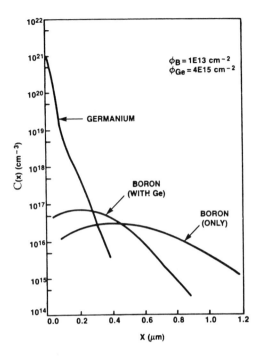

Fig. 6-11 Reduction of boron implant redistribution during field oxidation by co-implanting Ge. Figure shows implanted boron doping profile after field oxidation step with and without the presence of a co-implanted Ge dose. Boron doping profile is deeper without implanting Ge.[13] (© 1990 IEEE).

Several techniques have been studied to reduce the extent of the channel-stop dopant diffusion, including: (1) use of high-pressure oxidation (HiPOX) to grow the field oxide;[11,12] (2) co-implanting chlorine and boron into the field regions;[13] (3) use of a germanium-boron co-implant;[14] (4) use of a high-energy post-field-oxide channel-stop implant; and (5) implementation of a novel, field-implant-free well-drive process.[99]

HiPOX allows the oxide-growth temperature to be reduced, which reduces the diffusion length of the boron. The chlorine co-implant is performed in the field regions prior to field oxidation, causing the oxide to grow at a faster rate. Consequently, the same field oxide thickness can be attained in less time at the same temperature. The germanium-boron co-implant exploits the fact that boron diffuses with a lower diffusivity (by a factor of nearly three) in the presence of implanted germanium, and boron segregation effects are also reduced. The result is a 40% increase in field threshold voltage for the same dose of implanted boron, and a corresponding decrease in lateral-boron encroachment. Figure 6-11 shows the effect of the Ge on the vertical boron profile in the field region after a field oxide step of 165 minutes at 1000°C in steam. The boron implant dose was 1×10^{13} cm^{-2} at 100 keV, and the Ge dose was 5×10^{15} cm^{-2}

at 150 keV. The Ge significantly enhances the final surface concentration of boron, and maintains a generally shallower profile with greater peak concentration.

A high-energy channel-stop implant following the field oxide growth greatly reduces the lateral penetration of boron because it no boron is present during the long, high-temperature field oxidation. In one reported process, a 400-keV boron channel-stop implant was implanted through a 0.8 μm field oxide (this same implant is also used in the process to create a retrograde p-well profile in the active areas).[15,118] Implanting the channel-stop dose after field oxidation appears to become even more attractive as device dimensions shrink toward 0.5 μm because the field-oxide thickness is also reduced in advanced, submicron CMOS processes. For example, for 0.5 μm devices, this thickness is projected to be ~0.4 μm. Such thinner field oxides require implant energies $\leq$250 keV for boron (and $\leq$600 keV for phosphorus). High-energy implanters, with implant energies exceeding 1 MeV, are now commercially available, making these latter processes manufacturable. The application of MeV implantation to well formation and isolation in CMOS technology is described further in sections 6.6 and 6.7 and in chap. 8.

The novel field-implant-free approach is reported to be applicable to a p-well or twin-well CMOS process, and is described more fully in section 6.7.1.1. Briefly here, a sufficiently high boron concentration at the Si surface is achieved without a channel-stop implant by using a unique well drive-in process. After implanting the boron well dopants, most of the well dopant distribution is accomplished in a non-oxidizing ambient *after* field-oxide growth. The time-at-temperature during field-oxide growth makes up the first part of the well drive-in, during which time the boron near the oxide surface is depleted by impurity segregation effects. However, during the after-oxide drive-in, boron dopants deep in the bulk diffuse back toward the surface and replenish the boron lost near the surface to the field oxide (Fig. 6-12). Since no channel-stop implant is used, boron does not encroach into the active regions, and the problem of lateral boron diffusion is eliminated. The associated narrow-width effect is also thereby avoided. Nominal V_{TF}s >10V at isolation spacing of 1.2 μm were reported.

6.2.1.6 Grow Field Oxide. After the channel-stop implant has been performed, the field oxide is thermally grown by means of wet oxidation at temperatures of around 1000°C for 2-4 hours (to thicknesses of 0.8-1.0 μm). The oxide grows where there is no masking nitride, but at the edges of the nitride, some oxidant diffuses laterally. This causes the oxide to grow under and lift the nitride edges. Because the shape of the oxide at the nitride edges is that of a slowly tapering oxide wedge that merges into the pad oxide, it has been named a *bird's beak* (Fig. 6-13). The bird's beak is a lateral extension of the field oxide into the active area of the devices. Although, as we shall discuss in the following section, the length of the bird's beak depends upon a number of parameters – including the thicknesses of the buffer oxide, nitride, and isolation oxide (as well as the oxidation temperature and oxygen partial pressure) – for a typical 0.7-0.8-μm field oxide it is ~0.5 μm/side. This would make a lithographically defined 1-μm feature disappear on the chip following the field oxidation step (Fig. 6-14). Although this effect led to predictions that LOCOS isolation would have to be replaced for device dimensions smaller than 2 μm, optimization of process steps has allowed conventional LOCOS to

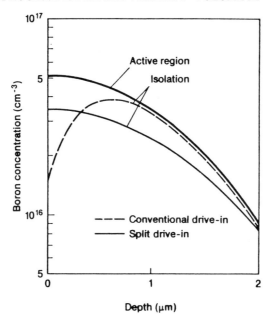

Fig. 6-12 SIMS profiles of boron well underneath field oxide and in the active area for split and non-split drive-in. Implanted boron dose: 8×10^{12} cm^{-2}. The active area profile is the same for both drive-in cases.[99] (© 1990 IEEE).

continue to be used for device-isolation spacings as narrow as 1.25-1.5 μm.[16,17] For dimensions smaller than this, modifications to basic LOCOS which reduce bird's beak had to be incorporated. One such modification is poly-buffered LOCOS, to be described later.

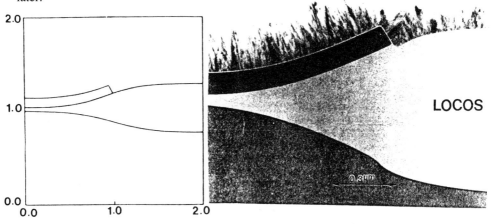

Fig. 6-13 Schematic of the bird's beak that occurs during semirecessed LOCOS.

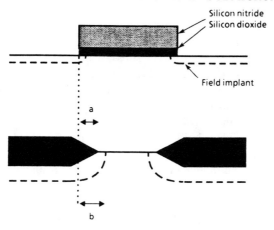

a: encroachment of field oxide
b: lateral diffusion of field dopants

Fig. 6-14 Bird's beak encroachment limits the scaling of channel widths to about 1.2-1.5 μm.[16] Reprinted with permission of Semiconductor International.

Another limitation of LOCOS-based isolation schemes for submicron structures is the *oxide field-thinning* effect.[17] The field-oxide thickness in submicron-isolation spacings is significantly less than the thickness of field-oxides grown in wider spacings (Fig. 6-15).[17,18] The narrower the width of the exposed substrate silicon region, the thinner the field oxide. For example, a field oxide that is grown to a thickness of 400 nm above a region of exposed Si that is 1.5-μm wide would be only about 290 nm thick if grown above a 0.8-μm-wide region of Si. In 0.2 μm-wide windows, the thinning can be as great as 80%. Thin field oxides that result from this effect can have a great impact

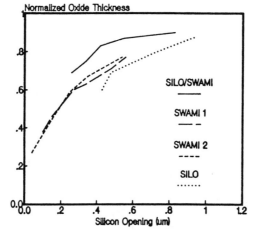

Fig. 6-15 Normalized field oxide thickness versus silicon opening for various advanced LOCOS processes.[17] (© 1985 IEEE).

on V_{TF} values and on the interconnect capacitances to substrate.

The field thinning effect is believed to be caused by higher compressive stress in the oxide growing in smaller openings.[19] The stress is sufficient to reduce the diffusivity of the oxidant through the oxide. Field oxides grown at 1200°C showed less thinning than those grown at 1000°C (in the same size openings). At 1200°C the viscosity of the growing oxide is reduced by roughly two orders of magnitude. This permits the oxide to flow and thereby reduce the growth inhibiting stress. Unfortunately, raising the growth temperature is not a feasible solution in most cases. Higher temperatures increase bird's beak length and exacerbate unwanted diffusion of channel-stop dopants in CMOS or BiCMOS. Indeed, the field-thinning effect and the need to maintain defect-free isolation structures (see next section), may limit the minimum space for LOCOS-type isolation structures with a field-oxide thickness of 550 nm to ~0.8 μm. Recently, however, it has been reported that use of HiPOX may be a way to reduce the severity of the problem (see section 6.4.1 for more details).

6.2.1.7. Factors Which Impact Bird's Beak Length and Shape.

We mentioned earlier that the length and shape of the bird's beak is impacted by a number of factors. They include the following: pad layer thickness and composition; silicon crystal orientation; temperature of the field oxide growth process; thickness of the nitride layer; mechanical properties of the nitride layer; and mask stack geometry. Let us consider each of these factors in more detail:

    1. *Pad layer thickness.* In general, lateral oxidation should be reduced by making the pad oxide thinner, leading to a shorter bird's beak (Fig. 6-16).[20] However, since the purpose of the pad oxide is stress reduction, it cannot be

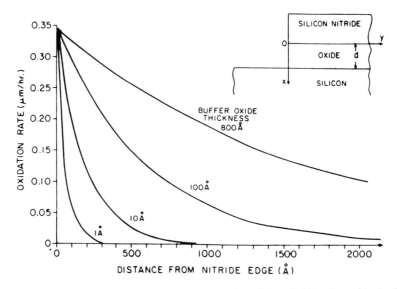

Fig. 6-16 Oxidation rates versus distance from the edge of the nitride edge with the buffer (pad) oxide thickness as a parameter.[20] (© 1982 IEEE).

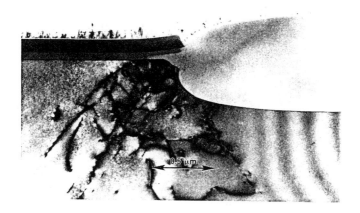

Fig. 6-17 Suppressed LOCOS. Bird's beak reduction is achieved by replacing the pad oxide of the conventional LOCOS structure with an oxynitride. Note that the oxynitride is hardly oxidized. TEM of cross section.[3] (© 1991 IEEE).

made arbitrarily thin. The minimum pad oxide thickness will depend on the oxidation conditions. Also note that LOCOS structures with no pad oxide have been investigated, termed SILO structures (*sealed interface local oxidation*). In such cases, a native oxide of 10-20Å is still usually present, giving rise to some bird's beak formation.

2. *Pad layer composition.* Although direct contact of the nitride with the silicon can dramatically reduce bird's beak effects (i.e., pad oxide thickness is zero), defects may be thereby produced in the silicon. A variation that has been investigated is to employ a pad layer composed of CVD oxynitride (SiO_xN_y), rather than a thermally grown oxide. The material properties of such layers may be a compromise between those of pure nitride and oxide - with respect to the oxidation masking capability of nitride and the stress relief qualities of oxide. Kuiper et al., studied the oxidation behavior of such films as a function of their composition.[22] They concluded that oxynitride films with composition ratios of $0< x/y <0.5$ (nitride rich) show better oxidation resistance during field oxide growth than do oxygen rich films. Figure 6-17 shows a TEM photo-micrograph of a LOCOS structure with a CVD oxynitride pad layer. Note that the bird's beak penetration is smaller in the latter structure, and that oxynitride pad layer is not noticeably oxidized.

3. *Silicon crystal orientation.* Since the oxidation rates of different crystal planes in silicon vary, the bird's beak lengths depend on the silicon crystal orientation. Shorter bird's beaks are found on <111> silicon wafers than on silicon wafers with <100> surface orientation.

4. *Field oxide process temperature.* Shorter bird's beaks are found as the field oxidation temperature is increased. The oxide is less viscous at higher temperatures. As it forms under the nitride edge it is more easily squeezed out by the pressure of the nitride mask which is resisting being lifted.

5. *Thickness and mechanical properties of the nitride layer.* In general, all other factors being equal, the thicker the nitride layer, the less bird's beak penetration. The thicker the nitride, the stiffer it will be, and thus will resist the edge lifting that accompanies bird's beak penetration. However, if the nitride film is too thick, it is likely to crack. Consequently, the thickness of masking nitride layers is usually chosen to be 250 nm or less.

The mechanical properties of the nitride are also a major factor that influences the bird's beak. It has been reported that at elevated temperatures Si_3N_4 is a more viscous than elastic material.[23] As a result, once the nitride mask edge is lifted up by the growing bird's beak, it will have no further tendency to compress the oxide grown under it. The nitride seems to have a higher viscosity than SiO_2, but this also depends on the stoichiometry of the nitride. Silicon-rich nitride films were found to exhibit a higher resistance to flow, resulting in less nitride bending and less encroachment of the field oxide under the nitride edge.

6. *Mask stack geometry.* The shape of LOCOS structures is also dependent on the mask geometries. That is, the following effects have been observed: (1) the bird's beak penetration is significantly greater at convex corners (particularly at the end of long, narrow mask stack structures, e.g., mask widths ≤ 1.0 μm); (2) bird's beaks are shorter at concave corners; and (3) bird's beaks are shorter for narrow mask features.[6,18] (It should be noted that these effects are less pronounced in the poly-buffered LOCOS process discussed in section 6.3).

This is explained as follows: At the end of long, narrow mask stack lines (Fig. 6-18), the nitride layer is less resistant to bending than along the narrow dimension of the line, hence allowing greater lateral oxidation to occur as the nitride is lifted. The bird's beak length at the end of the line can be 2-3 times the normal bird's beak length. Convex (270°) corners are also less resistant to bending than concave (90°) corners, allowing further lifting of the nitride edge, and greater lateral penetration at the convex corner.

The extended bird's beak penetration effect can impose limitations on packing density, since more overlap area is needed for contacts to the end of small device areas. In addition, the region of the longer bird's beak is susceptible to junction leakage because etchback of the thin long beak after *pn* junction formation can easily expose the junction.

7. *Isolation Lifting* (or *Bird's Beak Punchthrough*). If the bird's beak on either side of a mask-stack-isolation line penetrates under the line such that the

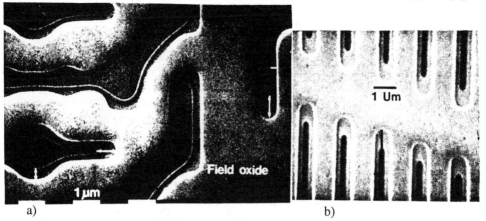

a)   b)

Fig. 6-18 Bird's beak dependence on mask geometry: (a) Top view of a CMOS RAM cell. The bird's beak length (white arrows) is different in concave and convex corners; (b) Enhanced bird's beak (EBB) at the end of narrow active areas. BB refers to the normal bird's beak.[3] (© 1990 IEEE).

active-area width reaches zero, it is said that *isolation lifting,* or *bird's beak punchthrough* has occurred. Figure 6-19a shows this effect.[131] The effect occurs for two reasons: (1) Wider isolation spacings permit the mask stack to deform at the edges, relieving the stress that is lifting the lines. As the isolation space is made narrower, the mask stack becomes more rigid with respect to edge bending, and thus will not deform. Instead the entire mask stack line will lift. Thus, an optimum nitride thickness must be used. That is, the nitride must be thick enough to suppress bird's beak penetration by resisting upward deformation at the mask line edges, yet it must not be so thick that

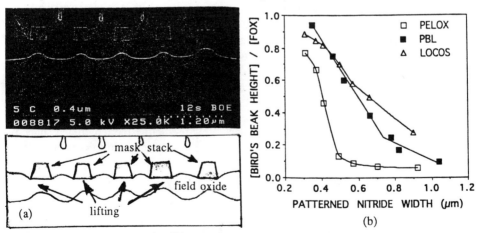

Fig. 6-19 (a) Bird's beak lifting[131]; (b) Bird's beak height under the center of the isolation line as a function of isolation line width, and for three different isolation technologies.[132] (© 1994 IEEE).

deformation cannot occur at all, instead giving rise to lifting. A suggested PBL mask stack with optimized layer thicknesses for both isolation widths and isolation spacings of 0.6 μm consists of 2500Å/500Å/100Å-thick nitride/ amorphous silicon/pad oxide layers, respectively.[131]; (2) As the active area dimension is decreased, the concentration of the oxidizing species merges at the center of the isolation line at a very early stage of field oxidation. In this case, as the field oxidation proceeds, the oxidizing species concentration quickly reaches supersaturation at all locations beneath the line, resulting in a surface-reaction limited growth condition. A uniform oxide punchthrough profile beneath the isolation line thus results (see Fig. 6-19a). This suggests that if the lateral diffusion of the oxidizing species under the nitride can be limited, oxide lifting can be reduced. In the PBL and PELOX processes (which are advanced variations of LOCOS described in section 6.4), nitride cladding of the mask-stack sidewalls is used to reduce this lateral diffusion for the purpose of suppressing the oxide lifting effect.[122]

Figure 6-19b shows the bird's beak height under the center of the isolation line as a function of isolation line width, and for three different isolation technologies.[132] Note that the advanced LOCOS isolation processes can reduce the effect for isolation spacings down to ~0.5 μm.

However, if isolation lifting occurs, the thicker oxide underneath the nitride mask must then be etched back, resulting in a reduced field oxide thickness elsewhere, which degrades the isolation of the small active spaces. In addition, increased field etchbacks are limited by the susceptibility of LOCOS to the field thinning effect in small active spaces. As a solution, a post-field-oxide implantation has been proposed in order to locally increase the well doping and compensate for the thinner field oxide. However, achieving acceptable MOSFET performance with this solution requires that a very critical alignment-sensitive photomasking step be used to keep the implant out of neighboring active regions. Reference 132 describes the integration of a PELOX isolation structure and a split-well drive-in scheme to realize the same benefits, but without the need for such an extra post-field oxide implant, allowing this scheme to provide adequate isolation for CMOS technology down to 0.35 μm.

From this list of factors, we can see that accurately predicting the length and shape of the bird's beak is a formidable task. We shall see in a later section the attempts that have been made to model such 2-D and 3-D oxidation effects. In practice, some experimentation is generally required to get the optimum conditions for making the desired device structures.

6.2.1.8 Use of High-Energy Ion Implantation to Introduce the Channel-Stop Dopant After Field Oxide Growth.
As noted earlier, the commercial availability of high-energy implanters now makes it possible to implant the channel stop dopants (chiefly boron) through the field oxide, rather than having to

implant them into the substrate prior to field oxide growth. This approach offers several attractive benefits. First, a higher concentration of boron at the surface under the oxide can be achieved with the same implant dose than if the implant is done prior to field-oxide growth. This is possible because the leaching of the boron that takes place during field oxide growth is avoided, and this leaching causes the boron surface concentration of at the silicon surface to be reduced (see section 6.2.1.5.) Thus, the field oxide thickness needed to attain the target V_{TFiso} value can be reduced. Second, such thinner field oxides exhibit smaller bird's beak. This means that smaller isolation spacing design rules can be used which, in turn, translates to a reduced chip size. Third, the thinner field oxide makes the topography of the wafer after the semirecessed field oxide growth step smoother. Smoother topography may extend the use of existing stepper tools for one or more device generations, and will delay the need to introduce chemical-mechanical polishing for back-end processing. Finally, the redistribution of channel-stop dopants by lateral diffusion during the field oxide growth step is largely replaced by lateral straggle of the dopant occurring from the high-energy implant step.[112] Since the latter effect results in approximately ~25% less lateral dopant spread, this also contributes to smaller isolation spacing design rules, and thus reduced chip size.

6.2.1.9 Strip the Masking Nitride/Pad-Oxide Layer.

Following field oxidation, the masking layer is removed. For several reasons, this removal process must be optimized (and during manufacture, carefully controlled) in CMOS technologies smaller than 2.0 μm.

First, since 20-30 nm of the top of the nitride is converted to SiO_2 (and oxynitride) during field oxidation, the removal of the nitride must in fact begin with a step to remove this layer. (The very top surface actually consists of a layer of approximately stoichiometric SiO_2. Beneath this is an oxynitride region that is graded in composition from SiO_2 to Si_3N_4 i.e., SiO_xN_y.) If wet chemical removal of the nitride is used, an HF "deglaze" step is first usually used to remove the SiO_2/mixed SiO_xN_y layer. (Note also that vapor HF is reportedly replacing wet HF deglaze processes in some advanced processes.[24]) Hot (180°C) phosphoric acid (H_3PO_4) is then used to etch the remaining nitride. The etch rates of SiO_2 in 5% HF, 0.5% HF and hot H_3PO_4, respectively are 293±73, 70±17, <1 Å/min. The etch rates of silicon nitride in these same chemicals are, respectively, 8, nil, and 50 Å/min. This indicates that etching in hot phosphoric acid offers excellent selectivity with respect to the underlying oxide and considerable overetching during this step can be used.[25]

However, during the deglaze step, the HF also etches the field oxide. Thus, an optimum deglaze etch time must be established. (If the deglaze does not completely remove the oxynitride layer, the remaining residue may delay the onset of nitride etching by the H_3PO_4 - as hot H_3PO_4 is ineffective at removing oxide. As a result, the nitride may not all be removed in the nominal time allotted for the nitride stripping process. Such inadequate removal of the nitride can sometimes result in scrapping of wafer lots. On the other hand, too long a deglaze step will excessively etch the field oxide.) To assist in the development of an optimal deglaze process, a thorough characterization of the material properties of the nitride film after field oxidation should thus be conducted.

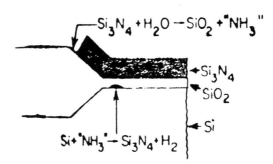

Fig. 6-20 Kooi's model for explaining nitride growth under the gate oxide.[26] Reprinted by permission of the publisher, The Electrochemical Society, Inc.

If a dry process is used to remove the oxidized nitride, the variation in the etch rates of the two layers must still be taken into account when choosing the etching conditions. The oxynitride layer generally etches more slowly than the underlying nitride. The amount of field oxide removed during this dry etch step also must be considered.

After stripping the nitride, the pad oxide must also be removed, so that a gate oxide can be grown over the active device regions. The etchant used to remove the pad oxide will also attack the field oxide, hence the conditions of this step must also be carefully determined and controlled. In fact, the field-oxide thickness-reduction is cumulative to the deoxidation of the nitride layer, the removal of the pad oxide, and removal of the sacrificial gate oxide (see next section). Typically, 100-200 nm of field oxide may be removed by the sum of these three etching steps. Some of the thinner part of the bird's beak will also be removed, reducing lateral oxide penetration.

6.2.1.10 Regrow Sacrificial Pad Oxide and Strip (Kooi Effect).

During the growth of the field oxide, another phenomenon occurs that can cause defects later when the gate oxide is grown. Kooi et al., discovered that a thin layer of silicon nitride can form on the silicon surface (i.e., at the pad-oxide/silicon interface) close to the border of the active regions, as a result of the reaction between the oxidizing species (O_2 or H_2O) and the silicon nitride (Fig. 6-20).[26] That is, NH_3 (or some other NH compound or nitrogen) is generated from the reaction between H_2O and the masking nitride during the field-oxidation step. This NH_3 then diffuses through the oxide and reacts with the silicon substrate to form silicon-nitride spots or ribbon (these regions are also sometimes called *white ribbon* because they have this appearance when viewed under an optical microscope due to light scattering, see Fig. 6-21). Under the field oxide the reaction of NH_3 with Si would not be very effective due to competition with the oxidation reaction of H_2O with Si. However, at some distance from the field oxide edge, under the nitride mask, the concentration of H_2O might be assumed to be low enough to allow an effective nitridation reaction to occur. This would allow some silicon nitride (or possibly, silicon oxynitride with oxidation masking capability), to form. Direct observation of this masking layer by transmission electron microscopy has also been reported.[139]

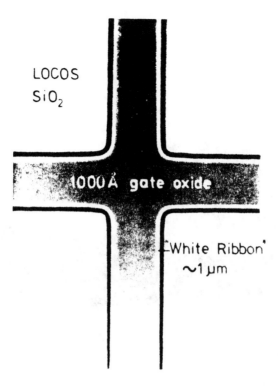

Fig. 6-21 Top view of a LOCOS structure with a "white ribbon" effect.[6] (© 1991 IEEE).

When the nitride mask and pad oxide layer are removed, there is a possibility that the nitride ribbon would remain present. When the gate oxide is subsequently grown, the growth rate becomes impeded at the locations where such silicon nitride remains. The gate oxide is thus thinner at these locations than elsewhere (Fig. 6-22), giving rise to problems of low-voltage breakdown of the gate oxide. One way to overcome this problem would be to etch the pad oxide long enough to also ensure that the ribbon is removed. Unfortunately, too much field oxide is removed at the same time.

Instead, the most widely method to eliminate the white ribbon problem is to grow a wet "sacrificial" gate oxide (typically 25 - 50 nm thick) after stripping the masking nitride and pad oxide. This sacrificial oxide layer is removed by wet etching before growing the final gate oxide.[27,28] The chemical removal of the sacrificial oxide will again consume part of the field oxide and, as noted above, must likewise be optimized.

A double sacrificial-oxide process has also been reported. Its benefit is a smoother active-area silicon surface on which the final gate oxide is grown. This results in smaller gate leakage currents (due to the onset of Fowler-Nordheim tunneling at higher fields), a lower interface state density, and a lower gate-oxide defect density.[29]

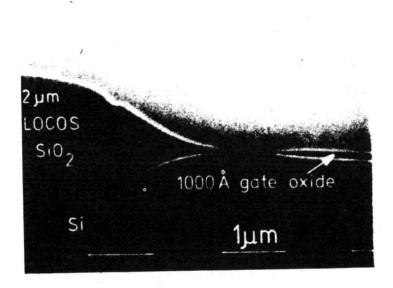

Fig. 6-22 SEM picture of a cross-section of a LOCOS structure with a "white ribbon" effect.[6] (© 1991 IEEE).

6.2.2. Planarizing Semirecessed LOCOS Structures

As described in chap. 4, Vol. 2, very planar surfaces are required for accurate lithography and for implementing multilevel interconnects in submicron ICs. However, semi-recessed LOCOS structures produce non-planar conditions (i.e., smooth steps) on the wafer surface. LOCOS structures modified to reduce bird's beak (such as PBL described in section 6.4), produce topographies with steeper steps than conventional LOCOS (even though the step heights are comparable). To return the wafer surface to a flat condition after semi-recessed LOCOS, efforts have been made to planarize semi-recessed LOCOS structures.

One example of such a planarization scheme is shown in Fig. 6-23.[15] A mask stack consisting of a 50 nm oxynitride pad layer and a 100 nm nitride film is first formed. An 800 nm field oxide is grown. Prior to planarization (by RIE etchback), a 200 nm thick layer of CVD oxide is deposited to fill the gaps between the nitride edge and field oxide (Fig. 6-23d). Then, when the field oxide is etched back, the gap will not be etched into the remaining planarized field oxide structure. (Fig. 6-23e). This procedure is reported to produce bird's beak free field oxide for thicknesses below 500 nm.

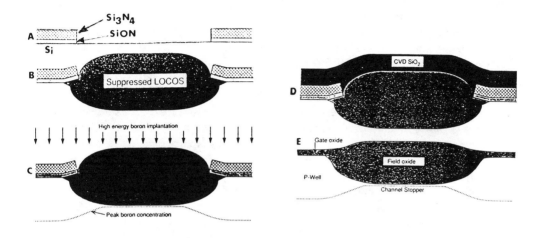

Fig. 6-23 A scheme to planarize semi-recessed LOCOS. In this example SLOCOS is combined with a high energy ion implantation scheme to provide channel stoppers and retrograde wells to make high density CMOS devices.[15] (© 1987 IEEE).

6.3 MODELING THE TOPOGRAPHY OF LOCOS STRUCTURES

For the case of 1-D oxidation, it is possible to accurately simulate oxide growth under virtually all practical conditions. When oxidation occurs in two dimensions, (e.g., "bird's beak" growth beneath the nitride-mask edge in LOCOS), simulation of oxide growth is more difficult. Complexities associated with 2-D oxidation include: (1) nonplanar geometries; (2) moving boundaries; and (3) volume expansion arising from the formation of new oxide at the Si surface. In the latter effect, the newly formed oxide expands and pushes out the old oxide, which rearranges itself through viscous flow.

Nevertheless, both empirical and physically based models have been developed to provide two-dimensional simulations of oxide growth in LOCOS structures. (Some process simulators such as SUPREM IV contain both types, and the user is able to select the desired model for a particular simulation). The *physical models* solve the complete set of differential equations governing both the oxide growth and the simultaneous viscous flow. Although such models can give accurate results, they are complex and require long computation times. The *empirical models* – which are expressed in terms of relatively simpler analytical functions – involve much less computational effort.

6.3.1 Empirical Models of 2-D Thermal Oxidation

Empirical models have been implemented to simulate the "bird's beak" of LOCOS structures. The 2-D model in SUPRA for local oxidation uses an empirically determined shape function, based on such input parameters as pad-oxide thickness, silicon-nitride thickness, oxidation temperature, and pressure. That is, the contour of the "bird's beak" is approximated with a complementary-error function whose parameters are defined by the particular LOCOS process conditions. The empirical model in Stanford's SUPREM IV is essentially the same as that used in SUPRA.

Another empirical model that also treats semi-recessed LOCOS oxide shapes was developed by Guillemot et al. and has been incorporated in the TSUPREM-4 simulator, available from TMA, Inc.[30] This model again uses a simple parametric relationship that is based on the analysis of experimental data. It characterizes the bird's beak by three main parameters: (1) the bird's beak length l_{bb}; (2) the extent the nitride edge has been lifted, H_2, and the depth of the bird's beak below the surface at the nitride edge, H_1. It also classifies the shapes of the bird's beaks that occur in semi-recessed LOCOS into two groups, depending on the stress exerted by the nitride masks (Fig. 6-24): (1) If the nitride layer is relatively thin, low mask stress exists and smooth birds-beak shapes occur (Case 1 in Fig. 6-24). For such shapes, two analytical complementary-error functions are used to fit the oxide contours: one for the oxide-silicon interface, and the other for the oxide-nitride interface. In Case 2, the nitride layer is thicker and the pad layer thinner. This causes stronger mask stresses, in which case the oxide becomes "pinched" beneath the nitride edge. Therefore, two functions are used to simulate the bird's beak contours at each interface: one on the left side of the pinch and the other on the right side. Figure 6-25 shows that in each case the bird's beak shape predicted by the simulation closely duplicates the shapes observed in SEM photos.

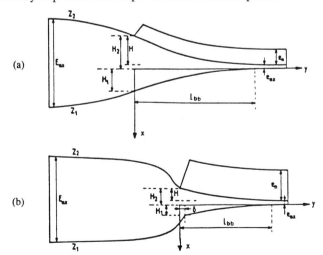

Fig. 6-24 The two shapes of the bird's beak with characteristic lengths (E_{ox}, l_{bb}, and H) and processing parameters (ε_{ox} and ε_n). (a) Shape 1 and (b) shape 2.[30] (© 1987 IEEE).

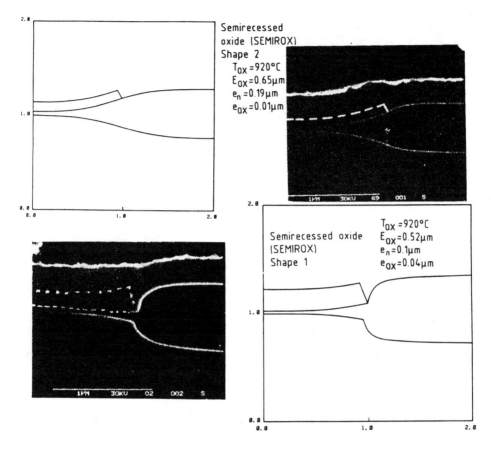

Fig. 6-25 Comparison between experimental and simulated field oxide shapes.[30] (© 1987 IEEE).

6.3.2 Physically Based Models of 2-D Oxidation

As mentioned above, the physically based models of 2-D oxidation solve the equations of the Deal-Grove linear-parabolic model (or the equivalent steady-state diffusion model) and at the same time account for the volumetric expansion due to oxide formation and viscous flow. The viscous-flow phenomenon was first quantitatively studied by Eer Nisse, using silicon wafers that had a thermal-oxide film on only one side.[46] Since the thermal-expansion coefficient of SiO_2 differs from that of silicon, the wafer was bowed when the oxidation temperature was less than 960°C. If the temperature was increased above 960°C, however, the wafers remained flat, which suggests that the stress due to thermal mismatch was relieved by the viscous flow of the oxide.

The first physically based model of 2-D oxidation that became available in a public-domain simulator was designed to handle LOCOS processes and was incorporated in the

Stanford Oxidation Analysis Program (SOAP).[31] It assumed that the growing SiO_2 films behave like viscous fluids that flow when the thermal-oxidation temperature exceeds 960°C, with the viscosity of the oxide determined by the curvature of the wafers. The viscosity of thermally grown SiO_2 films decreases exponentially with increasing temperature. Above 960°C the oxide may flow with relatively little viscous resistance.[32]

The oxidation process is modeled by assuming that two mechanisms occur: (1) oxidant diffuses through the SiO_2 to the SiO_2/Si interface, and (2) the oxide flows due to the volume expansion and associated stress buildup. The oxidant diffusion in the SOAP model is described by a generalized diffusion equation (rather than by the flux-conservation equations of the 1-D model given in Volume 1, chapter 7):

$$D \nabla^2 C = \frac{\partial C}{\partial t} \cong 0 \qquad (6 - 1)$$

The boundary conditions for this equation for LOCOS structures are nonhomogeneous, and hence cause the oxidant distribution to be different from place to place along the silicon/oxide interface. The volume-expansion rate therefore also varies with position. The flow of the oxide is described by a simplified Navier-Stokes equation as

$$\mu \nabla^2 V = \nabla P \qquad (6 - 2)$$

where μ, V, and P are the viscosity, the velocity, and the pressure of the oxide, respectively. To model the localized oxide structures well, one needs information on the mechanical properties of the materials used in LOCOS processing, namely SiO_2 and Si_3N_4.

The goal of simulating 2-D-oxidation is to determine the position of the oxide boundaries at the conclusion of the oxide-growth cycle. Since these boundaries are continuously moving, it is very difficult to obtain this information from the above equations. The SOAP program incorporates a boundary-value numerical technique to solve the integral form of Eqs. 6-1 and 6-2 by using Green's function. Details of this method are given in reference 31.

Figure 6-26 shows the simulation of two semirecessed LOCOS field oxides using SOAP. In Fig. 6-26a, the nitride mask is 25 nm thick. Since the stress is small, the oxide moves in a direction normal to the interface throughout its entire growth. In Fig. 6-26b the nitride mask is much thicker (175 nm), and it thus prevents the oxide from moving normal to the interface by forcing it to move laterally during growth. The compressive stress due to the thicker nitride film reduces oxide growth by making the SiO_2 flow toward the open surface.

At temperatures below 960°C, oxides no longer exhibit viscous behavior, but instead deform as nonlinear viscoelastic materials. This has consequences for mechanical stress and bird's beak. Another model must therefore be used to treat such conditions. Such a model was developed by Kao et al. and has been incorporated into SUPREM IV.[33, 34] This model takes into account the stresses that build up in the growing oxide film and how such stresses impact the growth rate. Experimental evidence to support the model shows that these stresses cause the oxide to grow most slowly at concave corners. The more general nature of this model allows it to simulate the growth of oxide in trenches as well as in LOCOS processes. Figure 6-27 shows a SUPREM IV simulation of an oxide grown in a trench in dry oxygen for 240 minutes at 950°C.[34] Thinning of the oxide in the lower corners is predicted for this structure. In addition, the stresses induced by growing oxide will be lower at higher temperatures. This implies that bird's beak dimensions will then be smaller, because the nitride edge can more successfully resist lifting if the oxide can flow aside.   Figure 6-28 compares the bird's beak length and edge lifting of various experimental LOCOS structures with simulation results obtained using SUPREM-IV. Relatively good agreement is displayed.

CREEP is another physically based 2-D oxidation simulator developed to incorporate the stress effects associated with the growth of thermal SiO_2.[35,36] This simulator incorporates a modified form of Kao's 2-D thermal-oxidation model. The major change from the earlier model is the use of a shear-stress-dependent viscosity model in lieu of the hydrostatic-stress-dependent model. CREEP simulations of 2-D oxide thicknesses on both convex and concave cylindrical silicon structures over a wide range of temperatures and curvature conditions show better agreement with experimental

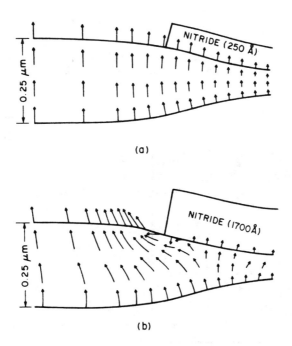

(a)

(b)

Fig. 6-26 Two-dimensional oxide growth simulated using SOAP with (a) a thin nitride (25 nm) masking layer, and (b) a thicker (170 nm) nitride masking layer.[31] (© 1983 IEEE).

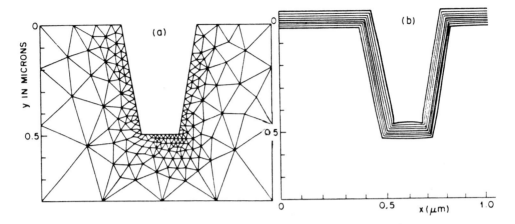

Fig. 6-27 Oxidation of a trench structure using SUPREM IV. (a) Initial grid. (b) Final oxide profile.[136]

measurements than do simulations based on previous models. The model used indicates that the effect of stress during oxidation on the linear-growth-rate constant dominates the two-dimensional profile-shape evolution.

Figure 6-29a shows the CREEP simulation of an oxide grown on a vertical step in wet oxygen for 3 minutes at 1000°C. This simulation clearly predicts the thinning of the oxide in the lower and upper corners of the step, as is observed in experimentally

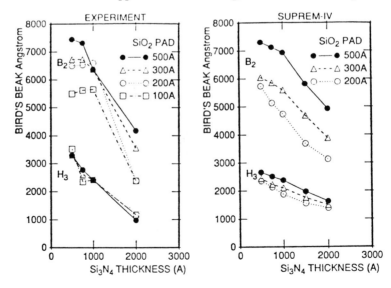

6-28 Comparison of SUPREM-IV simulations to parameterized data on LOCOS structures.[3] (© 1990 IEEE). Experimental data is from Bassous.[135]

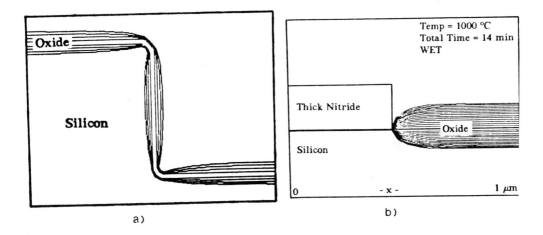

Fig. 6-29 (a) CREEP simulation of an oxide grown on a vertical step in wet oxygen for 3 minutes at 1000°C. (b) CREEP simulation of a SILO process using a 2-nm-thick pad oxide, a thick nitride mask, and an oxide-growth temperature of 1000°C.[35] (© 1986 IEEE).

grown oxides on trench structures. Figure 6-29b shows a CREEP simulation of a SILO process using a 2-nm-thick pad oxide, a thick nitride mask, and an oxide-growth temperature of 1000°C. CREEP is also capable of calculating the stress along the SiO$_2$/Si interface as a function of time and to simulate reflow of deposited oxides.

Oxidation-induced stress in LOCOS structures have been calculated by Isomae et al.,[37] and others.[123] Compressive stress in the bird's beak region is presumed to cause retardation of the oxidation rate (both the oxidant diffusion and the interface oxidation rate may be impacted) and thus influence the bird's beak shape. It is also reported that plastic deformation is initiated at the edge of the nitride mask, and expands into the silicon substrate as oxidation proceeds.[123]

6.3.3. Simulating Thermal Oxidation in 3-D Using Physical Models

Earlier we discussed that corners in the patterns of the mask stack can have a significant effect on the length of bird's beak: longer bird's beak arises at convex corners and shortened bird's beak at concave corners. Simulations with 3-D thermal oxide simulators confirm this effect. Results of 3-D numerical simulations with the aid of a supercomputer and the 3-D process simulator SMART-P[38] have been published by Unimoto and Odanaka.[39] In 3-D calculations of the stress in LOCOS structures, they assume elastic beam bending of the edges of the nitride mask during local oxidation though, as discussed earlier, according to Griffin[23] this may not be totally correct. Their simulation of the corner effects mentioned above quantitatively considered two factors: (1) the stress distribution in the LOCOS oxide; and (2) the local flux of oxidant. Figure 6-30 shows an example of calculations around corners in semi-recessed oxide patterns. In the case of a square "hole" structure (oxidation mask surrounded by LOCOS), the formation of bird's beak is significantly enhanced at the corners of the hole because the stress at the corners is lower and the flux of oxidant is larger at such a 270° corner. In the case of a "LOCOS island" structure, with concave (90°) corners, it is more difficult to bend the nitride edge at the corners, resulting in enlarged pressure at these locations. Hence, the bird's beak is reduced there.

These 3-D simulations also support the idea that it is important to limit the bending of the nitride edge by making the mask sufficiently thick in submicron isolation structures. That is, Odanaka's simulations confirmed that at the end of long, narrow (<2 μm-wide) nitride lines the bird's beak can be surprisingly long because the nitride edge can be easily lifted at such locations.

Another report studied the sensitivity of the bird's beak profile to variations in the

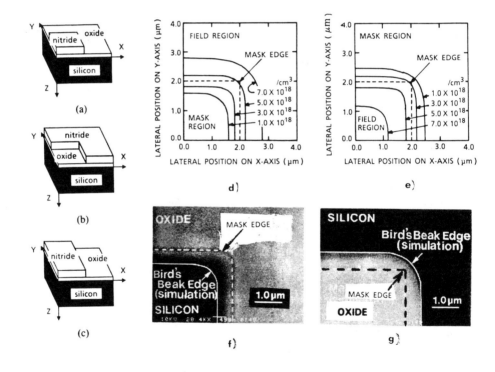

Fig. 6-30 Three typical nitride mask structures before field oxidation: (a) hole structure; (b) island structure; and (c) line structure. Calculated position of the bird's beak edge: (d) hole structure; (e) island structure. Top view SEMs of LOCOS structure after nitride and pad oxide stripping: (f) Hole structure; (g) Island structure. Solid and dashed lines show the bird's beak edge and the mask edge by simulation, respectively.[38] (© IEEE 1988).

active pattern geometries.[122] They used experimental data of bird's beak heights and widths for various active pattern widths for conventional LOCOS, poly-buffered LOCOS and PELOX (described in section 6.4). They also compared the data to simulation of the bird's beak profile obtain from SUPREM4 simulations.

6.4   POLY-BUFFERED LOCOS

To reduce the undesirable encroachment of bird's beak, various semirecessed- and fully-recessed LOCOS bird's-beak compaction schemes have been developed, including *polybuffered-LOCOS* (PBL), SILO, SWAMI, and OSELO. These have allowed LOCOS-based isolation structures to continue to be used in MOS ICs down to 0.6 μm. Of the above structures, we elect to discuss only PBL here, as it appears to be the most widely adopted LOCOS-based isolation structure for 1.0-0.5 μm ICs. (An example of a study favorably comparing PBL to SILO is given in ref. 40.) SILO (*sealed-interface local oxidation*) relies on interface sealing and SWAMI (*sidewall masked isolation*) on sidewall masking to reduce bird's beak to almost zero. However, these approaches are less attractive than PBL because they are susceptible to defect formation leading to either excessive diode leakage or gate-oxide degradation. SWAMI also involves a much more complicated process sequence. Fabrication details of these and other LOCOS-based structures can be found in Vol. 2, chap. 2.

All bird's-beak compaction schemes exploit the fact that a thinner pad oxide and a thicker nitride produce a shorter bird's beak. As the pad oxide is reduced and the nitride layer thickened, increasingly greater stresses arise during field oxidation. In conventional LOCOS structures this will eventually lead to defects in the silicon. In PBL, however, a polysilicon layer is deposited on the pad oxide before depositing the nitride layer. The polysilicon absorbs some of the stress produced during field oxidation, permitting the use of a thinner pad oxide and a thicker nitride film without the producing defects. A typical mask stack in a PBL process (Fig. 6-31a) consists of a very thin pad oxide (8-10-nm), an LPCVD poly layer (40-60 nm), and a thicker LPCVD nitride layer (e.g., 180-250 nm).[41,42,43]

PBL exhibits two other significant advantages. First, the dependence of bird's beak length on mask stack geometry discussed in section 6.2.1.7 appears to be less severe than in conventional LOCOS. A study of the mask geometry effects on bird's beak in PBL structures by Wils et al., reports this conclusion.[44] Second, the white ribbon problem seems to be mitigated by the PBL approach. The underside of the nitride mask is shielded from oxidation and thus less NH_3 is produced. With less NH_3 available, there is less propensity to form Si_3N_4 on the Si surface under the gate oxide.

A detailed explanation of how the poly provides stress relief is given in Ref. 45, but briefly, the poly apparently gets squeezed out of the edge of the mask stack by compressive forces arising from volume expansion (caused by the bird's beak oxide growth) and the rigidity of the thick top nitride. The small-grained nature of the poly allows some of it to be squeezed out, thereby relaxing the stress that would otherwise be applied to the silicon substrate. The subsequent oxidation of this squeezed-out poly also produces a feature on the field oxide named a *crab-eye*. Such features have been observed

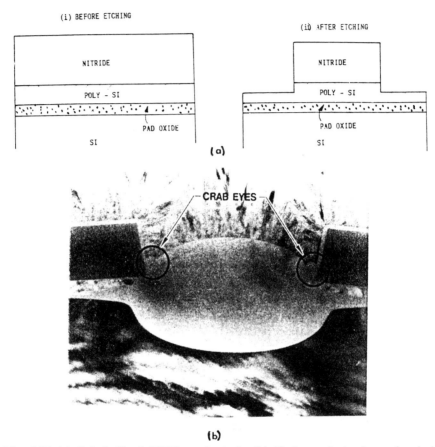

Fig. 6-31 (a) Poly-buffer LOCOS mask stack. (b) 'Crab eyes' at edges of poly-buffer LOCOS.[45] Reprinted by permission of the publisher. The Electrochemical Society.

in field oxides grown using PBL mask stacks (Fig. 6-31b). The formation of the crab-eye thereby also retards the oxidation rate near the mask edge by providing a longer oxide path to the substrate for the oxidizing species. As a result, the degree of lateral oxidation (which is responsible for bird's beak), is even further reduced. Conventional PBL processes yield a bird's beak of only 0.2-0.3 μm/side for field oxides of 400-600 nm thickness (compared to 0.5 μm per side for LOCOS). Leakage currents of the n^{+}-p junction comparable to those of a conventional LOCOS process are reported, provided the bird's beak penetration is not reduced below ~0.3 μm per side.

Reference 46 provides an extensive description of a PBL isolation technology optimized for an 0.8-μm CMOS process. By carrying out a full-factorial experimental plan the effects on defect formation, bird's-beak penetration, and isolation-leakage currents as a result of varying the pad-oxide-layer and nitride-layer thicknesses were studied. An additional description of a conventional PBL technology developed for a high-volume 0.8 μm CMOS process is given in ref. 47. Included is a discussion of how this process can be enhanced to provide wider manufacturing process-latitude. These reports also address some of the issues unique to the fabrication of PBL structures, including:

1. Special precautions should be taken to minimize oxidation of the poly layer prior to the deposition of the nitride layer (such as inserting the wafers into the nitride deposition tube more rapidly than the usual ~25 cm/min, and allowing no wet chemical cleanups of the poly between poly and nitride deposition). The presence of a significant poly-oxide layer obstructs the removal of the sandwich layers after field oxidation, and provides a more efficient path for lateral oxidation - leading to enhanced bird's beak encroachment.

2. When the PBL stack layer is patterned, it may be desired to leave approximately one-half of the poly layer (as well as the pad oxide layer) unetched. The remaining poly-plus-pad-oxide film serves as a screen layer to minimize damage and contamination during the channel-stop implant. The poly remaining on the pad oxide in the field regions is oxidized during the field oxidation step;

3. After field oxidation, the removal of the PBL stack is similar to the removal of the mask stack in conventional LOCOS, with two exceptions:

a. It has been reported that the action of the H_3PO_4 with respect to nitride etching is inconsistent when a poly layer is below the nitride. This can lead to inadequate removal of the nitride, and may even lead to scrapping wafer lots.[25]

b. The poly layer must be carefully stripped. In ref. 38, the poly is dry-etched in a manner that leaves the pad-oxide intact. The pad-oxide is then removed in a 10% HF solution, with a lengthy overetch used to remove a portion of the bird's beak that penetrates under the nitride. This reduces the final bird's beak encroachment to ~0.13 μm. In ref. 48, the removal of the poly by dry etching and by steam oxidation (followed by wet etching in HF) was studied. MOS capacitors fabricated after dry-etch removal of the poly showed worse gate-oxide endurance under high-field stressing than did those in which the poly was removed by steam oxidation.

c. In two other reports, wet stripping of the nitride/poly mask layers was compared with an all dry stripping process.[128,138] It was found that the gate oxides grown after the dry process exhibited worse oxide integrity behavior than those grown after the wet strip was performed. This degradation was blamed on damage (in the form of increased interface states in the substrate) created in the silicon substrate.

4. Voids can occur in the polysilicon layer, during field oxide growth (Fig. 6-32). In ref. 49 Lin et al, propose that these voids arise by a Kooi-like effect (see section 6.2.1.9) that causes nitridation of some of the poly grains, and oxidation of others during field oxide growth. They argue that the nitrided poly grains are removed when the nitride is stripped in hot H_3PO_4, resulting in voids in the poly along the mask stack edges. After the nitride is stripped, the oxided grains remain behind as a residue on the poly surface. If this residue is removed using dip in a weak (150:1) H_2O:HF solution, the etchant will also attack the pad oxide exposed by the poly voids. Then, when the poly is removed, the pad oxide may be breached, and the Si substrate attacked by the poly etch (assuming the selectivity of poly-to-SiO_2 is not high enough during poly removal). This will produce pits in the Si substrate. PBL isolation structures in which pitted substrates occur exhibit higher leakage currents than conventional LOCOS. It was suggested that the dip in weak HF be replaced with a short dry process that attacks the ribbon residue much faster than the pad oxide to prevent Si-substrate pitting.

Yang et al., however, observed that such voids occur in the poly before the nitride is removed, and also that they increase in density as the width of the active-area (nitride mask width) decreases.[50] A significant number of voids begin to appear when the width shrinks below 1.0 μm. Furthermore, as the nitride/poly thickness ratio is increased more voids are observed. Thus, it was

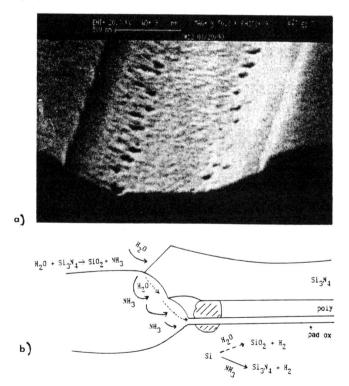

Fig. 6-32 Voids (or pits) are observed on polysilicon around the field oxide edge after nitride removal by hot phosphoric acid.[49] Reprinted by permission of the publisher. The Electrochemical Society.

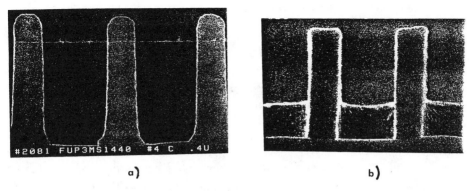

a)   b)

Fig. 6-33 "Microfoot" at the patterned resist/nitride interface: (a) Examples of 0.40 μm photoresist imaged over 2500Å nitride/500Å polysilicon/100Å pad oxide, in which the microfoot can be seen; (b) 0.40 μm lines imaged over 2000Å nitride/500Å polysilicon/100Å pad oxide. Microfoot does not occur. [129] This paper was originally presented at the Spring 1994 Meeting of the Electrochemical Society, Inc. held in San Francisco, CA.

proposed that the voids arise from stress between the nitride and poly layers. A thicker, narrower nitride feature does not bend upward as bird's beak oxide forms under the edges, producing more stress in the poly film. Yang postulates that the stress is relieved by void formation. It was also reported that voids were not observed if the oxidation temperatures exceeded 1000°C or if the poly deposition temperature was <500°C.

It has also been reported that some unique issues arise in patterning PBL mask layers. That is, standing waves introduced by the interaction of the nitride layer and photoresist can produce a "micro-foot" at the patterned resist/nitride interface (see Fig. 6-33a, which shows the presence of the micro-foot on resist features with 0.4 μm lines and spaces).[129] Because image variation and subsequent substrate etch profiles are critical in PBL processes to maintain and control active area encroachment, this foot must be eliminated. This is done by minimizing substrate reflectivity; i.e., by proper choice of the nitride film thickness. The substrate reflectivity is found to be a maximum when the nitride is 2500 Å thick, and a minimum when 2000 Å thick. Thus, use of a 2000 Å nitride film eliminates the micro-foot (as shown in Fig. 6-33b).

6.4.1. Modified PBL Processes

Several *modified* PBL processes have also been proposed. In the first, a thinner field oxide is grown, and the channel-stop implant is performed through this 220-nm-thick field oxide (Fig. 6-34).[51] The 100-keV boron implant that forms the channel stop also serves as the punchthrough implant in the active regions. Since the channel-stop implant is done after the field-oxide growth, much less boron encroachment occurs. In addition, a smaller field-oxide step is produced, thereby helping the planarity requirement. A thinner field-oxide region can be used because the process is designed for

0.7-μm (and smaller) device applications. At these short channel lengths, the doping of the substrate must be increased to prevent punchthrough. As a result, the dopant concentration of the channel stop also ends up being high enough to prevent field inversion, even with the use of such a thin field oxide.

6.4.1.1 Framed-Mask PBL (FMPBL).

Another advanced PBL process forms nitride spacers on the pad-oxide-poly-nitride stack after the nitride layer of the stack is patterned in the conventional PBL manner (Fig. 6-35).[52,53] These spacers are formed by depositing a second 1000Å-thick nitride layer and performing an anisotropic etch which stops on the underlying poly layer. Since the nitride spacers frame the masking stack (and also reduce the field isolation width to dimensions smaller than can be achieved lithographically), this process has been named *framed mask PBL* (FMPBL). Field encroachment of FMPBL isolation can be reduced by increasing the width of the nitride sidewall or the thickness of nitride-II, as opposed to increasing thickness of nitride-I (which has the potential for defect generation at high stress). A field-oxide etch-back step can be used to further reduce field-oxide encroachment. FMPBL provides excellent isolation characteristics (e.g., nominal V_{TF} values>10V) down to isolation spacings of 0.8-μm.

A variation of the FMPBL approach called a *reverse L-shaped sealed PBL* (RLS-PBL) technology has recently been reported.[54] It provides comparable bird's beak encroachment to the FMPBL method, but with improved reverse leakage currents of NMOS submicron devices. In this process the pad oxide of the (pad oxide/poly/nitride-1) mask stack is laterally undercut by 300-500 Å using a 15:1 HF etch for several minutes as a part of

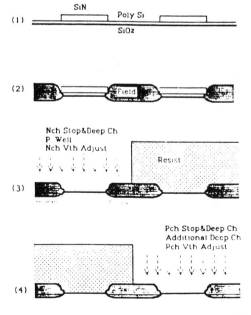

Fig. 6-34 Process flow of Advanced Poly Silicon Pad LOCOS (APPL).[51] (© 1988 IEEE).

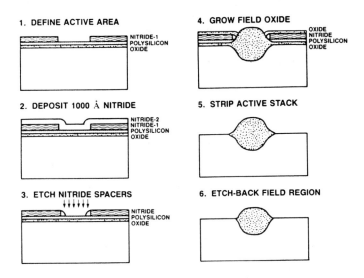

Fig. 6-35 Process flow for the advanced or etched-back FMPBL isolation scheme.[53] (© 1991 IEEE).

the mask stack patterning method (Fig. 6-36). The exposed portions of Si including the undercut portions were reoxidized to grow a very thin oxide as a new buffer layer. Next,

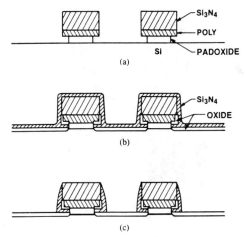

Fig. 6-36 Reverse L-shape sealed PBL process flow: (a) formation of side etched portions of pad oxide; (b) sealed nitride film deposition; and (c) RIE nitride etch. The pad oxide (100Å), polysilicon film (500Å), nitride cap (2000Å), and regrown oxide (60Å) are not shown to scale.[54] (© 1990 IEEE).

a thin (500 Å) LPCVD SiN film is deposited over the whole surface (nitride-2). The conformally deposited SiN layer also fills the etched portions of the pad oxide film (Fig. 6-36b). Finally, nitride spacers are formed by anisotropic etching of the nitride-2 film (Fig. 6-36c, which also shows the L-shaped nature of these interface-sealing spacers). Following a 600-nm field oxide growth virtually no bird's beak is observed. It is conjectured that this approach results in reduced transistor and diode leakage currents because the stresses created in the silicon lattice are absorbed by the polysilicon film which is sandwiched between the nitride and pad oxide via the specially designed L-shaped sealed nitride spacer.

An advanced form of the RLS-PBL technology, reportedly suitable for devices with 0.3 μm dimensions (e.g., 256-Mbit DRAM cells), was recently described, called PBR-LOCOS (Fig. 6-37).[55] During the mask-stack etch, the Si substrate is also aniso-tropically etched to a depth of 25-200 nm. Then, the exposed sides of the pad oxide (SRO-1) are selectively etched to form lateral undercuts of 30 nm using buffered HF. The exposed Si substrate and polysilicon surfaces are reoxidized to form a new stress-relief oxide (SRO-2), which extends into the lateral undercut areas as well. Next, a thin nitride layer is deposited and etched so that it remains on the sidewalls of the stack and

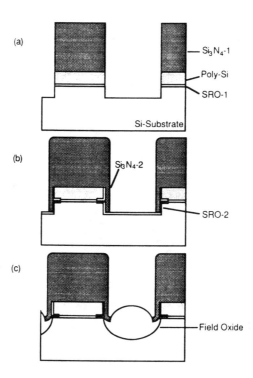

(a) — Si_3N_4-1
— Poly-Si
— SRO-1
Si-Substrate

(b) Si_6N_4-2
— SRO-2

(c) — Field Oxide

Fig. 6-37 PBR LOCOS process sequence. (a) After recess etching. (b) After nitride sidewall formation. (c) Field oxidation.[55] (© 1992 IEEE).

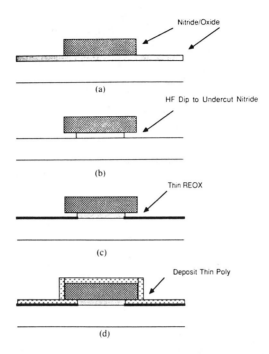

Fig. 6-38 PELOX process flow: (a) RIE nitride; (b) HF dip to undercut nitride and form cavity; (c) grow reoxidation; (d) deposit polysilicon encapsulation layer.[56] (© 1991 IEEE).

the trenched Si areas (SiN-2). Field oxide is then grown. Using PBR-LOCOS, bird's beak encroachment is reportedly suppressed to 0.15 μm for a 50 nm-deep Si trench. Junction leakage is almost identical to that of conventional semirecessed LOCOS and the punchthrough voltage of the parasitic field-oxide transistors exceeds 5V at isolation spacings of 0.3 μm. Furthermore, no anomalous leakage currents are observed in the subthreshold characteristics of MOS transistors formed using this technique, and gate oxide integrity in these devices is also excellent, implying that defect generation in the Si is not significant.

It has been noted that in the RLS-PBL approach the etching process that is used to form the nitride-2 spacers may represent a critical problem when attempting to implement this process. That is, the anisotropic nitride-spacer etch must stop on the nitride-1 layer of the mask stack, and thus there is no selectivity. A secondary concern is that the nitride-2 spacers will worsen the field thinning problem, as they will further narrow the spacing of the field oxide area.[133]

6.4.1.2 Polysilicon-Encapsulated LOCOS (PELOX).

Another variation of PBL, in which the poly layer does not extend over the entire pad-oxide/nitride interface is called *polysilicon-encapsulated local oxidation* (PELOX).[56,57] As shown in Fig. 6-38 the poly layer is "inserted" into a cavity between a thin pad-oxide layer (at the mask stack edges) and the nitride. That is, the initial mask consists of a conventional 50-nm-thick pad oxide and a 140-nm-thick CVD nitride. After patterning the nitride film, the uncovered pad-oxide layer is etched in diluted hydrofluoric acid. During this step, some of the pad oxide under the nitride is undercut, forming a cavity beneath the nitride edges that penetrates on each side to a depth of ~0.12 μm. Next, the exposed portions of the silicon are slightly re-oxidized. When a thin layer of poly (~300Å thick) is next deposited by CVD, it covers all the exposed surfaces, and fills the cavities under the nitride edges created when the original pad was undercut. Unlike the RLS-PBL process, no spacer-formation etch process is needed after the cavities have been filled. Instead, the wafers are transferred directly into the field-oxidation furnace. After the field oxide is grown, the oxidized polysilicon on top of the nitride mask is removed by wet etching, and finally the nitride mask is stripped.

By varying the thickness of the re-oxidized pad-oxide layer (called REOX in Fig. 6-38c), both the height and length of the bird's beak oxide may be minimized. The authors claim that if no re-oxidation is used, less than 0.1 μm bird's beak is observed. With 25 nm of regrown SiO_2 the bird's beak length is ~0.3 μm. Although some reoxidation is required to prevent defect formation in the silicon crystal, about 3 nm seems to be enough for this purpose. A second report combined PELOX with a shallow trench prior to growing the REOX pad layer and depositing the poly. The field oxide is more recessed than in either conventional-PBL or PELOX structures. Almost fully planar isolation with slightly larger encroachment than non-trenched PELOX was achieved with a 140 nm deep trench and 720 nm field oxide.[58] In addition, the small bird's beak in PELOX significantly reduces the degree of bird's beak punchthrough in 0.5 μm-wide active regions.

The enhanced field oxidation substrate recess of PELOX compared to conventional PBL also makes PELOX an attractive candidate for technologies smaller than 0.5 μm. That is, conventional PBL appears to be sufficiently robust for 0.8-0.5 μm technologies, but its susceptibility to field-oxide punchthrough at active spacings of ≤0.5 μm limits its ability to scale further.[59] On the other hand, PELOX, or nitride-clad-LOCOS (NCL) have been reported to be attractive candidates for 0.35 μm[132] and 0.25 μm CMOS processes, respectively.[133] The integration of PELOX into an existing PBL 1-MB DRAM baseline process is also described by Roth et al.[60]

6.4.1.3 Nitride-Clad LOCOS (NCL). Despite the fact that PELOX appears to be suitable for 0.35 μm CMOS technology, it has a problem that may prevent from being implemented in the next generation technology (i.e., 0.25 μm CMOS). That is, the oxidized poly mask layer must be stripped by a wet etch after the field oxide is grown. This etch steps thins down the field oxide, and may potentially degrade the isolation in narrow field regions.

To circumvent this difficulty, a modification to the PELOX process has been suggested that may be suitable for 0.25 μm CMOS.[134] That is, instead of using polysilicon to fill the oxide cavity under the nitride mask, very thin (~100Å thick) CVD-nitride-2 layer is deposited instead. Thus, the process has been dubbed *nitride-clad LOCOS* (NCL). Unlike in the RLS-PBL process, however, no nitride spacer-formation etch step is needed here. Instead, the wafers are immediately subjected to the field oxidation step. The thin nitride-2 layer is oxidized away during the initial portion of the field oxidation cycle. Then, only the relatively short etch step used in the conventional LOCOS process to remove the oxidized nitride is required prior to stripping the nitride (see section 6.2.1.9). Hence, less field oxide is removed in the NCL process, allowing it to be scaled to 0.25 μm technologies.

6.4.1.4 Mitigating the Field-Thinning Problem of LOCOS.

Recently, the field thinning problem has also been reported to be reduced in PBL by growing the field oxide under high pressure (HiPOX).[61,62,63] Field oxides were grown at 8-20 atm and 900-1000°C in steam with isolation spacings of 2.0-0.8 μm. Field oxide thinning as a function of decreasing isolation spacing was significantly reduced especially at 1000°C and 20 atm. Increases in nominal-V_{TF} of 30% were also observed in parasitic field MOSFETs in which $L = 1.0$ μm, compared to those in which the oxide was grown at 1 atm. Part of the V_{TFiso} increase was also attributed to the reduced encroachment of channel-stop boron during HiPOX field oxidation, since less time (at constant T) is needed to grow the same thickness of field oxide under HiPOX. Bird's beak length was also decreased by the HiPOX step.

Another technique for reducing the field thinning problem (and to reduce the encroachment of the field oxide at convex corners, as discussed in section 6.2.1.7) is to etch only the nitride layer of the PBL mask (i.e., leave the poly-buffer layer unetched) prior to the field oxidation growth step.[130] In addition, if a thinner field oxide (e.g., 150 nm thick) can be tolerated, these two effects are reduced in magnitude even further, especially if combined with the nitride-only etch approach.

6.5 SHALLOW TRENCH AND REFILL ISOLATION

Despite the advances made to decrease bird's beak and channel-stop encroachment in LOCOS isolation by PBL and other approaches, it appears that LOCOS-based techniques will eventually become inadequate for deep-submicron MOS technologies. The most probable successor to LOCOS in CMOS is the *shallow trench and refill* isolation structure. Here, a relatively shallow trench is first etched in the Si substrate (0.3-0.5 μm deep), and is then refilled with an insulator material (following a short thermal oxidation growth that is first grown on the trench walls to control the Si-SiO$_2$ interface quality). The surface is planarized after refill to complete the isolation structure.

Since bird's beak is entirely eliminated and channel-stop dopant redistribution is reduced, smaller isolation spacing is possible than with LOCOS. In addition, the structure is fully recessed, offering the potential of a completely planar surface. Furthermore, the problem of field-oxide thinning in narrow isolation spaces does not occur and the threshold voltage is constant as a function of channel width because of the elimination of the narrow-channel effect found in LOCOS (see chap. 5). Also, MOSFETs made with fully recessed oxide isolation exhibit larger g_m and smaller S_t values than those using semirecessed LOCOS. Finally, fully recessed structures with sharp lower corners provide improved isolation efficiency due to the so-called "corner effect."[64] That is, the field lines at the bottom corners of the trench spread out at the vicinity of the corner, leading to a higher threshold at the corners. Until the silicon surface at these corners is inverted, isolation is maintained.

Despite the impressive advantages of shallow trench isolation listed above, a variety of new difficulties associated with such structures have slowed their acceptance as replacements for LOCOS isolation. As we shall show, however, significant progress has recently been made toward overcoming these problems.

6.5.1. Early Shallow Trench and Refill Isolation

The earliest example of shallow-trench and refill is the so-called *buried-oxide* (or BOX) isolation technology. The original BOX technique (BOX-1) was introduced in 1981 (see Fig. 6-39i),[113] and an improved version was presented in 1983 (BOX-II, Fig. 6-39ii).[65] In the latter, shallow trenches (0.5-0.8 μm deep) are etched with an orientation-dependent Si etch to provide an inclination of the trench sidewalls of ~60°. Next a channel stop implant step is performed. (The inclination ensures that the sidewalls also receive sufficient doping during the channel stop implant step to prevent weak inversion of the sidewall Si surface. Thus, subthreshold leakage from source to drain along this parasitic conduction path is suppressed.) A thin thermal oxide (20-50 nm) is then grown to passivate the trench sidewalls. Next, CVD oxide is deposited to fill the trenches. This layer is etched back, leaving the oxide only in the recesses. Ideally, the top of the oxide

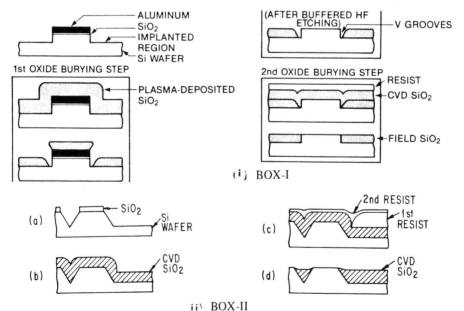

Fig. 6-39 (i) The BOX-I isolation process. (ii) The BOX-II isolation technique. (a) Si is etched using an oxide transfer mask. (b) Oxide is deposited by CVD. (c) Two layers of resist are applied, with the first being flowed. (d) The oxide is planarized using an RIE etchback technique which etches oxide and resist at the same rate.[65] (© 1983 IEEE).

should be level with the original silicon surface. Etchback was performed by eroding photoresist and SiO_2 at the same rate in a plasma (see chap. 4, Vol. 2). In the improved process, two layers of resist were applied, to try to produce a globally planarized surface prior to etchback. Active regions are those protected from etch when the trenches are formed.

These early BOX processes, however, exhibited several drawbacks, including:

1. Void formation occurred if the CVD oxide was deposited into 0.5 μm-wide trenches that are narrower than about 2 μm. However, more recently developed CVD-deposition processes have mitigated this problem.

2. Inversion of the silicon at the sidewalls of p-type active regions may occur, especially if vertical trench sidewalls are used to reduce the isolation spacing. This problem is made worse by boron segregation into the thin sidewall-passivating thermal oxide (which lowers its concentration at the sidewall surface, as discussed in following section, which defines isolation in CMOS and gives further details of this problem).

3. Despite complex planarization schemes, the early BOX processes were unable to yield adequately planar surfaces. (In particular, global planarity was poor.) More recently, new planarization approaches have been announced which may overcome this difficulty - e.g., chemical-mechanical polishing. Note that the topography of the trench-surface after etch should be smooth to enable a lower particle size detection limit and to provide a favorable surface for subsequent film nucleation.

4. This isolation structure can negatively impact the device operating behavior.[67,68,69,141] That is, in a conventional LOCOS-isolated MOSFET, a polysilicon gate that passes across the device will curve upward and away from the device once it reaches the isolation oxide, as shown in Fig. 6-40a. (This figure represents the cross section of the region under the gate of the MOSFET, where the source and drain of the device are situated above and beneath Fig. 6-40, which lies in the plane of the paper.) For this particular configuration of the polysilicon gate, the portion of the gate over the LOCOS region will have little effect upon the device behavior. Consequently, a simple 2-D simulation will give an adequate description of the behavior of the device, where the 2-D region is taken in the plane perpendicular to Fig. 6-40 and along the axis of the device, so that it includes the source and drain regions.

In the case of a shallow-trench-isolated MOSFET, the gate region runs flat across the isolation, as shown in Fig. 6-40b. Consequently, the part of the gate over the field region creates more of a two-dimensional fringing field on the corner and sidewall of the silicon mesa than in the LOCOS case of Fig. 6-40a. This establishes a *corner parasitic MOSFET* in parallel with the main device.[140] The parasitic device turns on at gate voltages lower than those required by the main channel, resulting in a "hump" in the drain current versus gate voltage

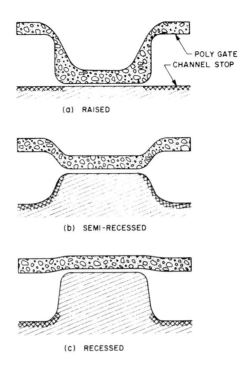

(a) RAISED

(b) SEMI-RECESSED

(c) RECESSED

Fig. 6-40 In (a) *grow-oxide-and-cut-window* isolation, and in (b) LOCOS isolation structures, the field oxide rises above substrate. (c) In trench isolation structures, the field oxide is flat with respect to the substrate surface (unless, if the trench oxide is overetched, a downward step exists at the edge of the active regions, see, for example Fig. 6-41).

subthreshold curves (Fig. 6-41). Thus, the parasitic device increases the subthreshold leakage current of the active device.

This effect becomes even stronger if the isolation region is partly etched below the silicon mesa top surface. Then, the gate wraps around the corner of the mesa as shown in Fig. 6-40c. Now the regions of the channel near the edges of the device will behave much differently than the region at the center of the mesa. Consequently, 3-D modeling is required to accurately simulate the device characteristics. Such simulations verify that the corner regions have lower threshold voltage than do the center regions of the device.

5. Thinning of the gate oxide at the trench edge is another concern. Thinned gate oxide not only degrades the gate oxide reliability but also worsens the parasitic device problem, since a thinner gate oxide increases the electric field strength at the trench corner.

6. Problems arose as result of the etchback step. That is, to ensure complete removal of the CVD SiO_2 from the active areas, the field oxide must be overetched by about 100 nm. The field oxide surface is then lower than active-area surface, causing a portion of the active-area sidewall to become exposed (Fig. 6-40c). This exacerbates the parasitic sidewall conduction described above, as well as to an enhanced inverse narrow-width effect (see chap. 5).

The combination of the above problems (especially the complex processing required to produce adequately planar surfaces), kept BOX isolation from displacing LOCOS-type isolation structures. However, the benefits offered by shallow-trench isolation are so attractive that work has proceeded to overcome the above problems. It appears highly likely that shallow-trench and refill isolation will become more widely adopted as dimensions approach 0.5 μm and smaller. Indeed, an isolation approach for NMOS that combined the best features of both BOX and LOCOS was reported by Fuse et al,[71] as is discussed in more detail in the following section.

6.5.2. Improved Shallow Trench and Refill Isolation Processes

Progress in overcoming the four major problems of early BOX isolation is summarized as follows:

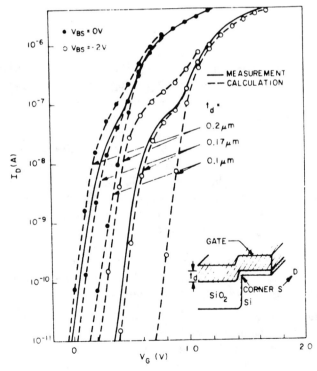

Fig. 6-41 Measured and simulated drain current versus gate potential for devices having a downward step in the field oxide (t_d).[66] (© 1981 IEEE).

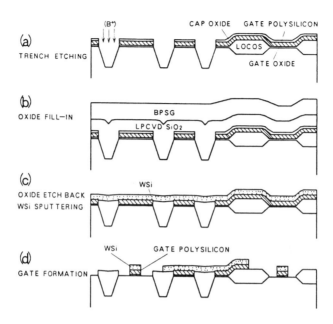

Fig. 6-42 Shallow trench process with tapered trenches.[70] (© IEEE 1992).

1. The problem of void formation when refilling narrow trenches with CVD SiO_2 has been ameliorated through the development of various advanced CVD techniques. Such CVD processes which exhibit less tendency to form void during trench filling include LPCVD TEOS, atmospheric-pressure ozone-TEOS, and various deposition-etchback approaches. A new shallow-trench process (Fig. 6-42) that produces tapered trenches by dry-etching with Cl_2 and N_2 gases (and which uses a cap oxide as a mask) attacks this problem from another direction.[70] Such tapered trenches can be more easily filled without void formation and the deposited dielectric can be planarized with less difficulty. However, the wider trenches have hollow tops (i.e., when the trench width is is greater than twice the depth), resulting in poor isolation characteristics in the resulting parasitic field transistors). Hence, the shallow tapered trench isolation structures are used only for small isolation spaces (<0.6 μm), with wider spaces being isolated using LOCOS structures. Film stress of the trench-fill dielectrics must also be smaller (<200 MPa) than in intermetal dielectric films, due to the use of thicker films.

2. Several approaches have been developed to overcome the inability to adequately planarize the surface through etchback. One involves the use of a block mask, whose function is to allow LOCOS oxide to be grown in wide isolation regions (see chap. 4, Vol. 2 for a discussion of complete global planarization through the use of a block mask). After employing the block mask, a variety of methods involving CVD deposition and etchback are used to planarize the remaining narrow isolation spaces. Many of these methods followed the early BOX methods of conventional resist etchback, but one novel technique used a thin SiO_2 layer (sputter deposited at low temperature) between double photoresists (the SiO_2 layer acts as an etchback layer) and a polysilicon film above active regions (as an etchback buffer). This process is called *planarization with resist/oxide/resist and polysilicon* (PRORPS).[71] Another technique used LOCOS to fill the wide spaces in the trench and spin-on-glass SOG to fill the narrow spaces. Three or four layers of SOG were spun on to get good planarization.[72] All of the above, however, are complex processes. A relatively new planarization method called chemical-mechanical polishing has been applied to this problem, as is discussed in subsequent paragraphs.

3. As described above, the subthreshold characteristics of narrow MOSFETs (e.g., 0.5 μm wide) isolated by refilled shallow- trench structures are sensitive to the shape of trench upper corner shape.[73] The edges of the silicon mesa at the upper corners are turned on by the portion of the gate that overlaps such corner regions (see also section 5.2.2). This edge effect becomes even stronger if the isolation region is partly eroded away, in which case the gate wraps around the corner of the device as shown in Fig. 6-40c. The optimum condition for the shallow trench isolation structure is thus a gate that runs flat across the isolation, requiring a planar surface prior to poly deposition. A process utilizing RIE etchback followed by a chemical-mechanical polishing step offers the ability to produce a highly planar surface after etchback. The top shape exhibits virtually no step. However, single wafer processing with *in situ* control of the CMP process is likely to be needed to obtain the exact surface required.

4. Inversion of trench sidewalls. This problem and techniques to overcome it are described in section 6.6.

A shallow trench isolation (STI) process incorporating the above improvements is described by Fazan and Mathews.[121] They project that this isolation approach will be feasible for DRAM generations as dense as 4 Gbits (minimum feature size of 0.12 μm). Another trench process that uses trenches with sloped sidewalls and CMP for etchback is described by Deleonibus.[127] Finally, Inowaka describes how a shallow-trench isolation process (with a minimum trench width of 0.28 μm) is applied to a 0.2 μm CMOS technology.[120]

6.6 CMOS ISOLATION TECHNOLOGY

In CMOS ICs isolation must exist not only between *like* kinds of devices (e.g., between two n-channel transistors or two p-channel transistors within a given well or within the substrate region) but also between devices of *opposite* polarity (e.g., between p- and n-channel devices separated by at least one well). The isolation of like kind of devices involves the same techniques used to isolate the devices in either NMOS or PMOS circuits (i.e., a combination of a thick field oxide and channel-stop doping). However, the isolation of p-channel from n-channel devices involves additional considerations, insofar as two opposite-type FETs must be separated physically by at least one well. That is, in CMOS isolation two additional requirements that arise in neither PMOS or NMOS technology must be simultaneously satisfied: (1) any possible leakage currents that could flow between a p-channel device adjacent to an n-channel device must be suppressed; and (2) the susceptibility of CMOS to latchup must be minimized. In this section, we describe isolation techniques to suppress the leakage currents between n- and p-channel devices. Latchup suppression is described in Vol. 2, chap. 6.

Interest in isolating n- from p-channel devices is very keen because CMOS isolation structures generally consume much more chip area than the isolation structures needed between like types of devices. That is, earlier in this chapter we showed that isolation between *like* kinds of MOS devices can be realized with isolation spacings ≤ 1.0 μm. But in single-well CMOS technologies the minimum required isolation spacing is about three times the depth of the well.[76] Thus, for a 4-μm-deep well, the minimum n^+ to p^+ spacing is ~12 μm. Even in twin-tub CMOS technologies with dual channel-stops, a minimum of 4-9 μm of lateral space is necessary for effective isolation. In advanced submicron CMOS technologies, it has been estimated that the minimum interwell (i.e., n^+-to-p^+) spacing is about three times the minimum intrawell (i.e., n^+-to-n^+ or p^+-to-p^+) spacing.

The large area penalty of p-channel-to-n-channel device isolation is the most important reason why CMOS technologies using conventional isolation methods cannot achieve as high a packing density as NMOS. Furthermore, while new techniques such as epitaxy greatly reduce latchup susceptibility as CMOS is scaled down, they generally do not suppress leakage currents in the parasitic MOS structures. Hence, the layout spacing between an n-channel and a p-channel device may be limited by isolation failure rather than by latchup.

In this section we describe why greater isolation spacing is needed in CMOS than in NMOS or PMOS, and how the minimum spacing for a given CMOS technology is determined. We begin by considering CMOS isolation from a qualitative perspective. Next, we give a description of how CMOS isolation is quantitatively modeled. Then, test structures for empirically assessing the adequacy of isolation among opposite-type FETs in a CMOS technology are described. Procedures for establishing the design rules for minimum CMOS-isolation-spacing from the simulation results and measured data are then presented. Finally, technological approaches for fabricating isolation structures in CMOS are discussed.

6.6.1 Qualitative Description of Isolation in CMOS

In CMOS structures, the isolation spacing between the n- and p-channel devices is defined as the sum of: (1) the distance between the edge of the n^+ region of the n-channel device and the edge of the well; and (2) the distance between the edge of the p^+ region of the p-channel device and the edge of the well (or, in other words, the n^+ to p^+ spacing, as shown in Fig. 6-43).[74] As noted in the introduction, the minimum isolation spacing in CMOS is much larger than that required in NMOS or PMOS technologies. Here we explore the reasons why this is the case.

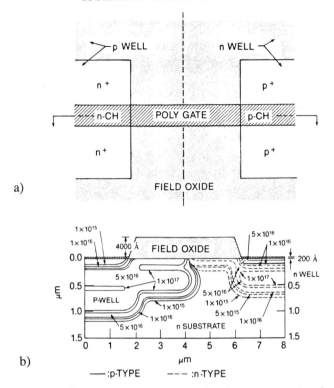

Fig. 6-43 (a) Layout top view of the isolation region between n-type and p-type transistors in CMOS. (b) Cross sectional view of a CMOS inverter showing the channel stops that are designed to prevent the surface under the field oxide from inverting.[74] (© 1986 IEEE).

An overall grasp of the issues of isolation in CMOS can be obtained by analyzing the various causes of leakage current in a CMOS inverter. The circuit schematic, layout, and a device cross-section of an n-well CMOS inverter is shown in Figs. 6-44a, b, and c, respectively. The layout actually shows two CMOS inverters connected in series, allowing the figure to be used to illustrate intra-well as well as inter-well isolation issues. In addition, the cross-section depicts an inverter with a different layout than the one shown in part (b) to enable us to show the source, drain, substrate and well contacts. Finally, note that n-well CMOS is chosen as the example CMOS architecture for this discussion, but the concepts are also equally valid for p-well and twin-well CMOS.

If a normally operating CMOS inverter is in one of its two logic states (i.e., it is not in transition between states), only a negligibly small leakage current I_{DD} should exist between V_{DD} and V_{SS}. To ensure that the total I_{DD} is within acceptably small limits, all of the sources of leakage between V_{DD} and V_{SS} need to be identified and characterized. Having such information in hand permits appropriate measures to be taken to assure that none of the leakage current components will exceed the maximum allowable I_{DD} value. From this perspective, we can identify the sources of such leakage by dividing them up into two groups: (1) those which arise as a result of leakage phenomena within active devices or from isolation breakdown between *like* types of devices, and; (2) those which occur as a result of isolation failure in CMOS structures (e.g., loss of isolation between devices in the well and in the substrate).

6.6.1.1 Leakage Currents in CMOS Gates Due to Active Device Phenomena and Intra-Well Isolation Loss.
The leakage-current phenomena associated with active devices and intra-well isolation structures have already been discussed in depth in chaps. 4 and 5 and in earlier sections of chap. 6. Therefore, they are considered here only in the context of their contribution to leakage in CMOS structures.

Recall first that if a CMOS inverter is in one of its two logic states, one of the two complimentary MOS devices of the inverter will be *OFF* (see Fig. 6-44a). In the *OFF* state there are two components of leakage current that the device itself can contribute to I_{DD}, namely the subthreshold drain current I_{Dst} (arising from either conventional subthreshold surface current or subsurface lateral punchthrough current) and the reverse-biased drain-substrate junction leakage current. By proper circuit and device design these leakage components can be kept adequately small under normal operating conditions.

In addition, leakage between the drain of one device and the source of neighboring devices within the same well (or substrate) constitutes another possible component of I_{DD} (see Fig. 6-44b). Such leakage can be suppressed by the techniques used to isolate two n-channel (or p-channel) devices from one another, as described earlier in the chapter. In most cases, leakage current due to inadequate isolation among intra-well devices is due to surface inversion effects which permit excessive subthreshold drain current to flow in the intra-well parasitic field transistors, as described in section 6.1.

6.6.1.2 Leakage Currents in CMOS Gates Due to Loss of Isolation Among Opposite-Type FETs.
Basic isolation among opposite-type FETs in CMOS involves several considerations. The first and most obvious involves the suppression of leakage across the *pn* junction which isolates the well from the substrate. To keep the component of I_{DD} due to this effect negligible, the well-substrate junction must always be kept under reverse bias. To ensure that this requirement is met (under normal operating conditions) the n-well (or n-substrate) is connected to the most positive circuit voltage (i.e., V_{DD}), and the p-well (or p substrate) to the most negative circuit voltage (i.e., V_{SS}), as shown in Fig. 6-44c for n-well CMOS.

Other components of I_{DD} in CMOS, however, can also arise from the loss of isolation involving leakage in the parasitic FETs created by the proximity of the active device source/drain regions and the well edges. There are two of these parasitic FETs formed at the edge of the n-well - one being a parasitic NMOSFET and the other a parasitic PMOSFET (as shown in Fig. 6-45). Notice that the n^+ and n-well (and the p^+ and p-substrate), form the source and drain for such parasitic NMOSFETs (and PMOSFETs), respectively. The p-substrate and n-well are the channels of these parasitic NMOS and PMOS FETs respectively, and the field oxide and poly (or Al) runners over the field oxide form the gate oxide and gates of these parasitic structures. However, it is important to note that unlike in active MOSFETs, the source and drain in these parasitic FETs are not symmetrical. That is, the substrate and well are deep junctions

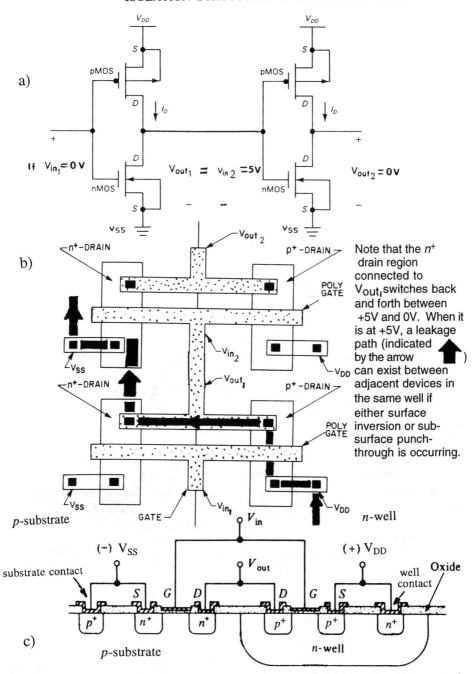

Fig. 6-44 (a) Circuit schematic of two CMOS inverters connected in series. (b) Layout of two *n*-well CMOS inverters connected in series. (c) Cross-section of a CMOS inverter, showing also the well and substrate contacts.

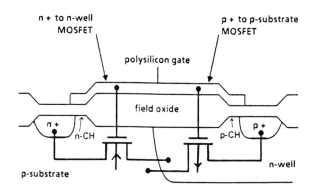

Fig. 6-45 Parasitic MOS transistors formed at the well edge in *n*-well CMOS.[91] (© IEEE 1987).

and the n^+ and p^+ regions are shallow junctions. Because a deeper drain junction and a highly conductive source always produce more subthreshold current (thereby representing a worst case condition for isolation), the *n*-well and *p*-substrate are designated as the drains when characterizing the behavior in these parasitic *asymmetric* FET structures.

Here we identify the phenomena in these parasitic FETs that can give rise to leakage current components in CMOS (again using *n*-well CMOS as the example CMOS architecture). Later we will describe techniques for mitigating these leakage currents. First, we point out that while the *n*-well (or *n*-substrate) is connected to V_{DD}, the n^+ source or drain regions can be biased at V_{SS}. (As an example, the n^+ source of the NMOS device in the CMOS inverter is connected to V_{SS}.) Thus, if a leakage path exists between the *n*-well and the n^+ source, the potential difference between the *n*-substrate and the n^+ regions can cause a component of I_{DD} to flow between V_{DD} and V_{SS}. The same problem arises between the p^+ source regions in the well and the *p*-substrate. It is also important to note that each of the parasitic FETs in which such leakage paths can arise act independently. Thus, when a CMOS technology is being developed, all of the parasitic FETs must be must be designed correctly to prevent any one of them from drawing a significant I_{DD}.

The leakage paths which can be established in the parasitic FETs of an *n*-well CMOS structure are the following:

1. Inversion of the channel region of the n^+-to-*n*-well parasitic FET.
2. Inversion of the channel region of the p^+-to-*p*-substrate parasitic FET.
3. Lateral subsurface punchthrough of the n^+-to-*n*-well parasitic FET.
4. Lateral subsurface punchthrough of the p^+-to-*p*-substrate parasitic FET.
5. Vertical punchthrough of the p^+-to-*p*-substrate parasitic FET.

Let us consider the *n*-well CMOS structure shown in Fig. 6-46. If the polysilicon gate is biased at $V_{DD} = 5V$, the channel region of the active NMOS device under the

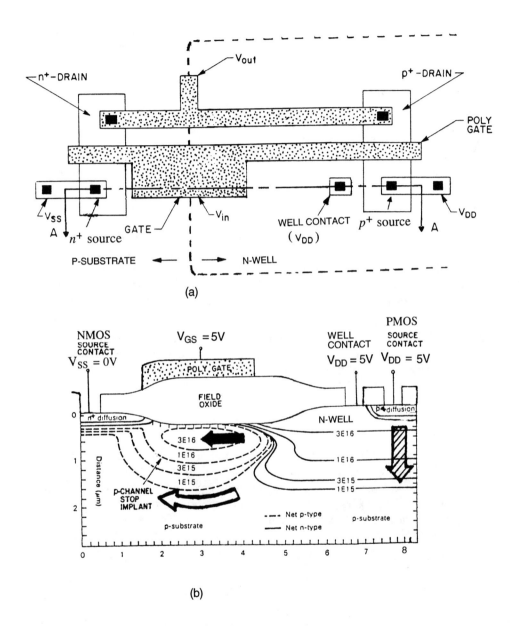

Fig. 6-46 (a) Layout of an *n*-well CMOS inverter; (b) Cross-section of this inverter taken through section A-A showing various possible leakage paths, including: ◀■ - lateral surface leakage path from n^+-to-*n*-well; ⬅ - lateral subsurface (punchthrough) leakage path from n^+-to-*n*-well; and ⬇ - vertical punchthrough path from p^+ (source)-to-*p*-substrate.

polysilicon gate is inverted to *n*-type. However, as long as the field region under the polysilicon in the *p*-substrate is not inverted, the active NMOS device remains isolated from the *n*-well by the *p*-substrate. However, if V_{TFiso} of the parasitic NMOSFET is not high enough, the surface of the *p*-substrate can invert under the field oxide, creating a path for current flow from the n^+ source to the *n*-well, causing the isolation provided by the well to be lost (path #1 above, and shown as   in Fig. 6-46b). The subsurface lateral punchthrough path in this device is also shown in Fig. 6-46b as   . This path can arise if the isolation spacing is decreased to a point where the punchthrough voltage of this parasitic FET becomes smaller than V_{DD} (path # 3 above). Vertical punchthrough from the p^+ source through the *n*-well to the *p*-substrate could also cause leakage in the parasitic PMOSFET (see also 6-46b). Finally, in *n*-well CMOS, leakage can also be due to surface-inversion and lateral-subsurface (punchthrough) phenomena in the p^+-to-*p*-substrate parasitic FET (paths #2 and #4 above).

6.6.1.3 Why n^+-to-p^+ Isolation Spacing is Greater than n^+-to-n^+ Spacing in NMOS (or p^+-to-p^+ Spacing in PMOS).

Having identified the possible leakage mechanisms arising from the two parasitic FETs formed at the edge of the well, we can go on to explain why larger n^+-to-p^+ spacing must be used to provide adequate isolation in CMOS. There are several reasons which underlie the need for larger n^+-to-p^+ spacing:

1. The technology of conventional well formation leads to lower concentrations of well doping at the Si surface near the well borders (i.e., due to lateral redistribution and interdiffusion of well dopants during the drive-in step that forms the well). Thus, if the p^+-to-*p*-well spacing gets too small, the maximum *n*-substrate concentration in the channel of the parasitic FET will eventually become too low to sustain an adequately large value of V_{TFiso}. Hence, leakage will occur at the surface of the channel of the parasitic FET.

2. Even if the doping concentration at the surface of the channels of the parasitic FETs is large enough to sustain an adequately large long-channel V_{TFiso}, subthreshold-leakage-currents between opposite type FETs in submicron CMOS may still become excessive as the isolation spacing is reduced below some minimum dimension. Three additional effects that can give rise to such increased subthreshold leakage components of I_{DD} in submicron CMOS are the following:

a. Short-channel V_T rolloff and DIBL in the parasitic FETs;

b. Short-channel and channel doping-profile effects that can increase the susceptibility to lateral subsurface punchthrough in the parasitic FETs;

c. Decreased lateral n^+-to-p^+ spacing (which leads to shallower well depths) can give rise to vertical punchthrough (between the source/drain junction in the well and the substrate). CMOS structures fabricated on silicon substrates with thin epitaxial layers are also more prone to vertical punchthrough.

Here we discuss dopant redistribution at the well borders and short-channel and lateral subsurface punchthrough effects in the parasitic FETs. Vertical punchthrough is discussed in section 6.6.5.

6.6.1.4 Effects on n^+-to-p^+ Spacing of Dopant Redistribution at the Well Borders. The need for large isolation-spacing dimensions in CMOS is due in part to the processes used to fabricate CMOS devices. Wells are typically driven in quite deeply to: (1) ensure that enough charge exists below the transistor to prevent vertical punchthrough to the substrate, and; (2) to reduce the gain of the vertical parasitic bipolar transistor (decreasing the gain of parasitic bipolars reduces latchup susceptibility). The deep well drive-in, however, also results in both substantial lateral diffusion of the well dopants (which increases the minimum distance from the p^+-region and the well border) and a reduction in the surface concentration near the border of the n-well. The interdiffusion (i.e., compensation) of the tub and substrate impurities in single-well CMOS (or the two tub impurities in twin-well CMOS) further reduces the net surface concentration near the border, making the threshold voltage of the parasitic MOS field transistors even smaller.

The effects of dopant redistribution and interdiffusion at the well border in single p-well and twin-well CMOS processes are illustrated in Fig. 6-47. A 2-D simulation of

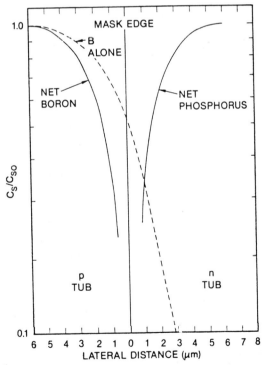

Fig. 6-47 Impurity surface concentration near the border of the two tubs in twin-tub CMOS.[77] (© 1980 IEEE).

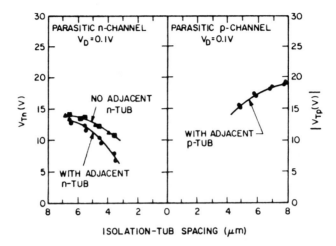

Fig. 6-48 Threshold voltage of n- and p-channel parasitic device as a function of the separation between the transistor edge and the tub border.[77] The upper curve in the left-hand graph shows the parasitic n-channel threshold-voltage reduction near the tub border when no adjacent n-tub is present. When an n-well is present, the threshold voltage is reduced (lower curve), since the interdiffusion of the two types of impurities reduces the net surface concentration of each dopant near the well border.[77] (© 1980 IEEE).

the surface doping concentration near the well border as a result of the well drive in is shown. (Note that this calculation assumes no extra channel-stop implants are used.) We see that near the border the net impurity concentrations at the surface are significantly decreased. The dashed line in Fig. 6-47 shows the reduction in net impurity concentration at the well boundary for the case in which only a boron well implant is used (single p-well). The solid curves represent the case when both boron and phosphorus well implants are used (twin well). We see that the slope of the curves in twin-well CMOS (Fig. 6-47) is greater than in conventional single-well CMOS. But, since the doping change occurs on both sides of the junction compared to a single side for the single-well case, these two effects offset each other. As a result, both technologies require comparable minimum n^+-to-p^+ spacings across the well. However, an advantage of the twin-well is that the well border is located close to its drawn position, while in the single-well case the well border is displaced by lateral diffusion of the well dopants. Thus, in single-well CMOS technologies, the circuit layout must be compensated for this displacement, either by design rules or by mask biasing. In twin-well CMOS processes like those of Fig. 6-47, this problem does not occur.

Figure 6-48 illustrates the effect on V_{TFiso} of the parasitic field transistors when the surface doping concentration near the well borders is reduced. Here, the experimental V_{TFiso} values of such structures (fabricated with the well processes that yield the well-border surface doping profiles of Fig. 6-47), are plotted as a function of the separation between the transistor edge and the well border.[77] The upper curve in the left-hand graph shows the parasitic n-channel threshold-voltage reduction near the tub border when no adjacent n-tub is present. Note that when an n-well is also present (twin-well CMOS), the threshold voltage is reduced even more than in the single-well case (lower curve), since the interdiffusion of the two types of impurities decreases the net surface concentration of each dopant near the well border. Unless the net dopant-reduction effects are somehow counteracted, the spacing between adjacent n^+ and p^+ devices must be kept quite large (e.g.,>10 μm) to prevent inversion beneath the field oxide.

If smaller spacings between n- and p-channel devices are to be possible, the channel-stop doping concentration must somehow be increased, particularly in the p-substrate regions of n-well CMOS. During field oxidation, boron segregates into the oxide, while phosphorus piles up at the silicon surface. As a result, in an n-well process a separate p-type channel-stop implant must be added to increase the surface concentration of the lightly doped p-substrate. Without such an implant, inversion between the n-channel devices in the substrate is likely to occur. In p-well technologies the well itself is an adequate n-type channel stop because heavier boron doping exists in the p-well. In the n-substrate of p-well CMOS the concentration of phosphorus is increased at the surface of the n-substrate during field oxide growth so that a separate substrate channel-stop implant may not be necessary.

Because of increased interdiffusion, two channel stops are needed in twin-tub processes to reduce the isolation distance as much as possible. In one recently described approach, an increase in the abruptness of the doping transition between the two wells is realized with two channel stops as follows. A double implant is used to simultaneously introduce the n-well dopant and n-well channel stop dopants. That is, a shallow arsenic implant is performed together with a phosphorus implant into the n-well regions. This increases the net n doping near the well edge because the smaller diffusivity of arsenic keeps it close to its original location during the drive in that diffuses the phosphorus deeply to form the n-well. In addition, a second shallow boron implant is done into the p-well following the well drive in. This increases the boron surface concentration near the well edge and thus compensates for the loss of boron due to lateral diffusion and for the diffusion of phosphorus into the p-well near the well border. This process is described in more detail in section 6.6.6.

6.6.1.5 Threshold Voltage Rolloff, DIBL, and Lateral Punchthrough in Submicron CMOS Parasitic Field FETs.

As n^+-to-n-well or p^+-to-p-substrate spacing is reduced, the magnitude of V_{TFiso} for either NMOS or PMOS parasitic FETs decreases for the same reasons that V_T decreases in active short-channel MOSFETs (or that V_{TFiso} decreases in parasitic field MOSFETs between like devices) as the effective channel length is reduced (see chap. 5 and section 6.1). V_{TFiso} also decreases as the drain bias is increased (DIBL), just as is observed in short-channel active MOSFETs. Lateral punchthrough from drain (n-well) to source (n^+ region) is more likely to occur in the inter-well parasitic FETs than in the intra-well parasitic FETs because of the deep drain in the former devices. Moreover, the two failure modes (field inversion and punchthrough), are coupled through 2-D effects.[74] For worst-case

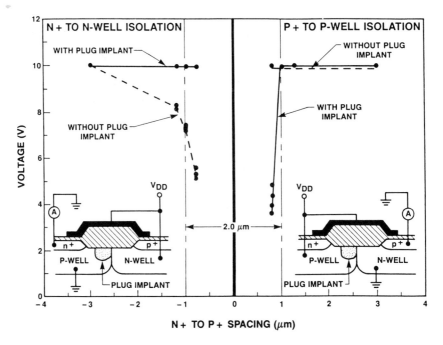

Fig. 6-49 Inter-well isolation voltage as a function of n^+ to p^+ spacing, demonstrating that proper implant selection can improve n-$+$ to n-well leakage without significantly degrading p^+ to p-well isolation. Interwell isolation voltage is defined as the voltage required for 1 pA/μm of interwell leakage. The n^+ to n-well isolation is preserved on the left and p^+ to p-well on the right. The test setup is depicted in the insets at the bottom of the figure.[84] (© 1991 IEEE).

considerations, field inversion must be experimentally determined with the drain bias set at its maximum value (e.g., V_{DD} + 10%). Punchthrough must be experimentally determined with the gate voltage set at its maximum operating value. Fig. 6-49, shows the results using these test structures to monitor the "plug"-implant CMOS isolation structure discussed in section 6.6.7.[84] Here the interwell isolation voltage V_{TFiso} is defined as the gate voltage at 1 pA/μm of interwell leakage.

6.6.2 Quantitative Modeling of CMOS Isolation

A qualitative description of the issues pertinent to CMOS isolation, as given in section 6.6.1, is useful for gaining an intuitive understanding of the overall problem. However, in the process of developing a new CMOS generation (or modifying an older one), a *quantitative* characterization of the isolation behavior of the parasitic FETs near the well borders is needed. As will be described in section 6.6.3, such characterization can be experimentally obtained from appropriate test structures and test procedures. That is, if a set of test structures that represent the parasitic well-edge FETs in a particular CMOS technology is available, their experimental V_{TFiso} and punchthrough voltage values can be obtained for each channel length dimension of interest. From plots of such experimental values it is easy to derive the minimum distance for safe operation at the supply voltage, usually V_{DD} plus 10% safety margin.

On the other hand, when a new CMOS process is being developed, a minimum n^+-to-p^+ spacing may be chosen as one of the design rules by the circuit designers. In this case, one would like to be certain early in the design cycle (namely, even before any circuits or device structures have actually been fabricated), that the parasitic well-edge FET structures of the new process will provide adequate isolation, thus allowing this isolation spacing design rule to be adopted for circuit design layout purposes. The experimental test data, in this case, would not yet be available. In fact, if the parasitic FETs could be properly designed prior to fabrication, the data from the test structures would merely serve to confirm the adequacy of the isolation characteristics as predicted from the simulation.

However, the isolation behavior of a well-edge parasitic FET with a given channel length can vary, depending on the device structure and fabrication techniques. In fact, the interdependence of doping profiles, thermal cycles, and device dimensions makes optimization of these parameters during process design a challenging task. To avoid many experimental runs for finding the optimal well-edge FET device configuration, quantitatively modeling of the isolation behavior of these structures is necessary. Such modeling early in the design cycle can also be used to determine whether or not adequate isolation is possible at the chosen minimum n^+-to-p^+ spacing, and if not, what the minimum achievable isolation spacing with the available process capabilities would be.

Such modeling of isolation behavior involves simulation of the subthreshold device characteristics of the parasitic FETs of interest. However, since the device structures of these parasitic FETs are quite different from those of conventional active MOSFETs, the simple analytical models of subthreshold behavior derived in chaps. 4 and 5 for such simulations are inadequate. That is, in submicron CMOS the parasitic devices are asymmetric FETs with deep drains, thick gate oxides, and short channel lengths. Furthermore, the doping in the channel regions is non-uniform in both the lateral and vertical dimensions. Hence, to quantitatively simulate the electrostatic potential and carrier concentrations as a function of position in the channel regions when the device is operated under subthreshold dc bias conditions, the Poisson equation and the current equations must be solved in two-dimensions. This can only be accomplished with two-dimensional process and device simulators, as described, in chaps. 1 and 2. Specific examples of simulating the parasitic well-edge FETs in CMOS are described in refs. 74 and 91. Here we summarize their results.

Basically, the first step in such quantitative modeling of CMOS isolation is to use a two-dimensional process simulator (such as SUPREM IV) to calculate the isoconcentration impurity contours of both well-edge FET isolation structures. Figure 6-50a shows the configuration of the test structure used to simulate n^+-to-n-well well-edge FET of an n-well CMOS technology, in which the doping concentration as a function of position has been plotted using a 2-D process simulator. By using the doping concentration results from this simulation procedure as an input to a two-dimensional device analyzer (such as GEMINI, MINIMOS, PISCES, or MEDICI), together with the appropriate bias conditions, the potential contours in the device can be obtained. An example of this type of simulation for the same device structure is shown in Fig. 6-50b.[91]

We noted earlier that the two mechanisms of isolation loss (leakage) in the parasitic well-edge FETs are inversion of the channel in the field region and punchthrough of the source and drain of the parasitic device. For analyzing the *onset of inversion* in the parasitic FETs it is useful to plot the surface potential versus lateral distance under the isolation field-oxide at various V_{GS} values for a given n^+-to-p^+ spacing. An example of this type of plot is shown in Fig. 6-52c. We show how this plot is derived with the aid of Fig. 6-51. That is, in Fig. 6-51a1 we show the structure of the n^+-to-n-well parasitic FET. Beneath it (a2 to a5), the surface potential $\varphi_{surf}(y)$ is plotted for various V_{GS} values (e.g., 0, 15, 20 and 25V, respectively). We see that the minimum surface potential exceeds 0.51 mV when V_{GS} is between 20 and 25V (~21.4V). In Fig. 6-51b we show the same $\varphi_{surf}(y)$ plots for the p^+-to-p-well FET (b1). Here the maximum surface potential drops below -51 mV when V_{GS} is between -5 (b4) and -10V (b5), i.e., at ~ -7V.

In Fig. 6-52a we show the layout and in Fig. 6-52b the cross-section and 2-D net doping contours of these two parasitic FETs together. This particular structure represents a configuration that would be found in a *quadruple-well CMOS technology* (see chap. 8). In Fig. 6-52c the variation of the surface potential versus lateral distance is plotted for various V_{GS} values for the structure of Fig. 6-52b. (Note that this structure has a 2 μm n^+-to-p^+ spacing, and that the field oxide overlaps the p-well on the left-hand side, and the n-well on the right-hand side.) The minimum surface potential φ_{surf} in the p-well becomes 0V when $V_{GS} = 20V$, and reaches 0.22V at $V_{GS} = 25V$, indicating that the surface is becoming inverted as V_{GS} exceeds about 20V. The minimum value of φ_{surf} becomes 0V in the n-well when V_{GS} reaches about -7V.

The following procedure can be used to specify the value of V_{TFiso} more precisely

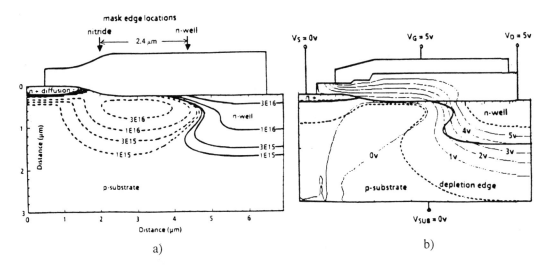

Fig. 6-50 2-D simulated: (a) doping contours; and (b) potential contours in the n^+-to-n-well parasitic MOSFET.[91] (© 1987 IEEE).

First, a specific carrier density is selected as an indicator of the onset of field inversion (e.g., 1×10^{11} cm^{-3}). Then, the value of φ_{surf} needed to establish this carrier concentration is found. Next, the value of V_{GS} necessary to produce this value of φ_{surf} is calculated, and this V_{GS} value represents the V_{TFiso} for the parasitic FET. The value of φ_{surf} can also be used to calculate the carrier density in the surface channel (and thus also at the V_{GS} necessary to establish this φ_{surf} value).

As an example, in Fig. 6-53 the minimum minority carrier concentration values in the parasitic channel versus V_{GS} are plotted for the structure depicted in Fig. 6-52b. If field inversion is defined as occurring when the minority carrier density exceeds ~1×10^{11} cm^{-3} (corresponding to a surface potential of 51 mV at 25°C), then the simulated value of V_{TFiso} of a 1 μm n^+-to-n-well structure as shown on the left hand side of Fig. 6-52b is 21.4V. Likewise, a 1-μm p^+-to-p-well parasitic FET will have a corresponding V_{TFiso} = -7.0V. Thus, a safe V_{GS} operational range for this CMOS technology with a 1 μm n^+-to-n-well spacing and a 1 μm p^+-to-p-well spacing (i.e., 2-μm n^+-to-p^+ spacing) is -7.0V<V_{GS}<21.4V.

The V_{TFiso} calculated for, say the n^+-to-n-well FET in the manner described above, can be found for various channel lengths (i.e., n^+-to-n-well spacings), and these simulated V_{TFiso} values can then be plotted versus this distance (as is done in Fig. 6-57a). The same can be done for the p^+-to-p-well FETs, as shown in Fig. 6-59. From these plots one can find the minimum n^+-to-p^+ spacing that can be used and still have adequate protection against loss of isolation due to field inversion in the parasitic FETs.

For simulating *lateral punchthrough*, the voltage applied to the well junction and to the neighboring source/drain regions must be considered in the simulations. Furthermore, the effect of the gate voltage applied to the field parasitic MOSFETs must also be included, since it can indirectly affect punchthrough by controlling the underlying surface potential and carrier density. An example of these simulations is given in Fig. 6-54, which illustrates 2-D equipotential contours for 2 μm isolation with 1.5 μm p^+-to-p-well spacing and 0.5 μm n^+-to-n-well spacing.[74] The n-well is tied to the supply voltage (5V), while the p-well and the substrate are tied to ground. The graph at the top shows good electrical isolation with a gate voltage of 10V due to the undepleted portion of the p-well surface, which is characterized by zero surface potential. However, if the gate voltage is raised to 20V, then punchthrough occurs from n^+ to n-well, because the p-well surface becomes fully depleted or inverted, as demonstrated by the fact that it is at positive potential. By analyzing a matrix of bias conditions and spacings, the design of the parasitic well-edge FETs can be optimized even before a single silicon wafer lot is processed, providing a great savings of development costs and time.

6.6.3 Experimental Characterization of Isolation in CMOS

The cross-sections of two test structures for measuring the degree of leakage in the diffusion-region-to-well-edge parasitic field MOSFETs in CMOS are shown in Fig. 6-55.[91] (Note that an n-well CMOS technology is again used here, but the same kind of

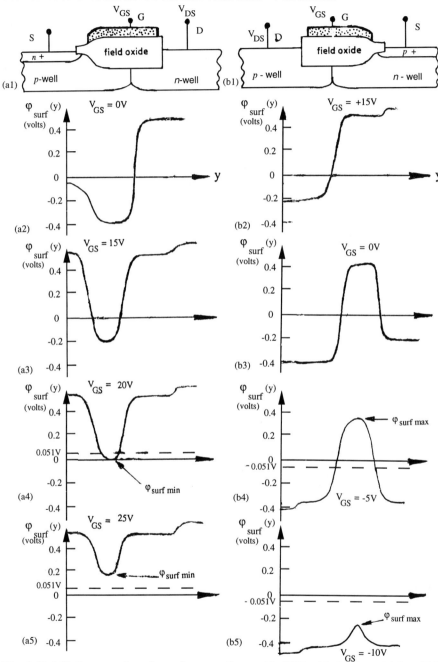

Fig. 6-51 (a1) Cross-section of an n^+-to-n-well parasitic FET with $L = 1$ μm; (a2 - a5) Plots of φ_{surf} in this structure for V_{GS} values of 0, 15, 20 and 25V. (b1) Cross-section of an p^+-to-p-well parasitic FET; (b2 - b5)) Plots of φ_{surf} in this structure for V_{GS} values of +15, 0, -5, and -10V.

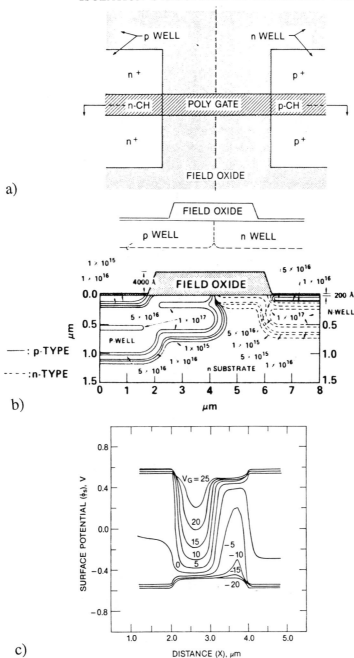

Fig. 6-52 (a) Layout and (b) cross-section and simulated 2-D net impurity contours in the CMOS isolation region of a quadruple-well CMOS technology; (c) Simulated surface potential for 2-μm isolation spacing at various gates voltage V_{GS}. (© IEEE 1986).

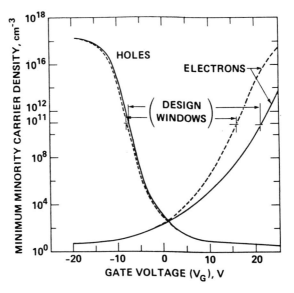

Fig. 6-53 Minimum minority carrier density under the 2-μm field oxide. For a total of 2-μm n^+-to-p^+ spacing, solid lines represent 1-μm p^+-to-p-well spacing and dashed lines present 1.5 μm p^+-to-p-well spacing.[74] (© 1986 IEEE).

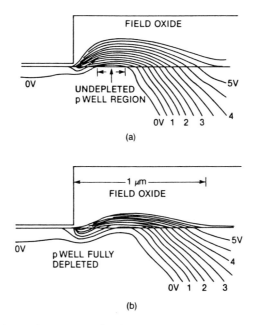

Fig. 6-54 2-D equipotential contours for 2-μm isolation with 1.5 μm p^+-to-p well and 0.5 μm n^+-to-n-well spacing. V_n = 5V, V_p = V_{sub} = 0V. (a) No punchthrough at 10V. (b) Punchthrough at 20V.[74] (© 1986 IEEE).

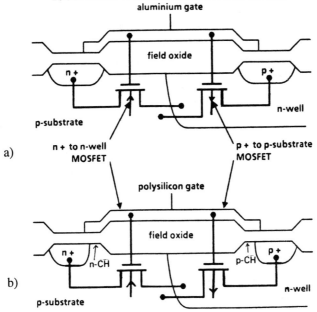

Fig. 6-55 Asymmetric parasitic FETs formed at n-well edge: (a) Aluminum gate structure; (b) Polysilicon gate structure.[91] (© 1987 IEEE).

test structures can be designed for p-well or twin-well CMOS.) These cross-sections indicate that both aluminum (Fig. 6-55a) and polysilicon (Fig. 6-55b) gate parasitic transistors exist in CMOS, and hence it is important to characterize each of these types to determine if one or the other might limit the minimum isolation spacing.

As noted earlier, in these test structures, the n^+ regions and n-well form the source and drain for the parasitic NMOSFETs while the p^+ and p-substrate serve as source and drain for the parasitic PMOSFETs. As in the NMOS isolation test structures described in section 6.1, two important differences exist between the two structures shown here: (1) the field oxide is thicker in the structures with aluminum rather than polysilicon gates (due to the addition of a dielectric layer to isolate aluminum from polysilicon where they overlap); and (2) the n^+ and p^+ regions in the polysilicon gate structures are self-aligned to the polysilicon gate edge instead abutting the LOCOS edges (see Fig. 6-55b), as occurs in the aluminum gate structures. Thus, a thin gate oxide region exists under the polysilicon between the n^+ and p^+ diffusion and the LOCOS edge. This region inverts at a very much lower voltage than the field, and the resultant inversion layers act as very shallow source and drain regions. Nevertheless, the true source and drain regions are kept further apart than in the aluminum gate case, and this tends to inhibit lateral punchthrough.

Note this implies that the polysilicon-gate parasitic-FET test structure is a good vehicle for characterizing V_{TFiso} under the polysilicon lines, but is not as good for characterizing the punchthrough voltage of actual parasitic CMOS FETs. That is, because lateral punchthrough is inhibited in the polysilicon gate test structure, this test structure does not test for the worst case conditions under which lateral punchthrough will occur in such parasitic FETs.

The isolation characteristics of these parasitic transistor structures are typically determined separately, as was done in the section on modeling, where one well-edge FET was modeled at a time (see Fig. 6-50b). Usually, both V_{TFiso} and the lateral punchthrough voltages are also determined using separate test procedures. A gate voltage needed to establish a predefined maximum drain/source leakage current in these transistors (e.g., 1 pA/μm width) in each case is measured as a function of the n^+-to-n-well or p^+-to-p-well distance. As noted earlier, for worst case considerations, V_{TFiso} must be measured at maximum drain bias, while punchthrough must be measured at highest gate voltage. The minimum n^+-to-p^+ spacing needed to maintain adequately small leakage currents between opposite device types in a CMOS technology for the specified power supply voltage (plus, usually, a safety margin of 10%) can be derived from the data obtained from such measurements.

Specifically, a minimum V_{TFiso} is selected for the CMOS technology being developed. The minimum distance for the n^+-to-n-well and p^+-to-p-well needed to establish this value for both the aluminum and polysilicon gate structures is determined from the experimental data. The larger of the sum of the two minimum spacings for each parasitic device is the minimum acceptable n^+-to-p^+ spacing to maintain adequate field inversion. The same procedure is used to choose the minimum n^+-to-p^+ spacing to maintain a sufficiently high punchthrough value. The larger of these two spacings (i.e., the minimum n^+-to-p^+ spacing to maintain an adequate V_{TFiso} value in each device, and the minimum n^+-to-p^+ spacing to allow an adequate punchthrough voltage in each device) is the minimum overall n^+-to-p^+ spacing value needed to provide adequate CMOS isolation. Note that since this distance also affects latchup, the final design rule must exceed both the value found from this experimental data and the one necessary for avoiding latchup.

It should also be noted that if both the leakage due to field inversion and punchthrough are measured simultaneously, the same values of V_{GS} and V_{DS} are applied simultaneously as their values are ramped up, as shown in Fig. 6-56.[78] The voltage at which some predetermined drain current is observed is then plotted, and these quantities are referred to as V_C and d in Fig. 6-56.

6.6.3.1 Experimental Characterization of Isolation in n^+-to-n-well Parasitic FETs.
Fig. 6-56a shows the measured values of field inversion voltages V_{TFiso} for n^+-to-n-well parasitic MOS structures as a function of n^+-to-n-well separation. V_{TFiso} is defined at parasitic FET drain current values of 10 pA, 1 nA, and 0.1 μA, and it assumes that the drain voltage is set at 5V as the gate voltage is ramped, for both the aluminum and polysilicon gate test structures.[91] Results from simulation data are also plotted, and good agreement with the measured data is found.* Below about

---

* It should be pointed out that the authors indicated that the fixed charge in the threshold equation used to calculate V_T was treated as a fitting parameter to match the experimental and

2 μm nominal n^+-to-n-well separations V_{TFiso} is seen to decrease due to short-channel V_T rolloff effects. That is, at n^+-to-n-well spacings smaller than about 2 μm, the depletion region of the n-well extends far enough toward the n^+ source that the short-channel V_T lowering and DIBL effects observed in active MOSFETs at smaller L values now also begin to occur in the parasitic field device.

The values of V_{TFiso} of the polysilicon-gate parasitic MOS transistors are lower than those of the aluminum gate devices because the field (gate) oxide is thinner in the former. But, the curves corresponding to the different subthreshold drain currents are closer together in the poly-gate devices, due to the smaller subthreshold swing S_t. (As discussed in chap. 4, S_t decreases as the thickness of the gate oxide is reduced.) Furthermore, the threshold lowering is smaller for polysilicon-gate FETs, again due to the thinner parasitic gate oxide. At the smallest n^+-to-n-well separations (1-1.5 μm), the faster V_T rolloff in the aluminum-gate FETs causes their V_{TFiso}s to become smaller than those of polysilicon-gate devices. As a result, it is the aluminum gate structures which ultimately limit the minimum n^+-to-n-well separation. Furthermore, the oxide quality and thickness control of the oxide between the poly and the aluminum is worse than that between the poly and substrate. Hence, the V_{TFiso}s of the aluminum gate

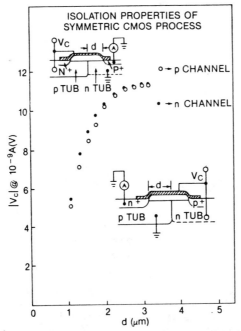

Fig. 6-56 Isolation characteristics of well-edge parasitic as a function of the distance from well edge to active area edge.[78] (© 1986 IEEE).

(* cont.) simulated long-channel V_T values (at values of $Q_{tot} < 2 \times 10^{12} q$ cm^{-2}). Thus, the significance of these simulations lies primarily in their predictions of the short-channel rolloff rather than their absolute values.

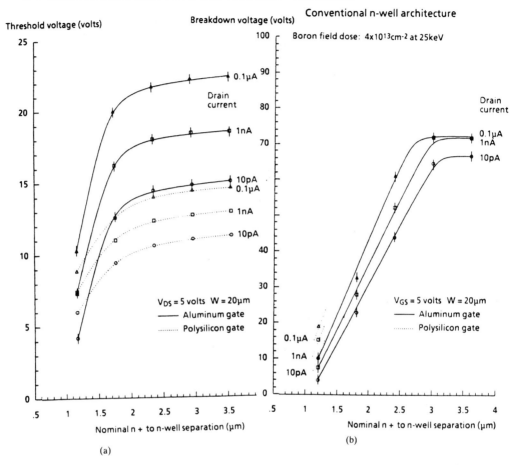

Fig. 6-57 (a) Threshold voltages V_{TFiso}; (b) breakdown voltages for the asymmetric n^+-to-n-well parasitic FETs.[91] (© 1986 IEEE).

structures are less reproducible from run to run. Thus, a greater margin of safety must be allowed (i.e., larger nominal values of V_{TFiso} for the aluminum devices are required).

Figure 6-57b shows the breakdown voltages (i.e., either due to punchthrough or avalanche breakdown, whichever occurs first) of the n^+-to-n-well parasitic test structures as a function of n^+-to-n-well spacing. They are measured by ramping the drain voltage until a voltage is reached which produces drain currents of 10 pA, 1 nA, and 0.1 μA, with $V_{GS} = 5$V. Also shown are the simulated values, and very good agreement between the two is again found. The breakdown voltages of n^+-to-n-well parasitic FETs indicate once again that the aluminum gate FETs ultimately determine minimum separation. Fig. 6-57b shows that at 1.2 μm n^+-to-n-well spacing, the polysilicon gate punchthrough voltages are all about twice the corresponding values for aluminum gate devices. At larger separations, breakdown in the polysilicon gate devices is limited by the dielectric strength of the thin gate oxide in the region where the polysilicon overlaps

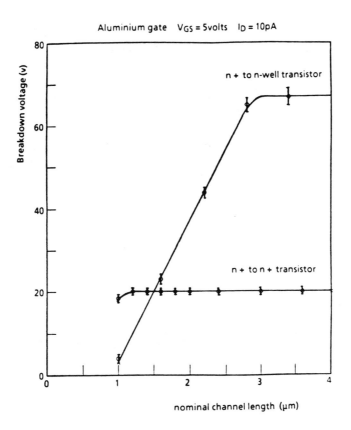

Fig. 6-58 Avalanche and punchthrough voltages for the symmetric (n^+-to-n^+) and symmetric (n^+-to-n-well) parasitic NMOSFETs.[92] (© 1987 IEEE).

the active area in the n-well (indicated as p-CH in Fig. 6-51a). Thus, punchthrough or avalanche breakdown cannot be measured in these structures.

As compared with the symmetric parasitic FETs previously described in section 6.1, punchthrough in asymmetric parasitic short-channel FETs is much more severe because of the deeper drains in these devices. In Fig. 6-58 the breakdown voltages of n^+-to-n^+ parasitic FETs and n^+-to-n-well devices are compared.[92] We observe that when the nominal channel length is reduced below 2 μm (i.e., n^+-to-n-well spacing), this parasitic device exhibits much smaller punchthrough voltages than does the n^+-to-n^+ parasitic FET.

6.6.3.2 Experimental Characterization of Isolation in p^+-to-p-substrate Parasitic FETs.

Measured and simulated field inversion voltages V_{TFiso} for p^+-to-p-substrate parasitic FETs are shown in Fig. 6-59 for both aluminum and polysilicon gate devices.[91] Again, agreement between the two is good. We observe, however, that the structure of this parasitic FET differs considerably from that of a conventional FET, and even that of the n^+-to-n-well FET. That is, the p-substrate (which acts as the drain) is not only deep, but wraps around under the p^+ source. Thus, there is the possibility of lateral and vertical leakage paths between the p^+ and p-substrate. But the vertical leakage path is not affected by the parasitic gate voltage, and hence may be neglected in the present discussion. We discuss vertical punchthrough in such devices in section 6.6.5.

We see in Fig. 6-59 that the V_{TFiso} values are much higher than those of n^+-to-n-well FETs, especially for the case of the aluminum gate devices. This is due to several effects, including the fact that higher doping is needed in the n-well to ensure adequate compensation of the boron, and that any fixed charge at the Si-SiO$_2$ interface is likely to be positive and therefore increase the magnitude of V_{TFiso}. Short-channel effects are also

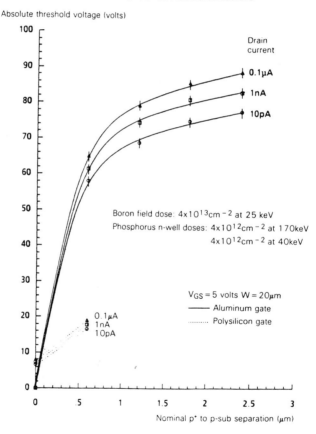

Fig. 6-59 Threshold voltages for the symmetric p^+-to-p-substrate parasitic FETs.[91] (© 1987 IEEE).

less severe, partly due to the larger doping in the n-channel, and partly because the drain (substrate) doping is lower than that of the channel. Thus, the drain-channel (substrate-well) depletion region width extends into the true substrate rather than encroaching through the well toward the p^+ source.

Since nominal p^+-to-p-substrate separation represents the separation of the nitride LOCOS mask and n-well resist mask, and the actual p^+ in the polysilicon device isabutted to the polysilicon edge rather than the nitride edge, the actual p^+ to p-substrate separation is larger than its nominal value by the length of the poly-overlapping thin oxide. The values of V_T can only be found at 0.6 μm or less, because of the dielectric breakdown in the thin oxide region. At nominal zero separation in the polysilicon devices, the actual p^+-to-p-substrate separation is about the same as the length of the poly-overlapping thin oxide, that is, 1.2 μm. In the case of an aluminum gate in which the p^+ is abutted to the LOCOS edge, the devices fail to operate.

Lateral punchthrough between the p^+-to-p-substrate is not seen until the nominal separation becomes smaller than 0.6 μm. As described earlier, this minimum punchthrough occurs mostly because the majority of the drain depletion region is extended into the lightly doped p-substrate, which serves as the drain in this structure. Vertical punchthrough between p^+ to p-substrate can be a more worrisome problem, particularly when the n-well depth is scaled down in submicron CMOS. This issue, as noted earlier, is discussed in section 6.6.5 which deals with vertical punchthrough.

6.6.4 Establishing the Minimum n^+-to-p^+ Isolation Spacing in CMOS from Modeling and Experimental Data

The data presented in Fig. 6-60a indicate that using conventional wells permits adequate isolation to be established between n^+ diffusions and n-wells in n-well CMOS at about 1.5 μm nominal separation (i.e., for this structure V_{TFiso} is ~10V at 1.5 μm, and V_{PT} is ~20V). Figure 6-60b also shows that this separation can be reduced to about 1.0 μm with retrograde wells. Likewise, it has been shown that p^+-to-p-substrate separations down to 0.6 μm can be achieved in n-well CMOS with either conventional or retrograde wells. Thus, it should be possible to realize full CMOS structures with about 2 μm n^+-to-p^+ separation using conventional n-wells, and about 1.6 μm separation with a retrograde-well technology. However, these results are obtained with isolated n^+-to-n-well and p^+-to-p-substrate parasitic transistors. To establish isolation design rules, it is necessary to show that adequate isolation exists at such small separations in full CMOS devices.

Figure 6-61 shows supply currents drawn by full CMOS structures with 1.8 μm n^+-to-p^+ separations (1.2 μm n^+-to-n-well edge and 0.6 μm p^+-to-n-well edge).[91] Fig. 6-61a shows the test structures used for this arrangement. The output node, connecting n^+ and p^+ diffusions closest to the well edge, is either shorted to ground ($V_{out} = 0$) or to the supply line ($V_{out} = V_{DD}$). These cases simulate an inverter with its output in either a Low or High state. The leakage current drawn by an ideal CMOS device between V_{DD} and V_{SS} should be zero in both cases, but any leakage due to

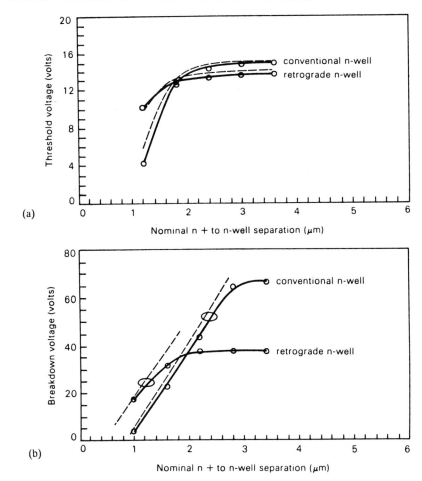

(a)

(b)

Fig. 6-60 Comparison of retrograde and conventional well structures for n^+ to n-well parasitic FETs: (a) field threshold voltage; and (b) n^+-to-n-well breakdown voltage. Solid lines: experimental data, dashed lines: modeled results, breakdown voltage is modeled by punchthrough only.[91] (© 1987 IEEE).

insufficient isolation between the n- and p-channel devices will show up as a component of the supply current.

Fig. 6-61b shows results for conventional-well devices. When $V_{out} = V_{DD}$, no potential difference exists between the n^+ diffusion and the n-well, and no leakage current should flow between them. The limiting phenomenon here is thus p^+-to-p-substrate breakdown, and consequently no breakdown should be observed below 20V. This indicates that the worst case for leakage is when the output node is shorted to ground. In such cases, the full supply voltage appears between the n^+ diffusion and the n-well, and the mechanism limiting the maximum operating voltage is instead n^+-to-n-well punchthrough leakage. The results shown in Fig. 6-61b for $V_{out} = 0$ are consistent

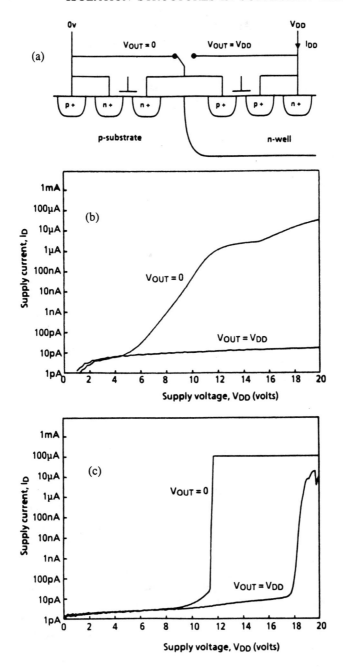

Fig. 6-61 Test structures and I-V curves for a full CMOS isolation structure: (a) test structure and measurement arrangement; (b) leakage current for conventional-well CMOS. (c) leakage current for retrograde well devices.[91] (© 1986 IEEE).

with the punchthrough breakdown voltages exhibited in Fig. 6-57b where at nominal n^+-to-n-well separation, the breakdown (punchthrough) voltage is ~10V. Figure 6-61b shows that at V_{DD} = 5V the leakage current is very close to the maximum acceptable value of 10 pA, and increases steeply as V_{DD} is increased above 5V. This demonstrates that the CMOS device under test provides barely adequate isolation at V_{DD} = 5V, but also that this does not provide adequate safety margin for 5V operation. However, by increasing the n^+-to-n-well spacing to 1.8 μm (n^+-to-p^+ separation = 2.4 μm), the maximum operating voltage becomes limited instead by junction breakdown, which in this case is just over 20V. Thus, the minimum n^+-to-p^+ separation acceptable for 5-V operation with conventional wells lies between 1.8 and 2.4 μm.

Figure 6-61c shows results for retrograde well devices with 1.8 μm n^+-to-p^+ separation. In these instances, the leakage current remains below 10 pA for supply voltages as high as 10V, providing a good safety margin for 5V operation. Again, the condition with V_{out} = 0 sets the lowest breakdown voltage, although n^+-to-n-well junction avalanche breakdown occurs at only a few volts higher than the onset of n^+-to-n-well punchthrough leakage.

In conventional LOCOS-isolated CMOS ICs, isolation among similar type transistors can be achieved with 1.0 μm isolation spacing. Isolation among opposite-type transistors is more involved, however, and modeling and measurement results show that it is possible to achieve isolation between an n- and p-channel transistor with approximately 2.4 μm isolation spacing. The use of retrograde wells can further reduce this isolation dimension to below 2 μm. At such small isolation dimensions, latchup becomes a major problem and ultimately may instead become the factor limiting the isolation spacing between NMOS and PMOS transistors.

The results presented above were obtained from n-well technologies, and thus, one might ask how well such might apply to p-well and twin-well processes. Although a p-well structure could be made by merely exchanging the n- and p-type dopants, (implying that the isolation characteristics would be comparable), data indicates that in one major respect the isolation behavior is somewhat different than for n-well CMOS. That is, the most important isolation leakage mechanism in submicron CMOS appears to be due to lateral punchthrough when the lateral spacing between the well border and source/drain regions outside the well is small. In the case of n-well CMOS, the boron channel-stop implant in the substrate must be fairly heavy due to boron segregation into the field oxide during field oxide growth. As a result, the boron profile in the substrate penetrates relatively deeply. This is exactly the type of substrate doping profile needed to prevent subsurface lateral punchthrough. In p-well CMOS, on the other hand, the phosphorus channel-stop dopant tends to pile up at the surface, yielding a shallower final phosphorus channel-stop doping profile in the substrate. This type of profile is less effective in suppressing lateral subsurface punchthrough. Thus, it may be more difficult to suppress p^+-to-p-well punchthrough in p-well CMOS.

In twin-well CMOS, both n-type and p-type devices lie inside a well. Thus, it might appear that the superior p^+-to-p-well isolation performance observed in the n-well CMOS results would be duplicated between the n^+-to-n-well in twin-well CMOS. However, the well profiles produced in fabricating the n-well CMOS for the above-cited study appear quite like twin wells, with the boron field implant extending as deep or deeper than the shallow n-well. Consequently, it is not expected that significantly better isolation is achievable using a twin-well technology.

6.6.4.1 Isolation-Spacing Design Rules for 0.35 and 0.25 μm CMOS.

Recent reports summarizing the work required to establish the minimum isolation spacings in submicron CMOS (as described above) indicate the following design rules will be needed in 0.35 μm and 0.25 μm CMOS technologies:[84,133]

1. For 0.35 μm CMOS, the minimum active pitch at which adequate *intrawell isolation* (n^+-to-n^+, or p^+-to-p^+) can be maintained appears to be about 1 μm (i.e., ~0.5 μm active region width plus 0.5 μm isolation spacing width). For LOCOS-based approaches, the minimum dimension for *interwell isolation* (i.e., n^+-to-p^+ spacing) is about three times that required for intrawell isolation. Thus, the minimum n^+-to-p^+ spacing for 0.35 μm CMOS is about 1.5 μm.

2. For 0.25 μm CMOS the above design rules can be scaled by about 30-40%. Using this criterion, the active pitch for 0.25 μm CMOS would be 0.6-0.7 μm. This means the minimum intrawell isolation spacing would be 0.3-0.35 μm, and that for interwell isolation spacing, would be 0.9-1.05 μm.

These design rules represent the nominal requirements. Obviously, a manufacturable isolation process will need to specify allowable tolerances to these dimensions to accommodate the inevitable variations in patterning technology.

6.6.5   Vertical Isolation in CMOS

By reducing the depth of the wells in CMOS, smaller n^+-to-p^+ spacing can be used. However, when shallow wells are implemented the problem of maintaining adequate vertical isolation must be addressed. That is, shallow wells are more prone to vertical punchthrough between the source/drain diffusions in the well and the underlying substrate. Retrograde wells (described in chap. 8), with their high doping levels at the well bottom provide excellent vertical isolation, even at well depths of the order of 1 μm,[115, 116] but adequate vertical isolation at such shallow well depths is much harder to achieve with conventional-well structures. Shallow wells fabricated with a significantly reduced thermal budget also allows the use of thinner epitaxial substrate material, and hence better latchup protection. At the same time, however, the shallow wells introduce a new constraint on the epitaxial layer thickness due to the degradation in vertical isolation caused by the underlying heavily doped substrate. As we will see, this is especially true in the case of n-well CMOS, where out-diffusion of boron from the heavily doped substrate imposes a major limitation on the minimum epitaxial layer starting thickness.

Example 6-1: An n-well CMOS process is to be developed for operation with a power-supply voltage of V_{DD} = 5 V. The substrate doping of the p-type wafers is 1x10^15/cm^3. Assume the n-well has a uniform doping profile with an average dopant concentration of 1x10^16/cm^3. The p-channel MOSFET sources and drains are to have junction depths of 0.4 μm and an average dopant density of $10^{18}/cm^3$. What is the minimum n-well depth needed to avoid vertical punchthrough to the substrate?

Solution: Vertical punchthrough will occur if the depletion region of the source/drain-to-well junction were to merge with the depletion region of the well-substrate junction when V_{DD} = 5 V (see section 5.5.2). The source-to-well junction is essentially a one-sided pn junction with a built-in voltage of V_{bi} = 0.82 V. In this case, the depletion-region width is calculated to penetrate into the n-well to a distance of ~0.35 μm, if the voltage applied across the junction is zero (i.e., both the source and the well are connected to V_{DD}). The np-junction to the substrate has a built-in voltage of 0.63 V, and the total depletion width of this junction at a 5 V bias is ~1.9 μm. We calculate that about 0.19 μm of this depletion region is in the n-well. The n-well must therefore be deep enough to accommodate the depth of the source junction (0.4 μm) as well as the sum of the depletion region widths in the well in order for vertical punchthrough to be avoided. While the total of these dimensions is 0.94 μm, it is good engineering practice to increase the depth of the well by about 50% to account for process variations. A reasonable well depth might therefore be 1.5 μm.

It is more feasible to fabricate CMOS having adequate vertical isolation with shallow conventional p-wells than with conventional n-wells. It has been demonstrated that successful p-well CMOS circuit operation can be achieved at V_{DD} = 5V with conventional well depths of approximately 1 μm.[117] Consider first the case when the n^+ source/drain diffusion in such shallow p-wells is biased more positively than the n-substrate. In this instance, the vertical punchthrough voltage is only 3-4 V. However, since the n-substrate is tied to V_{DD} and the n^+ region is biased between V_{DD} and V_{SS} this bias arrangement does not occur in normal circuit operation (except during transient overshoot of the voltage at the circuit node). Thus, a punchthrough voltage value of 3-4V is adequate in this case.

Let us also consider the case of vertical punchthrough current flowing in the opposite direction in a p-well CMOS structure. That is, when the substrate is biased at a higher potential than the n^+ region. In this case, in a p-well circuit under normal operating conditions, the n-substrate must always be at the most positive potential. In such circumstances (i.e., with the n-substrate at the higher potential and the n^+ region at V_{SS}), the n-substrate-to-n^+ punchthrough voltage is measured to be well above 10V. Since the substrate is usually tied to V_{DD} = 5V, under normal operation this punchthrough voltage value is also adequate for p-well CMOS operation.

Under some biasing conditions, however, shallow wells in n-well CMOS are much more prone to vertical punchthrough, and the problem becomes worse if the n-well CMOS is fabricated in a p-epi layer on a p^+ substrate. Note first that in n-well CMOS vertical punchthrough current flows between the p^+ region and the p-substrate through an n-well. In normal CMOS operation, the n-well is at V_{DD}, the p-substrate is at V_{SS} and the p^+ is biased between V_{DD} and V_{SS}. However, during transient overshoot, the p^+

or *p*-substrate can become negatively biased. Since this condition represents the worst case for vertical punchthrough, it is useful to analyze it in more detail.

The problem can be illustrated by considering an example of a conventional but shallow *n*-well with its doping profile (obtained using the process simulator SUPREM III) given as in Fig. 6-62a.[93] The well depth is 1.1 μm and the p^+ junction depth is about 0.3 μm. The simulated potential distribution for this case is depicted in Fig. 6-62b. In this figure, the p^+ is biased between +5V and -5V while the *n*-well and *p*-substrate are biased at normal operating voltages (i.e., the *n*-well is biased at $V_{DD} = 5V$ and the *p*-substrate at $V_{SS} = 0V$).[93] As the p^+ is varied from +5V to 0V, the potential energy barrier between the p^+ and *p*-substrate regions is always present, even when the p^+-to-*n*-well and *n*-well-to-*p*-substrate depletion regions meet. Consequently, under normal operating conditions, vertical punchthrough current is not expected to flow. When the p^+ potential reaches -5V, however, the barrier disappears, permitting punchthrough current to flow from the substrate up to the p^+. *p*-channel devices formed in such an *n*-well would thus be limited to operation at drain biases smaller than -10V.

Punchthrough current can also flow from the p^+ down to the substrate if the substrate is negatively biased (a condition also examined in Fig. 6-62b). However, because most of the well-to-substrate depletion region is in the lightly doped substrate rather than into the well, the p^+-to-substrate potential barrier cannot be lowered significantly until the substrate is at a large negative bias (<-70V).

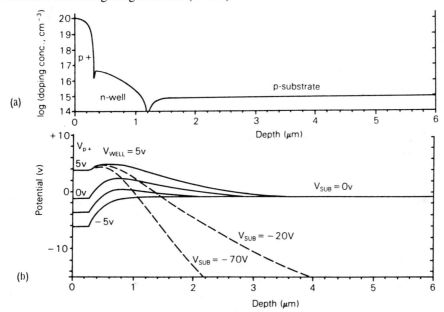

Fig. 6-62 Vertical doping and potential profiles for a 1.2 μm CMOS structure. (a) Net doping, and (b) potential profiles, solid lines: p^+ voltage varies with *p*-substrate grounded, dashed lines: substrate bias changes with p^+ fixed at 5 V. The *n*-well is always at 5 V. (c) Potential profile showing vertical punchthrough with p^+ more positive than *p* substrate.[93] (© 1987 IEEE).

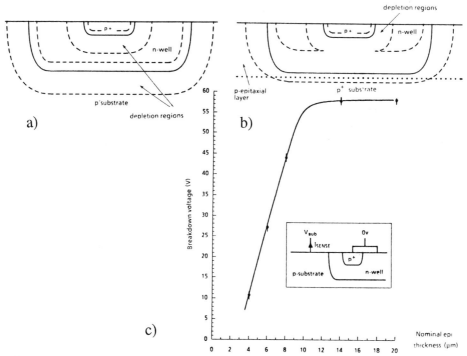

Fig. 6-63 (a) Influence of thin epitaxial layer on depletion regions in an *n*-well. (b) Thin epitaxial material. (c) Vertical punchthrough voltage versus nominal (i.e., as-grown) epi thickness in a CMOS structure with a 1.1 μm well depth. Sense current = 1 nA.[93] (© 1987 IEEE).

The situation is altered, however, if the *p*-substrate is replaced by a *p*-epi layer on a p^+ substrate. Epitaxial substrates are often required for latchup protection, especially as dimensions are reduced (see Vol. 2, chap. 6). As the minimum n^+-to-p^+ spacing is shrunk, the epitaxial layer thickness must also be reduced.[118] In the case of *n*-well technology, this means that the heavily doped p^+ substrate starts to approach the base of the *n*-well. Because the heavily doped substrate prevents the extension of the well-substrate depletion region down to the substrate, the depletion region is forced up into the well (see Figs. 6-63a and b). As a result, the V_{SUB} needed to lower the potential energy barrier is reduced, thus making it easier to cause vertical punchthrough. Figure 6-63c shows vertical punchthrough voltages measured in 1.2 μm deep wells as a function of nominal *p*-on-p^+ epitaxial thickness.[93] It indicates that the magnitude of V_{SUB} at the breakdown of vertical isolation decreases as the epi layer is thinned. At 4 μm nominal (as-grown) epi thickness, isolation breaks down at V_{SUB} of about -5V (i.e., if the p^+ diffusion is biased at +5V, the breakdown voltage is 10V). Therefore, vertical isolation may limit the use of the thinnest epi layer. Where thin epi layers are required for high-packing-density CMOS circuits in latch-up sensitive applications, the as-grown epitaxial layer thickness will need to be tightly controlled to avoid unacceptable degradation of vertical isolation.

6.6.6 LOCOS-Based Isolation in CMOS

The AT&T Twin-Tub V technology is an example of an advanced CMOS process that uses a LOCOS-based approach to isolate like devices.[79] The starting material is a p-epi layer on a p^+ substrate. The technology is implemented with a single-mask, self-aligned twin-well process that uses two channel-stop implants (as well as two separate well implants).

First, phosphorus and arsenic are sequentially implanted into the n-well areas, forming a high/low doping profile (channel-stop and well; Fig. 6-64). Since arsenic diffuses much more slowly than phosphorus, it will remain near the surface of the well during the drive-in step. This high arsenic concentration provides an effective channel stop for p-channel devices and also protects against punchthrough.

Next, a relatively thick masking oxide is selectively grown over the n-well region, and the p-well implant (boron) is then performed. Because the implant is blocked by the oxide that covers the n-wells, it enters the silicon only in the p-well regions (a self-aligned implant step). Both well regions are then driven in (with the thick oxide over the n-wells being retained), and a second boron implant (which will serve as the p-well channel stop) is carried out. This implant is kept shallow because a high pressure LOCOS process is subsequently used to grow the field oxide, minimizing the lateral and vertical impurity-profile spreading. Once again, the implant is self-aligned to the p-well regions by the presence of the oxide on the n-wells. The masking oxide is then removed, and a nitride masking layer is deposited and patterned to cover the active areas. Finally, the field oxide is formed.

This process makes it possible to achieve adequate isolation and a reduced tendency toward latchup with smaller device separations than are possible with an atmospheric-pressure oxide-growth process. Nevertheless, a 7-μm spacing must be used between the n^+ and p^+ regions in the Twin-Tub V structure to provide adequate isolation. Since this spacing still represents a significant layout-density limitation, alternatives to the LOCOS-only process are being vigorously pursued.

In another study using n-well technology, a high dose p-type channel-stop implant for the substrate (yielding a peak concentration of 5×10^{16} boron atoms/cm^3) allowed n^+ to p^+ spacings of 2.4 μm with conventional wells, and 1.8 μm spacings with retrograde wells.[82]

A novel LOCOS-based submicron-CMOS isolation approach employs a FMPBL isolation structure and a high energy boron "plug" implant.[84] The FMPBL with a conventional channel-stop implant provides nominal V_{TFiso}s in excess of 10V between NMOS transistors (intra-well isolation). The plug implant allows inter-well p^+ to n^+ spacings of less than 2.0 μm without the use of epi layers, trench structures, or retrograde wells. Instead, a low-dose of high-energy boron atoms are implanted through the field oxide (5500Å-thick) to form a p^+ plug just under the oxide in the p-well adjacent to the boundary of the n-well (Fig. 6-65). The lateral extent of the implant is controlled by implanting through a narrow slit in the implant mask. This plug effectively controls NMOS field leakage without degrading PMOS isolation. With the plug, lower implant channel-stop doses can be used, which helps curtail the narrow-width effect due to boron redistribution. Although the implant could be done before field oxidation, by doing it afterwards the problem of boron diffusion during the oxide growth step is circumvented.

6.6.7 Trench Isolation for CMOS

Trench isolation has also been explored for twin-tub CMOS as a means of implementing n^+-to-p^+ isolation structures, primarily as a means for achieving smaller interwell (n^+-to-p^+) isolation spacing. (Other advantages of trench isolation over LOCOS are described in section 6.5.) A trench at the n-well to p-well interface prevents dopant interdiffusion where the two wells join. Thus, dopant compensation (which lowers the surface dopant concentration at the well borders) is eliminated. This permits larger parasitic V_{TFiso} values to be maintained at smaller isolation spacings. Shallow and deep trenches of micron and submicron widths have been used to reduce p^+ to n^+ spacings to 2-2.5 μm.[85]

When trenches deeper than the well depth are used, they replace the reverse-biased *pn* junction as the isolation structure at the well sidewalls (Fig. 6-66). However, since fabrication of deep-trench isolation for CMOS is substantially more complex than shallow-trench isolation, and latch-up measurements have not fulfilled expectations, this approach has not yet been widely used for such applications. Nevertheless, some recent reports have described deep trench isolation structures as potential candidates for 0.5 μm (and smaller) CMOS technologies.[119,120] In this section we limit our discussion to shallow-trench isolation structures for CMOS. Readers interested in more details on deep-trench isolation are referred to chap. 2, Vol. 2 and the references.

While their use appears to permit smaller n^+-to-p^+ spacing, the presence of trench structures also gives rise to additional leakage paths not present in conventional CMOS isolation structures. These new paths can degrade the isolation between the active devices and the well. In some cases these paths can also increase the subthreshold leakage current within *active* devices. Generally, these new leakage phenomena involve the formation of an inversion channel along the vertical trench sidewall (see Fig. 6-67a).

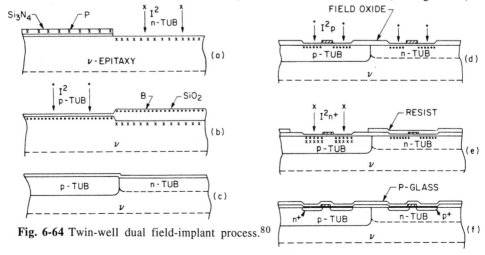

Fig. 6-64 Twin-well dual field-implant process.[80]

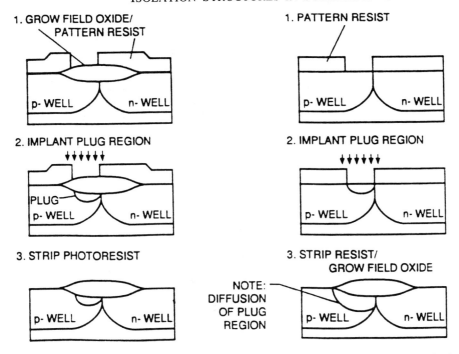

Fig. 6-65 Process flow for the plug implantation process. The figure shows that the implant can be performed either before (left) or after (right) field oxide growth.[84] (© 1991 IEEE).

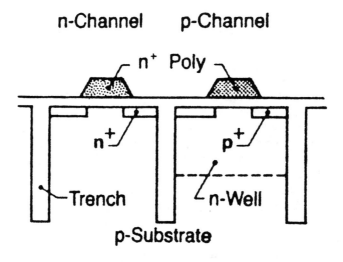

Fig. 6-66 Schematic of an *n*-well CMOS with deep trench isolation.[83] (© 1986 IEEE).

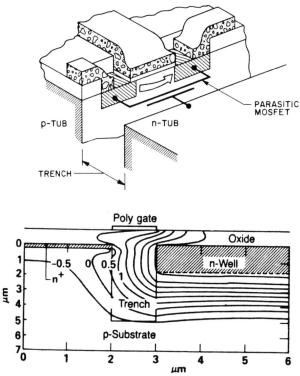

Fig. 6-67 (a) A parasitic sidewall MOSFET with the *n*-well as the gate and the trench serving as the gate oxide.[75] From S.M. Sze Ed., *High-Speed Semiconductor Devices*, Copyright 1990 by John Wiley & Sons. Reprinted with permission. (b) Cross-sectional view of a simulation of the 2-D equipotential contours in an *n*-well CMOS with trench isolation. The simulation is done at $Q_{fc} = 5\times10^{10}$ cm^{-2}, $N_A = 6\times10^{14}$ cm^{-3}, $V_{well} = 3V$, $V_{GS} = 0V$, $V_{sub} = -1V$.[137] (© 1983 IEEE).

The sidewall inversion is caused by the *horizontal* parasitic MOS device, in which the positively biased *n*-well acts as the gate electrode, and the trench dielectric serves as the MOS gate oxide (with a thickness equal to the trench width). If the *n*-well is biased at +5V, and the trench is narrow (e.g., ≤ 1 μm), inversion along the sidewall of the trench between the source and drain of the MOSFET can easily occur. (As shown in Fig. 4-67a, this is the trench sidewall that is outside of, but facing, the *n*-well.) In Fig. 6-67b, the simulated 2-D potential contours in a trench isolated CMOS structure are shown. Note that the potential on the sidewall of the trench on the *p*-substrate side is >0.5V, indicating that it is inverted.

It would appear that to take maximum advantage of such trench structures for reducing isolation spacing the active devices should be placed right at the tub edge (as shown in Fig. 6-67a). However, if an active NMOS device abuts an inverted trench sidewall, a conducting path will exist between the source and drain of the active NMOS device. This path will exist regardless of the bias on the "real" gate of the active

NMOS device, giving rise to an increase in the subthreshold leakage current of the active device. In practice, to avoid this problem, active devices are usually moved back somewhat from the tub edge.

Even if the NMOS device is moved back from the trench edge, the trench sidewall can still become inverted by a positively-biased n-well. If this happens and the poly over the field region also inverts the top surface of the p-well, it is possible for a leakage path from the NMOS source to the n-well to be established, as shown in Fig. 6-68.

Assuming that the leakage path of Fig. 6-68 is somehow suppressed (e.g., by implanting channel-stop dopants into the bottom of the trench), the inverted trench sidewall can still produce other, unexpected leakage paths. One such dc leakage path between V_{DD} (e.g., 5V) and V_{SS} (e.g., 0V) is illustrated in Fig. 6-69 for the case of two series-connected CMOS inverters which suffer from inadequate CMOS isolation.[87] This path arises from leakage along both the inverted surface of the field regions and the trench sidewall (which, in this example, is offset from the active device edge). Here V_{in1} to the first inverter is at logic 1 (i.e., $V_{in1} = V_{DD}$), causing the NMOS transistor of the first inverter to be turned ON. The output of the first inverter V_{out1} (and thus the input to the second inverter V_{in2}) is at logic 0. This causes the output of the second inverter V_{out2} to be at logic 1, and causes the PMOS device of the second inverter to be turned ON. The black highly conductive paths in Fig. 6-69 from V_{DD} to the edge of the n^+ region in the second inverter and from V_{SS} to the p^+ region in the first inverter are connected by a less-well-conducting parasitic conductive path. This path consists of an inverted region that runs under the poly of gate 1 in the p-tub, then along the inverted trench sidewall, then under the poly of gate 2 (note that for clarity, in Fig. 6-69 the path under the poly of gates 1 and 2 is drawn as running adjacent to the poly, whereas the path actually exists beneath the poly).

More severe trench-sidewall inversion problems are exhibited in p-wells than in n-wells. This is due to two interrelated phenomena. The first involves the dielectric (insulator) material used to fill the trench (typically SiO_2), and the resultant Si-SiO$_2$

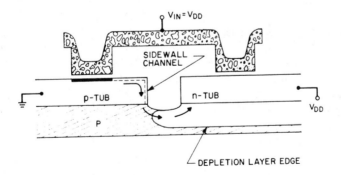

Fig. 6-68 A trench isolated p-well and n-well with a parasitic vertical sidewall MOSFET (with n-well as the gate) and a parasitic horizontal MOSFET (with the V_{in} poly line as the gate).[75] From S.M. Sze Ed., *High-Speed Semiconductor Devices*, Copyright 1990 by John Wiley & Sons. Reprinted with permission.

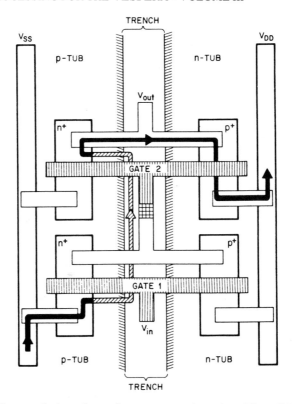

Fig. 6-69 A dc leakage path through two inverter stages in series. The solid black path is a good conducting route and the shaded path is a parasitic route. The parasitic consists of a field oxide corner under gate 1 (cf. Fig. 6-68), a sidewall path along the trench (cf. Fig. 6-67a), and a corner path under the V_{out} strap.[87] From S.M. Sze Ed., *High-Speed Semiconductor Devices*, Copyright 1990 by John Wiley & Sons. Reprinted with permission.

interface at the trench sidewall. The interface fixed or trapped charge that exists at an Si-SiO_2 interface is positive, which tends to lower the inversion threshold of *p*-channel regions (in this case the *p*-tub). To minimize this interface charge, a thin, good-quality thermal-oxide layer must be grown inside the trench. The oxide growth process, however, gives rise to the second problem. That is, during thermal oxidation some of the boron doping in the *p*-well segregates into the oxide. Thus, the boron surface concentration at the interface is reduced, further decreasing the inversion threshold. As a result, inversion of *p*-well trench sidewalls occur at lower threshold voltages than do those of an *n*-well for comparable well-doping concentrations. Finally, note that trench-etch processes often damage the Si surface in a manner that leads to increased interface trapped charge. This tends to worsen the problem of trench sidewall inversion in *p*-wells even more.

To counteract intra-well and inter-well leakage in trench-isolated CMOS several steps are necessary. First, the surface isolation path must be suppressed, by use of sufficient channel-stop doping between the active device and tub edge (as is also done in LOCOS-isolated CMOS).   Second, to avoid subthreshold leakage in single active devices, the devices are moved back somewhat from the trench edge. Third, inversion of the trench sidewall should be prevented.   One way to do this is to increase the trench width. However, this will increase the isolation spacing (as will moving the active devices away from the active device to the trench edge).   Because of these limitations, the

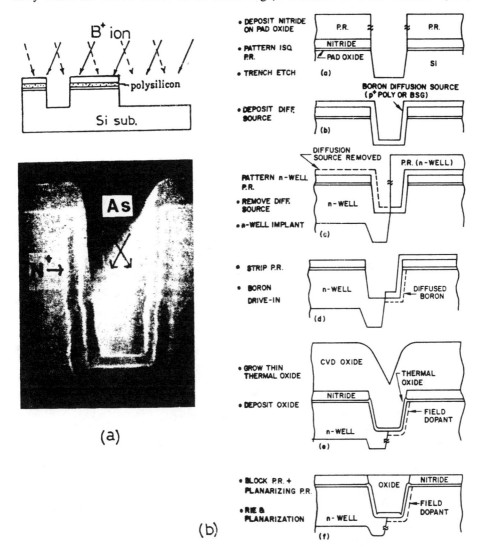

Fig. 6-70 (a) Schematic of oblique ion implantation and SEM cross section result of this procedure.[89] (© 1987 IEEE). (b) Shallow trench isolation process flow using a doped oxide as diffusion source of trench sidewall doping.[90] (© 1988 IEEE).

minimum n^+ to p^+ isolation distance in trench isolation in 1992 was still approximately 2-2.5 μm.

Another way to prevent inversion of the trench sidewalls is to increase the doping at the sidewall surface. Use of a direct, low-tilt-angle implant (e.g., boron, at an angle of 8° off the perpendicular to the top wafer surface, or at an angle of 82° off the perpendicular to the trench walls) is one reported way to do this (Fig. 6-70a).[89] However, since only one of the walls is doped by one implantation, the implant must be done four times, with the wafer rotated 90° after each step to ensure that all four walls of the trench are doped. In addition, this procedure is only effective for intra-well isolation (i.e., to isolate like-types of devices).

An alternative method for doping the sidewall of the p-well without doping the n-well with Si (thus making it suitable for CMOS inter-well isolation), was proposed by Davari et al.[90] In this approach, the p-well sidewall dopant is provided by boron diffusion from p^+ poly or borosilicate glass. The n-well does not require additional sidewall dopant as phosphorus piles up during the brief thermal oxidation of the trench prior to CVD oxide refill.

First a nitride/pad oxide mask stack is formed and patterned. Next, after shallow trenches are etched by RIE to a depth of 0.3-0.5 μm, a boron diffusion source (*in situ* doped p^+ poly or borosilicate glass, BSG) is deposited. A lithography step is then used to etch the poly of BSG away from the n-well sidewall and trench bottom (see Fig. 6-70b). A thermal cycle is then carried out to drive the boron into the sidewall and bottom of the p-well trench. No boron is diffused into the active device areas since they are covered with nitride. The boron source is then etched away, and the remainder of the trench refill process is conducted. The boron concentration at the sidewall surface is controlled by the segregation during the brief thermal 50-nm-thick oxide growth step. This approach has been used for trench widths as small as 0.8 μm. For 0.5 μm widths, control of sidewall doping and geometry is difficult, and hence for such dimensions control of sidewall parasitic MOSFETs represents a major obstacle to miniaturizing isolation.

These doping techniques have been used for ~0.8 μm wide trenches. For 0.5 μm widths, control of the sidewall doping and geometry effects is difficult.[73] No matter what technique is used, however, sidewall doping impacts the active devices through increased junction capacitance and source-substrate bias dependence. Control of sidewall parasitic MOSFETs thus represents a significant challenge for scaling CMOS isolation.

Trench-isolated 0.5-μm CMOS using shallow trenches filled with void- and seam-free TEOS/Ozone films has been implemented.[126] The 0.5 n- and p-channel MOSFETs showed no subthreshold degradation compared to the same device fabricated with LOCOS isolation. Field punchthrough voltages on intra-well and inter-well isolation structures were significantly higher than the control devices, which used PBL isolation (see Fig. 6-71). That is, punchthrough voltages were well above 10V and independent of trench isolation width.

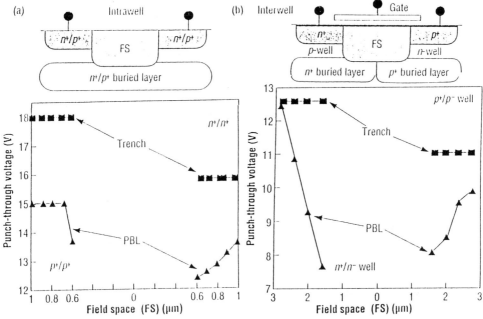

Fig. 6-71 Field punch-through voltages for trench isolation and PBL isolation. Consistently higher punchthrough voltage is observed for trench isolation with no degradation of subthreshold 0.5 μm MOSFET characteristics.[126] Reprinted with permission of Solid State Technology.

REFERENCES

1. J. Y. Chen, CMOS Science and Technology, Prentice-Hall, Englewood Cliffs, N. J., 1990, p. 237.

2. K. L. Wang et al., IEEE Trans. Electron Dev. ED-29, p. 541, 1982.

3. A. G. Lewis, R. A. Martin, and J. Y. Chen, "Retrograde and Conventional n-well CMOS technologies: A comparison," Internal Report, EIL-87-17, Xerox Palo Alto Research Center, October, 1986.

4. J.W. Lutze and J.P. Krusius, "Electrical Limitations of Advanced LOCOS Isolation of Deep Submicron CMOS," *IEEE Trans. Electron Dev.,* **ED-38**(2), p. 242, Feb. 1991.

5. J.A. Appels et al., *Phillips Research Rep.,* **25**, 118, (1970).

6. E. Kooi, *The Invention of LOCOS* IEEE Press, 1991, New York.

7. R. C. Jaeger, *Introduction to Microelectronic Fabrication*, 1988, Addison-Wesley, Reading, MA.

8. S. M. Sze, Ed., *VLSI Technology*, 2nd Ed., 1988 McGraw-Hill, New York.

9. D.R. Craven and J.B. Stimmel, *Semiconductor International,* June 1981, p. 59.

10. Cham et al., *Computer-Aided Design and VLSI Device Development* Kluwer Academic Publishers, Boston 1986.

11. L.C. Parrillo, "CMOS Active and Field Device Fabrication," *Semiconductor International*, April 1988, p. 64.

12. B. Cochran, "Tradeoffs in Submicron CMOS Process Design," *Semiconductor International,* May 1991, p. 146.

13. J.R. Pfiester and J.R. Alvis, "A Novel CMOS VLSI Isolation Using Ge/B Ion Implantation," *IEEE Electron Dev. Letts.*, August 1988, p. 391.

14. J.R. Pfiester and J.R. Alvis, "Improved CMOS Field Isolation Technology Using Selective Cl Implantation," *IEEE Electron Dev. Letts.,* November 1988, p. 561.

15. P. A. Van den Plas et al., *Field Isolation Process for Submicron CMOS*, Digest Symposium on VLSI Technology, Karuizawa, Japan, p. 19-20, 1987.

16. J. Manoliu, *Semiconductor Internat.,* April 1988, p. 90.

17. J. Hui et al., "Scaling Limitations of Submicron LOCOS Technology," *Tech. Dig. IEDM,* 1985, p. 392.

18. B. Coulman et al., *Ext. Abs. Electrochem. Soc. Meeting,* Spring 1989, p. 293.

19. J. W. Lutze, H. Perera, and J.P. Krusius, J. ECS, Vol. 137, No. 6, June 1990, p. 1867.

20. J. Hui et al., *IEEE Trans. Electron Dev.* **ED-29**, p. 554, 1982.

21. E. Kooi and J.A. Appels, "Selective Oxidation of Silicon and its Device Applications," *Semiconductor Silicon,* Electrochemical Society, 1973., p. 860.

22. A.E.T. Kuiper et al., "Oxidation Behavior of LPCVD Oxynitride Films," *Applied Surface Science* 33/34, p. 757, 1988.

23. P.B. Griffin and C.S. Rafferty, "A Viscous Nitride Model for Nitride/Oxide Isolation Structures," *IEDM Tech. Dig.,* p. 741, 1990.

24. R. A. Chapman et al., "High Performance Sub-Half Micron CMOS Using RTP," *IEDM Tech. Dig. 1991,* p. 101.

25. L. M. Loewenstein and C.M. Tipton, "Chemical Etching of Thermally oxidized Silicon Nitride: Comparison of Wet and Dry Etching Methods," *J. Electrochem. Soc.,* **138** (5) p. 1389, May 1991.

26. E. Kooi et al., *J. Electrochem. Soc.,* **123,** 1117, (1976).

27. T.A. Shankoff, *J. Electrochem. Soc.,* **129,** 1066, (1982).

28. C.A. Goodwin and J.W. Brossman, *J. Electrochem. Soc.,* **123,** 1117, (1976).

29. H.H. Tseng and P.J. Tobin, "A Double Sacrificial Oxide Process for Smoother Gate Oxide Interfaces," *Extended Abs. Meeting Electro. Chem. Soc.,* Spring, 1992, p. 392.

30. N. Guillemot et al., *IEEE Trans. Electron Dev.,* May 1987, p. 1033.

31. D.J. Chin et al., *IEEE Trans. Electron Dev.,* **ED-30**, July 1983, p. 993.

32. E.P. EerNisse, "Stress in Thermal SiO_2 during growth," *Appl. Phys. Lett.,* , **35** (1) 1 July, 1979.

33. D. Kao et al., *Tech. Dig. IEDM,* 1985, p. 388.

34. D.-B. Kao et al., "Two-Dimensional Thermal Oxidation of Silicon-II. Modeling Stress Effects in Wet Oxides," *IEEE Trans. Electron Dev.,* **ED-35**, January 1988, p. 25.

35. P. Sutardja, W.G. Oldham and D.B. Kao, *Tech. Dig. IEDM*, 1987, p. 264.

36. P. Sutardja, Y. Shacham-Diamond, and W.G. Oldham, *Tech. Dig. IEDM*, 1986, p. 526.

37. S. Isomae et al., "Oxidation-Induced Stress in a LOOCS structure," *IEEE Electron Dev. Letts.,* **EDL-7**, June 1986 p. 368.

38. S. Odanaka et al., "SMART-P: Rigorous three-dimensional process simulator on a supercomputer," *IEEE Tans. Computer-Aided Design,* p. 675, June 1988.

39. H. Unimoto and S. Odanaka, "Three-Dimensional Process Simulation of Local Oxidation of Silicon," *IEEE Tans. Electron Dev.,* **ED-38**, p. 505, March 1991.

40. R. L. Hodges, et al., *Ext. Abs. Meeting Electrochem. Soc.,* Spring 1991, p. 625.

41. R. Chapman et al., "0.8 μm CMOS Technology" *IEDM Tech. Dig.* 1987, p. 362.

42. Y. Han and B. Ma "Poly Buffer Layer for Scaled MOS", *VLSI Science &Technology* Electrochem. Soc., 1984, p. 334.

43. N. Hoshi et al., *Tech. Dig. IEDM,* 1986, p. 300.

44. N.A.H. Wils, P. A. Van den Plas, and A. H. Montree, "Dimensional Characterization of Poly Buffer LOCOS in comparison with Suppressed LOCOS," *Digest of ESSDERC,* Nottingham, England, p. 535, 1990.

45. J.M. Sung et al., "Crab-Eye Formation in Poly-Buffer LOCOS Isolation Technology," *J. Electrochem. Soc.,* **137**, p. 2350, 1990.

46. M. Ghezzo et al., *J. Electrochemical Soc.,* July 1989, p. 1992.

47. R. L. Guldi, et al., *J. Electrochemical Soc.,* December 1989, p. 3815.

48. J. M. Sung, et al., *IEEE Trans. Electron Dev.,* Vol. 38, p. 1970, Aug. 1991.

49. T. Lin, N. Tsai, and C. Yoo, "Twin-White-Ribbon Effect and Pit Formation Mechanism in PBLOCOS," *J. Electrochem. Soc.,* **138**(7), p. 2145, July, 1991.

50. H.S. Yang et al., "Poly-void formation in PBL Process," *Ext. Abs. Electrochem. Soc. Mtg.* Spring 1992, p. 442.

51. T. Nishihara et al., "A 0.5 μm Isolation Technology Using Advanced Poly Silicon Pad LOCOS (APPL)," *Tech. Dig. IEDM,* 1988, p. 100.

52. B.-Y. Nguyen, et al., *Ext. Abs. Electrochem. Soc. Conf.,* Spring, 1991, p. 614.

53. J. D. Hayden et al., *IEEE Trans. Electron Dev.,* **ED-38**, p. 876, April 1991.

54. J. M. Sung, et al., *Electron Dev. Letts.,* November 1990, p. 549.

55. N. Shimizu et al., "A Poly-Buffer Recessed LOCOS Process for 256 Mbit DRAM Cells," *Tech. Dig. IEDM,* 1992, p. 279.

56. S.S. Roth et al., "Polysilicon Encapsulated Local Oxidation," *IEEE Electron Dev. Letts.,* p. 92, March 1991.

57. S.S. Roth et al., *IEEE Trans. Electron Dev.,* **ED-39**, May 1992, p. 1085.

58. K.J. Cooper et al., "Recessed Polysilicon Encapsulated Local Oxidation," *IEEE Electron Dev. Letts.,* p. 515, October 1991.

59. S.W. Sun and K.C. Weng, "Effects of field-oxide volume ratio and interface-charge density on submicron modified LOCOS isolations," *Solid-State Electronics.,* vol. 32, April 1989, p. 333.

60. S.S. Roth et al., "PELOX Integrated PBL," *IEEE Trans. Semi. Manf.* Vol. 6, August, 1993, p. 246.

61. S.-P. Tay, S. Grant, and I. Wylie, "Submicron MOS Device Isolation Using HiPOX-PBL Technology," *Ext. Abs. Electrochem. Soc. Mtg.,* Ext. Abs. #287, Fall 1992, p. 410.

62. R.L. Hodges, F.T. Liou, and S.S. Kim, "Reduction of Oxide Thinning and Bird's Beak for PBL Isolation Using HIPOX," *Ext. Abs. Electrochem. Soc. Mtg.* Spring 1992, p. 421.

63. S. Deleonibus and S.S. Kim, "High Pressure Oxidation: The Key for Poly-Buffer LOCOS Scalability towards the Gigabit Density," *Ext. Abs. Electrochem. Soc. Mtg.* Fall 1993, p. 281.

64. E. DuBois et al., "A Study of the Electrical Performances of Isolation Structures," *IEEE Trans. Electron Dev.* **ED-37**(6), p. 1477, June 1990.

65. T. Shibata et al, *IEDM Tech. Dig.* 1983, p. 27.

66. T. Iizuka et al., "Double Threshold MOSFETs in Bird's-Beak Free Structures," *Tech. Dig. IEDM* 1981, p. 384.

67. D. C. Cole et al., "The Use of Simulation in Semiconductor Technology Development," *Solid-State Electronics*, Vol.33, No. 6, p. 591, 199.

68. D. Foty., J. Mandelman and T. Furukawa, "Behavior of an NMOS Trench-Isolated Corner Parasitic Device at Low Temperature," *Electrochemical Soc. Mtg. Fall, 1989,* p. 295.

69. T. Furukawa and J. Mandelman, "Process and Device Simulation of Trench Isolation Corner Parasitic Device," *Electrochemical Soc. Mtg. Fall, 1988,* p. 329.

70. K. Shibahara et al., "Trench Isolation with ∇-Shaped Buried Oxide for 256-Mbit DRAMs," *Tech Dig. IEDM*, 1992, p. 275.

71. G. Fuse et al., *Tech. Dig. IEDM* 1987, p. 732.

72. G. Smolinsky et al., "Material Properties of Spin-on Silicon Oxide (SOX) for Fully Recessed NMOS Field Isolation," *J. Electrochem. Soc.*, **137**(1) p. 229, January 1990.

73. K. Ohe et al., "Narrow-Width Effects of Shallow-Trench-Isolated CMOS with n^+ Polysilicon Gate," *IEEE Trans. Electron Dev.* **ED-36** June 1989, p. 1110.

74. J.Y. Chen and D.E. Snyder, "Modeling Device Isolation in High-Density CMOS," *IEEE Electron Dev. Letts.,* February 1986, p. 64.

75. J.R. Brews, "The Submicron MOSFET," in *High-Speed Semiconductor Devices,* Ed. S.M. Sze, John Wiley & Sons, New York, 1990, p. 183.

76. R. Chwang and K. Yu, "CHMOS - An *n*-Well Bulk CMOS Technology for VLSI," *VLSI Design,* Fourth Quarter, 1981, p. 42.

77. L.C. Parrillo et al., "Twin-Tub CMOS," *IEDM Tech Dig.,* 1980, p. 752.

78. S.J. Hillenius et al., "A Symmetric Submicron CMOS Technology," *Tech. Dig. IEDM,* 1986, p. 252.

79. M.-L. Chen et al., *Tech. Dig. IEDM,* 1986, p. 256.

80. L.C. Parrillo, G.W. Reutlinger, and L.K. Wang, U.S. Patent No. 4,435,895, March 31, 1984.

81. S.J. Hillenius and L.C. Parrillo, U.S. Patent No. 4,554,726, Nov. 25, 1985.

82. A.G. Lewis et al., *IEEE Trans. Electron Dev.,* June 1989, p. 1777.

83. J.Y. Chen, "CMOS-The Emerging Technology," *IEEE Circuits and Devices Magazine,* March 1986, p. 16.

84. J.D. Hayden et al., "A High-Performance Half-Micron Generation CMOS Technology for Fast SRAMS," *IEEE Trans. Electron Dev.*, **ED-38**(4), p. 876, April 1991.

85. Y. Nitsu et al., "Latchup Free CMOS Structure Using Trench Isolated CMOS Process," *Tech. Dig. IEDM 1985,* p. 509.

86. K.M. Cham and S.-Y. Chiang, "Study of Trench Surface Inversion Problem for the Trench Isolation Technology," *IEEE Electron Dev. Letts.,* Sept. 1983, p. 303.

87. *ibid.* ref. 75, p. 185.

88. K. Cham et al., *Tech. Dig. IEDM 1986, p. 296.*

89. G. Fuse, "A New Isolation Method with Boron-Implanted Sidewalls for Controlling Narrow-Width Effect," *IEEE Trans. Electron Dev.,* **ED-34**(2) p. 356, Feb. 1987.

90. B. Davari et al., "A Variable-Size Shallow trench Isolation Technology with Diffused Sidewall Doping for Submicron CMOS," *IEDM Tech. Dig.,* 1988 p. 92.

91. A. Lewis, et al., "Device Isolation in High Density LOCOS-Isolated CMOS,"*IEEE Trans. Electron Dev.,* Vol. ED-34, p. 1337 June 1987.

92. J. Y. Chen and A. G. Lewis, "Parasitic transistor effects in CMOS VLSI," *IEEE Circuits and Devices Magazine,* Vol. 4, p. 8, 1988.

93. A. G. Lewis et al., "Vertical Isolation in Shallow *n*-wWell CMOS Circuits," *IEEE Electron Dev. Lett.,* EDL-8, p. 107, 1987.

94. A.T. Wu et al., *IEDM Tech. Dig.,* 1989, p. 271.

95. J. Manoliu and J.O. Borland, "A Submicron Buried Layer Twin-Well for High Density CMOS," *Tech. Dig. IEDM,* 1987, p. 20.

96. L.C. Parrillo et al., "Twin-Tub CMOS-II," *Tech. Dig. IEDM,* 1982, p. 706.

97. M.-L. Chen et al. *Tech. Dig. IEDM* 1986, p. 256.

98. S.J. Hillenius and L.C. Parrillo, U.S. Patent No. 4,554,726, Nov. 25, 1985.

99. Ch. Zeller, C. Mazure, and M. Kerber, "Field-Implant-Free Isolation by Double-Well Split Drive-In," *IEEE Electron. Dev. Letts.,* p. 215, May 1990.

100. J.Y. Chen,"CMOS - The Emerging Technology," *IEEE Circuits and Devices Magazine,* March 1986, p. 16.

101. D.M. Brown et al., "Trends in Advanced CMOS PRocess Technology," *Proceedings of the IEEE,* December 1986, p. 1646.

102. R.D. Rung, C.J. Dell'Oca, and L.G. Walker, "A Retrograde *p*-well for High Density CMOS," *IEEE Trans. Electron Dev.,* ED-28, p. 1115, 1981.

103. R. Martin and J.Y. Chen, "Optimized Retrograde *n*-well for 1 μm CMOS, *Proc. Custom Integ. Circuits Conf.,* 1985, p. 199.

104. S.R. Coombs, "Scalable Retrograde *p*-well CMOS Technology," *IEEE Trans. Electron Dev.,* **ED-28**, p. 346, 1981.

105. Y. Taur et al., *IEEE J. Solid-State Circuits,* **SC-20,** p. 123, 1985.

106. G.J. Hu et al., *IEDM Tech. Dig.* 1982, p. 710.

107. Y. Mochizuki, "Special Report: High Energy Ion Implantation Technology," Nikkei Microelectronics, (Dec. 1991), p. 92.

108. M. Moslehi and K. Saraswat, "Thermal Nitridation of Si and SiO_2 for VLSI," *IEEE Trans Electron Dev.* **ED-32**, p. 116, January 1985.

109. P. Fahey, R.W. Dutton, and M. Moslehi, "Effects of Thermal Nitridation Processes on Boron and Phosphorus Diffusion in <100> Silicon," *Appl. Phys. Letts.,* **43**(7), p. 683 July, 1983.)

110. R. de Werdt et al., *Tech. Dig. IEDM,* 1987, p. 532.

111. K. Tsukamoto et al., *Nucl. Instrumentation & Methods,* B59/60, p. 584 (1991).

112. K. Tsukamoto et al., "High Energy Ion Implantation for ULSI: Well Engineering and Gettering," *Solid State Technology* P. 49, June 1992.

113. K. Kurosawa, T. Shibata, and H. Iizuka, "A new bird's beak free field isolation technology for VLSI devices," *IEDM Tech. Dig.* 1981, p. 384.

114. A. Stolmeijer, "A twin-well CMOS process employing high-energy ion implantation," *IEEE Trans. Electron Dev.,* **ED-33**, April, 1986, p. 450.

115. F.-S. Lai et al., *IEEE Trans. Electron Dev.,* **ED-33**, p. 1308, 1986.

116. R.A. Martin et al., *Tech. Dig. IEDM,* 1985, p. 403.

117. A.G. Lewis and S.L. Partridge, *IEEE Trans. Electron Dev.,* **ED-30**, p. 1680, 1983.

118. J.O. Borland and R. Koelsch, "MeV implantation technology: Next generation manufacturing with c rrent generation equipment," *Solid-State Technology,* December 1993, p. 28.

119. P.V. Gilbert et al., "Latch-Up Performance of a Sub-0.5 Micron Inter-well Deep Trench Technology," *Tech Dig. IEDM,* 1993, p. 731.

120. H. Inowaka et al., "Ultranarrow Trench-isolated 0.2 μm CMOS and its Application to Ultralow-power Frequency Dividers," *Tech Dig. IEDM,* 1993, p. 887.

121. P.C. Fazan and V.K. Mathews, "A Highly Manufacturable Trench Isolation Process for Deep Submicron DRAMs," *Tech Dig. IEDM,* 1993, p. 57.

122. P. U. Kenkare et al., "Sensitivity of Field Isolation Profiles to Active Pattern," *Tech. Dig. IEDM,* 1993, p. 479.

123. T. Uchida et al., "A Simulation of Plastic Deformation of Silicon During Thermal Oxidation," *Tech. Dig. IEDM,* 1993, p. 315.

124. P.E. Riley et al., "Reactor Characterization for a Process to Etch Si_3N_4 Formed on Thin SiO_2," *IEEE Trans. Semi. Manuf.,* Vol. 6, August 1993, p. 290.

125. P.K. Kenkare et al., "Scaling of Poly-Encapsulated LOCOS for 0.35 μm CMOS Technology," *IEEE Trans. Electron Dev.,* **ED-41**, January 1994, p. 56.

126. H. Wallace et al., "Applications of APCVD $TEOS/O_3$ Thin Films in ULSI IC Fabrication," *Solid-State Technology,* March 1994, p. 31.

127. S. Deleonibus et al., "Optimization of a shallow trench isolation refill process for high density non-volatile memmories using 100% chemical mechanical polishing," *Ext. Abs. of the Electrochemical Soc. Mtg.,* Spring 1994, p. 267.

128. M.A. Chonko, "Gate Dielectric Issues in 0.5μm Processing," *Ext. Abs. of the Electrochemical Soc. Mtg.,* Spring 1994, p. 256.

129. K.C. Brown et al., "Poly-Buffered LOCOS Isolation Pattern Definition," *Ext. Abs. of the Electrochemical Soc. Mtg.,* Spring 1994, p. 291.

130. S. Deleonibus, "The thickness and temperature dependence of field oxidation three-dimensional behavior: Example on Poly-Buffer LOCOS Isolation," *Ext. Abs. of the Electrochemical Soc. Mtg.,* Spring 1994, p. 273.

131. D. M. Rossman et al., Physical Characterization of Poly-Buffered LOCOS," *Ext. Abs. of the Electrochemical Soc. Mtg.,* Spring 1994, p. 295.

132. P.U. Kenkare et al., "Scaling of Poly-Encapsulated LOCOS for 0.35 μm CMOS Technology," *IEEE Trans. Electron Dev.,* **ED-41**, January 1994, p. 56.

133. P.U. Kenkare and J.R. Pfiester, "Extending LOCOS-based Approaches for Sub-0.5 μm CMOS," *Semiconductor International,* May 1994, p. 64.

134. J.R. Pfiester et al., "Nitride-Clad LOCOS Isolation for 0.25 μm CMOS," *Digest of 1993 Symp. of VLSI Tech.,* 1993, p. 139.

135. E. Bassous, H.N. Yu, and V. Maniscalco, "Topology of Silicon Structures with Recessed SiO_2," *J. Electrochem. Soc.* **123**, p. 1729, 1976.

136. M.E. Law, C. Rafferty, and R.W. Dutton, *SUPREM IV User's Manuel,* Technical Report, Integrated Circuits Laboratory, Department of Electrical Engineering, Stanford University, July, 1986.

137. K.M. Cham et al., "Characterization and modelling of the trench surface inversion problem for the trench isolated CMOS technology," *Tech. Dig., IEDM* 1983, p. 23.

138. H.-H. Tseng and P.J. Tobin, "Thin CVD Stacked Gate Dielectric for ULSI Technology," *Tech. Dig. IEDM,* 1993, p. 321.

139. T.T. Sheng et al., "From "White Ribbon' to 'Black Belt': A Direct Observation of the Kooi Effect Masking Film by Transmission Electron Microscopy," *J. Electrochem. Soc.,* **140**, p. L163, November 1993.

140. A. Bryant et al., "The Current-Carrying Corner Inherent to Trench Isolation," *IEEE Electron Dev. Letts.,* **EDL-14**, August 1993, p. 412.

141. N. Shigyo et al., "Three-Dimensional Analysis of Subthreshold Swing and Transconductance for Fully Recessed Oxide (Trench) Isolated $1/4\text{-}\mu$ m Width MOSFETs," *IEEE Transs. Electron Dev.,* **ED-35**, July 1988, p. 944.

PROBLEMS

1. Two n^+ diffused lines are running parallel in a substrate doped with 10^{15} boron atoms/cm^3. The substrate is biased to -5V, and both lines are connected to +5V. Using one-dimensional junction theory, calculate the minimum spacing needed between the lines to prevent their depletion regions from merging.

2. Explain why bird's beak and boron encroachment limit the maximum dimension in which conventional LOCOS isolation can be used.

3. Discuss each of the following drawbacks of LOCOS isolation technology:
   a) bird's beak encroachment
   b) boron encroachment;
   c) oxide thinning in narrow field oxide spacings
   d) non-planarity
   e) process complexity
   f) sensitivity of bird's beak encroachment on pattern geometry.

4. Explain how the frame-masked PBL (FMPBL) and the polysilicon-encapsulated LOCOS (PELOX) processes achieve a smaller bird's beak penetration length the conventional PBL.

5. Assume the field oxide beneath an $n+$ polysilicon line is 600 nm thick, and the p-type channel stop beneath this oxide is doped to 1×10^{17}/cm^3. Calculate V_{TF} and S_t if $Q_{tot} = 1\times10^{11}$ cm^{-2}.

6. If the nominal V_{TF} (i.e., measured when $I_{Dst} = 1$ μA) of an aluminum gate field oxide test device is 8V, what is the leakage current of this test structure when the aluminum line at 5V (assuming that $S_t = 0.5$V/dec at T = 300K)? If V_{TF} decreases to 6.5V when T is increased to 125°C, what is the leakage current in this case when the aluminum line is biased to 5V.

7. Based on Figs. 6-4 and 6-5 obtain the subthreshold swing S_t for the parasitic n- and p-channel FETs (both Al- and polysilicon gate devices) with a 2 μm separation between two n^+ and two p^+ diffusion regions.

8. If the circuit application requires that no more than 10 pA leakage flows between the $n+$ and n-well in a CMOS technology, and we have obtained the process and device data from Fig. 6-57a. What design rule should be specified to provide for the minimum n^+-to-n-well separation?

CHAPTER 7

THIN GATE OXIDES:

GROWTH and RELIABILITY

Gate oxide thickness has grown smaller with each generation of MOS ICs. Table 7-1 shows the evolution of MOSFET scaling from 1977 to 1991.[1] As the gate length shrank from 3.0 μm in 1977 to 0.6 μm in 1991, the gate oxide thickness went from 70 nm to 13.5-12.5 nm. During the shrinkage from 3.0 μm to 0.6 μm technologies, the power-supply voltage remained at 5V. At gate lengths below 0.5 μm, however, it is projected that the power supply voltage will have to be reduced. In fact, a reduction to 3.3V in some 0.5 μm CMOS technologies has already been implemented. The decrease in power-supply voltage is needed because the gate oxide thickness in such deep-submicron MOSFETs is 10 nm or less. As will be discussed, the oxide electric fields produced by 5V cause severe reliability problems in oxide films thinner than 10 nm.

The thickness of gate oxides is made as small as possible because the drive current in MOSFETs increases with decreasing gate oxide thickness. Since this trend extends to gate oxide thicknesses below 5 nm, it seems apparent that even thinner oxides will be specified as MOSFETs are scaled below 0.5 μm (see Table 5-3 in Section 5.6.1).

Table 7-1   Evolution of MOSFET Technology Since 1977[1]

Year of Introduction	1977	1979	1982	1985	1988	1991
Gate Length (μm)	3	2	1.5	1.1	0.9	0.6
Minimum Feature Size (μm)	3	2	1.5	1	0.7	0.5
V_{CC} (V)	5	5	5	5	5	5
MOSFET Gate Oxide (nm)	70	40	25	25	20	13.5
Junction Depth (μm)	0.6	0.4	0.3	0.25	0.2	0.15
NMOS I_{Dsat} @ $V_{GS} = 5V$ (mA/μm)	0.1	0.14	0.23	0.27	0.36	0.64
PMOS I_{Dsat} @ $V_{GS} = 5V$ (mA/μm)		0.06	0.11	0.14	0.19	0.31
Gate Delay @ FO = 1 (ps)	800	350	250	200	160	90

Furthermore, thin oxides (and shallow junction depths) are needed to control short-chan
-nel effects; i.e., thin gate oxides permit the gate to retain strong control of the channel
charge, and shallow junctions keep the drain field from extending far into the channel.

Table 5-4 in chap. 5 gives an estimate of MOSFET technology scaling made by Hu
in 1993.[1] As the gate length is decreased and approaches 0.1 μm it is predicted that gate
oxides of only 4 nm thickness will be used (albeit at a power supply voltage of 2.2V).
An example of a deep submicron CMOS technology (0.25 μm) is given by Chang et
al. of IBM, in which t_{ox} = 7 nm and V_{DD} = 2.5V.[2] Other studies predict that even thinner oxides will be needed in memory technology than in logic CMOS technologies. For
example, in 64 MB DRAMs the capacitor oxide thickness is estimated to be below 10
nm, and in EEPROMs tunneling oxides are even thinner than those used in DRAMs.

While the benefits of using thin oxides are apparent, there are two key issues which
must be satisfied to permit them to be utilized: (1) it must be possible to grow such
thin oxide layers precisely and uniformly across a wafer; and (2) MOSFETs with such
thin oxides must exhibit adequate reliability characteristics under normal circuit
operating conditions. These two issues are the subject of this chapter.

7.1 GATE OXIDE CHARACTERISTICS NEEDED FOR SUBMICRON MOSFETS

The desired characteristics of MOSFET gate oxides are the following:

1. The grown gate oxide thickness must closely match the thickness
specification of the MOSFET device design.

2. The specified oxide thickness must also be sufficiently uniform across the
entire wafer, and from wafer to wafer, and from run-to-run.

3. The gate oxide film and the Si/SiO$_2$ interface must exhibit adequately
small values of charge in the oxide and at the Si-SiO$_2$ interface (i.e., low Q_f,
D_{it}, Q_{ot} and Q_m values - see chap. 3).

4. The dielectric breakdown strength of the oxide must be sufficiently high
(e.g., >8 MV/cm), implying that the film is pinhole free and contains a
negligible number of defects that would lead to oxide breakdown at lower
electric fields.

5. The oxide film must exhibit a sufficiently long lifetime under normal
operating conditions (i.e., t_{BD} is adequate). This characteristic is related to #4.

6. The oxide should exhibit high resistance to hot-carrier damage (i.e., device
degradation should be low in the face of CHE or DAHC stressing).

7. If the oxide is to be used in a symmetric CMOS technology (i.e., in which
both p^+ and n^+ poly are used), the oxide film needs to be resistant to the
penetration of boron at the process temperatures used after gate doping. (Note
that this topic will be discussed in chap. 9.)

From the list of desired gate oxide characteristics given above, we see that thin oxide reliability issues fall into two categories:

a. Dielectric breakdown (which causes catastrophic failure of device).

b. Hot-carrier-injection degradation (as a result of which device characteristics are degraded).

In this chapter we cover gate oxide breakdown, and in chapter 9 we describe device degradation due to hot-carrier injection. However, here we will also cover all the mechanisms by which charge is injected into the gate oxide (section 7.3), including injection by "hot" as well as by "cold" carriers.

7.2 PHYSICAL PICTURE of SiO₂ and the Si/SiO₂ INTERFACE

Before setting out to describe the technology of growing thin gate oxides and their reliability, it is useful to discuss the physical and chemical properties of thermally grown SiO_2 and the physical picture of the Si/SiO_2 interface. We cover these topics in this section.

7.2.1 Physical and Chemical Properties of SiO₂

SiO_2 (silica) can be found in crystalline, vitreous, or amorphous forms. When the atomic structure of silica exhibits long-range order it is said to be in a *crystalline* form. Many varieties of crystalline silica exist, including quartz, crystobalite, coesite, etc. However, the type of silica encountered in silicon ICs (i.e., thermal silicon dioxide films grown under normal conditions) is not crystalline. Instead, it is silica in its *vitreous* (or *glassy*) form. Vitreous solids do not exhibit long range order. Instead, their structure is highly ordered only over short ranges. This glassy state of SiO_2 is also often referred to as *fused silica*. If no short-range order is exhibited by the silica, its structure is termed *amorphous*. Amorphous SiO_2 films may be encountered in oxides deposited under poorly controlled conditions. Since we are interested in thermally grown SiO_2 most of our discussion will focus on the glassy state of SiO_2 (fused silica).

The basic structural unit of silica is centered around the *structural formula* (SiO_4). The spatial arrangement of Si and O atoms is due to their respective valence (+4 and -2), their relative sizes, and their electrostatic interactions. These factors give rise to elementary SiO_2 cells of tetrahedric configurations. That is, a silicon atom (with a valence of +4) is located at the center of the tetrahedron, with oxygen atoms (O^{2-}) at each of the corners (Fig. 7-1a).[3] In crystalline SiO_2 (quartz), each oxygen atom belongs to two tetrahedra and is thus bonded to 2 silicon atoms. Such oxygen atoms are then known as *bridging oxygen atoms*. (Fig. 7-1b).[3] In vitreous or amorphous SiO_2 some of the vertices of the tetrahedra have *nonbridging oxygen atoms*, meaning they are not shared between two tetrahedra (Fig. 7-1d). The greater the ratio of bridging to non-bridging oxygens, the greater the cohesiveness of the SiO_2 structure.

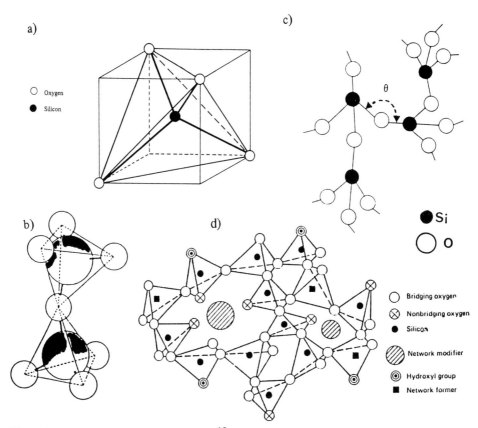

Fig. 7-1 (a) The basic structure of SiO_2.[18] (b) Three-dimensional representation of two neighboring SiO_4 cells, bridged by an oxygen atom. (c) Two-dimensional lattice representing vitreous SiO_2.[18] (d) The structure of thermally grown SiO_2 showing bridging and non-bridging oxygen atoms and dopant (i.e., network modifier) atoms.[132] (© IEEE 1965).

The interatomic distances (from the center of one atom to the center of its nearest neighbor) have been measured and found to have the following mean values: 1.62Å for the Si-O bond; 2.27Å for the O-O distance; and 3.12Å for the Si-Si distance. Note this implies that a 10 nm gate oxide is only 40-50 atomic layers thick!

The structure of fused silica is a continuous random network of tetrahedra, where the Si-O-Si bond angle varies from 110° to 180°, with the most probable value being 144°. A two-dimensional representation of the vitreous SiO_2 lattice is shown in Fig. 7-1c).[3]

The density of thermal SiO_2 (fused silica) is 2.20 g/cm³ which is smaller than that of quartz (2.65 g/cm³). In fused silica only 43% of the lattice space is occupied, making its structure much more open than that of quartz. Consequently, a large variety of impurity atoms can easily enter this oxide network and diffuse through it. Since it is difficult to directly assess the density of thin films, the refractive index of SiO_2 is usually measured instead, and the density is then inferred from it. A refractive index of 1.460 corresponds to a density of 2.20 g/cm^3. Generally, CVD oxides exhibit smaller densities than thermally grown SiO_2, and worse electrical and material properties correspond to less dense films. Hence, measurements of the index of refraction also provide a method for rapidly comparing the characteristics of deposited oxides.

7.2.2 The Si/SiO$_2$ Interface

The characteristics of the Si/SiO$_2$ interface, as well as the SiO_2 bulk characteristics, play an important role in the functioning of the gate dielectric. Hence, a discussion of the structure of this interface is also useful. In chap. 3 we introduced the concept of surface states and interface trapped charge, and their impact on the threshold voltage of MOSFETs. Here we consider these topics in further detail. We recall that surface states are extra allowed energy states for electrons that are present at the semiconductor surface, but not within the bulk.

The term *surface states* was coined by Tamm in 1932.[4] Using quantum mechanical calculations he showed that new electronic energy states arise in a crystal if the lattice is terminated at a surface. Such new states are confined to the region very close to the surface. He also calculated that these states will arise at interfaces (such as the Si/SiO$_2$ interface), as well as at free surfaces. Each of the states is associated with a single atom at the surface. Hence, an electron occupying one of these states is localized (i.e., forced to remain in a restricted region of space centered on that atom). Since such states thus effectively trap free carriers at the surface, they are also referred to as *interface traps*. The charge per unit area stored in the traps is symbolized by Q_{it}.

Although the theoretical basis of interface traps is well accepted and models exist that accurately detail the electrical behavior of the traps, the *physical origin* of these surface states has not been totally worked out. The weight of experimental evidence supports the view that surface states arise primarily from unsatisfied, or *dangling* bonds at the silicon surface (note also that such a silicon atom can be viewed as a *trivalent Si atom*).

From a qualitative perspective, the dangling bond model can be visualized with the aid of Fig. 7-2a. Here it can be seen that if a Si lattice is abruptly terminated along a given plane to form a surface, one of the four bonds of each Si atom at the surface is left dangling. There will thus be extra states on this surface because the energy field of the crystal is one-sided (i.e., the electrons in the surface region are bonded only from the side directed toward the bulk). It is plausible that the thermal formation of SiO_2 can tie up these surface Si bonds, and that along a perfect Si/SiO$_2$ interface (Fig. 7-2b) all such bonds could be tied up. In this case, surface states at the interface would be suppressed.[5] However, it is also plausible that such oxidation might not tie up all the bonds (Fig. 7-2c). If even a very small fraction of the number of dangling bonds was left unsatisfied, a significant number of surface states could exist. For example, on a (100) Si surface there are 6.8×10^{14} Si atoms per cm^2. If oxidation left 1/1000 of these bonds dangling, and each of them gave rise to a surface state, the density of interface trapped charges would be 6.8×10^{11} cm^{-2} (assuming one electronic charge is associated with each energy state). If a gate oxide thickness of 20 nm was being used, this would cause a threshold voltage shift of 0.63V. This indicates that if the dangling bond model correctly describes the origin of interface states, then only a relatively small number of residual dangling bonds can significantly perturb the device characteristics. Crystal defects near the surface or foreign atoms bonded at the surface are other interface perturbations that have been identified as possible sources of surface states.

As proposed by Deal,[6] surface states have the following properties:

> **1.** A surface state can trap or emit a carrier.

> **2.** The energy levels of these states are located within the forbidden gap.

> **3.** The surface state can be of either type: donor or acceptor. The classification is made in a manner analogous to bulk dopant atoms. That is:

>> **a.** A monovalent *donor* trap possesses two charge states +1 and 0. Its charge is positive (+1) when the trap is empty (i.e., its energy level E_T is above E_F), but is neutral (0) when full (when E_T is below E_F).

>> **b.** A monovalent *acceptor* trap possesses two charge states 0 and -1. When the trap is empty its charge is neutral (0) (i.e., its

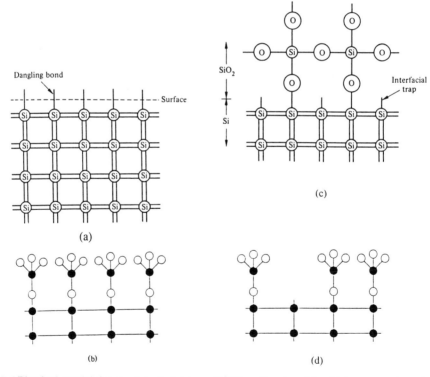

Fig. 7-2 Physical model for the interfacial traps.(a)"Dangling bonds" which occur when the Si lattice is abruptly terminated along a given plane to form a surface. (b) Post oxidation perfect interface. (c & d) Post oxidation dangling bonds that become interfacial traps.[118] Reprinted with permission of the publisher, the Electrochemical Society.

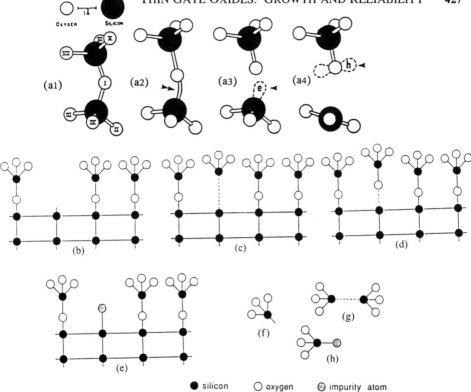

Fig. 7-3 (a) Strained and broken bonds: (a1) normal Si-O bonds; (a2) strained bond in vitreous silica ; (a3) broken bond represented with a trapped electron; (a4) broken bond represented with a trapped hole. Possible interface defects. (b) Si dangling bonds. (c) Si-Si stretched bond (or oxygen vacancy). (d) Si-O stretched bond. (e) impurity at interface. Possible oxide bulk defects: (f) Si dangling bond; (g) Si-Si stretched bond (or oxygen vacancy). (h) impurity in SiO_2.[5] (© IEEE 1988).

energy level E_T is above E_F), but when the trap is full its charge is negative (-1) (i.e., when E_T is below E_F).

4. Because they are mostly due to a disruption of the periodicity of the crystal lattice (and only less frequently caused by the presence of foreign impurities), interface states are not associated with well-defined energy levels. Instead, interface states are distributed throughout the entire band gap at closely spaced levels.

Figure 7-3 represents the bond stretching and broken bond model of the Si/SiO$_2$ bulk of Verwey[18] and of the Si/SiO$_2$ interface of Sakurai and Sugano.[5] That is, Fig. 7-3a depicts the stretched and broken Si-O bonds in the bulk, and Figs. 7-3b-d at the interface and Figs. 7-3e-h the possible defects in the oxide bulk. In Fig. 7-3b, the dangling Si bond at the surface is depicted as an *interfacial trivalent Si atom,* while in Fig. 7-3f, a dangling Si bond in the bulk is portrayed as a *trivalent Si atom.* Trivalent Si atoms introduce a deep trap level near the Si midgap when located at the interface (see Fig. 7-4) and a deep trap level in the SiO$_2$ bandgap when located in the oxide bulk (1 in Fig. 7-4). The weak Si-Si* and Si-O stretched bonds (Figs. 7-3c and 7-3d) at the interface introduce a continuum of deep trap levels, or if such stretched bonds exist in the bulk (Fig. 7-3g), they produce shallow trap levels. If a dangling Si bond is tied up with an impurity (most commonly H or OH) this is thought to produce an electron trap, while the oxygen vacancy (or weak Si-Si stretched bond) is considered to be the precursor of the hole trap. Thus, as we shall see, processes that decrease the electron trap densities tend to increase the hole trap densities.

An anneal in a hydrogen ambient (100% H_2 or 4%-H_2 forming gas) at approximately 450°C is normally the final step prior to assembly and packaging of the ICs. This step is thought to allow hydrogen to penetrate the gate oxide and tie up the remaining dangling bonds at the Si/SiO$_2$ interface not tied up by thermal oxidation (as suggested in Fig. 7-5). However, the Si-H or Si-OH bond can be easily broken by injected hot electrons, giving rise to interface traps. Thus, hydrogen introduced in the post-metal anneal or other process steps (i.e., during the steam reflow of an interlevel BPSG layer, or during the deposition of silicon nitride), can increase hot-electron degradation in a MOSFET. Consequently, it has been suggested that the ideal gate dielectric and all subsequent dielectric layers should contain as little hydrogen as possible to make them hot-electron resistant.

The defects in the oxide bulk and at the interface are believed to be responsible for:

1. Oxide integrity degradation (which may cause catastrophic failure).

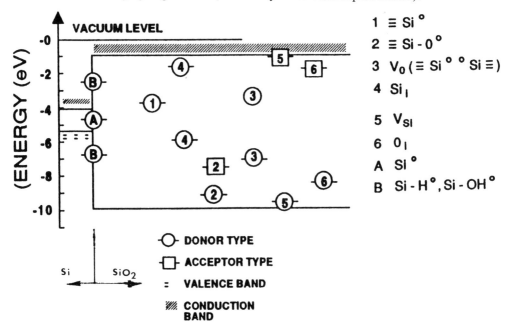

Fig. 7-4 Energy band diagram showing the energy levels of the various defects in the oxide-silicon interface and in the gate oxide.

* The weak Si-Si bond is more frequently referred to as an *oxygen vacancy*.

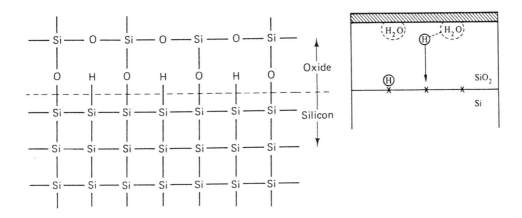

Fig. 7-5 How hydrogen can passivate the dangling bonds at the silicon surface shown in Fig. 7-2c and reduce the interface trap density. From D.L. Pulfrey and N. G. Tarr *Introduction to Microelectronic Devices*, p. 222. Copyright 1989. Prentice-Hall. Reprinted with permission.

   2. Hot-carrier induced degradation, which causes some of the device operating characteristics to be degraded (e.g., V_T and g_m), but the device may still work.

7.3   CARRIER INJECTION IN THE Si/SiO$_2$ SYSTEM

Failures in MOSFETs associated with the gate oxide (both catastrophic failures and device-characteristic-degradation failures) usually involve carriers injected into the gate oxide. A variety of carrier-injection mechanisms have been proposed for the Si/SiO$_2$ system.   Here we review the basic physics of the carrier injection phenomena in MOSFETs as useful background material for the discussion of gate oxide breakdown (this chapter), and hot-carrier degradation (chap. 9).

   Carriers can be injected either over an energy barrier (hot-carrier injection), or through a barrier (tunneling by cold carriers). The most important injection phenomena are:

   1. Channel hot electron (CHE) injection   Hot carrier injection phenomena

   2. Drain avalanche hot carriers (DAHC) injection   "

and

   3. Injection by Fowler-Nordheim tunneling   Cold carrier injection phenomena

   4. Injection by direct tunneling.   "

Hot carrier injection implies that the injected carriers are no longer in equilibrium with the lattice at the point of injection (i.e., they possess far more kinetic energy than they would normally acquire from the ambient lattice temperature). They gain such energy upon being accelerated by the high channel fields in the device. This is in contrast to tunneling injection phenomena, in which the carriers being injected are in equilibrium with the Si lattice (i.e., they are "cold") and do not become hot until after they are injected into the oxide and are accelerated by the oxide field to the gate electrode.

The energy-band diagram of the MOS structure, including the barrier heights for electrons and holes, is shown in Fig. 7-6. The oxide band gap is ~9 eV. The barrier that suppresses electron injection into the oxide (or *modified electron affinity*) is 3.1 eV, and the barrier for holes (*modified hole affinity*) is ~4.9 eV. Thus, the barrier to hole injection into the oxide is higher than that for electron injection.

7.3.1 Channel Hot Electrons (CHE)

Injection of channel hot electrons (CHE) occurs in MOSFETs biased to strong inversion. The electric field responsible for accelerating the carriers in this case is the lateral electric field. Ideally carriers flow only in the channel of the MOSFET since an energy barrier exists between the channel and the gate oxide (3.1 eV for electrons and 4.9 eV for holes). This barrier is important, since the electric field along the channel also has a vertical component. The vertical component pulls the carriers toward the gate, but the presence of the barrier suppresses the injection of the carriers into the oxide. Thus, the vertical field component merely acts to constrain the electrons to the silicon surface. However, if the carriers acquire sufficient energy from the lateral electric field and become 'hot', they can surmount this barrier and jump into the oxide conduction band. Since the barrier for electron injection is smaller, the probability of hot-electron injection is far greater than for hot-hole injection. Hence, the problem of hot-carrier injection is much worse in *n*-channel MOSFETs (in which electrons are the channel current charge carriers) than in PMOSFETs. Consequently, only *channel hot electron* (CHE) injection is generally considered to be important, and *channel hot hole* injection (which would be associated with PMOSFETs) is generally ignored.

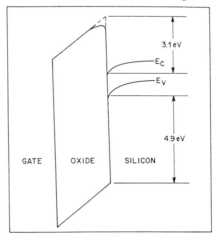

Fig. 7-6 Energy band diagram of a MOS device in the direction perpendicular to the surface. The barriers at the Si-SiO$_2$ interface are ~3.1 eV for electrons and ~4.9 eV for holes.

The energy-band diagram at the drain end of a MOSFET for the condition when hot electron injection can occur is shown in Fig. 7-7. Since the mean electron energy is a reasonably strong function of the electric field, and the fraction of hot electrons with an energy greater than the oxide barrier height is an exponential function of this mean energy, one expects most of the hot electron emission into the dielectric to occur where the channel field is the greatest. Figure 7-8a illustrates the field distribution along the channel for the saturation regime, which indicates that the channel electric field is very large near the drain in the pinchoff region. Thus, hot electrons are most likely to be generated in the pinchoff region of MOSFETs. The source of the electrons is the drain current, which is controlled both by the gate and drain voltages. More details on the channel electric field in short-channel MOSFETs and its effects on hot-carrier degradation are given in chap. 9. Nevertheless, once the channel hot electrons are injected into the oxide conduction band they can be transported to the gate electrode (in which case they represent a gate current), or they can be returned to the substrate, depending on the oxide field direction.

Figure 7-9 illustrates a plot of the gate current due to CHE versus gate voltage V_{GS}, with the drain voltage as the parameter. The CHE gate current initially increases as

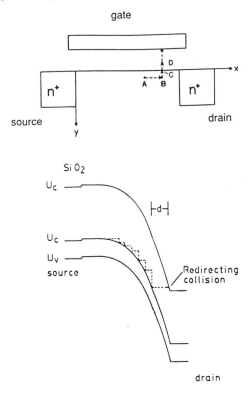

Fig. 7-7 The energy band diagram at the drain end of a MOSFET for the condition when hot electron injection can occur.

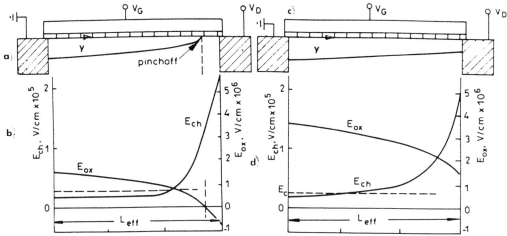

Fig. 7-8 (a) Cross section of MOS transistor operating in saturation. (b) The oxide and channel fields in the y-direction of the channel when the MOSFET is in saturation (i.e., $V_{GS} < V_{DS}$, here $V_{GS} = 6V$ and $V_{DS} = 8V$). (c) Cross section of a MOS transistor operating in linear regime. (d) The oxide and channel fields in the y-direction of the channel when the MOSFET is in the linear regime (i.e., $V_{GS} > V_{DS}$, here $V_{GS} = 15$ V and $V_{DS} = 8V$).[119] (© IEEE 1991).

V_{GS} is increased - due to the increase in the number of carriers in the channel. The gate current peaks at the point when $V_{GS} \cong V_{DS}$ because when V_{GS} is increased beyond V_{DS}, the MOSFET is driven toward the linear region of operation and the channel electric field is rapidly reduced. As the channel electric field decreases below its maximum value, fewer energetic electrons are produced. Thus, hot electron emission also declines. (Fig. 7-8b shows the electric field along the channel in the linear regime. It is seen that the maximum channel field strength is smaller than in the saturation regime case). Note, however, that as drain bias increases, hot-electron injection into the oxide increases because of increased channel field.

It should also be pointed out that when V_{GS} is smaller than V_{DS} the field in the oxide near the drain end of the channel is directed so that electrons in the oxide conduction band at that location are drifted back toward the substrate. In this case, many electrons that jump over the energy barrier into the oxide simply return to the MOSFET channel. Since only the electrons that reach the gate are detected as gate current, the gate current due to CHE will decrease as gate bias decreases even when electron emission at the Si/SiO$_2$ interface is increasing (because of higher electric field).

The two common models for gate current due to CHE are the *lucky electron model* and the *electron-temperature model*. In the lucky-electron model,[7] the probability of an electron suffering a collision within a certain distance is determined (as the electron is being accelerated along the channel by the drain bias). In MOSFETs with small channel lengths, it is calculated that a few "lucky" electrons may simply escape such energy loss collisions and only gain energy from being accelerated. These lucky electrons, become "hot", and acquire sufficient energy to be able to jump into the conduction band. (Collisions resulting in a carrier *gaining* energy from a collision are ignored). Using this model, the experimentally measured ratio of gate current to drain current has been successfully fitted at large drain voltages. The main discrepancy between the lucky-electron model and experimental data is that the model fails to describe the gate current observed under small drain bias.

The *electron-temperature model* assumes that the electron temperature T_e is higher than that of the lattice, and hence the electrons are not in equilibrium with the lattice.[8] The higher temperature of the channel electrons near the drain increases the number of electrons in the high-energy tail of the distribution. Some of these higher-energy electrons may be injected into the oxide. However, like the lucky-electron model this model predicts a much smaller gate current at low values of drain bias than is found experimentally.

Frey has presented an explanation of why gate current can occur at such low voltages. He noted that electrons can acquire (as well as lose) energy by collisions with the lattice.[9]   The highest-energy electrons are also the ones most likely to undergo such energy-gaining collisions - i.e., with optical (high-energy) phonons. Calculations show that enough energy-gaining collisions are possible even at drain voltages as small as 1.5V, to produce a significant number of high-energy electrons.

However, as channel lengths shrink below about 0.15 μm, Frey postulates that electrons in the channel may not be able to undergo enough energy-gaining collisions

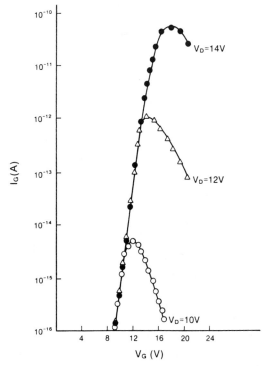

Fig. 7-9 Gate current due to channel hot electrons versus gate voltage, with V_{DS} as the parameter.[120] (© IEEE 1981).

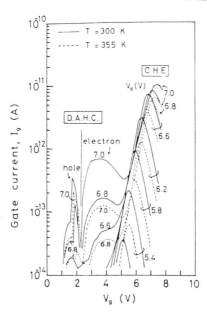

Fig. 7-10 At very low V_{GS}, I_G changes sign, indicating that hot holes are emitted into the gate oxide. Their presence at low V_{GS} is shown in this figure.[8] (© IEEE 1982).

before being collected at the drain. Consequently there will be fewer high-energy electrons available to cause hot-electron degradation reliability problems in such ultra-short-channel devices.

7.3.2 Injection of Drain Avalanche Hot Carriers (DAHC)

Energetic channel electrons accelerated by the lateral electric field can produce additional channel carriers (i.e., electron-hole pairs) by impact ionization in the channel region. The electrons created by impact ionization are either collected by the drain or injected into the oxide. The holes formed by this process give rise to substrate current, providing a measurable quantity for assessing the degree of impact ionization. Under conditions of gate bias much smaller than drain bias some of these holes can also cause a hot-hole gate current.

If the level of impact ionization is quite high a substantial substrate current can flow. Excessive hole flow into the substrate can lead to such undesirable behavior as snap-back or latchup. Hence, it is essential to monitor substrate current in a production environment and ensure that it does not become excessive in normal device operation.

As mentioned above, when V_{GS} is much smaller than V_{DS} (but V_{GS} is still greater than V_T), a gate current can flow due to injection of impact-ionization-generated hot holes (see Fig. 7-10). Since the magnitude of such hot-hole currents is very small (typically $<10^{-12}$ A) they are difficult to measure directly, especially in oxides thicker than 10 nm. However, indirect measurements using EPROM structures permit currents as small as 10^{-19} A to be detected. With these techniques, hole gate currents in oxides as thick as 25 nm have been observed.[10,11]   Figure 7-10 shows that hole gate currents arise when the gate voltage is much smaller than the drain voltage (e.g., $V_{GS} = 1.2V$ and $V_{DS} = 6V$). As V_{GS} is increased above 2V (while V_{DS} is kept fixed at 6V), the hot-hole gate current decreases to vanishingly small values.

As the gate voltage is increased beyond the hot-hole regime, however, the bias regime associated with drain-avalanche hot electrons (DAHE) is encountered (Fig. 7-10). Such DAHE gate current arises because as the voltage between drain and gate decreases (but the drain voltage remains at a constant, high value), the probability increases that hot electrons injected into the oxide conduction band can make it to the anode before being forced back into the substrate by the oxide field. This results in larger gate currents due to DAHE as the gate voltage initially rises. Further increases in gate voltage, however, lower the lateral electric field to such an extent that hot electrons generated by impact ionization events will not contribute significantly to the gate current. Thus, for sufficiently high gate voltages I_g is dominated by CHE.

While the shoulder region of gate current attributed to DAHE is not observed for thick oxides, it is detected in thinner oxides. Some workers have argued that this shoulder region current is not due to DAHE, but instead is due to the increased collection efficiency of the emitted electrons for thinner oxides. More work is required to resolve this issue.

Some models of hot-electron degradation in MOSFETs also attribute this degradation to avalanche-generated hot carriers. Others, however, dispute this view, arguing that there exists no physical basis for the expectation that secondary (impact-ionization, or avalanche generated) carriers could cause more degradation than the primary hot carriers (i.e., CHE). They note that CHE are, on average, more energetic and numerous by at least an order of magnitude than those secondary carriers generated by impact ionization.[12]

7.3.3 Fowler-Nordheim (FN) Tunneling

The phenomenon of carrier injection into the oxide by tunneling is due to the quantum-mechanical nature of the electron. In the classical sense, the oxide represents an impenetrable barrier to injection of electrons into the conduction-band of the silicon if they possess kinetic energies smaller than 3.1 eV. However, the wave nature of the electron (or hole) allows a finite probability of crossing the barrier even if the electron does not possess sufficient kinetic energy. This probability increases with larger gate electric fields and/or thinner barriers. As mentioned in the introduction, electrons injected by tunneling are generally considered to be in equilibrium with the lattice, and thus are characterized as being "cold," i.e., not "hot."

The first type of tunneling is called *Fowler-Nordheim tunneling*. Here electrons are injected by tunneling into the conduction band of the oxide through the triangular energy barrier. Once injected into the oxide conduction band, electrons are accelerated by the oxide field toward the anode (gate), causing a gate current. Figure 7-11a sketches the energy band diagram for this case assuming a positive bias is applied to the gate.

To determine the probability of an electron exhibiting FN tunneling through a barrier, Schroedinger's equation is solved for a triangular barrier. The WKB approx-

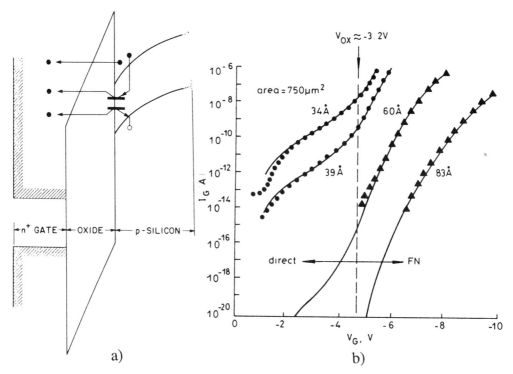

a)   b)

Fig. 7-11 (a) Energy-band diagram for the phenomenon of Fowler-Nordheim tunneling in the MOSFET gate oxide. Also shown are some possible interface-trap assisted leakage paths, with trap levels indicated by short, solid bars. From J.R. Brews, "The Submicron MOSFET," Chap. 3, in *High-Speed Semiconductor Devices*, Ed. Sze, p. 153. Copyright 1990, John Wiley & Sons. Reprinted with permission. (b) Theoretical and experimental tunneling I-V curves of Al-gate *n*-channel MOS structures under negative gate bias, illustrating the I-V characteristics of Fowler-Nordheim tunneling in 6 and 8.3 nm thick oxides and the calculated direct tunneling currents in 3.9 and 3.4 nm thick oxides.[15] (© IEEE 1983).

imation (discussed in most quantum mechanical textbooks) is invoked, and the following expression for the tunneling current expression is derived:

$$ J = A_F \varepsilon_{ox}^2 \exp(-B/\varepsilon_{ox}) \qquad (7-1) $$

where $A_F = 1.25 \times 10^{-6}$ A/V^2, B ~240 MV/cm, J is the current density in A/cm^2, and ε_{ox} is the oxide field in V/cm.[13] According to this equation, the oxide current is exponentially dependent on the electric field and experimental studies have found that the equation accurately describes the oxide current. This can be seen in Fig. 7-11b which shows the measured gate current and the gate current calculated using Eq. 7-1 in oxides 6 nm and 8.3 nm thick. The tunneling probability rapidly rises as ε_{ox} increases because the tunneling distance (i.e., the distance from the Si surface, through the triangular barrier, to the oxide conduction band) becomes smaller as ε_{ox} increases.*

It should also be noted that it may be possible for electrons to be hot but not possess sufficient energy to surmount the barrier. In this case, carrier injection may occur by allowing these hot carriers to tunnel through a smaller triangular barrier distance. Thus, a synergistic combination of processes which individually would not have caused injection may yet enable carriers to be injected. This effect was modelled by Ning and Yu.[14]

7.3.4 Direct Tunneling

For gate oxides thinner than 6 nm, the tunneling current is observed to exhibit a weaker dependence on oxide fields than that described by Eq. 7-1. This has been explained by attributing the gate current in such oxides to direct tunneling through the forbidden gap of the SiO_2 to the gate electrode Such direct tunneling is known to occur in thin oxides at low voltages. In direct tunneling, electrons tunnel through a trapezoid-shaped barrier as shown in Fig. 7-12. An expression for the tunneling probability can be derived, but

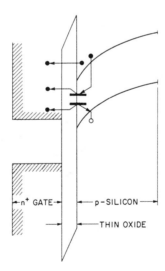

Fig. 7-12 Energy-band diagram for the phenomenon of direct tunneling through the gate oxide for thin oxides. Also shown are both unassisted tunneling and some possible interface-trap assisted leakage paths, with trap levels indicated by short, solid bars. From J.R. Brews, "The Submicron MOSFET," Chap. 3, in *High-Speed Semiconductor Devices*, Ed. Sze, p. 160. Copyright 1990, John Wiley & Sons. Reprinted with permission.

* Because the distance of tunneling between Si surface and the oxide conduction band decreases with increasing electric field.

no analytical expression is available as in the case of FN tunneling. Figure 7-11a also shows the direct tunneling current calculated from numerical analysis.[15]

For oxide thicknesses smaller than 3 nm the direct tunneling current becomes large enough that it removes carriers faster than they can be supplied by thermal generation. In such cases an inversion layer is kept from forming in an MOS capacitor. This appears to set a lower limit of ~3 nm on gate oxide thickness.

7.4 TESTS FOR GATE OXIDE RELIABILITY

Various types of tests are used to characterize the breakdown characteristics of gate oxides. Depending on the type of test employed, the breakdown phenomenon may bear a different name.

7.4.1 Measuring Dielectric Strength

The *dielectric strength* of an oxide - i.e., the maximum electric-field strength that can be applied before it breaks down (typically expressed in units of V/cm) is measured with a

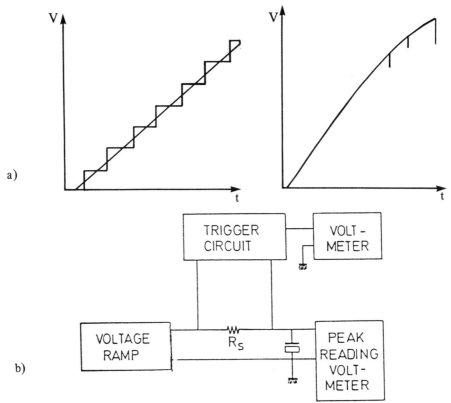

Fig. 7-13 (a) Breakdown voltage value of the gate oxide can be obtained by ramping or stepping the applied voltage and detecting sudden voltage drops at the electrode using a sensing resistor. (b) Diagram of the ramp-voltage oxide breakdown test setup.[16] Reprinted with the permission of the publisher, the Electrochemical Society.

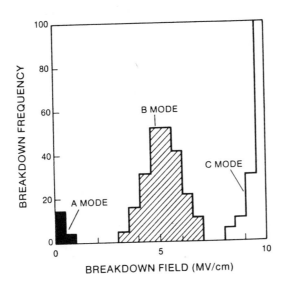

Fig. 7-14 Ramp voltage oxide breakdown data of Yamabe and Taniguchi.[17] (© IEEE 1985).

ramped-voltage test. That is, as shown in Fig. 7-13a a voltage that increases linearly with time (ramp voltage) is applied between the gate and substrate of the MOS-C test structure until the oxide breaks down. Breakdown is defined at the voltage value V_{BD} at which a sudden voltage drop across the oxide is observed. When measuring the dielectric strength of a set of oxide samples with the same thickness, the ramp rate is ($\Delta V/\Delta t$) is held constant (e.g., at a value of 0.1 or 1V/sec).* Figure 7-13b depicts the test setup for the ramped-voltage breakdown test.[16]

A histogram is usually used to plot the results of the ramped-voltage tests for a group of oxide samples, with the number (or fraction) of the group that failed within each voltage interval (e.g., within each 1 MV/cm, see Fig. 7-14).[17] The ramp breakdown tests are attractive because they require very little time. However, the V_{BD} data that is obtained is not directly relevant to practical concerns, since what is really needed is how long a given capacitor will survive at lower field strengths. A procedure for correlating V_{BD} to the time-to-breakdown at lower bias will be presented later.

On the other hand, a JEDEC-recommended current-ramp test applies a gate current that is ramped at a constant logarithmic rate until the oxide is broken down. In this test the charge-to-breakdown, Q_{BD} (see section 7.4.2.3), occurs in a very short time (i.e., approximately two to three seconds per capacitor), making it one of the most frequently used methodologies. Since it offers very poor reliability resolution, however, it can only be used to flag major oxide problems during the process.

* A variation of the ramped-voltage test is the *stepped-voltage test*, in which the voltage is stepped to various values, and held at those values for a constant time period.

7.4.2 Measuring Time-Dependent Breakdown Behavior

7.4.2.1 Time-to-Breakdown under Constant-Voltage Stressing. If
the electric field in the oxide $\mathcal{E}_{ox}$ is kept constant during the stress test (implying also
that the applied voltage is held constant), the biasing time (instead of the oxide voltage)
becomes the variable. The length of time t_{BD} elapsed until breakdown occurs is then
measured. The time-to-breakdown behavior of a group of oxide samples under such test
conditions is referred to as *time-dependent dielectric breakdown* (TDDB). Breakdown is
said to occur when the voltage across the oxide suddenly drops (Fig. 7-15.)[18] This test is
frequently referred to as the *constant-voltage time-to-breakdown* test.

7.4.2.2 Time-to-Breakdown under Constant-Current Stressing.
An alternative to the constant-voltage test is the *constant-current time-to-breakdown*
test. Here, a preset current is injected into the insulator (by Fowler-Nordheim injection),
and this value I_{inj} is held constant as the test proceeds. Voltage and time are recorded
until the voltage suddenly drops.[18] Results from such tests indicate that the time-to-

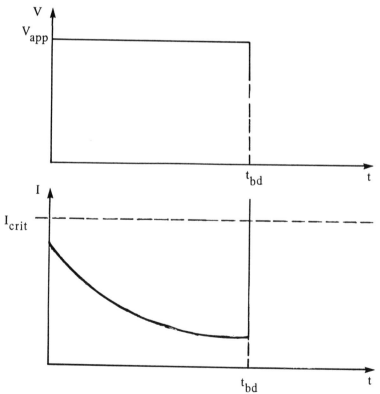

Fig. 7-15 (a) One technique for obtaining the time to breakdown t_{BD} is by applying a
constant voltage and detecting a sudden voltage drop.

breakdown is dependent on the value of the current density $J_{inj} = I_{inj}/A$ - the larger the current density, the shorter the time t_{BD} until breakdown occurs.

7.4.2.3 Charge to Breakdown (Q_{BD}).

If the constant-current test is used to determine t_{BD}, the product of the current density and t_{BD} provides another measure of the oxide breakdown behavior. This quantity is referred to as the *charge-to-breakdown* Q_{BD}. When comparing oxide breakdown behavior, those oxides exhibiting larger Q_{BD} are deemed superior. In a constant-current test the value of Q_{BD} is simply calculated from

$$Q_{BD} = J_{inj} \cdot t_{BD} \qquad (7 - 2)$$

If a constant-voltage test is used Q_{BD} can still be determined, but in this case the more general definition of Q_{BD} must be used (i.e., Q_{BD} is the time integral of J_{inj} from the time the bias is applied, to the time of breakdown)

$$Q_{BD} = \int_0^{t_{BD}} J_{inj} \, dt \qquad (7 - 3)$$

It has been found that for small values of J_{inj} the value of Q_{BD} for defect-free gate oxide films (i.e., intrinsic oxides) is constant as a function of the magnitude of J_{inj} (with a value of ~10 C/cm^2). For larger values of J_{inj} the value of Q_{BD} tends to decrease. We discuss this dependence of Q_{BD} on J_{inj} in section 7.5.1.

7.4.3 Mathematics of Reliability Characteristics

The dielectric strength ($\mathcal{E}_{ox}$ at breakdown observed in the ramp-voltage test), the time-to-breakdown t_{BD}, or charge-to-breakdown Q_{BD} are all important parameters that describe the breakdown of a single oxide sample. However, in a group of oxide samples of the same area and thickness, the above values will vary from sample to sample. Likewise, when a large number of MOS ICs (each containing an oxide of the same thickness and total gate oxide area) are operated under the same conditions, they will exhibit the same sort of variation in their breakdown parameters.

   The *reliability* of an oxide is defined as:

   the probability that it will not suffer breakdown under the stated operating conditions for the defined lifetime of the system.

To predict the reliability of circuits and systems in which such MOS ICs are used, the oxide reliability must be expressed in quantitative form. Here we present the terms and the mathematical functions with which oxide reliability is quantitatively characterized. In later sections, these terms and functions will be applied to specific examples. A more rigorous treatment of this subject is given in reference 19.

7.4.3.1 The Failure Unit (FIT).

If system contains a large number of electronic parts (e.g., MOS ICs) operated under the same conditions, a unit of failure rate can be used to characterize the reliability of the system. This unit of failure rate is the *Failure Unit* or FIT. One FIT is defined as 1 failure per 10^9 hours of device operation. (Note that other failure rate units, e.g., 1 failure per 1000 hours, have also been defined, but for electronic systems containing a large number of parts, the FIT is most useful.)

For example, 10 years of operation equals ~88,000 operating hours. If a system contains 1000 MOS ICs this corresponds to 8.8×10^7 device hours of operation in 10 years. Assume the failures are known to be caused by oxide breakdown and the system is designed to exhibit a failure rate of 1000 FIT. At this failure rate (1000 FIT), 1000 failures are expected to occur in 10^9 hours, so 88 failures should occur in 8.8×10^7 hours. Hence, 88 of the 1000 parts (~10%) are expected to fail during 10 years of operation. Likewise, it can be shown that if a system is designed for 100 FIT, the percentage of parts that are expected to fail in 10 years of operation is ~1%, and at 10 FIT, only 0.1%. Note that 100 FIT also corresponds to 0.01% failure per 1000 device hours of operation.

It should also be noted, however, that 1 FIT represents approximately 125,000 years of failure-free operation for one device. Thus, it is impossible to wait that long to determine whether all of a large number of similar devices have failed by then and to record the time of individual failure. As a consequence, some sort of *accelerated life testing* is needed to determine reliability. This type of approach is described in section 7.5.3.

7.4.3.2. The Cumulative Distribution Function.
Let there be N devices in a population, whose "reliability" one wishes to determine, and let these devices be placed under test at time $t = 0$. Assume that at time t it is observed $N_f(t)$ of the devices have failed and that $N_s(t) = N - N_f(t)$ devices have survived. The ratio of surviving devices to the number of original devices placed under test (N_s/N) is defined as the *reliability*. Similarly, the ratio of $N_f(t)/N$ is a measure of the unreliability of the devices and is usually termed the *cumulative distribution (or failure) function $F(t)$*. $F(t)$ describes the probability that a device will fail at a time before time t. In general, $F(t)$ has the following properties:

$$F(t) = 0 \quad t < 0 \quad\quad (7-4a)$$

$$0 \leq F(t) \leq F(t') \quad 0 \leq t \leq t' \quad\quad (7-4b)$$

$$F(t) \to 1 \quad t \to \infty \quad\quad (7-4c)$$

The *cumulative failure percentage* (i.e., the fraction of parts from a group of samples that will fail prior to a specific time t) can be obtained from $F(t)$. The time-to-failure data from the constant-voltage or constant-current tests are frequently plotted on a cumulative percentage failure graph, with the time axis scale plotted in terms of $\ln t$.

7.4.3.3 Probability Density Function.
The probability that a device will fail in the interval from t to $t + dt$ is determined by a function $f(t)$ referred to as the *probability density function*. It can be shown that $f(t)$ is the derivative of $F(t)$ with respect to time, or

$$f(t) = dF(t)/dt \quad\quad (7-5)$$

Furthermore, because all devices fail eventually,

$$\int_0^\infty f(t)\, dt \; = \; 1 \tag{7 - 6}$$

7.4.3.4 The Instantaneous Failure Rate.

In many applications, the two most important reliability quantities are the *cumulative percentage of failure* [determined using $F(t)$], and the *instantaneous failure rate*, $\lambda(t)$. The instantaneous failure rate is the failure rate during an interval of time divided by the population remaining at that time. In fact, $\lambda(t)$ may be the more critical of these two reliability functions. It can shown that $\lambda(t)$ can be calculated from $F(t)$ according to

$$\lambda(t) \; = \; f(t) / [1 - F(t)] \; = \; \{1 / [1 - F(t)]\} \; dF(t)/dt \tag{7 - 7}$$

The distinctive shape of the $\lambda(t)$ curve makes it the more useful measure of the reliability of a part. This 'bathtub'-shaped curve can be divided into three regions, as shown in Fig. 7-16. A high infant mortality rate is initially observed, followed by a constant random (and generally low) failure rate (midlife), and ultimately a wearout region. The infant failures are most often due to a manufacturing process defect that was not evident at wafer-level or package-level testing.

7.4.3.5 The Mean Time to Failure.

Another commonly used measure of reliability is the mean time to failure (MTTF) of the device or system, which can be expressed as

$$\text{MTTF} \; = \; \int_0^\infty t\, f(t)\; dt \tag{7 - 8}$$

MTTF is the device's average age at failure for a population whose reliability is represented by the function $(1 - [F\{t\}])$ with a probability density function of $f(t)$.

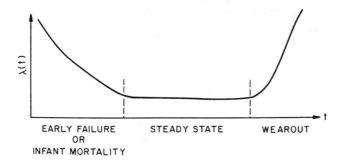

Fig. 7-16 Failure rate versus time for typical ICs.

7.4.3.6 The Weibull Cumulative Distribution Function. If the failure
rate of a group of parts varies as the power of the age of the device (as is observed to be
the case of oxide breakdown failures), the time-to-failure versus cumulative percentage
failure is likely to be well fitted with a *Weibull* (or *extreme*) *cumulative distribution
function.* The early failure of gate oxides can be represented by a Weibull distribution,
and Weibull plotting paper is often used in presenting oxide TDDB data. The failure rate
of parts whose failure statistics can be represented with the Weibull function is
expressed as

$$\lambda(t) = \frac{\beta}{\alpha} t^{\beta - 1} \tag{7 - 9}$$

where α and β are constants. From Eq. 7-9 we can calculate that

$$F(t) = 1 - \exp\left[-\frac{1}{\alpha} t^{\beta}\right] \tag{7 - 10}$$

and

$$f(t) = \frac{\beta}{\alpha} t^{\beta - 1} \exp\left[-\frac{1}{\alpha} t^{\beta}\right] \tag{7 - 11}$$

When experimental data is fitted to an assumed cumulative failure function to
determine the function parameters as well as the goodness of fit, appropriate plotting
paper must be used. That is, the scales of the paper must be such that the experimental
data will lie on a straight line if the data is well represented by the assumed distribution.
Such plotting paper is available for use with the Weibull distribution function. For the
Weibull distribution function

$$1 - F(t) = \exp\left[-\frac{1}{\alpha} t^{\beta}\right] \tag{7 - 12}$$

$$\ln\left\{\ln\left[\frac{1}{1 - F(t)}\right]\right\} = \beta \ln t - \ln \alpha \tag{7 - 13}$$

which is linear in the form $y = mx + b$. Figure 7-17 shows an example of Weibull
plotting paper; the ordinate is marked in cumulative percent failed devices $F(t)$, and the
abscissa is $\ln t$. If the experimental data are represented by a Weibull distribution, a
straight line is obtained when the data are plotted, as shown in Fig. 7-17. The slope of
the line is the parameter β. Note that if $\log t$ is the horizontal axis, the vertical axis can
be scaled either as $\ln \{\ln (1 - F[t])^{-1}\}$ or as F (see Fig. 7-17).

7.4.3.7. The Log-Normal Cumulative Distribution Function. The *log-
normal distribution. function* is another form of $F(t)$ that been empirically shown to
successfully describe the failure statistics of oxide breakdown. Many reports which
describe oxide TDDB experiments report their data using log-normal plotting paper. The
function $f(t)$ of the log-normal distribution is given by

$$f(t) = \frac{1}{\sigma t \sqrt{2\pi}} \exp\left[-\frac{1}{2}\left(\frac{\ln t - \mu}{\sigma}\right)^2\right] \tag{7 - 14}$$

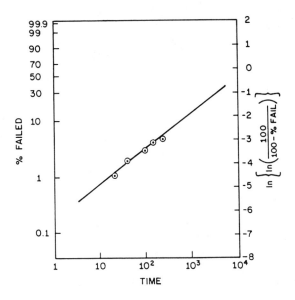

Fig. 7-17 An example of Weibull plotting paper showing the failure distribution for a typical device. From W.J. Bertram, "Yield and Reliability," Chap. 14 p. 632, in *VLSI Technology,* 2nd. Ed., S.M. Sze Ed., Copyright 1988 Bell Telephone Laboratories. Reprinted with permission.

$$= \frac{1}{\sigma\, t \sqrt{2\,\pi}} \exp\left[-\frac{1}{2}\left(\frac{1}{\sigma}\ln\frac{t}{t_{50}}\right)^2\right]$$

where μ is the *mean* and σ is the *dispersion* of the distribution. The median time to failure (the time when 50% of the devices have failed) is given by

$$t_{50} = e^{\mu} \tag{7-15a}$$

or

$$\ln t_{50} = \mu \tag{7-15b}$$

and the *dispersion* (or *scale parameter*) σ is approximately

$$\sigma \cong \ln\,(t_{50}/t_{16}) \tag{7-16}$$

where t_{16} is the time when 16% of the devices have failed (more precisely, 15.866%).
    The form of $F\,(t)$ is given by

$$F\,(t) = \int_0^t f(\tau)\,d\tau = \frac{1}{\sigma\sqrt{2\,\pi}}\int_0^t \frac{d\tau}{\tau}\exp\left[-\frac{1}{2}\left(\frac{\ln\tau - \mu}{\sigma}\right)^2\right] \tag{7-17}$$

Experimental data can be fitted to the log-normal distribution function by plotting the data on standard *log-normal plotting paper*, on which the ordinates have a normal probability scale and the abscissae have a logarithmic time scale (or vice-versa). A straight line representing the distribution is obtained if the probability distribution is log-normal. The value of the σ of the distribution can be estimated from the plot by the intersection of a line parallel to the experimental data and passing through the index point ⊕, with the sigma scale on the right hand side of the plot (see Fig. 7-18). The MTTF is the time shown on the log-normal plot of the TDDB data when the cumulative percent failure is 50 percent.

7.4.3.8 Characterizing the Reliability of Oxides in Terms of the Mathematical Reliability Functions.
As noted earlier, the quantities of most interest with respect to the reliability of an electronic system containing a large number of parts are: (1) the *cumulative failure percentage* of these parts during the expected lifetime of the system under the specified normal operating conditions; and (2) the *instantaneous failure rate* as a function of time over the system lifetime. Note that $\lambda(t)$ will generally vary during this time, but typically, a maximum value is specified. However, it may be possible to use a screening technique to prevent defective parts from being used in the system (by burn-in, as described in section 7-6). This can not only reduce the value of $\lambda(t)$, but can also make $\lambda(t)$ become essentially constant over the

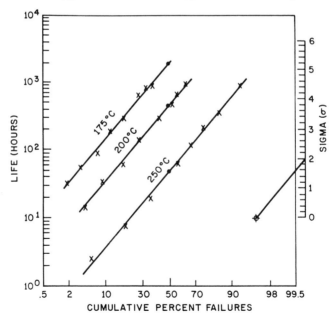

Fig. 7-18 An example of log-normal plotting paper showing device failure distribution at three temperatures. From W.J. Bertram, "Yield and Reliability," Chap. 14 p. 636, in *VLSI Technology*, 2nd. Ed., S.M. Sze Ed., Copyright 1988 Bell Telephone Laboratories. Reprinted with permission.

expected lifetime (i.e., the surviving parts behave like those in the constant (or random -failure) portion of the instantaneous failure rate curve shown in Fig. 7-16). In such cases, a single λ (t) value can be used to characterize the failure rate of the system.

The cumulative percentage of failure is usually determined from experimental values of TDDB data under normal or accelerated stress conditions (but, by using a relationship that correlates V_{BD} to t_{BD}, the cumulative percentage failure can also be determined as a function of experimental V_{BD} values, as will be discussed in section 7.5.3).

To determine values of λ (t) however, we must calculate them from Eq. 7-7. This implies that an analytical expression for F (t) must be available. The following two approaches are used to establish the analytical form of F (t) from the empirical cumulative failure data.

1. In the first approach, F (t) is assumed to exhibit either a Weibull or log-normal form. In this case, the data of cumulative percentage failure versus t_{BD} is plotted on the graph paper appropriate for the assumed form of F (t) (i.e., if we assume $F(t)$ has a log-normal form, the data is graphed on log-normal plotting paper). If a straight-line dependence is exhibited by this graphed data, the parameters needed to obtain the analytical form of F (t) can be extracted from the plot [e.g., μ and σ for the log-normal form of the F (t) function, or α and β for the Weibull form of the F (t) function]. Once these parameters are extracted, the analytical form of $F(t)$ can be determined, and this function can then be used in Eq. 7-7 to determine λ (t).

2. In the second approach (as is used in the oxide breakdown reliability model discussed in section 7.5.4), F (t) is derived indirectly. Here, oxide breakdown is assumed to be hastened by defects present in the oxide film.[20] For instance, when such a defect exists, the oxide breaks down at a smaller voltage than expected for a film of that nominal oxide thickness. Since the distribution of such defects is also used in estimating the yield of ICs, F (t) is likewise assumed to have a form (1 - Y), where Y is the function that estimates the yield (ratio of good chips to the number of chip sites per wafer). The experimental cumulative failure percentage data is then used to calculate Y, which in turn is used to establish the analytical form of F (t).

Specifically, if the defects are assumed to be uniformly distributed Y is assumed to follow the Poisson distribution

$$Y = \exp[-D(\Delta t_{ox})A].\qquad\qquad (7 - 18a)$$

If they are assumed to be nonuniformly distributed, Y has a Gamma function form

$$Y = \frac{1}{(1 + A D (\Delta t_{ox}) S)^{1/S}}\qquad\qquad (7 - 18b)$$

The data of cumulative percent failure versus t_{BD} is then used to establish a set of empirical data points representing the cumulative oxide defect density [$D(\Delta t_{ox})$] versus effective oxide thinning. (The procedure for doing this is described in detail in section 7.5.4.) Finally, an analytical function of $D(\Delta t_{ox})$ is fitted to this set of points (see for example, Eq. 7-40). The analytical form of this function is used to calculate the defect density value required in the function used to calculate Y. That is, once A and $D(\Delta t_{ox})$ are known, Y can found, and this allows an analytical form of $F(t)$ to be established (see Eq. 7-41). From this expression, $\lambda(t)$ can be found using Eq. 7-7.

7.5 THE PHENOMENON OF OXIDE BREAKDOWN

Thin oxide films undergo catastrophic breakdown when stressed by high electric fields. The maximum electric field that SiO_2 films (fabricated in normal IC processes) can withstand without instantaneously breaking down is approximately 12 MV/cm. However, not all oxide films of the same thickness undergo breakdown at the same electric field strength. Results of experiments on MOS-C structures in which an increasing electric field is applied until breakdown occurs indicate that such oxide failures fall into three groups (as shown in Fig. 7-14).

Some fraction of the sample population can withstand the highest electric fields (8-12 MV/cm). These constitute the C-mode group shown in Fig. 7-14. The high-field failure mechanism exhibited by this group is referred to as "intrinsic" failure. It is generally assumed that such oxides are defect free. Intrinsic oxide films are observed to fail at about the same time if they are stressed for long periods at lower electric fields.

Another fraction of the stressed oxides fail instantly upon the application of a relatively small gate bias, e.g., <1 MV/cm (the A-mode group in Fig. 7-14). It is believed that such MOS-Cs may already be shorted before the application of the low-strength field. Oxides that cannot withstand even such relatively low electric fields are thought to possess gross defects (such as pinholes).*

The remaining fraction of oxide films (the B-mode group in Fig. 7-14) suffers failure at electric fields of intermediate strength (2-6 MV/cm). The oxides of the B-mode group are thought to contain weak spots that do not produce instant shorting but may give rise to early failures of ICs under normal operating conditions (infant-mortality failures). Thus, B-mode failures are believed to be responsible for the early breakdown of oxides. Since such premature failures occur at various times, they are also referred to as *time-dependent dielectric breakdown* failures. Note that if 5V is applied across a 15 nm gate oxide, the oxide field falls in the range of the B-mode failures (~3 MV/cm). Hence, B-mode failures represent a serious problem for MOSFETs with such thin oxides. In this section we discuss the physical models of intrinsic failure (C-mode) and early failure (B-mode).

---

* A technique for gate oxide pinhole detection prior to metalizing the oxide has recently been described.[21] It works by carbonization of the Si surface by propane infiltration. After surface carbonization at the pinhole sites, the oxide is stripped, leaving behind SiC spots that are easily visible with an optical microscope.

Before beginning the discussion of breakdown models, one other general observation regarding breakdown should be mentioned. It appears that oxide degradation occurs in two stages. At first, the oxide is gradually weakened by the passage of gate current. At some point this weakening permits a continuous conductive path to be locally established in the oxide. The energy stored in the MOS-C is then abruptly discharged by the current flowing along this path. As a result, the oxide film (and also possibly the gate material above the oxide at that location), is vaporized at that spot.

Examination confirms that the breakdown is highly localized. That is, a conductive short of very small area is found at a specific location within the MOS-C (Fig. 7-19).[18] However, if the gate material over this spot is also completely vaporized, the capacitor itself may not be shorted. Such blowing of the gate material over the breakdown spot acts a self-healing mechanism. During oxide stress testing many such self-healing breakdown events may be observed on one capacitor.[22]

7.5.1 Qualitative Physical Models of Intrinsic Oxide Breakdown

The physical origin of intrinsic oxide breakdown is still not entirely understood. A

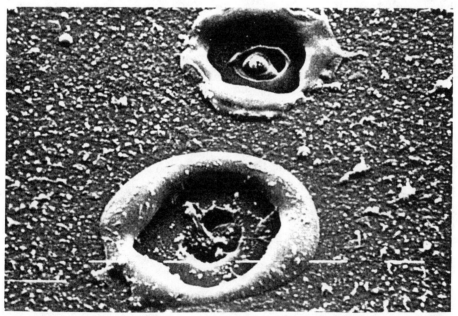

Fig. 7-19 A SEM photograph of two breakdown spots. The polysilicon electrode has melted away over 20 μm^2. The polysilicon is spread over a large area in the form of dust and little globules. The size of a dash is 1 μm. From D.R. Wolters and J.F. Verwey, "Breakdown and Wear-Out Phenomena in SiO$_2$ Films," Chap. 6 p. 329, in *Instabilities in Silicon Devices*. G.M. Barbottin and A. Vapaille Eds., Copyright 1986 Elsevier Science Publishers. Reprinted with permission.

number of models have been proposed to explain the phenomenon, but experimental evidence does not convincingly support one over the others. Here we describe the two leading models, the *hole-generation and trapping model* and the *lattice damage model*. Several other models have also been proposed including the electron-trapping model, the resonant tunneling model, and the electron trap-generation model. References are listed that give the details of the latter three.[23,24,25]

7.5.1.1 Hole Generation and Trapping Model. The most widely accepted theory of oxide breakdown is the *hole generation and trapping model*.[26,27,28] This model proposes that at sufficiently large fields electrons are injected into the conduction band of the oxide by Fowler-Nordheim tunneling. In the oxide conduction band these injected electrons are accelerated by the oxide field toward the anode, thereby gaining kinetic energy.* Some of these high-energy electrons generate electron-hole pairs within the oxide. A fraction of these generated holes are trapped at localized areas of the oxide, which, for some reason, have a greater probability to trap positive oxide charge than the "robust" oxide areas. (Some sort of 'super-fine' defects such as trivalent Si atoms in the bulk [resulting in a dangling bond], impurities, or very small micropores at such locations are believed to act as a 'seed' for the generation of 'larger' defects during high current injection.)** Locations with such a propensity to trap positive charge are postulated to make up only ~10^{-6} of the total oxide area.[28] The locally trapped holes increase the positive charge (and thus the cathode field) at such points in the oxide, causing the tunneling current density to increase there (a positive feedback effect). When the density of trapped-oxide hole charge Q_{ot}^+ at one of such locations reaches some critical value, the local tunneling current is increased to the point that breakdown occurs.

Several mechanisms for hole generation within the oxide by the energetic electrons have been suggested, including band-to-band impact ionization, trap-assisted impact ionization, and transitions between the conduction-band and valence-band tails of the SiO_2 (Fig. 7-20). The latter two effects could permit significant hole generation at even relatively low voltages (albeit at reduced generation rates).

The argument that trapped holes are the responsible species for oxide damage gains more plausibility once it is recognized that hole trapping in oxides is far more likely to

---

* Note that the *anode* and *cathode* are the terminals at which the polarity of the applied bias is, respectively, positive and negative. Thus, either the gate or the substrate in a MOS-C can be the cathode, depending on the polarity of the applied bias. In most cases, the gate of a MOS-C with a *p*-type substrate is biased positively in oxide stress tests (making the substrate the cathode). Occasionally, however, results are reported for the case of negative gate bias, in which case the gate becomes the cathode.

** It has been speculated by Sah that if the oxide film was microscopically uniform and free of such superfine defects, that the 'intrinsic' breakdown fields observed in normally fabricated thin oxide films (10-15 MV/cm) would be much higher (possibly by as much as by a factor of 5).[29] Under such conditions, if current runaway was not initiated by very-high Fowler-Nordheim injected gate currents, the field-strength might eventually become so strong that the electrons would be directly ripped from their silicon-oxide bonds, and the lattice would disintegrate or explode!

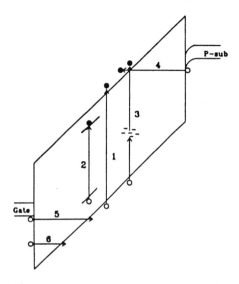

Fig. 7-20 Several possible mechanisms of the substrate hole current.[31] (© IEEE 1986).

occur than electron trapping. That is, electrons in the oxide conduction band are quite mobile (20-40 cm^2/V·s), and hence most are apparently swept rapidly from the oxide. However, the relatively low mobility of holes in the oxide (~2x10^{-5} cm^2/V·s) makes it far more probable that they will be trapped. The greater likelihood of hole trapping has been demonstrated by independent experiments, in which MOSFETs were exposed to ionizing radiation capable of generating electron/hole pairs and lattice damage. Such irradiated MOSFETs exhibited negative threshold voltage shifts, implying that positive charge accumulated in the oxide after being irradiated. From this it is inferred that if the lattice is damaged and both electrons and holes are available to be trapped on the damaged sites, positive charge (hole) trapping appears to be more probable than negative charge (electron) trapping.

It should be noted, however, that some electron trapping is also possible, and in fact it evidently occurs simultaneously with hole trapping as a result of the electron transport in oxides. This is evident from Fig. 7-21 which shows the measured and calculated gate current (using the quantitative model described in section 7.5.3) through a 13 nm-thick gate oxide as a function of V_{GB}.* The saturation of the gate current as V_{GB} increases implies that negative charge is being trapped throughout the oxide, as depicted in Fig. 7-22. (Note, however, that typical oxide films have been shown to trap only about one percent of the total injected electrons.[30])

Nevertheless, while trapped electrons may be accumulating throughout most of the oxide volume as gate current flows, the hole-trapping model assumes that such electron trapping does not contribute to the damage that leads to breakdown. Instead, only at

* Note that in this case, V_{GB} is negative, implying that the gate is the cathode, and electrons are injected into the oxide from the gate.

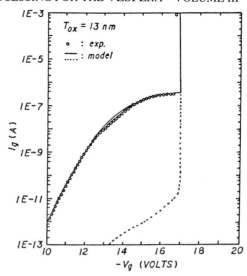

Fig. 7-21 I-V curve of a ramp-voltage test measured and simulated by the model. The dotted curve is the current carried by the weak area, which is responsible for breakdown.[121] (© IEEE 1985).

those local spots where hole trapping is dominant does such damage occur. The current density carried in these 'mini-defective' regions increases as the positive charge builds up. While this current component initially makes up only ~10^{-6} of the total tunneling current (since the defective areas consist of only ~10^{-6} of the total oxide area), the

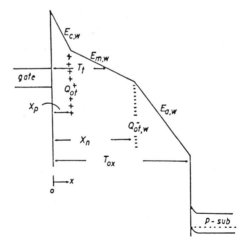

Fig. 7-22 SiO_2 energy diagram showing trapped holes Q_{ot}^+ and trapped electrons Q_{ot}^-.[121] (© IEEE 1985).

positive feedback effect causes such defect-region current to increase until it dominates the gate current flow and produces breakdown. (Figure 7-21 also shows the calculated current flowing in the mini-defective region, as the dashed curve. Notice that it rises until it eventually dominates the gate current, finally leading to breakdown).

The presence of hole flow in the gate oxide during oxide stressing (resulting from the generation of holes in the oxide as discussed above) has also been directly observed using two different approaches. In the first, the gate of an n-channel MOSFET is positively biased to cause Fowler-Nordheim tunneling of electrons into the oxide. This gives rise to a gate current I_g (consisting of electron flow) shown in Fig. 7-23.[31] At the same time, however, a small hole current is measured flowing from the substrate I_p (originating from holes generated in the oxide, as discussed above, which are then drifted to the substrate by the oxide field). The charge to breakdown due to I_g (Q_{BD}) is monitored versus Fowler-Nordheim (electron injection) fluence, as is the hole-charge-to-breakdown (Q_p) versus hole fluence. For low densities of gate current, the value of Q_{BD} in intrinsic oxides is found to be relatively constant at ~10 C/cm^2. The value of Q_p is also constant, but is much smaller, at a value of ~0.1 C/cm^2 (Fig. 7-24a).

In the second approach of directly examining the effect of hole flow on the breakdown characteristics of oxide, hot holes originating in the channel are injected into the oxide. That is, hot electrons are produced in the channel of an NMOSFET by the application of a high drain electric field (e.g., V_{DS} = 10V).[32] These hot electrons generate additional channel electron/hole pairs by impact ionization, as described in section 7.3.2. By keeping the gate voltage much lower than the drain voltage (e.g., V_{DS}

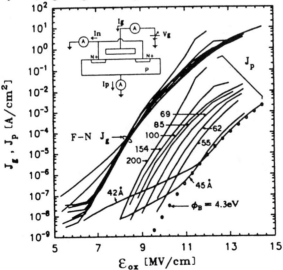

Fig. 7-23 Gate and hole current density versus oxide field for different oxide thicknesses. The gate currents follow the same Fowler-Nordheim characteristics as expected. The dependence of hole current on oxide thickness eliminates cold carrier tunneling as the origin of holes. The dotted curve labeled $\varphi_B = 4.3$ eV represents the theoretical J-$\mathcal{E}$ for valence band electron tunneling.[31] (© IEEE 1986).

= 10V and V_{GS} = 1.5V), any channel hot holes injected into the oxide conduction band will be drifted by the oxide field toward the gate. While hot electrons can also be injected and transported through the oxide (by making the gate voltage *larger* than the drain voltage), it was found that MOSFETs stressed with enough hot electrons to produce threshold voltage and transconductance degradation did not exhibit reduced Q_{BD} values if subjected to Fowler-Nordheim stressing after such hot electron stressing. On the other hand, stressing by hot hole injection prior to Q_{BD} testing, degraded the Q_{BD} of the oxides. That is for every 0.01 C/cm² of hole fluence, Q_{BD} was reduced by ~1 C/cm². This also appears to support the model assumption that hole transport through the oxide is somehow related to oxide breakdown.

One inconsistency between this model and experimental data is that Q_{BD} appears to *decrease* with increasing temperature. Since impact ionization is predicted to decrease with increasing temperature, the model would imply that Q_{BD} should also *increase* with temperature. Another question concerns the fact that oxide breakdown occurs at electric fields smaller than those that could cause band-to-band impact ionization in the oxides. This concern was addressed by postulating that trap-assisted ionization or transitions between the conduction-band and valence-band tails of the SiO_2 could be responsible for producing holes in the oxide, as mentioned above.

Nevertheless, if the mechanism of hole trapping is indeed chiefly responsible for oxide breakdown, it would be useful to characterize the origin, growth, and shrinkage of hole trap-center densities. As noted earlier, hole traps are thought to be caused by oxygen vacancies in bulk and/or dangling bond at the surface.

A recent study by Satake and Toriumi sheds some light on why Q_p is independent of (Fowler-Nordheim induced) gate current density, but that Q_p (and Q_{BD}) decreases with increasing temperature.[102] Their model postulates that hot holes in thin oxides are generated in the gate electrode, and that these holes are captured at traps (usually weak Si-O bonds randomly distributed throughout the oxide) having a small but finite repulsive barrier (as shown in Fig. 7-24b). The hole trapping induces local structural changes in the SiO_2 network (weak Si-O bond becomes a dangling bond), and the oxide band gap at these sites becomes smaller than that of SiO_2. Eventually a breakdown path whose conductivity is much larger than that in SiO_2 is created, leading to oxide breakdown. At room temperature, holes can easily be trapped at these sites by surmounting the repulsive barrier merely with the aid of thermal energy. Thus, oxide breakdown brought about by such trapping can occur without the help of the oxide field. At low temperatures, holes do not have enough thermal energy to overcome the barrier, and the traps remain unfilled unless the oxide field is increased such that the barrier is lowered (Fig. 7-24c). Thus, Q_p increases for smaller gate current densities at lower temperatures (Fig. 7-24d). This data supports the model that holes captured in the oxide causes local structural changes in the oxide lattice that eventually leads to oxide breakdown.

It has also been shown that the number of *electron* trap sites is related to the water diffused into the SiO_2 film.[33] Furthermore, the negative charge build up in ultra-dry SiO_2 is 1/10 that in wet oxides. These results suggest that the hydrogen contained in the oxide strongly affects the generation of electron traps in SiO_2. However, some of

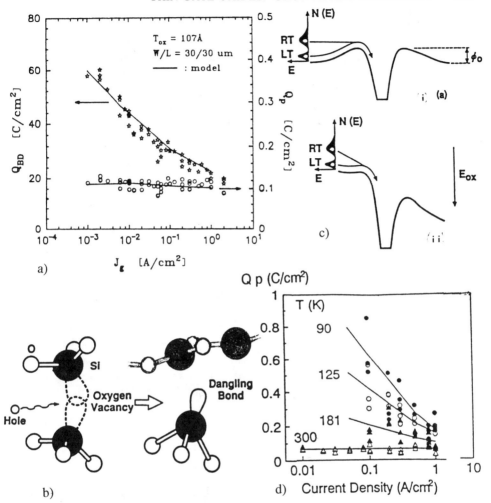

Fig. 7-24 (a) The charge-to-breakdown, Q_{BD}, and the hole-fluence-to-breakdown, Q_p, for a 107Å oxide under constant current stress. Q_{BD} increases with decreasing current density, while Q_p remains constant as predicted by the hole-trapping oxide breakdown model.[31] (© IEEE 1986). (b) Schematic picture of structural change in Si-O bonds caused by a trapped hole. Oxide vacancy acts as a hole trap. The hole trapping locally induces a structural change in the SiO_2 network. The conductivity in the changed structure becomes quite large compared to that of the initial SiO_2 due to its small band-gap. (c) Schematic picture for the repulsive hole trap with a finite energy barrier φ_0. Figures (i) and (ii) correspond to the trap without and with oxide field ε_{ox}, respectively. At room temperatures, holes are easily trapped with only the help of thermal energy. At low temperatures, barrier lowering by the electric field is needed for holes to be captured. (d) Hole-fluence-to-breakdown Q_p as a function of current density. At 300K, the oxide-field dependence of Q_p agrees with previous work [31]. However, note that Q_p has a strong oxide field dependence at lower temperatures.[102] (© IEEE 1993).

the hydrogen contained in the oxide is eliminated by high temperature annealing in dry N_2. Since the Si-OH structure is thought to be an electron trap, and oxygen vacancies in the bulk and dangling bonds at the surface are thought to be hole trap precursors, such N_2 anneals are expected to reduce electron traps, but also to increase hole traps. Since it does not appear to be possible to simultaneously achieve a reduction in electron and hole trap densities by annealing alone, other kinds of oxide quality improvement by adding small amounts of impurities to the oxide have been investigated, including fluorine and nitrogen. These approaches are described in chap. 9.

7.5.1.2 Wolters' Electron Lattice-Damage Model.

In the lattice-damage model of Wolters, it is agreed that electrons are injected into the conduction band of the oxide by Fowler-Nordheim tunneling where they undergo acceleration by the oxide field. Upon reaching the anode they have the highest energy. This energy is dissipated by creating atomic defects at the anode interface (e.g., breaking Si-O bonds). These defects are charged positively and thus they attract newly injected electrons. This mechanism directs the growth of tracks of defects into the dielectric. Such bond breaking proceeds from anode to cathode forming a conductive path. Figure 7-25 depicts the simulation of these tracks which evolve during random charge injection. Initially a large number of small tracks grow. The largest track will grow faster than the others. Tracks also tend to branch and closely resemble "trees" in the pre-breakdown stage. Eventually, a conductive path that has grown from the anode to cathode is produced.[34] Once the conductive path is established across the entire film thickness, the capacitor can be discharged through this path. Since this discharge occurs very rapidly, the energy stored in the capacitor must be quickly dissipated by the small volume of oxide material that

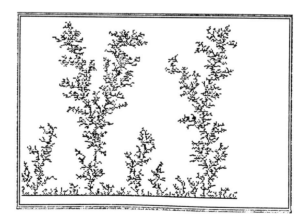

Fig. 7-25 Modeling of growing "trees" at the draining electrode of a capacitor under stress. Under charge injection the "trees" grow until they reach the opposite electrode and make a short.[34] This paper was originally presented at the Spring 1990 Meeting of the Electrochemical Society, Inc. held in San Francisco, CA.

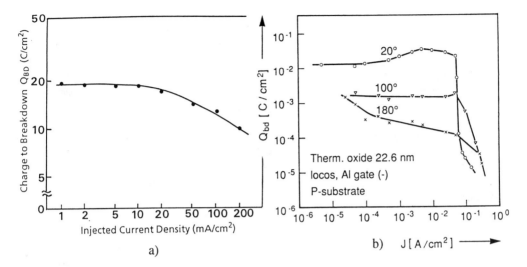

Fig. 7-26 (a) The dependence of the breakdown charge on the F-N injection current density. Q_{BD} is constant below certain current density and decreases gradually beyond it.[123] (© IEEE 1991). (b) Temperature effect on Q_{BD} values. Devices have often higher operation temperatures and hence, the lowering of Q_{BD} with T is an important aspect of end-of-life prediction.[34] This paper was originally presented at the Spring 1990 Meeting of the Electrochemical Society, Inc. held in San Francisco, CA.

constitutes the current path. This vaporizes the oxide along the path of current flow, and the capacitor is broken down. (The area of melted polysilicon above the breakdown spot, as shown in Fig. 7-19, is ~20 μm^2. For a breakdown spot of a few square microns in even a very small-area MOS-C [e.g., 0.02 mm^2], the energy density arising from the dissipation of the charge stored on the capacitor can exceed 10^5 J/cm^3. Such energy densities can indeed melt and evaporate polysilicon spots of 20 μm^2.)

Wolters has also observed that the average value of Q_{BD} is essentially constant as a function of Fowler-Nordheim injection current density (i.e., electron fluence) for low current densities. According to him, this precludes avalanche multiplication as a stepping stone in the oxide breakdown mechanism because the multiplication is strongly field dependent. This constancy of Q_{BD} has also been observed by Uraoka et al[35, 123] and Takeda et al (Fig. 7-26a).[122] Wolter's model also correctly predicts that Q_{BD} significantly decreases with increasing temperature (Fig. 7-26b).

In addition, Wolters argues that the critical parameter determining intrinsic oxide breakdown is Q_{BD}. He notes that while Q_{BD} is constant versus injected current density (J_{inj}) at low values of J_{inj}, its value decreases somewhat as J_{inj} rises (as shown by the curve fitted to the squares in Fig. 7-27a).[34] Thus, failure data from the four tests used to characterize oxide breakdown (ramp-voltage and ramp-current breakdown tests, and constant-voltage and constant-current TDDB tests) can only be meaningfully compared if the above facts are taken into account. That is, when any one of the four tests is performed, the total charge transported through the oxide Q is related to J_{inj} in a different manner (as is indicated by the lines given in Fig. 7-27a). From Fig. 7-27a we see that, in general, the Q versus J_{inj} curve for each test can intersect the Q_{BD} curve at a different point (i.e., when $Q = Q_{BD}$ breakdown occurs). Thus, it is not surprising that the tests may appear to give conflicting results with respect to oxide failure. However, if all four tests are designed so that the charge transported through the oxide intersects the Q_{BD} versus J_{inj} curve at the same point, all of the tests should yield identical failure data. Figure 7-27b shows that this indeed the case. That is, apart from the early (B-mode) failures, the predicted failure rates of the intrinsic oxide are identical, regardless of the type test used to produce such data.

7.5.2 Qualitative Models for the Physical Origin of B-Mode Failures in Oxides

While intrinsic failures are easier to study, the B-mode failures shown in Fig. 7-14 are more important. This is because oxide electric fields in submicron CMOS fall in the range at which B-mode failures occur (e.g., when $t_{ox} = 12.5$ nm and $V_{GS} = 5.0$, ε_{ox} is ~4.0 MV/cm). The B-mode failures of oxide films shown in Fig. 7-14 are believed to be due to defects in the oxide film that reduce its ability to withstand electrical stress. Such "walking wounded" oxide films will cause parts to fail prior to their designed lifetimes during normal operation. To build reliable systems, parts with such weaknesses must be screened out and excluded from use. Various types of defects have been proposed as being responsible for B-mode failures, including:

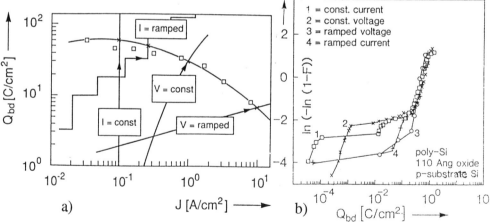

Fig. 7-27 (a) An example of the variation of Q_{BD} with injection current density. Lines in the figures depict the applied stress for different measuring techniques. In order to get comparable results, the lines should intersect the Q_{BD} curves at the same point. (b) Cumulative failure percentage F versus Q_{BD} for the various measuring techniques showing their correspondence. The differences in the tails are not only due to stochastical variations on the wafer but are caused by the different types of stress as well.[34] This paper was originally presented at the Spring 1990 Meeting of the Electrochemical Society, Inc. held in San Francisco, CA.

1. *Sodium contamination in the oxide film.* When a field is applied to the oxide, any positive ionic charges present in the oxide (e.g., Na^+) eventually drift toward the cathode. The proximity of these charges to the cathode increases the cathode field and enhances electron injection. This field increase continues as more charge builds up until the oxide ruptures.

It is thought that the origin of such Na^+ is the W-furnace filament. The sodium evaporates from the filament and then diffuses through the quartz furnace tube into the oxidation ambient. Periodic cleaning of the oxidation furnace tube by flowing a mixture of O_2 and a chlorine-containing gas (e.g., Cl, HCl, or TCA) through it for several hours (followed by an O_2 purge), is a standard technique used to reduce Na contamination from this source in the thermal oxide. Use of double-walled tubes (in which gas flowing in the outer tube carries away metal ions which have diffused through the outer wall), has also been reported to reduce Na (and other metallic) contamination.[36]

2. *Substrate metal contamination.* The presence of metals (especially Al, Fe, and Ca) on the Si surface prior or during oxide growth can significantly degrade the gate oxide properties. Metal contamination may exist in the starting material (in the form of heavy metal precipitates in the wafer),[37,38] or it may be introduced during processing. Examples of the latter include sputtering of stainless-steel fixtures and wafer holders by the beamline of ion implanters, diffusion of heavy metals from the heater coils through the quartz walls of diffusion and oxidation tubes (see above and Vol. 1, chap. 2), and metal-contaminated chemicals or DI water used in the cleaning process.[39] The latter reference also suggests adding complexing agents for Ca or Al to the cleaning solutions. An example is EDTA (ethylene diamine tetra acetic acid) which is an agent that binds metal ions (e.g., Ca and Al) in basic solutions through the unshared pair of electrons on the nitrogen atoms.

3. *Surface roughness.* With gate oxide films approaching 10 nm in thickness, uncontrolled surface roughness can significantly reduce the effective oxide thickness. A total Si-surface roughness of less than 5Å is now being specified as a requirement before gate oxide growth. This can be monitored using atomic-force microscopy, which enables 3-D subnanometer roughness measurements.

In the conventional RCA cleaning process used prior to gate oxidation, silicon surface roughening has been found to occur as a result of using $NH_4OH:H_2O_2:H_2O$ in the ratio of 1:1:5. If the process is modified, using instead a solution with less NH_4OH (e.g., ratios of ($NH_4OH:H_2O_2:H_2O = 0.05:1:5$,[40] or $0.25:1:5$[41]), the roughening is reported to become negligible.

Increased silicon surface roughness near the gate edge has also reportedly been measured with atomic force microscopy.[107, 108] This roughness is attributed to the high compressive stress caused by the field oxidation. The roughness degrades the oxide breakdown voltage. An annealing step after the field oxidation growth at 1000-1050°C (prior to the sacrificial gate oxide growth step) reportedly improves the breakdown voltage strength of the oxide films.

4. *Localized regions where the oxide is thinner.* Such thinning may be due to such causes as particulates embedded in the oxide during growth, the Kooi effect, or stress effects that locally reduce the oxide growth rate. The gate thinning problem is especially severe near the field edge due to the latter two effects (see Fig. 7-28a).[112, 130]

Note that stripping the sacrificial gate oxide in HF can result in impurities being left behind on the Si surface after the strip. These impurities cause a rough Si/SiO$_2$ interface that may thus result in a thinner SiO$_2$ film in some locations than others, and hence degrade the gate oxide reliability. Using ultra-high purity HF for this procedure appears to significantly improve the electrical breakdown yield.[42] The use of a stacked gate oxide (i.e., a two layer oxide, one layer thermally grown, and the deposited by CVD, see section 7.9.4.1) has also been reported to reduce this problem, since only the part of the gate oxide that is thermally grown is subjected to the thinning effects (see Fig. 7-28c).

5. *Crystalline defects in the substrate.* An example is the presence of SiO$_2$ precipitates near the surface of the Si.[43,129] These occur in Czochralski-grown silicon wafers containing oxygen dissolved in the lattice as result of the crystal growth process (see Vol. 1, chaps. 1 and 2). Unless the surface is made free of oxygen by a "denuding" step that out-diffuses the oxygen from the near surface regions, such precipitates can form near the surface during wafer processing steps. "Knock-on" oxygen from the implantation of heavy atoms (such as As) through screen oxides can also be responsible for the formation of such SiO$_2$ precipitates. Stacking faults are also possible crystalline-defect culprits. It has

Minimal Field Oxide Edge Thinning Problem

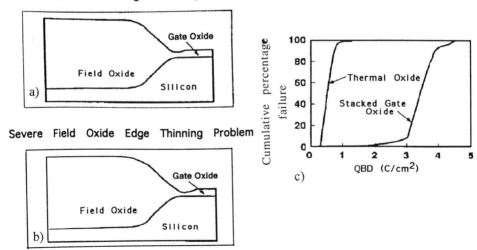

Fig. 7-28 Reduction of gate oxide thinning problem at field edge using stacked gate oxide. Nitride mask for PBL isolation is 2000Å thick.[112] (© IEEE 1993).

been reported that the presence of bulk defects which degrade gate oxide integrity can depend on the specific conditions of the ingot growth process (e.g., pull rate and thermal history of the ingot during the pulling process).

One measure that is reportedly effective in minimizing many of the defects listed above is the use of epitaxial- rather than bulk-Czochralski (CZ) wafers.[97,98] That is, epitaxial wafers show superior gate oxide integrity. Recently, a new high grade silicon bulk CZ wafer (which is termed a *Hi Wafer*) has been announced by Toshiba Semiconductor and Toshiba Ceramic.[99,100,124] In Hi-wafers a preprocessing high temperature anneal in high-purity hydrogen is used to form a zone denuded of oxygen near the wafer surface. Annealing in an inert ambient appears to result in lower surface oxygen levels than other ambients. Hi Wafers are reported to give gate oxide integrity results that are superior to conventional bulk CZ wafers and equal to those of epitaxial wafers (but at half the price of the latter).

7.5.2.1 Test Structure for Intrinsic Oxide Breakdown Measurements.

It should be mentioned that to measure the true intrinsic properties of an oxide, an appropriate test structure is needed (i.e., one that does not degrade the measured intrinsic properties). Most conventional MOS-C test structures used for characterizing oxide breakdown follow the design rule of not connecting a metal line to the poly gate inside the active MOS area. Instead the metal/poly contact is made as shown in Fig. 7-29a. In this case, however, the poly gate, overlaps the field oxide around the periphery of the MOS-C (field-oxide surrounded MOS-C). It has been shown that when an advanced isolation technology, such as poly-buffered-LOCOS (see Chap. 6), or SWAMI[44] (see Vol. 2, chap. 2), a slight amount of gate oxide thinning may occur at the gate edge (i.e., up to 30% of the nominal gate oxide thickness, due to stresses involved with 2-D oxidation growth effects[45,46] (see also chap. 6, section 6.3.2). Since the poly passes over a rather long section of such a thinner oxide, the measured breakdown characteristics of the oxide film will appear degraded, compared to those in which no such thinner regions occurs. To circumvent this problem, the test structure can be modified so that the poly gate is not allowed to overlap the field oxide, and the contact between the metal and poly is as shown in Fig. 7-29b.[125] In addition, following the poly gate definition, a short reoxidation step is carried out to produce a gate bird's beak (or *graded-gate oxide* - see chap. 5). This smoothly increases the gate oxide thickness at the edge, preventing the gate edge from becoming a weak spot, in terms of dielectric strength. Thus, with this improved test structure, the intrinsic oxide breakdown characteristics can be measured independent of edge effects.

7.5.2.2 Damage at the Gate Periphery Resulting from the Polysilicon Etch Process.

When the polysilicon gate is patterned by dry etching it is possible that during the overetch time the gate oxide may be removed from a small area adjacent to the gate periphery, even when the selectivity of the poly-to-SiO_2 of the etch process appears to be sufficiently high that the SiO_2 should not be completely removed. In such cases, the etch nevertheless "punches through" to the substrate and microtrenches are etched into the substrate near the gate periphery (Fig.

7-29c. This effect has been analyzed and modeled.[115] The cause of this microtrenching has been identified as ion scattering from the feature sidewalls, with a flux that is sufficient to sputter away the thin SiO_2 near the base of the sidewall and expose the substrate to the silicon etchant species.

The process engineer must minimize this damage to ensure adequate device reliability. Although the damage can be visually monitored with SEM/TEM, this is cumbersome. A special test structure has been suggested for electrical monitoring of such damage. It consists of an MOS-C with an additional polysilicon layer deposited and etched after the gate has been patterned (see Fig. 7-29d). This creates a conductive spacer over the region at the gate periphery and permits stress testing of the gate oxide at the periphery. If damage has occurred during the gate etch, such test-MOS-Cs will breakdown, or exhibit worse cumulative failure behavior than MOS-Cs without such conductive spacers over the damaged areas.[116] With the aid of such measurements the gate etch process can be adjusted to minimize such damage.

7.5.3 Empirical Quantitative Model of Intrinsic Oxide Breakdown

The exact physical origin of intrinsic oxide breakdown is still being debated. Nevertheless, the experimental evidence surrounding the breakdown event has led to the development of a statistical empirical model for oxide breakdown that allows the reliability of gate oxide films to be quite well estimated. The model can be applied to both "intrinsic" breakdown events (mode-C failures), and wearout events (mode-B failures).

The theoretical basis of the statistical reliability model for intrinsic failures is the following:[20] (1) Q_{BD} of intrinsic oxides (i.e., those containing no defects) is approximately constant (at ~10 C/cm^2) for relatively small Fowler-Nordheim tunneling current densities (i.e., less than 0.1 A/cm^2); and (2) Q_p is also constant at ~0.1 C/cm^2. Since $Q_p = J_g \alpha t_{BD}$ = constant (0.1 C/cm^2), where J_g is the Fowler-Nordheim gate current density, and α is the hole-generation coefficient, this implies that the breakdown time t_{BD} can be modeled as

$$Q_p \propto J_g \alpha t_{BD} \qquad (7-19)$$

where the gate current density due to Fowler-Nordheim tunneling is given by Eq. 7-1. Thus

$$J_g \propto \exp(-B/\mathcal{E}_{ox}) \text{ with } B = 240 \text{ MV/cm} \qquad (7-20)$$

and the hole-generation coefficient α is given by:

$$\alpha \propto \exp(-H/\mathcal{E}_{ox}) \text{ with } H \sim 110 \text{ MV/cm} \qquad (7-21)$$

where the oxide electric field, in terms of the voltage across the oxide V_{ox} and its thickness t_{ox}, is expressed as

$$\mathcal{E}_{ox} = V_{ox}/t_{ox} \qquad (7-22)$$

Therefore

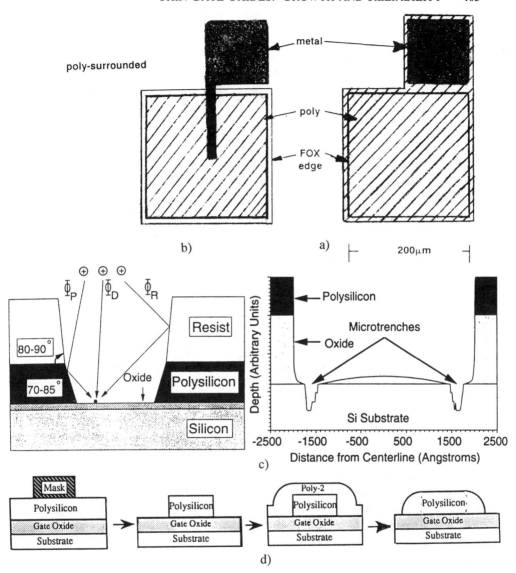

Fig. 7-29 (a) Layout of the conventional field-oxide-surrounded test structure with the gate poly expanded to the field-oxide area. (b) Layout of the gate-surrounded MOS capacitor.[125] (© IEEE 1992). (c1) Cross section of the film structure at polysilicon etching end point showing typical values of polysilicon and photoresist sidewall angles. (c2) Surface topography after etching. Note: microtrench locations correspond to the maxima in the flux profile.[115] Reprinted with the permission of the publisher, the Electrochemical Society. (d) Special test structure for electrical monitoring of such damage, consisting of an MOS-C with an additional polysilicon layer deposited and etched after the gate has been patterned.[116] This paper was originally presented at the Spring 1993 Meeting the Electrochemical Society.

$$Q_p \propto \exp(-G/\mathcal{E}_{ox}) t_{BD} \tag{7-23}$$

where

$$G = B + H \cong 350 \text{ MV/cm.} \tag{7-24}$$

Thus, the time required to accumulate a certain amount of Q_p to cause breakdown t_{BD} is proportional to:

$$t_{BD} \propto \exp(G/\mathcal{E}_{ox}). \tag{7-25}$$

The relation given by 7-25 can be made into an equation by finding the appropriate pre-exponential factor, which we will call $\tau_0(T)$. Then, in general, we can write

$$t_{BD} = \tau_0(T) \exp[G(T)/\mathcal{E}_{ox}] \tag{7-26}$$

The parameter G (T) and the pre-exponential factor $\tau_0(T)$ have been shown to depend on temperature (over a limited range of temperatures: 25°C-150°C) in the following way[47]

$$G(T) = G[1 + \{(\delta/k)[(1/T) - (1/300)]\}] \tag{7-27}$$

and

$$\tau_0(T) = \tau_0 \exp[(-E_b/k)(\{1/T\} - \{1/300\})] \tag{7-28}$$

where $\tau_0 = 10^{-11}$ sec, G = 350 MV/cm, $E_b = 0.28$ eV and $\delta = 0.0167$ eV.

Equation 7-26 is the model for the time-to-breakdown in intrinsic oxide films. At 300K, the equation is simply

$$t_{BD}(300K) = 10^{-11} \text{ (sec) } \exp[350 \text{ (MV/cm) } t_{ox} \text{ (cm)/ } V_{ox}(V)]. \tag{7-29}$$

Equation 7-29 can be used to predict the time to breakdown of a defect-free oxide film of a given thickness at 300K for various electric field strengths. On the other hand, if the voltage across the oxide is known, it can also be used to select the minimum oxide thickness for a specified oxide lifetime, e.g., 10 years. To predict t_{BD} at other operating temperatures, Eq. 7-26 must be used.

The theoretically derived Eq. 7-29 has since been experimentally verified, as shown in Fig. 7-30. Here, the value of log t_{BD} for several thin oxides (ranging from 52 to 103 Å) is plotted versus $1/\mathcal{E}_{ox}$. In addition, Eq. 7-29 using a value of G = 350 MV/cm, and $\tau_0 = 10^{-11}$ sec is also plotted. It can be seen that the agreement between the experimental data and Eq. 7-29 is very good. The value of τ_0 is obtained by extrapolating the curve of the experimental points until they intercept the t_{BD} axis (see Fig. 7-31).

Equation 7-26 is also the basis for extrapolating the lifetime under normal operating conditions from the lifetime measured at higher-than-normal stress voltages (*accelerated testing*). That is,

$$t_{BD2} = t_{BD1} (\tau_0/ t_{BD1})^{(1 - V_{ox1}/V_{ox2})} \tag{7-30}$$

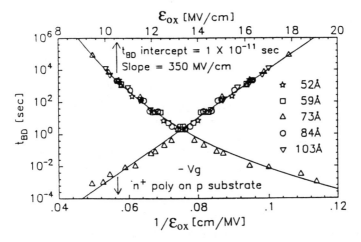

Fig. 7-30   Log (t_{BD}) versus $1/\mathcal{E}_{ox}$ for different gate oxide thicknesses. Log (t_{BD}) follows a linear relationship with $1/\mathcal{E}_{ox}$, not $\mathcal{E}_{ox}$. Small-area oxide samples (80 μm^2) were used such that intrinsic breakdown dominates and little statistical variation of t_{BD} at any one applied electric field was observed.[20] (© IEEE 1988).

Example 7-1: Use Eq. 7-29 to calculate the time to breakdown of 8 nm thick, defect-free oxide film if V_{ox} is 5V at 300K.

Solution: We use Eq. 7-29 to calculate t_{BD} with $t_{ox} = 8 \times 10^{-7}$ cm

$$t_{BD}(300K) = 10^{-11}(sec)\ e^{350\ (MV/cm)\ t_{ox}\ (cm)/V_{ox}(V)} \qquad (7\text{ - }31)$$

$$t_{BD} = 5.18 \times 10^{10}\ sec\ (i.e.,\ in\ excess\ of\ 1000\ years!). \qquad (7\text{ - }32)$$

Example 7-2: Calculate the minimum thickness of a defect-free oxide that could be used in a MOSFET that is to operate at 5.5V for 10 years at 150°C (425K) without suffering oxide breakdown.

Solution: Using Eqs. 7-27 and 7-28, the value of G(425K) = 283 MV/cm, and $\tau_0(425K) = 0.75 \times 10^{-11}$ sec. With these values we solve for t_{ox} assuming $t_{BD} = 10$ years (3×10^8 sec), to get

$$t_{ox\ min} = 5.5V/(283\ MV/cm)\ ln\ (3 \times 10^8\ sec/(.75 \times 10^{-11}\ sec) = 88\text{Å}$$

Example 7-3: What is the maximum electric field that can be applied across a gate oxide so that it will operate for 10 years without suffering breakdown at 125°C.

Solution: At T = 125°C $\cong$ 400K, and $t_{BD} = 10$ years $= 3.1 \times 10^8$ sec.

$$G(400K) = 297\ MV/cm\ and\ \tau_0(425K) = 0.75 \times 10^{-11}\ sec$$

Thus, using Eq. 7-26 and solving for ε_{ox} we get

$$\varepsilon_{ox} = V_{ox}/t_{ox} <6.7 \text{ (or} \cong 7) \text{ MV/cm}.$$

It should also be noted that V_{ox} is the voltage across the oxide, which is generally different than the applied gate voltage V_{GB}. The difference is due to band bending and the work-function difference. The worst case occurs for a MOS-C with an n^+ polysilicon gate and a p-substrate (which also corresponds to the structure of the NMOSFET), when the MOS-C is biased into inversion. Here, $V_{ox} \sim (V_{GB} - 0.2V)$. For a MOS-C with an n^+ polysilicon gate and an n-substrate (or for a MOS-C with a p-substrate biased into accumulation), the oxide field for the same V_{GB} is smaller [$V_{ox} \sim (V_{GB} - 1.2V)$]. This explains why n-channel devices exhibit higher oxide failure rates than p-channel devices in CMOS ICs.[48]

Another point that should be emphasized concerns the upper limit of oxide field strength for accelerated tests. Since the log (t_{BD}) versus $1/\varepsilon_{ox}$ plot is linear, one might be tempted to use very high fields to obtain t_{BD} data in a very short time, and then use Eq. 7-26 to extrapolate the t_{BD} value at smaller fields. However, if ε_{ox} becomes too large the Fowler-Nordheim current density begins to deviate from the theoretical J-ε_{ox} curve (see Fig. 7-32, inset). The upshot is that testing at such excessive fields will lead to overly optimistic extrapolated lifetimes. To avoid this undesirable outcome a maximum oxide field ε_{max} as a function of oxide thickness (for accelerated tests of "intrinsic" oxide breakdown), is suggested in Fig. 7-32.[49] By keeping ε_{ox} below ε_{max}, a higher confidence in the accuracy of the extrapolated lifetime is ensured. Note that the

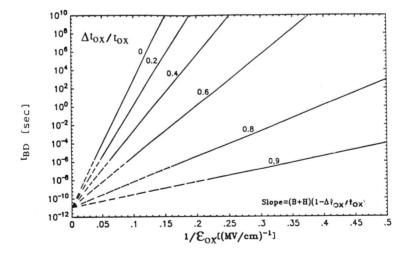

Fig. 7-31 An illustration of the dependence of t_{BD} on the severity of defects Δt_{ox} as a function of the oxide field ε_{ox}, using Eq. 7-26. The value of τ_0 is obtained by extrapolating the curve of the experimental points of Fig. 7-30 until they intercept the t_{BD} axis.[20] (© IEEE 1988).

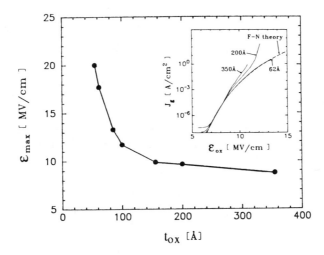

Fig. 7-32 Maximum recommended oxide field for extrapolating lifetime from log (t_{BD}) versus $1/\mathcal{E}_{ox}$ plots as a function of oxide thickness. At fields higher than $\mathcal{E}_{max}$, the J-$\mathcal{E}$ curve deviates from the theoretical Fowler-Nordheim values as shown in the inset. Fields should be kept to 20 percent below the $\mathcal{E}_{ymax}$ shown for testing of early failures.[49] (© IEEE 1987).

value of $\mathcal{E}_{max}$ given in this figure should be reduced by ~20% when accelerated field tests are used to study B-mode failures. This is necessary because the local oxide field at weak spots is higher than the nominal $\mathcal{E}_{ox}$.

On the other hand, Q_{BD} is independent of J and is therefore not affected by the distortion of the J-$\mathcal{E}_{ox}$ curve at high field. Thus, one can perform Q_{BD} measurements at high fields and extrapolate high-field Q_{BD} against $1/\mathcal{E}_{ox}$ to a low field. This low-field Q_{BD} can then be divided by the low-field current density to find the low-field lifetime $t_{BD} = Q_{BD}/J$. Using this approach it appears that highly accelerated testing (i.e., test times of only a few seconds) appears to be feasible, especially for very thin oxides.

7.5.4 Quantitative Models for B-Mode Failures

7.5.4.1 Reduced Barrier Height Model. In an early quantitative model of B-mode failures, Shatzkes et al. proposed that oxide defects may effectively lower the barrier for Fowler-Nordheim tunnel injection of electrons into the oxide conduction band. The breakdown mechanism, is then identical to intrinsic oxide breakdown at high fields. The breakdown distribution is merely shifted to lower fields because of the defect barrier lowering. Figure 7-33 shows a curve of oxide current versus electric field in such a defective oxide.[50] At low fields, more leakage current flows than would be expected in a defect-free oxide film (J_o). At low fields the leakage current characteristic is the same as if it were caused by Fowler-Nordheim tunneling if the oxide barrier was 2.4 eV instead of the normal 3.1 eV. Shatzkes found that capacitors with this excessive leakage also suffered the intermediate field breakdown with far greater frequency than the less leaky MOS capacitors.

7.5.4.2 Oxide Thinning Model.

The effect on the lifetime of oxides containing the B-mode failure defects listed in section 7.5.2 can be modeled by assuming that each such defect (as well as any others not listed) has the same effect on an "intrinsic" oxide film of a given thickness. That is, the presence of any one of these defects will cause an otherwise defect-free oxide to fail at a shorter time - corresponding to the time-to-failure of a thinner "intrinsic" oxide. Hence, any B-mode defect (weak spot) causes the oxide to behaves as a film having an effective thickness t_{oxeff} that is thinner than the nominal thickness t_{ox} by an amount Δt_{ox} (i.e., $t_{oxeff} = t_{ox} - \Delta t_{ox}$, see Fig. 7-34a).

Quantitatively, an oxide film of nominal thickness t_{ox} having no B-mode defects would fail at time t_{BD} given by Eq. 7-26. However, one containing a B-mode defect (that makes it appear to be thinner by Δt_{ox}) would fail at a time t_{BD} given by[20]

$$t_{BD} = \tau_0(T) \exp [G(T) (t_{ox} - \Delta t_{ox})/V_{ox}] = \tau_0(T) \exp [G(T) t_{oxeff}/V_{ox}] \quad (7 - 33)$$

The statistical variation of breakdown in the B-mode group is thus incorporated into the statistical distribution of Δt_{ox}. *That is, if we can determine the statistical variation of*

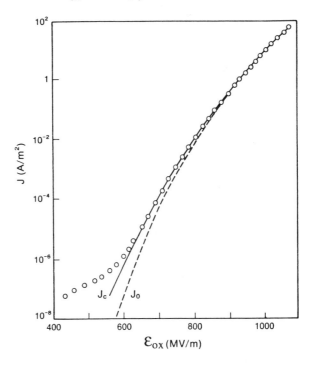

Fig. 7-33 J-V characteristics of defective oxide (J_c) compared to the theoretical J-V characteristics of an ideal oxide.[50] Reprinted with permission of IBM J. Research and Devel.

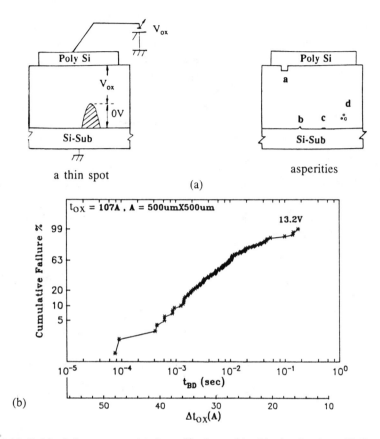

Fig. 7-34 (a) Oxide defects are modeled as effective oxide thinning by Δt_{ox}. b) Cumulative percentage failures versus time for a group of 0.25 mm^2 MOS-Cs with t_{ox} = 10.7 nm under a stress voltage of 13.2 V.[20] (© IEEE 1988).

B-mode defects in an oxide film we can estimate the failure rate and cumulative percentage of failures of such films under normal operating conditions. Note that the larger Δt_{ox} becomes, the sooner the oxide film will fail.

The statistical variation of Δt_{ox} in oxide films produced by a particular process in a specific fab environment can be inferred from time-dependent dielectric breakdown (TDDB) data of cumulative percentage failure versus time obtained from performing a constant-voltage stress test. For example, Fig. 7-34b shows the cumulative percentage failures versus time for a group of 0.25 mm^2 MOS-Cs (with an *n*-type substrate) with t_{ox} = 10.7 nm under a stress voltage of 13.2V. Using Eq. 7-34 we can find Δt_{ox} for each t_{BD} value Hence, from experimental data we can obtain a relation between cumulative percentage failure and Δt_{ox}. This relationship is also shown in Fig. 7-34. The data supports the notion that the short time to breakdown of the early failure samples corresponds to oxide samples containing spots with large Δt_{ox}.

7.5.4.3. The Cumulative Defect Density Function $D(\Delta t_{ox})$. To be able to project the lifetime of an oxide for arbitrary oxide areas, we need to obtain the *cumulative defect density as a function of Δt_{ox}* $D(\Delta t_{ox})$ [i.e., for a specific Δt_{ox}, $D(\Delta t_{ox})$ is the density of *all* the B-mode defects/cm^2 greater than Δt_{ox}]. Figure 7-35 is an example of a plot of $D(\Delta t_{ox})$ versus Δt_{ox}.

Basically, $D(\Delta t_{ox})$ is derived from the TDDB data of Fig. 7-34, but since obtaining $D(\Delta t_{ox})$ is the key to being able to predict the oxide reliability from experimental data, we will first outline the conceptual basis for how it is derived, and then give an example of how to actually calculate the values of $D(\Delta t_{ox})$ from a plot of cumulative percentage failure versus time.

Let us assume that oxide defects with varying degrees of severity are distributed over the wafer. Hence, the t_{BD} value for a particular oxide sample having a nominal thickness t_{ox} and area A is determined by the spot on that sample that has the largest Δt_{ox} value. For a group of samples each with the same oxide area, the percentage of samples that will fail below a specific t_{BD}, $P(t'_{BD} < t_{BD})$ is equal to the probability of finding a defect with an effective oxide thinning larger than Δt_{ox} in such an area ($P(\Delta t'_{ox} > \Delta t_{ox})$, or

$$P(t'_{BD} < t_{BD}) = P(\Delta t'_{ox} > \Delta t_{ox}) \qquad (7 - 34)$$

where Δt_{ox} and t_{BD} are related through Eq. 7-33. The complement of this is the probability of not finding a defect with an effective thinning greater than Δt_{ox}, i.e.,

$$P(\Delta t'_{ox} > \Delta t_{ox}) = 1 - P(\text{no defect with effective thinning} > \Delta t_{ox}). \qquad (7 - 35)$$

If the defects across a wafer are randomly distributed, implying a Poisson distribution can be used to estimate the probability, then

$$P(\text{no defect with effective thinning} > \Delta t_{ox}) = \exp(-A D[\Delta t_{ox}]) \qquad (7 - 36)$$

where A is the oxide area, and $D(\Delta t_{ox})$ is the cumulative defect density function. Combining Eqs. 7-34, 7-35, and 7-36 we get

$$P(t'_{BD} < t_{BD}) = 1 - P(\text{no defect with effective thinning} > \Delta t_{ox}) = 1 - \exp[-AD(\Delta t_{ox})] \quad (7 - 37)$$

On the other hand, if the defects are nonuniformly distributed across a wafer, a Gamma distribution function can be used, and Eq. 7-37 becomes

$$P(t_{BD}' < t_{BD}) = 1 - \frac{1}{(1 + A D (\Delta t_{ox}) S)^{1/S}} \qquad (7 - 38)$$

where S is a measure of the degree of clustering. In the limiting case of S --> 0, Eq. 7-37 reduces to Eq. 7-36.

The example of Fig. 7-35 shows that the defect density with increasing Δt_{ox} gets smaller. This trend explains why MOS-Cs of larger area are more likely to incorporate

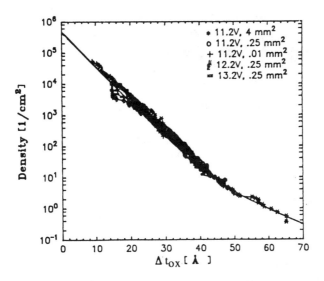

Fig. 7-35 $D(\Delta t_{ox})$ [i.e., Defect density as a function of Δt_{ox}], using Gamma distribution for the data in Fig. 7-34. Once $D(\Delta t_{ox})$ is derived for a given process, many reliability parameters such as yield, failure time, and optimum screen conditions can be determined.[20] (© IEEE 1988).

defects of larger Δt_{ox}'s and exhibit shorter t_{BD}s. This distribution of defect sizes is similar to the distribution of airborne particulates as a function of particle diameter.

Example 7-4: Calculate the value of $D(\Delta t_{ox})$ if: (a) $\Delta t_{ox} = 30\text{Å}$; and (b) $\Delta t_{ox} = 20\text{Å}$ for the oxide technology that yields the TDDB data of Fig. 7-34, assuming the defects are nonuniformly distributed and S = 0.6. The area of the oxide samples is 25 mm².

Solution: Since the defects are assumed to be distributed nonuniformly, we use the Gamma distribution and Eq. 7-38 to extract $D(\Delta t_{ox})$. That is, we solve Eq. 7-38 for $D(\Delta t_{ox})$, using S = 0.6 and A = 0.0025 cm² = 25x10⁻⁴ cm², or

$$D(\Delta t_{ox}) = \frac{1}{AS}\left\{\left[\frac{1}{1 - P(t_{BD}' < t_{BD})}\right]^S\right\} \qquad (7\text{-}39)$$

Then, using Fig. 7-34 we see that

$$P(t_{BD}' < t_{BD}) \cong 0.5 \text{ for } \Delta t_{ox} = 30\text{Å},$$

and

$$P(t_{BD}' < t_{BD}) \cong 0.9 \text{ for } \Delta t_{ox} = 20\text{Å}.$$

{i.e., from Fig. 7-34, $t_{BD} \sim 5 \times 10^{-3}$ sec for $\Delta t_{ox} = 30\text{Å}$. The probability that a failure will occur sooner is found from the cumulative failure percentage at $t_{BD} = 5 \times 10^{-3}$ sec, which in Fig. 7-34 is $\cong 50\%$. Thus, P $(t'_{BD} < 5 \times 10^{-3}$ sec$) \cong 0.5$.}
Using these values in Eq. 7-38 we find that

$$D(\Delta t_{ox}) \cong 330/\text{cm}^2 \quad \text{for} \quad \Delta t_{ox} = 30\text{Å}$$

$$D(\Delta t_{ox}) \cong 2000/\text{cm}^2 \quad \text{for} \quad \Delta t_{ox} = 20\text{Å}.$$

Note that these values correspond to the values shown in Fig. 7-35, on which the calculated $D(\Delta t_{ox})$ values for many more Δt_{ox} points are also plotted for this oxide process.

7.5.4.4. Using $D(\Delta t_{ox})$ to Predict Oxide Breakdown Reliability.
Once the calculated $D(\Delta t_{ox})$ points are plotted as shown in Fig. 7-35, a closed-form equation describing $D(\Delta t_{ox})$ as a function of Δt_{ox} can also be obtained from this experimental data by curve fitting a mathematical function to the set of the plotted points. This fitted curve can be used to predict the cumulative percentage of failure curves and the failure rates for any oxide area and stress voltage.

For example, the data in Fig. 7-35 can be curve fitted by the following equation:

$$D(\Delta t_{ox}) = a_1 \exp (b_1 \Delta t_{ox}) + a_2 \exp (b_2 \Delta t_{ox}) \tag{7 - 40}$$

where $a_1 = 13.1$, $a_2 = 6.3$, $b_1 = -0.26$, $b_2 = -0.11$ are fitting parameters. This equation is shown plotted in Fig. 7-35 as the solid line. Assuming a nonuniform distribution of defects, Eq. 7-38 can be used to formulate the cumulative distribution function F (expressed in terms of the percentage of failure) as a function of the oxide area, the oxide field, and time

$$F (A, V_{ox}, t_{BD}) = 1 - \frac{1}{\left[1 + A (a_1 e^{b_1 \Delta t_{ox}} + a_2 e^{b_2 \Delta t_{ox}}) \, S\right]^{1/S}} \tag{7 - 41}$$

where Δt_{ox} is related to V_{ox} and t_{BD} through Eq. 7-33. In other words, it is possible to derive F for a specific oxide thickness from a set of measurements at a single oxide stress voltage V_{ox} and oxide area A. This function F can then be used to estimate the cumulative percentage failure versus time for any area or stress voltage (for a specific oxide thickness and set of process conditions). In Fig. 7-36a, the theoretical F for various areas is plotted as the solid lines, and the experimental data as the points (with $t_{ox} = 107\text{Å}$). In Fig. 7-36b the theoretical F is plotted for various stress voltages for this same oxide thickness. Agreement between the estimated and the experimental values of F is reasonably good.

The instantaneous failure rate $\lambda (t)$ can also be predicted with the aid of Eq. 7-41. For example, a common specification of reliability of an electronic system is to have a failure rate of less than 0.01 percent per 1000 device hours (i.e., 100 FITs) before shipping the product to customers. From Eqs. 7-7, 7-26, and 7-41, one obtains

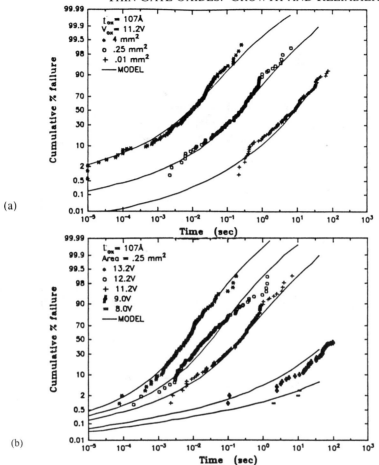

(a)

(b)

Fig. 7-36 Cumulative percentage failure versus time for (a) different areas and (b) different stress voltages of 10.7 nm oxide. Solid curves are derived from the defect density and Δt_{ox} models. Reasonable agreement between the data and model prediction is obtained.[20] (© IEEE 1988).

$$\lambda(t) = \frac{A}{1 + ADS} (a_1 b_1 e^{b_1 \Delta t_{ox}} + a_2 b_2 e^{b_2 \Delta t_{ox}}) \frac{V_{ox}}{t\,G} \qquad (7\text{-}42)$$

for the Gamma distribution, and with $S = 0$, for the Poisson distribution. Figs. 7-37a and 7-37b show the experimental and calculated failure rates. Reasonable agreement is again observed.

Equations 7-26, 7-41 and 7-42 constitute a quantitative model for the breakdown failure of oxides. That is they allow the following failure parameters of an oxide in a particular IC to be calculated: (a) Eq. 7-26 is used to find the oxide lifetime (t_{BD}) of a film with an effective oxide thickness t_{oxeff}, for a specific set of operating conditions (V_{ox} and T); (b) the cumulative failure of this oxide F (A, V_{ox}, t_{oxeff}) as a function of

time for a given oxide area and stress voltage is estimated from Eq. 7-41; and (c) the
failure rate λ (t) is calculated using Eq. 7-42.

It should also be noted that the $D(\Delta t_{ox})$ curves can be used to monitor the quality of
the oxide growth process. As discussed earlier, it is expected that the quality of the
oxide should depend on such factors the wafer quality (i.e., defect and metal precipitate
densities), the gettering conditions, the cleanliness of the process, and the oxide growth
and annealing conditions. By comparing the $D(\Delta t_{ox})$ curves of two different processes
or wafer lots, one can obtain a quantitative measure of the oxide breakdown
characteristics. Examples of applying the reliability model of oxide breakdown to such
cases are given in section 7.5.5.

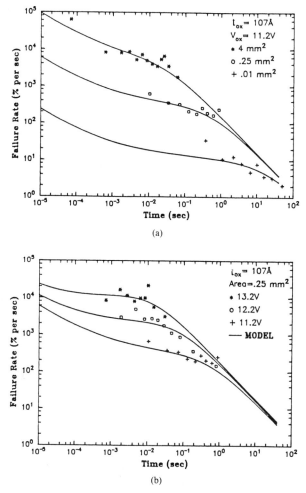

Fig. 7-37 Failure rate vs. time for (a) different areas and (b) different stress voltages of 10.7
nm oxide. Solid curves are derived from the defect density and Δt_{ox} models.[20] (© IEEE 1988).

7.5.4.5. Ramp-Voltage Breakdown Test for Obtaining $D(\Delta t_{ox})$

Data. Data for extracting $D(\Delta t_{ox})$ curves can be obtained using the ramp-voltage breakdown test instead of the constant-voltage TDDB test. Since the ramp-voltage test is much shorter than the constant-voltage test, this approach is very attractive. Note that a slow-ramped voltage (1-2V/sec) is used rather than the fast-ramped technique (100-200 V/sec) used to obtain dielectric strength (as described in section 7.4.1). A slow ramp allows TDDB failures to occur due to traps in the gate oxide, and yet each MOS-C can be tested in a matter of seconds.

The following equation gives the breakdown criteria in terms of the ramp-voltage test parameters.[51]

$$\{V_{BD}^2/RG (t_{ox} - \Delta t_{ox})\} \exp (- G [t_{ox} - \Delta t_{ox}]/V_{BD}) = \tau_0 \qquad (7 - 43)$$

where R is the ramp rate in volts per second, and V_{BD} is the ramp-breakdown voltage, and τ_0 is the pre-exponential term in Eq. 7-26 (i.e., the value of τ_0 is 10^{-11} sec).

In general, Eq. 7-43 has to be solved iteratively to find the value of $[t_{ox} - \Delta t_{ox}]$ corresponding to a measured V_{BD}. However, since the $[t_{ox} - \Delta t_{ox}]$ dependence of the exponential term in Eq. 7-43 dominates over the $[t_{ox} - \Delta t_{ox}]$ dependence of the pre-exponential coefficient, it is possible to obtain a reasonably accurate closed-form solution for $[t_{ox} - \Delta t_{ox}]$ by setting $[t_{ox} - \Delta t_{ox}]$ in the pre-exponential term to 80Å. Then Eq. 7-43 can be solved approximately for $[t_{ox} - \Delta t_{ox}]$ in the following form:

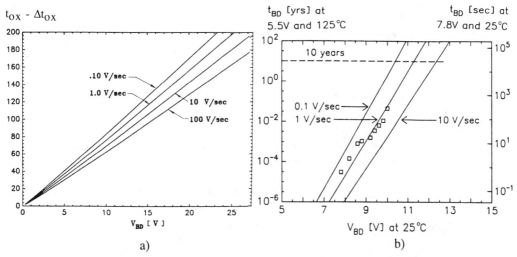

Fig. 7-38 (a) $t_{ox} - \Delta t_{ox}$ versus ramp breakdown voltage V_{BD} as a function of ramp rate. Using this figure, the $D(\Delta tox)$ curve can be derived from a ramp-voltage test.[20] (© IEEE 1988). (b) Correlation between t_{BD} and V_{BD} as predicted by Eq. 7-46. The experimental data were taken at 7.8V (for a constant voltage stress) and 1.0 V/s (for the ramp voltage stress) for a 125Å oxide [n^+ poly on (100) p substrate, biased in accumulation]. Each data point represents the breakdown voltage and time-to-breakdown for a specific cumulative failure percentage.[47] (© IEEE 1990).

$$(t_{ox} - \Delta t_{ox}) = \frac{V_{BD}}{G\,(T_{Vb\,d})} \ln \left(\frac{V_{BD}^2}{R\,G\,(T_{Vb\,d})\,\tau\,(T_{Vb\,d})\,80\text{Å}} \right) \qquad (7\text{-}44)$$

Figure 7-38a plots Eq. 7-44 (i.e., $[t_{ox} - \Delta t_{ox}]$ versus V_{BD} with ramp rate as the parameter). From such a plot, one can then relate V_{BD} to Δt_{ox}. Then, using a cumulative failure versus V_{BD} plot, one can extract $D(\Delta t_{ox})$. Once $D(\Delta t_{ox})$ is obtained, all the reliability predictions discussed earlier can be performed.

7.5.4.6. Correlating Ramp-Voltage Test Data and Constant-Voltage TDDB Data.
It has been proposed that the correlation between V_{BD} of the ramp breakdown test and the t_{BD} of a constant voltage test can be established.[47] That is, by substituting Eq. 7-44 into Eq. 7-33, an approximate relationship between V_{BD} of the ramp voltage test (at temperature T_{Vbd}) and the t_{BD} of the constant voltage test (performed at temperature T_{tbd}) is found

$$t_{BD} \cong \tau_o\,(T_{tbd}) \left| \frac{V_{BD}^2}{R\,G(T_{Vb\,d})\,\tau_o\,(T_{Vb\,d})\,80\text{Å}} \right|^{|G(T_{tb\,d})V_{BD}/\,G(T_{Vb\,d})\,V_{ox}} \qquad (7\text{-}45)$$

For the typical case where the ramp voltage test is performed at room temperature (T_{Vbd} = 25°C and T_{tbd} = T), Eq. 7-45 reduces to

$$t_{BD} \cong \tau_o\,(T) \left| 3.6 \times 10^8 \left(\frac{1}{V\,\text{sec}}\right) \frac{V_{BD}^2}{R} \right|^{[G(T)\,/350]\,(V_{BD}\,/V_{ox})} \qquad (7\text{-}46)$$

where $G(T)$ (in units of MV/cm) and $\tau_o(T)$ are given by Eqs. 7-27 and 7-28. This equation predicts that oxides with a lifetime of 10 years at 5.5V and 125°C will exhibit failure in a ramp-voltage test at $V_{BD} \sim 11.5$ V at 1 V/sec and a lifetime of 100 years at 125°C corresponds to $V_{BD} \cong 12$ V at 1 V/sec.

The theoretical correlation between V_{BD} and t_{BD} using Eq. 7-46 at T_{Vbd} = 25°C and T_{tbd} of 125°C and V_{ox} = 5.5V is plotted in Fig. 7-38b for various ramp rates (the left-hand axis represents these theoretical t_{BD} values). The experimental data for 125Å oxides correlating V_{BD} to the t_{BD} when the oxides are stressed at 7.8 V is also plotted, using the right-hand axis for representing the experimental t_{BD} values, with each point representing V_{BD} and t_{BD} for a specific cumulative percentage failure. (For example, the lowest experimental point corresponds to the V_{BD} and t_{BD} values at 10 percent cumulative failure in Figs. 7-39a and b.) Very good agreement between the theoretical and experimental data is seen. This implies that one can theoretically predict the lifetime of an oxide operating at different voltages and temperatures just by performing a simple ramp test at room temperature and carrying out the calculations needed to produce the curves as shown in Fig 7-38b. For example, the curves in Fig. 7-38b predict that an oxide sample (with any thickness and area) having any combination of V_{BD}s and ramp rates above the dashed line, will have a lifetime of more than 10 years at 5.5V.

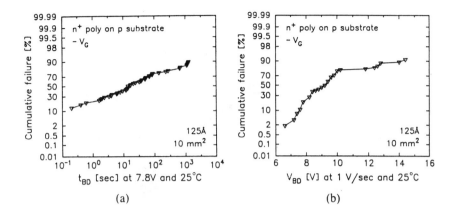

Fig. 7-39 (a) TDDB and (b) ramp breakdown data for 10 mm^2 125Å samples [n^+ polysilicon gate on (100) p substrate, biased in accumulation].[47] (© IEEE 1990).

7.5.4.7 Interface Trap Generation as a Measure of Oxide Damage Due to Charge Injected into the Oxide.

It has been observed that the passage of tunneling current through a thin gate oxide also introduces interface traps at the Si/SiO$_2$ interface. Furthermore, while breakdown may not occur until about 10 C/cm^2 of charge has passed through the oxide, interface traps are detectable even after 0.001 C/cm^2 of charge passage. Thus, measuring interface traps has been proposed as a more sensitive means of quantitatively measuring oxide damage prior to breakdown due to Fowler-Nordheim stressing of oxides.[52,53] Good agreement between TDDB values predicted from trap densities in the oxide caused by voltage stressing and measured TDDB values was found.[103] A physical model that describes how the traps are generated inside the oxide by high voltage stressing and how their presence in the oxide leads to wearout and breakdown in thin silicon oxides has also been developed.[104] The physical trap generation model was quantified to describe the measured breakdown distributions using a statistical model, the mathematical details of which are described in ref. 105.

Quasi-static CV curves of oxides before and after passage of charge through the oxide show that the CV curves after such stressing are degraded compared to the CV curves prior to stressing (Fig. 7-40), and the degree of degradation is correlated to the increase in trap density in the oxide. The more charge passed through the oxide, the more severe is the degradation. In section 7.10.4 we will describe how this method has been applied to measure oxide damage due to plasma etching.

7.5.5 Applications of the Oxide Breakdown Reliability Model

7.5.5.1 Projecting the Reliability of Gate Oxides with Various Thicknesses.

The oxide breakdown reliability model described in this chapter can

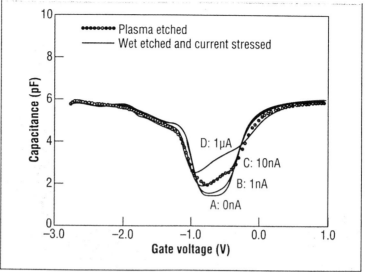

Fig. 7-40 Quasi-static CV curves of MOS-C structures prior to charge passage (Curve A = 0 nA), and after charge passage (Curves B - D). The creation of interface traps by current passage through the gate oxide degrades the CV curves.

be used to estimate and compare the reliability of different oxide technologies or thicknesses. Here we give an example of this procedure.

Example 7-5: Establish a set of curves which will allow the lifetime of various thin gate oxides of different thicknesses (e.g., 50-200Å thick) and arbitrary areas to be projected from accelerated stress data (assuming all are produced in the same process environment).

Solution: A group of MOS-Cs is fabricated for each oxide thickness of interest, with the gate oxide areas in all groups being equal. Then, the following procedure is used to estimate, for arbitrary area, the projected lifetimes of each of the oxide thicknesses:

1. Each group of MOS-Cs with a specific oxide thickness is subjected to ramp-voltage breakdown tests. The results, i.e., the cumulative percentage of failure versus V_{BD} for each oxide thickness are plotted (Fig. 7-41).

2. The experimental data from the previous step is used to calculate $D(\Delta t_{ox})$ versus t_{oxeff} for each oxide thickness. The procedure for obtaining $D(\Delta t_{ox})$ is:

a. For each value of V_{BD} for a given oxide thickness, we solve either Eq. 7-43, or Eq. 7-44 (the approximate form of Eq. 7-43), to get t_{oxeff}.

b. Using the calculations from part 2(a) we plot the cumulative percentage of failures versus t_{oxeff}.

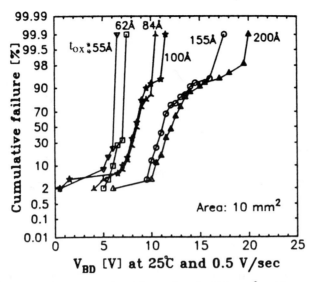

Fig. 7-41 Cumulative failure ramp breakdown data for 10 mm^2 oxide samples [n^+ poly-silicon gate (100) p substrate, biased in accumulation].[47] (© IEEE 1990).

c. We then find D(Δt_{ox}) versus t_{oxeff} for each oxide thickness. This is done by first finding the percentage of failures for a given t_{oxeff} from the plots generated in part 2(b), and then using Eqs. 7-37 or 7-38 to calculate D(Δt_{ox}) for that value of t_{oxeff} (using the area of the test MOS-Cs).

d. The values of D(Δt_{ox}) are then plotted versus t_{oxeff} for each oxide thickness (see Fig. 7-42). The experimental plot of D(Δt_{ox}) has now been obtained.

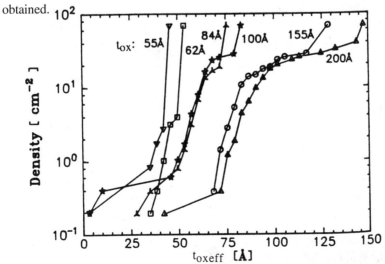

Fig. 7-42 Defect distribution for the oxide samples of Fig. 7-41.[47] (© IEEE 1990).

3. Now that $D(\Delta t_{ox})$ is available for each t_{oxeff}:

a. For a given operating temperature, we can calculate t_{BD} for each t_{oxeff} from Eq. 7-33.

b. From part 2, for a given t_{oxeff} we know $D(\Delta t_{ox})$. So from Eq. 7-37 or 7-38 we can determine the cumulative percentage of failures for any other specific oxide area.

c. Following the procedure of part 3b, the cumulative percentage of failures vs t_{BD} is now plotted (i.e., a point can be calculated for each t_{oxeff}).

4. From these curves we can find the cumulative percentage of failure for the various oxide thicknesses at that area for various times (Fig. 7-43). As an example, note that the cumulative failure for the 155Å oxide after 10 years is projected to be approximately 5%.

7.5.5.2 If a MOS IC is to have a Specific Lifetime (e.g.,10-Years), what is the Minimum Oxide Thickness that can be Used? (Assume the Maximum Cumulative Failure Percentage, Operating Temperature, and Oxide Area are Specified.)

Here we outline the procedure for selecting the minimum oxide thickness that will ensure a specific maximum cumulative failure rate over a 10-year lifetime at a specific operating temperature in a part that has a known gate oxide area.

1. Assume the $D(\Delta t_{ox})$ versus t_{oxeff} for each oxide thickness of interest has been established, as described in the previous section.

2. The maximum electric-field strength that allows defect-free (intrinsic) oxides to operate for a 10-years at 125°C is $\cong 7$ MV/cm (see section 7.5.3). If an oxide has a defect such that its effective oxide thickness $t_{oxeff} = t_{ox} - \Delta t_{ox}$ is reduced from the nominal thickness of t_{ox}, we must derate the maximum allowed electric

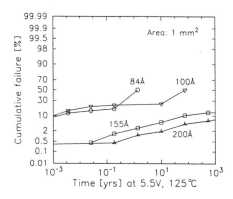

Fig. 7-43 Projected reliability during 5.5V operation is calculated from the defect density curves shown in Fig. 7-42.[47] (© IEEE 1990).

field and oxide voltage to obtain a 10-year lifetime at 125°C operation for this weakened oxide. That is, the maximum electric-field strength (as measured by V_{ox}/t_{ox}) must be derated to $\mathcal{E}_{max} = 7$ MV/cm (t_{oxeff}/t_{ox}), and the maximum voltage that can be applied to such a defective film having a nominal oxide thickness t_{ox} must be reduced to $V_{max} = (7$ MV/cm$)$ t_{oxeff} (cm).

3. For a specified cumulative failure percentage over 10 years (e.g., 3% cumulative failure) at some operating temperature (e.g., 125°C) and specific oxide area (e.g., 1 mm^2), Eq. 7-37 is used to calculate the value of $D(\Delta t_{ox})$ needed to ensure this cumulative failure percentage for that specific oxide area. (Eq. 7-37 is used because we also assume the defects are distributed uniformly). As an example, solving Eq. 7-37 for $D(\Delta t_{ox})$ indicates that a 3% cumulative percent failure in 10 years for a 1 mm^2 oxide corresponds to a $D(\Delta t_{ox})$ of 3 defects/cm^2 on the wafer.

4. Next, we use the plot of $D(\Delta t_{ox})$ versus t_{oxeff} to determine the value of t_{oxeff} corresponding to this value of $D(\Delta t_{ox})$. In this case, from Fig. 7-35 we see that a value of $D(\Delta t_{ox}) = 3$ defects/cm^2 corresponds to a t_{oxeff} of 55Å, and since the oxide under study was 125Å thick, Δt_{ox} is found to be 70Å.

5. Once the value of t_{oxeff} is known, we can calculate the $\mathcal{E}_{max}$ or V_{max} that can be applied to oxide films of this area at various thicknesses, using the relations given in step 2. On the other hand, if it is known that a specific voltage will be applied to the oxide (e.g., 5.5V), we can use the value of Δt_{ox} to calculate t_{oxeff} and then derate $\mathcal{E}_{ox}$ (intrinsic) or V_{ox} (intrinsic) to $\mathcal{E}_{max}$ or V_{max} accordingly. For example, if we know that at 125°C, a 10-year life can be had for an $\mathcal{E}_{ox}$ (intrinsic) of 7 MV/cm, then the thinnest intrinsic oxide that can live for 10 years at 125°C under a 5.5V stress is $t_{ox} \sim 80$Å. Since $\Delta t_{ox} = 70$Å, the thinnest oxides we can use (with an area of 1 mm^2) that will give a 10 year lifetime at 125°C with a maximum 3% cumulative failure are 150Å thick.

6. The calculation performed in part 5 can be repeated for other voltages to yield other minimum oxide thicknesses. In addition, other defect density values can be used when performing this calculation. A set of points can be plotted using this procedure, as is done in Figs. 7-44 to yield the minimum oxide thickness for a given oxide voltage, with the defect density (cm^{-2}) as a parameter. Note that if a higher defect density (corresponding to a higher cumulative failure rate) can be tolerated, these figures imply that a higher operating voltage could be used.

A final remark about oxide integrity models should be interjected. The structures for studying gate oxide integrity are MOS-Cs, in which the electric field is uniform across the entire device area. In MOSFETs, however, the oxide field can varies spatially along the channel due to the increase in the channel voltage from source to drain. Thus, one can speculate whether nonuniform injection would lead to a spatially non-uniform Q_{BD}

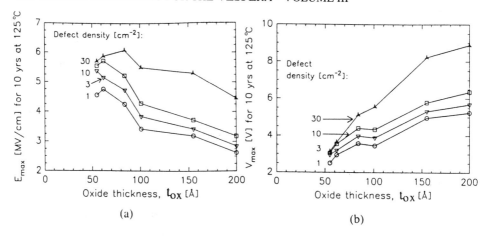

Fig. 7-44 Given a desired average failure rate and the oxide area, the largest acceptable defect density is calculated from Eq. 7-37. Using this defect density, it is possible to determine (a) the maximum allowable oxide field and (b) voltage for different oxide thicknesses or technologies.[47] (© IEEE 1990).

in MOSFETs. This might also yield different gate oxide integrity results in MOSFETs as compared to those obtained from tests using MOS-Cs.

7.6 SCREENING TESTS FOR OXIDE BREAKDOWN (BURN-IN)

As noted above, oxides in the B-mode group will fail at times sooner than those in the C-mode group (intrinsic oxides). *Burn-in* is a common technique used to screen out B-mode group parts. In this procedure, the intent is to operate the devices for some period of time, during which most of those parts that would undergo early failure actually do fail. Failing while undergoing burn-in is preferable to having the devices fail after they are installed in a system and delivered to the customer. By excluding such weak parts the reliability of the installed system can be significantly improved.

In general, burn-in conditions are selected so that the failure mechanisms that contribute to the early failures are presumably accelerated. In the case of oxide breakdown, this is achieved by burning-in under higher than normal voltages and temperatures. That is, application of high field and elevated temperature yields a much more efficient burn-in procedure than straightforward stress under normal operating conditions.

For example, Fig. 7-45 shows the theoretical failure rate curves at 5V predicted from the model for the parts that exhibit the cumulative defect density function of Fig. 7-35. These curves indicate that the failure rate of such products would stay higher than the specification of 0.01% per 1000 device hours (100 FIT) for more than 100 years. That is, only after 100 years of operation would a sufficient number of the weaker devices have expired so that the failure rate after that time would be less than 100 FIT.

To decrease the failure rate to an acceptably low rate more quickly, the failure of these weakest devices must be hastened by applying above-normal stress, i.e. screening.

The instantaneous failure rate of parts that fail by a mechanism that exhibits a log-normal distribution decreases monotonically in time. Early failure (B-mode) oxides have been shown to exhibit such log-normal behavior. Thus, the device failure rate (measured in this case as the fraction of the instantaneous population of oxides breaking down per unit time), decreases as the stress time increases. Figures 7-45 and 7-46 both depict typical experimental data expressing the instantaneous failure rate of a group of oxide capacitors as a function of time (that have not been subject to a burn-in screen).[54] The fact that the instantaneous failure rate decreases with time is the logical basis of the burn-in screen tests. That is, if a reliability engineer specifies a maximum allowable rate of failure of constituent MOS capacitors of, say, 100 failure units (100 FIT), the population may be burned-in until the instantaneous failure rate drops below this level.

Figure 7-47 presents an example of how such a burn-in procedure reduces the failure rate of parts under normal operating conditions.[55] The instantaneous failure rate of two groups of oxides is shown. In one group (black dots), a continuous stress of 2 MV/cm (which we assume to be the normal operating electric-field stress) is applied, while in the other group (white circles), a 2.5 MV/cm stress is applied for the first second of the test. Then the stress is reduced to 2 MV/cm. During this first second, the failure rate in the second group is increased. Upon dropping the stress to its normal operating value (2 MV/cm), however, the failure rate drops to a value well below that of the first group. That is, it falls to a value that is not attained by the first group until a much later time.

Unfortunately, while a longer burn-in time lowers the failure rate, it also increases the yield loss (i.e., the fraction of the parts that fail during burn-in). Thus, it is necessary to determine the optimal set of burn-in conditions that minimizes the burn-in time, yet

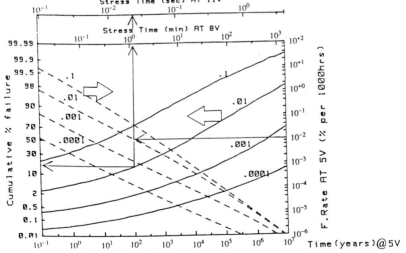

Fig. 7-45 Theoretical curves of failure rate and cumulative percent failures for different areas at 5-V operation. These curves are used for screening and screen yield optimization.[20] (© IEEE 1988).

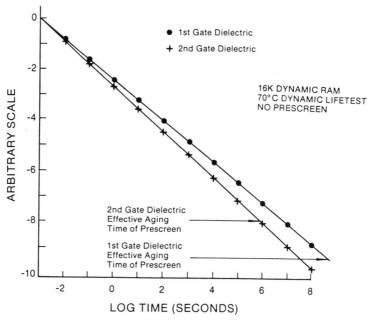

Fig. 7-46 Instantaneous failure rate data.[54] (© IEEE 1979).

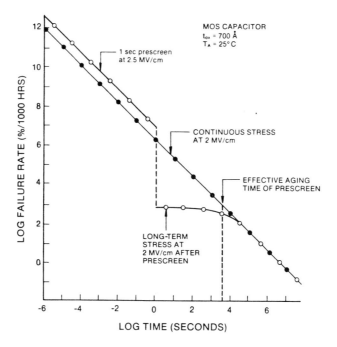

Fig. 7-47 Instantaneous failure rate data showing the effect of aging stress at elevated field.[54] (© IEEE 1979).

adequately lowers the failure rate with minimal yield loss. However, burn-in duration has often been set arbitrarily or determined by experimental results which are applicable to only certain lots of devices. It would be better to use a model that simulates the burn-in effects of various sets of burn-in conditions. Here we describe such an approach.

In order to determine the appropriate stress time, stress field, and stress temperature for optimally screening   oxides of a given area, operating voltage, and operating temperature, an accurate quantitative model of predicting the failure rate and TDDB behavior is required.   In fact, the model for t_{BD} due to B-mode failure described above has been applied to burn-in condition selection. Using this model, the reliability of oxides [characterized by a cumulative defect distribution $D(\Delta t_{ox})$] following a given burn-in condition can be projected for any oxide area, operating voltage, and temperature.[47]

7.6.1 Modeling the Effect of the Burn-In Stress on the Post-Burn-In Reliability of the Oxides.

With the addition of a burn-in step, oxide breakdown during post-burn-in operation occurs as a result of damage incurred during both the burn-in and the normal operation of the device. The subsequent lifetime of a device after a specific burn-in has been carried out t_{op} is calculated from

$$t_{op} = \tau_o(T_{op})\, e^{G(T_{op})\, t_{ox\,eff}/V_{op}}\left[1 - t_{BI}\, e^{-\,G(T_{BI})\, t_{ox\,eff}/V_{BI}}\right] \qquad (7\text{-}47)$$

where t_{BI} is the burn-in time, V_{BI} is the burn-in voltage, V_{op} is the operating voltage, and T_{BI} and T_{op} are the burn-in and operating temperatures, respectively. Comparing Eq. 7-47 with Eq. 7-33 we see that the first two product terms of Eq. 7-47 give the original oxide lifetime, i.e., the lifetime without burn-in t_{BD}. Thus, the quantity in square brackets represents the fraction of the original oxide lifetime remaining after burn-in, L_{BI}

$$L_{BI} = \left[1 - t_{BI}\, e^{-\,G(T_{BI})\, t_{ox\,eff}/V_{BI}}\right] \qquad (7\text{-}48)$$

This quantity (fraction of the lifetime remaining after burn-in, L_{BI}) is plotted in Fig. 7-48 as a function of the ramp breakdown voltage (using Eq. 7-43 to find the value of V_{BD} corresponding to the value of t_{oxeff} in Eq. 7-48), for the case of a burn-in test performed for 10 hours at 150°C at various burn-in temperatures. The expected lifetime at 5.5V and 125°C before burn-in is found using Eq. 7-33.

Plots such as those in Fig. 7-48 are used to determine the fraction of oxides that will be damaged by the burn-in to a degree that they will exhibit a significantly shorter lifetime after the burn-in (e.g., oxides whose life after burn-in is less than 90% of their original life). As an example, Fig. 7-48 indicates that after a burn-in of 7V for 10 hours at 150°C, only those oxides which originally would have exhibited a V_{BD} between 11.5 and 12V are predicted to have had their lifetimes reduced to less than 90% of their pre-burn-in value (note that those oxides which would have had $V_{BD}<11.5V$ would not have survived this burn-in). The same conclusion is drawn when comparing the projected lifetime after burn-in versus the original lifetime before burn-in as

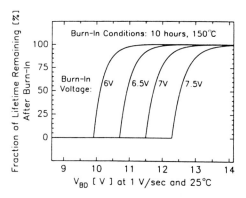

Fig. 7-48 The effect of a given burn-in condition on an oxide technology can be estimated based on a simple ramp voltage test. For example, following a 10-h burn-in at 7V and 150°C, all oxides with breakdown voltages below 11.5V are expected to fail. Of the oxides surviving burn-in, only those with 11.5V<V_{BD}<12V are expected to exhibit a reduction of more than 10% from their original lifetime (the lifetime without burn-in).[47] (© IEEE 1990).

shown in Fig. 7-49. Of the oxides that survive the burn-in, only the ones having lifetimes within one half of one decade have significantly reduced lifetimes (i.e., a reduction of more than 10% from the original lifetime) after burn-in. With the aid of Eq. 7-48, the optimal burn-in conditions can now be determined.

7.6.2 Procedure for Selecting an Optimal Set of Burn-In Conditions for Oxide Breakdown Screening

Here we outline the general procedure for selecting optimal burn-in conditions. Then we give an example which illustrates how the steps of this procedure are carried out.

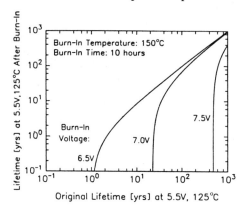

Fig. 7-49 Replot of Fig. 7-48 in terms of lifetime under operating conditions.[47] (© IEEE 1990).

We recall that the goal of burn-in is to *lower the failure rate* so that: (1) it becomes constant over the subsequent normal operating lifetime; and (2) its value becomes small enough to meet the reliability specification of the system. In addition, the yield loss due to burn-in should be minimized. The general procedure for establishing the design curves from which optimal burn-in conditions can be selected is the following:

1. When an optimal set of burn-in conditions is to be selected, it is assumed that the following parameters are given: the nominal oxide thickness t_{ox}, the oxide area A in the circuit being fabricated, the operating voltage V_{ox}, the operating temperature T_{op}, the expected lifetime after burn-in, and the allowable cumulative percent failure after burn-in over the expected lifetime of the oxides.

2. A plot of cumulative percent failure versus V_{BD} for oxide structures with the given t_{ox} and area A is first established from a ramp-voltage breakdown test.

3. The lifetimes t_{BD} (at the specified T_{op} and V_{op}) versus V_{BD} from Eq. 7-46 (using ramp rates of 0.1V/sec, 1V/sec, and 10V/sec as the parameter) are then calculated and plotted as shown in Fig. 7-38b.

4. A burn-in temperature T_{BI} is now selected (e.g., 150°C).

5. Equation 7-46 is then used to calculate the V_{BD}'s that correspond to oxide burn-in lifetimes t_{BI} for various burn-in voltages V_{BI} and the selected T_{BI}. That is, V_{BD} values for oxide lifetimes ranging from $t_{BI} = 1$ sec to 10^6 sec (in decade intervals), and V_{BI} values ranging from 5-10V, might be calculated.[*] If this group of calculated V_{BD} values is plotted versus V_{BI} (with t_{BI} as the parameter), a set of design curves is produced. An example of such a set of curves is shown in Fig. 7-50 for the case of $T_{BI} = 150°C$, $T_{op} = 125°C$, $V_{op} = 5.5V$, and R = 1V/sec. (Note that at this point readers might not yet be able to interpret this figure, as it also contains other relevant information that still needs to be described).

6. A set of plots of L_{BI} versus V_{BD} {as shown for example in Fig. 7-48 for the case of $T_{BI} = 150°C$, $T_{(Vbd)} = 25°C$, R = 1V/sec, and various burn-in voltages} are next computed. The values for such plots are calculated using Eq. 7-48, with a separate set of curves calculated for each t_{BI} used in step 5. A set of operating-lifetime-after-burn-in versus original-lifetime plots for each t_{BI} (with V_{BI} as a parameter) should also be developed (see Fig. 7-49).

7. Next, on the same set of design curves developed in step 5, we also plot the value of V_{BD} that pre-burn-in oxides would have to exhibit in order to be able to survive both the burn-in and the expected lifetime after burn-in. This is done as follows:

---

[*] One might also wish to compute the V_{BD}s for $t_{BI} = 3.6 \times 10^4$ sec, and plot these points on the design curve, as this corresponds to a burn-in time of 10 hours (the curve for this time is not plotted in Fig. 7-50).

a. First we calculate the value of V_{BD} that an oxide would have to exhibit if it only had to survive the stress of normal operation (i.e., no burn-in). This is done using the curves generated in step 3. As an example, if an oxide was operated at 125°C and 5.5V, Fig. 7-38b indicates it would need to exhibit a $V_{BD} = 11.3V$ to ensure an operating lifetime of 10 years (with no burn-in).

b. Second, from the plots developed in step 6 (see for example, Fig. 7-49), we note that for low values of V_{BI} (e.g., 6V or less in Fig. 7-49), the lifetime after the burn-in remains essentially the same as for the case of no burn-in. Thus, for the case of an oxide operated at 125°C and at a voltage of 5.5V, any oxide exhibiting a $V_{BD} \geq 11.3V$ will not have its original lifetime altered by burn-ins at 150°C for 10 hours and burn-in voltages smaller than approximately 6V.

c. We next superimpose another set of curves on the design curves of step 6. These are the curves that indicate the minimum original V_{BD} value that an oxide would have to exhibit if it was to survive both the burn-in and the expected operating lifetime (i.e., oxides exhibiting original V_{BD} values above this curve would be such survivors). The value of V_{BD} at the intercept of the vertical axis is the V_{BD} value needed by an oxide to survive merely the normal operating stress (in Fig. 7-38b equal to 11.3V). However, as V_{BI} is increased, the burn-in eventually starts to damage some oxides to the degree that their post-burn-in lifetime is significantly reduced. The value at which this begins to occur is determined from the curves of step 5 as follows: We see in Fig. 7-49 that at $V_{BI} = 6.5V$ for a 10 hour burn-in at 150°C, the original lifetime of a 11.3V oxide is reduced by ~10%, and at $V_{BI} = 7V$ it is reduced by 100% (i.e., all the oxides exhibiting original V_{BD} values smaller than 11.4V would be eliminated by the burn-in). Thus, in this case, the minimum original V_{BD} an oxide would have to exhibit in order to survive both the burn-in and a 10-year lifetime is greater than 11.4V. To find this value (which would become one of the points on these curves), we use Figs. 7-38b and 7-49. That is, from Fig. 7-49 we see that for an oxide to have a 10-year life after a 7V, 10-hour, 150°C burn-in, its original (i.e., pre-burn-in) projected lifetime would have to be 30-years. From Fig. 7-38b we see that this corresponds to an original V_{BD} of 11.6V. This value would become one of the points we would plot on the set of design curves of Fig. 7-50.

8. From the now-completed set of design curves we can determine a number of things about a burn-in test. First, from the design curves (such as those shown in Fig. 7-50) we can see that samples with original breakdown voltages between the dashed and solid lines in this figure are projected to fail during normal operating conditions after burn-in. Those with breakdown voltages above the solid lines are projected to satisfy the specified operating lifetime after burn-in. Thus, it is apparent that in order to achieve a low post-burn-in failure rate, a set of burn-in conditions (voltage, time, and T) should be chosen such that there is a small difference between the V_{BD} corresponding to the burn-in and the V_{BD}

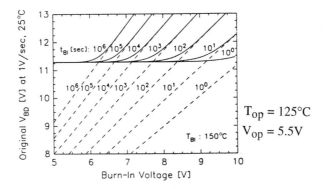

Fig. 7-50 Burn-in conditions can be optimized using the design curves shown here.   The optimal burn-in condition at T_{BI} = 150°C can be chosen using these curves and a breakdown voltage distribution characterizing the oxide technology.[47] (© IEEE 1990).

corresponding to the normal operating condition plus burn-in. Second, there are many combinations of voltage and time that can produce an equivalent difference between these values. In addition, the values of V_{BI} and t_{BI} to achieve such goals can be selected from the burn-in design curves described above.

9. After a set of burn-in conditions is chosen, we now have sufficient information to characterize the selection. That is, from the set of selected burn-in conditions and the design curves generated for the particular oxide technology and reliability specifications, we can determine: (1) the range of original V_{BD} values that will be screened out by the burn-in test; (2) the range of V_{BD} values that will correspond to early failures among the survivors of the burn-in.

10. Using the values from step 10 and the cumulative percent failure versus V_{BD} plot, one can determine: (a) the yield loss due to burn-in; and (b) the fraction of oxides that, having survived the burn-in, would still fail prior to the expected lifetime (cumulative percent failure during post-burn-in lifetime).

7.6.3 Example of Applying the Procedure for Determining an Optimal Set of Burn-In Conditions

Assume we are asked to choose a set of conditions for burning-in a set of ICs having a nominal gate oxide thickness of 125Å and a gate oxide area 10 mm². The expected operating lifetime is 10 years at an operating temperature of 125°C. The specified cumulative percentage failure after burn-in during the operating lifetime is 2%. How do we select a set of burn-in conditions to meet this goal?

First, we carry out a ramp-voltage breakdown test (with R = 1V/sec) on a set of MOS-Cs having the specified t_{ox} and oxide area at 25°C. The resulting cumulative percentage failure versus V_{BD} data is plotted as shown in Fig. 7-38a. The t_{BD} versus V_{BD} for the normal operating conditions (and T_{VBD} = 25°C) is computed and plotted as shown in Fig. 7-38b. If we choose a T_{BI} of 150°C, and a t_{BI} of 10 hours (3.6×10^4 sec), the V_{BD} as a function of V_{BI}, T_{BI}, and t_{BI} can computed using Eq. 7-46. The computed points of V_{BD} for these chosen burn-in parameters are plotted as the dashed line in Fig. 7-51.

Next, the L_{BI} versus V_{BD} curve, and the curve of lifetime after burn-in versus lifetime prior to burn-in (for several burn-in voltages and t_{BI} = 10 hours) are plotted from Eq. 7-48, as shown in Figs. 7-48 and 7-49. From Fig. 7-48, we see that Eq. 7-48 predicts that if oxides are subjected to a 10-hour burn-in at 150°C at 7V, all those with $V_{BD} \leq 11.4V$ will fail during burn-in, and hence will be screened out.

The values of V_{BD} (as a function of V_{BI}) that would have to be exhibited by the pre-burn-in oxides to be able to survive the burn-in *and* a 10-year lifetime at 5.5V at 125°C are then computed (with the aid of Figs. 7-48 and 7-49). These points are then plotted on Fig. 7-51 as shown by the solid line. (Note that for an oxide to have a projected 10-year lifetime at 5.5V and 125°C, it must exhibit an original V_{BD} = 11.3V). We see that at V_{BI} = 7V, the V_{BD} that would have to be exhibited by the oxides is 11.6V.

Based on the selected values of the burn-in and the information graphed in Fig. 7-51, we can draw the following conclusions about the burn-in procedure. First, since yield loss from burn-in is determined by the fraction of the total oxide population with a breakdown voltage of ≤11.4V, we estimate from Fig. 7-38a that the burn-in yield loss will be 75%. Second, after this particular burn-in, Fig. 7-51 indicates that only oxides with 11.4V<V_{BD}<11.6V are projected to fail during the subsequent 10-years of operation at 5.5V at 125°C. From Fig. 7-38a, we see that the percentage of oxides that exhibit V_{BD} between 11.0 and 12.V is very small, implying that the burn-in will probably achieve the goal of a cumulative percent failure of 2% after burn-in.

The corresponding average failure rate is determined by the fraction of the surviving population with 11.4V<V_{BD}<11.6V. Therefore, it is clear, that the burn-in condition

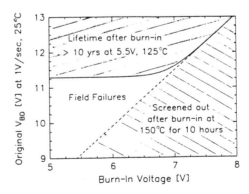

Fig. 7-51 Samples with breakdown voltages below the dashed line are screened out after burn-in; samples with breakdown voltages between the dashed line and the solid line are projected to fail during operation at 5.5V and 125°C and those with breakdown voltages above the solid line are projected to satisfy a 10-year lifetime specification.[47] (© IEEE 1990).

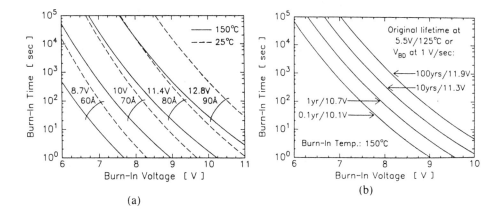

(a)   (b)

Fig. 7-52 Once an optimal burn-in condition is chosen using Fig. 7-50, equivalent burn-in conditions can be determined using the curves shown here. For example, burn-in conditions which screen out all oxides with breakdown voltages below 10V, i.e., $t_{oxeff}{<}70\text{Å}$ (see the 10V/70Å) curve for 150°C burn-in (a) or the 0.1-year lifetime/10.1V curve in (b) will have the same burn-in yield and projected reliability.[47] (© IEEE 1990).

has to be chosen such that the cumulative percentage that will fail during the operating lifetime (in this case that fraction of the population that exhibits failures with $11.4\text{V}{<}V_{BD}{<}11.6\text{V}$) is within the failure specification while keeping the yield loss from the burn-in as low as possible. If, for a given technology, a large fraction of the oxides have $11.4\text{V}{\leq}V_{BD}{\leq}11.6\text{V}$ ($80.5\text{Å}{<}t_{oxeff}{<}81.5\text{Å}$), as determined by taking the difference between the values of F ($V_{BD}=11.4\text{V}$) and F ($V_{BD}=11.6\text{V}$) on the cumulative percent failure versus V_{BD} plot, further screening is necessary to reduce the failure rate. Conversely, an oxide technology may have such a low fraction of oxides with $V_{BD}{\leq}11.6\text{V}$ (i.e., the defect density may be very low) that no screening is necessary.

Also note that since three variables must be selected (burn-in time, temperature, and voltage), it is possible to obtain the same burn-in yield and projected failure rate for many combinations of burn-in time, temperature, and voltage. As an example, if the optimal burn-in condition is determined from Fig. 7-50 to be 7V, 150°C, and $3{\times}10^4$ sec (corresponding to a breakdown voltage of 11.4V), all equivalent burn-in conditions are given by the 11.4V/80Å line in Fig. 7-52a or the 11.3V/10-year line in Fig. 7-52b. In other words, any burn-in voltage and time combination on the 11.4V/80Å line in Fig. 7-52a, or the 11.3V/10-year line in Fig. 7-52b can be used to screen out those oxides characterized by $V_{BD}{\leq}11.4\text{V}$ or $t_{oxeff}{<}80\text{Å}$ (i.e., to screen out those oxides that are projected to fail within 10 years at 5.5V at 125°C). Since it is desirable to select burn-in conditions which minimize testing costs, the shortest burn-in time (i.e., the maximum burn-in voltage) is usually picked. This maximum allowable voltage is usually set by such circuit or technology constraints as the junction breakdown voltage.

7.7 OXIDE BREAKDOWN MODULE IN BERKELEY RELIABILITY TOOL (BERT)

The oxide reliability model described above has been implemented in the *Circuit Oxide Reliability Simulator* (CORS) program,[56] which is part of a larger reliability simulator software package BERT.[57] CORS helps determine if the oxide quality for a particular process is high enough to meet the specified circuit lifetime under expected operating conditions with a sufficiently low failure rate. Thus, it should help circuit designers determine if a particular design is feasible for a given oxide process. The user is required to provide ramp-voltage breakdown statistics or time-to-breakdown statistics of test MOS-Cs. The simulator uses this data to derive $D(\Delta t_{ox})$ for the particular technology.

The CORS program generates statistics about circuit failures due to MOS oxide breakdown. It predicts the probability of circuit failure as a function of operation time, temperature, power-supply voltage, and input waveforms. In addition to supplying TDDB data, the user creates an input deck similar to an ordinary SPICE input deck. CORS then determines ε_{ox} for each oxide element in the circuit from the SPICE node voltages and a consideration of the work function difference between the electrodes. Figure 7-53 shows a block diagram of this oxide reliability simulator. Circuit failure statistics are calculated using the rule that if any MOSFET experiences breakdown, then the entire circuit fails. CORS is also a tool for optimizing burn-in, in that it can simulate the effect of burn-in in circuit reliability. The results of such simulations are useful for balancing conflicting goals such as cost, avoidance of hot electron degradation, and reduction of field failures due to oxide breakdown in choosing the burn-in condition for a product. HSPICE-compatible versions of the BERT simulator with software support are also commercially available (e.g., from BTA, Santa Clara, CA[127]).

7.8 MODELS OF THIN OXIDE GROWTH

The Deal-Grove model described in Vol. 1 for the growth of SiO_2 provides excellent agreement with experimental observations for thick oxides.[58] That is, the rate constants

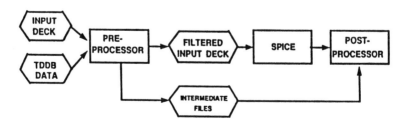

Fig. 7-53 Block diagram of oxide reliability simulator.[56] (© IEEE 1989).

derived in the Deal-Grove model allow the thickness of oxide films >350Å to be well predicted as a function of temperature, furnace ambient, silicon doping concentration, and silicon crystal orientation.   However, the model does not give a detailed understanding of the mechanisms that produce these dependencies nor is it relevant when the oxide is thinner than 350Å. This is particularly troublesome because gate oxide thicknesses of ≤100Å are needed for submicron MOSFETs.

Several physical mechanisms have been proposed as models for such enhanced oxidation including:[59]

1. Models based on *space-charge effects* where the oxidation enhancement in the thin regime is due to field-assisted oxidant diffusion.

2. Models based on the existence of structural defects in the oxide, such as micropores (~10Å in diameter). These allow the oxygen molecules to diffuse more rapidly.

3. Models based on *stress effects* that can lead to a larger value of the diffusivity of the oxidizing species.

4. Models which postulate that the increased solubility of the oxidant in the thin oxide could affect the growth rate by its influence on the oxidant concentration at the silicon surface.

5. A model by Massoud et al., based on the presence of a *thin surface layer in the silicon where additional reaction sites are available*. The concentration of these sites decays exponentially with a characteristic length L_2 in Eq. 7-50.

Despite the large number of models proposed to explain oxide growth in this very thin regime, none has yet been convincingly accepted as more valid than the others. Nevertheless, several empirical models have been developed that yield reasonable agreement with measured values of oxide thickness in the thin regime.

Massoud et al. demonstrated that a much better fit can be accomplished that with the Deal-Grove model alone by adding an additional term to the oxidation rate that decays exponentially with thickness. The expression for the growth rate in the classical Deal-Grove model (see Vol. 1, chap. 7)

$$\frac{d\,t_{ox}}{d\,t} = \frac{B}{(2t_{ox} + A)} \qquad (7\text{-}49)$$

then becomes

$$\frac{d\,t_{ox}}{d\,t} = \frac{B}{(2t_{ox} + A)} + C_2\,e^{-t_{ox}/L_2} \qquad (7\text{-}50)$$

where C_2 is a pre-exponential constant with a value of 3.2 eV, and L_2 is the characteristic decay length described in paragraph **5** above. For dry-oxidation of lightly doped substrates in the 800-1000°C range, L_2 was found to be $\cong$ 70Å, independent of surface orientation. Heavy doping was found to only slightly affect the oxidation rate enhancement in the thin regime. Equation 7-50 has been implemented in SUPREM III as the model for thin oxide growth in dry-oxygen.

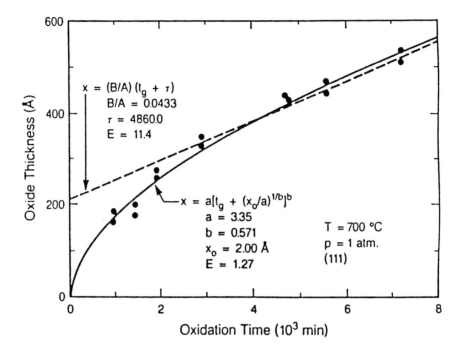

Fig. 7-54 Fits to oxide thickness versus oxidation time using the Deal-Grove model and the power-law model expression.[128]

Another empirical model for thin oxide growth has been developed by Reisman and Nicollian. By analyzing a vast amount of data, they were able to derive an empirical model that calculates the oxide thickness versus time using a general power law of the form

$$t_{ox} = a \ (t_g + \tau)^b \qquad (7 - 51)$$

where a and b are constants, and t_g is the growth time measured in a given experiment, and τ is the time to grow an oxide of thickness t_{oxi} already present on the surface.

A comparison between the power law description of oxide thickness and the Deal-Grove model is shown in Fig. 7-54. Data from Deal and Grove at 700°C are plotted on linear scales and Eq. 7-49 is plotted with measured values of A and B. Shown for comparison is Eq. 7-51 with the appropriate constants obtained by a fractional weighted least squares fit to the data.[60] Kouvatsos has extracted the a and b parameters of Eq. 7-51 at 950°C and 1100°C for oxide growth in O_2 diluted in He, and found very good fit to the Reisman-Nicollian power-law model.[61] This model has been implemented in the process simulator PREDICT-1 (see chap. 1).

7.9 TECHNOLOGY OF THIN OXIDE GROWTH

In this section we will describe the process technology of growing 10-20 nm thick gate oxides. As mentioned earlier, the goal is to grow uniform, reliable oxides of precisely the specified thickness - across each wafer, from wafer-to-wafer, and from run-to-run.

7.9.1 Oxidation Furnaces

Gate oxide growth is still carried out in production as a batch process. The typical load size is 150 wafers for 150 mm wafers and 100 wafers for 200 mm wafers (at 0.125" wafer-to-wafer spacing). Vertical furnaces are used almost exclusively for growing such gate oxides on 150-200 mm wafers (see Fig. 7-55).[62] In such furnaces neither the wafers nor the wafer holders make contact with the tube during loading or during the growth process. Thus, far fewer particles are generated than when loading was carried out by sliding a quartz boat into the horizontal furnace tube. (This approach was improved by cantilevering the load during insertion into the tube, then lowering the boat onto the tube, and withdrawing the cantilever, see Vol. 1, chap. 7). However, to achieve this same level of particle reduction in a horizontal furnace, a cantilever must be used to suspend the wafer load during the growth process. This necessitates use of a cantilever sufficiently rigid to hold the wafer load at high temperatures without sagging. As the wafers get larger, the load becomes heavier, making this approach too cumbersome. (Variable deflections of the cantilever rod may also cause problems in centering the load in the process tube, and the massive construction of cantilevers increases the amount of thermal energy transported from the wafers, leading to temperature nonuniformities in the wafers during oxide growth).

In the vertical furnace, lighter boat materials can be used, permitting the return to all-quartz boat construction. The lighter, more open boat design also enables virtually 360 degrees of line-of-sight radiant heat transfer between the wafers and furnace walls, thus improving the thermal uniformity characteristics. Additionally, gas-phase mass transport of the process gases is distributed uniformly along virtually the entire wafer circumference. Other advantages are: (1) precise control of wafer-to-wafer spacing in vertical furnace boats (which promotes better thickness uniformity); (2) ease of implementing automated wafer loading and unloading onto the boat (as well as boat loading into the furnace (in fact, loading wafers from plastic cassettes to the quartz boat is performed by Class-1 robots); and (3) contamination of the furnace by ambient atmosphere during load cycles is reduced. Thus, vertical furnaces have virtually replaced horizontal furnaces for 150 mm or larger wafers.

7.9.2 Control of Gate Oxide Growth Rates

Relatively slow growth rates must be used to reproducibly grow thin oxide films of precise thickness. A number of approaches to achieving such slower growth rates have been reported, including: growth in dry O_2 at atmospheric pressure at lower temperatures (800-900°C); growth at reduced total pressures (i.e., lower than atmospheric pressure);[63] growth a reduced partial pressures of O_2 (i.e., use of a diluent inert gas -

such as N_2,[64] Ar,[65] or He,[66] together with the gas containing the oxidizing species); and use of composite oxide films (i.e., using gate-oxide films consisting of a layer of thermally grown SiO_2 and an overlying layer of CVD SiO_2). By and large, however, the mainstream approach for 10-15 nm thick gate oxides is apparently to grow the oxide film at atmospheric pressure and lower temperatures (800-900°C). With this approach, processes using modern vertical oxide furnaces can grow 10 nm oxides to within 0.1 nm (100Å ± 1-2Å) across the wafer, from wafer-to-wafer, and from run to run.

Note that particle densities resulting from gate oxide growth processes are very low in modern vertical furnaces for a number of reasons. Besides avoiding contact between the boat and the furnace walls, particle generation by vibration of wafers standing vertically in the boat (as can occur in horizontal furnaces) is suppressed. In addition, particles present in the vertical furnace are likely to fall in the annular space between the wafers and furnace walls. Each wafer is protected from these particles by the wafer just above it. Particle densities of less than $0.05/cm^2$ (at sizes <0.2 μm) are now being specified for oxide furnaces.

The oxidation process is also inherently a particle reducer (as opposed to a supplier). That is, many particles are carbonaceous, and are thus consumed by the oxidation process itself (being turned into gaseous CO_2 or CO). However, other types of particles, such as silicon particles (from scribe marks, laser marking tools, or scratches), or metallic precipitates, etc., are of course not removed, and can represent problems. Particulates are more likely to be introduced from other fabrication processes than from the oxide furnace. In fact, the cleanest wafers (e.g., ≤10 particles per 200 mm wafer), and the most reproducible gate oxide films, are routinely achieved on wafers as received from the silicon wafer suppliers.

7.9.3 Factors Impacting Gate-Oxide Thickness Uniformity

Some of the factors that can adversely impact the control of oxide thickness uniformity include: (1) the presence of native oxide films on the Si surface prior to gate oxide growth; (2) growth of the oxide during ramp up and ramp down; (3) pre-oxidation cleaning effects; and (4) the residual water content of the O_2 gas in dry-oxidation processes. (Although the doping concentration in the Si substrate can also impact the oxide growth rate, this factor is not significant in gate oxidation processes since the substrate doping is relatively light.) Let us discuss the important factors in more detail.

A thin "native oxide" grows on bare silicon at room temperature and usually achieves a maximum thickness of about 1 nm (10Å).[67] Although there is some controversy concerning the exact nature of this oxide, (i.e., organic contamination, adsorbed H_2O, or true oxide), its presence undoubtedly affects subsequent oxidation. Nevertheless, the native oxide growth is self-limiting, and seems to attain most of its final thickness (10Å) within 24 hours after a bare Si surface has exposed to atmosphere. Thus, by either rigidly controlling the time between cleaning (HF dip) and oxide growth to within an hour, or by allowing at least 24 hours as the minimum time between cleaning and oxide growth, the native oxide layer thickness from run-to-run can be kept sufficiently constant so that the final oxide layer thickness will not be impacted by this

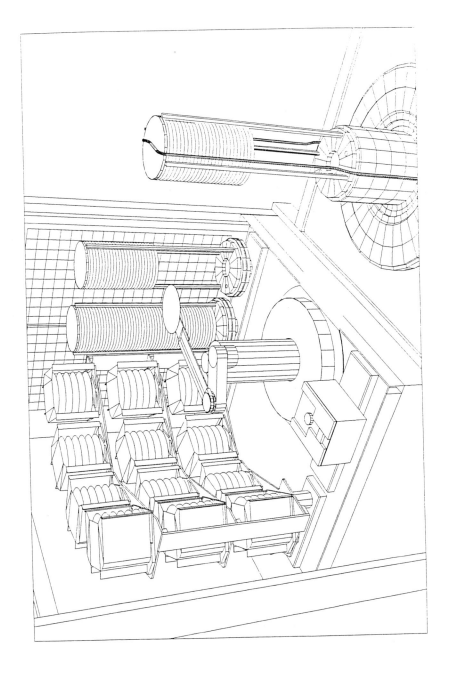

Fig. 7-55 Vertical furnace for growing thin gate oxides.   (a) Robotic loading of vertical quartz boat. Courtesy of Semitherm.

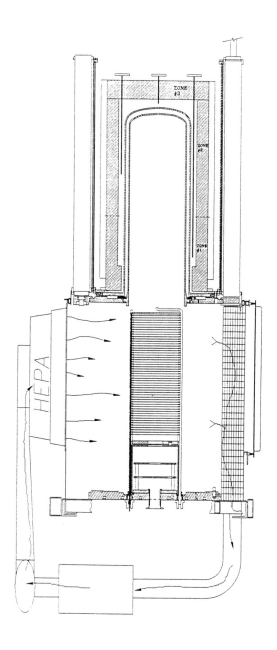

Fig. 7-55 Vertical furnace for growing thin gate oxides. (b) Furnace tube and boat. Courtesy of Semitherm.

factor. (The time wafers are permitted to remain in the DI rinse water after the HF dip may also need to be specified and controlled.)

Ohmi has also reported that native oxide can be prevented from forming by storing the wafers after cleaning in a gas ambient containing very little residual oxygen and moisture.[68] He also reported that native oxide growth can occur as a result of rinsing wafers with exposed Si in DI water containing high concentrations of dissolved oxygen (>600 ppm). To suppress such growth, he suggests rinsing such wafers in DI water containing very little (i.e., <20 ppm) dissolved oxygen, and then drying the wafers by blowing with N_2 gas.[69]

The furnace temperature during insertion is typically 700°C. The temperature is then ramped up to the growth temperature (~15°C/min). To prevent (uncontrolled) oxide growth during the temperature ramp up and ramp down of the furnace, the procedure is normally carried out in an ambient of N_2 and 2-4%O_2 (i.e., the oxygen is present to prevent either nitridation or micropitting of the Si surface exposed to pure N_2 at elevated temperatures). In another approach to control oxide growth and control surface microroughness during ramp up, Morita describes a technique of growing a "pre-oxide" of 4Å thickness in ultraclean O_2 at 300°C, and then ramping the wafers up to temperature in ultraclean Ar.[70] Yet another technique was reported by Wu et al., in which wafers were loaded at a lower temperature (600°C) into an N_2 ambient to reduce thermal stress and minimize native oxide growth. This is followed by a ramp-up to 900°C. The method includes a 60 minute pre-annealing step at 900°C prior to the oxide growth process, and a 15 minute N_2 anneal after the oxide is grown.[114]

Pre-oxidation cleaning procedures can have significant impact on the growth rate. With respect to cleaning, common procedures involve the use of acidic or basic hydrogen peroxide solution, sputter cleaning, in situ gas cleans using HCl, or flash heating to high temperatures. All of these cleans leave the surface in different states with varying surface films. For example, cleans composed of as base-acid-HF sequence produce a silicon surface that can oxidize up to 20% faster than a base-only clean. Apparently, the different cleans, on fundamentally different surface structures, can produce a change in the interfacial reaction rate which affects the linear oxidation rate constant.[71]

For dry O_2 oxidations there is also the requirement that trace amounts of water be controlled. A relatively small amount of water (125 ppm) in O_2 is sufficient to increase the oxidation rate at 980°C enough to throw the oxidation process out of spec for a sub-0.5 μm technology. In situ gas analysis with an RGA can monitor trace moisture in dry-oxidzing ambients to improve gate oxide thickness uniformity.[133]

7.9.4 Gate Oxide Growth Processes for 10-20 nm thick Gate Oxides on 150-200 mm Wafers

Gate oxide processes for submicron MOSFETs down to ~0.5 μm generally vary from company-to-company, and the exact details are usually proprietary. Despite this fact, some general statements can be made about thin gate oxide growth in this regime. As noted earlier, the processing is carried out in vertical furnaces, with wafer loads of 100-

150 wafers. Dummy wafers (e.g., 5 at the top and bottom of the wafer holder) are used to prevent thickness nonuniformity on wafers at the ends of the boat.

Prior to the gate oxide growth step, various procedures, as described in section 7.5.2 are carried out to optimize the gate oxide breakdown characteristics after it is grown. These include the growth and stripping of a sacrificial gate oxide (to counteract the Kooi effect), and careful cleaning procedures (see section 7.9.4). The wafers are then loaded onto quartz carriers by robotic wafer handling, and the carrier is moved into the hot zone of the furnace at insertion rates of ~15 cm/min for 150 mm wafers and ~10 cm/min for 200 mm wafers, with the furnace temperature during such insertion at ~650-700°C.

After being loaded, the furnace temperature is ramped to the oxide growth temperature. During this time, the wafers are held in an N_2 ambient (or maybe an Ar ambient) to prevent uncontrolled oxide growth during ramp up. As noted earlier, a small percentage of O_2 is also included in the inert ambient to slightly oxidize the wafer. This prevents thermal nitride from forming, which could inhibit subsequent oxidation. In addition, extended exposure of bare Si wafers to inert high temperature gases can result in the formation of micropits.[72] When the furnace reaches the growth temperature a short time for temperature stabilization of the wafers is allowed (e.g., 5 min) before the oxidizing gases are introduced. (In some furnaces, the furnace is pumped out prior to introducing pre-heated process gases.)

The growth process is usually carried out at atmospheric pressure, either in dry O_2, or in some cases in a 3-step process (i.e., the growth time is divided into parts: 1/3 dry O_2/1/3 wet O_2/1/3 dry O_2).* Typical process temperatures range from 800-900°C with the total growth time in the range of 15-30 minutes. Many processes use a chlorine-containing gas as well as O_2. HCl or trichloroethane (TCA - $C_2H_2Cl_3$) have been widely used for this purpose (2-4% concentration in the O_2 is typical).[73] Some of these may also be 3-step processes (e.g., 1/3 dry O_2/ 1/3 dry O_2 + TCA/ 1/3 dry O_2).[109]

The drawbacks of using HCl stem from its highly corrosive nature. That is, small leaks can cause damage to the gas cabinet electronic circuitry. Also, to prevent corrosion of the gas lines careful measures must be employed to exclude any moisture. TCA is much less corrosive. It is also the safest organic chloride available (with a relatively high toxic limit value [tlv] of 350 ppm), and generally only a catastrophic container failure may result in harmful release. However, TCA has been identified as an ozone depleter, and thus its use is also being phased out.** New gases, including 1,2,-trans dichloroethylene (t-DCE) have been introduced as substitutes for TCA, and are commercially available from Schumacher, Olin Hunt, and others.

---

* In a few processes, purely wet oxidation may be carried out, usually where it is desired to keep as low a thermal budget as possible (i.e., where very shallow junctions are needed and have been formed prior to the oxide growth step).

** Note that both the Montreal Protocol and the U.S. Clean Air Act will not regulate TCA that is used as a 'feedstock' material. So TCA is not restricted for use in applications like silicon oxidation, where it is a feedstock for chlorine atoms. Despite this fact, many U.S. semiconductor manufacturers are replacing TCA with t-DCE, which has been dubbed "the more responsible ecological choice." Its environmental half-life is four days, compared to six years for TCA.[74]

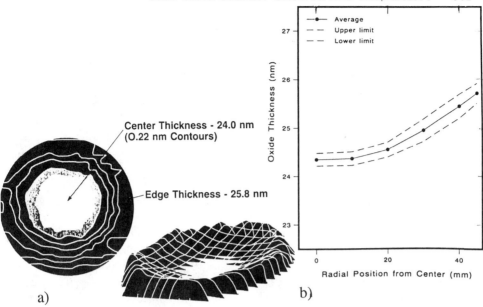

Fig. 7-56 Radial oxide thickness variations in oxides grown in O_2 + HCl: (a) thickness contour map for a single wafer, (b) oxide thickness as averages over an entire boat of wafers, as a function of radial position. These graphs illustrate the oxide thinning towards the center of the wafer.[73] Reprinted with the permission of the publisher, the Electrochemical Society.

However, it has been reported that use of Cl-containing gases in the oxide growth process can cause oxide thickness non-uniformity (see Fig 7-56).[73]

Some gate oxide growth processes, however, reportedly do not use chlorine-containing gases. The philosophy behind such approaches is that the Cl is primarily used to enhance local uniformity of the thin oxide film. This same goal is believed to be achievable by using meticulous and frequent cleaning of the furnace quartzware (which also prevents inadvertent Na contamination). In such cases, the use of chlorine is considered to be unnecessary.

Upon concluding the oxide growth process, the wafers are usually subjected to a post-oxidation anneal (POA), most commonly in N_2 at either the oxide growth temperature, or a somewhat higher temperature (50-100°C higher). A report comparing a 900°C/60 min POA in N_2 + 5%O_2 with a 1000°C/20 min POA in N_2 + 5%O_2 for 20 minutes claims that the higher temperature POA improves the oxide Q_{BD} and t_{BD} values.[75] (The small percentage of oxygen in the N_2 annealing ambient is thought to bridge non-bridging positively-charged oxygen atoms, and to increase the probability of oxidizing free Si trivalent atoms at the Si-SiO$_2$ interface.) Thus, surface states and fixed oxide charge are reduced. (Some reports also indicate that POA in Ar may result in incrementally lower oxide defect densities and reduced electron traps. Argon, however, is 3 to 5 times as expensive as N_2, so the increased performance may not justify the added production cost.[76]) Note that another approach, involving a two-step oxidation has also been reported to improve the quality of the oxide. Here an initial 30-40Å oxide is grown, followed by an anneal at 1050°C for 60 min in Ar. Then the second oxidation step is performed to obtain the desired oxide thickness. The anneal in argon is postulated to cause viscous flow of the oxide allowing relaxation and release of built-up strains.[77]

Following the POA the furnace temperature is ramped back down, and the wafers are unloaded. The thickness of the grown oxide is measured with either a reflection spectrophotometer or an ellipsometer.[78] (UV-reflection spectrophotometers can measure thinner films than visible-light spectrophotometers, i.e., repeatable to <1 Å on 50Å oxides).

7.9.5 Alternative Gate Oxide Growth Processes

7.9.5.1 Stacked Gate Oxide Films (Thermally Grown SiO$_2$ Layer and CVD SiO$_2$ Layer).
An alternative technique for forming the gate dielectric film by using a stack of thermal and CVD oxide layers has been investigated. This approach attempts to decrease the density of low-voltage defects (the A-mode defects shown in Fig. 7-14) in thin (<15 nm) gate oxide films. In one report, a three-step process sequence was used to fabricate a gate oxide film that had low defect density and interface state density.[79] A 5-nm-thick thermal oxide was first grown at 850-900°C in a mixture of O$_2$:TCA. Next, a 5-nm-thick LPCVD (0.2-0.3 torr) SiO$_2$ layer was deposited by TEOS pyrolysis at 625-650°C. Finally, a third layer of oxide was thermally grown underneath the first grown layer by performing an oxidation during the densifying anneal at 850-900°C. During this third step three events occur: the CVD oxide is densified, the traps get annealed out and a planar stress-free Si/SiO$_2$ interface is formed by the newly grown SiO$_2$ layer. The decrease in low-voltage defects is attributed to a mismatch of the micropores (10-25Å in diameter) that occur in both the thermal oxide and CVD layer. That is, there is high probability that these weak spots will not occur in both layers at the same location at the thermal/LPCVD oxide interface (Fig. 7-57a). In addition, since less silicon is consumed than in a conventional thermal oxide fewer weak spots originating from substrate defects (such as metal-contamination-related defects in the bulk) are incorporated into the bottom thermal oxide.

In a second report, a 11-nm-thick LPCVD TEOS layer was deposited at 650°C on a 4-nm-thick thermal oxide layer (grown at 900°C in O$_2$ and HCl) followed by a densification step to form a 14-nm-thick gate oxide. The densification was performed at 950°C in a 1% oxygen ambient diluted with argon, so that the shrinkage of the CVD layer during the anneal was offset by simultaneous thermal SiO$_2$ growth, resulting in a negligible effect on the final thickness of the stacked oxide. The temperature of the anneal is also important, as a lower one (i.e., 900°C) resulted in a less densified CVD layer, which allowed enhanced diffusion of oxidizing species during the later poly reox step, resulting in a larger gate bird's beak (see section 5.2.3.1). This can impact the electrical channel length in small MOSFETs. That is, whereas the 950°C anneal produced devices with electrical channel lengths comparable to those with thermal gate oxides, those with 900°C anneals had significantly longer electrical channel lengths.

Like the oxide in the report above, a significantly smaller number of low-voltage defects are also observed.[80,81] In later work, the results of hot-carrier and Fowler-Nordheim stressing on these films was reported. That is, the stacked films exhibited less degradation due to such stressing (i.e., less V_T-shift and degradation of the subthreshold slope S_t were observed in MOSFETs with these stacked gate oxides than with those made with thermal gate oxides).[113]

Moazzami and Hu investigated the impact of the dielectric deposition and growth sequence and the ratio of thermal to LPCVD oxide thickness on gate dielectric integrity.[82] They suggest that the decrease in low-voltage defects in such stacked gate dielectrics is not due to mismatch of the micropores, but to the filling of the micropores by the LPCVD oxide film (see Fig. 7-57b). If this assertion is correct (implying that only a very thin LPCVD oxide layer is necessary to fill micropores in the thermal oxide layer), it is projected that the stacked oxide technology can be scaled further by reducing the thickness of the thermal oxide layer. For example, with a 5-nm-thick thermal oxide layer, a total stacked oxide thickness as thin as 7 nm (suitable for 0.25-μm CMOS technology) appears feasible. They also note that for oxide technologies that are not

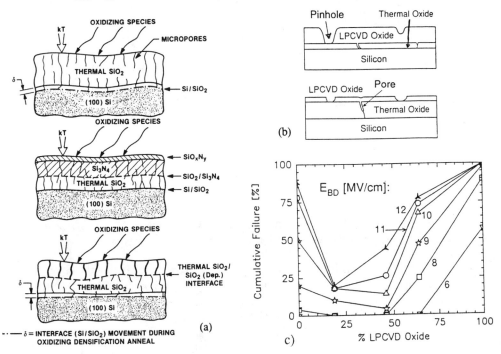

Fig. 7-57 (a) Effects of oxidizing densification anneal: (*i*) SiO_2 films, (*ii*) SiO_2 -Si_3N_4 dual dielectric: (*iii*) Thermal SiO_2 -CVD Dep SiO_2 multilayered stacked film.[79] (© IEEE 1988). (b) Thermal reoxidation does not eliminate a pinhole in the LPCVD oxide layer. (c) By introducing a thermal oxidation step prior to the LPCVD oxide deposition, the defect density is improved appreciably.[82] (© IEEE 1993).

believed to contain micropores (such as wet thermal oxide), stacked oxide technology may not lower A-mode defect density significantly. In addition, CVD SiO_2 processes are more subject to particulate formation than are thermal SiO_2 processes. Thus, gate oxide processes involving a CVD step will need to demonstrate that this problem can be overcome in order to be considered for mainstream production processes.

In another recent report, the advantages of the stacked gate dielectric was demonstrated for overcoming the following problems: gate thinning at the field edges; decreased oxide reliability following removal of the poly-buffer LOCOS nitride/poly mask by dry etching, and; damage of the gate oxide by MERIE plasma etch processes. The merits of using an N_2O oxynitride layer together with a CVD TEOS layer to form the stacked gate dielectric were also discussed.[112]

7.10 GATE OXIDE DAMAGE FROM PLASMA PROCESSING

Plasma processes use glow discharges to lower the process temperature and obtain directional ion bombardment (see vol. 1, chaps. 9 and 16). By their nature, glow discharges result in some wafer-surface charging, which is normally not significant. However, if this charging occurs on conductor films formed on the wafer surface, under some circumstances a thin (i.e., gate) oxide under these conductors can be severely degraded by such charging. That is, the oxides can be either completely shorted or weakened to the degree that they will fail early during normal device operation. Since such oxide damage may represent even further IC yield loss by enhancing the oxide's vulnerability to hot-carrier-induced degradation, the issue of plasma-induced degradation is a critical one for VLSI processing.

Evidence indicates that non-uniformities in the plasma across the wafer surface can give rise to significant local charge build-up. Here we describe models of how such charge build-up occurs and how it may damage the gate oxide, as well as suggested methods to avoid or mitigate the problem. A second plasma damage mechanism, radiation induced damage, is also briefly discussed at the conclusion of section 7.10.

7.10.1 How Isolated Conductor Regions on a Wafer Surface Can be Charged Up by an RF Plasma

When a plasma is generated with an rf power supply, the reactor electrodes are subjected to an alternating polarity voltage (i.e., at 13.56 MHz frequency in many RIE etchers). During the first half of the rf cycle (i.e., when a positive bias is applied) the electrode surface attracts electrons from the plasma. When the bias is negative (in the second half of the rf cycle of the voltage waveform) the electrode surface attracts positive ions from the plasma. Thus, the electrode is impinged upon by both positive and negative charges. These charged particles will therefore also bombard the surface of wafers mounted on such electrodes (see also Vol. 1, chap. 9).

In a uniform plasma a condition of balance is reached in which the flux of electrons during the positive part of the rf signal is equal to the flux of ions during the negative part of the signal. Charging is not a problem because precise recombination of opposing charges occurs and the surface potential stays close to that of the substrate.

However, if the plasma is non-uniform, ion and electron currents do not have to balance locally over the rf cycle (although there must be a net balance over the electrode as a whole).

If the effective electrode surface is a conductor, surface currents flow to balance the local nonuniformity in conduction currents from the plasma. If the surface is an insulator, this imbalance can cause the surface to charge locally. Specifically, if an island of conductor material is sitting on an oxide (and this island is elsewhere not connected to the substrate (e.g., a poly line that serves as a gate electrode), the locally unbalanced ion and electron currents can charge the conductor. The surface area of such a conductor exposed to impingement by the charged plasma species is referred to as the *antenna* surface (see Fig. 7-59). Since the antenna can sit on both thick oxide (field regions) and thin oxide (gate regions) the antenna/thin oxide area-ratio can exceed unity. The charging will result in an increased voltage across the gate oxide and a decreased voltage across the plasma sheath. This charge buildup will continue until the currents balance or the oxide begins to conduct. The positive feedback mechanism that drives the charge buildup is caused by the exponential dependence of electron current on sheath voltage. If the oxide begins to conduct (i.e., by Fowler-Nordheim tunneling), charge passage through the oxide may cause damage that can eventually lead to oxide breakdown. In particular, if the time integrated oxide current approaches Q_{BD} for the oxide, significant damage is incurred.

Let us consider the degree of charging from a quantitative perspective.[83] If the plasma is uniform, and positive and negative charges balance over a single rf cycle, the amount of charging of a gate *during* the cycle is very small. For instance, if we have a gate oxide thickness t_{ox} of 10 nm, an impinging ion current density J_i of 10 pA/μm^2 during the second half of the cycle, a 13.56 MHz excitation frequency, and an antenna/thin oxide area-ratio (antenna ratio) of 1000, the maximum gate voltage excursion in 1 rf cycle ΔV_g will be less than

$$\Delta V_g = \frac{J_i \times 1000}{2 \, f \times C_{ox}} = \frac{10 \text{ pA/}\mu\text{m}^2 \times 1000}{2 \times 13.56 \text{ MHz} \times 345 \text{ nF/cm}^2} = 0.11 \text{V} \qquad (7\text{-}52)$$

where C_{ox} is the oxide capacitance per unit area.

However, when the ion and electron currents are not in local balance, net charging over each rf cycle occurs. It continues until a steady-state oxide voltage is reached. At this point the Fowler-Nordheim tunneling current through the oxide balances the net current collected by the antenna. To get some idea of how long it takes for such a steady-condition is reached, let us assume that the ion current density J_i is larger than the electron current density J_e (e.g., $J_i = 10$ pA/μm^2 and the time-average electron current density $<J_e> = -8$ pA/μm^2), the time needed to reach a steady-state gate voltage of 10V ($t_{charging}$) is approximately

$$t_{charging} = \frac{C_{ox} \times V_g}{(J_i - <J_e>) \times 1000} = \frac{345 \text{ nF / cm}^2 \times 10 \text{ V}}{2 \text{ pA / }\mu\text{m}^2 \times 1000} = 17.3 \text{ } \mu\text{sec} \qquad (7\text{-}53)$$

Thus, after this short charging time a steady-state bias of 10V exists across the oxide in this example. At this steady-state condition, the voltage on the gate remains nearly constant, with a small-amplitude, superimposed 13.56 MHz ripple, similar to the effect calculated in Eq. 7-52. Plasma charging can therefore be approximated as a dc stress to the oxide. Note that both positive and negative charging can occur with voltages over 50V possible for thick dielectrics in very nonuniform plasmas. The actual voltage seen by a gate is reduced because the tunneling currents flowing the rough the gate oxide limit the peak charging voltage.

7.10.2 Causes of Non-Uniformities in Plasmas

The non-uniformities in a plasma which can give rise to local imbalances in collected charge can result from a variety of factors, including the following: (1) poor electrode design;[84] (2) non-uniform and/or time-varying magnetic fields;[83] (3) gas composition; e.g., use of highly electronegative gases (such as SF_6);[85] and (4) gas flow conditions inside the plasma reactor that cause unstable plasmas. Besides plasma nonuniformity there is concern that the drive toward higher plasma densities will increase charge damage since the charged particle currents are higher.

An example of how a non-uniform magnetic field causes plasma non-uniformities is shown in Fig. 7-58. Here a magnetic field in a MERIE (magnetically enhanced RIE)

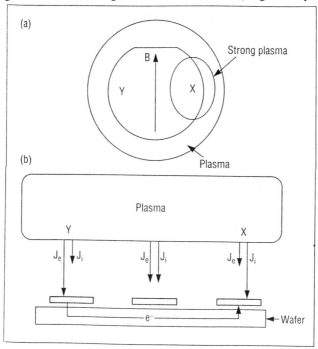

Fig. 7-58 (a) A strong plasma is present in region X during static MERIE etching. (b) A possible plasma-charging current path.[83] Reprinted with permission of Solid State Technology.

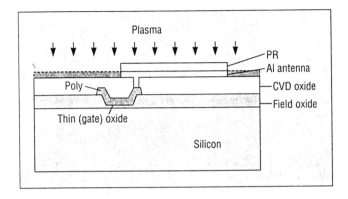

Fig. 7-59 Device cross-section of "antenna structure."[83] Reprinted with permission of Solid State Technology.

reactor with a static magnetic field is depicted. (Note that this is not necessarily the exact magnetic-field configuration of any particular MERIE reactor.) The effect of this magnetic field non-uniformity is to cause the electron flux to be larger than the ion flux near the wafer periphery, and the (positively charged) ion flux to be greater near the wafer center. Such magnetic field non-uniformities can also arise in ECR as well as MERIE plasma etchers.

7.10.3 Test Structures Used to Characterize Plasma-Induced Oxide Damage

Special test structures can be used to maximize the charging sensitivity of oxides to plasma damage. Measurements on these test structures can then be compared to results on product wafers. The two types of test structures most widely used to enhance the effects of plasma damage on thin oxides are: (1) large area capacitors; and (2) so-called "antenna" structures (structures with a large conductor area on thick oxide connected to a relatively small-area gate electrode on thin oxide - see Fig. 7-59. Note that both types of test structures should also be layed out in area-intensive and edge-intensive configurations (Fig. 7-60). This is because damage may be proportional to gate periphery or area (as will be discussed in section 7.10.5.)

Oxide degeneration tends to increase with capacitor size because defects in the grown oxide tend to exhibit the same density distribution as particulates that cause chip defects (see section 7.5.4.3). That is, there is a greater likelihood of a defect being present in a capacitor as it's area is increased.

Antenna structures increase the density of Fowler-Nordheim tunneling current in thin oxides during plasma exposure by increasing the collected dc or rf currents which drive the Fowler-Nordheim tunneling current. That is, collected charge is proportional to the antenna electrode area or edge length (depending on whether the entire surface or just

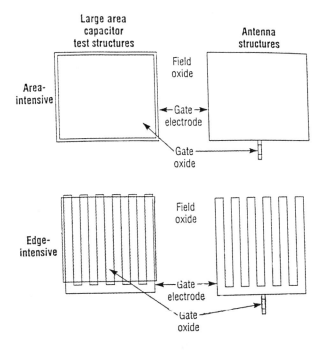

Fig. 7-60 Top view comparison of large area capacitor and antenna damage test structures with area-intensive and edge-intensive configurations. Field oxide is grown wherever gate oxide is not.[86] Reprinted with permission of Solid State Technology.

the edges are exposed to the plasma).[86] After the small area of thin oxide of the antenna structure is stressed by the collected charge, it is subjected to one of the electrical tests which measures oxide integrity (e.g., ramped-voltage V_{BD} or charge-to-breakdown [Q_{BD}] testing). Note that the antenna structure is less sensitive to damage but is probably more representative of real device structures than the large area capacitor. The antenna:gate-area ratio is usually varied (e.g., from 16:1 to 1000:1 for gate oxide areas of 20 μm x 20 μm (400 μm^2).

Large capacitors with area- and edge-intensive configurations are recommended for studying oxide damage during gate etching and ashing. Such structures are useful as monitors of both gate-oxide quality and overall damage because they are very sensitive to oxide defects. Antenna structures are effective for measuring damage from charge buildup after gate formation (i.e., interconnect etching) as well as damage that occurs during gate formation and ashing.

The threshold voltage of a MOSFET structure subjected to charging current damage will change due to the generation of interface states (as described in the next section). Although the shift in V_T may be small, a technique for monitoring such small V_T shifts has been suggested. It involves the use of a differential pair amplifier containing two MOSFETs. One MOSFET of the pair has a gate connected to an antenna with small area, and the other to an antenna of larger area. The input offset voltage of the pair will vary if a change in the V_T of the two MOSFETs is not equal. The MOSFET whose gate is connected to the larger antenna will suffer more V_T shift than the other in the differential pair. Thus, the input-offset voltage of the circuit will increase proportionally to the increase in antenna area after a plasma processing step that causes oxide damage.[111]

7.10.4 Electrical Tests for Measuring Oxide Damage

The damage to gate oxides by oxide charging during plasma etching is measured after the oxide has been exposed to the plasma-etching process suspected of causing the damage. The same test techniques as those used to characterize the reliability of gate oxides (as described in section 7.5) can be used to monitor the damage from the plasma charging. That is, the oxide can be tested for: (1) increased Fowler-Nordheim leakage, as described in section 7.5.4.1; (2) the time-to-failure, t_{BD}, or charge-to-breakdown, Q_{BD}, using either a constant-voltage or constant current oxide breakdown test, as described in section 7.4.2.2; (3) V_{BD} using a slow-ramp voltage breakdown test, as described in section 7.5.4.5; (4) degradation of the CV characteristics (which is correlated to the degree of interface state generation by the injected charge), as described in sect. 7.5.4.7.

From the latter test, the stress charge that is passed through the oxide as a result of the plasma charge buildup can also be extracted from the CV measurements. That is, a group of MOS-Cs are fabricated with gates defined by wet etching (i.e., they are not exposed to any plasma charging process). These control samples are then subjected to known values of injected charge using a constant-current test setup. The injected charge causes these control MOS-Cs to exhibit degraded CV curves. Such degraded CV curves become the reference curves for extracting the charge injected during plasma etching. As an example, the CV curve of a plasma etched large-area MOS-C (16,000 μm^2) is superimposed on a set of CV reference curves of the same size control MOS-Cs that were respectively subjected to various known values of injected stress charge (as shown in Fig. 7-40). The plasma-etched CV curve matches the 10 nA reference curve quite well, indicating that the plasma-etched sample collected an average of 10 nA of charging current during the time of etch.

A non-plasma bias-temperature stress has also been reported to be a predictor of how susceptible an oxide will be to plasma charging. In the study, 12 nm-thick oxides were subjected to a -7V stress at 200°C for 15 min. The threshold-voltage shift after such bias-temperature stressing was correlated to the percentage failure in a slow-ramped voltage breakdown test after plasma-charging stress. Good correlation was found, suggesting that this bias-temperature stressing may be used to predict oxide susceptibility to plasma charging.[87]

Annealing in forming gas (e.g., at 400°C for 30 min) has been suggested as a technique to reverse plasma etch damage. Such an anneal is effective in passivating the interface traps caused by plasma etching (i.e., by the formation of Si-H bonds). This is evidenced by the disappearance after annealing of the CV shifts caused by the plasma process. Thus, it may appear that the annealing step heals the plasma damage.

However, the bonds formed between hydrogen and silicon during annealing are very weak (0.3 eV), and thus are more likely to be easily broken when the oxide is electrically stressed. This indeed occurs if the gate oxide is subjected to Fowler-Nordheim stressing after the annealing step (i.e., about 60% of the traps reappear subsequent to such electrical stressing). The oxides also continue to exhibit premature failure in time-dependent breakdown tests. The conclusion is that the damage caused by oxide charging is latent and remains even after annealing.

7.10.4.1 Wafer Mapping to Determine Positional Dependence of Damage on the Wafer Surface.

Wafer mapping is also commonly used to locate the positions on the wafer where damage is most severe. From this information clues are obtained as to the possible cause of the damage. Figure 7-61 shows a wafer map of failed test MOS-Cs after being exposed to an Ar magnetron plasma with a nonuniform magnetic field. The position of the failures was correlated to this non-uniformity and the magnet was redesigned, reducing the damage problem.[88]

As another example, Fig. 7-62 shows a wafer map of the oxide-charging current across a wafer extracted from CV measurements as described in the previous section. This demonstrates the value of the CV measurement technique for monitoring plasma-oxide damage. That is, such spatial patterns would be very difficult to extract from oxide breakdown data because the latter become confounded with the random distribution of oxide defects.

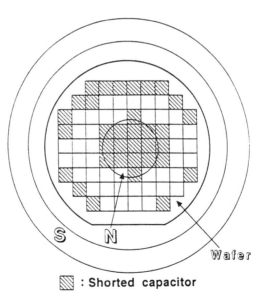

▨ : **Shorted capacitor**

Fig. 7-61 (a) Gate oxide breakdown mapping in wafer exposed to an Ar magnetron plasma with a nonuniform magnetic field as shown in (b). (b) Magnetic field distributions as a function of distance from wafer center and magnet.[88] This paper was originally presented at the Spring 1992 Meeting of the Electrochemical Society, Inc. held in San Francisco, CA.

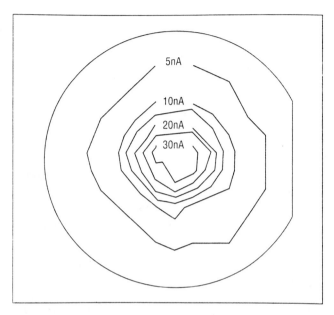

Fig. 7-62 Wafer map of the oxide-charging current across a wafer in a RIE etcher as extracted from CV measurements.[83] Reprinted with permission of Solid State Technology.

7.10.5 Oxide Damage Models in Various Plasma Etching Processes

7.10.5.1 Oxide Damage During Polysilicon or Metal Etch
Processes. The first report of oxide damage during plasma etching was made by Watanabe and Yoshida in 1984.[89] They observed that the gate oxide could be destroyed by dielectric breakdown during reactive ion etching (RIE) of the polysilicon gate layer under some etching conditions. The mechanism of breakdown is not obvious, since the conductor is protected by a resist mask after the gates become isolated. A model has been proposed by Fang and McVittie to explain the mechanism of this damage.[90]

That is, as the doped polysilicon gate film is being plasma etched, non-uniformities in the plasma cause local unbalanced ion and electron currents. During most of the actual etching process the polysilicon film completely covers the wafer. Thus, the exposed poly-Si provides a low resistance path across the wafer so that surface currents can flow and balance the local nonuniformity in conduction currents from the plasma. No charge builds up during this phase, and no oxide damage occurs.

As the etching of polysilicon film is nearly completed, the long surface conduction paths across the wafer become too resistive or eventually discontinuous, and thus surface current paths are broken. Islands of gate electrode start to appear, and local charge buildup may begin. This results in a brief period (estimated to be a few seconds) during which the gate can be sufficiently charged to cause a significant Fowler-Nordheim tunneling current.

As noted earlier, the charging rate is determined by the net local current imbalance and the amount of exposed gate area in the islands. In the model by Fang and McVittie, the charge collector area during the transitory charging period is represented as a 'halo' of residual poly film around the resist edge (Fig. 7-63). That is, the charging current is collected by such halo regions around the mask. This model implies that the gate periphery may be important in determining the charging current. That is, the stress-producing current may depend on the perimeter of the polysilicon. This hypothesis must be tested for each plasma etch process using area-intensive and edge intensive test structures.[86]

During the overetch period, this 'halo' eventually disappears, and only the gate electrode edges are exposed to the plasma. Thus, current collection decreases significantly because it is limited by the small sidewall area. Further damage to the gate oxide from current tunneling is unlikely after the etch reaches endpoint. This model is supported by plasma measurements, SPICE simulations, and etching damage results.

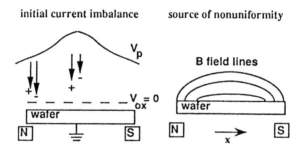

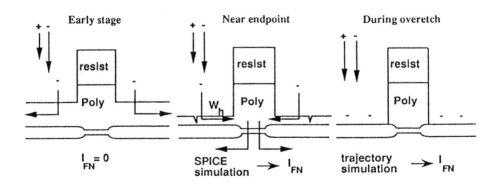

Fig. 7-63 The sequence leading to charge damage during poly-Si etching. Initially, surface currents prevent charging. Near endpoint, the long surface conduction paths across the wafer become too resistive, and excess current charges the gate and flows through the substrate. During overetch, current collection is limited by the small sidewall area.[86] (© IEEE 1992).

A report from the Microelectronics Center of North Carolina (MCNC) in 1992 studied cumulative breakdown failure of 11 nm-thick gate oxides in MOS-C in which the polysilicon gate was dry etched. They found that oxide breakdown failures after dryetch increase as the polysilicon gate perimeter-to-area ratio is made larger. Since the trend is to use ever larger polysilicon perimeter-to-area ratios, there is concern that the polysilicon gate etching process may become a serious yield limiter in submicron CMOS processes.[101]

The type of oxide damage that occurs during polysilicon etching described by the above model is also likely to occur during the etching of other conductors, including aluminum thin films, and during the oxide-spacer etch used to form the spacers in LDD MOSFETs (if the etching is continued past end point).[110]

7.10.5.2 Oxide Damage During Resist Stripping.

In contrast to conductor pattern etching, when a plasma photoresist stripping process is carried out, the entire wafer surface is exposed to the reactive environment during the overetching step. In this case, any charging current that is present is thus proportional to both the pad area and the overetch time. Consequently in-plasma ashing is potentially a more damaging process. However, since there is no need for resist stripping to be anisotropic, the process can be carried out in a charge-free afterglow.

Solvent and low molecular weight residues from the resist can also contribute to plasma nonuniformity. In high rate strippers, the wafer is typically heated to ~200°C at the start of the cycle. At this temperature, light materials volatilize rapidly and the transient gas load can change the plasma's composition and electrical properties. Remote strippers generally avoid this difficulty because the flow and pressure of the feed gas are usually enough to prevent downstream products from reaching the plasma source.

It should be noted that other process steps besides plasma etching may also cause oxide damage by charging, including ion implantation[131] and pre-metal sputter-etch cleaning.[91] Generally speaking, however, charge build-up in these processes does not seem to represent as severe a problem as charging due to plasma etching.

7.10.5.3 Radiation Induced Oxide Damage.

Another mechanism besides that due to plasma non-uniformities has been identified as a cause of gate oxide damage by the plasma, namely UV induced generation of traps and trapped charge at the exposed gate/thin oxide edge. That is, O_2 plasmas are known to emit light from the visible range down to 130 nm (i.e., down to the UV range). Although such UV radiation is unable to penetrate through the poly-Si gate layer to damage the oxide below, it can strike the exposed edge of the oxide. If the oxide is charged so that the field in the oxide is not sufficient to cause damage on its own (e.g., 1 MV/cm), the presence of this field may enhance UV degradation. Thus, edge-intensive structures can suffer this type of damage during the overetch of the poly-Si gate.

7.10.6   Procedures for Reducing Plasma-Induced Oxide Damage

Various measures can be taken to reduce oxide damage during plasma processing. These include: (1) reducing the excitation frequency;[92] (2) modifying the electrode design of the plasma etcher (e.g., by altering the magnet design in a MERIE etcher);[88] (3) eliminating highly electronegative gases such as SF_6 from the etch process;[85] (or, as another example, add O_2 to HBr during the polysilicon etch);[93] (4) modifying the pre-oxide cleaning process;[91] (5) selecting an oxide growth process that yields an oxide less susceptible to charging damage;[94,95]* and (6) utilizing device design techniques, such as limiting conductor area or edge length on field oxide attached to a gate electrode to reduce charge collection.

Since it seems that resist ashing in any process that subjects the wafer to charged particle bombardment can potentially become a source of oxide charge damage, resist should be stripped with processes that do not cause such damage (such as wet stripping, ozone ashing, or ashing in the charge-free afterglow of a plasma [downstream etching]).

It has also been reported that it may be possible to anneal out oxide damage incurred during plasma etching with an anneal at 650°C prior to metallization. This step is believed to detrap the holes thought to be responsible for the oxide damage.[96] However, another report indicates that while it appears that a post-plasma-etch heat treatment does seem to completely passivate the interface traps formed by plasma charging, these traps reappear after subsequent stressing. (The anneal is thought to form Si-H bonds that tie up the traps, but such bonds are weak and can be easily broken when electrically stressed.) Thus, this report concludes that the damage caused by oxide charging is latent and remains, even after annealing.

Another approach minimizing damage gate oxide during the LDD spacer etch involves depositing a protective dielectric layer over the gate electrode (e.g., 1500Å of thermal TEOS deposited) prior to gate electrode etching. After the gate is patterned, the spacer oxide layer is deposited by CVD, and then the spacers are created with an anisotropic dry etch step. The thicker oxide atop the gate remains intact during spacer oxide overetching. This prevents charge buildup across the gate oxide because the conductive surface of the gate is not exposed to charging currents, even during overetch time.[110]

As a final comment, it has been observed that those oxides which survive plasma processes that cause charge-up damage show longer lifetimes (t_{BD}) than those oxides not subjected to such processes. This is not surprising since the effect of plasma stressing is, in a sense, similar to oxide burn-in. However, the yield from such quasi-burn-in stressing may be intolerably low since the conditions of stress are inadvertent and certainly not optimized (as is possible in a genuine burn-in test). Hence, plasma oxide charge-up is still considered to be detrimental, and is not a substitute for burn-in.

---

* Interestingly, some evidence indicates that use of TCA during the dry-oxide growth process makes the oxide more susceptible to plasma charging damage than an oxide grown in dry-O_2 without a chlorine-containing gas.[94]

REFERENCES

1. C. Hu, "Future CMOS Scaling and Reliability," *Proceedings IEEE* May 1993, p. 682.
2. W.S. Chang et al., "A High-Performance 0.25 μm CMOS Technology: II - Technology," *IEEE Trans. Electron Dev.,* April 1992, p. 959.
3. S. Rigo, "Silica Films on Silicon," in *Instabilities in Silicon Devices - Vol. 1,* Ch. 1 Eds. G. Barbottin and A. Vapaille, (Elsevier) North-Holland, Amsterdam, 1986.
4. I.E. Tamm, *Phys. Z. Sowjetunion* 1, 733, (1932).
5. P. Roblin, S. Samman and S. Bibyk, "Simulation of Hot-Electron Trapping and Aging in *n*MOSFETs," *IEEE Trans. Electron Dev.,* **ED-35**, December 1988, p. 2229.
6. R.R. Razouk and B.E. Deal, *J. Electrochem. Soc.* **126,** p. 1573, (1979).
7. S. Tam, P.K Ko, and C. Hu, "Lucky-Electron Model of Channel Hot-Electron Injection in MOSFETs," *IEEE Trans. Electron Dev.,* **ED-31**, (1984), p. 1116.
8. E. Takeda et al, "Submicrometer MOSFET Structures for Minimizing Hot-Carrier Generation," *IEEE Trans Electron Dev.,* **ED-29**, (1982), p. 611.
9. J. Frey, "Where Do Hot Electrons Come From?" *IEEE Circuits and Devices Mag.,* Nov. 1991, p. 31.
10. Y. Nissan-Cohen, "A novel floating-gate method for measurement of ultra-low hole and electron gate currents in MOS transistors," *IEEE Trans. Electron Dev. Lett.,* **EDL-7**, 1986, p. 561.
11. N.L. Saks et al., "Observation of Hot-Hole Injection in NMOS Transistors Using a Modified Floating-Gate Technique," *IEEE Trans. Electron Dev.,* **ED-33**, October 1986, p. 1529.
12. J.M. Pimbley et al., *Advanced CMOS Process Technology,* VLSI Electronics Microstructure Science, Vol. 19, Academic Press, Inc., San Diego CA, 1989, p. 186.
13. Y. Nissan-Cohen, J. Shappir, and D. Frohman-Bentchkowsky, "Measurements of Fowler-Nordheim Tunneling Currents in MOS Structures under Charge Trapping Conditions," *Solid-State Electron.* **28** (7) p. 717, (1985).
14. T.H. Ning and H.N. Yu, "Optimally induced injection of hot electrons into SiO_2," *J. Appl. Phys.,* vol. 45, p. 5373, (1974).
15. C. Chang et al., "Carrier tunneling related phenomena in thin oxide MOSFETs," *Tech. Dig. IEDM,* 1983, p. 194.
16. C.M. Osburn and D.W. Ormond, *J. Electrochem. Soc.,* **121**, (1972) p. 526.
17. K. Yamabe and K. Taniguchi, "Time-dependent dielectric breakdown of thin thermally grown SiO_2 films," *IEEE Trans. Electron Dev.,* **ED-32**, p. 423, (1985).
18. D. Wolters and J.F. Verwey, "Breakdown and Wearout Phenomena in SiO_2 Films," chap. 6, in *Instabilities in Silicon Devices - Vol. 1,* Ch. 1 Eds. G. Barbottin and A. Vapaille, (Elsevier) North-Holland, Amsterdam, 1986.
19. W.W. Hines and D.C. Montgomery, *Probability and Statistics in Engineering and Management Science,* Wiley, New York, 1972.
20. J.C. Lee, I.-C. Chen, and C. Hu, "Modeling and Characterization of Gate Oxide Reliability," *IEEE Trans. Electron Dev.,* **ED-35** December 1988, p. 2268.
21. J.P. Lee and A.J. Steckl, *J. Electrochem Soc.,* June 1993, p. L89.

22. P. Solomon, "Breakdown in Silicon Dioxide - A Review," *J. Vac. Sci. Technol.,* **14**, 1122, (1977).

23. E. Harari, "Dielectric breakdown in electrically stressed thin films of SiO_2," *J. Appl. Phys.*, **vol. 49**, no. 4, p. 2478, 1978.

24. B. Ricco et al., "Novel mechanism for tunneling and breakdown of thin SiO_2 films," *Phys. Rev. Lett.,* **51**, 1795 (1983).

25. Y. Nissan-Cohen and T. Gorczyca, "The Effect of Hydrogen on Trap Generation, Positive Charge Trapping, and Time-Dependent Dielectric Breakdown of Gate Oxides," *IEEE Electron Dev. Letts.,* vol. 9, June 1988, p. 287.

26. T.H. DiStefano and M. Shatzkes, "Impact ionization model for dielectric instability and breakdown," *Appl. Phys. Lett.* vol. 25, no. 12, Dec. 1974, p. 685.

27. N. Klein and P. Solomon, "Current runaway in insulators affected by impact ionization and recombination," *J. Appl. Phys.,* vol. 47, no. 10, 1976, p. 4364.

28. I.C. Chen, S. Holland, and C. Hu, "Electrical breakdown of thin gate and tunneling oxides," *IEEE Trans. Electron Dev.,* p. 413, Feb., 1985.

29. C.T. Sah, in *Properties of Silicon*, INSPEC, London, 1988, p. 587.

30. T.H. Ning, C.M. Osburn, and H.-N. Yu, "Threshold instability of IGFETs due to emission of leakage electrons from silicon substrate into silicon dioxide," *Appl. Phys. Lett.,* **29**, 198 (1976).

31. I.C. Chen, S. Holland, and C. Hu, "Oxide breakdown dependence on thickness and hole current-enhanced reliability of ultra-thin oxides." *Tech. Dig. IEDM,* 1986, p. 660.

32. I.C. Chin, et al., "The Effect of Channel Hot-Carrier Stressing on Gate-Oxide Integrity in MOSFETs," *IEEE Trans. Electron Dev.,* **ED-35**, Dec. 1988, p. 2253.

33. D.L. Griscom, "Diffusion of radiolytic molecular hydrogen as a mechanism for the post irradiation buildup of interface states in SiO_2 on Si structure," *J. Appl. Phys.,* vol. 58, p. 2524, 1985.

34. D.R. Wolters and A.T.A. Zeegers-van Duijnhoven, "Breakdown of thin dielectrics," *Ext. Abs. Mtg. of Electrochem. Soc.,* Spring 1990, p. 272.

35. Y. Uraoka et al., "Evaluation technique of gate oxide reliability with electrical and optical measurements," *Proc IEEE 1989 Conf. Microelectronic Test Structures,* March 1989, p. 97.

36. M.W. Hillen et al., *Insulating Films on Semiconductors,* J.F. Verwey and D.R. Wolters, Eds., North-Holland, New York, (1983), p. 274.

37. K. Honda , A. Ohsawa, and N. Toyokura, "Breakdown in Silicon Oxides - Correlation with Cu Precipitates," *Appl. Phys. Letts.,* vol. 45, no. 3, p. 270, Aug. 1, 1984.

38. K. Honda, A. Ohsawa, and N. Toyokura, "Breakdown in Silicon Oxides - Correlation with Fe Precipitates," *Appl. Phys. Letts.,* vol. 46, no. 6, p. 582, Mar. 15, 1985.

39. S. Verhaverbeke et al., "The Effect of Metallic Impurities on the Dielectric Breakdown of Oxides and Some Ways of Avoiding Them," *Tech. Dig. IEDM,* 1991, p. 71.

40. M. Miyashita et al., "Dependence of Surface Microroughness of CZ, FZ, and Epi Wafers on Wet Chemical Processing," *J. Electrochem. Soc.,* August 1992, p. 2133.

41. M. Meuris et al., "Investigating techniques to improve gate-oxide integrity," *Microcontamination,,* May 1991, p. 31.

42. D. Dimetrius et al., "Effects of HF-Last Clean Process Sequence on Gate-Oxide Quality," *Abs. Mtg. Electrochem. Soc.*, Fall 1993, p. 473.

43. M. Liehr, G.B. Bronner, and J.E. Lewis, "Stacking-Fault-Induced Defect Creation in SiO_2 on Si (100)," *Appl. Phys. Lett.*, **vol. 52**, no. 22, p. 1892, May 30, 1988.

44. W.M. Greene, P.J. Marcoux, and C.K.Lau, "Time Dependent Dielectric Breakdown: Lateral Areal Defects and Isolation Edge Defects," *Abs. Mtg. Electrochem. Soc.*, Fall 1991, p. 437.

45. R. Burmester, M. Kerber, and C. Zeller, "Optimisation of polysilicon oxidation for 0.8 μm technology," in *Proc. ESSDERC 88, J. de Physique*, coll. C4, suppl. 9, vol. 49, Sept. 1988, p. C4-545.

46. K. Shiozaki et al., "Influence of Field Isolation Stress on Gate Oxide Reliability," *Abs. Mtg. Electrochem. Soc.*, Spring 1992, p. 444.

47. R. Moazzami and C. Hu, "Projecting Gate Oxide Reliability and Optimizing Reliability Screens," *IEEE Trans. Electron Dev.*, **ED-37**, July 1990, p. 1643.

48. J.M. Soden and C.F. Hawkins, "Reliability of CMOS ICs with Gate Oxide Shorts," *Semiconductor International,* May 1987, p. 240.

49. I.C. Chen and C. Hu, "Accelerated Testing of Time-Dependent Breakdown of SiO_2," *IEEE Electron Dev. Letts.*, **EDL-8**, April 1987, p. 140.

50. M. Shatzkes, M. Av-Ron, and R.A. Gdula, "Defect-related breakdown and conduction in SiO_2," *IBM J. Res. Dev.* **24**, 469 (1980).

51. I.C. Chen, S. Holland, and C. Hu, "A quantitative physical model for time-dependent breakdown in SiO_2," in *Proc. Intl. Rel. Physics Symp.*, p. 24, 1985.

52. D.J. Dumin et al., "Correlation of Wearout and Breakdown in Sub-10 nm Silicon Oxide," *Tech Dig. IEDM,* 1988, p. 718.

53. D.J. Dumin and J.R. Maddux, "Correlation of Stress-Induced Leakage Currents in Thin Oxides with Trap Generation Inside the Oxides," *IEEE Trans. Electron Dev.*, **vol. 40**, May 1993, p. 986.

54. D.L Crook, "Method of Determining Reliability Screens for Time Dependent Dielectric Breakdown," *Proc. 17th Int. Rel. Phys. Symp.* 1, San Francisco CA, April 1979.

55. *ibid.*

56. E. Rosenbaum et al., "Circuit Reliability Simulator - Oxide Breakdown Module," *Tech. Dig. IEDM,* 1989, p. 331.

57. C. Hu, "IC Reliability Simulation," *IEEE J. Solid State Circuits,* p. 241, March, 1992.

58. B.E. Deal and A.S. Grove, "General relationship for the thermal oxidation of silicon," *J. of Appl. Phys.* vol. 36, p. 3770, 1965.

59. H.Z. Massoud , J.D. Plummer & E.A. Irene, *J. Electrochem. Soc.,* **132**, 1985, p. 2693.

60. A. Reisman et al., *J. Electron. Mat.* **16**, p. 45, (1987).

61. D.N. Kouvatsos and M.K. Hatalis, "Thin silicon dioxide films grown at very low oxygen partial pressure in oxygen diluted by helium," *Abs. Mtg. Electrochem. Soc.*, Fall 1992, p. 399.

62. R. Pong "LPCVD - Are Vertical Reactors the Answer?", *Microelectronics Mfg. and Test.,* July, 1990, p. 1.

63. A.C. Adams, T.E. Smith, and C.C. Chang, *J. Electrochem. Soc.*, **127**, p. 1787 (1980).

64. Y.J. van der Meulin, *J. Electrochem. Soc.*, **119**, p. 530 (1972)

64. Y.J. van der Meulin, *J. Electrochem. Soc.,* **119**, p. 530 (1972)

65. H.Z. Massoud, J.D. Plummer and E.A. Irene, *J. Electrochem. Soc.,* **132**, p. 2685 (1985).

66. D.N. Kouvatsos and M.K. Hatalis, "Thin silicon dioxide films grown at very low oxygen partial pressure in oxygen diluted by helium," *Abs. Mtg. Electrochem. Soc.,* Fall 1992, p. 399.

67. A. Licciardello, O. Puglisi, and S. Pignataro, "Effect of Organic Contamination on the Oxidation Kinetics of Silicon at Room Temperature," *Appl. Phys. Lett.,* vol. 48 (1), p. 41, Jan. 6, 1986.

68. M. Morita et al., *J. Appl. Phys.,* July 15, 1990, p. 1272.

69. M. Miyawaki, S. Yoshitake, and T. Ohmi, "Improvement of Al-Si Contact Performance in Native-Oxide-Free Processing," *IEEE Electron Dev. Lett.,* , **11**, October 1990, p. 448.

70. M. Morita and T. Ohmi, "Pre-Gate Oxide Si Surface Control," *Abs. Mtg. Electrochem. Soc.,* Spring 1992, p. 380.

71. G. Gould and E.A. Irene, "The Influence of Silicon Surface Cleaning Procedures on Silicon Oxidation," *J. Electrochem. Soc.,* vol. 134 (4) , p. 1031, April 1987.

72. A. Reisman, S. Edwards, and P. Smith, *J. Electrochem. Soc.,* **vol. 132**, p. 284, (1990).

73. C.M. Osburn et al., "Silicon Gate Oxide Thickness Uniformity during HCl Oxidation," *J. Electrochem. Soc.,* **vol. 138**, January 1991, p. 268.

74. *Semiconductor International*, March 1993, p. 21.

75. M.K. Khan and L. Schmidt, "A Simple Way to Improve Gate Oxide Quality," *Semiconductor Internat.,* September 1989, p. 136.

76. *Semiconductor International,* October 1988, p. 42.

77. A. Battacharyya et al., *J. Electrochem. Soc.* **Vol. 132**, August 1985, p. 1900.

78. T.S. Choo, C.L. Lee, and T.F. Lei, "Measurement of Ultrathin (≤ 100Å) Oxide Films by Multiple-Angle Incident Ellipsometry," *J. Electrochem. Soc.,* June 1991, p. 1756.

79. P.K. Roy et al., "Synthesis and Characterization of High Quality Ultrathin Gate Oxides for VLSI/ULSI Circuits," *Tech. Dig. IEDM* 1988, p. 714.

80. H.H. Tseng, P.J. Tobin, J.D. Hayden, and K.-M. Chang "Advantages of CVD Stacked Gate Oxide for Robust 0.5 μm Transistors," *Tech. Dig. IEDM*, 1991, p. 75.

81. H.H. Tseng and P.J. Tobin, "A Robust Gate Dielectric for Submicron Technology," *Semicond. Internat.*, July 1992, p. 68.

82. R. Moazzami and C. Hu, "A High Quality Stacked Thermal/LPCVD Gate Oxide Technology for ULSI," *IEEE Electron Dev. Lett.,* **14**, February 1993 p. 72.

83. H. Shin et al., "Plasma Etching Charge-Up Damage to Thin Oxides," *Solid-State Technology*, August 1993, p. 29.

84. H. Shin et al., "Spatial Distributions of Thin Oxide Charging in Reactive Ion Etched and MERIE Etcher," *IEEE Elect. Dev. Lett.,* vol. 14 (2), p. 88, February 1993.

85. C.T. Gabriel, "Gate Oxide Damage from Polysilicon Etching," *J. Vac. Sci. Tech. B* vol. 9 (2), p. 370 (1991).

86. C.T. Gabriel and J.P. McVittie, "How Plasma Etching Damages Thin Gate Oxides," *Solid-State Technology,* June 1992, p. 81.

87. S. Fang and J.P. McVittie "Thin-Oxide Damage from Gate Charging During Plasma Processing," *IEEE Electron Dev. Letts.,* May 92 p. 288.

88. M. Sekine et al., "Gate Oxide Breakdown Phenomena in Magnetron Plasma," *Ext. Abs. Mtg. Electrochem. Soc.,* Spring 1992, p. 126.

89. T. Watanabe and Y. Yoshida, "Dielectric Breakdown of Gate Insulator Due to RIE," *Solid State Technology,* April 1984, p. 213.

90. S. Fang, S. Murakawa, and J.P. McVittie, "A New Model for Thin Oxide Degradation from Wafer Charging in Plasma Etching," *Tech. Dig. IEDM* 1992, p. 61.

91. I.-W. Wu et al., "Breakdown Yield and Lifetime of Thin Gate Oxides in CMOS Processing,"*J. Electrochem. Soc.,* June 1989, p. 1638.

92. K. Tsunokuni, K. Nojiri, M. Nawata, "Dependence of RF Frequency on Gate Oxide Breakdown During Microwave Plasma Etching," *Ext. Abstr. 38th Mtg. Jap. Soc. Appl. Phys.,* p. 499, (1991).

93. W.M. Greene, J.B. Kruger, G. Kooi, "Magnetron Etching of Polysilicon: Electrical Damage," *J. Vac. Sci. Tech. B* vol. 9 (2), p. 1638 (1989).

94. S. Fang and J.P. McVittie, "Thin Oxide Damage from Charging During Plasma Processing," *IEEE Elect. Dev. Lett.,* vol. 13 (5) p. 288, May 1992.

95. W. Ting, et al., "MOS Characteristics of Ultrathin SiO_2 Prepared by Oxidizing Si in N_2O," *IEEE Elect. Dev. Lett.,* vol. 12 (4) p. 416, April 1991.

96. S. Fang and J.P. McVittie, "Thin Oxide Damage from Charging During Plasma Processing," *IEEE Elect. Dev. Lett.,* vol. 13 (5) p. 288, May 1992.

97. J. Borland, "Borland's Overview of the Latest in Intrinsic Gettering," *Semiconductor Internat.* Part 1, April 1989 p. 144, & part 2, May 1989, p. 154.

98. T. Ohmi et al., *IEEE Symposium on VLSI Technology,* Section 3-4, p. 24, June 1992.

99. "Special Report on Flash Memory and Hi Wafers," *Nikkei Microdevices,* p. 34, June 1993.

100. S. Samata et al., *Japan Society of Applied Physics Spring Meeting,* sections 30a-ZS-1 -4, p. 676, April 1993.

101. P.H. Singer, "Evaluating Plasma Etch Damage," *Semiconductor International,* May 1992, p. 78.

102. H. Satake and A. Toriumi, "Substrate Hole Current Generation and Oxide Breakdown in Si MOSFETs under Fowler-Nordheim Electron Tunneling Injection," *Tech. Dig. IEDM,* 1993, p. 337.

103. D.J. Dumin et al., "Use of Wearout Measurements to Analyze TDDB Distributions in Thin Silicon Oxides," *Ext. Abs. Electrochem. Soc. Mtg.,* Spring 1994, p. 204, Abs. No. 133.

104. D.J. Dumin, "Wearout and Breakdown in Thin Silicon Oxide," *Ext. Abs. Electrochem. Soc. Mtg.,* Spring 1994, p. 200, Abs. No.131.

105. J. Sune et al., *Thin Solid Films,* **185,** 347, 1990.

106. R. Winkler and G. Behnke, "Gate Oxide Quality Related to Bulk Properties and Its Influence on DRAM Device Performance," *Ext. Abs. Electrochem. Soc. Mtg.,* Spring 1994, p. 778, Abs. No.488.

107. K. Shiozaki et al., "Improvement of Stress-Induced Surface Microroughness for Highly Reliable Gate Oxide," *Ext. Abs. Electrochem. Soc. Mtg.,* Spring 1994, p. 207 , Abs. No.135.

108. M. Gardener, J. Seaton and J. Fulford, "The Role Silicon Surface Has Upon Producing Highly Reliable Tunnel/Gate Dielectrics," *Ext. Abs. Electrochem. Soc. Mtg.*, Spring 1994, p. 211, Abs. No.137.

109. A. Philiposian and K. Van Wormer,"Temperature Measurement Studies in Atmospheric Thermal Silicon Oxidation Reactors," *Ext. Abs. Electrochem. Soc. Mtg.*, Spring 1994, p. 223, Abs. No.145.

110. C. Gabriel and M. Weiling, "Gate Oxide Damage Reduction during LDD Oxide Etch," *Ext. Abs. Electrochem. Soc. Mtg.*, Spring 1994, p. 322, Abs. No. 205.

111. H. Shin, Z.-J. Ma, and C. Hu, "Impact of Plasma Charging Damage and Diode Protection on Scaled Thin Oxide," *Tech. Dig. IEDM* 1993, p. 467.

112. H.-H. Tseng and P.J. Tobin, "Thin CVD Stacked Gate Dielectric for ULSI Technology," *Tech. Dig. IEDM,* 1993, p. 321.

113. H.-H. Tseng et al., "A Comparison of CVD Stacked Gate Oxide and Thermal Gate Oxide for 0.5 μm Transistors Subjected to Process-Induced Damage," *IEEE Trans. Electron Dev.,* **ED-40**, March 1993, p. 613.

114. S.L. Wu, C.L. Lee, and T.F. Lei, "Characterization of Ultra-Thin Oxide Prepared by Low-Temperature Wafer Loading and Nitrogen Pre-Annealing before Oxidation," *J. Appl. Phys.,* vol. 72, p. 1378, 1992.

115. T.J. Dalton et al., "Microtrench Formation in Polysilicon Plasma Etching over Thin Gate Oxide," *J. Electrochemical Soc.,* August 1993, p. 2395.

116. S. Krishnan and J. McKee, "A Monitor for Polysilicon Etch Damage at the Gate Periphery," *Ext. Abs. Electrochem. Soc. Mtg.,* Spring 1994, p. 328, Abs. No.208.

117. S. Ma and J.P. McVittie, "Effect of Exposed Gate Oxide Edge on the Separation of Plasma Charging and Radiation Induced Damage," *Ext. Abs. Electrochem. Soc. Mtg.,* Spring 1994, p. 326, Abs. No. 207.

118. B.E. Deal, *J. Electrochemical Society.,* **121:** 198C (June 1974).

119. J.J. Sanchez and T.A. DeMassa, "Review of Carrier Injection in the Silicon/Silicon-Dioxide System," *IEE Proceedings-G* **138**, No. 2, June 1991.

120. B. Eitan and D. Frohman-Bentchkowsky, "Hot Electron Injection into the Oxide in *n*-channel MOS Devices," *IEEE Trans. Electron Dev.,* **ED-28**, p. 328, (1981).

121. C. Hu, "Thin Oxide Reliability," *Tech. Dig. IEDM,* 1985 p. 368.

122. E. Takeda et al., "VLSI Reliability Challenges," From Device Physics to Wafer Scale Systems," *Proceedings of the IEEE,* **81**, May 1993, p. 653.

123. Y. Uraoka et al., "Evaluation Technology of VLSI Reliability Using Hot Carrier Luminescence," *IEEE Trans. on Semiconductor Mfg.,* **4**, August 1991, p. 183.

124. S. Samata et al., "Hydrogen Annealing of Silicon Wafer," *Ext. Abs. Electrochem. Soc. Mtg.*, Fall 1993, p. 426, Abs. No. 264.

125. M. Kerber, "Entirely Gate-Surrounded MOS Capacitor to Study the Intrinsic Oxide Quality," *IEEE Trans. Electron Dev.,* **ED-39**, December 1992, p. 2814.

126. R. Moazzami et al., "Projecting the Minimum Acceptable Oxide Thickness for Time-Dependent Dielectric Breakdown," *Tech. Dig. IEDM,* 1988 , p. 710.

127. BTA, P.O. Box 4868, Santa Clara CA 95054.

128. A. Reisman et al., *J. Electron. Mat.* **16**, p. 45 (1987).

129. H. Abe et al., "Analysis of Defects in Thin SiO_2 Thermally Grown on Si Substrate," *Tech. Dig. IEDM,* 1985, p. 372.

130. H. Uchida et al., "The Effect of Oxide Charges at LOCOS Isolation Edges on Oxide Breakdown," *IEEE Trans. Electron Dev.,* **ED-40,** October 1993, p. 1818.

131. H. Muto et al., "A Mechanism of Gate Oxide Deterioration During As^+ Ion Implantation," *IEEE Trans. Electron Dev.,* **ED-38,** June 1991, p. 1296.

132. A.G. Revesz, "The Defect Structure of Grown Silicon Dioxide Fims," *IEEE Trans. Electron Dev.,* **ED-12,** p. 97, (1965).

133. M. Moinpour, "In Situ Reactor Analysis for Silicon Nitride and Silicon Dioxide Thin Films," *Ext. Abs. Electrochem. Soc. Mtg.,* Spring 1994, p. 223, Abs. No. 146.

PROBLEMS

1. Describe the difference between hot and cold carrier injection in MOSFETs.

2. Explain why the peak value of substrate current I_{sub} and gate current I_G occur at different values of V_{GS} for a fixed value of V_{DS}.

3. Explain why it appears that the minimum gate oxide thickness in MOSFETs may be 30Å.

4. Using the data plotted in Fig. 7-18, determine the value of the dispersion (σ) of the log-normal cumulative distribution function plotted therein, as well as the mean time to failure at 200°C and 250°C.

5. Calculate the value of $D(\Delta t_{ox})$ if: (a) $\Delta t_{ox} = 40$Å; and (b) $\Delta t_{ox} = 15$Å for the oxide technology that yields the TDDB data of Fig. 7-34, assuming the defects are nonuniformly distributed and S = 0.8. The area of the oxide samples is 75 mm^2.

6. Assume that a chip having a total gate oxide area per chip of 75 mm^2 is to be manufactured and the defect density due to weaknesses in the gate oxide of the specific chosen thickness is found to be $D(t_{ox}) = 40/cm^2$. Calculate the manufacturing yield of this chip if: (a) the defects are assumed to be uniformly distributed; and (b) the defects are assumed to be nonuniformly distributed, and   S = 0.5.

7. Use Eq. 7-29 to calculate the time to breakdown of 10 nm thick, defect-free oxide film if V_{ox} is 5V at 300K. If a defect in the film reduces the thickness to 6 nm, calculate the new time to breakdown at the same gate voltage and operating temperature.

8. Calculate the minimum thickness of a defect-free oxide that could be used in a MOSFET that is to operate at 3.5 V for 10 years at 150°C (425K) without suffering oxide breakdown.

8. What is the maximum electric field that can be applied across a gate oxide so that is will operate for 2 years without suffering breakdown at 125°C.

9. Using Eq. 7-51 calculate the time to grow a 10 nm oxide film at 700°C on bare (111) silicon, assuming that the constants a and b at 700°C equal a = 3.35 and b = 0.571.

10. List some of the advantages of vertical furnaces that have caused them to replace horizontal furnaces fro the growth of thermal oxides in submicron technologies.

CHAPTER 8

WELL FORMATION IN CMOS

Both n- and p-channel transistors must be fabricated on the same wafer in CMOS technologies. Obviously, only one type of device can be fabricated on a given starting substrate. To accommodate the device type that cannot be built on this substrate, regions of a doping type opposite to that present in the starting material must be formed. These regions are called *wells* (or sometimes *tubs*) and are usually (but not always) the first features to be defined on a starting wafer. The well-formation process starts with a uniform, lightly doped p- or n-type substrate. Excess dopants of the opposite type are then selectively implanted or diffused to attain the proper well depth and doping profile in the well regions. The doping type in the wells becomes the identifying characteristic of the CMOS technology (e.g., p-well or n-well CMOS). Conventional well-implant doses range from $2x10^{12}$-$8x10^{12}$/cm^2 at energies from 100-200 keV. The term "conventional" in this sense refers to wells formed by low-energy (<200 keV) ion implantation and a thermal drive-in. Alternative well-formation techniques that do not require a drive-in will also be discussed separately. Epitaxial n-on-n^+ or p-on-p^+ starting substrates have also come into widespread use, since they help reduce the susceptibility of CMOS circuits to latchup.

As well as being of the correct doping type, the well and substrate must be electrically isolated from each other under every operating condition. As noted in chap. 6, to ensure that *pn* junctions are not forward-biased during circuit operation, if a p-type substrate is used as the starting material of an IC, the substrate must be connected to the most negative circuit voltage. If an n-type substrate is used, it must be connected to the most positive circuit voltage. When wells are present, however, the well regions must also be connected to the appropriate circuit voltages to prevent forward-biasing of the junctions within the well (and between the well and substrate). Because the wells are totally junction-isolated from the rest of the wafer, it is especially important that provisions for well connections be made at the top surface of the wafer. That is, in non-well technologies, it may still be possible to contact the substrate from the backside of the wafer even if no provision is made for a substrate contact from the top surface. Obviously, such backside connections cannot be established to the well regions.

The dopant concentration near the surface of the well is one of the factors that impact V_T, carrier mobility, source/drain capacitance, and field isolation. The well concentration deeper beneath the surface affects other characteristics of MOSFET behavior such as latch-up and vertical punchthrough (i.e., between drain and well-substrate junctions).*

---

* To ensure that vertical punchthrough will not occur, the depletion regions of the drain/well and well/substrate junctions must be prevented from merging. That is, the depth of the well/substrate junction must be deep enough (typically >1.5 μm) so that it is greater than the sum of the widths of the two depletion regions in the well, even when a reverse bias of V_{DD} is

8.1 *p*-WELL, *n*-WELL, and TWIN-WELL TECHNOLOGIES

There are many trade-offs involved in the optimization of a CMOS process. The choices revolve around the highly interrelated parameters of circuit performance, layout density, fabrication cost, and susceptibility to latchup. As described in previous chapters, obtaining the best circuit performance from an MOS device involves maximizing the drive current and minimizing junction capacitances and body effect - all characteristics which favor lower doping concentrations in the device body. Optimizing density, however, requires raising these same doping concentrations (to avoid punchthrough and to achieve high values of threshold voltage in the parasitic field-transistors). Higher density is thus achieved by allowing closer packing of adjacent *n*- and *p*-channel transistors. Conversely, latchup tolerance can also be improved by keeping *n*- and *p*-channel transistors farther apart (see chap. 6, Vol. 2), but this in turn lowers circuit density.

These complex interacting tradeoffs converge on several processing configurations that are determined at the outset of the processing sequence through the selection of the type of well doping.[1,2] It is therefore useful to consider the ramifications of the well-type choice with respect to its impact on circuit applications. Because at least one of the device types must be located in the well, the selection of well architecture influences device and circuit behavior. In particular, the performance of devices in the well for the most part suffer as a consequence of the higher well doping. That is, they exhibit higher junction capacitance, increased sensitivity to body effect, and decreased transconductance (due to reduced carrier mobility). Furthermore, substrate current (e.g., due to hot-carrier effects) is harder to collect from the well regions. The issue thus becomes one of deciding which device type (if any) should be subjected to such performance degradation.

Figure 8-1 shows the five basic well structures employed in CMOS technologies. Figure 8-1a illustrates the *single p-well structure*, in which *p*-wells are fabricated in an *n*-type starting substrate. NMOS devices are made in the well, and PMOS transistors in the substrate. If the dopant types of the *p*-well technology are reversed, a *single n-well structure* is obtained (Fig. 8-1b). The structures in Figs. 8-1c to 8-1e involve approaches in which *both p*- and *n*-wells are formed. CMOS technologies employing such structures are called *twin-well, dual-well,* or *twin-tub CMOS*. The first two of these (Figs. 8-1c and 8-1d) are designed to be fabricated on a particular substrate type, like the single *p*- and *n*-well structures. The third of these twin-well technologies (Fig. 8-1e), however, is independent of starting material type.

In the next sections we will outline the pros and cons of both the single *p*-well and *n*-well configurations, as well as those of the more complex well configurations that have been developed (e.g., twin-well and retrograde-well CMOS).

---

* (cont.) applied to the drain (see example 8-1 in this chapter.). In conventional-well CMOS structures, this depth is achieved by a long, high-temperature drive-in (up to 1200°C) following the well implants. For example, in one twin-well process the well-implants are followed by a drive-in at 1100°C for 500 minutes (8 1/3 hours).[13]

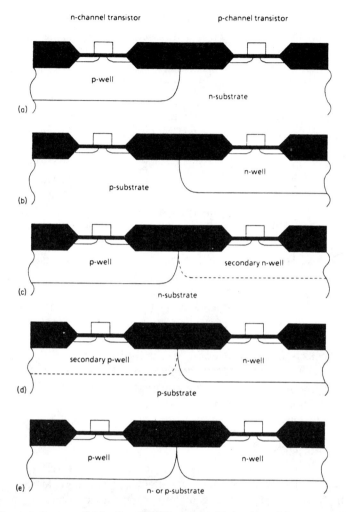

n-channel transistor   p-channel transistor

p-well

n-substrate

(a)

p-substrate

n-well

(b)

p-well   secondary n-well

n-substrate

(c)

secondary p-well   n-well

p-substrate

(d)

p-well   n-well

n- or p-substrate

(e)

Fig. 8-1 Well structures available for CMOS circuit fabrication: (a) *p*-well CMOS; (b) *n*-well CMOS; (c) *p*-well with secondary *n*-well (twin-well constrained to *n*-substrate); (d) *n*-well with secondary *p*-well (twin-well constrained to *p*-substrate); (e) twin-well CMOS on *n* or *p*-substrate. A.G. Lewis and J.Y. Chen, "Current Trends in MOS Process Integration," in N.G. Einspruch and G. Gildenblatt, Eds. *Advanced MOS Device Physics,* Academic Press, San Diego CA, 1989, Reprinted with Permission.

8.1.1 *p*-Well CMOS

The *p*-well process, illustrated in Fig. 8-1a, involves the creation of *p*-regions in an *n*-type substrate to permit the fabrication of NMOS devices. The *p*-wells are formed by implanting a *p*-type dopant into an *n*-substrate at a high enough concentration to overcompensate for the substrate doping and to give adequate control over the *p*-type doping in the well. The starting n-type substrate, however, must also have sufficient doping to ensure that the characteristics of devices fabricated in the substrate regions are adequate (a minimum doping concentration of 3×10^{14}-$1 \times 10^{15}/cm^3$ is required). If the p-well is doped too highly, however, the performance of the n-channel devices will be degraded through lower carrier mobility, increased source/drain to p-well capacitance, and increased sensitivity to body-biasing effects. The p-well doping is therefore usually selected to be about five to ten times higher than the doping in the n-substrate.

p-well CMOS was the first type of CMOS that could be practically manufactured, and such circuits were introduced in the late 1960s. The first companies to commercially offer CMOS components produced many designs in p-well technology. As this experience was spread throughout the industry, p-well CMOS became widely established.

There were several reasons for choosing p-well CMOS at that time. First, the earliest MOS ICs were based on a metal-gate PMOS process which utilizes an n-substrate. The work-function of aluminum is such that enhancement-mode PMOS devices can be made in a lightly doped n-type substrate without the need for additional channel doping. Thus, when CMOS circuits were invented (to take advantage of the reduced power consumption possible with CMOS), it was simplest to manufacture them merely by adding a p-well to the basic PMOS process. Second, higher channel doping levels were needed to permit sufficiently large V_T values to be established in the enhancement-mode NMOS transistors. Such higher doping was also needed in the field regions of the NMOS sections of the circuit to ensure adequate isolation (see chap. 6). These requirements are compatible with the need to have well surface concentrations five to ten times larger than the substrate doping level. Finally, it was relatively simple to manufacture p-wells with the existing process fabrication technology. That is, in the late 1960s ion implantation was not yet available and it was necessary to introduce the well dopants by chemical diffusion. At the doping levels required in the wells it was much easier to achieve adequate doping profile control using boron rather than phosphorus diffusion processes.

There are also several circuit and system advantages of p-well over n-well CMOS. First, p-well technology may be the better choice for pure-static logic, in which a good balance between the performance of both MOS device types is beneficial. (The performance of the PMOS and NMOS devices are "more balanced" because the carrier mobility reduction associated with higher well doping is compensated by forming the NMOS devices in the p-well; i.e., the electrons have higher mobility.) Second, it is attractive for applications that require an isolated p-region (such as those using an npn bipolar transistor as an on-chip driver or an n-channel FETs for an analog input). Third, p-well CMOS is less susceptible to field-inversion problems than n-well CMOS (which uses a lightly doped p-substrate), and can thus be slightly easier to fabricate. (We will describe later how p-well CMOS can use the inherent substrate and well doping as the channel stops, whereas n-well CMOS must use a separate substrate channel-stop process.) Fourth, if the so-called retrograde-well process (rather than a diffusion of a shallow implant) is used to form the wells, p-well technology is more feasible. It is easier to form a p-retrograde well than an n-retrograde well, since boron ions penetrate deeper than arsenic or phosphorus ions at the same implant energy. Finally, p-well

CMOS may be better for fabricating SRAMs. Since the alpha-particle-induced soft-error rate (SER) becomes significant even in SRAMs if feature sizes are scaled to submicron dimensions, the cells should be made inside a well. The sensing of the state of an SRAM cell depends on the current provided by the cell. As a result, high-gain NMOS devices are more desirable for the pass gates and drivers in the cell, and must be built in a p-well. Furthermore, it facilitates the use of polysilicon load resistors in 4-transistor memory cells and buried contacts.

Some of the disadvantages of p-well CMOS are the following: (1) Since NMOS transistors are fabricated in the p-well, their characteristics will be degraded compared to those made in a lightly doped substrate. In CMOS circuits that rely heavily on optimum NMOSFET behavior, this can lead to reduced circuit performance; (2) Substrate currents, the result of impact-ionization generated carriers in short-channel devices (see chaps. 7 and 9), are much larger in NMOS than PMOS devices. It is more difficult to collect these carriers from a well than from the substrate. Since the NMOSFETs in p-well CMOS are in the well, this represents a disadvantage of submicron CMOS p-well technology.

8.1.2 *n*-Well CMOS

By the late 1970s, the technological barriers that prevented enhancement-mode NMOS transistors from being manufactured were overcome. Primarily, the introduction of ion implantation made V_T control in NMOSFETs a simple, straightforward procedure. As a result, NMOS technologies ousted PMOS in high-speed, high-packing-density ICs. By the mid-1980s, however, the power dissipation in VLSI NMOS ICs became intolerably high (see chap. 6, Vol. 2), and CMOS development was pursued as a mainstream replacement technology for NMOS. For those companies that had been producing NMOS as their main IC product, n-well CMOS appeared to be an attractive approach for making the switch to CMOS.

In the n-well process, shown in Fig. 8-1b, the p-channel devices are formed in the more heavily doped n-well, while the NMOS devices are made in the substrate. Since it was now feasible to build NMOS devices in lightly doped substrates, this made it possible to make n-channel devices in an n-well CMOS process that were identical to those made by NMOS technology. Thus, virtually all of the experience that had been amassed in fabricating high-performance NMOS could be transferred to an n-well CMOS process. Furthermore, CMOS circuits could be made that exploited existing NMOS device design. The availability of ion implantation for introducing well dopants into the substrate (instead of having to rely on diffusion), now made dopant control of n-wells much more feasible. This lead to the successful development of n-well CMOS technology.

As a result, virtually all EPROMs, microprocessors, and dynamic RAM designs in the generations of technology built with 1.25-2.0 μm dimensions were implemented with n-well CMOS. Mixed CMOS-NMOS designs were also made, in which the high noise immunity and negligible stand-by-power dissipation of CMOS was exploited in the input/output sections, and faster NMOS devices were used internally.

However, it should be noted that *n*-well technology also has some disadvantages. First, as mentioned earlier, it is more sensitive to field-inversion problems than *p*-well CMOS. Second, it may be more difficult to build pure-static, high-performance logic circuits with *n*-well CMOS.

8.1.3 CMOS on Epitaxial Substrates

As described in vol. 2, chap. 6, heavily doped substrates with a more lightly doped surface epitaxial layer have been utilized to suppress latchup in CMOS.[4] When such starting material is used with single-well CMOS, the epitaxial layer is doped to a concentration equal to that of the substrate in a nonepitaxial wafer used for that process. If a twin-well CMOS process is used, the epitaxial layer is doped to a level significantly lower than that required for building either the *p*- or *n*-channel MOSFETs (see section 8.1.4).

The epitaxial layer is made thicker than the well depth, since the dopants in the heavily doped substrate under the epi layer diffuse toward the surface as the well dopants are diffused toward the bulk (Fig. 8-2). Thus, some of the epitaxial layer becomes more heavily doped during the CMOS process flow. The process is designed so that the bottom of the well is eventually adjacent to the heavily doped substrate region.

Either *n*-epi on n^+ substrates or *p*-epi on p^+ substrates can be used, with each method having advantages and drawbacks. Because the problems with *n*-epi on n^+ are more serious, *p*-epi on p^+ is more widely used. The major limitation of the latter

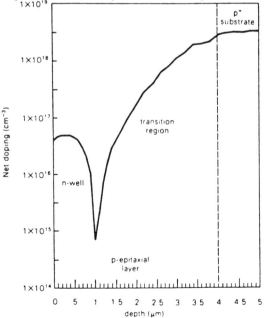

Fig. 8-2 A *p*-on-p^+-epi doping profile and diffused *n*-well profile measured after the entire CMOS process has been completed. The as grown epi thickness is 4 μm and the final lightly doped epi thickness is about 2 μm.[3] (© 1987 IEEE).

approach is that the outdiffusion of boron from the p^+ is much more severe than is the outdiffusion of As or Sb in n-epi on n^+. (The reason for this is that boron diffuses much more rapidly than antimony, which is the most widely-used n^+ dopant material.) Thus, a thicker p^-- epitaxial layer must be used.

In addition, the transition region between the p^+ substrate and the p^--epi layer is thicker, producing a larger series resistance (R_{sub}), which in turn reduces latchup immunity. On the other hand, the p-on-p^+ material is less sensitive to process-induced defects, and the p-type substrate provides higher conductivity under NMOS devices. Such additional conductivity is desirable, since it reduces the voltage drops caused by the substrate currents (generated as a result of the hot-carrier effects in short-channel devices). It is especially important in the regions containing NMOS devices, since the hot-electron substrate current is much higher in such devices than in PMOS devices.

The n-on-n^+ epitaxial substrates also offer some advantages. First, SRAMs are often built on n-type substrates, because the p-well-to-n-substrate junction provides protection from radiation-induced discharging of the memory's n-type storage nodes in the p-well.[5] Second, retrograde p-wells are easier to implement because their implantation energy requirements are much lower. Third, the n-to-n^+ transition region is smaller than that in p-on-p^+ substrates, and the smaller value of R_{sub} provides improved latchup protection.

The limitations of n-epi on n^+ involve the process by which the heavily doped substrate is grown. Antimony (Sb) is the n-type dopant used, both because its diffusion coefficient is so low and because it exhibits much less lateral autodoping than arsenic (the other slow-diffusing n-type dopant). The problem with Sb is that its segregation coefficient, k_0, is very small (i.e., $k_{0,Sb} = 0.023$; see, Vol. 1, chap. 1), and a large quantity of Sb must therefore be put into the Si melt to ensure that a sufficiently heavily doped ingot will be produced. Furthermore, in even the most highly refined Sb there are high concentrations of unwanted heavy metals, which become incorporated into the growing silicon crystal. Finally, the oxygen content of the Sb-doped crystal is relatively small, due in part to the special growing conditions used when the Sb-doped ingot is pulled.[6,7] As a result, intrinsic gettering techniques that would immobilize the metals in the substrate are not as effective as they are in p-on-p^+ epi. For these reasons, n-on-n^+ substrates are less frequently chosen when epi-CMOS is implemented.[4]

A problem that exists with both types of epitaxial substrates for CMOS is that the wells cannot be made too deep, since the lateral diffusion would then take up too much area. On the other hand, if the wells are too shallow, vertical punchthrough (between the substrate and the source/drain regions of devices in the well) will ensue.[8] In this case, appreciable leakage current can flow along this vertical path. As noted, punchthrough can occur if the depletion regions of the p^+/n-well junction and the n-well/p^+-substrate junction merge. The problem is even more severe in the case of the heavily doped p^+ substrate, due to the high degree of boron outdiffusion. A major limitation is thus imposed on the minimum epitaxial-layer thickness.

Another problem of epi-CMOS is back-surface autodoping. For example p-type 20 Ω-cm (7×10^{14} boron/cm^3) epi on a 0.005 Ω-cm (2×10^{19} boron/cm^3) substrate is representative of epi for CMOS devices. If the back surface of the substrate is not

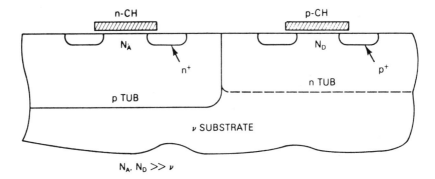

Fig. 8-3 Cross section of a twin-well 1.2-μm CMOS structure.[5] Reprinted with permission of Semiconductor International.

sealed (e.g., by using a sealing layer such as undoped silicon dioxide or silicon nitride), boron evaporation from the substrate can contribute to autodoping on the front surface during the entire epi deposition cycle. This widens the epi/substrate interface and may even prevent the epi from reaching the 20 Ω-cm specified resistivity. Note that if silicon nitride is used as a sealing layer it should only be used in thin layers (e.g., less than 100 nm thick) since its high intrinsic stress causes it to bow the silicon.[9]

8.1.4 Twin-Well CMOS

With the twin-tub approach, two separate wells are formed for n- and p-channel transistors on a lightly doped substrate (Figs. 8-1c and 8-3). The substrate may be either a lightly doped wafer of n or p material, or a thin, lightly doped epitaxial layer on a heavily doped substrate. In either case, the level of the well surface doping is significantly lower than that required for building either the p- or n-channel MOSFETs. Each of the well dopants is implanted separately into the lightly doped surface region and is then driven in to the desired depth.

In twin-well CMOS, the doping profiles of each of the device types can be set independently, since the constraint of single-well CMOS does not exist (i.e., that the well doping must always be higher than the doping of the substrate in which one type of device is made). This was originally cited as an advantage of twin-well CMOS over single-well CMOS, with the argument made that both device types could thus be optimized.[12] This benefit for 1-2 μm CMOS has been questioned by Chen,[2] who points out that in modern single-well CMOS processes, an additional implant is used to prevent punchthrough without the need to raise the entire substrate-doping concentration. By incorporating this additional implant, it is possible to build higher-performance devices than can be achieved with the twin-well approach, in terms of junction capacitance and sensitivity to body effect.

Twin-well CMOS does offer some significant benefits for devices with submicron-channel lengths (although these advantages are gained at the cost of greater process complexity). The first, and most important advantage arises when devices with submicron channel lengths are fabricated. Since it is recognized that the two device types perform similarly as channel lengths approach 0.5 μm, it is useful to provide symmetrical n- and p-channel devices. Furthermore, at submicron dimensions the body doping of both transistor types must be raised significantly to prevent punchthrough and to maintain adequate threshold-voltage levels. Thus, the advantage of having one type of MOS transistor in a lightly doped region (to optimize its performance at the expense of the other) disappears. It is instead more beneficial to produce two types of active device wells, each with its own optimized doping profile (i.e., formed by separate implants into a lightly doped substrate).*

The second advantage of the twin-well process is that it is compatible with the technologies of either isolation by selective epitaxial growth (SEG) or trench isolation.[1] Both approaches restrict the lateral diffusion of the dopants in each of the wells. In addition, sidewall inversion along the trench is less likely when both device sidewalls are butted against a trench that has been formed in a more highly doped well.[10] Finally, when deep trenches are used with a thin epitaxial layer on a heavily doped substrate, latchup can be eliminated. The combined use of the twin-well process and advanced isolation techniques allows n^+ to p^+ spacing to be dramatically reduced in comparison to single-well technologies.

A third benefit is that the combination of epitaxial substrates and the twin-well process allows either substrate type to be chosen with no effects on transistor performance and essentially no change in process flow. Such flexibility is useful since some applications are best met with n^+ substrates and others with p^+ substrates. This advantage may be important if a single process is needed for implementing designs with different applications.

Finally, self-aligned channel stops can be easily implemented in the twin-well approach, allowing the spacing between n- and p-channel devices to be reduced. Although this spacing reduction is not as great as it would be if trenches or SEG were used, the process is much less complex with the twin-well method.

A twin-retrograde-well 0.7-μm-CMOS process for fabricating 1-Mbit SRAMs has been reported.[11] The high energy implants also allow a restricted thermal budget to be used, thus reducing the up-diffusion from the p^+ substrate. This permits the use of a thinner epi layer (which also helps prevent latch-up), and allows implantation of the channel-stop dopants after the field oxide has been grown and planarized (consequently, minimizing lateral diffusion of the boron channel-stop dopants). We discuss retrograde-well CMOS in more detail in section 8.3.

* It is not useful to start with a substrate doped to the optimum level needed for just one of the submicron devices. If this were done, a single well of much higher doping would have to be established for the other type of submicron device, which would unnecessarily degrade the device performance. It is possible, with the twin-well approach, to have both types placed in a well of optimum doping profile.

8.1.5 Summary of CMOS Well-Technology Issues

The selection of a particular CMOS process depends largely upon circuit applications, and to a lesser degree on technology evolution. For VLSI circuits with 1-2 μm design rules n-well CMOS has been the more widely used single-well technology, both because n-channel devices can be optimized in the p-substrate and because most circuits use more NMOS than PMOS devices. In circuits that use transistor channel lengths smaller than 1 μm, twin-well and retrograde-well technology are more attractive. As noted, the price paid for their benefits is increased process complexity.

The optimum process-integration design strategy is to first select the well technology (and to decide whether or not to use epitaxial substrates), and then to select the isolation method. Once these decisions have been made, the well depth and doping profile can be determined. The well depth impacts the lateral-diffusion distance of the well and the vertical-punchthrough voltage. The doping profile affects transconductance, threshold voltage, source/drain punchthrough, junction capacitance, carrier mobility, source/drain-to-substrate breakdown, sensitivity to body effect, and hot-electron effects.

As previously discussed, early CMOS used lightly doped n-type wafers and diffused p-wells (in which the NMOSFETs were fabricated). The p-well approach was initially adopted because NMOSFETs could only be reliably produced in more heavily doped regions until ion implantation was developed in the mid 1970's (see chaps. 5 and 6, Vol. 2). Eventually, however, n-well as well as p-well single-well CMOS processes were implemented. Later twin-well processes were introduced, and these now dominate the newest CMOS fabrication lines (although older n- and p-well single-well technologies are still used to fabricate a variety of CMOS products).

The well-formation process was also one that quickly exploited the technology of ion implantation. The doping precision required in the well gave implantation a significant edge over diffusion as a method for introducing the dopants into the substrate. Advances in implantation technology are allowing development of processes involving multiple implants and higher energies to avoid the long, high-temperature drive-in and to form retrograde well profiles (as will be discussed in sections 8.3 and 8.4).

8.2 CONVENTIONAL FORMATION OF WELLS AND CHANNEL STOPS

There are several issues associated with conventional-well and channel-stop formation that are covered in this section, including: (1) alignment of subsequent patterns to the well locations; (2) process sequences for forming twin-well and channel-stop regions, and; (3) novel well-formation schemes that reduce mask count and process complexity.

8.2.1 Aligning Subsequent Patterns to the Wells

The wells are often the first features to be formed in the CMOS process flow. However, the implant process that introduces the well dopants does not produce visible features on the wafer surface. Thus, it is necessary to provide some indirect indication of the well locations so that subsequent layers can be aligned to them. Here we illustrate some

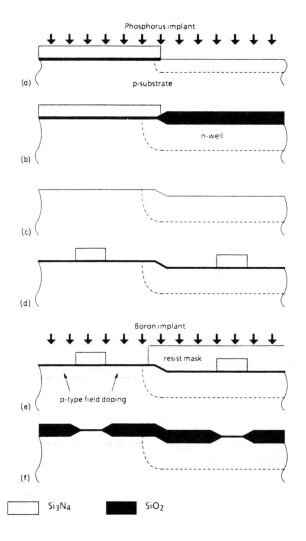

Fig. 8-4 Conventional *n*-well architecture with *n*-well as first mask. (a) Pad oxide/nitride well mask and well implant. (b) Well oxidation and drive-in. (c) Nitride/oxide strip. (d) LOCOS pad oxide/nitride mask and active area definition. (e) NMOS field implant. (f) LOCOS field oxidation. A.G. Lewis and J.Y. Chen, "Current Trends in MOS Process Integration," in N.G. Einspruch and G. Gildenblatt, Eds. *Advanced MOS Device Physics,* Academic Press, San Diego CA, 1989, Reprinted with Permission.

methods that have been developed to provide such alignment marks. For simplicity we utilize an *n*-well CMOS structure in depicting the process flows, but later we show how these methods can be incorporated into twin-well CMOS processes.

In the first approach the wells are the initial features created on the wafer. Here a nitride mask is employed to both define the well locations and to serve as an oxidation mask (see Fig. 8-4a and 8-4b). That is, the patterned nitride/resist layer blocks the phosphorus n-well-implant from penetrating to the p-substrate (or p-well) regions. Part of the drive-in step after the implant is carried out in an oxidizing ambient with the nitride mask layer left in place. This causes a thermal oxide layer to be grown selectively over the n-well regions. At the conclusion of the drive-in process, this oxide is stripped. Since the oxide growth consumes some silicon in the n-regions and since no such silicon loss occurs in the regions covered by the nitride mask, a step is produced on wafer surface when the oxide is stripped (Fig. 8-4c). This step is also is self-aligned to the well edge, therefore providing a visible indication of the well boundaries that allows the active area features to be aligned to them. (Subsequent layers, however, are usually aligned to the active area.) The disadvantage of this approach is the step that is created on the wafer surface. In submicron processing such nonplanar topography is undesirable.

The second approach is a simpler process and it also avoids the creation of the step produced in the previous method (see Fig. 8-5). Here, however, the first features to be defined are the active areas (Mask #1). That is, a nitride mask stack layer is patterned first and all subsequent layers are aligned to the active area pattern. Then the well mask (Mask #2) is aligned to the active area pattern, and the well implant is performed. Note that the implanted dopants must penetrate the nitride mask stack. This does not present a serious difficulty, but it does mean that the n-well tends to be shallower and slightly less-heavily doped beneath active regions than under the field areas. Both the first and second approaches require three masking steps (including the boron channel-stop implant that is performed after the well implant - but prior to the LOCOS field oxidation process). However, the second approach offers the benefit of needing fewer oxidations and depositions.

The first method can be applied to a twin-well process by growing an oxide after the n-well implant (Mask #1), but not doing much of the drive-in step during this oxidation. Then the nitride mask is stripped and a second p-well mask is aligned to the n-well oxide (Mask #2). After doing the p-well implant the well drive-in process is performed. An even easier (i.e., one mask) procedure would be to use the n-well oxide to mask the p-well implant (instead of using the second mask). The second method can also be applied to a twin-well process but two masks must be used to create the twin wells. However, if a shallow p-well is acceptable, the same resist mask that is used to form the channel-stop region in Fig. 8-4e (Mask #3) can be used to form the shallow p-well. In this case the p-well implant must be performed at a higher energy than the field implant in order to penetrate the thin nitride mask layer.

The third method utilizes an initial alignment mark etched into the silicon surface prior to forming any device features. This mark is also used as an automatic alignment target by the wafer stepper. Figure 8-6 shows an example of such an alignment pattern.[16] The use of such initial alignment marks is likely to increase with the proliferation of automatic stepper alignment.

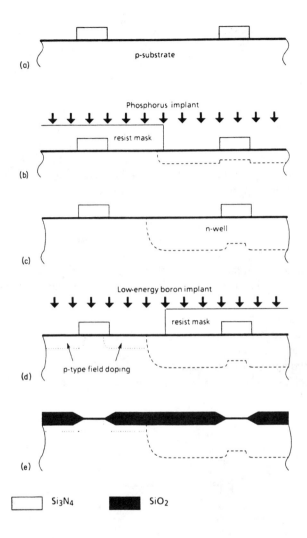

Fig. 8-5 Conventional *n*-well architecture with active area as first mask. (a) Active area definition using LOCOS nitride mask. (b) *n*-well mask and implant. (c) *n*-well drive-in. (d) boron field implant, and (e) LOCOS field oxidation. A.G. Lewis and J.Y. Chen, "Current Trends in MOS Process Integration," in N.G. Einspruch and G. Gildenblatt, Eds. *Advanced MOS Device Physics,* Academic Press, San Diego CA, 1989, Reprinted with Permission.

8.2.2 Twin-Well and Channel-Stop Formation.

The most obvious method of forming twin wells is to use two masking steps, each of which blocks one of the well implants. A procedure for forming twin-wells with a single masking step, however, has also been suggested (see Fig. 8-7).[12] In this method, a single mask is used to pattern a nitride/oxide film formed on the bare silicon surface (*Mask #1*). The openings in the film become the *n*-well regions, and phosphorus is implanted into them (e.g., at 80 keV). Next, a thermal oxide is selectively grown on the *n*-well regions, to a thickness that is sufficient to block the boron implant used to form the *p*-wells. (The nitride mask layer is used to prevent the oxide from growing in the *p*-well regions.) The pad-oxide/nitride mask layer is then stripped, exposing the silicon in the *p*-well regions. The *n*-well regions are however, still covered with the oxide grown earlier. Thus, during the *p*-well implant (e.g., at 50 keV), this oxide masks the *n*-well regions, permitting the boron to enter the silicon only in the *p*-well areas.

Next the wells are driven in (e.g., at 1100°C for 500 min). At the conclusion of this drive-in step the concentrations in the wells for an 0.8-μm-CMOS process are ~1×10^{16}/cm^3 for the *p*-well, and ~3×10^{16}/cm^3 for the *n*-well. The *n*-well is selected to have a higher doping concentration (i.e., to improve the punchthrough performance of the PMOS devices and to eliminate the need for a separate channel-stop implant for the *n*-well). A higher concentration in both wells would still produce devices with relatively low capacitances at the bottoms of the source/drain-to-well junctions.

The channel-stop implant procedure is also usually included in the part of the processing sequence in which the wells are formed. In one reported twin-well process,[13] only a *p*-well channel-stop implant (boron) is used, because the doping in the *n*-well is high enough (3×10^{16} cm^{-3}) that a separate channel stop implant is not required. In this case, an unmasked boron implant is performed following both well implants, but prior to field-oxide growth.

In a second approach,[14] an additional mask can be used to provide both *n*-well and *p*-well channel stops (Fig. 8-8a). Note that in this procedure, a mask is saved by

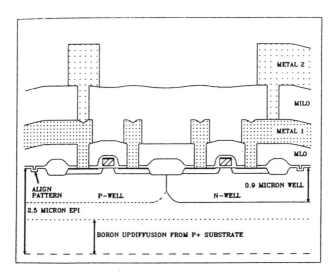

Fig. 8-6 Twin-well CMOS showing initial alignment mark.[16] (© 1991 IEEE).

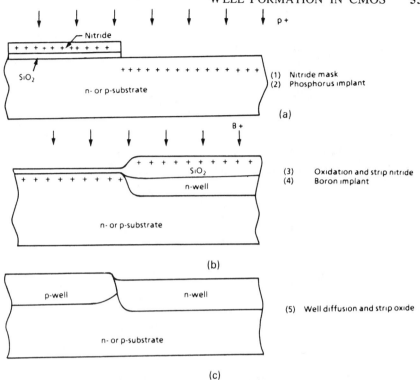

(1)   Nitride mask
(2)   Phosphorus implant

(a)

(3)   Oxidation and strip nitride
(4)   Boron implant

(b)

(5)   Well diffusion and strip oxide

(c)

Fig. 8-7 Twin-well CMOS process using a single mask to form both wells. (a) P+ implant for the *n*-well. (b) B⁻ implant to form the *p*-well (blocked by the *n*-well oxide). (c) well drive-in for both wells.[12] (© 1982 IEEE).

performing a blanket boron implant. As a result, the boron channel stop dopant ends up in the *n*-well as well as in the *p*-well. Hence, the phosphorus channel stop dose must be increased to compensate for the boron's presence in the *n*-well field regions. The disadvantages of this method include the additional alignment step between the channel stops and the well masks, the interdiffusion that occurs during the oxidation step, and the asymmetry of the doping profiles. (The latter is due to the increased phosphorus concentration that must overcompensate the nonselective boron channel stop).

A variation of this method that requires no masks at all to create the channel stops has been developed to overcome the above drawbacks (Fig. 8-8b).[14,15] In this sequence, both arsenic and phosphorus are co-implanted into the *n*-well regions. This places both the dopants that form the well and the channel stop into the *n*-well regions prior to implanting of the *p*-wells. An oxide is then selectively grown on the *n*-well regions and the boron dopant for the *p*-wells is implanted. After the wells have been driven in, the oxide over the *n*-wells is retained, and a second boron implant is carried out. This implant serves as both a channel stop in the *p*-well *field* regions and a punchthrough-prevention implant in the *active* regions of the *p*-well.

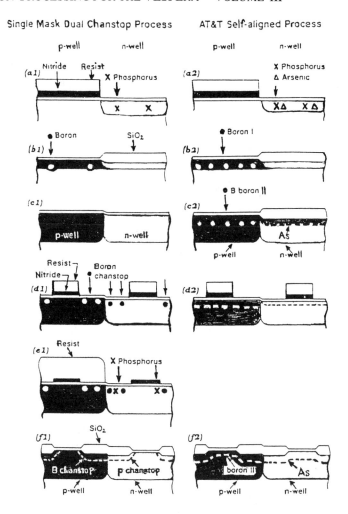

Fig. 8-8 (a) Twin-well CMOS with a single-mask dual channel stop process. (b) ATT twin-well CMOS process which requires no masks to form the dual channel stops (self-aligned process.)[15] (© IEEE 1981).

It should also be noted that the minimum separation between two wells of the doping type at two different potentials is limited by electrical isolation. In single-well processes, to prevent punchthrough in the lightly-doped substrate between two such wells, adequate spacing between them must be allowed.

8.2.3 Split Well-Drive-In Process

In another report, the long, high-temperature drive-in step is performed in a novel manner, allowing the *p*-well transistors to be fabricated without use of a channel-stop implant.[17] After the p-well implant is carried out, the field oxide is first grown without driving the implanted well dopants. During this step, some of the implanted boron impurities segregate into the field oxide, leaving a surface concentration as low as would exist after any field oxide step. Next, the remainder of the well drive-in step is performed in a non-oxidizing ambient. The well dopant deep in the bulk now back-diffuses toward the surface, raising the Si-SiO$_2$ interface concentration by a factor of 2-3 (to 2-3x10^{16} cm^{-3} in this case, see Fig. 8-9). The well concentration at surface of the field regions is only about 1.5x lower than at the surface in the active regions. V_{TFiso}s greater than 10 V (at I_D at 0.5 pA/μm at V_{DS} = 8V) can be produced for isolation lengths of 1.2 μm. It has been observed that for very narrow NMOSFETs (e.g., 0.35 μm) fabricated with the split-well drive-in scheme, V_T is decreased by ~100 mV compared to wider channel devices (e.g., 5 μm). This occurs because boron also diffuses from the channel regions to the field regions during the post-oxidation drive-in step. Such diffusion occurs because, as described earlier, the boron concentration at the silicon surface in the field regions has been reduced during the field oxide step by boron segregation effects.

8.3 RETROGRADE-WELL CMOS

As previously discussed, conventional wells are formed in single- and twin-well CMOS technology by implanting the well dopants and then diffusing them to the desired depth. However, lateral as well as vertical diffusion occurs, which has the effect of reducing packing density. For example, since the lateral diffusion is ~0.7 times the junction

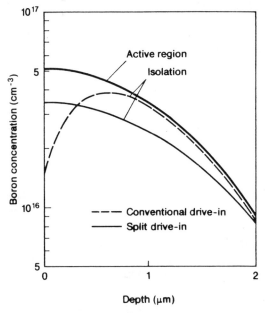

Fig. 8-9 SIMS profiles of boron well underneath field oxide and in the active area for split and non-split drive-in. Implanted boron dose: 8x10^{12} cm^{-2}. The active area profile is the same for both drive-in cases.[17] (© 1990 IEEE).

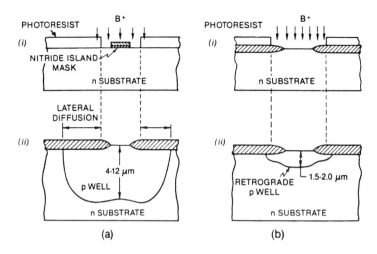

Fig. 8-10 Formation of (a) conventional and (b) retrograde *p*-well CMOS structures.[19] (© 1981 IEEE).

depth, a typical diffused well of 3 to 4 μm results in a lateral spread of well dopant of ~2 to 3 μm. If a higher energy implant is used to place the dopants at the desired depth without significant additional diffusion (i.e., the high-energy implant is performed after the active area isolation structures [field oxide] is already in place, and only a short anneal at a relatively low temperature is used to activate the implant), much less lateral dopant spread occurs. This is because ion implantation is a more anisotropic dopant distribution process than diffusion. That is, the lateral implant straggle is ~0.7 μm and barely exceeds one micron after all thermal processing.[18] In addition, since the high-energy implanted wells are formed after the LOCOS isolation step, lateral spread of the well dopants is further reduced. Hence, the 7-9 μm n^+-to-p^+ spacing required for a twin-well 1.2 μm CMOS process which uses conventional wells, can be reduced to ~5 μm if retrograde wells are used instead.

Figure 8-10 depicts the cross-section of a high-energy implanted *p*-well in comparison with a conventional diffused well. In this example, the implanted *p*-well is formed by boron implantation at 400-600 keV, followed by a brief 30 min anneal at 1000°C (instead of the 6-20 hour drive-ins at 1100-1150°C used for conventional-well formation). Notice the lateral spread associated with the *p*-well is greatly reduced.

Such high-energy implants also cause the peak of the implant to be buried at a certain depth within the silicon substrate (depending on the implantation energy, but at roughly 1 μm for the energies most frequently used), and the impurity concentration decreases as the doping profile approaches the wafer surface (see Fig. 8-11). Since the well profile in this case is different from that of conventionally formed wells (in which the doping concentration after drive-in is highest at the surface, and decreases monotonically with depth), such deeply implanted wells are known as *retrograde wells*. It is estimated that, in order to avoid excessive spread of the active device electrical parameters, the surface concentration after the retrograde implant should be at least five times smaller than its final value, which is set by shallower low-dose implants specifically designed for threshold and punchthrough control. Comparison of the doping profiles in conventional and implanted p-well profiles (obtained by simulation) is shown in Fig. 8-11.[19] The retrograde-doping profile is retained by minimizing the temperature cycles of later process steps (e.g., by using RTP). Retrograde wells can be implemented on both bulk and epitaxial wafers.[20]

Besides the potential benefit of increased packing density, retrograde wells offer the following advantages:[1]

1. A retarded electric field is created in the parasitic vertical bipolar transistor, thereby reducing its current gain. This affords some protection against latchup.

2. Susceptibility to vertical punchthrough is reduced without having to significantly raise the surface doping concentration.

3. The conductivity in the bottom of the well is increased, which also provides additional latchup protection.

4. A higher threshold voltage can be achieved in the field regions of the p-wells if the boron implant is done following field oxidation (i.e., the boron does not segregate out into the oxide during the field oxide growth step).[19]

5. Lateral diffusion of the channel-stop boron is also eliminated, thereby reducing encroachment of the boron into the active regions. This lessens narrow width effects in the active devices.

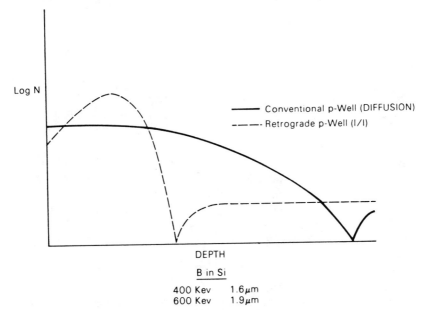

Fig. 8-11 Comparison of conventional and retrograde well p-well profiles.[19] (© 1981 IEEE).

6. Greater flexibility exists in retrograde structures to optimize channel doping profiles for active device performance. That is, in conventional wells (especially shallow ones), the surface doping is primarily determined by the need to maintain sufficient vertical isolation. In retrograde structures, however, vertical isolation is secured by the high doping level towards the well bottom. Thus, it is possible to adjust the surface doping profile to a larger extent. This helps to achieve adequate short-channel device characteristics with retrograde wells.

7. The shallower well depth should also make the drain of the parasitic n^+-to-n-well (or p^+-to-p-well) parasitic FETs shallower. This should improve both the short-channel threshold roll-off and the punchthrough characteristics of these parasitic structures, as is discussed further in chap. 6.

However, several concerns associated with the retrograde process should also be mentioned. First, the process requires a thick photoresist as a masking material for the high-energy implant. Typical resist thicknesses are about 5 μm, and special exposure and development techniques are required for this process. Second, there is concern about the annealability of the damage caused by the high-energy implant. Third, the retrograde implant may cause both the junction capacitance and the body factor to be significantly increased. The p^+-to-n-well junction capacitances measured in retrograde-well structures formed with a 700 keV implant have been shown to be about twice the values obtained in conventional wells. While this can adversely impact the propagation delay, circuit performance is also impacted by a number of other parasitic capacitances, and the net result on typical CMOS circuit speed and power dissipation is often relatively small. For example, in a simulation of a 32-bit CMOS arithmetic logic unit (ALU), it was found that the circuit delay increases by about 7% as the p-channel junction capacitance increases by 30 percent.[1]

When the retrograde well is formed by means of very high-energy implants, however, the doping concentration under the bottom of the source and drain regions is decreased, which reduces the junction capacitance. This implies that if such high-energy ion implanters (~1 MeV) become available for production, some of the disadvantages of retrograde wells can be overcome.[18] In addition, the higher doping that will be required in the wells for fabrication of submicron CMOS devices may mean a less severe junction capacitance penalty.

Although both p-type[21] and n-type[22] retrograde wells have been demonstrated (see Figs. 8-12a and 8-12b,[20] and Fig. 8-12c,[23] respectively), the p-type technology has been more widely implemented. This is because at least 600-keV beam energies are required for the formation of n-type (phosphorus) retrograde wells suitable for 0.5-0.8 μm CMOS. As of 1994 such machines were commercially available, but had only begun to be introduced into mainstream production environments. Retrograde p-type wells adequate for 0.5 μm devices require implants with energies of ~300 keV at a dose of ~1×10^{13} cm^{-2}. Such p-well implants can be achieved by implanting singly ionized boron at 300 keV or doubly ionized boron at 150 keV. (The required p-well energy is smaller because boron has a larger projected range than either As or P; see Vol. 1, chap. 9). Although the doubly ionized boron approach is achievable with conventional

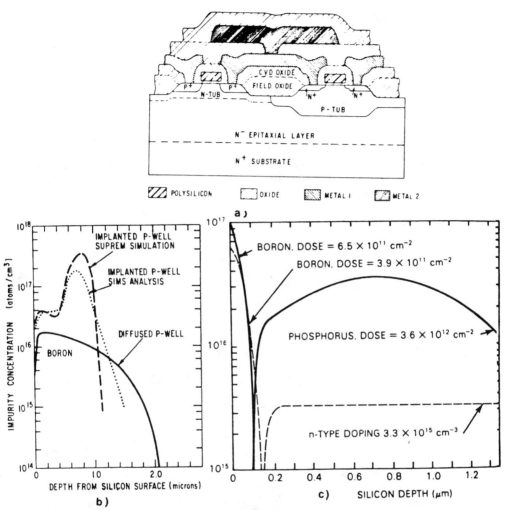

Fig. 8-12 (a) Twin-tub device cross section in which a retrograde p-well is used. General Electric AVLSI Process. (b) Retrograded p-well implanted impurity concentration profile. General Electric AVLSI process. Also shown is a conventionally thermally diffused well.[20] (© 1986 IEEE). (c) Simulated doping profiles in PMOS channel regions: dashed lines, lightly doped substrate; solid lines, retrograde n-well.[23] (© 1982 IEEE).

production implanters it is not a routine process to implement.* Subject to the precautions mentioned in the footnote, retrograde well CMOS processes have been

* One problem is that a large fraction of double-ionized ions, as high as 20%, can interact with gas molecules at the entrance of the acceleration column and become single-charged ions because of partial neutralization. These ions would only penetrate into silicon about half the desired range, distorting the profile and causing abnormalities of the threshold

the successfully implemented in a production environment with good results. However, these have primarily been limited to custom and advanced system applications, where higher costs of retrograde well processing are justified by the higher density and performance benefits offered by the retrograde-well device structures.

Two examples in which a 300 keV boron implant is used to form a retrograde *p*-well CMOS structure have recently been published. In the first, this *p*-well structure (together with a 1.2 μm epi layer) allowed an NMOS device-to-device spacing of less than 1 μm to be used when an optimized field implant was employed.[25] In the second, the *p*-well was fabricated with a 320 keV implant (using, in fact, doubly-charged boron accelerated at 160 keV), and a 5 min 1100°C RTP anneal. Together with the use of a 2-2.5 μm epi layer, a sub-half micron CMOS structure was fabricated (which permitted an n^+ to p^+ spacing of less than 2.5 μm).[16]

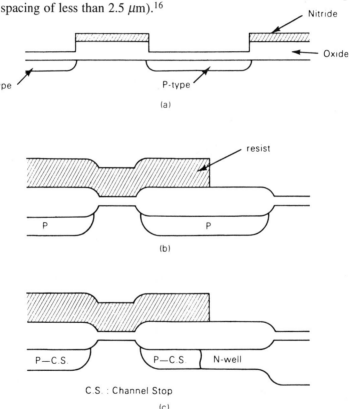

Fig. 8-13 A simplified retrograde *n*-well process. (a) Nitride mask for active area and B$^+$ implant for *p*-type channel stop.; (b) photoresist mask for *n*-well; and (c) high energy P$^+$ implant and any additional shallow implants in the *n*-well.[18] (© 1986 IEEE).

* (cont.) voltage and other electrical parameters. Thus, if a high-current implanter is not available, a medium-current implanter of the post-analysis type should be used to eliminate single-charge ions before they reach the wafers.[24]

However, an n-well retrograde CMOS process using a 700-keV phosphorus implant has also been demonstrated.[18] The process sequence used to form this retrograde n-well CMOS structure (with the well implant performed after field oxidation) is shown in Fig. 8-13. The active areas are first defined using nitride masking. Next, a blanket low-energy boron channel-stop implant is performed. The field oxidation is then carried out and the retrograde n-well implant step is performed. A 30 minute, 1000°C anneal follows the implant. Note that the blanket boron channel-stop dopant is overcompensated in the n-well regions by the phosphorus implant. This retrograde-well process permits very small ($\sim$2 μm) n^+-to-p^+ spacings.

Some advanced twin-well CMOS processes with both retrograde n- and p-wells, (using short [$\sim$5 min] RTP well-drive-in steps), have also been reported for submicron applications.[26] Scaling CMOS to 0.5 μm and below reduces the well depths required to prevent vertical punchthrough and latchup. In addition, the well depth and well-dopant concentration can be reduced if additional, lower energy implants are precisely located with respect to the transistor structure to suppress punchthrough of the MOSFET channels and to enhance the field isolation characteristics.

One novel method of achieving such short well-drive-in times is to enhance the effective diffusion rate. It has been demonstrated that the diffusion of boron and phosphorus is substantially enhanced by oxynitridation in an NH_3 ambient with a thin oxide layer over the diffusion region.[27]* These factors combine to produce a trend of lower implant energy in retrograde wells for scaled devices at and below 0.5 μm.

A twin-retrograde-well 0.7-μm-CMOS process for fabricating 1-Mbit SRAMs on p^--on-p^+ epi substrates has been reported.[11] The high energy implants also allow a restricted thermal budget to be used, thus reducing the up-diffusion from the p^+ substrate. This permits the use of a thinner epi layer (which also helps prevent latch-up), and also allows implantation of the channel-stop dopants after the field oxide has been grown and planarized (thus minimizing lateral diffusion of the boron channel-stop dopants).

The use of retrograde wells for both the n- and p-wells of a twin-tub CMOS process has also been reported.[29] The approach was called *quadruple-well CMOS* to emphasize the fact that for each type (n- or p-well), two wells were needed, one in the active area, and another, shallower one in the field region. The deep and shallow wells, however, are created simultaneously using the same higher energy implant steps. That is, since the implant is carried out after the field oxidation (and after the LOCOS nitride mask has been stripped), in regions of the wafer where no field oxide exists the implant penetrates deeply, but in regions where the implant must penetrate the field oxide, it enters the Si substrate less deeply (creating a shallower well there).

Another approach for fabricating retrograde wells without the need for very high ion implantation is to use epitaxy. Such a method for forming an n-well CMOS structure is shown in Fig. 8-14. Shallow, heavily doped wells are formed in the p-substrate by ion implantation of a slow diffusing dopant (typically arsenic) in order to prevent significant redistribution during subsequent processing. A p-type epitaxial layer is then grown to a thickness of a few microns, creating an n^+ buried layer. A low-energy phosphorus implant is then used to complete the n-wells. No drive-in is needed if it is

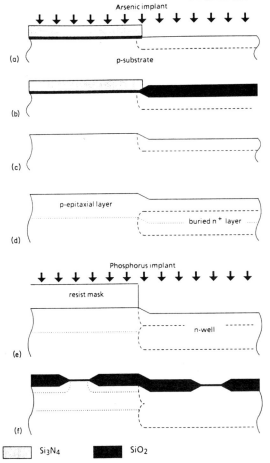

Fig. 8-14 Retrograde *n*-well architecture based on epitaxy. (a) Oxide/nitride well mask and buried layer implant. (b) Well oxidation. (c) Nitride/oxide strip. (d) Epitaxial growth. (e) Surface *n*-well implant. (f) Boron field implant and standard LOCOS field oxidation. From A.G. Lewis and J.Y. Chen, "Current Trends in MOS Process Integration," in N.G. Einspruch and G. Gildenblatt, Eds. *Advanced MOS Device Physics,* Academic Press, San Diego CA, 1989, Reprinted with Permission.

arranged that the surface phosphorus implant merges with the buried layer to complete the *n*-well. The formation of buried layers in this way is especially well-suited to BiCMOS technologies.

8.3.1 Retrograde Well Technologies to Improve Isolation

Since retrograde wells are formed by a high-energy implantation step following the LOCOS oxidation growth process, lateral diffusion of the well dopants is greatly reduced compared to a conventional well process. This results in significant saving of layout space. Isolation among opposite type devices is also expected to be improved.

Here we present data that supports this latter claim, as a supplement to the material on isolation presented in chap. 6.

The comparison of isolation performance between conventional-well and retrograde-well CMOS structures was performed using an n-well process and aluminum-gate MOSFETs.[18] To establish a fair comparison, equal well depths were used in the active area of both the conventional-well and retrograde-well structures.

The process sequences used to form both the conventional-wells and retrograde-wells in an n-well CMOS process are shown in Figs. 8-15a and 8-15b, respectively.[30] The active areas are first defined in both structures using nitride masking. In the retrograde structures, a blanket low-energy boron channel-stop implant is performed next. In the case of the conventional well, the n-well resist mask is aligned to the patterned nitride, and the n-well implant (phosphorus) is carried out, followed by a blanket low-energy boron channel-stop implant. The field-oxide is now grown on both structures. In the retrograde-well structure, the n-well implant step is carried out after the field oxidation, followed by a short (~30 min) anneal at 1000°C. In both structures, the boron channel stop dopant is overcompensated in the n-well regions by the phosphorus implant.

Because the retrograde well is formed by high-energy ions penetrating the field oxide in the field regions the well depth there is only half of the well depth in the active regions. The shallower well depth in the field regions of the retrograde-well structure (compared to the well field-region depth in the conventional-well structure) is advantageous. That is, it creates a shallower drain for the n^+-to-n-well parasitic FET,

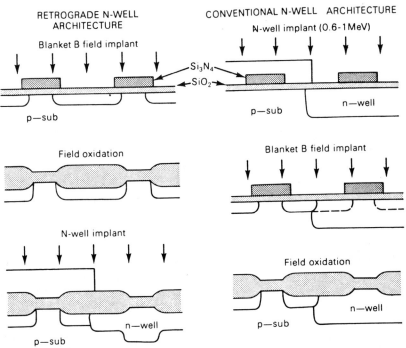

Fig. 8-15 Process architectures for retrograde and conventional n-well CMOS structures.[30]

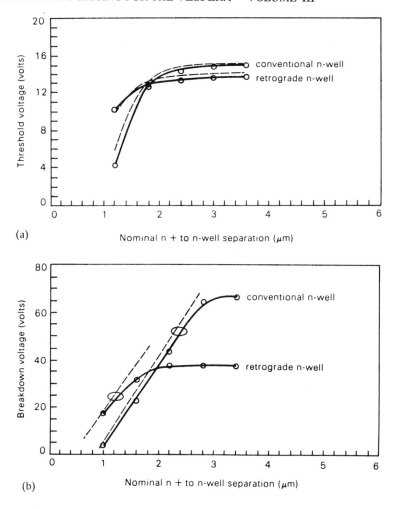

Fig. 8-16 Comparison of retrograde and conventional well structures for n^+ to n-well parasitic FETs: (a) field threshold voltage; and (b) n^+-to-n-well breakdown voltage. Solid lines: experimental data, dashed lines: modeled results, breakdown voltage is modeled by punchthrough only.[37] (© 1987 IEEE).

thereby improving isolation. At the same time, the depth of the well in the active region is greater, so that the performance of the devices in the well are not significantly degraded because the n-well doping concentration near the surface remains sufficiently low. In addition, in the active regions the peak of implanted profile is near the bottom of the well, which is beneficial for vertical isolation. Meanwhile, the implant profile peaks near the Si surface in the field areas, which is again better for producing a channel stop and for preventing p^+-to-p-substrate lateral punchthrough.

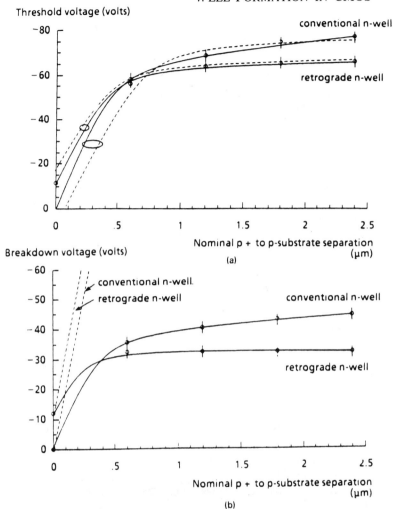

Fig. 8-17 Comparison of retrograde and conventional well structures for p^+ to p-well parasitic FETs: (a) field threshold voltage; and (b) p^+-to-p substrate breakdown voltage. Solid lines: experimental data, dashed lines: modeled results, breakdown voltage is modeled by punchthrough only.[37] (© 1987 IEEE).

The measured and simulated V_{TFiso}s and breakdown voltages (all defined at a drain current in the parasitic FET test structure of 10 pA) for n^+-to-n-well parasitic transistors in both the conventional and retrograde aluminum-gate CMOS test structures are shown in Figs. 8-16a and 8-16b. At large n^+-to-n-well separations, avalanche breakdown at the well-substrate junction occurs before lateral punchthrough occurs. The lower value of avalanche breakdown in the retrograde structures is attributed to higher well doping. As described earlier, shallower retrograde wells should exhibit less propensity to degradation caused by short-channel effects (e.g., to threshold lowering and DIBL). These predictions are confirmed from the experimental V_{TFiso} and punchthrough data.

Figure 8-17a gives the V_{TFiso} values for lateral p^+-to-p-substrate parasitic devices. The absolute values are much larger than those for the n^+-to-n-well devices. These higher values are due in part to the greater field doping required in the n-well to guaranty sufficient compensation of the boron. The larger values are also partly caused by the fixed charge at the Si-SiO$_2$ interface, which is generally positive and thus increases the magnitude of the threshold voltage of the p-channel transistors. It is also evident that short-channel effects are much less severe in these p-channel parasitic devices, especially for the retrograde structures; the thresholds do not decrease until the channel length approaches 0.5 μm. This effect is caused by the higher channel (n-well) doping in these parasitic transistors, and to the drain (substrate) doping being lower than the channel (n-well) doping.

Figure 8-17b depicts the breakdown voltages exhibited by the same p^+-to-p-substrate devices, and comparison with Figs. 8-17a and b again shows the superior performance of these structures. In these types of parasitic FETs, the p-substrate, which is considered to be the drain, is not only deep but wraps around under the source (see Fig. 6-45). Thus, both lateral and vertical leakage paths may possibly exist between the p^+ source and the p-substrate. The limiting values of breakdown voltage for retrograde n-well structures is set by well to substrate avalanche breakdown, as is the case of the n^+-to-n-well transistors. In conventional wells, however, the limit is set by p^+-to-p-substrate vertical punchthrough breakdown. Thus, the maximum breakdown voltage shown on Fig. 8-17b for these devices is not the same as that shown in Fig. 8-16b, even though the drain-channel junction is in fact the same in both cases.

The application of retrograde wells for both the n- and p-wells to a twin-tub CMOS process has also been reported. The approach, as described in the previous section, was called *quadruple-well CMOS* to indicate that for each well type (i.e., n- or p-), two wells were needed, one in the active area, and another, shallower one in the field region (see Fig. 8-18). The two shallow wells actually function as self-aligned channel stops, in which the surface concentration of the well dopants is tightly restricted on each side of the well boundary. That is, as shown in Fig. 8-19 the reduction of the net impurity concentration is restricted to a small distance from the boundary of the well edge. Specifically, the surface doping concentration near the well boundary is decreased significantly only within a few tenths of a micron from the boundary, instead of a few microns, as occurs in a conventional twin-well structure (see Fig. 6-47). Experimental data shows that at a 4 μm n^+-to-p^+ separation, subthreshold leakage in the isolation region is <1 pA for gate voltages between -15V and +20V (Fig. 8-20). Simulation data indicate that it is possible to obtain adequate isolation with a 2 μm n^+-to-p^+ separation.

A CMOS process based on high energy implantations without epi-layers or trenches that allows n^+-to-p^+ spacings as small as 1.5 μm has been reported. To realize such small isolation spacing, the n-well was formed with 700 keV, 1x10^{13} cm^{-2} phosphorus and 1.5 MeV, 3x10^{13} cm^{-2} boron implantations. A unique feature of the well structure in this report is that these same two implantations simultaneously form not only the two retrograde wells and the n-well and p-well channel stops, but the boron implant also

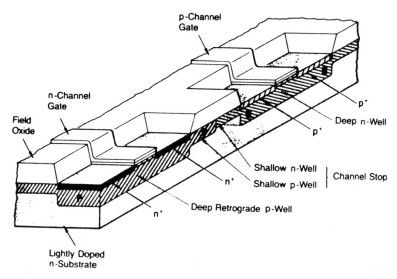

Fig. 8-18 Cross section of a quadruple-well CMOS device.[36] Reprinted with permission of VLSI Design.

formed a deep, buried p^+ layer under the phosphorus n-well profile. The p^+ layer eliminates the need for substrates with an epi layer, since the low resistivity substrate required to suppress latchup is created by the high energy implantation. It was also reported that the high energy implantation did not induce any excess leakage or measurably degrade MOS transistor characteristics.

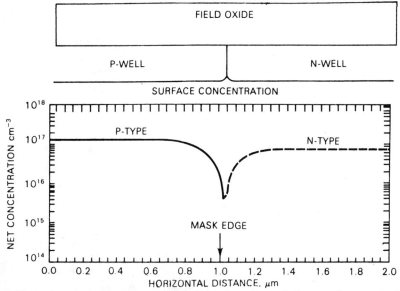

Fig. 8-19 Surface impurity concentration at the boundary of the p- and n-retrograde wells in quadruple-well CMOS.[29] (© 1986 IEEE).

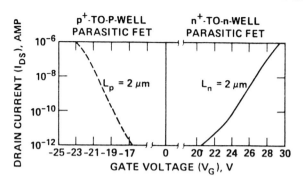

*L_p: p^+-TO-p-WELL SPACING, L_n: n^+-TO-n-WELL SPACING

Fig. 8-20 Subthreshold characteristics of symmetric parasitic FETs in quadruple-well CMOS.[29] (© 1986 IEEE).

8.4 FUTURE TRENDS IN WELL FORMATION

It seems that high-energy ion implantation will find more application for generating profiled wells. Profiled wells are achieved by multiple implants at varying energies. They offer the ability to independently control several MOSFET characteristics, including threshold voltage, hot-carrier generation, punchthrough voltage, junction capacitance, latchup susceptibility, soft-error immunity, and the body-effect coefficient. The optimization of well profiles for improving device performance has been termed "well engineering."[31]

Unlike a conventional well, which has an almost flat impurity distribution, a profiled well can have an impurity profile tailored to independently optimize a variety of device characteristics. Figure 8-21 shows the impurity profile of a multiply-implanted well and the relation of the device characteristics to the profile.[32]

In profile-implanted wells formed with high-energy implants, the wells are implanted after LOCOS isolation. In the n-well, multiple high-energy implants of phosphorus ions form a profiled well for active as well as isolation regions (with a thick photoresist serving as the p-well mask). Subsequently, low-energy implants are performed to adjust the PMOS V_T. A profiled p-well is next produced in the same way.

The deepest implant of the well in this example is fabricated with a 1 MeV implant. These implanted dopants form a heavily doped buried layer (10^{18}-10^{19} cm^{-3}) at a depth of 2-4 μm that serves to reduce latchup susceptibility. Such a p^+ buried layer is more effective than an epitaxial layer in reducing substrate resistance and suppressing latchup, thus eliminating the need for an epi layer. The ability to use non-epi substrates when wafer sizes reach 150 mm and 200 mm represents a major cost savings, as the cost of 200 mm epitaxial wafers are ~$100 US higher than bulk-CZ wafers. The replacement of epitaxial wafers with MeV implantation processing also alleviates problems with autodoping control and backside sealing.[35]

The use of MeV implantation avoids the long (3-21 hour), high-temperature (1150-1200°C) well-formation drive-in step of the conventional process. This minimizes

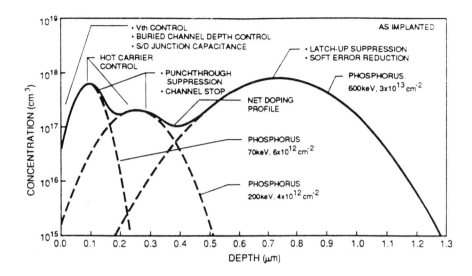

Fig. 8-21 The relation between device characteristics and the impurity concentration at various depths in multiple implanted well.[32] Reprinted with permission of Solid State Technology.

thermally induced stress in large wafers that can cause wafer warpage, bow, and flatness degradation, as well as offering simplified processing with shorter fabrication times. Process simplification also results from the fact that the retrograde-well and field-isolation regions are formed by the same implant (after field oxidation). As noted in section 8.3.1, implantation through field oxide can also improve active device isolation characteristics. Employing MeV implantation to dope the bottom of the well more heavily leaves more room to tailor the doping profile at the top of the well in the channel area with lower energy implants.

Concern has existed that the high-energy implants may cause damage that will degrade device and circuit performance. Increased junction leakage is observed if the dose or energy are too low (i.e., $<3 \times 10^{14}$ cm^{-2} and ~1-1.5 MeV, respectively). Recent studies, however, indicate that if the dose and energy exceed 3×10^{14} cm^{-2} and 1.5 MeV, respectively, leakage due to implant damage is dramatically reduced with both boron and phosphorus implantation. In fact, when an optimum combination of dose, energy, and annealing process is used, *less* leakage is observed than in control devices having no buried layer. This behavior is believed to be caused by gettering of electrically active damage or impurity defects away from the depletion regions of active transistors by secondary defects near the concentration peak of the buried layer. The effect is called "self-gettering." For all of the above reasons it appears that high-energy implantation will become more widely used to form wells in device generations at and below 0.5 μm.

8.5 AFTER-GATE IMPLANTATION (AGI)

An alternative technique which exploits high-energy implantation to reduce the complexity of CMOS process called *after-gate implantation* (AGI) has been suggested. That is, by performing all implantations after the gate electrodes are patterned (wells, channel-stop doping, and source/drain), the number of mask steps can be reduced.

Figure 8-22 illustrates this approach, in which only seven masks are required to form a single *p*-well CMOS structure.[33] The LOCOS-isolation field-oxide regions are formed first, then the polysilicon gates are deposited and patterned. Using a mask that obscures the PMOS regions, the NMOS *p*-well implant, multiple-channel implants, and the n^+ source/drain implants are carried out. Then a mask is used to cover the NMOS areas, and the PMOS-channel and p^+ source/drain implants are performed. Since the well and channel implantations must penetrate the field oxide and the polysilicon gate, they must be carried out at higher energies. The *p*-well implant energy is 600 keV (at a dose of 1×10^{13} cm^{-2}), and the NMOS devices receive low-dose channel implants of 135 keV, 175 keV, and 215 keV. The channel of the PMOS devices receives two low-dose, higher-energy phosphorus implants (at 220 keV and 440 keV). Such multiple-channel implants are used in both NMOS and PMOS devices to avoid unacceptable V_T variations caused by polysilicon gate thickness variations encountered in processing (and to improve the punchthrough resistance of the device structures). Studies also indicate

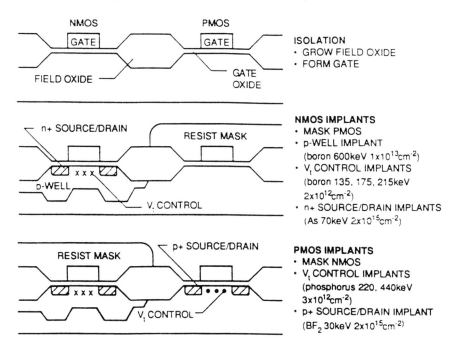

Fig. 8-22 After-Gate Implant (AGI) process sequence.[33] (© 1986 IEEE).

that the high energy AGI does not degrade the gate oxide integrity[32] nor the MOS transistor characteristics.[34]

The AGI process thus offers the benefits of implantation processing freedom and flexibility, as well as reduced CMOS process complexity. The low doses required for the well and channel implantations can be performed with a medium-current implanter which may also have a higher energy implantation capability.

REFERENCES

1. J.Y. Chen, "CMOS - The Emerging Technology," *IEEE Circuits and Devices Magazine,* March 1986, p. 16.
2. J.Y. Chen, *CMOS Devices and Technology for VLSI*, Prentice-Hall, Englewood Cliffs, N.J., 1990.
3. A.G. Lewis et al., *IEEE Trans. Electron Dev.*, **ED-34**, 2156, (1987).
4. T. Yamaguchi et al., *IEEE Trans. Electron Dev.*, **ED-31**, p. 205 (1984).
5. L.C. Parrillo "CMOS Active and Field Device Fabrication," *Semiconductor International*, April 1988, p. 64.
6. W. Wijaranakula et al., *J. Electrochem. Soc.,* December 1988, p. 3113.
7. H. Tsuya et al., *Japanese J. Appl. Phys.*, **22**, L16 (1983).
8. A. G. Lewis et al., "Vertical Isolation in Shallow n-Well CMOS Circuits," *IEEE Electron Dev. Lett.*, EDL-8, p. 107, 1987.
9. K. Tanno, F. Shimura, and T. Kawamura, *J. Electrochem. Soc.,* **128**, p. 395 (1981).
10. J. Manoliu and J.O. Borland, "A Submicron Buried Layer Twin-Well for High Density CMOS," *Tech. Dig. IEDM*, 1987, p. 20.
11. R. de Werdt et al., *Tech. Dig. IEDM,* 1987, p. 532.
12. L.C. Parrillo et al., "Twin-Tub CMOS-II," *Tech. Dig. IEDM*, 1982, p. 706.
13. R.A. Chapman et al., "A 0.8 μm CMOS Technology," *Tech. Dig. IEDM*, 1987, p. 362.
14. M.-L. Chen et al. *Tech. Dig. IEDM* 1986, p. 256.
15. S.J. Hillenius and L.C. Parrillo, U.S. Patent No. 4,554,726, Nov. 25, 1985.
16. R.A. Chapman et al., "High Performance Sub-Half Micron CMOS Using Rapid Thermal Processing," *Tech. Dig. IEDM* 1991, p. 101.
17. Ch. Zeller, C. Mazure, & M. Kerber, "Field-Implant-Free Isolation by Double-Well Split Drive-In," *IEEE Electron. Dev. Letts.,* p. 215, May 1990.
18. R. Martin and J.Y. Chen, "Optimized Retrograde n-well for 1 μm CMOS, *Proc. Custom Integ. Circuits Conf.,* 1985, p. 199.
19. R.D. Rung, C.J. Dell'Oca, and L.G. Walker, "A Retrograde p-well for High Density CMOS," *IEEE Trans. Electron Dev.,* ED-28, p. 1115, 1981.
20. D.M. Brown et al., "Trends in Advanced CMOS Process Technology," *Proceedings of the IEEE,* December 1986, p. 1646.
21. S.R. Coombs, "Scalable Retrograde p-well CMOS Technology," *IEEE Trans. Electron Dev.,* **ED-28**, p. 346, 1981.
22. Y. Taur et al., *IEEE J. Solid-State Circuits,* **SC-20,** p. 123, 1985.

23. G.J. Hu et al., "Design and Fabrication of *p*-channel FET for 1-μm CMOS technology," *IEDM Tech. Dig.* 1982, p. 710.

24. A. Stolmeijer, "A twin-well CMOS process employing high-energy ion implantation," *IEEE Trans. Electron Dev.*, **ED-33**, April, 1986, p. 450.

25. A. Shida et al., 3.3V BiNMOS Technology Using NPN Transistors without Buried Layers," *Tech. Dig. IEDM,* 1991, p. 93.

26. Y. Mochizuki, "Special Report: High Energy Ion Implantation Technology," Nikkei Microelectronics, (Dec. 1991), p. 92.

27. M. Moslehi and K. Saraswat, "Thermal Nitridation of Si and SiO_2 for VLSI," *IEEE Trans Electron Dev.* **ED-32**, p. 116, January 1985.

28. P. Fahey, R.W. Dutton, and M. Moslehi, "Effects of Thermal Nitridation Processes on Boron and Phosphorus Diffusion in <100> Silicon," *Appl. Phys. Letts.*, **43**(7), p. 683 July, 1983.

29. J.Y. Chen, "Quadruple-well CMOS for VLSI Technology," *IEEE Trans. on Electron Dev.*, **ED-31**, p. 910, 1984.

30. A.G. Lewis, R.A. Martin, and J.Y. Chen, "Retrograde and conventional *n*-well CMOS technologies: A Comparison," Internal Report, EIL-87-17, Xerox Palo Alto Research Center, Oct. 1986.

31. K. Tsukamoto et al., *Nucl. Instrumentation & Methods,* B59/60, p. 584 (1991).

32. K. Tsukamoto et al., "High Energy Ion Implantation for ULSI: Well Engineering and Gettering," *Solid State Technology* P. 49, June 1992.

33. H. Mikoshiba et al., "A Novel CMOS Process Utilizing After-Gate Implantation Process," *Dig. of Tech. Papers, 1986 Symp. VLSI Tech.*, p. 41.

34. J. Pfiester et al., "A Self-aligned Elevated Source/Drain MOSFET," *IEEE Trans. Electron Dev.,* September 1990, p. 365.

35. J.O. Borland and R. Koelsch, "MeV implantation technology: Next generation manufacturing with current generation equipment," *Solid-State Technology*, December 1993, p. 28.

36. J.Y. Chen, *VLSI Design* July 1984, p. 78.

37. A.G. Lewis et al., "Device Isolation in High Density LOCOS-Isolated CMOS," *IEEE Trans. Electron Devices,* **ED-34**, p. 1337, June 1987.

PROBLEMS

1. An *n*-well n^+ polysilicon-gate CMOS process starts with a substrate doping of 3×10^{15}/cm^3. The well doping near the surface of is approximately constant to a level of 3×10^{16}/cm^3. The gate oxide thicknesses are both 40 nm, and $Q_{tot} = 3\times10^{10}$/cm^2.

(a) Calculate the threshold voltages of the *n*- and *p*-channel transistors.

(b) Calculate the boron doses needed to shift the NMOS threshold to +1V and the PMOS threshold to -1V. Assume that the threshold shifts are achieved through shallow ion implantations.

2. In a *p*-well CMOS technology, the *n*-substrate has a doping concentration of 1×10^{15}/cm^3, and a *p*-well concentration neat the surface of 5×10^{16}/cm^3. Calculate the source/drain junction capacitances (cm^{-2}) and body effect coefficients for both *n*- and *p*-channel MOSFETs assuming the gate oxide is 20 nm thick in both devices.

3. Describe the split well-drive process, and the advantages it offers compared to the conventional well-drive process.

4. Comparing retrograde well to conventional well, what is the most important difference in process technology and finished device structure? How does it affect device isolation?

5. In a (p^+-diffusion)-n-well-(p-on-$p+$ substrate)structure, the n-well is uniformly doped at 1×10^{16} cm^{-3} and is 1 μm deep, the p-epi thickness is 4 μm and is uniformly doped at 1×10^{15}/cm^3, and the p^+ diffusion is 0.4 μm deep. If a substrate bias generator is needed and the p^+ diffusion and n-well are both biased at 5V, what is the maximum (in absolute value) substrate voltage that can be applied before punchthrough occurs?

CHAPTER 9

HOT-CARRIER RESISTANT PROCESSING
AND DEVICE STRUCTURES

One of the more serious problems posed by the continued shrinking of MOSFETs into the submicron regime is the *hot-carrier effect*. If device dimensions are reduced and the supply voltage remains constant (or is not reduced as rapidly as the structures are scaled), the lateral electric field in the channel increases. This causes the inversion-layer charges to be accelerated (heated) to an extent that they can cause a number of harmful device phenomena (hot-carrier effects). Figure 9-1 depicts hot-carrier generation and the current components which result from such generation. The most important hot-carrier effect is the damage inflicted to the gate oxide and/or the Si-SiO$_2$ interface. This leads to a time-dependent degradation of various MOSFET characteristics, including threshold voltage (V_T), linear region transconductance (g_m), subthreshold slope (S_t), and

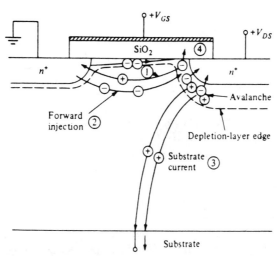

Fig. 9-1 Hot-carrier generation and current components. 1 Holes reaching the source. 2 Electron injection from the source. 3 Substrate hole current. 4 Electron injection into the oxide.

559

saturation current (I_{Dsat}). The lifetimes of conventional MOSFET structures when subject to such degradation may be reduced below acceptable limits (i.e., to less that 10 years of operation) in NMOS devices with channel lengths smaller than 1.5 μm, and in PMOS devices with submicron channel lengths. As a result, it has been necessary to develop techniques to combat this problem. The purpose of this chapter is to discuss hot-carrier effects in MOSFETs and the approaches developed to overcome them.

Techniques for Reducing Hot-Carrier Degradation. The degradation of device performance arising from hot-carrier effects can be suppressed by various methods. Most involve modifying the conventional MOSFET structure or strengthening the gate oxide and the Si-SiO$_2$ interface against hot-carrier damage. As an introduction to the material of this chapter, a list of the general categories of approaches to suppress hot-carrier degradation is presented here:

1. The common driving force of all hot-carrier phenomena is the channel electric field $\mathcal{E}_y$. Specifically, the greatest control over hot-electron effects is exerted by the *maximum channel electric field* $\mathcal{E}_{ymax}$, which occurs at the drain end of the channel. Thus, a key underlying goal in reducing hot-carrier degradation is to reduce the magnitude of $\mathcal{E}_{ymax}$. Toward this end, the factors that impact $\mathcal{E}_{ymax}$ in a MOSFET must be understood, and useful tools for gaining such understanding are models for $\mathcal{E}_{ymax}$. We thus begin the chapter by reviewing a simple model for $\mathcal{E}_{ymax}$ in non-graded-drain MOSFETs, and later we extend it to include graded-drain (i.e., LDD) MOSFETs.

2. One obvious way to decrease $\mathcal{E}_{ymax}$ is to reduce the voltages applied to the device (e.g., by lowering the power-supply voltage from 5V to 3.3V). The decision to implement such power supply reductions, however, is not in the hands of the device designer or process engineer.

3. The structure of the conventional MOSFET can be modified such that it is less sensitive to hot-carrier degradation. Such modifications attempt to reduce $\mathcal{E}_{ymax}$ as well as to separate the maximum current path in the channel from the maximum electric field location. This is accomplished by developing special drain field-reducing structures designed to accomplish these objectives. A discussion of the evolution of such structures constitutes the bulk of this chapter.

4. The resistance of the gate oxide and the Si-SiO$_2$ interface to hot-carrier degradation can be increased, thereby allowing a larger $\mathcal{E}_{ymax}$ to be applied. As an example, the density of trapping sites in the gate oxide can be reduced through the use of special processing techniques (which are described in section 9.14).

9.1 MODEL FOR THE MAXIMUM LATERAL ELECTRIC FIELD $\mathcal{E}_{ymax}$ IN NON-GRADED-DRAIN MOSFETS

The maximum lateral electric field in a MOSFET, $\mathcal{E}_{ymax}$, occurs near the drain. It has been determined that no significant hot-carrier effects occur at values of $\mathcal{E}_{ymax}$ smaller than 4×10^4 V/cm (i.e., the field value at which electrons are velocity saturated). Hence, when hot-carrier effects are being considered, it is only necessary to be concerned with the MOSFET being operated in saturation, and then only with the lateral electric fields in the velocity-saturated region (VSR) of the MOSFET. Note that the VSR was introduced in section 5.4.3 of chap. 5.

A rigorous calculation of the field near the drain is a complex procedure, requiring a numerical analysis of the two-dimensional Poisson equation. An example of the results of one such analysis which shows $\mathcal{E}_y$ within an NMOSFET as a function of channel length is shown in Fig. 9-2. Nevertheless, in chap. 5 we showed how a reasonably accurate analytical model of $\mathcal{E}_{ymax}$ in the VSR of non-LDD MOSFETs could be derived using the pseudo-2D approach to solving the Poisson equation in the MOSFET channel. This model gives good agreement with the values of $\mathcal{E}_{ymax}$ obtained from numerical analysis. According to this model the value of $\mathcal{E}_{ymax}$ is given by Eq. 5-70, which for the case when $(V_{DS} - V_{DSsat})/l >> \mathcal{E}_{sat}$ becomes [1,2,8]

$$\mathcal{E}_{ymax} = (V_{DS} - V_{DSsat}) / l \qquad\qquad (9-1)$$

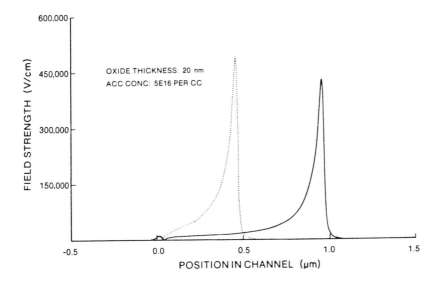

Fig. 9-2 $\mathcal{E}_y$ within an NMOSFET as a function of channel length for two devices with channel lengths of 1.0 μm and 0.5 μm, and the same value of $t_{OX} = 20$ nm.[146]

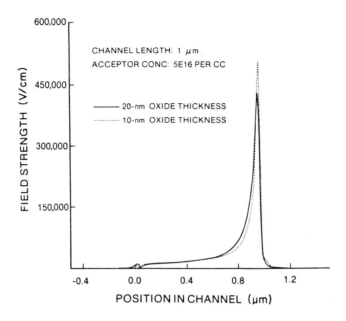

Fig. 9-3 ε_y within an NMOSFET as a function of channel length and gate oxide thickness for two devices with a channel length (1.0 μm) and two values of t_{ox}, 10 and 20 nm.[146]

where[9]

$$l \approx 0.22 \, t_{ox}^{1/3} \, r_j^{1/3} \qquad \text{for} \quad t_{ox} \geq 15 \text{ nm} \qquad (9\text{-}2a)$$

and

$$l \approx 1.7 \times 10^{-2} \, t_{ox}^{1/8} \, r_j^{1/3} L^{1/5} \quad \text{for} \quad t_{ox} < 15 \text{ nm, and } L < 0.5 \, \mu\text{m} \qquad (9\text{-}2b)$$

and t_{ox} is the gate oxide thickness and r_j approximately corresponds to the source/drain junction depth. As we calculated in section 5.4.3, when t_{ox} is ~15 nm and r_j ~0.35 μm, l ~ 0.15 μm. Equations 9-2a and 9-2b imply that l is independent of L until L becomes small enough that it approaches l. That is, for larger values of L than this, the channel length still has an influence on ε_{ymax}, but only through the V_{DSsat} term of Eq. 9-1, and this dependence is weaker than a linear one. A model for calculating V_{DSsat} was presented in chap. 5 (Eq. 5-37), which we also repeat here for convenience:[3]

$$V_{DSsat} = \frac{\varepsilon_{sat} L \, [V_{GS} - V_T]}{(V_{GS} - V_T) + \varepsilon_{sat} L} \qquad (9\text{-}3)$$

An example of the dependence of ε_y on t_{ox} as calculated using numerical analysis for an NMOSFET with $L = 1$ μm is shown in Fig. 9-3. Here we see that the device with a thicker t_{ox} has a smaller ε_{ymax}, as is also predicted by the model of Eqs. 9-1 and 9-2.

9.2 SUBSTRATE CURRENTS DUE TO HOT CARRIERS

While the time-dependent degradation of MOSFET device parameters is the hot-carrier effect that receives the most attention, another important one involves the substrate current I_{sub} generated by such hot carriers. Since I_{sub} can be correlated to long-term device degradation, it can be used to predict the device lifetime. However, I_{sub} can also adversely impact MOSFET operation in other ways as well. Hence, it is useful to examine the phenomenon of I_{sub} prior to the discussion on how to characterize hot-carrier degradation.

If electrons in the channel of a MOSFET acquire more than about 1.5 eV of energy, impact ionization can result upon their collision with the lattice. Electron-hole pairs are generated from such collisions, with the total number being exponentially dependent on the reciprocal of the electric field, $-1/\mathcal{E}_{ymax}$. The electrons produced in this manner are either attracted to the drain (adding to the drain current) or if possessing sufficient energy, they may be injected into the oxide. The generated holes, on the other hand, enter the substrate and constitute a parasitic substrate current I_{sub} (Process 3 in Fig. 9-1). Such substrate current differs from the current which arises in *pn*-junction avalanche breakdown in that its magnitude is much smaller than the drain current. I_{sub} is thus classified as a *low-level-avalanche multiplication effect*. Nevertheless, I_{sub} can itself produce several problems, and thus must be kept below some maximum tolerable value. The problems which can be directly caused by I_{sub} include the following:

1. If some of the holes that should constitute I_{sub} are instead collected by the source (i.e., instead of by the body contact), and this collected hole current causes a voltage drop in the substrate material on the order of 0.6V, the substrate-source *pn* junction will begin to conduct significantly. Electrons will then be injected from the source to the substrate, just like electrons injected from emitter to base of an *npn* transistor (the forward injection shown in Fig. 9-1). These extra injected electrons can, in turn, gain sufficient energy as they travel toward the drain to cause additional impact ionization and create new electron-hole pairs. A positive-feedback mechanism thus exists, one that can sustain itself if the drain voltage exceeds a certain value. This is observed externally as a form of breakdown, referred to as a *snapback breakdown*. A particularly clear explanation of this effect, including the reason for the negative-resistance, or "snapback," portion of the curves, is given in reference 4.

2. Excessive I_{sub} may induce latchup in CMOS circuits.

3. As some of the holes are accelerated during their passage out of the drain-substrate depletion region, they may acquire enough energy to cause secondary impact ionization far from the drain region. Some the electrons generated in this manner may escape the drain field and, instead of being collected by the drain, may then travel to other nodes on the chip to be collected. This may lead to a reduction of the storage time of dynamic circuit nodes in DRAMs (i.e., manifested as a degradation of the refresh time).[5] This excess electron current is reported to be around 10^{-4} times smaller than the substrate ionization impact current itself.

4. If a substrate bias-generator circuit is included on-chip, its output becomes less negative as I_{sub} is increased.

As noted earlier, I_{sub} can also be used as a monitor to correlate device degradation with predicted device lifetime. The reason that I_{sub} is chosen for this purpose is that both device degradation and I_{sub} are driven by a common driving force, namely the lateral electric field in the channel of the MOSFET. The magnitude of I_{sub} depends exponentially on the maximum value of this field $\mathcal{E}_{ymax}$.

An example of how I_{sub} is experimentally observed to depend on decreasing channel length is seen in Fig. 9-4.[6] This figure shows the maximum I_{sub} generated at a voltage of 5V versus the effective channel length for MOS transistors processed with the same technology (i.e., t_{ox} and r_j have identical values in all of the devices). Since I_{sub} also increases with $\mathcal{E}_{ymax}$, according to the model of Eqs. 9-1 and 9-2, the magnitude of I_{sub} would grow even more rapidly with shrinking L_{eff} if the oxide thickness and junction depth were scaled together with the channel length.

Two common methods are used to display the empirical data when I_{sub} in a MOSFET is being characterized through measurement methods. In the first (shown in Fig. 9-5), I_{sub} is plotted against the gate voltage V_{GS}, with V_{DS} as the parameter. The initial increase in I_{sub} with increasing V_{GS} observed in such plots is due to the rise in the population of electrons in the channel as V_{GS} is first increased. (We also recall that I_D increases as V_{GS} is made larger). Since this raises the number of electrons that can be heated, it implies that there are a larger number of electrons capable of participating in impact ionization. Eventually, however, when V_{GS} approaches V_{DS}, the lateral electric field begins to decrease. From that point on, I_{sub} decreases even as V_{GS}

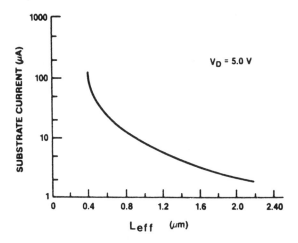

Fig. 9-4 The maximum substrate current due to impact ionization produced at a drain voltage of 5V vs. L_{eff} for MOSFETs with t_{ox} = 250Å.[6]

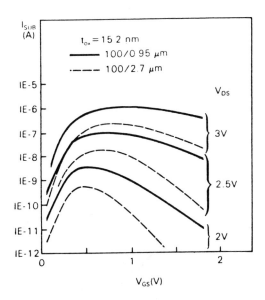

Fig. 9-5 Substrate current characterized as a function of V_{GS} with V_{DS} as a parameter.[7] (© IEEE 1984).

continues to rise.   In the second approach used to display I_{sub} data, we plot $(\ln I_{sub})$ versus $1/V_{DS}$, with the gate voltage as the parameter (as shown in Fig. 9-6). In this type of plot I_{sub} values are typically observed to follow a series of straight lines.

While both types of plots are useful for depicting the empirical behavior of I_{sub}, the resulting experimentally generated curves fail to reveal a simple relationship between I_{sub} and V_{GS}, V_{DS} and device parameters such as t_{ox}, r_j, and L. However, a rudimentary analytical model that allows I_{sub} to be calculated based on the these terminal voltages and device parameters was derived by Chan et al., as follows:[7]

$$I_{sub} = 1.2 \, (V_{DS} - V_{DSsat}) \, I_D \exp \, (-1.7 \times 10^6 / \mathcal{E}_{ymax}) \qquad (9 - 4)$$

$$= 1.2 \, (V_{DS} - V_{DSsat}) \, I_D \exp \, (-3.7 \times 10^5 \, t_{ox}^{1/3} \, r_j^{1/3} / \, (V_{DS} - V_{DSsat}) \qquad (9 - 5)$$

By plotting Eq. 9-5 (in terms of log I_{sub} versus V_{GS}, with V_{DS} as the parameter) a set of curves shown as the dashed lines in Fig. 9-7 is obtained. If the measured values of (log I_{sub}) are also plotted on the same figure (as is done in Fig. 9-7 using solid lines), good agreement between the model and the experimental data is observed. We also note that the I_{sub}-V_{GS} curves exhibit a bell-shape, with their maximum values occurring at low gate voltages. This shape results because, as noted earlier, $\mathcal{E}_{ymax}$ decreases as V_{GS} increases, but I_D increases monotonically. Thus, I_{sub} peaks where a

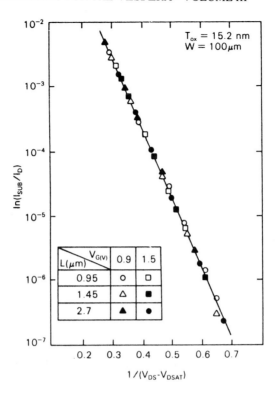

Fig. 9-6 Substrate current characterized as a function of $1/V_{DS}$ with V_{GS} as a parameter.[7] (© IEEE 1984).

significant number of carriers are available, but ε_{ymax} has not yet been significantly reduced. These circumstances exist when $V_{GS} \approx 0.4 V_{DS}$. The whole I_{sub} curves shift upward or downward depending on the drain bias.*

9.3 MODELS OF HOT-CARRIER DEGRADATION PHENOMENA

Generally speaking, a negative charge builds up in the gate oxide and/or at the Si-SiO$_2$ interface of MOSFETs as a result of hot-carrier injection from the silicon into the oxide. This charge contributes to the total oxide charge term Q_{tot} in the expression for the device threshold voltage (see chap. 3, Eq. 3-72). Furthermore, in NMOSFETs this charge continues to accumulate with time under conditions of operation that produce

---

* Note that Eq. 9-5 has been verified for MOSFETs with uniform channel doping. In order to be able to treat the complex channel and drain doping profiles found in short-channel MOSFETs (e.g., the doping profile of an LDD), some extracted parameters need to be added. Specifically, the bias and size dependencies of ε_{sat} of Eq. 9-3 need to be taken into account.

hot-carrier stress. Due to the polarity of the trapped charge, the resulting V_T shift in n-channel devices is positive, which in turn causes both the drain current I_D and the transconductance g_m to be reduced. Reduced current, of course, will lead to reduction of circuit speed. Threshold voltage drift will cause the inverter transfer characteristics and linear circuit offset to drift. The concern is that such hot-carrier stressing may eventually cause a circuit to fail the speed specification or to experience racing conditions (or to otherwise become unacceptable).

Figure 9-8 shows typical I_D-V_{DS} characteristics of an NMOSFET before and after stressing. Notice that the decrease in I_D is larger if the source and drain are reversed after stressing. As we will describe in further detail in the next section, this indicates that the hot-carrier-induced negative charges are located near the drain (see Fig. 9-9a).

It is not clear exactly what sort of mechanism is responsible for such charge buildup, but most agree that it is caused either by interface trap generation[10] or by oxide trapped charge.[11] However, mounting evidence points to interface trap generation as the main degradation mechanism of NMOSFETs having normal quality oxides, operated at room temperature, and stressed under the V_{GS} condition that causes the largest I_{sub}.[17]

Some hypotheses blame hot electrons, others hot holes, and still others the combined effect of hot electrons and hot holes for the generation of such interface traps. However, hot holes alone have been effectively discounted as the culprits because it is observed that if I_{sub} is kept fixed (which implies that the hot-hole generation rate is not changing) and the degradation is monitored as a function of V_{GD}, degradation increases

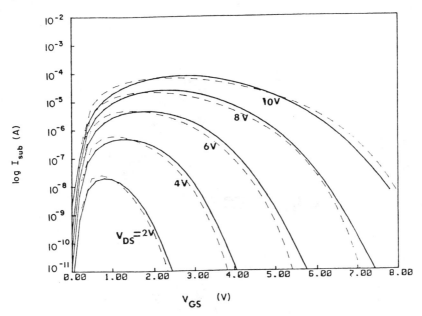

Fig. 9-7 Example of the calculated values of I_{sub} (dashed lines) using (Eq. 9-5) compared to the measured values of I_{sub}, depicted by the solid lines.[147]

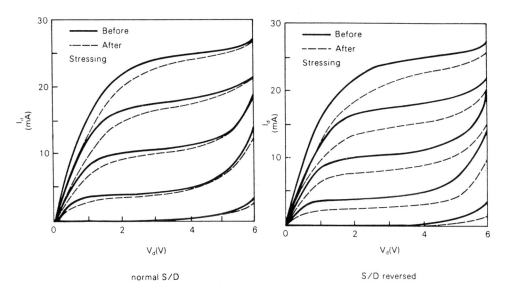

Fig. 9-8 Typical I_D-V_{DS} characteristics of an NMOSFET before and after hot-carrier stressing.[148] (© IEEE 1984).

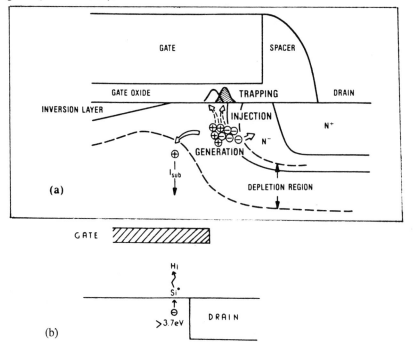

Fig. 9-9 (a) Illustration of hot-carrier effects, including hot-carrier generation, injection, and trapping.[92] (© 1988 IEEE) (b) Physical model for interface trap generation.[17] (© IEEE 1985).

monotonically with increasing V_{GD}. Increasing V_{GD} tends to attract electrons to the gate and to repel holes. This implies that hot-electron injection is at least partially responsible for the degradation.

9.3.1. Si-H Bond Breaking Model

One of the simplest microscopic degradation models is based on the assumption that damage arises from the creation of interface states. They are proposed to be generated as follows:[18] If $V_{GS}<V_{DS}$ in NMOSFETs, hot-electrons bombard the Si-SiO$_2$ interface against a field that tries to repel them. However, if the electrons possess sufficient energy to overcome the barrier of the Si-SiO$_2$ interface and the repelling field, they can break chemical bonds at the interface (Fig. 9-9b). Most likely the bonds that are broken are Si-H bonds. (The breaking of Si-H bonds by energetic electrons is a mechanism that has been confirmed by experiment.[12]) Such Si-H bonds at the interface can be formed during process steps such as BPSG reflow in steam, CVD of Si$_3$N$_4$, or the final post-metal anneal in H$_2$ or forming gas. The strength of Si-H bonds is about 0.3 eV. Hence, the barrier energy that would have to be overcome to break the bond would be the sum of the Si-SiO$_2$ energy barrier (~3.2 eV) plus this bond strength (0.3 eV) and the retarding potential difference between the current path and the interface (assuming $V_{GS}<V_{DS}$). Thus, a hot electron would have to possess ~4.0 eV of kinetic energy to cause such bond breaking and to create an interface trap. The resultant trivalent Si atom at the Si-SiO$_2$ interface becomes an electron trap. That is, if the bond created by separating the H atom from the Si atom is filled by trapping an electron (as opposed to when it was filled by the H atom), the site has a net negative charge. Such broken bonds accumulate with time, and their filling with electrons would account for the buildup of negative charge at the Si-SiO$_2$ interface under hot-carrier stressing. It should be noted that while this microscopic model is intuitively satisfying, its authors admit that there is no direct proof of its correctness.

9.3.2 Hot-Hole and Hot-Electron Trapping Model

Another microscopic model of interface trap generation proposes that both hot holes and hot electrons play a role in causing the device degradation.[13] That is, neutral trapping centers at a density N_t^0 are postulated to exist in the 'fresh' SiO$_2$ film (i.e., not yet having been subjected to hot-carrier injection). These sites are thought to exist within a distance of about 10 nm from the interface. Such neutral centers are initially able to trap only holes (i.e., but not any electrons) that are injected into the oxide. Such hole trapping converts them from neutral to positively charged sites. The density of positive charge centers initially grows during hot-carrier stressing, with their density at any time given by N_t^+. Due to their positive charge, these sites are attractive to electrons, and are also capable to trapping one of them. The latter electron trapping events give rise to two further effects. First, the charge of the trapping site is returned to neutral, with the symbol of the density of such centers being written as N_{the}^0. Second, an interface state is produced (by a mechanism that is still not understood) that becomes charged to a negative state during the transconductance measurement. Their density is denoted by N_{it}^-.

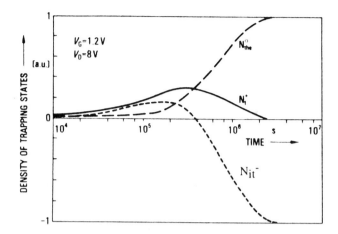

Fig. 9-10 The evolution (as a function of hot-carrier stressing time), of the densities of the different trapping states N_t^0, N_t^+, N_{the}^0, and N_{it}^-. (© IEEE 1984).[13]

Such negatively charged interface states are deemed to be responsible for the negative effective charge that builds up at the Si-SiO$_2$ interface as a result of the hot-carrier stressing. Eventually all of the original neutral sites (N_t^0) become converted to neutral sites (N_{the}^0) and corresponding interface states (N_{it}^-). The evolution of the densities of these respective charge centers (as a function of hot-carrier stressing time), is shown in Fig. 9-10.

Despite the fact that the degradation mechanisms in either model cannot be directly observed, the amount of degradation (both of V_T and g_m) is observed to follow the bias dependence of substrate current (see Fig. 9-11). Hence, it has been postulated that by monitoring I_{sub} we are, in effect, also monitoring the degradation in an actual device.

This becomes the rationale for using I_{sub} as a universal monitor of hot-carrier stressing in NMOSFETs, as will be described in the next section. However, others point out that attempting to infer the degree of degradation of two different devices by measuring the bias voltages at which the same I_{sub} values are produced may not be valid. This is because knowing the magnitude of I_{sub} does not provide any information as to how far beneath the Si-SiO$_2$ interface are the impact-ionization-generated carriers created. That is, if the carriers which constitute I_{sub} are being created deep within the substrate, not much damage should occur in the device (because the I_D current path, which is populated by the hot carriers that cause impact ionization, is too far from the surface to permit many of these hot carriers to be injected into the oxide). Conversely, for the same value of I_{sub} arising from impact-ionization near the interface, much more degradation would be expected. Furthermore, it is observed that different bias conditions can cause different degrees of degradation, even at the same value of I_{sub}. Perhaps this is due to the fact that the measured value of I_{sub} incorporates hot carriers of *all* energies, but only a small fraction of these may have sufficient energy to be injected into the oxide and cause degradation. Furthermore, the degradation is known to be localized along a small region of the device channel (as will be discussed in the upcoming section). Hence, this damage must be caused by injection only in that region. This local component of injected current is not necessarily related to the average value of I_{sub} in a simple manner.

One final aspect of using I_{sub} to compare degradation in different MOSFETs should also be mentioned. That is, hot-carrier degradation is smaller in MOSFETs with thinner oxides, when compared to devices having the same channel length but a thicker oxide, if both are stressed to exhibit the same value of I_{sub}.[14] It is speculated that this happens because the gate electric field is stronger in the devices with the thinner oxides, which causes the electrons injected against this field to be repelled more strongly. Thus, fewer hot electrons with sufficient energy arrive to cause degradation. On the other hand, the devices with thinner t_{ox} exhibit larger I_{sub} for the same stressing conditions. As a result, the maximum power-supply voltage that can be applied to avoid hot-carrier degradation is essentially independent of t_{ox} as L is decreased (see Fig. 9-12).[15] Nevertheless, this is another example that using I_{sub} as a comparator of damage in devices with differing structures may not be valid.

9.3.3 Location of the Hot-Carrier Damaged Region

The location of the damaged region due to hot-carrier stress is found to be above or adjacent to the drain of the device. The lifetime of devices is impacted by the spatial non-uniformity of this damage in that a device which focuses the hot carriers in a small area behaves differently than one that spreads them over a wide area. The extent of the damaged region is a function of device geometry, of the duration and conditions of stress, and of spatial distribution of oxide and interfacial defects.

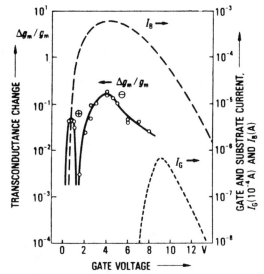

Fig. 9-11 The dependence of I_{sub}, and g_m on V_{GS} for a given value of V_{DS}. Note that both exhibit the same dependence on V_{GS}.[13,149] (© IEEE 1984).

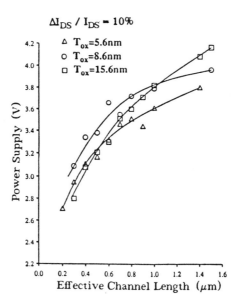

Fig. 9-12 Voltage required to insure 10 years of device lifetime for t_{ox} = 56Å, 86Å, and 156Å.[15] (© IEEE 1988).

Several reports indicate that damage occurs initially at the lateral position of $\mathcal{E}_{ymax}$. The damaged region grows toward the drain, and also at a slower rate toward the source. In very short channel devices the damaged region can grow to a significant fraction of the channel length.[16] However, it has also been reported that the length of the damaged region is independent of channel length; i.e., it appears to have the same length in devices with L_{eff} from 0.95 μm down to 0.15 μm. Thus, the damaged region becomes a larger fraction of the channel length as the devices shrink. This causes the percent degradation in I_D to increase more rapidly as L_{eff} is made smaller for the same stressing time and the same value of I_{sub} (Fig. 9-13).[42]

9.4 CHARACTERIZING MOSFET DEGRADATION DUE TO HOT-CARRIER EFFECTS

As we have been discussing, channel hot carriers in a MOSFET can cause device degradation. Earlier we described models for the driving force that produces such hot carriers ($\mathcal{E}_{ymax}$), as well as microscopic models for the mechanisms believed to be responsible for the damage that they cause. In this section we discuss how to characterize hot-carrier device degradation in a quantitative manner. That is, we identify the device parameters that are degraded, and examine how such damage is measured. Then we indicate how to determine if a device can be operated for a suitably long lifetime without exhibiting excessive hot-carrier degradation. This entails designing stress tests to verify the device reliability, as well as the issue of accelerated stress testing. In this discussion we also consider the effects of dc versus ac stressing, and the effects of device degradation on circuit behavior. That is, the reduction in a *device* parameter due to hot-carrier stressing may in fact result in a smaller percentage degradation in a corresponding *circuit* parameter. For example, a 10% reduction in I_D may cause the circuit switching speed to drop by only 1%. If this is not taken into account, the device may end up being "overdesigned" in an attempt to mitigate what appears to be excessive hot-carrier *device* degradation. The price for such unnecessary protection may entail increased process complexity and/or the sacrifice in performance of some other device parameter (for example, current drive capability), through the introduction of a more complex drain structure (e.g., an LDD). This issue has been addressed in reliability simulators (e.g., CAS), which we will also describe in this section.

9.4.1 Device Parameters that are Impacted by Hot-Carrier Damage

We have indicated previously that hot-carrier damage can degrade the I_D-V_{DS} characteristics of a MOSFET during long-term operation under normal operating conditions, or during a stress test (see Fig. 9-8). At least four device parameters contribute to such degradation, namely: shift in threshold voltage ΔV_T; reduction in

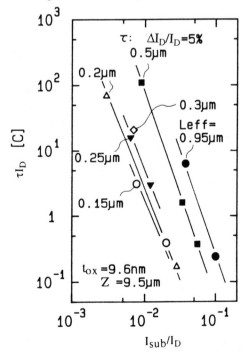

Fig. 9-13 Lifetime plot, τI_D versus I_{sub}/I_D. τ is defined as the time when $\Delta I_D/I_D$ reaches 5% at V_{GS} - V_T = 1.5V.[42] (© IEEE 1990).

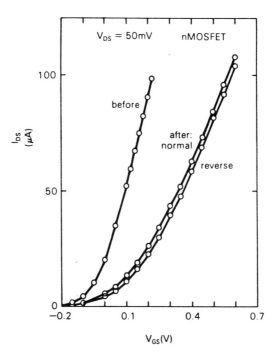

Fig. 9-14 I_D vs V_{GS} characteristics before and after hot-carrier stressing.[19] (© IEEE 1985.)

drain current ΔI_D; reduction in the linear transconductance Δg_m; and shift in subthreshold swing ΔS_t. Figure 9-14 shows an example of the changes in V_T and g_m after severe stressing.[19] The device under test in this example is 100 μm wide, with a 2 μm-wide gate length. Note that V_T here is defined as the gate voltage at which an I_D of 0.1 μA/μm occurs with V_{DS} = 50 mV. Thus, V_T in this figure is the gate voltage at I_D = 10 μA. The value of g_m is the linear slope of the curves in this figure. Note that the linear transconductance or drain current is usually measured since hot-carrier damage will lead to a larger change in g_m in the linear- rather than the saturation-region of operation.

9.4.2 How to Determine if a MOSFET Can be Operated Under Normal Operating Conditions without Exhibiting Failure due to Hot-Carrier Degradation?

We now consider the problem of how to determine if a MOSFET can be operated under normal conditions without exhibiting failure due to hot-carrier damage. To do this, we must first decide what actually constitutes device failure, and then choose an appropriate device failure criterion. Second, we must identify a monitor (e.g., I_{sub}) that is correlated to the stress mechanisms responsible for causing the failure-inducing damage. By tracking the monitor level during the test, the degree of stress applied to the device at any time can be determined. Third, the bias conditions of the stress test at the power-supply voltage of normal operation (e.g., 5.5V, which is 5.0V nominal plus 10% margin) must be chosen. Most commonly, the combination of V_{GS} and V_{DS} that yields the maximum value of the monitor signal (e.g., maximum I_{sub} value, corresponding to $V_{GS} \approx 0.45V_{DS}$) is used, as this represents the worst-case stress conditions that the device will experience under normal operating conditions.[*] The device can then be operated under such bias conditions, with I_{sub} being continuously monitored. Periodically the test can be interrupted to measure the device parameter selected as the indicator of failure (e.g., ΔV_T or Δg_m). The stressing continues until the failure criterion is reached, with the time to reach such failure being the hot-carrier device lifetime τ. That is, τ is defined as the stress time at which the change in the device parameter value being monitored reaches the chosen failure criterion.

9.4.2.1 Selecting a Criterion that Identifies Device Failure Due to Hot-Carrier Damage.
The first step in determining the hot-carrier reliability of a MOSFET is to select an appropriate criterion indicating that a device has "failed." Most such criteria are based on a specific degree of change in one of the four device parameters listed above. Quite a number of such criteria have been used, apparently somewhat arbitrarily. The ranges of change that have been picked to signal device failure are: shifts in V_T of 10 to 100 mV, and percent changes in I_D or linear g_m of between 3% and 10%.[20] In Fig. 9-15 we note that in non-LDD MOSFETs the shift in V_T is linearly related to the percentage change in g_m, with, for example, a 10 mV shift in V_T corresponding to a 3% change in g_m (with the degradations being caused by conditions of maximum I_{sub} for several V_{DS} values).[17]

While the value of the change in device parameter selected to indicate failure has often been selected somewhat arbitrarily, Ning et al.[21] who performed some of the earliest work on the lifetime of MOSFETs under hot-carrier stressing selected the value in a more logical manner. They described a process with a minimum gate length of 1.3 μm $\pm$ 0.3 μm. They reasoned that the shortest allowable gate length of 1.0 μm would exhibit the worst case hot-carrier degradation, but would also have the highest "fresh" (pre-stressed) value of g_m. They argued that such short devices could afford to relinquish some of their initial g_m advantage to hot-carrier degradation, and still perform as well as the nominal length (1.3 μm) devices. Thus, the device failure criterion was

---

[*] Note that not everyone agrees that selecting bias conditions which correspond to the worst-case value of the stress-signal monitor is an appropriate way to design a hot-carrier stress test for a device. That is, if device operation under normal conditions does not expose the device to such high levels of stress monitor signal, the test overstresses the device, and a pessimistic value of its lifetime compared to normal operating conditions will be obtained. This may again make it appear that hot-carrier protection structures need to be incorporated in a device design, when this may not be the case. On the other hand, if the stress time is derated to a time which more realistically mirrors the actual stress that a device will experience during normal operation, the test will reveal a more accurate estimate of the hot-carrier reliability of the device. As we will see, such considerations exist in the hot-carrier reliability simulators that are currently available.

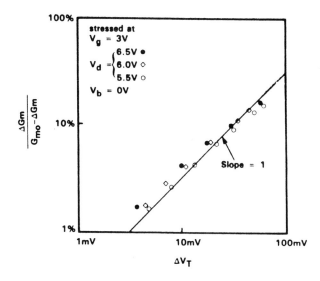

Fig. 9-15 The linear relationship between ΔV_T and Δg_m in non-LDD MOSFETs.[17] (© IEEE 1985).

chosen by Ning as follows: The 1.0 μm devices would be stressed until they lost 30% of their initial transconductance, at which point it would be deemed that they had failed. The time to failure would be the device hot-carrier degradation lifetime. In addition, Ning et al. recognized that the device would not face a continuous dc stress during normal operating circuit conditions. Thus, they estimated a duty cycle of 3% (the fraction of time in which the MOSFET is "ON" in their particular circuit application). This would allow a 10 year (10^5 hr) circuit operation requirement to be assessed by a continuous dc stress in only 3000 hours (~4 months).

9.4.3 Accelerated Testing of Hot-Carrier Device Lifetime

Devices are often designed with the goal of reliable operation (under normal operating conditions) of at least ten years (10^5 hours ~ 3.6×10^8 sec). That is, devices should be able to operate for ten years without exceeding the chosen hot-carrier failure criterion. However, having to wait for ten years to verify the reliability of a device is obviously not practical. Instead, it is necessary to establish some ways to accelerate the stress test to obtain accurate estimates of time-to-failure τ in less time. One way, as mentioned above, is to carry out a dc stress test and then extrapolate the results to normal (i.e., ac) operation. This can reduce the test time by an order of magnitude (or more).

Another means of accelerating the failure time is to increase the stress level. This can be done by increasing V_{DS} beyond the normal power-supply voltage and adjusting the V_{GS} value until a maximum I_{sub} is produced (to $V_{GS} \approx 0.45V_{DS}$). I_{sub} in this case will be higher than that observed under the supply voltage value, leading to shorter times to device failure. Since it has been observed that τ and I_{sub} are related by a power-law function, by measuring τ at several higher values of V_{DS}, one can extrapolate from these high-stress lifetimes a value of τ at the lower power-supply voltage value.

The general relationship that has been observed to exist between τ and I_{sub} is*

$$\tau = B \, Z \, (I_{sub})^{-m}/(I_D)^{m-1} \qquad (9-6)$$

Since I_D is proportional to Z, but does not vary much otherwise, a simpler, approximate form of Eq. 9-6 that appears to give good agreement with experimental results for devices smaller than ~1.0 μm is[22]

$$\tau \approx B \, (I_{sub}/Z)^{-m} \qquad (9-7)$$

where Z is the device width. As a result, when characterizing device lifetime using accelerated stress testing, the relationship between the measured values of τ and I_{sub}/Z is often graphed (for several values of V_{DS}) on a log-log plot (as shown in Fig. 9-16). It should be noted that while the value of m in Eqs. 9-6 and 9-7 is roughly independent of technology (and typically is found to be around 3), B appears to vary quite widely. This variation in B is due to a number of factors, such as hydrogen concentration, mechanical stress, and drain-gate overlap. Nevertheless, it is generally advisable to empirically determine the values of both m and B for each device structure by constructing a plot such as the one shown in Fig. 9-16 and extracting the particular values from it. As illustrated in Fig. 9-16 such a plot yields straight lines with a slope of -3, which appears to support the validity of Eq. 9-7.[23] In any case, one can extrapolate the lifetime that would be exhibited by a device operated at the normal power-supply voltage from such a plot.**

Expressions that provide a reasonable fit to experimental data and hence yield useful first order estimates of τ in non-LDD MOSFETs are given as follows:[17]

$$\tau \approx 10^6 \, [I_{sub}/Z]^{-3} \qquad (9-8a)$$

$$\approx 3 \, (I_{sub}/I_D)^{-3} \qquad (9-8b)$$

Another method for plotting data in a form that is suitable for extrapolating τ at normal operating voltages from τ measured at higher V_{DS} stress voltages is to plot log τ versus $(1/V_{DS})$, with V_{GS} chosen to produce maximum I_{sub} for each particular value of V_{DS}.

---

* It appears that the more general relationship given by Eq. 9-6 must be used to accurately extrapolate τ in larger devices operated at higher power-supply voltages (such as MOSFETs designed for use in analog circuits or non-volatile memory applications). Since, Eq. 9-6 gives accurate results for the case of both large devices operated at high V_{DS} values and short-channel devices, it is used in the circuit hot-carrier device degradation simulator SCALE instead of Eq. 9-7 to calculate τ.

** Note that Eq. 9-6 can also be graphed on a log-log plot, and this often done in the literature by first converting Eq. 9-6 to the form $\tau I_D \propto (I_{sub}/I_D)^{-m}$ and then plotting τI_D versus I_{sub}/I_D on such a plot.

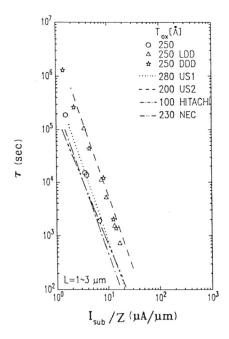

Fig. 9-16 Device lifetime τ versus I_{sub} /Z for various technologies.[23] (© IEEE 1987).

Since according to Eq. 9-5, ln I_{sub} is approximately linearly dependent on (1/V_{DS}), this plot should also yield straight lines. As shown in Fig. 9-17, this appears to be the case.[24] This approach is also a somewhat more straightforward way to visualize how τ depends on V_{DS}.

Despite the fact that the relationship given by Eq. 9-6 appears to permit the lifetime of a particular device structure to be accurately extrapolated from accelerated stress test data, this does not mean that we can create a universal curve of τ versus I_{sub} for all devices. Instead, when comparing τ of two or more device structures, it is customary to graph either the change in the selected device parameter (e.g., percentage change in I_D) versus stress time for each device on the same plot (Fig. 9-18), or τ versus (1/V_{DS}) for each device on the same plot (Fig. 9-19). Such plots permit us to compare the susceptibility of different device structures to hot-carrier degradation.

Note that the hot-carrier degradation of NMOSFETs by the I_{sub} model of Eqs. 9-6 and 9-7 assumes that the device is stressed at the condition of maximum I_{sub} (i.e., V_{GS} ≈ 0.45V_{DS}). Since devices may not be subjected to such gate voltages during normal operation, a model for degradation for all gate voltages would be useful to characterize device degradation under conditions of other than maximum I_{sub}. Such a model has been reported by Woltjer and Paulzen in 1992.[25] They develop a model which predicts

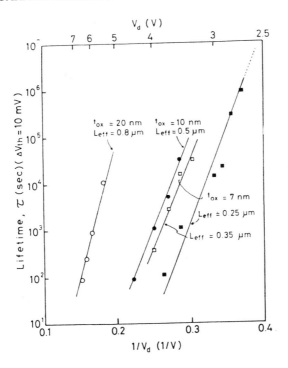

Fig. 9-17 Log τ versus $1/V_{DS}$ plot is an alternative way of plotting lifetime data to enable lifetime to be extrapolated.[24] (© IEEE 1983).

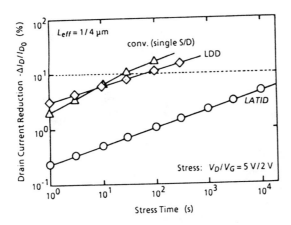

Fig. 9-18 Stress time dependence of hot-carrier-induced I_D degradation measured at V_{GS}/V_{DS} = 3V/3V (S/D reversed after stress) for the 1/4 μm LATID, conventional, and LDD devices.[117] (© IEEE 1989).

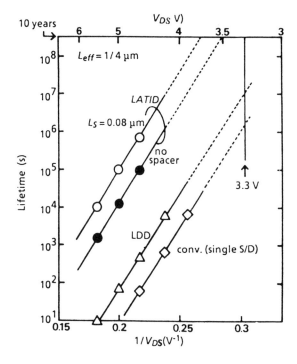

Fig. 9-19 Device lifetime reaching 10% I_D degradation (the more severe 10% Δg_{max} degradation for single S/D) versus the $1/V_{DS}$ for the 1/4 μm LATID, conventional, and LDD devices.[117] (© IEEE 1989).

the generation of interface states at all V_{GS} values for a given value of V_{DS}, and they select a maximum value of the generated interface states as the failure criterion, instead of ΔV_T, ΔI_D, etc.

9.4.4 Hot-Carrier Lifetime Under AC Stressing

Although most hot-carrier reliability stress testing is carried out under dc stress conditions, MOSFETs in an actual circuit are generally stressed in a dynamic (ac) manner. It is therefore important to understand device degradation under dynamic stressing. Modeling and characterization on simple circuits such as inverters, source followers, and transmission gates has been performed.[26] It was found that fast switching of an inverter's input voltage raises V_{GS} above V_T when the output voltage is still high. This corresponds to the condition of high substrate current generation because the driver transistor is biased at $V_{GS} > V_T$ and V_{DS} across the device is also high. Pulsed measurements made on an inverter chain has provided the following simple correlation between static and dynamic lifetime:

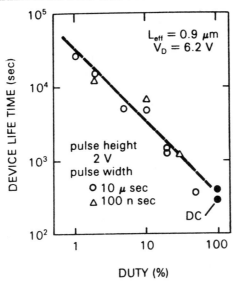

Fig. 9-20 Lifetime versus duty cycle measured after dynamic (ac) hot-carrier stressing.[150] (© IEEE 1986).

$$\tau_{dynamic} \;=\; \tau_{dc\ stress}\ /(duty\ cycle) \qquad\qquad (9\text{-}9)$$

The experimental confirmation of this relationship is shown in Fig. 9-20. If Eq. 9-9 is valid, this allows extrapolation of dc-stress device lifetime to the actual device lifetime under ac stress. Extrapolating $\tau_{dynamic}$ by use of a linear relationship is referred to as the quasi-static model of device lifetime.

Many initial reports claimed that enhanced degradation for ac stress was due to transient effects during the falling gate-voltage edges.[27-32] These effects have more recently been attributed to measurement difficulties, and thus it has been concluded that the quasi-static model given by Eq. 9-9 is valid for real digital circuits.[33, 34]

9.4.5 Effect of Device Degradation on Circuit Performance

There are two major components which determine the circuit level performance degradation. They are the amount of stress-induced degradation of the device and the sensitivity of circuit performance to the degradation of the individual devices. In a circuit environment, knowing the former is insufficient.[35] For example, a heavily degraded device may not cause significant circuit degradation if the circuit is insensitive to the effects of the degraded parameter. Conversely, a mildly stressed device may cause severe performance degradation due to circuit sensitivity. Traditionally, however, emphasis has been placed on estimating the stress and degradation sustained by individual devices. A test structure that permits hot-carrier degradation in CMOS circuits is described in ref. 36. More recently, several circuit level hot carrier simulators have been introduced, and these will be discussed next.

9.4.6 Hot-Carrier Reliability Simulation

9.4.6.1 SCALE.

SCALE (Substrate Current and Lifetime Evaluator) calculates device degradation due to transient voltages (ac stress), which allows the degradation of individual devices in a circuit environment (i.e., where they are subjected to ac stress) to be simulated.[37] SCALE is linked to SPICE externally in a pre- and post-processor fashion so that it functions as an independent simulator. But by using SCALE and SPICE together as a simulator system, the circuit designer can easily identify those devices within the circuit most susceptible to adverse hot-electron degradation effects. Appropriate measures can then be taken to enhance the hot-carrier reliability of these devices.

SCALE carries out the simulation based on a quasi-static approach in the following way: m and B of Eqs. 9-6 and 9-7 are first supplied by the user. SCALE then calculates the lifetime τ under dc-stress that would cause the failure criterion to be met under normal operating bias voltages, using Eq. 9-5 to model I_{sub},[*] and Eq. 9-6 to model τ. (We will hereafter denote the failure criterion in symbolic form as the change in the parameter subscripted with the letter f, e.g., $[\Delta I_D/I_{Do}]_f$.) Next, the pre-processor takes the input deck and requests SPICE to calculate the transient voltages at the drain, source, gate, and substrate of all user-selected devices in the circuit. That is, it determines these voltages for each time interval of the period of the SPICE analysis (namely, the time of one switching cycle). With this information, and Eq. 9-5, the value of I_{sub} during each of these time intervals can be determined. Since the value of I_{sub} is known, the fraction of the total degradation of $[\Delta I_D/I_{Do}]_f$ during each of these time intervals can be calculated. By summing the fractional values of $[\Delta I_D/I_{Do}]_f$ for each time interval over one switching cycle the fractional degradation occurring during a single switching cycle is found. Finally, the lifetime due to ac stress for each device in the circuit can be computed by finding the time needed to reach $[\Delta I_D/I_{Do}]_f$. This time corresponds to the time per cycle multiplied by the number of cycles that must elapse to cause $[\Delta I_D/I_{Do}]_f$. As an example, in Fig. 9-21, a significant I_{sub} value is seen to occur only during the time interval around the 21.3 ns time of the switching cycle, as only then is V_{GS} within the range of $0.25V_{DS}$ to $0.5V_{DS}$ when V_{DS} is high. Thus, only during that fraction of the switching cycle is the device being subjected to hot-carrier stress sufficient to cause hot-carrier damage.

The system structure of SCALE is depicted in Fig. 9-22, where we see that SCALE is connected to SPICE in pre- and post-processor configurations. The pre-processor takes the input deck and BSIM parameters and requests a SPICE run to obtain the transient voltage waveforms at the drain, gate, source, and substrate of the user-selected device. The post-processor then calculates the transient substrate current using Eq. 9-5 and the transient drain voltages computed by SPICE. The value of I_D also needed in Eq. 9-5 is calculated by using the BSIM model for I_D.

---

[*] Note that Eq. 9-5 has been verified for MOSFETs with uniform channel doping. In order to be able to treat the complex channel and drain (e.g., LDD) doping profiles found in short-channel MOSFETs, some extracted parameters have been introduced.

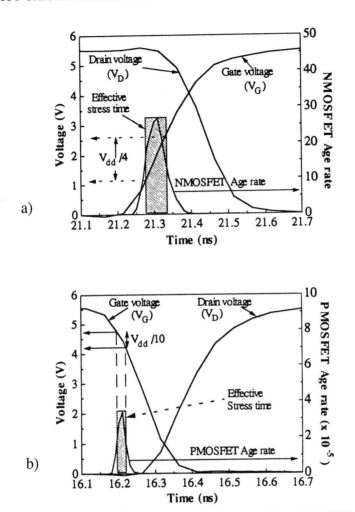

Fig. 9-21 (a) NMOSFET aging rate during circuit transient. The NMOSFET aging rate is a function of the substrate current. The overlap time is a quarter of the rise time. (b) PMOSFET aging rate during circuit transient. The aging rate is a function of the gate current and the effective overlap time is about a tenth of the fall time.[41] (© IEEE 1993).

9.4.6.2 Simulators that Relate the Device-Level Degradation Parameters to Circuit Performance (CAS and HOTRON).

As we have mentioned earlier, it is not sufficient to characterize just the degree of degradation of device parameters. Instead, it is necessary to relate the device-level degradation parameters directly to circuit output behavior and performance. That is, it has been demonstrated that not all devices will affect the circuit output equally. Each device may have different performance sensitivities towards the output, and this relationship may

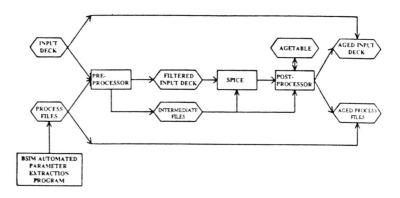

Fig. 9-22 Schematic configuration of how SCALE is incorporated as a pre-and post-processor to be used with SPICE.[151] (© IEEE 1988).

also change with the power-supply voltage. Several simulators have been developed to predict the effects of hot-carrier degradation on MOS circuit behavior, including the *circuit aging simulator* (CAS),[38] and HOTRON.[39] These simulators can directly simulate the entire circuit using degraded device parameters calculated from the hot-carrier degradation models Eqs. 9-6 and 9-7. The simulator CAS is thus a superset of SCALE in that transient substrate current and device lifetime can also be calculated using CAS.* However, CAS is also linked to SPICE so that at any time the device parameters that are degraded by hot-carrier effects can be substituted for the fresh device parameters, and the change in circuit behavior (i.e., aged output compared to fresh output) can be computed using SPICE (see Fig. 9-23).

A set of design guidelines for estimating hot-carrier lifetimes of devices under dynamic stress, as well the hot-carrier lifetimes of some classes of circuits in which such devices are being operated, have been developed using CAS.[41] The conversion from the lifetime under dc stress to the lifetime under ac stress can be accomplished by multiplying the dc stress lifetime by a dc-to-ac conversion factor, namely for NMOSFETs by NTF, and for PMOSFETs by PTF. These conversion factors have are termed *lifetime factors* and are found to be

$$\text{NTF} = 4 / (f\, t_r) ; \qquad \text{PTF} = 10 / (f\, t_f) \qquad (9 - 10)$$

where f is the operating frequency, and t_r and t_f are the rise and fall times of the V_{GS} signal. Figure 9-24 shows the calculated values of NTF (Fig. 9-24a) and PTF (Fig. 9-24b) as a function of f and t_r and t_f. As an example, for an operating frequency of 100 MHz and an input rise time of 0.35 ns, the NTF of NMOSFETs and the PTF of PMOSFETs, are 120 and 300 respectively. Thus, an NMOSFET operated under such

---

* A timing-simulator-based version of CAS, called IRSIM-CAS has also been developed. It is much faster than the standard CAS mentioned above, allowing it to be used to simulate hot-carrier aging of circuits containing thousands of transistors in a reasonable time.[40]

What CAS Does

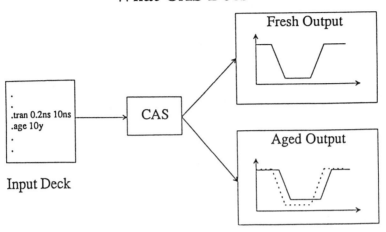

Fig. 9-23 CAS calculates the output of a circuit based on the device parameters as degraded by hot-carrier stressing.

an ac stress would exhibit a lifetime 120 times as long as the one predicted by a dc stress test.

Such guidelines have also been formulated for converting ac-stress lifetime of a device in a circuit to the circuit degradation lifetime with the aid of so-called *speed degradation factors*, NSF for NMOSFETs, and PSF for PMOSFETs. These factors take the following forms:

$$NSF = 1 / [2 k_n (1 + t_{ro} / t_{fo})] \qquad (9-11a)$$

$$PSF = 1 / [2 k_p (1 + t_{fo} / t_{ro})] \qquad (9-11b)$$

NSF and PSF appear to be about 1/4 and 1/2 for inverters.

Figure 9-25 shows how NTF and NSF translate dc-stress lifetime to circuit speed degradation. If a 10% $\Delta I_D/I_D$ of an NMOSFET is reached in 0.2 years under worst-case dc stress condition, it will take 16 years to produce a 10% $\Delta I_D/I_D$ if NTF = 120, and this $\Delta I_D/I_D$ degradation will cause a slow down of 2.5% of inverter speed under ac operation at 100 MHz if NSF = 1/4.

Although the circuit-level simulators discussed above can estimate hot-carrier lifetimes under ac stressing, they have generally not yet incorporated the latest understanding of ac stress degradation. A report that presents some guidelines that takes these effects into account, and which have been incorporated into another hot-carrier reliability simulator named ADHOC is given in ref. 54.

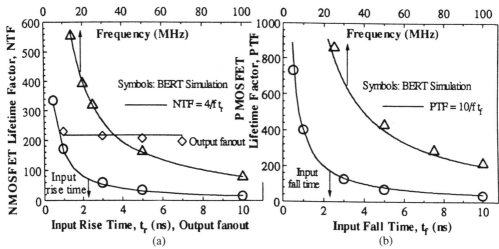

Fig. 9-24 (a) NMOSFET lifetime factor NTF as a function of input rise time, operating frequency, and output fanout factor. The frequency curve is for t_r = 0.5 ns and the input rise time curve is for f = 25 MHz, t_{ox} = 17.5 nm, L_{eff} = 0.5 μm. (b) PMOSFET lifetime factor PTF as a function of input rise time, operating frequency, and output fanout factor. The frequency curve is for t_f = 0.5 ns and the input fall time curve is for f = 20 MHz, t_{ox} = 17.5 nm, L_{eff} = 0.5 μm.[41] (© IEEE 1993).

9.5 DECREASING HOT CARRIER DEGRADATION BY MODIFYING THE MOSFET STRUCTURE

As was pointed out earlier, device lifetime (and other hot-carrier effects) can be improved in a number of ways, including, reducing the bias voltages, significantly strengthening the gate oxide against hot-carrier damage (i.e., in effect increasing B in Eq. 9-6), or

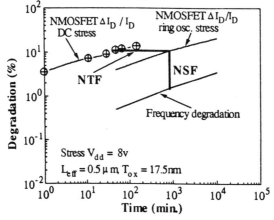

Figure 9-25 NMOSFET lifetime factor NTF, and NMOSFET speed degradation factor NSF, translate dc device degradation to circuit speed degradation.[41] (© IEEE 1993).

modifying the MOSFET structure. If the power-supply voltage cannot be reduced (e.g., it may need to be kept at 5V for system-compatibility reasons), and if the gate oxide cannot be sufficiently strengthened against hot-carrier degradation to provide adequate operating lifetimes, then the only remaining option is to modify the MOSFET structure.

A quantitative example will concretely demonstrate why a way must be found to reduce $\mathcal{E}_{ymax}$ in submicron MOSFETs. Assume that a 1 μm NMOSFET has the following structural and electrical device parameters: $t_{ox} = 20$ nm, $r_j = 0.25$ μm, $V_{DS} = 5V$, and $V_{DSsat} = 1V$. In this case, from Eq. 9-2a, $l \approx 138$ nm $= 1.38 \times 10^{-5}$ cm, and $(V_{DS} - V_{DSsat}) = 4V$. Then, from Eq. 9-1, $\mathcal{E}_{ymax} \approx 2.9 \times 10^5$ V/cm. Now we can roughly estimate the hot-carrier lifetime of the device using Eq. 9-8b. We first use Eq. 9-5 to model I_{sub}/I_D in this device. Then we insert this I_{sub}/I_D value into Eq. 9-8b to find τ. Equation 9-5 yields a value for I_{sub}/I_D ~0.015, and then Eq. 9-8b predicts that such a device will have a hot-carrier lifetime τ of only 1×10^6 sec or ~0.4 year. Obviously, this lifetime is too short (the design goal is typically 10 years). Clearly, a way to increase τ needs to be found.

Equation 9-1 suggests that one way to modify the MOSFET structure to reduce $\mathcal{E}_{ymax}$ is to increase the magnitude of l. According to Eq. 9-2, this can be accomplished by increasing t_{ox} or $r_{j'}$ (or both). However, increasing either of these parameters will worsen the susceptibility of the MOSFET to short-channel effects (as was discussed in chap. 5). Thus, another tack must be taken to modify the device structure other than by using this approach.

An alternative approach in *n*-channel MOSFETs is to create a lightly doped (n^-) buffer region between the heavily As-doped (n^+) drain and the channel, *outside of the channel*. In other words, the idea is to produce a MOSFET device having a drain with a *graded*, or *lightly-doped* extension. Qualitatively, $\mathcal{E}_{ymax}$ is reduced by such a buffer region because the maximum electric field in a reverse-biased *pn* junction is highest when the junction is abrupt. By replacing the abrupt drain doping profile of a conventional MOSFET with a drain that has a more gradually decreasing lateral doping profile (i.e., a *graded drain*), the voltage drop becomes shared by the drain and the channel [in contrast to an abrupt n^+/p drain junction, in which almost the entire voltage drop occurs across the lightly doped (channel) side of the junction]. From a simple quantitative perspective using the model for $\mathcal{E}_{ymax}$ given by Eq. 9-1, $\mathcal{E}_{ymax}$ is significantly reduced by the presence of such a lightly doped region because this is another way to increase the denominator of Eq. 9-1.

Graded-drain regions can be created in MOSFETs in a number of ways, including: (1) using phosphorus in place of As as the dopant of the source/drain regions; (2) adding fast diffusing phosphorus to an As-doped drain region, and driving the phosphorus laterally ahead of the arsenic with a high temperature diffusion step (to create a so-called *double-diffused drain* [DDD] structure); and (c) pulling the highly doped (n^+) drain region away from the gate edge with an "oxide spacer" to create a so-called *lightly doped drain* (LDD) structure. Here we describe these approaches in more detail, focusing on the LDD, as it is the most important technique for forming graded-drain MOSFETs. Table 9-1 shows the evolution of the AT&T Twin-Tub CMOS technology,

Table 9-1 Evolution of Device Structures in AT&T's Twin-Tub CMOS Technology Development[43]   (Twin-Tub VI announced in 1989)[44]

	Twin-Tub I	Twin-Tub II	Twin-Tub III	Twin-Tub IV	Twin-Tub V	Twin-Tub VI
Design Rule	3.5 μm	2.5 μm	1.75 μm	1.25 μm	0.9 μm	0.6 μm
L_{eff}	2 μm	1.5 μm	1.3 μm	1.0 μm	0.75 μm	0.4 μm
t_{ox}	600 Å	350 Å	250 Å	200 Å	150 Å	125Å
Device Structure	Conventional	Conventional	DDD	LDD	N&P LDD	N-DDD

which gives an indication of how graded-drain structures were incorporated into MOS devices as the devices were scaled.

9.5.1 Phosphorus-Drain Structure

The simplest method to incorporate a graded-drain region into a conventional (i.e., single As drain) MOSFET device, is to replace the arsenic with phosphorus as the source/drain donor impurity.[45] This structure is called the (single) *phosphorus-drain MOSFET*. The faster-diffusing phosphorus provides additional lateral length to the drain dopant profile, which widens the depletion region of the drain-channel junction, and thus reduces the maximum lateral electric-field strength $\mathcal{E}_{ymax}$.

To keep the sheet resistivity of the source/drain regions reasonably low, the dose of the phosphorus implantation must be greater than $1x10^{15}$ cm^{-2}. The resulting device exhibits values of I_{sub} about an order of magnitude smaller than those made with As-doped drains. The reduction in $\mathcal{E}_{ymax}$ is actually due to both the graded phosphorus diffusion profile and the much deeper source/drain junction depth. However, because of this deep source/drain junction, short channel effects are much more difficult to suppress in phosphorus-drain structures. Thus this method is not suitable for NMOSFETs with gate lengths smaller than about 1.3 μm.[46]

9.5.2 Double Diffused Drain (DDD)

While the single phosphorus-drain is not suitable for alleviating the hot-carrier reliability problem in short-channel MOSFETs, if arsenic and phosphorus are simultaneously used as drain dopants, additional improvement in hot-carrier reliability can be obtained with less excessive lateral encroachment into the MOSFET channel. The two dopants are co-implanted into the same region (using two separate implants, i.e, a medium phosphorus dose [e.g., $1x10^{14}$ to $1x10^{15}$ cm^{-2}] and a heavy arsenic dose [e.g., $5x10^{15}$ cm^{-2}] both at $0°$ tilt angle). This initially aligns both dopants to the same gate edge. Since these two implants are followed by a high temperature anneal step, in which both dopants diffuse simultaneously, the structure is called a *double-diffused drain* (DDD). However, the faster-diffusing phosphorus is driven farther under the gate edge (and elsewhere, see Fig. 9-26) than the arsenic, creating a less abrupt concentration gradient for the drain. Figure 9-27 shows a typical impurity distribution

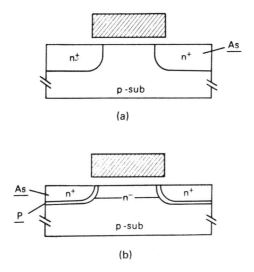

Fig. 9-26 An NMOSFET with (a) conventional single drain; and (b) double-diffused drain.

along the channel direction of a DDD MOSFET. The doping profile of a conventional single-As-drain MOSFET is also depicted for comparison.[47] A significant reduction in ε_{ymax} occurs in the DDD, as is shown in Fig. 9-28. For devices with channel lengths greater than about 1.25 μm, I_{sub} reduction factors of 4 to 6 are typically obtained. It should be noted that some DDD structures are implemented using the oxide spacer technology generally associated with the LDD. In such structures, the implants are carried out after spacer formation.

The DDD structure is attractive because it adds little complexity to the process sequence. That is, it can be introduced into a CMOS process flow without any extra masking steps, whereas an NMOS LDD process may require an extra masking step to prevent the n^- implant from entering the PMOS source/drain regions. Furthermore, since the medium-dose phosphorus implant (n^-) and the high dose arsenic implant (n^+) are aligned to the same gate edge, the relative position between the n^- and n^+ edges (which is the basis of all graded-drain structures), is determined only by the high temperature anneal process. Thus, the DDD structure exhibits relatively consistent device characteristics and I_{sub} values.

On the other hand, this approach permits no freedom to optimize the length of the n^- region and simultaneously achieve a shallow junction. This limits the degree to which ε_{ymax} can be reduced. That is, in order to get an n^- region of sufficient length, a long thermal drive needed. Unfortunately, this also causes a deep *vertical* phosphorus junction. Since shallow junctions are needed to prevent short-channel effects (see chap. 5), as the gate length approaches 1 μm in DDD structures, the deep vertical junction degrades the short-channel behavior to an unacceptable degree. The long drive-in also causes redistribution of dopants in the channel, which is also undesirable.

In addition, it should be mentioned that selecting the correct process and device parameters which yield an optimized DDD structure involves significant process and device calibration. That is, too much phosphorus or excessive diffusion will yield punchthrough problems, while too little phosphorus will provide inadequate protection from hot-electron degradation. Furthermore, if an oxide spacer is used, the gate/drain overlap depends strongly on the width of the oxide sidewall spacer, which could make such devices very susceptible to hot-carrier degradation unless the spacer width is tightly controlled.

For 5V supply voltages, the DDD structure is therefore not suitable for devices with gate lengths smaller than 1.25 μm. As shown in Table 9-1 it was used in the 1.75 μm ATT CMOS-III technology, but not in the following 1.25 μm CMOS-IV process.[43] However, it is reported that the DDD structure has returned in the ATT 0.6-μm CMOS-VI technology, in which a smaller (3.3V) power-supply-voltage is used.[44]

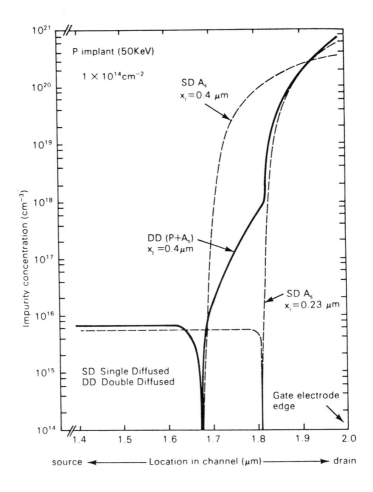

Fig. 9-27 Lateral impurity profiles for two single-diffused drain structures and one double-diffused drain structure.[47] (© IEEE 1985).

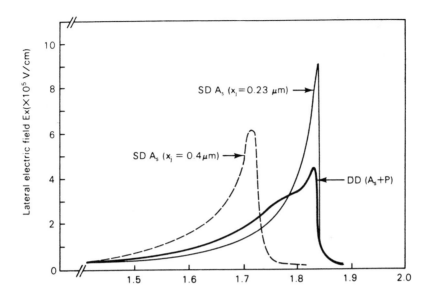

Fig. 9-28 Lateral electric field distributions associated with the three structures shown in Fig. 9-27.[47] (© IEEE 1985).

9.6 LIGHTLY DOPED DRAIN (LDD) STRUCTURES

The most widely used device structure for increasing the hot-carrier reliability in 5V-NMOSFETs with gate lengths smaller than 1.25 μm is the *lightly doped drain* (LDD), and in the upcoming sections we will describe it in detail. First we present models that allow the degree to which ε_{ymax} is reduced in an LDD to be estimated in terms of the device parameters and bias voltages, as well as models which predict the performance penalty that must be paid by using an LDD in a MOSFET device. Next we discuss the process sequence used to fabricate a conventional LDD, and then we examine the limitations of such structures. Finally we describe how modifications have been made to the conventional LDD structure to overcome these limitations.

In the LDD structure, as first described in 1980 by Ogura et al.,[48,49] the drain is formed by two implants (Fig. 9-29). One of these is self-aligned to the gate electrode, and the other to the gate electrode on which two oxide sidewall spacers have been formed. The purpose of the first implant dose is to produce a lightly doped section of the drain at the gate edge near the channel.

Figure 9-30 shows the electric-field profile at the drain of a MOSFET, both with and without a conventional LDD structure (as obtained from 2-D numerical analysis of the MOSFET device). In this case, the LDD provides about a 30-40% reduction in ε_{ymax}. Since we noted earlier that the average energy of the hot-electrons is exponentially dependent on ε_{ymax} this reduction ought to significantly decrease the damage caused by such carriers in the MOSFET. Hence, the hot-carrier reliability of the LDD device should also be greatly increased. However, this benefit comes at a price, namely the lowering of the drive current of the MOSFET.

While 2-D numerical analysis techniques provide accurate simulations of the lateral electric field in both non-LDD and LDD MOSFETs, it would be useful if analytical models were available to estimate ε_{ymax} and the resultant reduction in I_D in LDD devices. Here we describe such analytical models for estimating both phenomena in LDD MOSFETs.

9.6.1 Modeling ε_{ymax} in LDD MOSFETs

9.6.1.1 Simple Model for Estimating ε_{ymax} in LDD MOSFETs

The LDD reduces ε_{ymax} because some of the drain voltage is dropped across the n^- region. This voltage drop does not occur in non-graded-drain devices because such an n^- region is absent. The simplest quantitative model for estimating the reduction of ε_{ymax} in an LDD assumes that the voltage dropped across the n^- region is as high as possible.[18] For this to occur, the lateral electric field would have to be roughly constant across the entire length of the n^- region L_{n^-}, and be equal to its maximum possible value ε_{ymax}. In this case, a modified form of the equation used to calculate ε_{ymax} in a non-LDD device in saturation (Eq. 9-1) would also be appropriate for estimating ε_{ymax} in an LDD. The condition mentioned above causes Eq. 9-1 to be modified as follows:

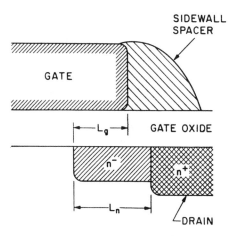

Fig. 9-29 Cross section of the drain end of an LDD device, showing the sidewall spacer, the gate overlap length, L_g, and the length of the lightly doped drain region L_{n^-}.

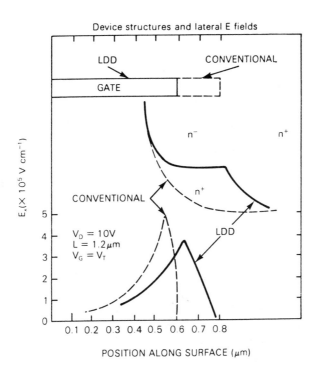

Fig. 9-30 Magnitude of the electric field at the Si-SiO$_2$ interface as a function of distance: $L = 1.2 \ \mu m$, $V_{DS} = 8.5$ V, $V_{GS} = V_T$.[48] (© 1980 IEEE).

$$\mathcal{E}_{ymax} \text{ (LDD)} = (V_{DS} - V_{DSsat} - \mathcal{E}_{ymax}L_{n\text{-}})/ \ 0.22 \ t_{ox}^{1/3}r_j^{1/3} \qquad (9 \text{-} 12)$$

which after some algebraic manipulation becomes

$$\mathcal{E}_{ymax} \text{ (LDD)} = (V_{DS} - V_{DSsat})/ \ (0.22 \ t_{ox}^{1/3}r_j^{1/3} + L_{n\text{-}}) = (V_{DS} - V_{DSsat})/l' \ (9 \text{-} 13)$$

Equation 9-13 offers an alternative perspective of the phenomenon of $\mathcal{E}_{ymax}$ reduction in an LDD device. That is, Eq. 9-13 suggests that the potential difference $V_{DS} - V_{DSsat}$ is no longer dropped across the effective length of the velocity saturation region $l = 0.22 \ t_{ox}^{1/3}r_j^{1/3}$, but instead is dropped across l', which is the sum of l and $L_{n\text{-}}$, or $l = (0.2 \ t_{ox}^{1/3}r_j^{1/3} + L_{n\text{-}})$. It should be noted that in practice, the electric field will not be constant across $L_{n\text{-}}$ and therefore the term $\mathcal{E}_{ymax}L_{n\text{-}}$ in Eq. 9-12 should in fact be reduced by some factor. Nevertheless, Eq. 9-13 suggests that the effect of an LDD structure is to raise the maximum acceptable value of V_{DS} over that of a conventional MOSFET, regardless of L.

9.6.1.2 Analytical Model for Calculating $\mathcal{E}_{ymax}$ in LDD MOSFETs Using the Pseudo-2D Approach to Solving the Poisson Equation.
The above model is useful for providing some rough quantitative insight into the behavior of LDD MOSFETs but gives no help in designing an LDD structure for a given MOSFET with respect to selecting L_{n^-}, the n^- dose, or the degree of overlap of the n^- region under the gate. Furthermore, while this model helps to explain why an LDD reduces $\mathcal{E}_{ymax}$, it implies that this reduction will continue to increase as L_{n^-} grows longer. However, this is not the case. Instead it has been observed that there is some L_{n^-} length beyond which $\mathcal{E}_{ymax}$ no longer significantly decreases. Furthermore, the above model gives no clue as to how the implant dose is related to the reduction of $\mathcal{E}_{ymax}$, nor as to the location of $\mathcal{E}_{ymax}$ with respect to the gate edge.

A more elaborate analytical model for $\mathcal{E}_{ymax}$ in LDD MOSFETs which provides some of this information was described by Lee et al.[50] This model was based on the same pseudo-2-D solution approach of the Poisson equation of Ko et al., as was discussed in more detail in chap. 5, section 5.4.3.3. Here the doping is assumed to be constant throughout each device region (i.e., in the n^- and n^+ regions of the drain, and the channel region). The solution of the 2-D Poisson equation based on this pseudo-2D method provides the value of $\mathcal{E}_y$ versus y in the device. The maximum value found is $\mathcal{E}_{ymax}$. The location of $\mathcal{E}_{ymax}$ can therefore also be obtained from this model. The dependence of $\mathcal{E}_{ymax}$ on the doping concentration in the n^- region can also be determined with this model. Finally, a field reduction factor (FRF) is defined which gives the ratio of $\mathcal{E}_{ymax}$ in an LDD device to $\mathcal{E}_{ymax}$ of a non-LDD device with the same dimensions. This permits various LDD MOSFET structures to be quickly compared with respect to their effectiveness in decreasing $\mathcal{E}_{ymax}$.

Lee et al. used the model to calculate the FRF in LDD devices for three general device structures: (a) one in which the n^- region is completely overlapped by the gate; (b) one in which there is zero overlap between the n^- region and the gate; and (c) one in which a partial overlap exists between the n^- region and the gate. They drew several conclusions about the LDD device from their analysis: (1) The device with full n^--to-gate overlap can potentially provide the largest FRF of the three structures; (2) The maximum FRF in an LDD is about 0.5, and this occurs in full-overlapped structures having an optimum doping (and a maximum length of L_{n^-}). That is, if a longer L_{n^-} region is used, the FRF no longer increases. On the other hand, the resistance of the current path between the source and drain terminals does continue to rise as L_{n^-} grows longer, which will cause I_D to decrease; (3) In partially overlapped devices, the location of $\mathcal{E}_{ymax}$ depends on the doping level in the n^- region. That is, for light n^- doses the $\mathcal{E}_{ymax}$ location is at the n^-/n^+ junction (i.e., it exists beyond the edge of the gate), while for higher n^- doses the location of $\mathcal{E}_{ymax}$ moves to the p/n^- junction (i.e., under the gate). As we shall see, when $\mathcal{E}_{ymax}$ is located under the gate, devices exhibit improved hot-carrier reliability.

While this model is useful in providing insight into the general directions that LDD device-design should take, it does not provide enough information to be able to predict the actual hot-carrier lifetimes of LDD devices designed only from the data provided by the model. That is, the assumption is still made that an LDD MOSFET with the smallest value of $\mathcal{E}_{ymax}$ will yield a device structure with the highest hot-carrier reliability. Unfortunately, this is not always the case. Instead, other factors enter into the picture, as will be discussed in the section that examines the issues of hot-carrier reliability in LDD devices (section 9.7.2). We will also describe methods that are better able to predict hot-carrier hardness in LDD devices (section 9.10). These are based on more rigorous simulation procedures than those used in the above model.

9.6.1.3 Model for the Series Resistance Introduced by the n^- Region of the LDD.
The value of the resistance R_{n^-} introduced by the n^- region of an LDD can be simply modeled if we assume that the doping concentration in the n^- region is uniform (with a value N_D) along the distance L_{n^-} and to the depth of the region r_j. In this case, we can model R_{n^-} in an NMOSFET according to:

$$R_{n^-} = L_{n^-}/(q \, \mu_n \, N_D \, r_j) \, Z \tag{9 - 14}$$

where Z is the width of the device and μ_n is the mobility of the electrons in the n^- region (e.g., 800 cm^2/Vsec). The impact of R_{n^-} on I_D is described in section 9.7.1.1.

9.6.2 Overview of the Process Sequence to Form LDDs

The basic process sequence used to form early LDD MOSFETs in simple NMOS technologies is shown in Fig. 9-31. The poly gate is patterned with an RIE etch process designed to produce a poly feature with vertical sidewalls (Fig. 9-31b). In some processes the thermally grown gate oxide beyond the edges of the gate is kept in place after the poly etch, in an attempt to maintain a high quality interface under the sidewall oxide. This requires a polysilicon etch with extremely high selectivity to oxide, since the gate oxide is normally quite thin (e.g., 12.5-20 nm thick). Next, the n^- implant (also called the *graded-drain,* or *tip* implant) is carried out with phosphorus to form the lightly doped region of the drain. In early LDDs the doses ranged from 5x10^{12} to 1x10^{13} cm^{-2} at energies of 40-60 keV (Fig. 9-31c). Note that the n^- region at this point is essentially self-aligned to the gate electrode. The n^- implant is carried out using a medium-current implanter with the ion beam tilted at 7° (to minimize implant channeling effects - see vol. 1, chap. 9).

Following the n^- implant step a thin oxide is thermally grown on the patterned poly gate using a short dry-oxidation process (this step is called *poly re-ox*). A conformal CVD oxide film is then deposited. A popular method is to decompose TEOS at 725°C, as this produces a film with excellent conformality, and if the poly profile is vertical, no re-entrant profile. A conformal deposition process produces a thicker film at the edge of the gate-to-active area step than on flat areas. Thus, an anisotropic dry-etch process will clear the oxide in the flat areas while leaving spacers at the sidewalls of the poly

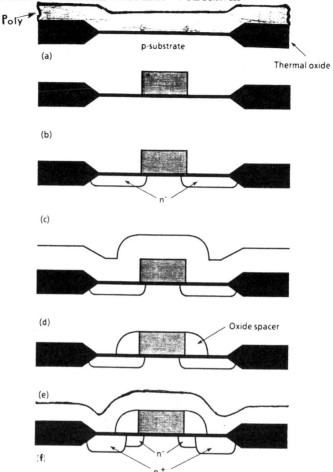

Fig. 9-31 Basic process sequence to form an LDD NMOSFET. (a) After poly deposition; (b) after poly etch; (c) LDD implant; (d) spacer deposition; (e) spacer etch; (f) n^+ implant and passivation.

gate (Fig. 9-31d). If the spacers are etched to endpoint with minimal overetch, the spacer height will be close to the same height as the poly. For poly gate thicknesses of 0.3 μm and a deposited oxide film thickness of ~0.3 μm, spacer widths of ~0.2 μm are typically obtained. A discussion of spacer thickness and shape dependence, with respect to variations in the deposited film thickness, conformality, overetch time etc. is given in ref. 51.

It should also be noted that to account for variations in the spacer oxide layer thickness, some overetch is needed in the etch step that creates the spacer. During the overetch time the spacer shape is altered (i.e., its thickness and height from the top of the poly gate will change). In addition, the field oxide and the silicon in the source/drain regions are also etched. Excessive overetching of these regions is undesirable from device isolation and junction leakage viewpoints, respectively. Figure 9-32 shows a SEM photograph of an NMOS transistor with an oxide spacer at the conclusion of the spacer etch process, where the n^+ gate and drain regions have been decorated with a selective etch (the n^- region is not visible). Note that the silicon in the drain has been slightly etched during the spacer overetch as shown by the depression in the silicon surface to the right of the gate. Leakage of the source/drain junctions, localized in the junction directly beneath the spacer edge has been reported in oxide-spacer LDDs. This problem has been attributed to the silicon loss and etch damage in the substrate arising from the spacer etch,[52,53] and to defects formed by the subsequent n^+ implant and anneal. (The shape of the oxide spacer produced by the spacer etch process has also been reported to impact the formation of these defects.[54])

After the oxide spacers are formed, a high dose n^+ source/drain implant is carried out with a high-current implanter. Typically, arsenic is implanted at a dose of about 5×10^{15} cm^{-2} and at energies of 40-80 keV. This forms the low-resistivity drain region, which is merged with the lightly doped n^- region. Because the spacer serves as a mask for the As implant, the heavily doped n^+ region is self-aligned to the sidewall spacer edges and is thus offset from the gate edge. Since the edge of the n^+ region is further away from the channel than would be the case in a conventional drain structure, the depth of the heavily-doped region of the drain can be made somewhat greater without adversely impacting the device operation (e.g., 0.3 μm deep versus 0.18 μm deep). The increased junction depth lowers both the sheet resistance and the contact resistance of the drain. Deeper junctions also provide better protection against junction spiking. An anneal is then performed to cause the n^- dopant to sufficiently diffuse laterally under the gate edge and to activate the implanted n^+ dopants. (Actually, the entire thermal budget after n^- implant determines the degree of lateral diffusion, and this is often dominated by the interlevel dielectric densification and reflow step, e.g., 950°C for 20 min.)

By introducing the sidewall spacer after the n^- implant to laterally offset the n^+ implant, the LDD structure offers more freedom in optimizing the n^- length than the DDD structure. That is, the n^- length is controlled by the lateral spacer dimension and thermal drive cycle, and is made independent from the n^+ junction depth. If a salicide

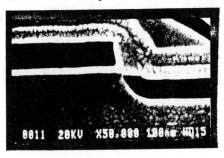

Fig. 9-32 SEM photograph of an NMOS transistor with an oxide spacer at the conclusion of the spacer etch process, where the n^+ gate and drain regions have been decorated with a selective etch (the n^- region is not visible).[67] Reprinted with permission of Semiconductor International.

process is being implemented, an oxide spacer is also needed to prevent shorting of the gate and the source/drain regions, and this structure is intrinsic to the LDD approach. However, as we shall describe in the next section, the conventional LDD has other problems and disadvantages, and improvement in hot carrier resistance in the basic LDD structure is obtained only by trading off device performance.

9.7 PERFORMANCE AND HOT-CARRIER LIMITATIONS OF THE CONVENTIONAL LDD

As emphasized earlier, the reason LDDs are incorporated into submicron MOSFETs is to increase their hot-carrier reliability. It would be ideal if this benefit could be obtained without degrading the other performance characteristics of the device. However, the introduction of an LDD generally does cause some performance degradation, primarily by causing a reduction in the drive current of the MOSFET. An example of this effect is illustrated in Fig. 9-33,[55] which compares the drain current in conventional and LDD MOSFETs as their gate length and n^- dose is varied. The LDD MOSFETs exhibit smaller I_D values. To make matters worse, if LDD MOSFETs are poorly designed they may even be more susceptible to hot-carrier degradation than comparable non-graded-drain MOSFETs.

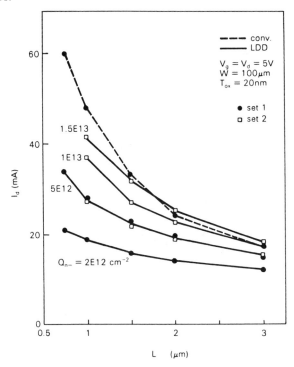

Fig. 9-33 Drain current in LDD MOSFETs with various gate lengths.[55] (© 1984 IEEE).

A report was published in 1985 that compared 1.0 μm non-graded-drain, DDD, and early LDD MOSFET structures.[56] The performance and hot-carrier reliability of the DDD at such gate lengths was somewhat better than that of the early LDD, but it appeared that the DDD would exhibit intolerable short-channel behavior if the supply voltage remained at 5V and the device dimensions were further reduced.

On the other hand, this study indicated that the LDD structure could be designed into smaller MOSFETs without excessively degrading their short-channel behavior. With this in mind, it became important to understand why early LDDs caused performance and hot-carrier reliability degradation. That is, if these drawbacks could be overcome, the LDD could be used to combat hot-carrier effects in MOSFETs with $L<1$ μm. Here we examine in detail the device structure and processing factors that are responsible for the limitations of the early LDD structure. An understanding of these issues also provides a background for the upcoming discussion of modifications to the basic LDD structure, as these were developed to overcome its limitations.

9.7.1 Performance Degradation in LDD MOSFETs

We have noted that the drive capability of conventional LDD MOSFETs, even when "fresh" (i.e., prior to hot-carrier stressing) is worse than that of non-graded-drain MOSFETs. That is, the introduction of an LDD is typically accompanied by a 10-20% reduction in I_D. In poorly designed LDD MOSFETs this performance degradation can be even larger. The reasons for such drive current decrease are discussed in this section. Note, however, that the gate/drain overlap capacitance is normally lower in LDD devices (because the LDD region is partially depleted), which recovers some of the reduced circuit performance. A study of the impact of the LDD on the gate-to-drain capacitance of the MOSFET is given in refs. 57 and 58. The overall loss in circuit performance of the combined effects is observed to be between 4-8%.

9.7.1.1 I_D Decrease Due to Added Resistance of n^- Regions. The most obvious reason that the drive current is reduced in an LDD MOSFET is that the n^- regions of the LDD add segments of lower doping along the current path between the source and drain. Hence, a higher total resistance exists along the current path between the source and drain terminals. As described in chap. 4, the series resistance of the MOSFET can be modeled using an equivalent circuit model as shown in Fig. 9-34.[59] Here we see that using the n^- regions is equivalent to adding two parasitic resistors each with a resistance R_{n^-} to the total source/drain resistance. A simple model for computing the value of R_{n^-} was given in section 9.6.1.3. As also noted earlier, this extra parasitic resistance in practice typically causes a 10-20% loss in both drain current and transconductance compared to non-LDD devices. Note that both the source and drain n^- parasitic resistors act to decrease I_D in the linear region, while only the source n^- resistor causes I_{Dsat} to decrease (because the I_{Dsat} is not impacted by a resistance change across the drain-channel junction). Thus, the effect of R_{n^-} on I_D is most pronounced in the linear (triode) region. (Note that an increase in the channel resistance as a result of hot-carrier damage will also cause the largest decrease in I_D in the linear region, and hence this quantity is often monitored when conducting studies of hot-carrier degradation.)

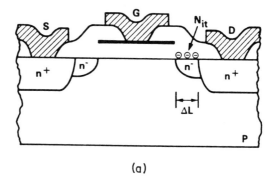

(a)

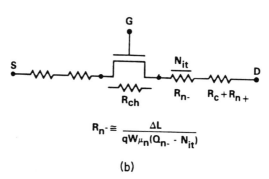

$$R_{n^-} \cong \frac{\Delta L}{qW\mu_n(Q_{n^-} - N_{it})}$$

(b)

Fig. 9-34 Schematic diagrams showing (a) the two-section drain model and the external channel pinch-off effect, and (b) the equivalent circuit of the graded drain device structures.[59] (© 1984 IEEE).

However, in a device in which the source and drain parasitic resistance values are not identical (i.e., in asymmetric MOSFETs, which are discussed in section 9.7.1.5), the values of I_{Dsat} will not be identical if the source and drain terminals are reversed. As this can pose a problem in some circuits, we will discuss this issue in more detail later.

To minimize the value of R_{n^-} we could adjust several parameters. Primarily the doping concentration of the n^- region could be increased and its length L_{n^-} decreased. However, both of these variations impact the effectiveness of the LDD structure. That is, the optimum value of L_{n^-} has been found by two different studies to be either: (1) the same length as the effective length of the saturation region in a comparable non-graded -drain device, $L_{n^-} \approx l$;[50] or (2) equal to the depletion region width w_D on the n^- side of the p/n^- junction.[60] In practice both of these distances are comparable. This implies that if a longer value for L_{n^-} is chosen, no further reduction in $\mathcal{E}_{ymax}$ will be obtained, but a larger R_{n^-} will result (than would exist if L_{n^-} was shorter).*   However,

---

* As L_{n^-} is increased, initially the depletion layer corresponding to doping in the n^- region and the drain voltage spreads out in order to sustain the drain electric field. This spreading continues until L_{n^-} becomes wide enough to sustain the drain field (i.e., which corresponds to a value of L_{n^-} equal to the depletion layer width in the n^- region). Hence, increasing L_{n^-} beyond l serves only to increase the parasitic series resistance with no further benefit in lateral field reduction.

if the n^+ region intrudes into the n^- depletion region (i.e., if L_{n^-} is shorter than w_D), the effective depletion-layer width is determined by L_{n^-}. Thus, L_{n^-} should be neither too short, nor too long.

Choosing the optimum doping concentration value is more complicated. Upper and lower bounds to the doping can be deduced from the limiting cases. That is, at one extreme, if the doping is too high the n^- region merely becomes an extension of the heavily doped n^+ region, and sufficient reduction in $\mathcal{E}_{ymax}$ is not achieved. At the other extreme, a very lightly doped n^- region hardly changes the structure from that of a conventional MOSFET with a high $\mathcal{E}_{ymax}$ at the heavily doped drain. Selecting the optimum doping between these two extremes involves various tradeoffs between performance and hot-carrier degradation. The relationship between these two characteristics is not straightforward, as will be discussed in section 9.10.

In practice, in early LDD MOSFETs the n^- dose was generally chosen to be in the range of 5×10^{12} cm^{-2} to 1×10^{13} cm^{-2} (which is roughly equal to a concentration of $2\text{-}4 \times 10^{17}$ cm^{-3} in an n^- region of 0.25 μm in depth), as these values resulted in MOSFETs with the smallest I_{sub} values as well as I_D values that were about 20% below those of conventional 1 μm MOSFETs (see Fig. 9-33, for the conventional MOSFET and the LDD MOSFET at $L = 1$ μm and n^- dose = 1×10^{13} cm^{-2}). More recently, as is described in section 9.11, the n^- dose in modified-conventional LDDs has been increased to $4 \times 10^{13}\text{-}1 \times 10^{14}$ cm^{-2}. However, in such fully-overlapped LDD structures as the IT-LDD (proposed for 0.5 μm MOSFETs), the n^- dose has been decreased back to the lighter range. Some of the reasons for these choices will be considered in the upcoming section that deals with designing LDD MOSFETs for high hot-carrier reliability.

9.7.1.2 Doping Compensation Effects that can Increase R_{n^-} in Deep Submicron LDD MOSFETs.

As device dimensions shrink, the doping concentration in the channel must be increased to achieve sufficiently high values of V_T and punchthrough voltage in submicron devices. At $L = 0.5$ μm, the peak channel doping concentration is estimated to be $\sim 2 \times 10^{17}$ cm^{-2}. Thus, it is possible for this doping to compensate the n^- doping such that R_{n^-} is significantly increased (which in turn will decrease I_D).[61] It may be necessary to develop process sequences that somehow prevent the channel dopants from being introduced into the n^- regions. One such approach is described in section 9.12.1.3.

9.7.1.3 Increase of R_{sh} by Weak Overlap of the Gate and Drain.

If the edges of the drain and gate are offset, a gap exists between the gate edge and the drain. A segment of the channel between source and drain thus extends over this gap. This condition (as well as the condition of only slight-edge-overlap between gate and drain), is referred to as *weak overlap*. The condition of weak overlap can lead to a degradation of both the performance (drive current) and hot-carrier reliability of a MOSFET. In this section, we former issue, and in section 9.7.2 the latter.

The decrease in drive-current performance arises because weak overlap results in an

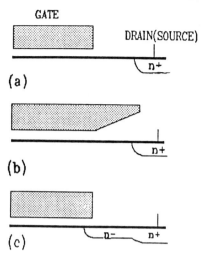

Fig. 9-35 Weak overlap occurs as a result of three conditions in a MOSFET: (a) offset of the drain edge from the gate edge in a single-drain MOSFET; (b) by a *gate bird's beak* (or *graded-gate oxide*, GGO; and (c) offset (or slight overlapping) of the gate and drain edges in an LDD. Note that gate offset and GGO may occur simultaneously, which can increase the severity of the weak overlap condition.[62] (© 1986 IEEE).

increase in R_{sh}. This effect occurs because the segment of the channel in the gap is under less control by the gate than is the channel region at the center of the gate. Consequently, this section is not inverted as strongly and the total channel resistance is increased. Basically, weak overlap[62] occurs as a result of three conditions in a MOSFET: (1) offset of the drain edge from the gate edge in a single-drain MOSFET (Fig. 9-35a). Such offset may occur for several reasons, as we shall discuss later; (2) weak overlap caused by a *gate bird's beak* (or *graded-gate oxide*, GGO, see Fig. 9-35b); and (3) offset (or slight overlapping) of the gate and drain edges in an LDD (Fig. 9-35c). Note that gate offset and GGO may occur simultaneously, which can increase the severity of the weak overlap condition.

9.7.1.4 The Impact of Poly Re-Ox on Weak Overlap in MOSFETs.
As described in chap. 5, the poly re-ox step grows a sidewall on the patterned poly gate and also gives rise to a graded-gate oxide, or GGO (9-35b). Weak overlap can be caused in MOSFETs as a result of both oxidation effects.[63,64] If the poly gate has been doped prior to re-ox, the poly sidewall oxide will grow much more rapidly than on the more lightly doped substrate regions (e.g., if 150Å of oxide is grown on the substrate about 500Å of oxide will grow on the doped poly). Thus, even if the gate and drain are overlapped prior to a poly re-ox step, the doped gate edge can retreat more rapidly (as a result of the rapid oxidation of the poly sidewall) than can the diffusing drain dopants which try to catch this retreating edge. As a result, the drain edge may end up being offset from the gate edge after re-ox even if alignment had existed prior to the process.

As noted in chap. 5, the GGO can provide several benefits to a MOS device, including improved gate-oxide edge integrity and lower gate-to-drain overlap capacitance. For example, the poly gate etch process may form microtrenches in the gate oxide at the periphery of the gate edge, causing all the oxide there to be removed (see Fig. 7-29d). The re-ox step can heal such damage. The heavy source/drain implant can also damage the gate oxide, even if it is covered by the CVD spacer.[106] A moderate re-ox process (which gives rise to a minor GGO) is effective in healing the former and preventing the latter damage. However, if a more extensive re-ox process is performed, i.e., in which the lateral penetration and increase in oxide thickness at the gate edge of the GGO is excessive, the performance of the device can be degraded by causing a weak gate/drain overlap effect (for different reason than is caused by the lateral offset of the gate and drain). That is, even if the drain edge ends up beneath the gate edge, the thicker oxide at the gate edges caused by GGO reduces the degree of inversion in the channel at the gate edge compared to that in the center of the gate. Since the lateral penetration of the GGO increases as the GGO thickens at the gate edge, these two effects can combine to worsen the reduction in the value of the drain current (or transconductance, as shown in Fig. 9-36). Here we see that the edge of the drain must be driven further under the gate edge (i.e., λ must be increased) to negate the effect of the GGO on transconductance.

A number of measures have been proposed to minimize the extent of poly oxide growth and GGO during poly re-ox. First, a short re-ox time and a relatively low oxide growth temperature should be chosen. Second, the re-ox step should be performed in a dry rather than a wet oxidation ambient. Finally, the poly can be doped after the re-ox step, namely during the n^+ implant step that is used to doped the source/drain regions (rather than before gate patterning, as is usually done).[65,66] The latter approach is effective because undoped poly oxidizes less rapidly than does heavily doped poly.

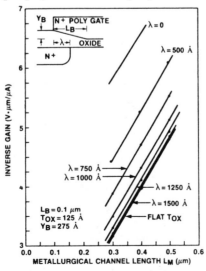

Fig. 9-36 Simulated results of inverse gain versus metallurgical channel length for different offset distances λ with $L_B = 0.1 \ \mu m$ and $Y_B = 275$Å.[66] (© 1989 IEEE).

9.7.1.5 Off-Axis Implant Effects in MOSFETs, Leading to Weak Overlap Problems and Asymmetrical MOSFET Device Characteristics.
Formation of the source/drain regions of a MOSFET is accomplished by means of ion implantation, with the polysilicon gate used as the implant mask. To produce shallow junctions the implant has traditionally been done off-axis (typically, at an angle of 7°), as this avoids channeling (see Vol. 1, chap. 9). However, an off-axis implant can also cause asymmetric doping of the source and drain regions.[68-72,76] That is, lateral shadowing (S in Fig. 9-37) of the substrate occurs on one side of the poly gate, and penetration of dopants through the leading corner of the poly on the other side. The impact of off-axis implants on the device characteristics can be examined by considering the n^- and n^+ implants separately.

If the implant that forms the lightly doped region of the drain is done off-axis, the as-implanted region in the shadow of the gate will have its edge displaced from the gate edge. As a result, there will be no overlap of the implanted region and this gate edge upon the conclusion of the implant. Even after a drive-in step, the overlap of this edge with the gate will be less than the overlap of the nonshadowed implant region edge and the gate. If the less-overlapped side is used as the source, the extra resistance introduced will reduce I_{Dsat} (I_{Dsno} in Fig. 9-37), thus degrading circuit speed. However, if the drain side has less overlap, the extra resistance will not affect I_{Dsat} (curve I_{Ddno} in Fig. 9-37). The asymmetry in drive current when the same device is connected in these two ways

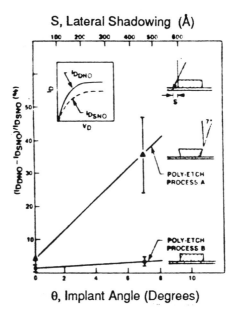

Fig. 9-37 Percent asymmetry in saturated drain currents ($V_{DS} = V_{GS} = 5V$) versus source/drain implant angle for LDD NMOS devices having reentrant- and vertical-wall polysilicon gates. Insert schematically shows source-non-overlap (S_{NO}) and drain-non-overlap (D_{NO}) I-V behavior.[67] Reprinted with permission of Semiconductor International.

can be as much as 40% and this can be catastrophic in circuits that require closely matched device characteristics.

The asymmetrical I_D-V_{DS} problem is severely worsened if the poly gate etch produces a structure with re-entrant angled sidewalls (rather than vertical sidewalls) as is shown in Fig. 9-37.[67] Thus, if an implant process with a 7° tilt angle is used, an etch process that produces vertical sidewalls on the poly (or polycide) is critical. This means that unless a 0° tilt angle is used in the implant processes, the etched profiles of the gate electrodes must also be monitored (and not just in the top views used to measure critical dimension, but in cross-section to expose re-entrant angles).

The problems arising from such n^- implant-shadowing can be alleviated by various measures, including the following:

1. A poly-etch process that produces vertical sidewalls in the poly gates should be used.

2. Excessive reoxidation of the polysilicon gate after it has been patterned should be avoided. (Note that minimizing re-ox also prevents a gap from being established between the drain region edge and the edge of the gate).

3. A vertical implant (0°) through a screen oxide can be used to reduce channeling, instead of using a 7° tilt implant.[27]

4. A poly-etch process that produces a slight positive bevel to the poly sidewall profile can be combined with a smaller angle (3° vs 7°) off-axis implant.[68]

5. The implant can be carried out at 7°, but in two segments, each at half the total dose. The wafer is repositioned by 180° after the first segment of the implant, so that each edge of the gate is the leading edge of the gate during one-half of the total implant, with respect to beam shadowing. In this way the implanted region on both sides of the gate will be symmetrical.

Let us next examine how the n^+ implantation can also impact the structure of the LDD.[73,75] If this implant is also performed at a 7° off-axis, additional asymmetric implant effects can occur. That is, on the side of the gate that is not shadowed, the arsenic atoms penetrate the leading corner of the spacer and thereby enter the substrate under the spacer to some extent. If the 7° tilt angle of the n^- region was from the opposite direction, the n^- region at the drain will have been offset from the gate. Therefore, if the spacer is too narrow, the tilted n^+ implant can wipe out the lightly doped drain-extension region. When this happens, the device can entirely lose the hot-carrier protection that was to be provided by the LDD structure, and it will become vulnerable to degradation by hot-carrier effects. To avoid this, a spacer with sufficient width must be employed, and a higher n^- dose will also offer more protection. Some guidelines for choosing the proper spacer width to deal with this problem are given in reference 74.

9.7.1.6 Implanter Issues that Impact the LDD Process Sequence.
Medium current implanters are used to perform the n^- implants. In early machines the wafer holder could be inclined so that the beam struck the wafer surface at a fixed, non-$0°$ angle. However, electrostatic scanning was typically the method used to deflect the beam over the wafer surface, and this causes the beam angle at the wafer surface to vary (e.g., from $3°$ to $9°$ when the nominal beam angle is $7°$), as the beam is scanned. The n^+ implant is carried out in high-current implanters which use fully mechanically scanned beams. Mechanical scanning reduces the beam scan-angle variations that occur with electrostatic scanning. (In some cases the n^- implant dose was actually carried out at $0°$ on high current implanters to try to take advantage of this benefit.)

Later generations of medium current implanters have been introduced which permit more options. First, the scanning system has been modified so that reduced scan-angle variations are caused. Second, they offer the capability of angular repositioning of the wafer so that both edges of the gate of a MOSFET can be implanted with an off-axis implant to achieve symmetrical doping of both the source and drain sides of the device.

9.7.1.7 Process integration issues which arise when an LDD is integrated into a CMOS Technology.
If an NMOS LDD structure is incorporated in a CMOS technology some issues must be addressed that do not arise in NMOS technology. Specifically, an extra mask is needed if it is desired to prevent the n^- implant dopants from being introduced into the source/drain regions of the PMOS devices. This is especially necessary if an LDD structure is also to be used in the PMOS devices. On the other hand, since the p^+ source/drain implant dose is heavy enough so that any n^- dopant implanted into the PMOS source/drain regions will be compensated by that dose, if no LDD is needed in the PMOS device, a blanket n^- implant can be carried out without the need for an extra mask step.

In the latter case, however, the p^+ source/drain implant step must be performed prior to the formation of the oxide spacer (to prevent the p^+ dopants from being offset from the gate edge by the spacer). This means that the p^+ dopants will be subjected to the anneal steps of the n implants. As a result, the depth of the PMOS source/drain junctions will be greater than if it was not necessary to subject them to this anneal cycle. In section 9-8 we will discuss how the use of disposable spacers is one possible way to circumvent this problem.

9.7.2 Hot Carrier Reliability Issues in Early LDDs

In early LDD MOSFETs, the criterion for selecting an optimum device structure for hot-carrier resistance was frequently based on monitoring I_{sub} for a given set of bias conditions and choosing the structure that exhibited the smallest I_{sub} value. This was done because the smallest I_{sub} value is correlated to the smallest value of $\mathcal{E}_{ymax}$. [If a tradeoff was made between low substrate current and high drain current, the devices which exhibited the lowest I_{sub}/I_D ratios were deemed best (see Eq. 9-5, which indicates that this ratio is an indicator of the $\mathcal{E}_{ymax}$ value).]

Although this assumption may be correct, unfortunately it is not always the case that devices with smaller $\mathcal{E}_{ymax}$ necessarily exhibit better hot-carrier reliability. In fact, as discussed previously, some early LDDs which apparently had smaller ε_{ymax} values than comparable non-graded-drain devices actually exhibited *worse* susceptibility to degradation after hot-carrier stressing. Hui and Moll reported that unless some minimum overlap between the gate and the n^- region of the drain was ensured, the LDD device would exhibit poor hot-carrier reliability.[77] They noted that LDD devices with extra thermal drive-in demonstrated significantly less hot-carrier degradation, and they surmised that the discrepancies in hot-carrier reliability among early LDD stressing reports was likely due to the different temperature cycles used in the various LDD devices.

It was eventually learned that a phenomenon dubbed the *structure-dependent degradation effect* could exacerbate hot-carrier degradation even as ε_{ymax} was being reduced.[55,78] Actually, two effects contributed to the problem. First, the location of ε_{ymax} is dependent on the doping concentration in the n^- region. That is, ε_{ymax} moves closer to the edge of the n^+ region of the drain if the n^- implant dose is low (e.g., 5×10^{12}-to-1×10^{13} cm^{-2}, which was the dose typically chosen in early LDDs). Second, since the damage due to hot-carrier injection is localized in the gate oxide above the location of ε_{ymax} this would have placed the damage in the spacer region of the channel (see Fig. 9-38b). Since this segment of the channel is outside of the edge of the gate, it will tend to already be less heavily inverted. The accumulation of damage-induced negative charge in the oxide above this location has the effect of reducing the level of inversion even more, thus causing the parasitic resistance to increase. In turn, the drain

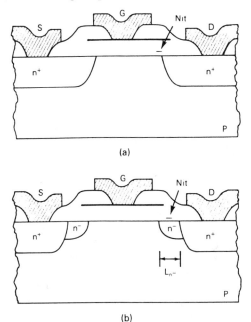

(a)

(b)

Fig. 9-38 Degradation in early LDDs (b) was above the drain current path beyond the edge of the gate. In conventional MOSFETs (a), the edge of the drain is under the gate.

current (and V_T and g_m) are decreased. (In extreme cases the charge buildup can cause the segment to be completely depleted, cutting off the device.)[55,78] This can cause the hot-carrier lifetime to decrease even more rapidly than in a non-graded-drain device, in which ε_{ymax} is located beneath the gate edge. Another issue that compounds the problem is that the deposited oxide in the spacer region may not have as a good a quality as the thermal oxide beneath the gate, and thus may be more susceptible to damage by the injected hot carriers.

One simple cure for the above problem is to use a somewhat higher n^- dose. Although the price is a somewhat higher value of ε_{ymax}, this also has the effect of moving the location of ε_{ymax} to the p/n^- junction, which is also beneath the gate edge. Here, the gate field counteracts the damage in the oxide, resulting in less channel depletion than before. Also, the heavier doping makes it harder to deplete the n^- region. These effects combine to make the device much more resistant to hot-carrier degradation. Devices with such higher n^- doses are referred to as moderately doped LDDs (M-LDDs), and are discussed further in section 9.11.2.1. Another way to guaranty that this problem does not occur is to fully overlap the n^- region with the gate. Devices have been designed to accomplish this, and we will also describe them later (e.g., fully overlapped structures: section 9.12.1, and LATID structures: section 9.12.2).

9.8 DISPOSABLE SPACERS

Instead of forming the oxide spacer after the n^- implant, and then doing the n^+ implant, an alternative process sequence can be used to form the LDD. That is, the spacer can be formed first, followed by an n^+ implant. Then the spacer is removed and the n^- implant is performed (hence the name *disposable spacer*). The benefits of disposable spacers apply mainly to CMOS technology, and they include the following: (1) the process becomes more flexible, allowing LDD formation in both or either NMOS and PMOS devices; (2) If both types of LDD structures are required they can be formed with only two masks (details later), whereas 3 or maybe even 4 masks are needed if the conventional sequence is used; (3) the p-implants for the PMOS device can be performed after the n-implants are annealed. Shallower source/drain junctions in PMOS devices can thus be fabricated since the p-implants do not have to be subjected to the n-implant anneal cycle; (4) As noted earlier, in the conventional LDD sequence the silicon substrate may be damaged during the overetch time of the oxide spacer etch formation process. Such damage has been blamed for junction leakage.[79] This problem is avoided in the disposable spacer process, since the damage is prevented during the disposable spacer etch (see below). Spacer etching is also simplified, because a sharp endpoint signal is easily detected as a large area is cleared at the end of etching, and; (5) The damage from the n^+/p^+ source/drain implant steps can be annealed prior to LDD implant step, thus allowing shallower n^- and p^- regions to be formed. Shallower junctions result in improved short-channel behavior.

The first disposable spacer process to be published used a polysilicon disposable spacer.[80] Here, a layer of polysilicon (instead of the conventional LTO oxide) is deposited on the reoxidized, patterned poly gate structure. The polysilicon is anisotropically etched back to form a poly spacer. This polysilicon etch, which has high

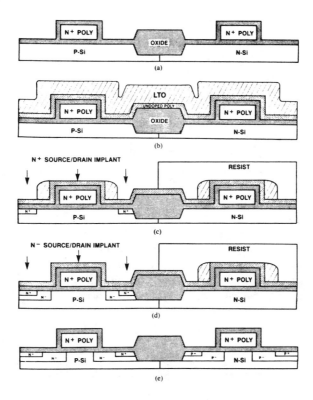

Fig. 9-39 Key processing steps for the NMOS device using the disposable sidewall spacer technology: (a) after poly etch and reoxidation: (b) after the 300-Å undoped poly and undoped LTO deposition; (c) after RIE of the LTO to form the sidewall spacers, which is followed by the n^+ source/drain implant with resist covering the PMOS areas; (d) with resist in place, the LTO sidewall spacers are stripped in 10:1 BOE and the n^- source/drain implant is performed; and (e) after the poly buffer is removed by etch or thermal oxidation.[81] (© 1988 IEEE).

selectivity to oxide, stops on the thin oxide over the source/drain regions without damaging the underlying silicon. The polysilicon spacers are removed after the n^+ implant, and the n^- implant is carried out. Note that in this process there is also virtually no loss of field oxide during the spacer formation etch step because of the high selectivity to the field oxide.

The next reported disposable spacer process was a *disposable oxide-sidewall-spacer process*,[81] in which a thin poly layer (300Å thick) was formed by LPCVD between the re-oxidized poly gate and the LTO spacer oxide. The thin poly under the spacer acts as an effective etchstop layer if a spacer-etch process with high etch selectivity of LTO to polysilicon is used. The oxide spacers are removed after the n^+ implant by a wet chemical etch step (10:1 BOE) which also does not attack the thin poly layer that covers the gate structure (see Fig. 9-39).[81] The thin poly layer can later be removed by wet or dry etching, or it can be thermally oxidized prior to the completion of the process. A variation of this process that uses CVD silicon nitride in place of the LTO oxide as the disposable spacer material has also been described.[82] Since hot phosphoric acid is used to strip the nitride spacers, fewer defects occur in the re-ox oxide layer beneath the thin poly protective layer than when the BOE spacer removal etch process is used to remove the disposable LTO spacers. A thinner re-ox oxide can thus be used. This is advantageous as less gate-bird's beak (GGO) is formed in the gate oxide at the edges of the poly gate during the re-ox process.

If a salicide process is to be included in a CMOS technology, the disposable polysilicon spacer fabrication sequence described earlier must be modified in several ways. First, an additional permanent oxide spacer must be formed after all the LDD implant steps are completed (to permit the silicide to be formed on both the source/drain and poly gate regions without shorting between them). A sequence for fabricating a dual-gate CMOS technology (i.e., p^+ poly for PMOS and n^+ poly for NMOS) with disposable poly spacers is shown in Fig. 9-40.[84] To permit this technique to be used when devices are scaled to 0.5 μm an additional modification is made. That is, a thin CVD TEOS oxide is deposited on the re-oxidized polysilicon gate before the poly spacer layer is deposited. This is done because a sufficiently thick oxide layer must exist under the poly spacer film (i.e., at least 150Å) to prevent damage to the substrate during the

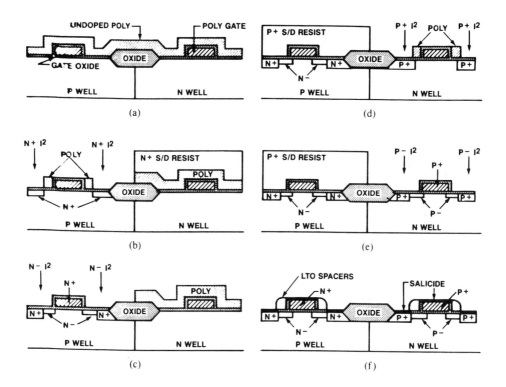

Fig. 9-40 Disposable polysilicon spacer process.[84] (© 1991 IEEE).

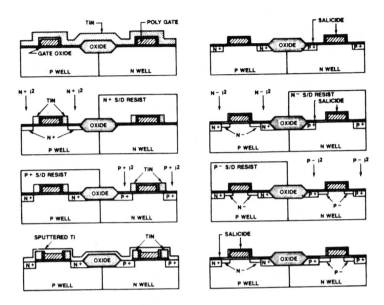

Fig. 9-41   Disposable TiN spacer process.[85] (© 1989 IEEE).

overetch time of the spacer formation process. If such a thick oxide film was grown during the poly re-ox step, the gate birds beak that would result would penetrate too far into the channel in devices (because of the heavy doping of the poly gate) whose gate lengths approached 0.5 μm. The use of the CVD TEOS film in combination with a thinner thermal oxide film formed during poly re-ox will sufficiently suppress the gate bird's beak and yet provide an adequately thick oxide under the poly spacer. Also note that to permit the dual gate technology to be implemented, the poly over the PMOS regions is not etched back to form spacers until both the n^+ and n^- implants are performed.

However, a technique has also been reported that allows a single disposable spacer to be used to form both the LDD and the salicide regions. But this approach requires the use of a different disposable spacer material than polysilicon, namely TiN. The disposable TiN spacer process sequence is shown in Fig. 9-41.[85] A technique that uses $CoSi_2$ disposable spacers has also been described.[86]

9.9 SUMMARY OF THE LIMITATIONS OF EARLY LDD DEVICES

In many cases, early LDD devices were able to provide improved hot-carrier reliability compared to conventional single-drain MOSFETs. However, these early LDDs also exhibited many drawbacks, including the distinct possibility that if they were improperly designed, or if the manufacturing processes were not tightly controlled, their hot-carrier reliability could no better (or even worse) than that exhibited by conventional MOSFETs. The following reasons summarize why early LDD devices were prone to such variability.

First, the n^- implant dose in early LDDs was too low, which degraded the drain current more than necessary, even prior to hot-carrier stressing. Second, this low dose caused the location of $\mathcal{E}_{ymax}$ to be outside of the edge of the gate, and also made the n^- region under the spacer susceptible to depletion by the hot-carrier damage that was highest above the point of $\mathcal{E}_{ymax}$. It was possible for the latter two effects to combine and severely degrade the hot-carrier reliability of the device. Third, the above problems were exacerbated by the fact that the 7° tilt angle used in the LDD implants, together with non-optimized GGO, caused significant asymmetrical I_{Dsat} characteristics in 1 μm and smaller devices. Finally, the optimum field-reduction-factor (FRF) in the conventional LDD could not be achieved as this would have required a fully overlapped LDD structure. To achieve a fully overlapped n^- region, the vertical depth of the n^-/p junction would have ended up being too deep to control short-channel effects in submicron MOSFETs. For all these reasons, modifications to early LDD structures were needed to make them capable of providing hot-carrier protection in sub-micron devices. The design and fabrication effort undertaken to achieve such hot-carrier- resistant device structures in submicron devices has been termed *drain engineering*.

9.10 SUMMARY OF THE METHODS TO BE USED IN DESIGNING EFFECTIVE LDD STRUCTURES

Some of the weaknesses exhibited by early LDD structures arose because the guidelines used to design them were based on erroneous or incomplete understanding of the behavior of the structure. That is, it was believed that the most important issue with respect to hot-carrier reliability was to reduce $\mathcal{E}_{ymax}$ as much as possible. Simulations were carried out to calculate $\mathcal{E}_{ymax}$ for various values of L_{n^-} and n^- dose, and the drive currents of MOSFETs with the corresponding n^- regions were also computed. Device designs based on the values of n^- and L_{n^-} chosen from these analyses were fabricated, and I_{sub} was measured as a monitor of $\mathcal{E}_{ymax}$ to ensure that sufficient hot-carrier stability was indeed achieved from these choices. However, it was learned later that such factors as the location of the $\mathcal{E}_{ymax}$ point, and the "structural degradation effect" also played an important role in how much the LDD increased the lifetimes of the devices. Consequently, merely knowing $\mathcal{E}_{ymax}$ and I_{sub} in a device was not enough to determine whether an LDD was optimally designed.

Instead, optimization of an LDD MOSFET involves many device parameters besides the n^- dose, implant energy, and the value of L_{n^-}. These include the value of the offset of the n^- dose from the gate edge as a result of the re-ox step, the thermal budget after the n^- implant, and the channel doping (the latter two determine the gate-to-n^- overlap). Selecting the optimum set of these parameters to obtain the most effective LDD structure for the device at hand is a complex task.

The dilemma faced by process and device engineers is to how to devise an optimized drain structure in the face of all the possible choices. From a realistic perspective only a reduced number of the alternatives can possibly be investigated, partly due to the time-consuming lifetime stress tests. These tests constitute an essential input and represent perhaps the ultimate criterion for selecting the best structure among the different possibilities. However, the necessity of conducting such lifetime tests runs up against a major obstacle. That is, the time pressure of shorter device-design cycle times conflicts with the need to investigate a broader spectrum of drain structures since the hot-carrier sensitivity increases as the devices continue to shrink. The only way to be able to carry out lifetime tests on a wide spectrum of drain structures in a short period of time when designing a next-generation MOSFET is to rely on simulation results to identify the most promising alternatives.

Such simulation, however, must be able to provide information beyond the values of $\mathcal{E}_{ymax}$ and I_{sub} that were the outputs of the early simulators. Such information permitted only the physics of degradation to be better understood and/or rough technological choices to be made. Unfortunately, this usually did not provide sufficient data to allow the degradation behavior of the actual devices to be correctly predicted. That is, an increase in $\mathcal{E}_{ymax}$ or I_{sub} does not necessarily translate into a lifetime reduction. Transistor degradation is also related to the damage of the gate oxide and Si-SiO$_2$ interface near the gate edge, both of which arise from hot-carrier injection. For an improved optimization of the drain structure, such effects require more evaluation than merely the value of $\mathcal{E}_{ymax}$. That is, the physical process which causes the degradation must also be considered in the simulation. A self-consistent calculation of the amount and position of the oxide damage is required in order to be able to carry out a direct evaluation of the device lifetime.

One such modeling tool for carrying out the above simulation task was developed by Hansch et al. in 1991.[87] This tool allows the time development of the device degradation under a dc stress condition to be directly monitored. It is able to predict the location and amount of gate oxide damage during the stress experiment by calculating the injection of carriers into the oxide region along the direction from the source to drain and by solving the continuity equation to obtain the carrier distribution in the oxide. This simulation routine was incorporated as a module of the device simulator MINIMOS IV. With such a simulation capability it becomes possible to direct and concentrate experimental efforts toward better devices while simultaneously helping to reduce development time and cost.

9.11 IMPROVED CONVENTIONAL (OXIDE-SPACER-BASED) LDD STRUCTURES

In section 9.6.1.2 we indicated that to optimize the hot-carrier resistance of the LDD structure, the n^+ region should be located at the edge (or just under the edge) of the gate, and the n^- region should be located entirely under the gate. Unfortunately, this optimum device structure is not easy to fabricate. That is, achieving full n^- overlap in an oxide-spacer-based LDD dictates the use of a very narrow spacer together with a substantial thermal drive-in. Unfortunately, in submicron CMOS technologies this approach would cause the S/D junctions in both the NMOS and PMOS transistors to be too deep to control short-channel effects. In fact, in the limit of very short spacer widths the LDD would essentially revert back to being a DDD structure, making it subject to the same minimum channel-length constraints.

While alternative device structures with fully overlapped n^- regions have been developed, these require quite complex manufacturing sequences. Nevertheless, when gate lengths shrink below $L = 0.5$ μm their implementation may become necessary. Thus we will consider such alternative structures in later sections.

On the other hand, oxide-spacer-based LDDs with only *partial n^--to-gate overlap* have also been developed that provide adequate hot-carrier lifetimes for gate lengths that approach 0.5 μm. Such partial-overlap LDDs are less complex to fabricate than the full-overlap structures, but are no more susceptible to short-channel effects than early LDDs. Hence, some of them have been designed into 0.6-1.5 μm CMOS technologies. Here we describe such *modified oxide-spacer-based LDDs*.

The evolution of modified LDD devices has involved the following three approaches to improving characteristics of the conventional LDD:[90]

1. The doping concentration in the n^- region of the LDD structure is increased to improve the drive-current capability and to reduce the "structural degradation effect" that worsens the hot-carrier lifetime of the conventional LDD. The latter problem is alleviated by this approach because the location of ε_{ymax} apparently moves beneath the edge of the gate when the doping concentration in the n^- region is sufficiently increased. The structures that exploit this approach are the *moderately-doped LDD* (M-LDD) and the *metal-coated LDD* (MLD).

2. The vertical profile of the n^- region is modified in an attempt to steer the path of current away from the surface of the MOSFET and to separate the location of ε_{ymax} and the path of maximum current flow in the device. The structures that pursue this approach are the *buried LDD* (B-LDD), the *profiled LDD* (P-LDD), and the *sloped-junction LDD* (SJLDD).

3. Dopants are selectively implanted beneath the n^- region to reduce the susceptibility of submicron LDD structures to short-channel effects. The structure that pursues this approach is the *double-implanted LDD* (DI-LDD).

9.11.1 Increasing the Doping in the n^- Region of the LDD

9.11.1.1 Moderate Lightly Doped Drain (M-LDD). The first approach to improving the conventional LDD involves only an increase in the doping of the n^- region of the drain. This was first proposed by Kinegawa in 1985, who dubbed the resulting device the *moderate lightly doped drain* (or M-LDD) structure.[88] Another report detailing the characteristics of the M-LDD was published by Krieger et al. in 1991.[89] The spacer width and thermal budget after n^- implant are basically the same as in the conventional LDD, but the dose of the n^- implant is increased from 5×10^{12}-2×10^{13} cm^{-2} to 4×10^{13}-1×10^{14} cm^{-2}.

The increased n^- doping implies that ε_{ymax} is not reduced as much as in the conventional LDD, but several problems of that structure are overcome such that the

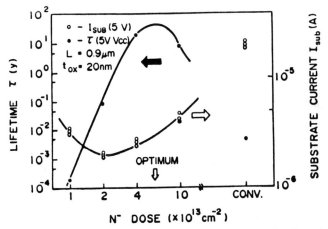

Fig. 9-42   The dependence of device lifetime and substrate current level on the n^- region implant dose in the LDD device structure. The minimum substrate current point is at 2×10^{17} cm^{-2} and the maximum lifetime point is at $5\text{-}6 \times 10^{13}$ cm^{-2}.[88] (© 1985 IEEE).

M-LDD exhibits increased hot-carrier resistance and improved drive current. Figure 9-42 shows the lifetime τ and I_{sub} of the LDD device as a function of the n^- implant dose. It is seen that τ in the M-LDD structure can be longer than that of a conventional LDD (in which $n^- = 1 \times 10^{13}$ cm^{-2}), despite the fact that I_{sub} is larger. In fact, at an optimal n^- doping ($n^- = 5\text{-}6 \times 10^{13}$ cm^{-2}), the M-LDD exhibits four to five orders of magnitude improvement in lifetimes over the conventional LDD with channel lengths down to 0.8 μm (for $V_{DD} = 5$V).[88] It is believed that this structure can be effectively used for devices with L_{eff} down to 0.6 μm.[89] Indeed, the advantages of the M-LDD are so great that to a large extent it has been incorporated into many devices (see for example ref. 81) - which are nevertheless generally still classified as LDD, but are actually M-LDD.

The benefits of increasing the n^- region doping in the MLDD arise for several reasons. First, the sheet resistance of the n^- region is lower than that of the light LDD, even prior to stressing. This improves the M-LDD current drive over that of lighter dosed LDDs. Second, the value of the current drive in the M-LDD is apparently much less sensitive to variations in the oxide spacer thickness than in the light-dose LDD. Third, the increased doping apparently moves the location of $\mathcal{E}_{ymax}$ under the gate edge, such that the damaged region in the oxide also lies beneath the gate edge, rather than outside the gate-overlap area as occurs in the light-dose LDD. Thus, the structural degradation effect that leads to more rapid hot-carrier degradation in light-dose LDDs is overcome. Finally, it should be noted that while gate-n^- overlap in the M-LDD is greater than in the light-dose LDD (in Krieger's report this overlap was found to be ~0.15 μm), it appears that the resultant increase in gate-to-drain capacitance does not significantly degrade the gate delays if an M-LDD is used in place of a light-dose LDD in such digital circuits.

9.11.1.2 Metal-coated LDD (MLD). The *metal-coated LDD* (MLD) is another oxide-spacer-based LDD structure that increases the doping in the n^- region above the levels used in light-doped LDDs.[91] Here, however, a deeper phosphorus implant dose is used than in the M-LDD and a silicide (e.g., $TiSi_2$) is also formed atop the n^+ source/drain regions (Fig. 9-42b). The deeper n^- implant steers the path of maximum current somewhat away from the position of maximum field at the surface. This reduces the impact ionization rate. As a result, a smaller I_{sub} occurs than is observed in light-dose LDDs with the same gate lengths. The silicide layer reduces the sheet resistance of the drain even further.

It has been shown that the MLD structure can sustain 5-V operation in MOSFETs with $L_{eff} = 0.6$ μm, and the structure has reportedly been incorporated into the ATT Twin-Tub CMOS V technology.[92] In ref. 92 several issues were also raised relative to integrating the MLD structure into a CMOS process, including: ensuring that the gate-drain overlap is large enough to cover implant shadowing effects that can result in asymmetrical device characteristics; choosing a spacer width that is optimized to prevent bridging between the gate and source-drain while ensuring consistent silicide formation in a production environment, and not incurring excessive S/D resistance; and adjusting the p-LDD doping to overcome the blanket n-LDD implant under worst case implant condition, saving a masking step to form both n- and p-LDD devices (see chap. 8).

9.11.2 Tailoring the Vertical Doping Profile of the n^- Implant to Improve the Conventional LDD

Besides increasing the n^- doping concentration, exploiting the effect of variations in the vertical doping profile of the n^- region have also been explored. Several structures have been proposed that employ an n^- LDD region whose peak concentration is beneath (instead of at) the surface. Reportedly this produces devices with better hot carrier resistance.

9.11.2.1 Buried-LDD (B-LDD). In the first of such devices, termed the *buried-LDD* (B-LDD)[93] or the *sloped-junction LDD* (SJ-LDD)[94] a deep (e.g., 165 keV) n^- implant is used. (see Fig. 9-43a). The n^- implants in the two respective structures are As [BLDD] and P [SJLDD]. The deep implant produces a vertical retrograde n^- doping profile, which causes the contour of the channel/n^- junction to be inclined at a non-perpendicular angle to the Si surface (see Fig. 9-43b). Since the electric field of a *pn* junction is roughly normal to the junction contour, the channel/n^- junction field will thus assist the gate field $\mathcal{E}_x$ in steering the electron current (and the impact ionization region) away from the surface and deeper into the silicon bulk. As the location of $\mathcal{E}_{ymax}$ remains at the surface, the current path is steered away from this point and less heating of the channel carriers results. Not only are there fewer hot carriers (as indicated by a reduction in I_{sub}), but these also have a lower probability of being able to traverse the increased distance to the Si-SiO$_2$ interface without recombining. Hence, less injection (and thus less oxide damage) results, and longer hot-carrier lifetimes are obtained.

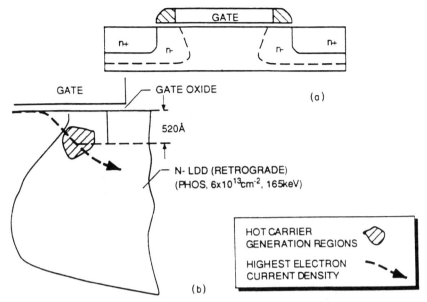

Fig. 9-43 (a) Schematic cross-section of the drain region of the *buried LDD* (B-LDD) structure.[93] (© 1985 IEEE); (b) Electric-field lines are normal to the buried *pn* junction, which steers the drain current away from the surface in this structure.[94] (© 1988 IEEE).

In the *graded-buried LDD* (GB-LDD)[95] the deep arsenic implant of the B-LDD is combined with the light *n⁻* phosphorus dose of the conventional LDD (see Fig. 9-44). This results in a buried *n⁻* profile that has a higher surface concentration than the B-LDD and which is also graded in the lateral direction when a thermal drive is carried out. This structure exhibits even better hot-carrier resistance than the BLDD, as seen in Fig. 9-45.

9.11.2.2 Profiled-LDD (P-LDD).
If the implanted regions of the buried LDD structures just described are too deep, the concentration at the surface of the *n⁻* regions just under the gate are reduced. This will cause degraded lifetime and increased parasitic drain resistance[96] (the latter effect is worsened by current crowding as described in ref. 145). This is one reason why the GB-LDD exhibits improved lifetimes compared to the B-LDD.

The GB-LDD structures can be even further improved by combining a very shallow moderately doped *n⁻* region (e.g., As @ 50 keV) just under the surface, with a deeper retrograde *n⁻* region (e.g., phosphorus, $1\text{-}5\times10^{13}$ cm⁻²) formed by a high-energy implant ($\geq$150 keV). The shallow, abrupt As layer serves to increase the surface doping concentration and to reduce the impact of current crowding effects at the source end on the S/D resistance. After the two *n⁻* implants are performed, a high temperature anneal is used to laterally diffuse the phosphorus more than the arsenic. After subsequent oxide spacer formation, the *n⁺* source/drain region is formed. Such a structure was first proposed by Toyoshima et al., in 1985, and the process sequence for forming it is

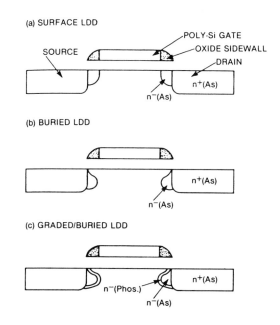

Fig. 9-44 Schematic cross-section of the *graded buried LDD* (GB-LDD).[95] (© 1986 IEEE).

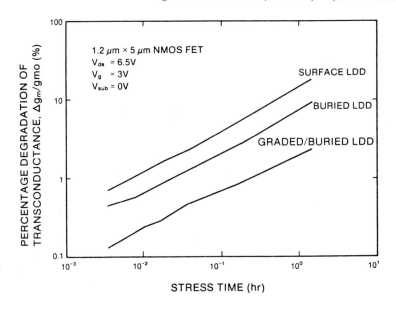

Fig. 9-45 Measured degradation in MOSFET transconductance under hot electron stress for the conventional LDD, B-LDD, and GB-LDD structures.[95] (© 1986 IEEE).

shown in Fig. 9-46.[97] A similar structure was reported by Chen et al., but they also added a TiSi$_2$ salicide layer.[92]

The P-LDD approach thus seeks to achieve all of the following objectives:

1. Reduction of the maximum electric field ε_{ymax} in the silicon, as compared to the conventional LDD.

2. Ensuring that the injection position (i.e., the ε_{ymax} point) is located under the gate edge.

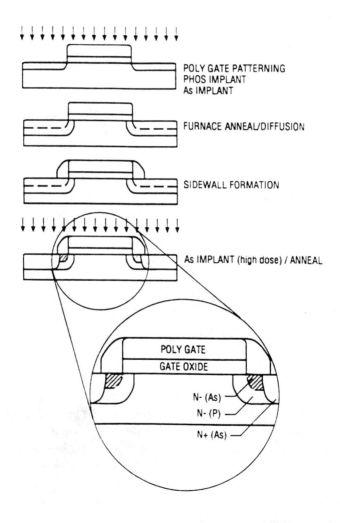

POLY GATE PATTERNING
PHOS IMPLANT
As IMPLANT

FURNACE ANNEAL/DIFFUSION

SIDEWALL FORMATION

As IMPLANT (high dose) / ANNEAL

POLY GATE

GATE OXIDE

N- (As)

N- (P)

N+ (As)

Fig. 9-46   Profiled LDD (PLDD) process sequence.[97] (© 1985 IEEE).

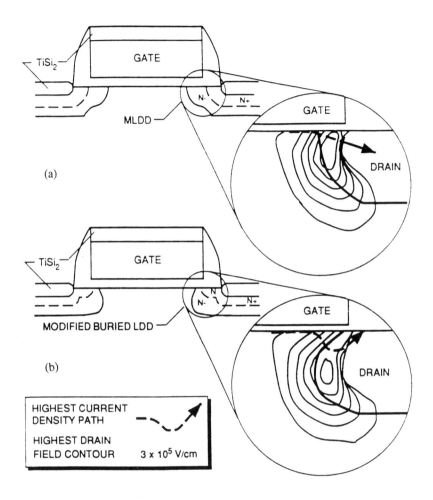

Fig. 9-47 Structure and lateral-field distribution for (a) MLD structure. (b) modified profiled LDD structure.[92] (© 1988 IEEE).

3. Separation of the point where the electric field in the silicon is at a maximum from the point of maximum current flow in the channel.

4. Ensuring that the impact-ionization region is pushed below the silicon sur-face to reduce the probability of hot carriers reaching the Si-SiO$_2$ interface.

5. Minimization of the increase in the parasitic resistance due to the LDD structure.

A simulation of the electric field and current path in this device is also shown in Fig. 9-47, where it is compared with those in an MLD-type structure. We see that in the

P-LDD structure there are two electric field peaks, but both are under the gate edge (Objective #2). We also observe that the current path is steered beneath the surface (Objective #4) and through the saddle point between these two peaks (Objective #3). A reduction in I_{sub} and the ratio of I_{sub}/I_D compared to MLD devices is also observed in P-LDDs, implying that $\mathcal{E}_{ymax}$ is reduced even more than in MLD-type devices (Objective #1). Objective #5 is met by the use of the shallow As n^- implant. Because the structure satisfies all of the above objectives it has been perceived as one of the most promising of the modified oxide-spacer-based LDD structures with respect to achieving high drive current and hot-electron resistance performance for MOSFETs down to 0.6 μm.[98] The lateral and vertical doping gradients in such structures, however, are quite complex, and this could cause manufacturing difficulties. Furthermore, it still requires a long high-temperature anneal to form the lightly graded region, and this may degrade the short-channel performance of such structures to a degree that they may not be suitable for devices with $L \leq 0.5$ μm.

9.11.3 Improving the Short-Channel Performance of the Conventional NMOS LDD

As noted in chap. 5, as MOSFET gate lengths are made shorter, various unwanted short-channel effects occur. One such effect in NMOSFETs is subsurface-DIBL (or punchthrough). While punchthrough stopper implants are used to suppress this problem, they become less effective as the gate length approaches 0.5 μm. An alternative technique to suppress punchthrough in such deep submicron LDD NMOSFETs is to locally implant p-type dopants (in NMOSFETs) under the lightly doped tip region of the LDD as shown in Fig. 9-48a. Such implants have been termed "halo" implants, and were first proposed for use in LDD NMOSFETs by Codella and Ogura in 1985. They called devices containing "halo" implants *double-implanted LDDs* (DI-LDDs).[99] Note that the use of halo-type implants as punchthrough stoppers in PMOSFETs is discussed in section 5.8.3.4.

Because the implanted dopant raises the doping concentration only on the inside walls of the source/drain junctions, the channel length can be decreased without needing to use a higher-doped substrate. That is, punchthrough does not set in until a shorter channel length because of the "halo." A penalty in increased sidewall junction capacitance is paid, but this cost is smaller than that incurred should the bottom area of the junctions lie above heavily doped substrate material. The maximum halo doping is determined by the onset of low-level avalanche breakdown of the pn^+ junction as is shown in Fig. 9-48b. Careful implant control is also essential to avoid compensation effects due to overlapping n- and p-dopants.

A halo NMOSFET with $L = 0.35$ μm was reported that operated at 3V with $t_{ox} = 15$ nm. The junction depth r_j was ~0.14 μm and the p-halo peak doping was ~3×10^{17} cm^{-3}. A more recent report applied a *large-angle tilt* implantation (LAT - see section 9.12.2) of boron ions in NMOS and phosphorus in PMOS (Fig. 9-48c) to form a halo-like punchthrough suppression region in each device, called SPI (*self-aligned pocket implantation*).[101,102] In NMOSFETs this approach first creates a conventional LDD structure, using an n^- implant, a spacer oxide, and an n^+ implant. Note that the n^- dose will usually have to be increased to avoid compensation by the p^+ pocket implant. This is followed by the formation of $TiSi_2$ (salicide process). The SPI step is performed next, using a 40 keV, $8x10^{12}$ cm^{-2} phosphorus implant at a tilt angle of 25-30° to create the pockets of dopants. The gate/spacer structure and the $TiSi_2$ layer both act as self-aligned implant masks to define the regions into which the pocket dopant can penetrate.

Devices with channel lengths as small as 0.2 μm that still exhibited long-channel subthreshold V_T behavior were fabricated. Another report by Duvvury et al. indicated that unless the doping profile of the p^+ halo implant was correctly optimized, the DI-LDD would exhibit more susceptibility to electrostatic-discharge damage.[103]

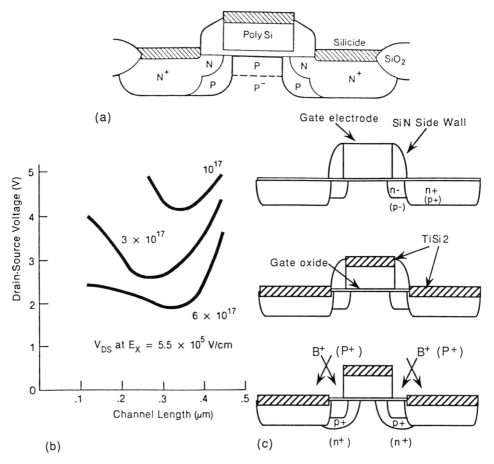

Fig. 9-48 (a) DI-LDD device cross-section. (b) Drain-Source voltage limit from low-level avalanche breakdown versus channel length for various peak halo doses.[99] (© 1985 IEEE). (c) Process sequence of SPI for NMOSFET and (PMOSFETs).[101] (© 1991 IEEE).

9.12 FULLY OVERLAPPED LDD STRUCTURES

As noted in section 9.6.1.2, an LDD structure with the gate fully overlapping the n^- region appears to be the optimum structure with respect to hot-carrier resistance and drive-current performance. Yet, this device structure is difficult to fabricate in submicron devices using the conventional oxide-spacer-based LDD approach. That is, the long thermal drive-in step required to drive the n^- region completely under the gate also produces a deep vertical junction, such that short-channel effects become excessive.

A variety of other device structures have been proposed to achieve the full-overlap condition, including the inverse-T structure (IT-LDD), the large-angle-tilt implanted drain (LATID) structure, the asymmetrical halo-source gate-overlapped LDD structure (HS-GOLD), and the high-dielectric-spacer structure. Here we describe these structures in more detail.

9.12.1 Inverse-T Gate LDD (ITLDD) and Gate-Drain Overlapped Device (GOLD) Structures

9.12.1.1 Inverse-T Gate LDD Structure.
The first fully overlapped LDD structure was described by Huang et al. in 1986.[104,105] They named it the *inverse-T gate LDD* since the gate resembles that shape (see Fig. 9-49). Note that the conductive lateral poly extensions at the base of the gate completely overlap the n^- region of the LDD. The full overlap is produced by self-aligning the n^- region to the inside edge of

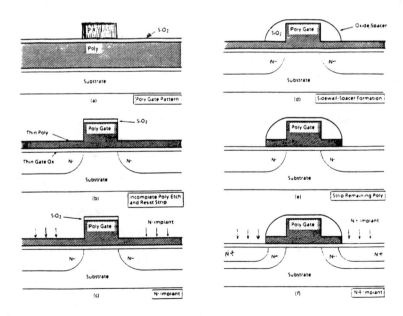

Fig. 9-49 Process sequence for ITLDD.[104] (© 1986 IEEE).

the inverse-T gate (by implanting phosphorus through the thin poly extensions), and by aligning the n^+ region to the outside edge of the gate. The latter alignment is achieved by forming an oxide spacer and then carrying out the n^+ implant. The n^+-to-gate offset is eliminated by this second self-alignment. (The remaining thin poly outside of the spacer regions is etched away prior to the n^+ implant.) No thermal step is needed to drive the n^+ dopants beneath the oxide spacer, and only a short RTP anneal is needed for implant dopant activation. Furthermore, since ε_{ymax} is certain to be under the gate edge, a lower n^- dose can be used than in an M-LDD. Typically, n^- doses of 1×10^{13} cm^{-2} are used. The lower n^- doping helps reduce the gate-to-drain overlap capacitance.

IT-LDD structures with L as small as 0.6 μm have been found to exhibit excellent current drive, hot-carrier resistance, and short-channel behavior (punchthrough resistance). Hot-carrier lifetimes greater than 10 are years projected for 0.6 μm IT-LDD devices at 5V operation.

Despite the performance benefits that this structure provides, the original IT-LDD also has a number of serious limitations besides the obvious increase in process complexity, including the following:

1. *Difficulty in controlling the processes that form the poly extensions.* The key process in the sequence of fabricating the IT-LDD is the incomplete etch of the poly gate. An etch step creates the thin (50-100 nm thick) poly-gate extension regions. But it is difficult to control the poly thickness in a production environment because of the non-uniformity of the poly CVD and plasma etch processes, and because there is no natural etchstop or endpoint signal. Any nonuniformity in the thickness of these extensions results in changes to the vertical doping profile of the LDD n^- region.

2. *Damage of the gate oxide edge by the n^+ implant.* When the n^+ implant is carried out, the gate oxide at the outer edges of the poly gate is exposed to this implant. Arsenic implants through thin oxides at doses $\geq 1\times10^{14}$ cm^{-2} have been identified as processes that degrade their dielectric breakdown voltage.[106] Hence, IT-LDD structures in which the gate oxide at the gate edge is not protected from the n^+ implant are prone to gate-oxide breakdown failures.

3. *Increase in gate-to-drain overlap capacitance.* The gate-to-drain overlap capacitance of the IT-LDD is higher than in non-fully overlapped LDD structures, despite the fact that a lower n^- dose can be used in the IT-LDD.

4. *Doping compensation problem in submicron LDDs is not corrected.* The problem of increased source/drain resistance due to compensation effects is not solved. This problem arises from the interaction of regions of high doping in the channels - needed in submicron devices - with those of comparable doping concentration, but opposite doping type, in the n^- regions.

We will see how modifications were made to the original IT-LDD structure to overcome these disadvantages.

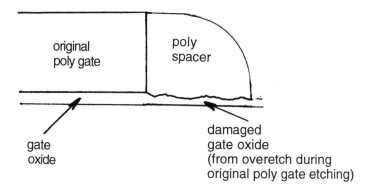

Fig. 9-50 Poly spacer acting as a poly gate extension can result in damaged oxide beneath the poly spacer that is subject to early breakdown.

Also note that poly extensions on a conventional poly gate could be created more simply, i.e., by forming poly spacers (instead of oxide spacers) after the n^- implant (see Fig. 9-50). The problem with this approach, however, is that when the original poly gate is etched (with an anisotropic etch to produce vertical sidewalls on the poly), some overetching must be employed. The exposed gate oxide is damaged during the overetch time and such damaged oxides exhibit early gate-oxide breakdown failures when subsequently covered by the poly spacers. Note that no re-ox can be used, because the poly spacer must make electrical contact to the main poly region to be able to act as an extension of the gate.

9.12.1.2 Gate-Drain Overlapped LDD (GOLD). A device quite similar to the IT-LDD structure was proposed by Izawa et al. in 1987,[107,108] which they termed the *gate-drain overlapped device* (GOLD). The GOLD device (Fig. 9-51) has two improvements designed to overcome two of the drawbacks of the IT-LDD structure described above. First, the poly gate film is deposited in two layers, with the first layer exposed to oxygen after deposition to allow a native oxide (5-10Å thick) to form on the surface at that time. When the two layer film is later etched to form the thin poly extensions, the native oxide layer serves as an etch stop - which should improve the control of this key poly etch process. Second, prior to implanting the n^+ region, the thin poly extensions are oxidized by a process that is called SELOCS (*selective oxide coating of silicon-gate*). This step serves two functions: (1) the length of the overlap of the gate and the n^- region overlap can be adjusted by this step; and (2) the gate oxide at the edge of the gate is now protected from exposure to the n^+ As implant, thus preserving the gate oxide integrity of the MOSFET. (Note, however, that no information is provided as to how to ensure a good electrical contact between the two poly layers of the gate separated by the native oxide.)

9.12.1.3 Modified IT-LDD Structures.

Several other versions of the IT-LDD structure have been reported which seek to improve the manufacturability and/or performance of the structure even further. The first is called an *inverse-T gate fully overlapped LDD* (FOLD),[109] which is an IT-LDD structure made with a more formidable etchstop layer between the two poly layers than the native oxide layer used in the GOLD structure. This etchstop layer is either a very thin (40Å) thermally grown oxide layer (Fig. 9-52a), or a PVD TiN layer (Fig. 9-52b), as both materials exhibit good selectivities to poly during reactive ion etching. The use of this etchstop further improves the control of the thickness of the poly extensions. In the process that uses the thermal oxide grown on the first poly layer, another thin layer of poly (300Å thick) must be deposited after the inverse-T poly gate is patterned and the thermal oxide etchstop layer is removed (with a short HF dip). The extra thin poly layer permits the upper and lower layers of the initial poly stack (which are separated by the thermal oxide etchstop) to be electrically connected. In the structure that uses the TiN etchstop, the extra poly layer is not needed. In both cases, As is used to form the n^- region as no additional drive-in is required to achieve n^- overlap. This structure exhibits adequate hot-

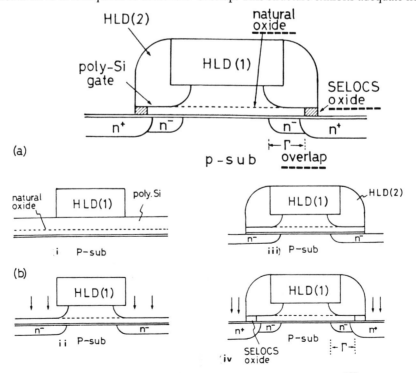

Fig. 9-51 (a) Schematic cross section; and (b) Process sequence of GOLD.[107] (© 1989 IEEE).

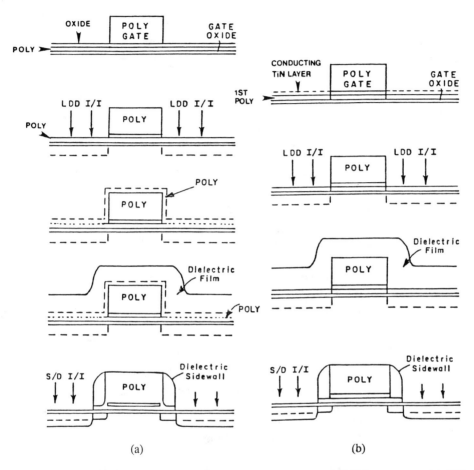

(a)   (b)

Fig. 9-52 (a) Process sequence for forming the FOLD structure; (b) FOLD structure with TiN etchstop layer.[109] (© 1989 IEEE).

carrier lifetimes for devices with $L = 0.35$ μm at a power supply of 3.5V.

A similar structure to the FOLD is the *total overlap with polysilicon spacer structure* (TOPS).[110] Instead of a thermal oxide etchstop layer in the poly gate stack, a 400Å CVD oxide layer is used (Fig. 9-53). The two poly gate layers are electrically connected with a poly spacer that is formed (in lieu of an oxide spacer) after the n^- implant is carried out. Note that it would be very difficult to form a salicide structure on the TOPS device as there is no oxide spacer to prevent the gate and source/drain from shorting during the silicidation step, and that neither the FOLD nor the TOPS structure provides protection of the oxide at the gate edges from the n^+ implant.

We noted earlier that it would be possible to create poly extensions on a conventional poly gate more simply by forming poly spacers (instead of oxide spacers) after the

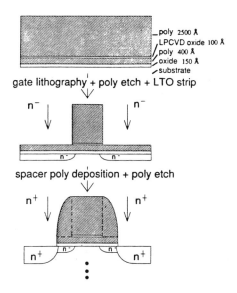

poly   2500 Å
LPCVD oxide 100 Å
poly   400 Å
oxide   150 Å
substrate

gate lithography + poly etch + LTO strip

n⁻   n⁻

spacer poly deposition + poly etch

n⁺   n⁺

Fig. 9-53 TOPS structure layered gate and polysilicon spacer formation. Gate and spacer definition are accomplished by plasma etching with oxide endpoint detection. Typical CVD thicknesses are shown.[110] (© 1990 IEEE).

n^- implant. However, the gate oxide ending up beneath these poly spacers would be damaged by the poly etch. This would make such fully overlapped structures subject to early gate oxide breakdown failures. However, by re-growing gate oxide above the active regions exposed to the poly gate etch, as is done in the poly   re-ox process, the resulting fresh oxide would exhibit adequate reliability. Unfortunately, if poly spacers were formed at this point, it appears that they could not serve as gate extensions, as they would be electrically disconnected from the gate.

However, in another IT-LDD-like structure proposed by I. Chen et al.,[111] poly extensions are formed after a re-ox process as described above, and the oxide grown on the poly sidewalls is apparently so heavily damaged by the n^+ implant that the gate and the poly spacer become electrically connected together. Hence, we can identify this structure as a *damaged re-ox layer fully overlapped structure*. Furthermore, by adding an additional oxide spacer to the edge of the poly spacer (Fig. 9-54),[112] the n^- overlap distance can be controlled (i.e., it becomes a partially overlapped device), and the oxide at the gate edge can be protected from the damage due to the n^+ implant in the same way that SELOCS protects the gate oxide in GOLD structures. In the partially overlapped device, the gate-to-drain capacitance is also significantly reduced, compared to a fully overlapped IT-LDD device.

Instead of using a dome-shaped poly spacer, as was done in the TOPS and in the damaged re-ox layer fully overlapped devices, M. Chen et al. suggest the use of *L-shaped spacers* (Fig. 9-55).[113] These are connected to the main gate poly by a $TiSi_2$ strap that is formed when a salicide is created on this structure. To prevent the gate and

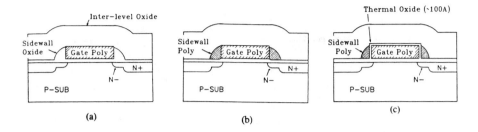

Fig. 9-54 Cross-sectional view of the (a) oxide spacer; (b) poly-spacer; and (c) oxide-padded poly spacer devices. The poly-spacer devices are permanent poly-sidewall to achieve the gate-to-drain overlap. For the oxide-padded poly-spacer device, due to the heavy source/drain implant, the thin thermal oxide between the gate and the poly spacer becomes conductive enough to keep the poly spacers at the same potential as the poly gate.[111] (© 1990 IEEE).

drain from shorting during the silicidation reaction, a nitride spacer is formed above the L-shaped spacer. It is much easier to integrate a salicide into this IT-LDD structure than in other IT-LDD structures.

The final IT-LDD structure we describe was proposed by Pfiester et al. in 1989. Here a novel approach is taken to forming the inverse-T gate.[114,115] That is, the main region of the gate is formed by selectively depositing poly, as shown in Fig. 9-56. After the main gate regions have been formed, a second layer of poly is blanket deposited to form the thin extension regions of the gate (see Fig. 9-56 again). The remainder of the process is similar to the conventional IT-LDD sequence. The advantages of this struc-

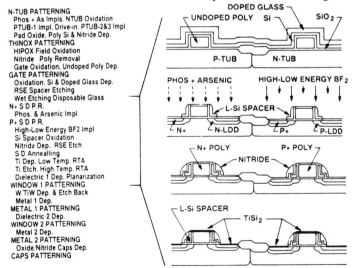

Fig. 9-55 Process sequence for self-aligned silicided L-shaped Si spacer LDD CMOS devices.[113] (© 1990 IEEE).

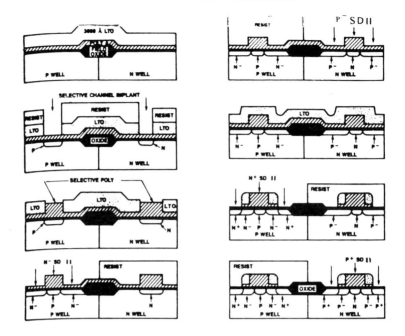

Fig. 9-56 Process sequence for forming self-aligned LDD/channel implanted ITLDD process with selectively-deposited poly gates for CMOS VLSI.[114] (© 1989 IEEE).

ture are: (1) a simpler, more manufacturable process sequence results, and (2) the channel dopants are only introduced into the region directly under the gate, not elsewhere. This avoids the compensation problem described in section 9.7.1.2 that occurs as heavier channel doping is encountered with shrinking channel length.

9.12.2 Large-Angle-Tilt Implanted Drain (LATID)

We have noted that fully overlapped drain structures can be fabricated with the IT-LDD approach, but that complex processing sequences are required that may be difficult to manufacture. A highly flexible technique for forming fully overlapped drains in submicron MOSFETs that is much simpler and also offers structure control and device performance improvements is based on large-angle-tilt implantation (LATID).[116-118,125] That is, this technique uses large tilt angles and target wafer rotational repositioning during implantation, without removing the wafer from the implant platen. The implant process sequence used to fabricate LATID is depicted in Fig. 9-57, together with the lateral doping profile that results (Fig. 9-58).

The first implant is performed after the poly gate is patterned, using an angle of 45-60° with a moderate phosphorus dose ($1-2 \times 10^{13}$ cm^{-2}) and energy (40-100 keV). This implant is carried out twice, with the wafer rotated 180° between these two implants, so that penetration of dopant under the gate is symmetrical. (In some circuit layouts in which some gates are oriented at right angles to other gates, four implants

90° apart would be needed.)   The function of this implant is to introduce the n^- region dopant under the gate at the desired depth and doping concentration without having to use a diffusion step. After the n^- implant is performed, a gate sidewall spacer (0.08-0.10 μm) is formed, followed by a conventional high dose As implant that self-aligns the n^+ source/drain region to the gate, sets the gate/n^+ drain offset, and determines the source/drain junction depth.   Note that to implement the LATID structure, an ion implanter that can vary the wafer tilt angle and also provide *in situ* repositioning of the wafer is needed.   Recently, medium-current implanters that feature the capability of precise angle control (i.e., the beam angle remains constant across the wafer surface) and rotational repositioning of the wafer have become available. Note that the LATID structure requires no additional mask sets, and can be implemented as a "drop in" process module in current CMOS production processes, for example, as a reliability/ performance enhancement or as a part of a process "shrink."

The LATID technique permits the length of the gate/n^- overlap region, the horizontal and vertical concentration profiles of the n^- region, and the n^+-to-gate region overlap to be set independently.   That is, the length of the lateral penetration of the n^- region can be increased by making the tilt angle larger (see Fig. 9-59). The length of the n^- region and its junction depth can be adjusted by the selection of the implant species and implant energy.   The local peak concentration is set independently by the implant dose. These n^- parameters can be optimized independently of the n^+ drain-to-gate overlap, which is adjustable by the gate sidewall-spacer width.

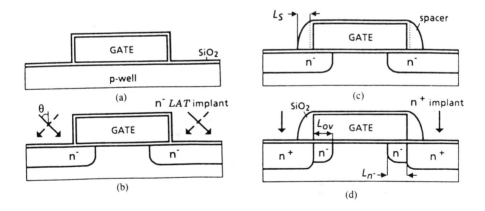

Fig. 9-57 Process sequences for 1/4 μm LATID FETs with ultrathin sidewall spacers. (a) 8.5-nm oxide formation and gate etching. (b) n^- LAT implant (tilt angle 45°). (c) formation of ultrathin ($L_S \leq 0.08$ μm) spacers. (d) n^+ implant and rapid thermal annealing (1000°C, 10 sec.)[117] (© 1989 IEEE).

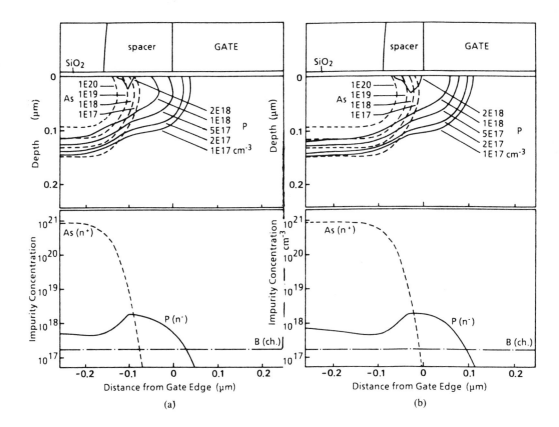

Fig. 9-58 Simulated 2D drain profiles and lateral ones near the surface (depth = 0.2 μm) for (a) conventional LDD; and (b) LATID with spacer devices after thermal annealing at 900°C for 10 min.[120] (© 1992 IEEE).

The LATID structures reportedly exhibit improved hot-carrier reliability and performance. NMOS LATID devices with a 0.5 μm gate length demonstrated extrapolated hot-carrier lifetimes of more than 10 years under 5V operation. The same device also exhibited high punchthrough immunity, i.e., similar to that of the control LDD device. The current drive capability was increased (i.e., by more than 50%) compared with the LDD control. The gate-to-drain capacitance is also reportedly significantly decreased below that of a conventional drain MOSFET.[119] It appears that the LATID device will be suitable for building MOSFETs to at least 0.25 μm, using power supplies of 3.3V.[120]

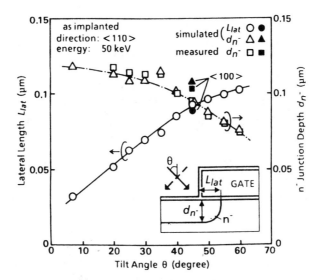

Fig. 9-59 Simulated lateral length L_{lat} from the implant-mask edge and n^- junction depth d_{n^-} at the gate edge (defined schematically in the inset figure) as a function of tilt angle θ for a constant ion flux N_{n^-} of 4×10^{13} cm^{-2}. Data of d_{n^-} estimated from SIMS measurements are also shown.[119] (© 1992 IEEE).

The gate-overlap capacitance of early (first-generation) LATID devices, however, was too high. This drawback was mitigated by incorporating a small (<0.1 μm) gate sidewall spacer in the second-generation LATID structures.[121] The resulting gate-overlap capacitance was reduced to a value comparable to that of a conventional LDD, even though the n^- region is well overlapped by the gate in the LATID. The small sidewall

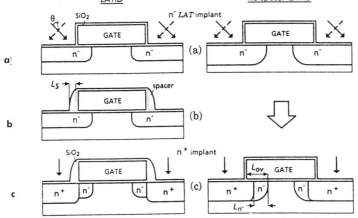

Fig. 9-60 Process sequence for LATID and *no-spacer* LATID. (a) n^- LAT implant after sidewall oxidation. (b) sidewall-spacer formation. (c) n^+ implant and annealing at 900°C for 10 min.[122] (© 1991 IEEE).

spacer is also needed to protect the gate oxide at the edge of the gate from being degraded by the n^+ implant, as described in the discussion on fabricating the IT-LDD.

An advanced LATID structure that also incorporates a self-aligned pocket implant that is also formed in combination with a LAT implant was described by Hori et al. in 1992.[122,123] Both NMOS and PMOS transistors can be built using this technique. The process sequence for fabricating this structure is illustrated in Fig. 9-60, where we also observe that a $TiSi_2$ film on the gate and source/drain regions and an epi substrate are also included. A dual-gate CMOS process is utilized, such that the PMOS transistor gates are doped p-type, and the NMOS gates n-type. Hence, both transistor types are surface-channel transistors. An inverter built with this CMOS process operates with a delay time of 30 ps and a power dissipation of 0.72 pJ.

Another LATID structure that deliberately incorporates a graded-gate oxide (GGO) region has also been described (see Fig. 9-61).[124] The GGO is formed by a poly re-ox step in a wet ambient at 850°C. This increases the 7-nm gate oxide thickness to about 25 nm at the edge of the gate. The presence of the GGO serves several functions in this structure. First, the vertical (gate) electric field is significantly smaller than that of the conventional LATID structure. This strongly suppresses the gate induced drain leakage (GIDL) current, which is high in LDDs (see chap. 4). Second, the gate-to-drain overlap capacitance is reduced as a result of the thicker gate oxide near the gate edges, where the gate-to-drain overlap occurs. This improves the propagation delay and power dissipation of the device compared with the conventional LATID fully overlapped MOSFET. These advantages in 0.6 μm T-gate LATID MOSFETs are obtained while maintaining comparable hot-carrier resistance as that of conventional 0.6 μm LATID structures.

9.12.3 High Dielectric Spacers

Fully overlapped LDDs have been created using IT-LDD and LATID structures. Another approach to obtaining the benefits of the fully overlapped LDD is to follow the conventional LDD process sequence, but to replace the oxide spacer with a spacer of higher dielectric constant (e.g., Si_3N_4, where $\varepsilon = 7.5$, or Ta_2O_5, where $\varepsilon = 30$), forming a so-called *high-dielectric spacer LDD* (H-LDD).[126-128] The effect of this replacement is to make a partially-overlapped LDD behave more like a fully overlapped LDD, especially as the gate lengths shrink to 0.5 μm or less. The use of high dielectric LDD spacers enhances the *gate fringing field* (GF) effects, which in turn increase the interaction of the gate and the n^- region beyond the gate edge. Up till now, the spacer material used for this purpose has been Si_3N_4. But since the GF effects are stronger if ε is larger, alternative spacer materials, such as Ta_2O_5 have also been considered. Furthermore, since the GF effects also become greater as devices are scaled down, the GF field becomes a more important factor in trying to exploit the benefits of scaled devices.

The H-LDD structure is shown in Fig. 9-62. Note that it could be created without the use of a poly sidewall and spacer-bottom oxide (Fig. 9-62b), but the Si/Si_3N_4 interface contains too high a density of interface states, and thus this structure exhibits poor hot-carrier resistance. The use of a thin poly sidewall and spacer-bottom oxide (Fig. 9-62c), reduces this problem, and the structure actually exhibits less degradation

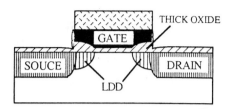

Fig. 9-61 T-gate overlapped LDD device structure.   The device has the thick gate-oxide above the LDD region.[124]   (© 1991 IEEE).

than an oxide-spacer LDD when $L = 0.5$ μm (see Fig. 9-63).   The hot-carrier reliability of the H-LDD is enhanced by the GF effect for other reasons as well.   First, the GF effect suppresses the structural degradation effect (negative charges built up in the spacer oxide deplete the n^- region and cause its resistance to rise).[128] This keeps the reduction of I_D during hot-carrier stress even smaller.   Second, the GF effect causes the impact ionization rate to decrease because the high drain potential edge is pushed and moves toward the drain n^+ region.   In essence, the GF effects enlarge the effective channel length, thereby reducing $\mathcal{E}_{ymax}$.

The drive-current capability of the H-LDD is also increased by the GF effect.   That is, the GF increases the vertical field in the source n^- region, causing the electron density to increase there.   Therefore, the LDD characteristic parasitic resistance of the n^- region under the LDD spacer decreases.   Then R_S becomes smaller, resulting in a higher g_m.

A sensitivity study of the impact of varying the thickness of both the polyoxide sidewall thickness and spacer bottom oxide on the performance and reliability of the H-LDD structure was recently reported.[129] This was a theoretical study that used the process and device simulators SUPREM IV and PISCES-2B to examine how the lateral electric field, drive current, and subthreshold leakage were altered as these two oxide thicknesses were varied and a high-dielectric spacer was used for the LDD structure.   The

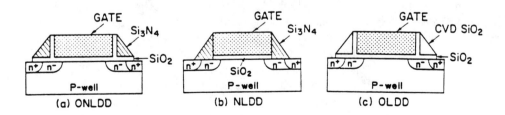

Fig. 9-62 Schematic cross section of three different LDD spacer structures.   The oxide under the nitride film is fabricated by the re-ox step. (a) Si_3N_4/SiO_2 spacer (ONLDD); (b) Si_3N_4 spacer (NLDD);   (c) oxide spacer (OLDD).[126]   (© 1988 IEEE).

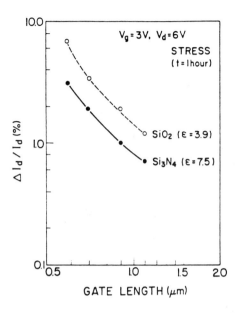

Fig. 9-63 Drain current degradation rate versus gate length for CVD-oxide spacer LDD and CVD-nitride spacer (with a 20 nm thick poly oxide).[127] (© 1989 IEEE).

results indicated that the structure can be optimized to give good performance and high hot-carrier reliability in devices with $L = 0.5 \, \mu$m.

9.12.4 Asymmetrical MOSFET Structure: Halo-Source-GOLD (HS-GOLD)

A novel approach to allow devices with gate lengths below 0.25 μm to possess adequate hot-carrier reliability is an asymmetrical MOSFET structure proposed in 1989 by Buti et al. They called this structure the *halo-source gate-overlapped drain* (HS-GOLD), and it is shown in Fig. 9-64.[130,131] Here the LAT implantation technique is used to form both a gate-overlapped structure only on the drain side of the gate (GOLD), as well as a halo implant punchthrough stopper (Halo Source - HS) only on the source side. This is accomplished by using two separate 45° implants, *p*- and *n*-type respectively. Superior hot carrier reliability and high punchthrough resistance were reported for this device, even at $L = 0.2 \, \mu$m. It is estimated that the structure would be adequate for gate lengths as small as 0.15 μm at a power supply voltage of 3.5V. The fabrication parameters used to build the structure are shown in Fig. 9-64b, including the LAT implant parameters. Figure 9-64c illustrates the doping profiles for a 0.5 μm device.

The key feature of this structure is that the n^- region and the *p*-type punchthrough stopper are completely separated. If the device was symmetrical, the *p*-type halo region would abut the n^- region doping. This would reduce the breakdown voltage and degrade hot carrier reliability. By separating these two regions in the asymmetrical device, the punchthrough resistance and hot-carrier reliability can be independently optimized, something that is not possible in a symmetrical MOS structure.

Another important benefit of using the lightly doped region only on the drain side is that the parasitic series resistance and gate overlap capacitance are smaller than in a symmetric structure. For MOSFETs with L below 0.25 μm these two parameters become limiting factors in device and circuit performance, and hence their reduction is crucial. The main drawback of asymmetrical structures is that their use may restrict the flexibility of circuit layout, especially in some IC applications.

9.13 HOT-CARRIER EFFECTS IN PMOS TRANSISTORS

It is not necessary to use LDDs in PMOS devices whose gate lengths are longer than about 1.0 μm. The reason is that hot-carrier effects are not serious in such devices operated at 5V. That is, the impact-ionization rate due to holes (i.e., the number of

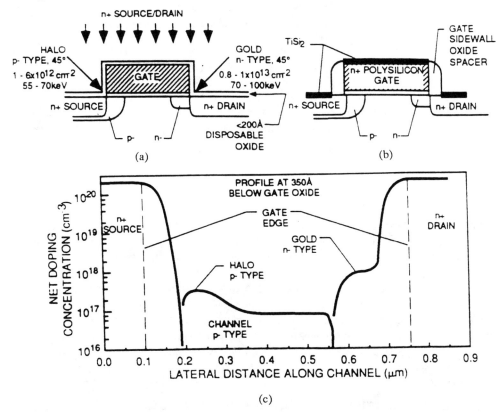

Fig. 9-64 The *halo-source gate-overlapped drain* (HS-GOLD) structure; (b) the fabrication parameters used to build this asymmetrical structure, including the LAT implant parameters; (c) the doping profiles for a 0.5 μm HS-GOLD device.[130] (© 1989 IEEE).

electron-hole pairs generated by a hot hole) is 1 or 2 orders of magnitude lower than that due to electrons at a given electric field. A secondary reason is that the buried-channel behavior associated with PMOS transistors with n^+ poly gates results in a deeper current path and possibly a lower electric field, both of which reduce hot carrier effects. At submicron channel lengths, however, hot-electron effects in PMOS begin to become significant.

It has been reported that two hot-carrier effects predominate in submicron PMOS devices. Both are apparently caused by hot electrons generated through impact ionization. These hot electrons are then injected into the oxide and become trapped. Hot-hole injection does not appear to cause significant degradation, despite the fact that holes are far more numerous in the channel of PMOSFETs than electrons. That is, hole injection into the oxide is far less probable than electron injection because the potential energy barrier for holes at the $Si-SiO_2$ interface is higher. In addition, when PMOS devices are operated in saturation (i.e., $V_{GS}<V_{DS}$), the gate-bias polarity favors electron drift through the oxide (which is opposite to that in NMOS), but retards the drift of holes. In fact, in PMOS devices only gate current due to hot-avalanched electrons has been measured, and no gate current resulting from channel hot holes has been reported in the literature.

9.13.1 Model for Hot-Carrier Damage in PMOSFETs

A qualitative model for the mechanism responsible for the PMOS device degradation mentioned above is as follows: At high channel fields, channel holes are sufficiently accelerated to cause impact ionization, thereby generating electron-hole pairs. If some of these generated electrons can gain sufficient energy from the channel field and then also happen to be scattered in the right direction, they can be injected into the gate oxide. Some of such injected electrons become trapped, and negative charge is thus built up in the oxide near the drain.[132,133]

It has been reported that the most severe degradation in PMOSFETs is observed under bias conditions corresponding to peak gate current I_{Gmax}. In general, I_{Gmax} in PMOSFETs occurs at low gate bias. That is, the worst stressing condition for PMOSFETs is at low V_{GS} (roughly $V_{GS} = -1.25V$ when $V_{DS} = -8V$) because its corresponding oxide field results in a maximum gate current and a maximum stress-induced V_T-shift (although the maximum substrate current occurs at higher V_{GS}, i.e., $V_{GS} \sim 0.4V_{DS}$ or roughly -3V in this case). Again this condition is opposite to the results observed in NMOSFETs, in which the worst degradation is observed at the gate voltage corresponding to the largest substrate current. This is because in PMOSFETs when V_{GS} is increased (i.e., made more negative) the electron injection into the gate oxide is suppressed. A study of hot-electron damage in PMOSFETs with p^+ gates is given in Ref. 134.

9.13.2 Hot-Electron Induced Punchthrough (HEIP)

The chief way in which PMOS devices are impacted by hot-electron trapping in the oxide is that a negative charge buildup in the oxide occurs near the drain. This

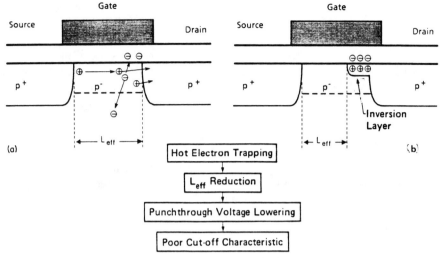

Fig. 9-65 Schematic diagram of the hot electron injection into the gate oxide of PMOSFETs.[136] (© 1987 IEEE).

eventually inverts the n-type Si surface near the drain, resulting in an extension of the p^+ drain region, as illustrated in Fig. 9-65. As a result, the effective channel length appears to shrink. This reduction in L_{eff} is even more severe in the buried-channel PMOS devices (used in CMOS technologies that have an n^+ polysilicon gate), because their buried-channel nature makes them more vulnerable to source-drain punchthrough, and consequently increases subthreshold leakage. This effect is called hot-electron-induced punchthrough (HEIP).[135,136]

Figure 9-66 shows the effects of hot-carrier stress (i.e., decrease in punchthrough

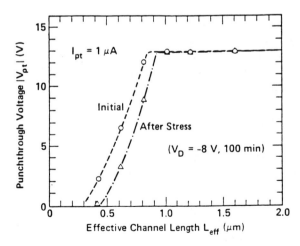

Fig. 9-66 Punchthrough voltage as a function of initial effective length for PMOS devices before and after stressing.[136] (© 1987 IEEE).

voltage as a function of stress time) in buried-channel PMOSFETs whose values of L_{eff} prior to stressing are 0.8 and 0.6 μm.[135] After only 2 hours of stress, the punchthrough voltage of the 0.6 μm device is seen to have decreased by a factor of two. A short lifetime (<10 days) was exhibited by the 0.6 μm PMOS devices under the worst-case condition for evaluating the submicron PMOSFET hot-carrier reliability. That is, the stress condition was chosen to give maximum gate current (i.e., V_{DS} = -8V and V_{GS} = -1.2V). The change in V_T (with V_T in this case defined by the V_{GS} value when I_D = -10 nA) after stressing was measured in the low gate voltage condition as a measure of HEIP-induced L_{eff} reduction, with the source and drain terminals interchanged (as this represents the worst-case stress condition for evaluating hot-carrier reliability in PMOSFETs). A model of PMOSFET hot-carrier degradation based on the shortening of L_{eff} due to hot-carrier damage is given in ref. 139.

A second effect arising from the negative charge buildup in the oxide of PMOS devices is also observed. That is, this buildup tends to reduce the magnitude of V_T. The combined effects of a smaller value of L_{eff} and a smaller V_T value result in an increase in I_D, which is usually desirable in MOSFETs, but in some circuit applications may play a detrimental role.

It should also be noted that, contrary to what occurs in NMOS, both of the above effects tend to saturate in PMOS. This can be understood by noting that the electrons trapped near the drain reduce the gate electric field present there in PMOS devices. Eventually, hot electrons injected into the oxide are drifted less strongly through the oxide to the gate, or they may even be repelled back into the Si without causing further damage. As a result, this effect does not appear to limit PMOS devices fabricated with p^+ polysilicon gates as long as L_{eff} is $\geq$0.6 μm.[134] Still, LDD structures appear to be needed for p-channel devices fabricated with n^+ polysilicon gates when L_{eff} gets to be 0.8 μm or less.[135] Figure 9-67 shows the hot-carrier lifetime improvement gained by using a p-channel LDD. It compares conventional 0.95 μm PMOS devices with 0.8 μm LDD PMOSFETs. The LDD devices have superior reliability despite their shorter gate lengths, and an extrapolation of the data to V_{DS} = 5V implies that lifetimes in excess of 10 years are possible. As noted in section, the incorporation of a PMOS LDD structure generally requires an additional mask step, although some processes that avoid this penalty (e.g., disposable spacers) have also been reported.

It should be noted, however, that a recent report indicates that graded-drain (i.e., LDD) PMOS structures exhibit *worse* hot-carrier degradation than abrupt drain (non-LDD) PMOSFETs.[137] Thus, the use of an LDD in PMOS might not automatically guarantee longer lifetimes, and separate solutions to the hot-carrier problem in PMOSFETs might have to be considered. For example, the hot-carrier resistance of buried-channel PMOS devices is reported to increase as t_{ox} is decreased. PMOS devices with gate oxides of 7 nm thickness exhibit very little degradation. The thin oxide appears to prevent the damaged region caused by trapped hot electrons that were injected into the oxide from spreading along channel toward the source.[138]

The LDD structure also helps to reduce subthreshold leakage in PMOS devices, where excessive junction depths caused by lateral diffusion have been a problem. The use of LDD basically increases L_{eff}, hence compensating for the L_{eff} reduction caused by hot-electron injection. A new LDD structure for PMOS devices, called a *halo* LDD, is described in chap. 5.[63] In this structure, a deeper phosphorus implant is placed below the lightly doped drain-extension p-type implant. The punchthrough resistance of the PMOS device is reported to be significantly improved by this LDD structure.

9.13.3 Hot-Electron Induced Degradation in p^+-Poly PMOSFETs

Because of short-channel effects, when the channel length of PMOS devices gets to 0.5 μm or smaller, it is likely that n^+ poly will no longer be suitable as the gate material. Instead, PMOS devices will have to be fabricated with p^+ poly gates (see chap. 5). With a p^+ poly gate, PMOSFETs become surface channel devices. LDDs may still be need to be used in such devices, but their main roles will be to permit shallower source/drain junctions to be created immediately adjacent to the active channel region, and to provide electrical conductivity between the active channel region and the p^+ source/drain.

As noted in chap. 5, in surface-channel PMOSFETs, boron penetration from the p^+ poly into the substrate through the thin gate oxide can occur during high temperature annealing. This boron penetration causes a positive V_T shift and an increase in S_t. It also can cause such other undesirable effects as an increase in electron trapping, a decrease in low-field hole mobility,[186] and a degradation of current drive due to polysilicon depletion.*[187] Furthermore, it has been reported that boron penetration is enhanced when a BF_2^+ implant is used to dope the poly as compared to a B^+ implantation. This implies that the fluorine contained in the gate poly enhances boron penetration. Since this results in a large amount of boron incorporation in the gate oxide, the oxide reliability (and the hot-carrier device reliability) of such PMOSFETs comes into question. A report by Mogami indicates that the hot-carrier lifetime in both B^+-doped and BF_2^+ doped p-type poly devices is independent of the amount of boron penetration.[140] On the other hand, the lifetime of BF_2^+ doped devices is about 100 times longer than that of B^+ doped devices. This may be due to the larger critical energy for electron trap generation during hot-carrier stress in BF_2^+ gates, as this should result in less electron trapping in the gate oxide for the BF_2^+ gate. It has been reported that a fluorine-incorporated oxide has high immunity to hot-carrier-related degradation because the Si-F bonding energy is higher than Si-H bonding energy (see section 9.14).

One suggested way to way to suppress boron penetration of the gate dielectric is to use silicon oxynitride instead of SiO_2. Such oxynitride layers can be fabricated with

---

* The *polysilicon depletion effect* occurs when boron, as it penetrates the gate oxide, crosses from the p^+ polysilicon gate into the oxide. The concentration of boron in the region of poly near the poly-oxide interface is thereby reduced. This causes a depletion region to arise in the poly adjacent to the poly-oxide interface. Its presence is manifested as an increase in the "equivalent" gate oxide thickness.[188] As the dopant concentration at the polysilicon/oxide interface is reduced, this effect increases. Thus, a gate oxide material that suppresses boron penetration of the gate dielectric would also mitigate this problem.

a number of different techniques, and the effectiveness in suppressing boron penetration of each of them is compared in reference 141. The details of oxynitride formation are discussed in section 9.14. Another approach to limiting boron penetration is to reduce the thermal budget after the boron is implanted into the gate poly. Figure 9-68 shows the degree of boron penetration as a function of gate oxide thickness, post-implant anneal temperature, and B^+ or BF_2^+ implant.[143] Yet another technique involves *in-situ* boron doping of the gate poly, followed by selective doping of the NMOSFET gate poly.[142] This method yields less boron penetration than boron doping of the poly by implantation followed by an activation anneal. Finally, a co-implantation of boron and fluorine into an as-deposited amorphous-silicon gate layer is reported to result in minimum boron diffusion into the silicon substrate while providing a reduction in the interface state density at the oxide/silicon interface.[144]

9.14 STRENGTHENING OXIDES AGAINST HOT-CARRIER INJECTION

Altering the structure of the MOSFET is one approach to reducing the degradation effects of hot-carrier injection. Another is to make the gate oxide and oxide-silicon interface more resistant to hot carriers. This strategy entails development of gate dielectrics with the following two properties: (1) the as-formed films should exhibit very low densities of oxide trapping centers, interface state traps, and fixed oxide charge; and

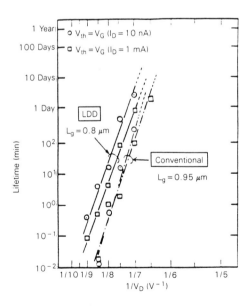

Fig. 9-67 Device lifetime versus reciprocal stressing drain voltage for submicron LDD PMOS devices. Data for conventional PMOS device is also plotted for comparison.[136] (© 1987 IEEE).

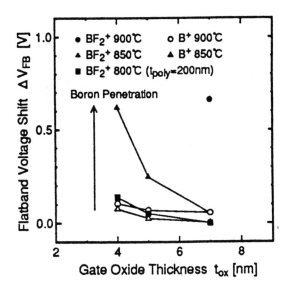

Fig. 9-68 Dependence of ΔV_{FB} due to boron penetration, determined from C-V characteristics, on t_{ox}. For $t_{ox} \leq 5$-nm thick, samples with 900°C annealing after BF_2^+ implantation, V_{FB} values are unmeasurable because of their anomalous C-V curves, due to excess large boron penetration.[143] (© 1993 IEEE).

(2) these densities should not increase when the MOSFETs in which these films are used as gate dielectrics are subjected to hot-carrier stressing. In films with such properties the density of states available for occupancy by hot carriers injected into the oxide is small - both in the as-formed films and after being subjected to hot-carrier stressing. The ability of injected hot-carriers to cause device-degradation is thereby limited, since the number of trapping sites they can occupy is small. In this section we describe the processing techniques developed for the purpose of attaining the above goals.

9.14.1 Minimizing Hydrogen and H_2O at the Si-SiO$_2$ Interface

We have previously mentioned that the presence of excess hydrogen and/or water in MOSFET gate oxides has been identified as a factor which makes the devices more prone to hot-carrier degradation. Here we consider this topic in more detail.

9.14.1.1. The role of hydrogen in hot-carrier degradation. Excess hydrogen at the Si-SiO$_2$ interface is reported to be one of the culprits responsible for the increase in interface state density in MOSFETs during hot-carrier stressing. Earlier we indicated that atomic hydrogen appears to play a benign role in MOSFETs behavior. That is, hydrogen tends to passivate the Si-SiO$_2$ interface traps, most probably by the formation of Si-H bonds which eliminate dangling bonds at the Si-SiO$_2$ interface.

However, it is also known that such Si-H bonds can easily be broken by high-energy electrons. Hence, such bonds are likely to be broken by injected hot-carriers or ionizing radiation, thereby generating interface states.

Some amount of hydrogen is always incorporated into the MOS gate oxide because of its almost universal presence during processing. Especially large amounts of hydrogen are present during such elevated-temperature processing steps as: epitaxial growth; LPCVD of Si_3N_4; deposition of TEOS; reflow in steam; and the final sintering step in hydrogen (100 percent H_2 or 4-percent H_2[forming gas]). Hydrogen can also be incorporated into the gate oxide during high-temperature anneal steps when hydrogen-rich layers (e.g., PECVD nitride) are present on the wafer. It has been observed that charge-to-breakdown, trap generation rates, and hot-carrier degradation are worse in gate oxides which have been exposed to hydrogen at high temperature.

In early studies of hot electrons, water diffusion experiments into very dry oxides suggested that the amount of trapped charge was related to the water content in the oxide. As the moisture in the oxide was increased, so did the number of trapped electrons. In these experiments, hydrogen evolution was also observed to occur. The amount of hydrogen lost was found to have a 1:1 correspondence with the amount of negative charge produced.[153] In avalanche experiments, interface state generation for wet oxides showed a substantial increase over dry oxides, suggesting that hydrogen or water-containing trapping centers were also involved. Further evidence that implicated hydrogen was found from experiments in which the final sinter of MOSFETs was performed in various ambients (i.e., in either hydrogen or nitrogen at 450°C for 30 minutes). As shown in Fig. 9-69, devices annealed in hydrogen display a higher degradation rate, with device lifetimes improving by two orders of magnitude when

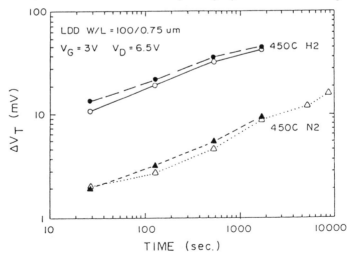

Fig. 9-69 Comparison of degradation rates in LDD devices annealed in hydrogen and nitrogen ambients (450°C 30 min). The degradation rate is greatly reduced in nitrogen-annealed devices. The two lines in each group correspond to different wafers from the same split.[154] (© IEEE 1985.)

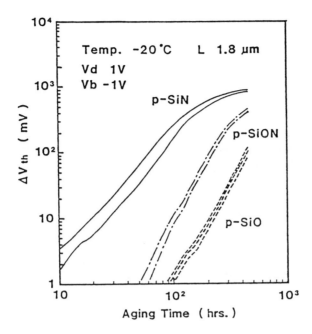

Fig. 9-70 Threshold voltage shift in MOSFETs under hot-carrier stressing with three different passivation layers.[155] (© IEEE 1986.)

nitrogen is used as the sintering ambient.[154] Another study showed that the susceptibility of the MOSFET to hot-carrier degradation after a hydrogen sinter step could be reduced by performing an additional anneal in nitrogen. This nitrogen anneal apparently permits the hydrogen introduced in the first sinter step to be released. Again, the conclusion is that excess hydrogen in the gate oxide is involved in increasing hot-carrier degradation.[189]

Devices encapsulated with PECVD nitride films have also been reported to exhibit larger hot-carrier degradation effects than those encapsulated with PECVD SiO_2 (see Fig. 9-70). The PECVD SiN films are known to contain large amounts of hydrogen. It has been proposed that hydrogen atoms from such encapsulation layers diffuse into the gate oxide layer and generate hot electron traps. The SiN layer must be present on the device during electrical stressing in order to induce the majority of the instability.[155]

9.14.1.2 Hydrogen introduced at high temperatures. Experiments have demonstrated that hydrogen introduced into MOSFET gate oxides at high temperatures (e.g. ≥800°C) exacerbates the hot-carrier degradation observed when hydrogen is introduced at lower temperatures.[156] That is, anneals in H_2 at 900°C for one hour reduce the charge-to-breakdown Q_{BD} in MOS-Cs by an order of magnitude, and also cause the electron trap density to increase by close to an order of magnitude. Finally, the interface state density after hot-carrier stressing also increases by an order of magnitude in the hydrogen-annealed structures (see Fig. 9-71). In this figure we also see that exposure of the wafers to an 825°C hydrogen-containing ambient (in an LPCVD SiN deposition process) causes a smaller, but still significant, increase in the interface trap density. One conclusion from these observations is that operations which expose the gate oxide to hydrogen at such high temperatures should, if possible, be avoided. One example of avoiding high temperature hydrogen involves the replacement of PSG with BPSG as an interlevel dielectric film. This switch is beneficial because the reflow of BPSG (a process used to planarize and smooth contact hole steps in the interlevel dielectric prior to metal deposition) can be performed in a nitrogen ambient rather than in the steam ambient required for the reflow of phosphosilicate glass.

A possible model for why high-temperature hydrogen makes the Si-SiO$_2$ interface more susceptible to hot-carrier damage is that the Si-H or Si-OH bonds in the oxide bulk and in the Si-SiO$_2$ interface act as precursors for the formation of new electron traps. These new traps might be generated when H bonds are broken, either directly by the energetic carriers, or indirectly by a reaction of the bonded H with atomic hydrogen (whereupon molecular hydrogen is released). In either case, a dangling bond is formed in the oxide. It should be mentioned that Si-H bonds are also present in samples which are subjected only to the low temperature 400°C sintering anneal but not to the higher-temperature hydrogen step, which in this case is the 825°C LPCVD SiN deposition process. At 400°C, however, the hydrogen is likely to form Si-H bonds only with silicon atoms which have a dangling bond. At higher temperatures, however, hydrogen may react with strained Si-Si or Si-O bonds to form additional H bonds. This model is

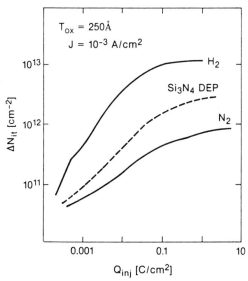

Fig. 9-71 The generated interface trap density ΔD_{it} as a function of the injected charge at tunneling injection, for hydrogenated (H$_2$) and control (N$_2$) wafers, and for a wafer which was exposed to 825°C LPCVD of Si$_3$N$_4$ (dashed line). The Si$_3$N$_4$ layer of 1000°C was deposited after PSG deposition and immediately removed by a dry etch.[156] (© IEEE 1988.)

supported by SIMS results which showed that oxides annealed in deuterium (an isotope of hydrogen) at 900°C had a deuterium content 40 times greater than the content in oxides which were annealed in deuterium at 400°C.

9.14.1.3 Moisture in Gate Oxides as a Contributor to Hot-Carrier Degradation.

The presence of H_2O in gate oxides has also been found to increase their susceptibility to hot-carrier degradation, for reasons closely related to those involving atomic hydrogen. The degradation is thought to be due to the diffusion of either H, OH, H_2, or H_2O whereupon these species form Si-H and Si-OH bonds at the Si-SiO$_2$ interface (which are precursors of interface states [•Si•] generated by hot-carrier stress).[157]

Early experimental studies showed that if minute quantities of water-related impurities (such as H and OH) are introduced into gate oxides, hot-carrier degradation of these oxides is accelerated.[158] Later, it was observed that ultra-dry oxides (gate oxides grown in ambients of less than 1 ppm water content) exhibit significantly less hot-carrier degradation than do oxides grown in conventional dry-oxide growth processes.[157] This result again indicates that removing water and hydrogen from the gate oxide and from high-temperature fabrication processes following the gate oxide formation improves MOS device endurance against hot carriers. Ohji also noted that after gate oxide growth the ultra-dry oxides were nevertheless exposed to hydrogen (i.e., during the 620°C poly CVD process, as a result of the pyrolysis of SiH_4). However, the ultra-dry oxides still exhibited less hot-carrier degradation than the conventional dry oxides. This suggests that hydrogen may have a less damaging effect than water. That is, hydrogen may diffuse rapidly through the oxide to terminate interface traps, but may not remain in the oxide itself, whereas water may be retained as part of the SiO_2 network.[159]

It is also appears that water and/or SiOH can diffuse into gate oxides from PECVD TEOS films[160] or from spin-on glass (SOG) films.[161] Such moisture is incorporated in the TEOS films as a result of the deposition process, and into the SOG films by absorption from the atmosphere after deposition.

9.14.2 Gate-Oxide Damage by Metal Etching

It has also been reported that gate-oxide hot-carrier reliability is worsened by radiation damage generated by RIE etching of the second-layer metal of a two-level metal interconnect. A sinter temperature of 375°C following this etch process was not high enough to anneal the damage.[162] That is, after hot-carrier stressing a large increase in the interface state density was observed after hot-carrier stressing and the metal etch step, and the 375°C sinter. While raising the sinter temperature to 450°C improved the device aging characteristics, the damage was not entirely removed unless the sinter temperature was increased to more than 500°C. This not only indicates that the device degradation is due to a buildup of radiation damage caused by second-layer metal patterning, but also that developing a diffusion-barrier-layer technology that can withstand sinter temperatures in excess of 500°C would be quite useful.

9.14.3 Nitrided Oxides

Besides reducing the hydrogen and moisture content, another general approach to strengthen gate oxides is to modify their chemical composition. The main such modification involves thermally incorporating nitrogen into the gate oxide films, as is discussed in this section.

9.14.3.1 Thermal nitridation of SiO₂. Thermal nitridation of SiO_2 films (as first introduced by Ito et al.,[166] and Naiman et al.[167]), was carried out by exposing the oxide films to pure ammonia (NH_3) at atmospheric pressure and high temperatures (900-1200°C). This results in the formation of a "nitrided" oxide film with an index of refraction higher than that of the oxide. Analysis by Auger emission spectroscopy (AES) indicates that for nitridation times of ~1 hour most of the film still consists of silicon dioxide, with nitridation occurring primarily at the silicon surface and the silicon/dielectric interface (see Fig. 9-72).[165] The nitridation mechanisms appear to be the addition of nitrogen atoms to the SiO_2 lattice and silicon nitride growth at the silicon-oxide interface. That is, a fast reaction between SiO_2 and NH_3 apparently occurs at the top surface of the oxide film, but NH_3 also rapidly diffuses to the Si-SiO_2 interface, where it reacts with the silicon. In the heavy nitridation process described above (i.e., nitridation carried out in an NH_3 atmospheric-pressure ambient at 900-1200°C), nearly stoichiometric silicon nitride is formed in the surface and interfacial regions. After a few minutes, however, the nitridation reaction mainly continues in the bulk, with the surface and interface nitrogen concentration remaining essentially constant. In the bulk of the oxide layer, only partial   conversion to nitride usually occurs, probably because the surface nitrogen layer impedes the diffusivity of the NH_3 into the bulk.[163,164,165]

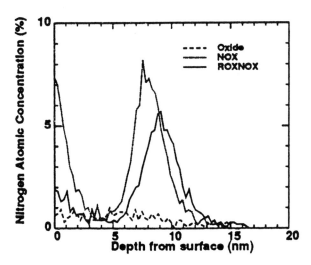

Fig. 9-72 Auger profiles of nitrogen in 11 nm low-pressure furnace nitrided and reoxidized nitrided oxide.[221] (© IEEE 1992.)

9.14.3.2 NH₃ Oxides as MOSFET Gate Dielectrics.

When gate oxide films are subjected to such nitridation, they exhibit stronger resistance to interface-state generation (ΔD_{it}) under hot-carrier stress and provide a barrier to various dopants and contaminants (including boron and sodium). The increased stability of the Si-SiO$_2$ interface is due to the pileup of nitrogen at the interfacial region.[182] The nitrogen atoms are thought to terminate dangling Si bonds at the Si-SiO$_2$ interface, and/or dangling bonds in the bulk associated with Si vacancies. The Si-N bonds which are formed are harder to break than Si-H bonds. Unfortunately, if the nitridation is carried out as described above (i.e., a 1 hr furnace operation at 1000°C at atmospheric-pressure in an anhydrous-NH$_3$ ambient), both a high fixed-charge density Q_f[168] and a large number of electron traps Q_{ot} are generally produced in the dielectric film.[169] These charges and traps result in shifted threshold voltages, degraded inversion-layer mobilities, and reduced stability under hot-carrier stressing. Thus, oxide layers nitrided in this manner are not suitable for use as gate dielectrics in MOSFETs.

Later, however, it was discovered that a reoxidation step following nitridation reduces the density of electron traps.[170, 171, 172] (The re-oxidation process consists of exposing the nitrided oxides to a high-temperature oxidizing ambient.) The names given to such gate dielectrics are thus *re-oxidized nitrided oxides*, *ROXNOX*, *RNO*, or *ONO*. (Note that the thickness of the nitrided oxide films remains basically unchanged during the re-oxidation step. That is, as long as the nitrogen-rich layer at the Si-SiO$_2$ interface remains intact, oxygen is prevented from reaching the silicon and growing more SiO$_2$ during the reoxidizing cycle. However, if excessive re-oxidation takes place, the dense interface layer may dissipate, permitting thermal oxidation to resume. In such cases, the film thickness will increase during re-oxidation.)

A model for why such re-oxidation reduces the electron trap density was proposed by Hori, Iwasaki, and Tsuji.[173,174] They observed that hydrogen-containing species (i.e., NH$_x$, -H, and -OH) are formed by the dissociation of NH$_3$ during the nitridation step. When such species are incorporated into the SiO$_2$ film they are known to cause electron traps (see Fig. 9-73).[179] Hori et al. also found that hydrogen concentration in SiO$_2$ films increases both as a function of temperature and nitridation time in NH$_3$ (see Fig. 9-74), as do flatband voltage shifts. This would explain how the NH$_3$ nitridation step is responsible for causing electron traps in the oxide, and also the correlation between the increase in hydrogen concentration and flatband voltage shift. Hori et al. also found that the hydrogen concentrations in the nitrided films are reduced during the re-oxidation step (see Fig. 9-74b - where the arrow shows the effect of a re-oxidation at 1150°C for 60 sec of an oxide nitrided at 950°C for 60 sec. - and Fig. 9-75), and that hydrogen concentration levels comparable to those of control oxides can be reached by sufficient re-oxidation. At the same time, they determined that the nitrogen concentration at the Si-SiO$_2$ interface (which is responsible for strengthening the interface against interface state generation) is only decreased slightly by the re-oxidation step (see Fig. 9-75, which shows the AES profiles of an NH$_3$-furnace nitrided oxide [a] immediately after nitridation, and [b] after an additional 100 min. 1000°C reoxidation step).[182] Thus, they concluded that "the re-oxidation procedure seems to be one of most promising processes for obtaining nitrided oxides of excellent integrity because it can eliminate the H-

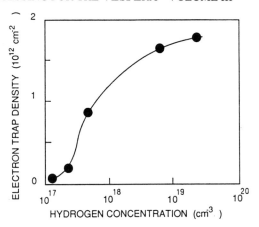

Fig. 9-73 The relationship between hydrogen contained in the oxide and the electron trap density, measured by nuclear reaction analysis and avalanche injection, respectively.[179] (© IEEE 1993.)

containing species while keeping the nitrogen concentrations in the interfacial region of the film unchanged."

9.14.3.3 Low-Pressure and RTP NH₃ Oxides (Lightly Nitrided Reoxidized NH₃ Nitrided Oxides).

While reoxidation reduces the density of electron traps in films produced by high-temperature (>900°C) atmospheric-pressure furnace nitridation, the resulting ROXNOX films still exhibit some significant drawbacks. First, the density of electron traps may not be sufficiently reduced in case of either excessive nitridation or insufficient reoxidation. Furthermore, the reoxidation of nitrided oxides formed by heavy nitridation does not reduce the fixed charge densities to levels required by high-performance scaled MOSFETs with high inversion-layer mobilities.

As a result, modifications to the nitridation process have been sought to overcome these limitations, including low-pressure furnace nitridation processes, RTP nitridation and re-oxidation processes, and replacing NH₃ with N₂O in the nitridation step. We will the discuss the first two of these approaches here, and N₂O oxides in the next section. The intent in all of these approaches is to reduce both the concentration of hydrogen and nitrogen in the film. That is, Q_f, D_{it}, and Q_{ot} all increase, peak, and turnaround with increasing nitridation. The buildup and turnaround in these electrical parameters occur more gradually in oxides subjected to low-pressure and RTP nitridation than in atmospheric nitridation.[180] (In fact, early nitrided oxides used heavy nitridation to exploit the turnaround in Q_f to minimize the fixed positive charge. Despite this approach the value of Q_f in such films generally nevertheless remains higher than the levels required by high-performance MOSFETs with high inversion-layer mobilities.[181]) Furthermore, when coupled with a reoxidation step, low-pressure and RTP nitrided oxides exhibit virtually no interface-state generation under hot-carrier stress.[152] Thus,

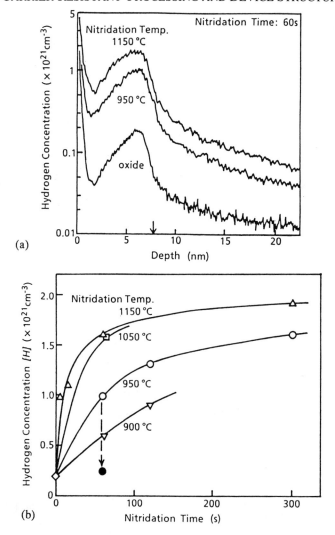

Fig. 9-74 (a) Hydrogen SIMS depth profiles of an oxide and oxides nitrided at 950 and 1150°C for 60 sec. The thickness of the starting oxide is 8 nm. The hydrogen concentration increases monotonically as temperature increases. (b) Hydrogen concentration [H] versus nitridation time for oxides nitrided at 900, 950, 1050, and 1150°C. [H] increases monotonically as nitridation proceeds. The dashed arrow and ▪ in the figure indicate the effect of reoxidation at 1150°C for 60 sec following a nitridation at 950°C for 60 sec.[173] (© IEEE 1988.)

relatively light nitridations in the pre-turnaround regime can be used to optimize the electrical properties of the dielectric. A comprehensive study of the effect of interfacial nitrogen concentration [N_{it}] on MOSFET characteristics has shown that optimum MOSFET device behavior is obtained with *very lightly nitrided* oxides, or when [N_{it}] is in the range of 0.2-1 atomic percent, as obtained by SIMS.[204]

In the low-pressure furnace processes the maximum temperature was also limited to 950°C[175] and 850°C,[176] respectively. To form a 10-nm-thick gate oxide with the 850°C low-pressure furnace nitridation process, the initial oxide film growth time is 55 minutes. This is followed by a 1 hour nitridation step in NH_3 at 0.1 atmospheric pressure, and a 3 hour re-oxidation step. The reoxidation step reduces the nitrogen concentration at the surface and bulk of the film, but without significantly reducing the nitrogen concentration near the interface, or without increasing the film thickness. Such oxides exhibit less than 8 atomic percent of nitrogen in the interfacial nitride region, and a negligible concentration of nitrogen in the oxide bulk.

Several RTP ROXNOX processes have also been reported.[174,177,178,207,208] An example of the Si, O, and N profiles in a 10 nm-thick ROXNOX film formed by one of these processes is shown in Fig. 9-76. We see that the nitrogen concentration at the Si-

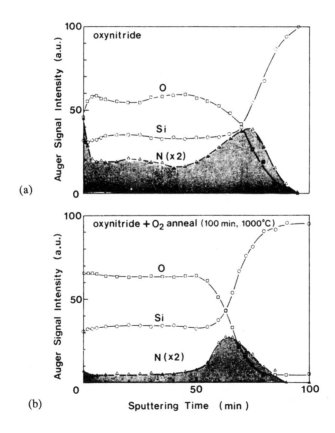

Fig. 9-75 Auger electron spectroscopy profiles of oxygen, silicon, and nitrogen in a furnace nitrided film immediately after NH_3 nitridation, and after reoxidation.[182] (© IEEE 1988.)

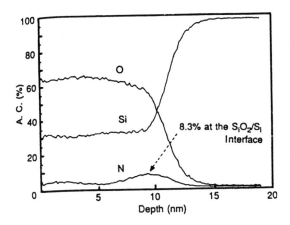

Fig. 9-76 Si, O, and N profiles in a 10-nm-thick RTP ROXNOX film.[177] (© IEEE 1986.)

SiO_2 interface is lower than that found in an atmospheric-pressure furnace-nitrided oxide. The RTP reoxidation is also effective in reducing the hydrogen concentration resulting from the RTP NH_3 nitridation step, as is shown in Fig. 9-77. Note that in some RTP processes the oxide is grown in a furnace operation, while in others RTP is also used to grow the initial oxide films. The range of temperatures and times used to nitridate thin gate oxide films using RTP is 950-1150°C and 15-300 sec, respectively. The range of temperatures used to reoxidize these nitrided films with RTP and dry oxygen is also 950-1150°C. Typically, RTP reoxidation times are 60 sec, and temperatures at the high end of this range are used. The specific processing conditions for a particular gate dielectric

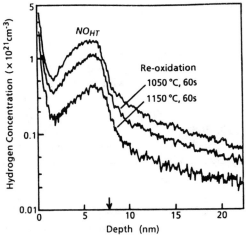

Fig. 9-77 Hydrogen SIMS depth profiles of nitrided oxide (NO_{HT}) and nitrided oxide reoxidized at 1050°C and 1150°C for 60 sec. An arrow indicates the position of the Si-SiO_2 interface.[174] (© IEEE 1989.)

film must be established by trading off electrical performance parameters because each combination of nitridation and reoxidation conditions will yield a different set of Q_f, D_{it}, and Q_{ot} values.

Sufficient reoxidation can return the fixed charge density back to the original values of a pure oxide. However, such reoxidation may be excessive, insofar as it may decrease the interface immunity to hot-carrier stress and/or it may lead to a relatively large increase in the film thickness, for the reasons cited earlier. Thus, ROXNOX films are generally reoxidized only to a degree in which the fixed-oxide-charge density remains somewhat higher than that of pure oxides. These fixed charge levels contribute to mobility degradation and reduction of the transconductance. Hence, post-reoxidation annealing in an inert ambient has been explored as a technique to further reduce Q_f without degrading the other electrical parameters of the ROXNOX film. One report examined the effects of RTP reoxidation and inert post-reoxidation annealing.[183] In another, a post-reoxidation anneal was added to the 850°C low-pressure furnace nitridation process described earlier, and has been is named a *fixed-charge anneal* (FCA).[184,185] The FCA is a nitrogen anneal which is performed after the polysilicon gate film is deposited, but before the poly doping implant step. Since it appears that it takes only a short time to significantly reduce Q_f in ROXNOX films once the temperature reaches 1000°C, the FCA can be carried out in either a furnace or by RTP. In ref. 184, 20 and 30 sec RTP anneals in N_2 at 1000°C were used with 45Å- and 65Å-thick films, respectively. The effective mobility of electrons is also increased by more than 12% in such FCA-treated ROXNOX NMOSFETS, while hole mobilities are increased by more than 30%. This is due to the reduction of Q_f in the films.

9.14.3.4 Oxynitridation of Silicon in N_2O Ambients. Although ROXNOX films exhibit better hot-carrier resistance than do pure oxides, some practical issues make them troublesome to manufacture. First, the ROXNOX formation sequence is complex and difficult to optimize, especially for CMOS applications. For example, the combination of nitridation and reoxidation steps used in the ROXNOX process may leave excess hydrogen in the film. In that case, the density of electron traps will be higher than in a pure oxide film. Since electron trapping is the dominant degradation mechanism in PMOS devices, PMOSFETs with such films will exhibit worse hot-carrier degradation.[216] On the other hand, if the reoxidation step is excessive, the film can lose its strength against interface-state generation by hot-carriers. Thus, NMOSFETs containing such films would be prone to more hot-carrier degradation. The gate dielectric thickness might also grow too thick. Another drawback is that the best NH_3-nitrided films always exhibit higher densities of positive fixed charge (Q_f) than do the best SiO_2 films. The fixed charge arises as a result of the nitridation process. Finally, the ROXNOX process generally involves multiple high-temperature steps, which are undesirable for ULSI CMOS applications.

A solution to some of the problems of NH_3-nitrided films is to avoid the incorporation of hydrogen in the film in the first place. One way to accomplish this is to replace NH_3 with N_2O as the nitriding ambient. Such N_2O-based techniques have indeed proved to be more fruitful because of the hydrogen-free nature of the processing.

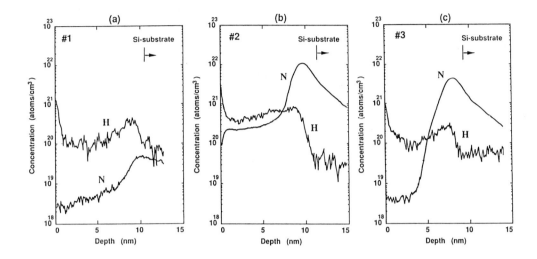

Fig. 9-78 SIMS depth profiles of N and H in three kinds of oxide films: (a) pure SiO_2 (#1); (b) NH_3-nitrided SiO_2 (#2); and (c) N_2O-nitrided SiO_2 (#3). (© IEEE 1990).

This approach was first employed to grow a gate dielectric by directly reacting N_2O at the silicon surface in an RTP system.[190,191,196,199] Since there is no hydrogen in N_2O, this process results in films with significantly less incorporated hydrogen than NH_3-nitride films. Figure 9-78 shows SIMS profiles of dielectric films prepared by: (a) thermally oxidizing silicon; (b) nitriding an oxide film in NH_3; and (c) growing a film on silicon by RTP in an N_2O ambient.[191] We see that the hydrogen concentration in the N_2O film is significantly smaller than in NH_3 film. It is also evident that the nitrogen concentration in the N_2O film is highest at the Si-SiO_2 interface. Early studies of such films concluded that they are self-limiting in thickness, as is shown in Fig. 9-79a.[190,200] The build up of the nitrogen concentration was thought to block the oxidation reaction that occurs simultaneously at the interface. Later work showed that the thickness was not self-limiting (see Fig. 9-79b),[201,202] and that the thickness in fact, increases approximately as $(time)^{1/2}$. This seems to indicate that the growth is instead limited by the diffusion of N_2O through the oxide bulk (rather than through the nitrogen-rich layer).[202] The discrepancy in the apparent growth mechanisms may have been explained by Okada et al., who observed significant retardation of the growth only at relatively high (~0.9 at %) interfacial nitrogen concentrations, which is higher than observed in some N_2O furnace processes.[203] However, the interfacial reactions may still dominate growth rates for short times and thin oxides.

Nevertheless, the nitrogen profile in the N_2O film is similar to that in the ROXNOX film, yet this is achieved with only a one-step process (i.e., no reoxidation is necessary). The peak nitrogen concentration (at the Si-SiO_2 interface) is ~0.5%, which is less than that found in furnace-nitrided in NH_3 under atmospheric pressure (2-10 at.%). Further-

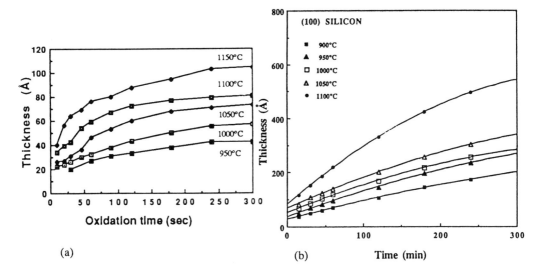

Fig. 9-79 (a) N$_2$O oxynitride thickness versus oxidation time using RTP for various process temperatures. Ramping rate was 200°C/sec. Oxide thickness was measured at a fixed refractive index (1.46).[190] (© IEEE 1990.) (b) N$_2$O oxynitride thickness versus time in a furnace anneal process. (© Electrochemical Society 1993.)[201]

more, residual hydrogen incorporation into the film is no longer a concern. This is evidenced by the low electron trapping density exhibited by such films. NMOSFETs fabricated with such films also exhibited less tendency toward hot-carrier degradation than those made with control oxides (i.e., they showed smaller values of ΔD_{it}), and were also less susceptible to the creation of electron traps throughout the oxide under hot-carrier stressing.[192]

However, several limitations were still observed in these N$_2$O-grown oxynitrides. First, larger initial values of D_{it} were observed than in pure oxide films (Fig. 9-80), even though the rate of their generation under hot-carrier stressing was much smaller (see also Fig. 9-80).[192] Second, the initial Q_f values were also somewhat higher. Third, the slow growth-rate of such films make them only practical for ULSI applications which use dielectric films thinner than 100Å (see Fig. 9-79). Fourth, the maximum mobility of electrons in MOSFETs made with such films is ~5% less than in MOSFETs with oxide gate dielectrics (but the mobility is actually higher at large lateral electric fields - see Fig. 9-81).[193] The most severe limitation, however, is that such RTP N$_2$O-grown films exhibit unacceptably large nonuniformities in composition and thickness across a wafer.[194] Such non-uniformities would limit the use of such films in ULSI MOS devices. Temperature nonuniformities in the RTP chamber, gas depletion, and heat-transfer effects were some of the phenomena suspected of leading to these nonuniformities.

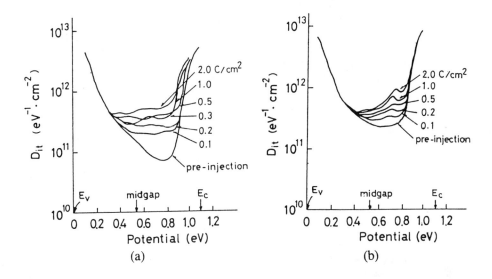

Fig. 9-80 Changes in the interface trap densities of MOS capacitors with (a) pure SiO_2 and (b) SiO_xN_y by Fowler-Nordheim electron injection. Electrons were injected from the gate electrodes into the oxide films at the current density of ~10 mA/cm^2.[192] (© IEEE 1991.)

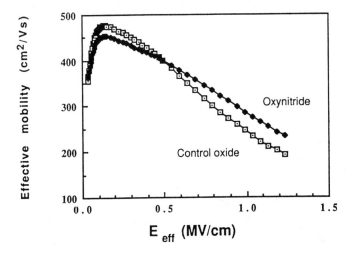

Fig. 9-81 Effective electron mobility versus effective normal field of NMOSFETs with 65Å-thick gate dielectric. The mobility values were calculated using the linear region I_D versus V_{GS} curves (V_{DS} = 100 mV), with a Z/L ratio of 75-μm/ 60-μm. The maximum effective mobility of the oxynitride is 5% lower than that of the control oxide. However, the high-field mobility of the oxynitride shows a 10% improvement.[193] (© IEEE 1991.)

Nevertheless, it was found that growth of such N_2O dielectrics in a furnace (rather than by RTP) resulted in films with thickness uniformities comparable to those of pure oxide films, and with adequate compositional uniformity as well.[195,197] The process described in these reports was a 950°C furnace step in N_2O, which grew 60Å-thick dielectric films having a nitrogen concentration at the Si-SiO_2 interface of ~3%. Hot-carrier degradation of PMOSFETs with such films was excellent since electron-trap densities in these films was also low.

9.14.3.5. Oxynitridation of Oxides in N_2O.

Unfortunately, the use of an N_2O furnace process to directly grow a dielectric film on bare silicon still results in layers that were too thin for reasonable thermal budgets. That is, at 950°C only 50Å films are grown in 40 minutes. To increase the oxide thickness, higher oxidation temperatures and/or extended times would be required. However, such high-thermal-budget processing steps are undesirable in ULSI applications. In addition, the charge-to-breakdown of such direct-N_2O furnace oxides is significantly degraded.[202,205,206]

To overcome these limitations, it was decided to instead investigate a two-step operation, i.e., in which oxides are first grown in O_2, and are then subjected to an oxynitridation step in N_2O. When N_2O is used as a post-oxidation annealing ambient, a wide range of final oxide thicknesses is achievable with much smaller thermal budgets. Processes using this two-step N_2O sequence have been described using atmospheric-pressure furnace,[198,202,209,217] low-pressure-furnace,[210] and RTP[211] conditions. Figure 9-82 shows an example of such a two-step process performed in a conventional furnace at atmospheric pressure.[209] Typically, the oxide is grown in dry O_2 in a furnace at 850-900°C. The N_2O step is usually carried out at 800-850°C for 5-40 minutes. In the process described in ref. 217, 50Å SiO_2 films are grown in dry O_2 at 850°C for 30 minutes. During the second step in N_2O at 950°C, an additional 35Å of oxide is grown to form films with a final thickness of 85Å.

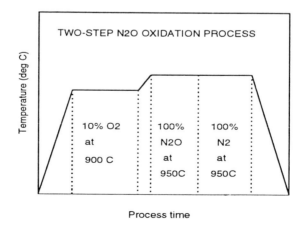

Fig. 9-82 Two-step oxidation and N_2O nitridation process in a conventional furnace.[209] (© IEEE 1993.)

PMOSFETs made by oxynitridation of SiO_2 in N_2O also exhibit enhanced hot-carrier immunity compared to devices made with pure oxide. This is thought to be due to the fact that electron trapping is suppressed in devices with such N_2O dielectrics.[218] Consequently, it has been suggested that the optimum N_2O oxynitride process is oxidation in O_2 followed by nitridation in N_2O, rather than oxidation in N_2O alone.

In the low-pressure approach[210] it was reported that a minimum pressure of between 1 and 50 torr of N_2O was needed before a measurable amount of nitrogen was incorporated into the oxide. However, at low pressures of N_2O just beyond the minimum needed for the onset of nitrogen incorporation, the concentration of nitrogen at the interface could be well controlled, but at the same time, minimal additional oxide was grown during the oxynitridation step. Thus, tight control of the final film thickness could be maintained.

As noted in a previous paragraph, the oxide film continues to grow during the second (i.e., N_2O) step. However, if re-oxidation of N_2O oxides is carried out after they are formed, unusual behavior occurs. That is, new SiO_2 grows at the Si-SiO_2 interface, and the existing N-rich layer remains intact and is displaced away from the interface by growth of the new oxide (see Fig. 9-83).[223] The resulting film does not have as good hot-carrier resistance as films that have not been reoxidized, and hence the step seems to be pointless. However, understanding the phenomenon that takes place during reoxidation of the N_2O oxide is important because it is something that does occur when the poly reox step is carried out after poly patterning. That is, a sidewall oxide is grown

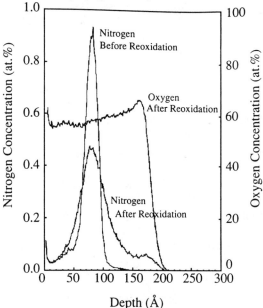

Fig. 9-83 SIMS profile of the oxynitride film grown from 100% N_2O at 1100°C before reoxidation, and after 85 min reoxidation.[223] Reprinted with permission of the Electrochemical Society.

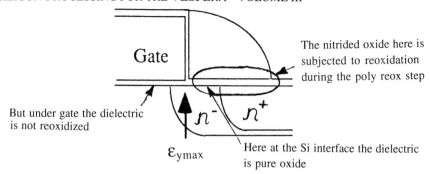

Fig. 9-84 LDD MOSFET with N_2O nitrided oxide as gate deielectric. The position of ε_{ymax} is such that hot carriers are injected into the gate dielectric under the spacer. If the gate dielectric at that location has been reoxidized such that pure oxide exists instead of nitrided oxide at the silicon-dielectric interface, the device will exhibit the same hot-carrier resistance as an LDD MOSFET made with a pure oxide.

during the poly reox step. Thus, in fact, it also represents a reoxidation of the N_2O oxide that will exist under the spacers of an LDD MOSFET. The reox step therefore grows an oxide under the N-rich layer of the oxide film that will exist under the spacers (see Fig. 9-84). Now, hot carriers are injected into the dielectric and spacers near the polysilicon edge, as shown in Fig. 9-84 (where the position of the simulated peak electric field of an LDD in which the n^+ region does not overlap the gate edge, is depicted). The region of maximum hot-carrier damage in the device is located at that point. Since the oxide at the $Si-SiO_2$ interface is no longer an N_2O oxide, but has been returned to a pure oxide, LDD MOSFETs fabricated with such reoxidized N_2O gate dielectrics exhibit hot-carrier degradation characteristics no better than LDD MOSFETs made with a pure oxide gate dielectric.[224]

A novel device structure has been proposed that would mitigate this effect. That is, we noted earlier that one form of degradation caused by the fixed oxide charge in nitrided oxides is a reduction in the peak channel mobility of both P- and NMOSFETs. This is apparently due to the presence of nitrogen at the interface.[221] While special process techniques (such as the fixed-charge anneal[185]) have been used to reduce this problem, a novel LDD structure has also been reported to overcome it. That is, a pure gate oxide is used under the gate of a MOSFET to yield the highest mobility of carriers in the channel, but a nitrided oxide process is used to reoxidize the poly sidewall after patterning (see Fig. 9-85). Since most gate-oxide hot-carrier-damage occurs outside of the channel region (i.e., under the spacer), by having a strengthened interface in those locations the device simultaneously exhibits significantly improved hot-carrier resistance and a higher drive-current capability compared to an LDD MOSFET made with an oxide spacer and a conventional poly reox process.[222]

We should also mention that adding nitrogen to gate oxides has also been reported by several other novel techniques, including implantation of nitrogen through the polysilicon gate,[212] N_2O nitridation of CVD oxides,[213] oxidation of deposited oxide on nitrided surface (ODON),[214] and oxidation of the silicon surface beneath a CVD oxynitride.[215]

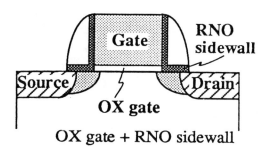

Fig. 9-85 Novel LDD MOSFET that has a pure oxide gate dielectric and a reoxidized nitrided poly sidewall. The latter feature is created during the reox of the poly (i.e., after poly patterning, but prior to spacer dielectric film deposition).[222] (© IEEE 1991.)

9.14.3.6 Fluorinated Oxides.

The presence of fluorine in the gate oxide has also been reported to increase the hot electron resistance of devices fabricated with such oxides.[225,226] Such fluorine may inadvertently be introduced from a BF_2^+ source/drain implant, or from an LPCVD-W or LPCVD WSi_x process. In the latter two processes fluorine is produced during the reaction of WF_6 and SiH_4.[227] Other reports confirm that a deliberate incorporation of fluorine into the gate oxide (from implanting fluorine into a polysilicon film, and then diffusing it into the gate oxide) produces a more hot-electron resistant interface.[228,229] The increased hot-carrier resistance of the F-containing oxides is thought to be due to fluorine atoms which form Si-F bonds. These are stronger than Si-H bonds. The presence of the fluorine implies that some of the Si-H bonds are replaced by Si-F bonds, thus yielding a stronger oxide.

Unfortunately, the presence of fluorine in the gate oxide increases the penetration of boron (from p^+ poly gates) though the gate oxides. Although various approaches have been examined to suppress this effect, many of them rely on methods that prevent fluorine from entering the gate oxide. As a result, use of nitrided oxides to suppress hot-carrier degradation has been pursued much more vigorously than use of fluorinated oxides. Nevertheless, a recent report has indicated that MOSFETs using a WSi_x polycide process exhibit significantly improved gate oxide hot-carrier hardness and higher carrier mobility as a result of the fluorine incorporated by the WSi_x polycide process.[230]

REFERENCES

1. T.Y. Chan, P.K. Ko, and C. Hu, "Dependence of channel electric field on device scaling," *IEEE Electron Dev. Lett.*, **EDL-6**, October 1985, p. 551.
2. P.K. Ko, R.S. Muller, and C. Hu, "A Unified Model for Hot-Electron Currents in MOSFETs," *Tech. Dig. IEDM,* 1981, p. 600.
3. C. Sodini, P.K. Ko, and J.L. Moll, "The Effect of High Fields on MOS Device and Circuit Performance," *IEEE Trans. on Electron Dev., ***ED-31**, October 1984, p. 1386.

4. D.K. Schroeder, *Advanced MOS Devices*, Vol VII in the Modular Series on Solid-State Devices, Reading MA, Addison-Wesley, 1983.

5. P.K. Chatterjee, *Tech. Dig. IEDM*, 1979, p. 14.

6. M.L. Woods, "MOS VLSI Reliability and Yield Trends," *Proceedings IEEE,* December 1986, p. 1715.

7. T.Y. Chan, P.K. Ko, and C. Hu, "A Simple Method to Characterize Substrate Current in MOSFETs," *IEEE Electron Dev. Letts.,* **EDL-5**, December 1984, p. 505.

8. P. K. Ko, "Hot Electron Effects in MOSFETs," Doctoral Thesis, Dept. of EECS, University of California, Berkeley, June 1972.

9. J. Chung et al., "New Insight into Hot-Electron Currents in Deep-Submicrometer MOSFETs," *Tech. Dig. IEDM,* 1988, p. 200.

10. C. Hu et al., "Hot-electron-induced MOSFET degradation - model, monitor, and improvement," *IEEE Trans. Electron Dev.*, **ED-32**, February 1985, p. 375.

11. E. Takeda and N. Suzuki, "An Empirical Model for Device Degradation due to Hot Carrier Injection," *IEEE Trans. Electron Dev. Letts.*, **EDL-4**, p. 111, 1983.

12. E.H. Nicollian and J.R. Brews, *MOS Physics and Technology*, Wiley, 1983.

13. K.R. Hoffmann, W. Weber, C. Werner, and G. Dorda, "Hot-Electron and Hole-Emission Effects in Short N-MOSFETs," *IEEE Trans. Electron Dev.*, **ED-32**, March 1985, p. 691.

14. M. Yoshida et al., "Increase in Resistance to Hot Carriers in Thin Oxide MOSFETs," *Tech. Dig. IEDM*, 1985, p. 254.

15. J. Chung et al., "Hot-Electron Currents in Deep-Submicrometer MOSFETs," *Tech. Dig. IEDM*, 1988, p. 200.

16. P. Woerlee et al., "The Impact of Scaling on Hot-Carrier Degradation and Supply Voltage of Deep Submicron NMOS Transistors," *Tech. Dig. IEDM,* 1991, p. 537.

17. C. Hu, "Hot-Carrier Effects," Chap. 3, in *Advanced MOS Device Physics*, N.G. Einspruch and G. Gildenblat, Eds., Vol. 18, VLSI Electronics Microstructure Science, Academic Press, San Diego, CA, 1989, p. 119-160.

18. C. Hu et al., "Hot-electron-induced MOSFET degradation - model, monitor, and improvement," *IEEE Trans. Electron Dev.*, **ED-32**, February 1985, p. 375.

19. P. Yang and S. Aur, "Modeling of Device Lifetime due to Hot Carrier Effects," *Proc. of 1985 Internat. Symp. on VLSI Tech.*, p. 227.

20. R.A. Chapman et al., "An 0.8 μm CMOS Technology for High Performance Logic Applications," *Tech. Dig. IEDM* 1987, p. 362.

21. T.H. Ning et al., "1 μm MOSFET VLSI Technology: Part IV - Hot Electron Design Constraints," *IEEE Trans. Electron Dev.,* **ED-26**, 346 (1979).

22. T.Y. Chan, C. I. Chiang, and H. Gaw, "New Insight into Hot-Electron-Induced Degradation of *n*-MOSFETs," *Tech. Dig. IEDM,* 1988, p. 196.

23. J.Y. Choi, P.K. Ko, and C. Hu, "Hot-Carrier-Induced MOSFET Degradation: AC versus DC stressing," *Dig. Tech. Papers Symp. VLSI Tech. 1987*, p. 45.

24. E. Takeda and N. Suzuki, "An Empirical Model for Device Degradation due to Hot Carrier Injection," *IEEE Trans. Electron Dev. Letts.*, **EDL-4**, p. 111, 1983.

25. R. Woltjer and G. Paulzen, "Universal Description of Hot-Carrier-Induced Interface States in NMOSFETs," *Tech. Dig. IEDM,* 1992, p. 535.

26. F.-C. Hsu and K.Y. Chiu, "Hot-Electron Substrate-Current Generation During Switching Transient," *IEEE Trans. Electron Dev.*, **ED-32**, (1985), p. 375.

27. K.R. Hoffmann, W. Weber, C. Werner, and G. Dorda, "Hot-Carrier Degradation Mechanism in N-MOSFETs," *Tech. Dig. IEDM*, 1984, p. 104.

28. W. Weber, C. Werner, and A. Schwerin, "Lifetimes and Substrate Currents in Static and Dynamic Hot-Carrier Degradation," *Tech. Dig. IEDM*, 1986, p. 390.

29. K.L. Chen, S. Saller, and R. Shah, "The Case of AC Stress in the Hot-Carrier Effect," *IEEE Trans. Electron Dev.*, **ED-33**, March 1986, p. 424.

30. B.S. Doyle et al., "Dynamic Channel Hot-Carrier Degradation of MOS Transistors by Enhanced Electron-Hole Injection into the Oxide," **EDL-8**, May 1987, p. 237.

31. J.Y. Choi, P.K. Ko, and C. Hu, "Hot-carrier induced MOSFET degradation under AC stress," *IEEE Trans. Electron Dev. Letts.*, **EDL-8**, p. 333, 1987.

32. R. Bellens et al., "Analysis of Mechanisms for the Enhanced Degradation During AC Hot Carrier Stress of MOSFETs," *Tech. Dig. IEDM*, 1988, p. 212.

33. W. Weber et al., "Dynamic Degradation in MOSFETs - Part II: Application in the Circuit Environment," **ED-38**, (1991), p. 1859.

34. K.R. Mistry et al., "Circuit Design Guidelines for *n*-Channel MOSFET Hot Carrier Robustness," *IEEE Trans. Electron Dev.*, **ED-40**, July 1993, p. 1284.

35. J. Winnerl et al., "Influence of Transistor Degradation on CMOS Performance and Impact on Lifetime Criterion," *Tech. Dig. IEDM*, 1988, p. 204.

36. S.C. Hu and M.P. Brassington, "Test Structure to Measure HC Degradation in CMOS Circuits," *IEEE Trans. Electron Dev.*, **ED-38,** August 1991 p. 1958.

37. M.M. Kuo et al., "Simulation of MOSFET lifetime under AC Hot-Electron Stress," *IEEE Trans. Electron Dev.*, **ED-35**, July 1988, p. 1004.

39. S. Aur, D. Hocevar, and P. Yang, "HOTRON - A Hot-Electron Effect Simulator," *Proc. ICCAD,* 1987, p. 256.

40. E.R. Minami et al., "Prediction of Hot-Carrier Degradation in Digital CMOS VLSI by Timing Simulation," *Tech. Dig. IEDM,* 1992, p. 539.

41. K.N. Quader, P.K. Ko, and C. Hu, "Projecting CMOS Circuit Hot-Carrier Reliability from DC Device Lifetime," *Tech. Dig. IEDM,* 1993, p. 511.

42. H. Hazama, M. Iwase, and S. Takagi, "Hot-Carrier Reliability in Deep Submicrometer MOSFETs," *Tech Dig. IEDM,* 1990, p. 569.

43. M.-L. Chen, "CMOS Hot-Carrier Protection with LDD," *Semiconductor Internat.*, April 1988, p. 88.

44. C.Y. Lu et al., "High Performance Salicide Shallow-Junction CMOS Devices for Submicrometer VLSI Application in Twin-Tub VI, **ED-36**, *IEEE Trans. Electron Dev.,* November 1989, p. 2530.

45. E. Takeda, H. Kume, and T. Toyabe, " Submicrometer MOSFET structure for minimizing hot carrier generation," *IEEE Trans. Electron Dev.* , **ED-29**, (1982), p. 611.

46. H. Mikoshiba, "Comparison of Drain Structures in *n*-Channel MOSFETs," *IEEE Trans. Electron Dev.*, Jan. 1986, p. 140.

47. M. Koyonagi, H. Kaneko, and S. Shinizu, "Optimum design of n^+-n- double-diffused drain MOSFET to reduce hot-carrier emission," *IEEE Trans. Electron Dev.*, **ED-32,** (1985), p. 562.

48. S. Ogura et al., "Design and Characteristics of the Lightly Doped Drain-Source (LDD) Insulated Gate FET,"*IEEE Trans. Electron Dev.*, **ED-27**, 1980, p. 1359.

49. P.J. Tsang et al., "Fabrication of High-Performance LDD FETs with Oxide Sidewall Spacer Technology," *IEEE Trans. Electron Dev., * **ED-29**, April 1982, p. 590.

50. K. Marayam, J. C. Lee, and C. Hu, "A Model for the Electric Field in Lightly-Doped Drain Structures," *IEEE Trans. Electron Dev.*, **ED-34**, July 1987, p. 1509.

51. S. H. Dhong and E. J. Petrillo, "Sidewall Spacer Technology for MOS and Bipolar Devices," *J. Electrochem. Soc.*, Feb. 1986, p. 389.

52. J. Sweeney et al., "Substrate Bias Dependent Leakage in LDD MOSFETs," *Tech. Dig. IEDM,* 1988, p. 230.

53. M. Weling and C. Gabriel, "Contact and Spacer Etch Dependent Junction Leakage in Sub-Micron CMOS Technology," *Ext. Abs. Mtg. Electrochem. Soc.,* Spring 1994, Abs. # 206, p. 324.

54. S. Onishi et al., "Mechanism of the Sidewall Process Induced Junction Leakage Current of LDD Structure," *J. Electro.Chem Soc.,* **Vol. 138**, May 1991, p. 1439.

55. F. Hsu and K. -Y. Chiu, "Evaluation of LDD MOSFETs Based on Hot-Electron-Induced Degradation," *IEEE Electron Dev. Letts.*, **EDL-5** (1984) p. 162.

56. H. Mikoshiba, "Comparison of Drain Structures in *n*-Channel MOSFETs," *IEEE Trans. Electron Dev.*, Jan. 1986, p. 140.

57. H. Ishiuchi et al., "Measurement of Intrinsic Capacitance of Lightly Doped Drain (LDD) MOSFETs, *IEEE Trans. Electron Dev.*, **ED-32**, November 1985, p. 2238.

58. T. Smedes and F.M. Klaassen, "Effects of the Lightly Doped Drain Configuration on Capacitance Characteristics of Submicron MOSFETs," *Tech. Dig. IEDM*, 1990, p. 197.

59. F.C. Hsu and H.R. Grinolds, "Structure-enhanced MOSFET Degradation Due to Hot-Electron Injection," *IEEE Electron Dev. Letts.*, **EDL-5** (1984) p. 71.

60. R. Izawa and E. Takeda, "The Impact of *n*⁻ Drain Length and Gate/Drain-Source Overlap on Submircmeter LDD Devices for VLSI," *IEEE Electron Dev. Letts.,* **EDL-8**, October 1987, p. 480.

61. A. Hamada et al., "*n*⁻ Source/Drain Compensation Effects in Submicrometer LDD MOS Devices," *IEEE Electron Dev. Letts.,* **EDL-8**, September 1987, p. 398.

62. P. Ko et al., "The Effects of Weak Gate-to-Drain (Source) Overlap on MOSFET Characteristics," *Tech. Dig. IEDM*, 1986, p. 292.

63. P.K. Ko et al., "Enhancement of hot-electron currents in graded-gate oxide (GGO)-MOSFETs," *Tech. Dig. IEDM*, 1984, p. 88.

64. T. Y. Chan, A.T. Wu, P.K. Ho, and C. Hu, "Effects of the Gate-to-Drain/Source Overlap on MOSFET Characteristics," *IEEE Electron Dev. Letts.*, **EDL-8**, July 1987, p. 326.

65. L.C. Parrillo et al., "Disposable Polysilicon LDD Spacer Technology," *IEEE Trans. Electron Dev.,* **ED-38**, January 1991, p. 39.

66. J. Pfiester et al., "Poly-gate sidewall oxidation-induced submicrometer MOSFET degradation," *IEEE Electron Dev. Letts.*, **EDL-10**, August 1989, p. 367.

67. L. Parrillo, "CMOS Active and Field Device Fabrication," *Semiconductor International*, April 1988, p. 64.

68. T. Mizuno et al., "A New Degradation Mechanism of Current Drivability and Reliability of Asymmetrical LDD MOSFETs," *Tech. Dig. IEDM,* 1985, p. 250.

69. Y. Oowaki et al., "Analysis of LDD Transistor Asymmetry Susceptibility in VLSI Circuits," *Tech. Dig. IEDM*, 1985, p. 492.

70. T. Chan, et al. "Asymmetrical Characteristics in LDD and Minimum-overlap MOSFETs," *IEEE Electron Dev. Letts.*, **EDL-7**, January 1986, p. 16.

71. R. Gregor, "Some Consequences of Ion Beam Shadowing in CMOS Source/Drain Formation," *IEEE Electron Dev. Letts.*, **EDL-7**, December 1986, p. 677.

72. T. Hamamoto et al, "Asymmetry of the Substrate Current Characteristics Enhanced by Gate Bird's Beak," *IEEE Symp. VLSI Tech., Dig. of Tech. Papers*, p. 67, 1990.

73. G. Krieger wt al., "Shadowing Effects Due to Tilted Arsenic Source/Drain Implant," *IEEE Trans. Electron Dev.*, **ED-36**, November 1989, p. 122458.

74. J. Pfiester et al., "Asymmetrical High Field Effects in Submicron MOSFETs," *Tech. Dig. IEDM*, 1987, p. 51.

75. F.K. Baker and J. Pfiester, "The Influence of Tilted Source-Drain Implants on High Field Effects in Submicron MOSFETs," *IEEE Trans. Electron Dev.*, **ED-35**, December 1988, p. 2119.

76. B.S. Doyle, C. Bergonzoni, and A. Boudou, "The Influence of Gate Edge Shape on the Degradation in Hot-Carrier Stressing of *n*-Channel Transistors," *IEEE Electron Dev. Letts.*, **EDL-12**, July 1991, p. 363.

77. J. Hu and J. Moll, "Submicrometer device design for hot-electron reliability and performance," *IEEE Trans. Electron Dev. Letts.*, **EDL-6**, July, 1985, p. 350.

78. Y. Toyoshima et al., "Mechanism of Hot-Electron Induced Degradation in LDD-MOS," *Tech. Dig. IEDM*, 1984, p. 786.

79. J. Sweeney et al., "Substrate Bias Dependent Leakage in LDD MOSFETs," *Tech. Dig. IEDM*, 1988, p. 230.

80. L.C. Parrillo et al., "A versatile, high-performance, double-level-poly, double-level-metal, 1.2 μm CMOS technology," *Tech. Dig. IEDM*, 1986, p. 244.

81. J. R. Pfiester et al., "LDD MOSFETs using Disposable Sidewall Spacer Technology," *IEEE Electron Dev. Letts.*, **EDL-9**, 1988, p. 189.

82. J. R. Pfiester et al., "A poly-framed LDD sub-half-micrometer CMOS technology," *IEEE Electron Dev. Letts.*, **EDL-11,** 1990, p. 529.

83. L.C. Parrillo et al., "An advanced 0.5 μm CMOS disposable spacer technology," *VLSI Symp. Dig.*, p. 31, 1989.

84. L.C. Parrillo et al., "Disposable Polysilicon LDD Spacer Technology," *IEEE Trans. Electron Dev.*, **ED-38**, January 1991, p. 39.

85. J. R. Pfiester et al., "An integrated 0.5 μm CMOS disposable TiN LDD/Salicide spacer technology," *Tech. Dig. IEDM*, 1989, p. 781.

86. H. Ronkainen et al., "The Use of Disposable Double Spacers and Self-Aligned CoSi$_2$ for LDD MOSFET Fabrication," *IEEE Electron Dev. Letts.*, **EDL-12,** 1991, p. 125.

87. W. Hansch, C. Mazure, A. Lill, and M.K. Orlowski, "Hot-Carrier Hardness Analysis of Submicrometer LDD Devices," *IEEE Trans. Electron Dev.*, **ED-512**, March 1991, p. 512.

88. M. Kinugawa et al., "Submicron MLDD MOSFET for 5V Operation." *1985 Symp. VLSI Tech., Dig. of Tech Papers*, p.116.

89. G. Krieger et al., "Moderately Doped NMOS (M-LDD) - Hot Electron and Current Drive Optimization," *IEEE Trans. Electron Dev.*, **ED-38**, January 1991, p. 121.

90. J.J. Sanchez, K.K. Hsueh, and T.A. DeMassa, "Drain-Engineered Hot-Electron-Resistant Device Structures: A Review," *IEEE Trans. Electron Dev.*, **ED-36**, June 1989, p. 1125.

91. Y. Tsunashima et al., "Metal-coated Lightly-Doped Drain (MLD) MOSFETs for Submicron VLSI," *1985 Symp. VLSI Tech., Dig. of Tech Papers*, p.114.

92. M.-L. Chen et al., "Suppression of Hot-Carrier Effects in Submicron CMO Technology," *IEEE Trans. Electron Dev.*, **ED-35**, December 1988, p. 2210.

93. H. Grinolds, M. Kinugawa, and M. Kakumu, "Reliability and Performance of Submicron LDD NMOSFETs with Buried As *n-* Impurity Profiles," *Tech. Dig. IEDM*, 1985, p. 246.

94. S. Jain et al., "Sloped-junction LDD (SJLDD), MOSFET structures for improved hot-carrier reliability," *IEEE Electron Dev. Lett.*, Oct 1988, p. 539.

95. C. Wei et al., "Buried and Graded/Buried LDD Structures for Improved Hot-Electron Reliability," *IEEE Electron Dev. Letts.*, **EDL-7**, June 1986, p. 380.

96. J.M. Ford and D. Stemple, "The Effects of Arsenic Drain Profile on Submicrometer Salicide MOSFETs," *IEEE Trans. Electron Dev.*, **ED-35**, March 1988, p. 302.

97. T. Toyoshima et al., "Profiled Lightly Doped Drain (PLDD) Structure for High Reliability NMOSFETs," *Proc. of VLSI Symposium*, 1985, p. 362.

98. R. Simonton, "Ion Implantation Applications in CMOS Process Technology," in *Ion Implantation Technology*, J.F. Zeigler, Ed., Elsevier Science Pub., New York, 1992.

99. C. Codella and S. Ogura, "Halo Doping Effects in Submicron DI-LDD Design," *Tech. Dig. IEDM*, 1985, p. 230.

100. T. Hori and K. Kurimoto, "A New Half-Micron *p*-Channel MOSFET with LATIPS (Large-Tilt-Angle Implanted Punchtrhough Stopper), *Tech. Dig. IEDM*, 1988, p. 394.

101. T. Hori et al., "A Self-Aligned Pocket Implantation (SPI) Technology for 0.2 micron Dual-Gate CMOS," *Tech. Dig. IEDM*, 1991 p. 641.

102. T. Hori et al., "High-Performance Dual Gate CMOS Utilizing a Novel Self-Aligned Pocket Implantation (SPI) Technology," *IEEE Trans. Electron Dev.*, **ED-40**, September 1993, p. 1673.

103. C. Duvvury et al., "Reliability Design of p^+ Pocket Implant LDD Transistors," *Tech. Dig. IEDM*, 1990, p. 215.

104. T. Huang et al., "A novel submicron LDD transistor with inverse-T gate structure," *Tech. Dig. IEDM*, 1986., p. 742.

105. T. Huang et al., "A new LDD transistor with inverse-T gate structure," *IEEE Electron Dev. Letts.*, April 1987., p. 151.

106. M. Stinson and C. Osburn, "Effects of Ion Implantation on Deep-submicrometer Drain-engineered MOSFET Technologies," *IEEE Trans. Electron Dev.*, **ED-38**, March 1991, p. 487.

107. R. Izawa, T. Kure, and E. Takeda, "Impact of the Gate-Overlapped Device (GOLD) for Deep Submicrometer VLSI," *Tech. Dig. IEDM*, 1987, p. 38.

108. R. Izawa, T. Kure, and E. Takeda, "Impact of the Gate-Overlapped Device (GOLD) for Deep Submicrometer VLSI," *IEEE Trans. Electron Dev.*, **ED-35**, December 1988, p. 2088.

109. D.S. Wen et al., "A self-inverse T-gate fully overlapped LDD device for sub-half micron CMOS," *Tech. Dig. IEDM*, 1989, p. 765.

110. J.E. Moon et al., "A New LDD structure: total overlap with polysilicon spacer (TOPS)," *IEEE Electron Dev. Letts.*, **EDL-11**, 1990, p. 221.

111. I.-C. Chen, C.C. Wei, and C.W. Teng, "Simple Gate-to-Drain Overlapped MOSFETs Using Poly Spacers for High Immunity to Channel Hot-Electron Degradation," *IEEE Electron Device Letters*, **EDL-11**, February 1990, p. 78.

112. I. Chen, R. Chapman , and C. Teng, "A Sub-half micron Partially Gate-to-Drain Overlapped MOSFET Optimized for High Performance," *Tech. Dig. IEDM,* 1991 p. 545.

113. M. Chen et al., "Self-Aligned Silicided Inverse -T Gate LDD Devices for Sub-Half Micron CMOS," *Tech. Dig. IEDM*, 1990, p. 829.

114. J. R. Pfiester et al., "An self-aligned LDD/channel implanted ITLDD process with selectively-deposited poly gates for CMOS VLSI," *Tech. Dig. IEDM,* 1989, p. 769.

115. J. R. Pfiester et al., "An ITLDD CMOS process with self-aligned reverse sequence LDD/channel implantation," *IEEE Trans. Electron Dev.*, **ED-38,** Nov. 1991, p. 2460.

116. T. Hori et al., "A new submicron MOSFET with LATID (LArge-Tilt-angle, Implanted Drain) structure," *Symp.VLSI Tech., Dig. of Tech. Papers,* 1988, p. 15.

117. T. Hori et al., "1/4 μm LATID (LArge-Tilt-angle, Implanted Drain) technology for 3.3V operation," *Tech. Dig. IEDM,* 1989, p. 777.

118. F. Matsuoka et al., "Drain Structure Optimization for Highly Reliable Deep Submicron *n*MOSFETs with 3.3V High Performance Operation on the Scaling Trend," *Tech. Dig. IEDM,* 1990, p. 832.

119. T. Hori et al., "Gate-capacitance Characteristics of Deep-submicron LATID MOSFETs," *Tech. Dig. IEDM,* 1991, p. 375.

120. T. Hori et al., "Deep Submicrometer LATID Technology," *IEEE Trans. Electron Dev.,* **ED-39,** October 1992, p. 2312.

121. M. Inuishi et al., "Gate Capacitance Characteristics of Gate/*n*- Overlap LDD Transistor with High Performance and High Reliability," *Tech. Dig. IEDM*, 1991, p. 371.

122. A. Hori et al., "High Carrier Velocity and Reliability of Quarter-Micron SPI (Self-Aligned Pocket Implantation) MOSFETs," *Tech. Dig. IEDM*, 1992, p. 699.

123. T. Hori et al., "High-Performance Dual Gate CMOS Utilizing a Novel Self-Aligned Pocket Implantation (SPI) Technology," *IEEE Trans. Electron Dev.,* **ED-40**, September 1993, p. 1673.

124. K. Kurimoto and S. Odanaka, "A T-Gate Overlapped LDD Device with High Circuit Performance and High Reliability,"*Tech. Dig. IEDM*, 1991, p. 541.

125. M. Inuishi et al., "A High Performance and Highly Reliable Dual Gate CMOS with Gate/*n*- Overlap LDD Applicable to Cryogenic Operation," *Tech. Dig. IEDM*, 1989, p. 773.

126. T. Mizuno et al., "Si_3N_4/SiO_2 Spacer Induced High Reliability in LDD MOSFET and its Simple Degradation Model," *Tech. Dig. IEDM,* 1988, p. 234.

127. T. Mizuno et al., "High Dielectric LDD Spacer Technology for High Performance MOSFET Using Gate-Fringing Field Effects," *Tech. Dig. IEDM,* 1989, p. 613.

128. T. Mizuno et al., "Gate-Fringing Field Effects on High Performance in High Dielectric LDD Spacer MOSFET s," *IEEE Trans. Electron Dev.,* April 1992, p. 982.

129. J.C. Guo et al., "Performance and Reliability Evaluation of High-Dielectric LDD Spacer on Deep Sub-Micrometer LDD MOSFET," *IEEE Trans. Electron Dev.,* **ED-41**, July 1994, p. 1239.

130. T. Buti et al., "Asymmetrical Halo Source- GOLD Drain (HS-GOLD) Deep Sub-half Micron n-MOSFET Design for Reliability and Performance," *Tech. Dig. IEDM,* 1989, p. 617.

131. T. Buti et al., "A New Asymmetrical Halo Source- GOLD Drain (HS-GOLD) Deep Sub-half Micron n-MOSFET Design for Reliability and Performance,"*IEEE Trans. Electron Dev.,* **ED-38**, August 1991., p. 1757.

132. K.K. Ng and G.W. Taylor, "Effects of Hot-Carrier Trapping in n- and p-Channel MOSFETs," *IEEE Trans. Electron Dev.,* **ED-30**, (1983), p. 871.

133. T. Tsuuchiya and J. Frey, "Relationship Between Hot-Electrons/Holes and Degradation for p- and n- Channel MOSFETs," *IEEE Trans. Electron Dev.*, **EDL-6**, p. 8, 1986.

134. Y. Hiruta et al., "Impact of Hot-Electron Trapping of Half-Micron PMOSFETs with p^+ Poly -Si Gate," *Tech. Dig. IEDM,* 1986, p. 718.

135. M. Koyanagi et al., "Investigation and Reduction of Hot-Electron Induced Punchthrough (HEIP) Effect in Submicron PMOSFETs," *Tech. Dig. IEDM,* 1986, p. 722.

136. M. Koyonagi et al., "Hot-Electron Induced Punchthrough (HEIP) Effect in Submicron PMOSFETs," *IEEE Trans. Electron Dev.*, **ED-34**, 1987, p. 839.

137. B.S. Doyle and K.R. Mistry, "Anomalous Hot-Carrier Behavior for LDD p-Channel Transistors," *IEEE Electorn Dev. LEtts.,* **EDL-14**, November 1993, p. 536.

138. S. Odanaka and A. Hiroki, "Gate-Oxide Thickness Dependence of Hot-Carrier-Induced Degradation in Buried p-MOSFETs," *Tech. Dig. IEDM,* 1990, p. 565.

139. R. Woltjer and G.M. Paulzen ,"Oxide Charge Generation During Hot-Carrier Degradation in PMOSTs," *Tech. Dig. IEDM,* 1993, p. 713.

140. T. Mogami et al., "Hot-Carrier Effects in Surface-Channel PMOSFETs with BF_2^+ or Boron-implanted Gates," *Tech. Dig. IEDM,* 1991, p. 533.

141. A.B. Joshi et al., "Oxynitride Gate Dielectrics for p^+-Polysilicon Gate MOS Devices," *IEEE Electron Dev. Letts.,* **EDL-14**, December 1993, p. 560.

142. T. Eguchi et al., "New Dual Gate Doping Process using In-Situ Boron Doped-Si for Deep Submicron CMOS Device," *Tech. Dig. IEDM,* 1993, p. 831.

143. K. Uwasawa et al., "Scaling Limitations of Gate Oxide in p^+ Polysilicon Gate MOS Structures for Sub-Quarter Micron CMOS Devices," *Tech. Dig. IEDM* 1993, p. 895.

144. H.-H. Tseng, et al., "The Effect of Silicon Gate Microstructure and Gate Oxide Process on Threshold Voltage Instabilities p^+ -Gate p-Channel MOSFETs with Fluorine Incorporation," *IEEE Trans. Electron Dev.,* **ED-39**, July 1992, p. 1687.

145. T. Noguchi et al., "Parasitic Resistance Characteristics for Optimum Design of Half Micron MOSFETs," *Tech. Dig. IEDM,* 1986, p. 730.

146. J.M. Pimbley, M. Ghezzo, H.G. Parks, and D.M. Brown, *Advanced CMOS Process Technology,* Vol. 19, VLSI Electronics Microstructure Science, Ch. 5, "Relibility," Academic Press, San Diego, CA, 1989.

147. *ibid.* Ref. 17, this chapter, p. 130.

148. F.H. Hsu and K.Y. Chiu, "A Comparative Study of Tunneling, Substrate Hot-Electron, and Channel Hot-Electron Injection Induced Degradation in Thin-Gate MOSFETs," *Tech. Dig. IEDM*, 1984, p. 96.

149. E. Takeda, A. Shimizu, and T. Hagiwara, "Role of hot-hole injection in hot-carrier effects and the small degraded channel region in MOSFETs." *IEEE Electron Dev. Letts.,* **EDL-4,** p. 329, (1984).

150. T.K. Horiuchi, H. Mikoshiba, K. Nakamura, and F. Hamano, "A Simple Method to Evaluate Device Lifetime Due to Hot-Carrier Effect Under Dynamic Stress," *IEEE Trans. Electron Dev. Letts.,* **EDL-7**, p. 377, (1986).

151. P.M. Lee et al., "Circuit Aging Simulator (CAS)," *Tech. Dig. IEDM,* 1988, p. 134.

152. G.J. Dunn and S.A. Scott, "Channel Hot-Carrier Stressing of Reoxidized Nitrided Silicon Dioxide," *IEEE Trans. Electron Dev.,* **ED-37**, July 1990, p. 1719.

153. R. Haruta et al., "Improvement of Hardness of MOS Capacitors to Electron-Beam Irradiation and Hot-Electron Injection by Ultra-Dry Oxidation of Silicon," *IEEE Electron Dev. Letts.,* **EDL-10,** January 1989, p. 27.

154. F. Hsu and K. Chiu, "Effects of Device Processing on Hot-Electron Induced Device Degradation," in *VLSI Symp. Tech. Dig.,* 1985, p. 108.

155. J. Mitsuhashi, S. Nakao, and T. Matsukawa, "Mechanical Stress and Hydrogen Effects on Hot Carrier Injection," *Tech. Dig. IEDM,* 1986, p. 387.

156. Y. Nissan-Cohen and T. Gorczyca, "The Effect of Hydrogen on Trap Generation, Positive Charge Trapping, and Time-Dependent Dielectric Breakdown of Gate Oxides," *IEEE Electron Dev. Letts..,* **EDL-9,** June 1988, p. 288.

157. Y. Ohji et al., "Effects of Minute Impurities (H, OH, F) on SiO_2/Si Interface as Investigated by Nuclear Resonant Reaction and Electron Spin Resonance," *IEEE Trans. Electron Dev.,* **ED-37** August 1990, p. 1635.

158. R.B. Fair and R.C. Sun, "Threshold voltage instability in MOSFETs due to channel hot-hole emission," *IEEE Trans. Electron Dev.,* **ED-28** p. 83, January 1981.

159. R. Haruta et al., "Improvement of Hardness of MOS Capacitors to Electron-Beam Irradiation and Hot-Electron Injection by Ultra-Dry Oxidation of Silicon," *IEEE Electron Dev. Letts.,* **EDL-10,** January 1989, p. 27.

160. M.T. Takagi, I. Yoshii, and K. Hashimoto, "Characterization of Hot-Carrier-Induced Degradation of MOSFETs Enhanced by H_2O Diffusion for Multilevel Interconnection Processing," *Tech. Dig. IEDM,* 1992, p. 703.

161. N. Lifshitz and G. Smolinsky, "Hot-Carrier Aging of the MOS Transistor in the Presence of Spin-on Glass as at the Interlevel Dielectric," *IEEE Electron. Dev. Letts..,* **EDL-12,** March 1991, p. 140.

162. M.L. Chen et al., "Hot-carrier aging in two-level metal processing," *Tech. Dig. IEDM,* p. 55, 1987.

163. Y. Hayafuji and K. Kajiwara, "Nitridation of Silicon and Oxidized Silicon," *J. Electrochem. Soc.* , **129**, (1982).

164. Y. Hayafuji, K. Kajiwara, and S. Usui, "Shrinkage and Growth of Oxidation Stacking Faults During Thermal Nitridation of Si and Oxidized Silicon," *J. Appl. Phys.,* **63,** 8639 (1982).

165. J.A. Nemetz and R.F. Tressler, "Thermal Nitridation of Silicon and Silicon Dioxide for Thin Gate Insulators," *Solid State Technology*, p. 209, September 1983.

166. T. Ito, T. Nozaki, and H. Ishikawa, "Direct thermal nitridation of silicon oxide films in anhydrous ammonia gas," *J. Electrochem. Soc.* , **127**, September 1980, p. 2053.

167. M.L. Naiman et al., "Properties of thin oxynitride gate dielectrics produced by thermal nitridation of silicon dioxide," *Tech. Dig. IEDM,* 1980, p. 562.

168. C.-T. Chen et al., "Study of electrical characteristics on thermally nitrided SiO_2 films," *J. Electrochem. Soc. ,* p. 875, 1984.

169. S.-T. Chang, N.M. Johnson, and S.A. Lyon, "Capture and tunnel emission of electrons by deep levels in ultrathin nitrided oxides on silicon," *J. Appl. Phys. Lett.,* **44**, March 1984, p. 316.

170. S.K. Lai, J. Lee, and V.K. Dham, "Electrical properties of nitrided oxide systems for use in gate dielectrics and EEPROM," *Tech. Dig. IEDM,* p. 180, 1983.

171. S.S. Wong et al., "Composition and electrical properties of nitrided-oxide and re-oxidized nitrided oxide," in *Proc. Symp. Silicon Nitride Thin Insulating Films,* **ECS vol. 83-8,** p. 346, 1983.

172. F.C. Hsu and K.-Y. Chiu, "A comparative study of tunneling, substrate hot-electron and channel hot-electron injection induced degradation in thin-gate MOSFETs," *Tech. Dig. IEDM,* p. 96, 1984.

173. T. Hori, H. Iwasaki, and K. Tsuji, "Charge-Trapping Properties of Ultrathin Nitrided Oxides Prepared by Rapid Thermal Annealing," *IEEE Trans. Electron Dev. ,* **ED-36**, July 1988, p. 904.

174. T. Hori, H. Iwasaki, and K. Tsuji, "Electrical and Physical Properties of Ultrathin Reoxidized Nitrided Oxides Prepared by Rapid Thermal Processing," *IEEE Trans. Electron Dev. ,* **ED-36**, February 1989, p. 340.

175. W. Yang, R. Jayaraman, & C.G. Sodini, "Optimization of low-pressure nitridation/re-oxidation of SiO_2 for scaled MOS devices," *IEEE Trans. Elect. Dev.,* **ED-35**, p. 939, 1988.

176. B. J. Gross, K.S. Krisch, and C.G. Sodini, "An Optimized 850°C Low-Pressure-Furnace Reoxidized Nitrided Oxide (ROXNOX) Process," *IEEE Trans. Elect. Dev.,* **ED-38**, September 1991, p. 2036.

177. H.S. Momose et al., "Hot-Carrier Related Phenomena for N- and PMOSFETs with Nitrided Gate Oxide by RTP." *Tech. Dig. IEDM,* 1989, p. 267.

178. A. Wu et al., "Gate bias polarity dependence of charge trapping and time dependent dielectric breakdown in nitrided and reoxidized nitrided oxides," *IEEE Electron Dev. Letts.,* **EDL-10**, p. 443, October 1989.

179. E. Takeda et al., "VLSI Reliability Challenges: From Device Physics to Wafer Scale Systems," *Proceedings of the IEEE*, May 1993, p. 653.

180. W. Yang, R. Jayaraman, and C.G. Sodini, "Optimization of Low-Pressure Nitridation/Reoxidation of SiO_2 for Scaled MOS Devices," *IEEE Trans. Electron Dev.,* **ED-35**, July 1988, p. 935.

181. M.A. Schmidt et al., "Inversion layer mobility of MOSFETs with nitrided oxide gate dielectrics," *IEEE Trans. Electron Dev.,* **ED-35**, 1988, p. 1627.

182. T. Kaga and T. Hagiwara, "Short- and Long-Term Reliability of Nitrided Oxide MISFETs," *IEEE Trans. Electron Dev.,* **ED-35**, 1988, p. 929.

183. P. J. Wright, A. Kermani, and K.C. Saraswat, "Nitridation and Post-Nitridation Anneals of SiO_2 for Ultrathin Dielectrics," *IEEE Trans. Electron Dev.,* ED-37, August 1990, p. 1836.

184. H. Fang, et al., "Low-Temperature Furnace-Grown Reoxidized Nitrided Oxide Gate Dielectrics as a Barrier to Boron Penetration," *IEEE Electron Dev. Letts.,* **EDL-13,** April 1992, p. 217.

185. H. Fang et al., "Ultrathin Furnace Reoxidized Nitrided Oxide Gate Dielectrics for Extreme Submicrometer CMOS Technology," *Tech. Dig. IEDM*, 1992, p. 623.

186. J.R. Pfiester et al., "The effects of boron penetration on p^+ polysilicon gated PMOS devices," *IEEE Trans. Electron Dev.*, **ED-37**, p. 1842, 1990.

187. J.S. Cable, R.A. Mann and J.C.S. Woo, "Impurity barrier properties of reoxidized nitrided oxide films for use with p^+ polysilicon gates," *IEEE Electron Dev. Letts.*, **EDL-12**, p. 128, 1991.

188. C. Wong et al., "Doping of n^+ and p^+ Polysilicon gates in dual-gate CMOS process," *IEDM Tech. Dig.* , 1988, p. 238.

189. F.C. Hsu, J. Hui, and K.Y. Chiu, "Effect of Final Annealing on Hot-Electron-Induced MOSFET Degradation," *IEEE Electron Dev. Letts.*, **EDL-6**, July 1985, p. 369.

190. H. Hwang et al., "Electrical and Reliability Characteristics of Ultrathin Oxynitride Gate Dielectric Prepared by Rapid Thermal Processing in N_2O, *Tech. Dig. IEDM*, 1990, p. 421.

191. A. Uchiyama et al., "High Performance Dual-gate Sub-halfmicron CMOSFETs with 6 nm-thick Nitrided SiO_2 Films in an N_2O Ambient," *Tech. Dig. IEDM*, 1990, p. 425.

192. H. Fukuda et al., "Novel N_2O - oxynitridation technology for forming highly reliable EEPROM tunnel oxide films," *IEEE Electron Device Letters*, **EDL-12** (1991) p. 587.

193. H. Hwang et al., "Improved reliability characteristics of submicrometer MOSFETs with oxynitride gate dielectric prepared by rapid thermal oxidation," *IEEE Electron Device Letters*, **EDL-12**, (1991), p. 495.

194. T.Y. Chu et al., "Thickness and Compositional Nonuniformities of Ultrathin Oxides Grown by Rapid Thermal Oxidation of Silicon in N_2O, *J. Electrochemical Soc.*, **138**, June 1991, p. 113.

195. W. Ting et al., "MOS Characteristics of Ultrathin SiO_2 Prepared by Oxidizing Si in N_2O," *IEEE Electron Device Letters*, **EDL-12** (1991), p. 416.

196. H. Fukuda, T. Arakawa, and S. Ohno, "Highly reliable thin nitrided SiO_2 films formed by rapid thermal processing in an N_2O Ambient," *Jap. Jnl. of Appl. Phys.,* **vol. 29**, p. 2333, 1990.

197. G.Q. Lo et al., "Improved Performance and Reliability of MOSFETs with Ultrathin Gate Oxides Prepared by Conventional Furnace Oxidation of Si in Pure N_2O Ambient," *Symp. VLSI Tech.* p. 43, 1991.

198. J. Ahn W. Ting, and D.-K. Kwong, "Furnace nitridation of thermal SiO_2 in pure N_2O ambient for ULSI Applications," *IEEE Electron Device Letters*, **EDL-13**, 1992, p. 117.

199. H. Hwang et al., "Electrical Characteristics of Ultrathin Oxynitride Gate Dielectric Prepared by Rapid Thermal Oxidation of Si in N_2O, *Appl. Phys. Lett.*, **57**, 1990, p. 1010.

200. Z. Liu et al., "The Effects of Furnace Annealing on MOSFETs," *Tech. Dig. IEDM,* 1992, p. 625.

201. S.C. Sun, T.S. Chen, and H.Y. Chang, "Thermal Oxidation of Silicon in Pure N_2O," *Ext. Abs. Mtg. Electrochem. Soc.*, Spring 1993, Abs. #749, p. 1080.

202. N.S. Saks et al., "Characteristics of Oxynitrides Grown in N_2O," *Ext. Abs. Mtg. Electrochem. Soc.*, Spring 1994, Abs. #162, p. 251.

203. Y. Okada et al., "Evaluation of Interfacial Nitrogen Concentration of RTP Oxynitrides by Reoxidation," *J. Electrochem. Soc.,* **140**, p. L87, June 1993.

204. H.S. Momose et al., "Very Lightly Nitrided Oxide MOSFETs for Deep-Sub-Micron CMOS Devices," *Tech. Dig. IEDM*, 1991, p. 359.

205. A. Joshi et al., "High-Field Breakdown in Thin Oxides Grown in N_2O Ambient," *IEEE Trans. Electron Dev.* , **ED-40**, p. 1437, August 1993.

206. Y. Okada et al., "The relationship between growth conditions, nitrogen profile, and charge-to-breakdown of gate oxynitrides grown from pure N_2O," *Appl. Phys. Letts.*, **63**, p. 194, 1993.

207. T. Hori, S. Akamatsu, and Y. Odake, "Deep-Submicrometer CMOS Technology with reoxidized or annealed nitrided-gate dielectrics prepared by rapid thermal processing," *IEEE Trans. on Electron Devices*, **ED-39**, January 1992, p. 118.

208. T. Hori, T. Yasui, and S. Akamatsu, "Improved hot-carrier immunity in submicrometer MOSFETs with reoxidized nitrided-gate dielectrics prepared by rapid thermal processing," *IEEE Trans. on Electron Devices*, **ED-39**, January 1992, p. 134.

209. H.G. Pomp et al., "Lightly N_2O nitrided dielectrics grown in a conventional furnace for E^2PROM and 0.25 μ m CMOS, *Tech. Dig. IEDM*, 1993, p. 463.

210. M.S. Soo et al., "Very Light Nitridation of Thin Gate Oxide in Low Pressure N_2O Ambients," *Ext. Abs. Mtg. Electrochem. Soc.*, Spring 1994, Abs. #168, p. 262.

211. Y. Okada et al., "The Performance and Reliability of 0.4 Micron MOSFETs with Gate Oxynitrides Grown by Rapid Thermal Processing Using Mixtures of N_2O and O_2," *IEEE Trans. Electron Dev.* , **ED-41,** p. 191, February 1994.

212. S. Haddad and M.S. Liang, "Improvement of Thin Gate Oxide Integrity Using Through-Silicon-Gate Ion Implantation," *IEEE Electron Dev. Letts.*, **EDL-8**, p. 58, 1987.

213. J. Ahn et al., "High Quality Thin Gate Oxide Prepared by Annealing Low-Pressure CVD SiO_2 in N_2O," *Appl. Phys. Letts.*, **59**, p. 283, 1991.

214. I. Rahat, J. Shappir, and D. Ben-Atar, "Novel Interface Nitridation Process for Thin Gate Oxides," *IEEE Trans. Electron Dev.*, **ED-40**, November 1993, p. 2047.

215. L. Manchanda et al., "A Boron-Retarding and High Interface Quality Thin Gate Dielectric for Deep-Submicron Devices," *Tech. Dig. IEDM*, 1993, p. 459.

216. B. Doyle and A. Philipossian, "p-Channel Hot-Carrier Optimization of RNO Gate Dielectrics Through the Reoxidation Step," *IEEE Electron Dev. Letts.*, **EDL-14**, April 1993 p. 161.

217. G.Q. Lo, J. Ahn, and D.L. Kwong, "Improved Hot-Carrier Immunity in CMOS Analog Device with N_2O-Nitrided Gate Oxides," *IEEE Trans. Electron Dev.*, **EDL-13**, September 1992, p. 457.

218. G.Q. Lo et al., "P-Channel MOSFETs with ultrathin N_2O gate Oxides," *IEEE Electron Device Letters*, **EDL-13** (1992), p. 111.

219. Z. Liu et al., "Improvement of Charge Trapping Characteristics of N_2O-Annealed and Reoxidized N_2O-Annealed Thin Oxides," *IEEE Electron Dev. Letts.*, **EDL-13**, October 1992, p. 519.

220. Z. Liu et al., "Effects of N_2O Anneal and Reoxidation on Thermal Oxide Characteristics," *IEEE Electron Dev. Letts.*, **EDL-13**, August 1992, p. 402.

221. C.G. Sodini and K.S. Krisch, "Silicon Oxynitride Gate Dielectrics for Scaled CMOS," *Tech. Dig. IEDM,*, 1992, p. 617.

222. S. Kusonoki et al., "Hot-Carrier-Resistant Structure by Reoxidized Nitrided Oxide Sidewall for Highly Reliable and High-Performance LDD MOSFETs," *Tech. Dig. IEDM*, 1991, p. 649.

223. Y. Okada et al., "Evaluation of Interfacial Nitrogen Concentration of RTP Oxynitrides by Reoxidation," *J. Electrochem. Soc.* , **140**, June 1993, p. L87.

224. Y. Okada and P.J. Tobin, "Hot-Carrier Degradation of LDD MOSFETs with Gate Oxynitride Grown in N2O," *IEEE Electron Dev. Letts.*, **EDL-15**, July 1994, p. 233.

225. E. F. Da Silva, *Tech. Dig. IEDM*, 1987, p. 848.

226. P. Wright et al., "Hot-Electron Immunity of SiO_2 Dielectrics with Fluorine Incorporation," *IEEE Electron Device Letters*, **EDL-10**, August 1989, p. 347.

227. V. Jain, D. Pramanik, K.Y. Chang, and C. Hu., "Improved Sub-micron CMOS Device Performance in CVD Tungsten Silicide," *1991 Symp. VLSI Tech.*, p. 91.

228. Y. Nishioka et al., "Hot-Electron Hardened Si-Gate MOSFET Utilizing F Implantation," *IEEE Electron Device Letters*, **EDL-10**, April 1989, p. 141.

229. N. Kasai, P. Wright, and K.C. Saraswat, "Hot-Carrier Degradation Characteristics for Fluorine Incorporated NMOSFETs," *IEEE Trans. Electron Dev.*, **ED-37**, June 1990 p. 1426.

230. I.C. Chen et al., "Performance and Reliability Enhancement for CVD Tungsten Polycided CMOS Transistors Due to Fluorine Incorporated in the Gate Oxide," *IEEE Electron Dev. Letts.*, **EDL-15**, September 1994.

PROBLEMS

1. Explain the difference between CORS and CAS.

2. Explain the difference between electron traps in SiO_2 and interface state traps.

3. Qualitatively describe the advantages and disadvantages of LDD MOSFETs.

4. Calculate ε_{ymax} in a non-LDD MOSFET having a 1 μm channel length, t_{ox} = 200 nm, r_j = 0.2 μm, V_T = 0.7V, V_{GS} = 5V, and V_{DS} = 5V. (b) Use Eq. 9-4 to calculate I_{sub} in this device if I_D = 100 μA.

5. Calculate ε_{ymax} in an LDD MOSFET having a 1 μm channel length, t_{ox} = 200 nm, r_j = 0.2 μm, V_T = 0.7V, V_{GS} = 5V, and V_{DS} = 5V using Eq. 9-13. Assume the L_{n^-} region in this device is 0.2 μm in length.

6. (a) An n-channel MOSFET has a tox of 20 nm, an L_{eff} = 1 μm, r_j = 0.2 μm, and V_T = 0.6V. If the device is biased at V_{GS} = 3V and V_{DS} = 5V, calculate the saturation voltage V_{DSsat} and the maximum electric field. If this device is built using an LDD and the n^- length of the LDD is 0.2 μm, find the decrease in the maximum electric field in the LDD device. If the FET channel width is 10 μm and the S/D sheet resistance in the LDD region is 100 Ω/square, calculate the additional S/D resistance due to the LDD insertion and compare it with the intrinsic FET resistance.

7. List some advantages of using disposable spacers for fabricating LDD MOSFETs. What are some of their drawbacks?

8. Discuss the advantages and disadvantages of the following device structures compared to conventional LDD MOSFETs:

        a) Fully overlapped drain structures
        b) Buried LDD structures
        c) Large-angle-tilt implanted drain structures
        d) LDD MOSFETs with high-dielectric spacers
        e) Asymmetrical MOSFET structures (Halo-Source GOLD)

9. Why have LDD structures not been necessary in PMOS devices until deep submicron gate lengths are encountered?

10. Explain briefly why N_2O nitrided oxides have proved to be superior to NH_3-nitrided gate dielectrics.

APPENDIX A

MATRIX METHODS

A.1 INTRODUCTION TO MATRICES

Matrices and their algebra are vital to modern engineering mathematics. They represent an enormously effective means by which data and other mathematical quantities of interest can be manipulated in an elegant and efficient manner. The practical use of finite difference and finite elements are greatly facilitated by the use of matrices. Hence, we present here a few of the important basic concepts of matrices and matrix algebra.

A *matrix* is a rectangular array of elements arranged in rows and columns. The elements may be numbers, variables, functions, derivatives, or even other matrices. The following set of m linear algebraic equations serves to illustrate a common notational convention used relative to matrix representation of a linear system of equations.

$$
\begin{aligned}
a_{11}x_1 + a_{12}x_2 + \ \ldots \ + a_{1n}x_n &= b_1 \\
a_{21}x_1 + a_{22}x_2 + \ \ldots \ + a_{2n}x_n &= b_2 \\
\vdots \qquad \vdots \qquad\qquad \vdots \qquad \vdots \\
a_{m1}x_1 + a_{m2}x_2 + \ \ldots \ + a_{mn}x_n &= b_m
\end{aligned}
\tag{A - 1}
$$

The set of variables x_1, x_2, $\ldots$, x_n, and a set of m dependent variables b_1, b_2, $\ldots$ b_m are related through the $m{\times}n$ coefficients a_{11}, a_{12}, ..., a_{mn}. Using matrix notation we write Eq. A-1 more compactly as follows:

$$
\begin{bmatrix}
a_{11} & a_{12} & \cdots & a_{1n} \\
a_{21} & a_{22} & \cdots & a_{2n} \\
\vdots & \vdots & \cdots & \vdots \\
a_{m1} & a_{m2} & \cdots & a_{mn}
\end{bmatrix}
\begin{Bmatrix}
x_1 \\ x_2 \\ \vdots \\ x_n
\end{Bmatrix}
=
\begin{Bmatrix}
b_1 \\ b_2 \\ \vdots \\ b_m
\end{Bmatrix}
\tag{A - 2}
$$

The $m{\times}n$ array of a's is referred to as the coefficient matrix $[\mathbf{A}]$ or $[a_{i,j}]$ and the independent variables as the $\{\mathbf{x}\}$ or $\{x_j\}$ vector. In addition, the dependent quantities on the right-hand side are grouped in a separate array called the $\{\mathbf{B}\}$ or $\{b_{i,j}\}$ vector.

A.1.1 Vectors and Scalars. Matrices with only one row and n columns $(1{\times}n)$ or one column and m rows $(m{\times}1)$ are called vectors. The symbol $\{\ \}$ is used to indicate a row or column vector. Matrices with only one element $(1{\times}1)$ are called scalars. For example, the 3x1 matrix $\{\mathbf{A}\}$

$$\{\mathbf{A}\} = \begin{Bmatrix} 2 \\ 10 \\ -3 \end{Bmatrix}_{3 \times 1} = \{a_{i,j}\}, \quad i = 1,2,3 \; j = 1 \qquad (A - 3)$$

is a *column vector*.

A.1.2 The Square Matrix. A matrix having an equal number of columns and rows is called a *square matrix*. Square matrices play an important role in engineering and have properties that are unique. For example, the determinant and inverse can only be defined if the matrix is a square matrix.

A.1.3 The Identity Matrix. The identity matrix is a square matrix whose off-diagonal elements are equal to zero and diagonal elements are equal to one. Since identity matrices are unique, they are designated by the letter I and sometimes written as

$$[\mathbf{I}]_n = \begin{bmatrix} 1 & 0 & \cdots & 0 \\ 0 & 1 & \cdots & 0 \\ \vdots & \vdots & \vdots & \vdots \\ 0 & 0 & \cdots & 1 \end{bmatrix} \qquad (A - 4)$$

A.1.4 The Diagonal Matrix. Diagonal matrices are square matrices whose off-diagonal elements are equal to zero and whose diagonal elements can take on any value. These matrices are very important and occur frequently when one solves systems of ordinary differential equations. Furthermore, "diagonalizing" is used to mean that a nondiagonal square matrix is reduced to one which is diagonal.

A.1.5 The Augmented Matrix. This is a matrix that can be formed from two other matrices. Consider the matrices [**A**] and [**B**]:

$$[\mathbf{A}] = \begin{bmatrix} a_{11} & a_{12} \\ a_{21} & a_{22} \end{bmatrix} \qquad [\mathbf{B}] = \begin{bmatrix} 1 & 0 \\ 0 & 1 \end{bmatrix}$$

Then a third matrix [**C**] is the augmented matrix if

$$[\mathbf{C}] = \begin{bmatrix} a_{11} & a_{12} & \vdots & 1 & 0 \\ a_{21} & a_{22} & \vdots & 0 & 1 \end{bmatrix} \qquad (A - 5)$$

Note that [**C**] can only be defined if both [**A**] and [**B**] have exactly the same number of rows. The dashed line in [**C**] is used to separate the elements of [**A**] and [**B**]. Augmented matrices are useful in solving sets of linear algebraic equations.

A.1.6 The Upper-Triangular Matrix. This is a square matrix often denoted as [U] in which all elements below the diagonal are zero and the rest of the elements can take on any value. That is:

$$[U] = \begin{bmatrix} a_{11} & a_{12} & \cdots & a_{1n} \\ 0 & a_{22} & \cdots & a_{2n} \\ \vdots & \vdots & \vdots & \vdots \\ 0 & 0 & \cdots & a_{mn} \end{bmatrix} \qquad (A-6)$$

The solution of linear algebraic equations using the Gaussian elimination method results in an upper-triangular matrix.

A.1.7 The Lower-Triangular Matrix. This is a square matrix often denoted as [L] in which all elements above the diagonal are zero and the rest of the elements can take on any value. That is:

$$[L] = \begin{bmatrix} a_{11} & 0 & \cdots & 0 \\ a_{21} & a_{22} & \cdots & 0 \\ \vdots & \vdots & \vdots & \vdots \\ a_{m1} & a_{m2} & \cdots & a_{mn} \end{bmatrix} \qquad (A-7)$$

A.2 MATRIX MULTIPLICATION

If we wish to obtain the product of two matrices [A] and [B], which is equal to a third matrix [C]:

$$[C] = [A][B] \qquad (A-8)$$

matrix [C] can only be defined if the number of rows of matrix [B] is equal to the number of columns of matrix [A]. That is,

$$[C]_{mxL} = [A]_{mxn}[B]_{nxL} \qquad (A-9)$$

Here m is the number of rows of matrices [A] and [C]; n is the number of columns of [A] and the number of rows of [B]; L is the number of columns of [B] and [C].

To illustrate the procedure for finding the products of the matrices consider the following example:

$$[A] = \begin{bmatrix} a_{11} & a_{12} & a_{13} \\ a_{21} & a_{22} & a_{23} \end{bmatrix} \qquad [B] = \begin{bmatrix} b_{11} & b_{12} \\ b_{21} & b_{22} \\ b_{31} & b_{32} \end{bmatrix}$$

Let us define

$$[C] = [A]_{2x3}[B]_{3x2} = \begin{bmatrix} c_{11} & c_{12} \\ c_{21} & c_{22} \end{bmatrix} \qquad (A-10a)$$

where

$$
\begin{aligned}
c_{11} &= a_{11}b_{11} + a_{12}b_{21} + a_{13}b_{31} \\
c_{12} &= a_{11}b_{12} + a_{12}b_{22} + a_{13}b_{32} \\
c_{21} &= a_{21}b_{11} + a_{22}b_{21} + a_{23}b_{31} \\
c_{22} &= a_{21}b_{12} + a_{22}b_{22} + a_{23}b_{32}
\end{aligned}
\qquad \text{(A - 10b)}
$$

We see that the process involved in multiplying two matrices causes us to use an *entire row* of [A] and an *entire column* of [B] to obtain a *single element* of [C]. That is, "c_{11}," is determined by combining the products of the elements in the first column of [B] with the elements of the first row in [A], "c_{12}" is determined by combining the products of the elements in the second column of [B] with the elements of the first row in [A]; ... etc.

Example A-1: Find the product [A] [B] for the following matrices.

$$
[A] = \begin{bmatrix} 2 & 1 \\ 3 & -4 \end{bmatrix}
\qquad
[B] = \begin{bmatrix} a & c & 0 \\ b & d & 0 \end{bmatrix}
$$

Solution:

$$
[C]_{2x3} = \begin{bmatrix} 2 & 1 \\ 3 & -4 \end{bmatrix} \begin{bmatrix} a & c & 0 \\ b & d & 0 \end{bmatrix}
$$

$$
= \begin{bmatrix} 2a + b & 2c + d & 0 \\ 3a - 4b & 3c - 4d & 0 \end{bmatrix}
$$

A.3 MATRIX INVERSION

There are instances where the solution of matrices involves the calculation of the inverse matrix. The inverse of a matrix [A] is a property of square nonsingular matrices (determinant is not zero) and is denoted [A^{-1}]. In addition,

$$
[A][A^{-1}] = [I] \qquad \text{(A - 11)}
$$

Note that only square matrices can have an inverse.

Several methods for inverting matrices are available, including: the *Cramer's rule* method; the *Gauss-Jordan method;* the *reducing matrix method*; and the *partitioning method*. Here we show the Gauss-Jordan method - an extension of the Gauss-Jordan method for solving matrix equations.

Suppose we have two 3x3 square matrices **A** and **B** such that [A]$^{-1}$ = [B], then by definition [A] [B] = [B] [A] = [I], or more explicitly,

$$\begin{bmatrix} a_{11} & a_{12} & a_{13} \\ a_{21} & a_{22} & a_{23} \\ a_{31} & a_{32} & a_{33} \end{bmatrix} \begin{bmatrix} b_{11}b_{12}b_{13} \\ b_{21}b_{22}b_{23} \\ b_{31}b_{32}b_{33} \end{bmatrix} = \begin{bmatrix} 1 & 0 & 0 \\ 0 & 1 & 0 \\ 0 & 0 & 1 \end{bmatrix}$$

Then if we form an augmented matrix $[[\mathbf{A}] : [\mathbf{I}]]$

$$[[\mathbf{A}] : [\mathbf{I}]] = \begin{bmatrix} a_{11} & a_{12} & a_{13} & \vdots & 1 & 0 & 0 \\ a_{21} & a_{22} & a_{23} & \vdots & 0 & 1 & 0 \\ a_{31} & a_{32} & a_{33} & \vdots & 0 & 0 & 1 \end{bmatrix}$$

we can use the Gauss-Jordan method to reduce this augmented matrix to the form:

$$[[\mathbf{I}] : [\mathbf{B}]] = \begin{bmatrix} 1 & 0 & 0 & \vdots & b_{11}b_{12}b_{13} \\ 0 & 1 & 0 & \vdots & b_{21}b_{22}b_{23} \\ 0 & 0 & 1 & \vdots & b_{31}b_{32}b_{33} \end{bmatrix}$$

where $[\mathbf{B}]$ is the inverse of $[\mathbf{A}]$. This method of determining the inverse is summarized in one step for an $n{\times}n$ matrix:

$$[[\mathbf{A}] : [\mathbf{I}]] \; {\longrightarrow} \; [[\mathbf{I}] : [\mathbf{B}]] \tag{A - 12}$$

Example A-2: Use the Gauss-Jordan elimination method to determine the inverse of $[\mathbf{A}]$:

$$[\mathbf{A}] = \begin{bmatrix} 1 & 2 \\ 2 & -1 \end{bmatrix}$$

Solution: First, multiply the first row by -2 and add it to the second row

$$\begin{bmatrix} 1 & 2 & \vdots & 1 & 0 \\ 2 & -1 & \vdots & 0 & 1 \end{bmatrix} \quad {\longrightarrow} \quad \begin{bmatrix} 1 & 2 & \vdots & 1 & 0 \\ 0 & -5 & \vdots & -2 & 1 \end{bmatrix} \;\; -2R_1 + R_2$$

Next, divide row two by -5

$$\begin{bmatrix} 1 & 2 & \vdots & 1 & 0 \\ 0 & 1 & \vdots & 2/5 & -1/5 \end{bmatrix} - R_2/5 \quad {\longrightarrow} \quad \begin{bmatrix} 1 & 0 & \vdots & 1/5 & 2/5 \\ 0 & 1 & \vdots & 2/5 & -1/5 \end{bmatrix} \;\; -2R_2 + R_1$$

Finally, multiply row two by -2 and add it to the first row to get the final augmented matrix. The inverse of $[\mathbf{A}]$ is simply equal to the right-hand portion of this augmented matrix, namely,

$$[\mathbf{A}]^{-1} = \frac{1}{5} \begin{bmatrix} 1 & 2 \\ 2 & -1 \end{bmatrix}$$

A.4 MATRIX METHODS FOR SOLVING SIMULTANEOUS LINEAR ALGEBRAIC EQUATIONS

As noted in the text, the solution of simultaneous linear algebraic equations is probably one of the most important procedures in modern engineering computations. For example, the finite element method and the finite difference method both involve the solution of systems of linear algebraic equations. Two classes of methods are available for solving a set of linear algebraic equations: *direct methods*, and *iterative methods*. The direct methods are based on elimination, and include Cramer's Rule, Gauss elimination method, the Gauss-Jordan elimination method, and Crout's Method. The iterative methods include Jacobi's method (and its variations), the Gauss-Seidel method (and its variations), the successive-overrelaxation (SOR) method, the alternating-direction implicit (ADI), and Stone's strongly implicit method. An good (but compressed) survey by Duff on the subject of the various matrix methods for solving a set of linear algebraic equations is listed in reference 1. A text dealing with this topic is A. George and J.W.H. Liu, *Computer Solution of Large Sparse Positive Definite Systems,* Prentice-Hall, Inc. Englewood Cliffs, N.J. (1981).

A.4.1 Direct Methods

A.4.1.1 Cramer's Rule. This method is widely taught as a procedure for solving a set of simultaneous linear algebraic equations. However, since it is likely to be familiar to readers and because it less efficient than other techniques, we do not emphasize it here.

A.4.1.2 Gauss-Jordan Elimination Method. This method is basically an extension of the Gauss method presented in the next section. The difference is that there is no need for back-substitution using this method. This is accomplished quite simply by eliminating the coefficients above the diagonal in the coefficient matrix. Consider the typical case of three equations with three unknowns

$$
\begin{aligned}
a_{11}x_1 + a_{12}x_2 + a_{13}x_3 &= b_1 \\
a_{21}x_1 + a_{22}x_2 + a_{23}x_3 &= b_2 \\
a_{31}x_1 + a_{32}x_2 + a_{33}x_3 &= b_3
\end{aligned}
\qquad (A-13)
$$

The Gauss-Jordan process operates on the augmented matrix

$$\begin{bmatrix} a_{11} & a_{12} & a_{13} & \vdots & b_1 \\ a_{21} & a_{22} & a_{23} & \vdots & b_2 \\ a_{31} & a_{32} & a_{33} & \vdots & b_3 \end{bmatrix}$$

(A - 14)

By successive operations of dividing rows by numbers, interchanging rows, and subtracting a multiple of one row from another, we try to reduce this matrix to the form

$$\begin{bmatrix} 1 & 0 & 0 & \vdots & b_1^* \\ 0 & 1 & 0 & \vdots & b_2^* \\ 0 & 0 & 1 & \vdots & b_3^* \end{bmatrix}$$

(A - 15)

in which case the solution is readily obtained as

$$x_1 = b_1^*$$
$$x_2 = b_2^*$$
$$x_3 = b_3^*$$

(A - 16)

If the matrix of the coefficients [**A**] is nonsingular, the process described can be carried out in full. Although this method requires more computational effort than the Gauss method, we present it because it provides a direct method for solving the inverse problem discussed earlier.

Example A-3: Solve the following set using the Gauss-Jordan method:

$$2x_1 - 4x_2 + 6x_3 = 5$$
$$x_1 + 3x_2 - 7x_3 = 2$$
$$7x_1 + 5x_2 + 9x_3 = 4$$

Solution: Forming the augmented matrix, we proceed by reducing the first column to that of an identity matrix. Thus

$$\begin{bmatrix} 2 & -4 & 6 & \vdots & 5 \\ 1 & 3 & -7 & \vdots & 2 \\ 7 & 5 & 9 & \vdots & 4 \end{bmatrix}$$

Next, divide row one by 2

$$\longrightarrow \begin{bmatrix} 1 & -2 & 3 & \vdots & 2.5 \\ 1 & 3 & -7 & \vdots & 2 \\ 7 & 5 & 9 & \vdots & 4 \end{bmatrix} \quad R_1/2$$

Then add the negative of row one to row two, and multiply row one by -7 and add it to row three:

$$\begin{bmatrix} 1 & -2 & 3 & \vdots & 2.5 \\ 0 & 5 & -10 & \vdots & -0.5 \\ 0 & 19 & -12 & \vdots & -13.5 \end{bmatrix} \begin{array}{l} \\ -R_1 + R_2 \\ -7R_1 + R_3 \end{array}$$

Now divide row two by 5:

$$\longrightarrow \begin{bmatrix} 1 & -2 & 3 & \vdots & 2.5 \\ 0 & 1 & -2 & \vdots & -0.1 \\ 0 & -19 & -12 & \vdots & -13.5 \end{bmatrix} \begin{array}{l} \\ R_2/5 \\ \end{array}$$

Then multiply row two by 2 and add it to row one, and also multiply row two by -19 and add it to row three:

$$\begin{bmatrix} 1 & 0 & -1 & \vdots & 2.3 \\ 0 & 1 & -2 & \vdots & -0.1 \\ 0 & 0 & 26 & \vdots & -11.6 \end{bmatrix} \begin{array}{l} 2R_2 + R_1 \\ \\ -19R_2 + R_3 \end{array}$$

Next, divide row three by 26:

$$\longrightarrow \begin{bmatrix} 1 & 0 & -1 & \vdots & 2.3 \\ 0 & 1 & -2 & \vdots & -0.1 \\ 0 & 0 & 1 & \vdots & -0.44 \end{bmatrix} \begin{array}{l} \\ \\ R_3/26 \end{array}$$

Finally, add row three to row one, and also multiply row three by 2 and add it to row two.

$$\begin{bmatrix} 1 & 0 & 0 & \vdots & 1.85 \\ 0 & 1 & 0 & \vdots & -0.99 \\ 0 & 0 & 1 & \vdots & -0.45 \end{bmatrix} \begin{array}{l} R_3 + R_1 \\ 2R_3 + R_2 \\ \end{array}$$

Note that this form is exactly the same as is given in Eq. A-15. The solution to the set of equations is then given as

$$x_1 = 1.85$$
$$x_2 = -0.99$$
$$x_3 = -0.45$$

Note also that roundoff errors may be introduced depending on the number of significant figures used in manipulating the matrices. This may become significant if a large set of equations is to be solved.

A.4.1.3 Gauss Elimination Method. An alternative to the Gauss-Jordan method is the simple *Gauss method.* This is one of the most popular and efficient methods for solving an *nxn* system of equations. Since less computations are needed for the Gauss elimination method than for the Gauss-Jordan method, the simple Gauss method is preferred. Here we use the same steps as in the Gauss-Jordan method, but the goal is to produce a matrix with zeros *below the diagonal.* Each unknown is then determined from this matrix by back-substitution. That is, we first seek to achieve a matrix of the form

$$\begin{bmatrix} 1 & b_{12} b_{13} & \vdots & c_1^* \\ 0 & 1 & b_{23} & \vdots & c_2^* \\ 0 & 0 & 1 & \vdots & c_3^* \end{bmatrix} \qquad \text{(A - 17)}$$

The corresponding set of equations from this matrix is then

$$\begin{aligned} x_1 + b_{12}x_2 + b_{13}x_3 &= c_1 \\ x_2 + b_{23}x_3 &= c_2 \qquad \text{(A - 18)} \\ x_3 &= c_3. \end{aligned}$$

Now x_3 can be obtained from the last equation and this value can be substituted in the next-to-last equation. This allows us to solve for x_2, which is then substituted together with the known value of x_3 in the first equation, to obtain x_1.

Example A-4: Solve the following set of equations using the Gauss Elimination method:

$$\begin{aligned} 2x_2 + 4x_3 &= 6 \\ 4x_1 + x_2 - 3x_3 &= 1 \\ 3x_1 - 8x_2 + 2x_3 &= 2 \end{aligned}$$

Solution: Using the augmented matrix approach and switching the second and first equations (so that $a_{11} \neq 0$) gives

$$\begin{bmatrix} 4 & 1 & -3 & \vdots & 1 \\ 0 & 2 & 4 & \vdots & 6 \\ 3 & -8 & 2 & \vdots & 2 \end{bmatrix}$$

We begin by dividing the first row by 4: thus

$$\begin{bmatrix} 1 & 0.25 & -0.75 & \vdots & 0.25 \\ 0 & 2 & 4 & \vdots & 6 \\ 3 & -8 & 2 & \vdots & 2 \end{bmatrix} \quad R_1/4$$

Multiplying the first row by -3 and adding it to the third row eliminates x_1 from all equations except the first. Hence

$$\begin{bmatrix} 1 & 0.25 & -0.75 & \vdots & 0.25 \\ 0 & 2 & 4 & \vdots & 6 \\ 0 & -8.75 & 4.25 & \vdots & 1.25 \end{bmatrix} \quad -3R_1 + R_3$$

The second row is now divided by 2 to give

$$\begin{bmatrix} 1 & 0.25 & -0.75 & \vdots & 0.25 \\ 0 & 1 & 2 & \vdots & 3 \\ 0 & -8.75 & 4.25 & \vdots & 1.25 \end{bmatrix} \quad R_2/2$$

Finally, multiplying the second row by 8.75 and adding it to the third row eliminates x_2 from the third equation. That is,

$$\begin{bmatrix} 1 & 0.25 & -0.75 & \vdots & 0.25 \\ 0 & 1 & 2 & \vdots & 3 \\ 0 & 0 & 21.75 & \vdots & 27.5 \end{bmatrix} \quad 8.75R_2 + R_3$$

Obviously, the original set of equations has now been transformed to an upper-triangular form. Hence, dividing row 3 by 21.75 and expressing the set in algebraic form yields

$$\begin{aligned} x_1 + 0.25x_2 - 0.75x_3 &= 0.25 \\ x_2 + 2x_3 &= 3 \\ x_3 &= 1.264 \end{aligned}$$

These equations are now solved by back-substitution to give

$$\begin{aligned} x_3 &= 1.264 \\ x_2 &= 3 - 2\,(1.264) = 0.472 \\ x_1 &= 0.25 - 0.25\,(0.472) + 0.75\,(1.264) = 1.080 \end{aligned}$$

Note that in this and the other direct solution method example there is no rounding off error and the answer is exact.

A.4.1.4 Cholesky's Method.

The classical Gaussian elimination method described above is not suitable for the systems of equations that must be solved in microelectronics because the size of the coefficient matrix is generally both large and sparse (most of its coefficients are zero). In addition, in many cases a set of tridiagonal linear matrix equations result. Therefore, some modifications of the classical Gaussian elimination algorithm are introduced to account for the zero entries and to utilize the relative simplicity of the tridiagonal set. One common approach is to decompose the augmented matrix into the product of a unit upper-triangular matrix and a lower-triangular matrix (Cholesky's method, also called Crout's method, or the LU-decomposition method). In Cholesky's method (also known as Crout's method) *triangular factorization* is applied to the coefficient matrix e.g., [A] of the equation

$$[A]\{x\} = \{b\} \qquad (A - 19)$$

which yields

$$[A] = [L] [L^T] \qquad (A - 20)$$

where [L] is a *lower triangular matrix* and [L^T] is the transpose of the [L] matrix, and [L^T] is also an *upper triangular matrix* (see section A.1 of this appendix for definitions of these terms). Using (A-20) in (A-19) we get

$$[L] [L^T] \{x\} = \{b\} \qquad (A - 21)$$

and by substituting $\{y\} = [L^T] \{x\}$, we can find $\{x\}$ by solving the triangular systems

$$[L]\{y\} = \{b\} \qquad (A - 22)$$

and

$$[L^T] \{x\} = \{y\}. \qquad (A - 23)$$

Example A-5: Solve the following matrix equation for $\{x\}$ using the Cholesky method.

$$
\begin{bmatrix}
4 & 1 & 2 & 1/2 & 2 \\
1 & 1/2 & 0 & 0 & 0 \\
2 & 0 & 3 & 0 & 0 \\
1/2 & 0 & 0 & 5/8 & 0 \\
2 & 0 & 0 & 0 & 16
\end{bmatrix}
\begin{Bmatrix}
x_1 \\ x_2 \\ x_3 \\ x_4 \\ x_5
\end{Bmatrix}
=
\begin{Bmatrix}
7 \\ 3 \\ 7 \\ -4 \\ -4
\end{Bmatrix}
$$

Solution: The coefficient matrix of the above equation can be factored to yield (A-20) where [L] in (A-20) in this case is

$$
[L] =
\begin{bmatrix}
2 & & & & 0 \\
0.50 & 0.50 & & & \\
1 & -1 & 1 & & \\
0.25 & -0.25 & -0.50 & 0.50 & \\
1 & -1 & -2 & -3 & 1
\end{bmatrix}
$$

Solving $[L]\{y\} = \{b\}$, we obtain

$$\{\mathbf{y}\} = \begin{Bmatrix} 3.5 \\ 2.5 \\ 6 \\ -2.5 \\ --0.5 \end{Bmatrix}$$

and then solving $[\mathbf{L}^T]\{\mathbf{x}\} = \{\mathbf{y}\}$ yields

$$\{\mathbf{x}\} = \begin{Bmatrix} 2 \\ 2 \\ 1 \\ -0.8 \\ --0.5 \end{Bmatrix}$$

A.4.2 Iterative Methods

Iteration is defined as a computational procedure in which the desired result is approached through a repeated cycle of operations, each of which more closely approximates the desired result. Iterative methods can be used to solve a set of simultaneous linear algebraic equations. Such methods yield an approximation to the solution of a system of such equations, but unlike the direct methods they may not always yield a solution, even if the determinant of the coefficient matrix is not zero. Consequently, for these techniques to work, certain other conditions must be considered:

1. The set of equations must posses a strong diagonal. This is a necessary but not a sufficient condition for a solution to be found.

2. A sufficient condition for a solution to be found is that the absolute value of the diagonal coefficient in any equation must be greater than the sum of the absolute values of all other coefficients appearing in that equation.

These two conditions can often be satisfied for a variety of practical problems encountered in engineering.

Iterative techniques are often used when dealing with sparse matrices. They offer the advantage that less computer memory is required for solving a set of algebraic equations than would be required using direct techniques (such as Gaussian elimination). Another important advantage of iterative methods is that round-off errors in the solution are limited to those incurred in the final iteration, and are normally negligible. This is because the values used in the previous iteration are treated as initial estimates and updated independently of the rounding error. On the other hand, direct solution methods are subject to cumulative round-off errors which can be come significant for large coefficient matrices or ill-conditioned systems of equations. The main disadvantage of iterative methods is that they depend on the numerical conditioning of the matrix and may fail to converge in some situations.

Here we present two of the most basic iterative methods in some detail. This presentation is designed to give readers some flavor for how iterative methods arrive at a solution. The more advanced methods, which are the methods more likely to be found in simulation software packages, are mentioned briefly in the final section, with references that provide more details on their procedures. Their complexity puts them outside of the scope of this text.

A.4.2.1 Jacobi's Method. One of the simplest iterative methods for solving linear algebraic equations is Jacobi's method. The following example illustrates this technique:

$$a_{11}x_1 + a_{12}x_2 + a_{13}x_3 = b_1 \qquad\qquad (A-24a)$$
$$a_{21}x_1 + a_{22}x_2 + a_{23}x_3 = b_2 \qquad\qquad (A-24b)$$
$$a_{31}x_1 + a_{32}x_2 + a_{33}x_3 = b_3 \qquad\qquad (A-24c)$$

The solution process begins by solving for x_1 from Eq. A-124a, then x_2 is determined from Eq. A-24b, and finally x_3 is determined from Eq. A-24c. In addition, a dummy index k is introduced to number the iterations performed in approximating the solution. In particular the equations used to get the next iteration from the last one are

$$x_1^{k+1} = (b_1/a_{11}) - (a_{12}/a_{11})x_2^k - (a_{13}/a_{11})x_3^k$$
$$x_2^{k+1} = (b_2/a_{22}) - (a_{21}/a_{22})x_1^k - (a_{23}/a_{22})x_3^k \qquad\qquad (A-25)$$
$$x_3^{k+1} = (b_3/a_{33}) - (a_{31}/a_{33})x_2^k - (a_{32}/a_{33})x_3^k$$

Thus, if we assume an initial vector $\{x\}^k = \{x_1^k, x_2^k, x_3^k\}$ and substitute it into Eq. A-25, a new vector $\{x\}^{k+1}$ is calculated. This process is continued until sufficient accuracy is achieved. That is, until

$$\{x\}^{k+1} \cong \{x\}^k, \quad k = 0, \dots, N \qquad\qquad (A-26)$$

where N is the number of iterations performed. In general, for an $n{\times}n$ set, Eq. A-25 can be expressed in the following matrix form:

$$
\left\{ \begin{array}{c} x_1 \\ x_2 \\ \vdots \\ x_n \end{array} \right\}_{k+1} = \left\{ \begin{array}{c} B_1 \\ B_2 \\ \vdots \\ B_n \end{array} \right\} - \left[\begin{array}{ccccc} 0 & A_{12} & \cdots & A_{1n} \\ A_{21} & 0 & \cdots & A_{2n} \\ \vdots & \vdots & \cdots & \vdots \\ A_{n1} & A_{n2} & \cdots & 0 \end{array} \right] \left\{ \begin{array}{c} x_1 \\ x_2 \\ \vdots \\ x_n \end{array} \right\}_k \qquad (A-27)
$$

where

$$
\begin{array}{lll}
B_i & = b_i/a_{ii} & i = 1, \;.... \; n \\
A_{i,j} & = a_{ij}/a_{ii}, & i = 1, \;.... \; n, \quad j = 1, \;... \;, n \\
k & = 0, \;... \;, N &
\end{array}
$$

The reader is to be reminded that Eq. A-27 is guaranteed to converge if condition 2 is met. Otherwise a solution may or may not be possible. Also, computer software packages for solving sparse matrices using the Jacobi conjugate gradient method (a variation of the Jacobi method) are available - such as ELLPACK, developed at Purdue University.[2]

Example A-6: Solve the following set of linear algebraic equations using the Jacobi method:

$$
\begin{array}{rcl}
5x_1 - 2x_2 + x_3 & = & 4 \\
x_1 + 4x_2 - 2x_3 & = & 3 \\
x_1 + 2x_2 + 4x_3 & = & 17
\end{array}
$$

Solution: First check the diagonal coefficients and determine whether the iterative procedure is suitable. Thus

$$
|5| > |\text{-}2| + |1| \;\text{---}\!> \; 5 > 3 \; \text{O.K.}
$$

$$
|4| > |1| + |\text{-}2| \;\text{---}\!> \; 4 > 3 \; \text{O.K.}
$$

$$
|4| > |1| + |2| \;\text{---}\!> \; 5 > 3 \; \text{O.K.}
$$

Obviously, the iterative approach will converge. Therefore, expressing the set in the form of Eq. A-20 yields

$$
\left\{ \begin{array}{c} x_1 \\ x_2 \\ x_3 \end{array} \right\}_{k+1} = \left\{ \begin{array}{c} 0.8 \\ 0.75 \\ 4.25 \end{array} \right\} - \left[\begin{array}{ccc} 0 & -0.4 & 0.2 \\ 0.25 & 0 & -0.5 \\ 0.25 & 0.5 & 0 \end{array} \right] \left\{ \begin{array}{c} x_1 \\ x_2 \\ x_3 \end{array} \right\}_k \qquad (A-28)
$$

Assuming an initial iteration $\{x\}_0 = \{0\}$ and substituting into equation yields our first approximation to the solution. That is,

$$\begin{Bmatrix} x_1 \\ x_2 \\ x_3 \end{Bmatrix}_1 = \begin{Bmatrix} 0.8 \\ 0.75 \\ 4.25 \end{Bmatrix} - \begin{bmatrix} 0 & -0.4 & 0.2 \\ 0.25 & 0 & -0.5 \\ 0.25 & 0.5 & 0 \end{bmatrix} \begin{Bmatrix} 0 \\ 0 \\ 0 \end{Bmatrix}_0 = \begin{Bmatrix} 0.8 \\ 0.75 \\ 4.25 \end{Bmatrix}_1$$

Substituting $\{x\}_1$ into Eq. A-28 gives the second approximation to the $\{x\}$ vector:

$$\begin{Bmatrix} x_1 \\ x_2 \\ x_3 \end{Bmatrix}_2 = \begin{Bmatrix} 0.8 \\ 0.75 \\ 4.25 \end{Bmatrix} - \begin{bmatrix} 0 & -0.4 & 0.2 \\ 0.25 & 0 & -0.5 \\ 0.25 & 0.5 & 0 \end{bmatrix} \begin{Bmatrix} 0.8 \\ 0.75 \\ 4.25 \end{Bmatrix}_1 = \begin{Bmatrix} 0.25 \\ 2.675 \\ 3.675 \end{Bmatrix}_2$$

The process is continued until successive values of each vector are sufficiently close in magnitude. For the example at hand, the first ten iterations are shown in Table A-1.

Table A-1. Successive Approximations of Solution (Jacobi's Method)

Variable	Iteration									
	1	2	3	4	5	6	7	8	9	10
x_1	0.8	0.25	1.14	1.24	1.02	0.92	0.98	1.02	1.01	0.99
x_2	0.75	2.68	2.53	1.89	1.79	1.99	2.07	2.02	1.98	1.99
x_3	4.25	3.68	2.85	2.70	2.99	3.10	3.02	2.97	2.98	3.01

A.4.2.2 Gauss-Seidel Method. This method converges more rapidly than the Jacobi method. However, it is constrained by the same conditions outlines in the previous section. The Gauss-Seidel solution procedure presupposes that the new solution values are a better approximation to the exact solution than the initial assumed values. This is true for most problems. Consequently for the 3x3 set given by Eq. A-19 the solution for the new values becomes

$$\begin{aligned} x_1^{k+1} &= (b_1/a_{11}) - (a_{12}/a_{11})x_2^k - (a_{13}/a_{11})x_3^k \\ x_2^{k+1} &= (b_2/a_{22}) - (a_{21}/a_{22})x_1^{k+1} - (a_{23}/a_{22})x_3^k \qquad (A-29) \\ x_3^{k+1} &= (b_3/a_{33}) - (a_{32}/a_{33})x_1^{k+1} - (a_{32}/a_{33})x_2^{k+1} \end{aligned}$$

Comparison of Eq. A-25 with A-29 clearly shows that one need not assume an initial x_1 value. Instead, x_1 is computed by assuming x_2 and x_3. Then the new x_1 value and the assumed x_1 value are used to calculate a new x_2 value. This procedure is continued by substituting the new x_1 and x_2 values to determine a new x_3 value.

Note that the Gauss-Seidel method will converge under the same conditions required for convergence of the Jacobi method. For many engineering problems, this condition can be satisfied. For example, the Poisson equation is readily solved using the Gauss-Seidel method. The Gauss-Seidel method (or variations thereof) are more widely used than the Jacobi method whenever an iterative solution is sought, because it converges faster.

Example A-7: Rework Example A-6 using the Gauss-Seidel method.

Solution: Since the Jacobi method converged for this particular example, the Gauss-Seidel technique should also converge. Consequently, expressing the set in the form of Eq. A-29 yields:

$$
\begin{aligned}
x_1^{k+1} &= 0.8 + 0.4x_2^k - 0.2x_3^k \\
x_2^{k+1} &= 0.75 - 0.25x_1^{k+1} + 0.5x_3^k \\
x_3^{k+1} &= 4.25 - 0.25x_1^{k+1} - 0.5x_2^{k+1}
\end{aligned}
\qquad (A - 30)
$$

Now, assuming initial values of $x_2 = 0$ and $x_3 = 0$ and substituting into Eq. A-30 gives for $k = 0$

$$
\begin{aligned}
x_1^1 &= 0.8 + 0 - 0 = 0.8 \\
x_2^1 &= 0.75 - 0.250 (0.8) + 0 = 0.55 \\
x_3^1 &= 4.25 - 0.250 (0.8) - 0.5 (0.55) = 3.775
\end{aligned}
$$

This process is continued by substituting the new x_2^1 and x_3^1 into Eq. A-30 permitting the determination of yet another set of x values. Computations for the first seven iterations are summarized in Table A-2.

Table A-2. Successive Approximations of Solution (Gauss-Seidel Method)

Variable	Iteration 1	2	3	4	5	6	7
x_1	0.8	0.265	1.249	0.956	1.002	1.001	0.999
x_2	0.55	2.571	1.887	2.008	2.003	1.999	2.000
x_3	3.775	2.898	2.994	3.007	2.998	3.000	3.000

Note that the results obtained in five iterations are more accurate than those obtained in ten iterations using the Jacobi method.

A.4.2.3 Advanced Iterative Solution Techniques. Although, in principle, the simple iterative methods (Jacobi or Gauss-Seidel) can be used to solve a set of linear algebraic equations, in practice, several other methods are better suited for this task. That is, other techniques with increased rate of convergence have been developed, and it is generally one of these that are typically used in the software packages that solve such equations.

The first of these advanced iterative methods the *successive over-relaxation* (SOR) method (and its variations, such as the *block SOR method*).[3] The SOR method is essentially an enhanced form of the Gauss-Seidel method. It converges more rapidly as a result of multiplying the *residual* (the difference between the latest estimate of the unknown and the previous estimate) by a relaxation factor ω so that

$$x_{ij}{}^{k+1} = x_{ij}{}^{k} + \omega (x_{ij}{}^{k+1} - x_{ij}{}^{k}) \qquad (A-31)$$

The optimum relaxation factor is chosen to provide either a minimum error in a specific number of iterations or to ensure convergence of the solution to a required tolerance in the minimum number of iterations. The procedure for selecting ω starts with $\omega = 1$ (equivalent to the Gauss-Seidel method), but then increases or decreases ω by 0.1 (or less) in the succeeding iterations until the residuals monitored change sign, which is an indication of an oscillating solution.

The other two advanced iterative methods are implicit methods: (1) the *alternating-direction implicit* methods;[4] and (2) *Stone's strongly implicit method.*[5] Both were developed to solve discretized elliptic partial differential equations, such as the Poisson equation.

The Jacobi, Gauss-Seidel and SOR methods can also be significantly accelerated by applying several other methods including the conjugate gradient method, the conjugate residual (GCR) method, the Chebyshev method, and the incomplete Cholesky-conjugate gradient (ICCG) method.[6]

A.5 NON-LINEAR ALGEBRAIC EQUATIONS

We noted in section that the set of discretized equations at each node of a device grid is a set of nonlinear algebraic equations. (Nonlinear algebraic equations are defined as those which contain powers of variable(s) and/or transcendental functions.) To solve such equations, the object is to find the so-called zeros of the equation. That is, given

$$y = f(x) \qquad (A-32)$$

we seek values of x such that y is zero. The x values that result in $y = 0$ are referred to as the roots of the function $f(x)$. No general algebraic method is available for solving all nonlinear algebraic equations, and a variety of iterative techniques with varying degrees of accuracy and rates of convergence have been developed (including the one we present here, the *Newton-Raphson method*). The degree of accuracy attained for a given root is directly related to the amount of computational effort and the method being used.

We show this method because it provides an example of an iterative numerical procedure used to solve a nonlinear algebraic equation and it illustrates the principle of convergence.

A.5.1 Graphical method

This method does not linearize the nonlinear equations, but in fact solves for the roots directly using a graphical solution method. It's chief role is to establish a range of values for the real roots of a given function (i.e., it provides no information relative to complex roots). That is, it is mainly used to find first approximations of the roots; these are then used as the initial estimate in more accurate numerical techniques. Basically, the function f(x) is evaluated at a number of points, and the results are plotted. The locations where the function crosses the x-axis are the roots. Figure A-1a a shows how the graphical method is applied for approximating the real roots of the function $y = x^3 - 6x^2 + 11x - 6$. If a more accurate estimate is needed, the scales of the ordinate and abscissa can be altered, as shown in Fig. A-1b.

A.5.2 Newton-Raphson Method

Iterative methods are generally used to find more accurate values of the roots of nonlinear algebraic equations. One of the more popular iterative methods is the *Newton-Raphson method*. It offers the benefit of converging to an accurate solution relatively quickly. However, it suffers from the limitation that an initial value close to the root must first be estimated and the derivative of the function must be evaluated. That is, if the initial estimate of the root is not sufficiently close to the actual root, the method may not always converge to a root.

To find the k+1th iteration of the approximation of the root of a nonlinear algebraic equation using the Newton-Raphson method, the following equation is used:

$$x^{k+1} = x^k - f(x^k) / f'(x^k) \qquad\qquad (A - 33)$$

where x^{k+1} = the approximate root after k+1 iterations
x^k =   the approximate root after k iterations
$f(x^k)$ =   functional value at x^k
$f'(x^k)$ = first-derivative of the function at x^k
k = 1, 2, ...

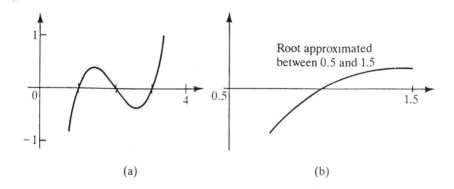

(a)   (b)

Fig. A-1 Procedure used in approximating the real roots of the function
$y = x^3 - 6x^2 + 11x - 6$.

For a system of nonlinear algebraic equations, the Newton-Raphson technique can also be used to find the roots. For a set of equations, the equation above in matrix form is

$$\{x\}^{k+1} = \{x\}^k - [J]_k^{-1} \{f\}^k \tag{A-34}$$

where $[J]$ is the square matrix of the partial derivatives called the *Jacobian* (and $[J]^{-1}$ is the inverse of the Jacobian).

Example A-8: Finding the Roots of a Set of Nonlinear Algebraic Equations Using the Newton-Raphson Method. Estimate one set of roots for the following system of nonlinear algebraic equations:

$$
\begin{array}{ll}
x_1^2 + x_2^2 = 18 & f_1(x_1, x_2) = x_1^2 + x_2^2 - 18 \\
x_1 - x_2 = 0 & f_2(x_1, x_2) = x_1 - x_2
\end{array}
$$

Solution: This system has an exact solution of $x_1 = \pm3$, $x_2 = \pm3$. However, let us use the Newton-Raphson method to estimate these roots. If a graphical procedure is used to obtain an initial estimate of the roots, we might get $x_1 = 2$ and $x_2 = 2$.

$$\begin{Bmatrix} x_1 \\ x_2 \end{Bmatrix} = \begin{Bmatrix} 2 \\ 2 \end{Bmatrix}_1$$

Then the Jacobian is determined and its inverse is evaluated, or

$$[J] = \begin{bmatrix} \dfrac{\partial f_1}{\partial x_1} & \dfrac{\partial f_1}{\partial x_2} \\[2mm] \dfrac{\partial f_2}{\partial x_1} & \dfrac{\partial f_2}{\partial x_2} \end{bmatrix} = \begin{bmatrix} 2x_1 & 2x_2 \\ 1 & -1 \end{bmatrix}$$

and

$$[J]^{-1} = \frac{1}{2x_1 + 2x_2} \begin{bmatrix} 2x_1 & 2x_2 \\ 1 & -1 \end{bmatrix}$$

Therefore, evaluating $[J]$ at the initial assumed values of $x_1 = 2$ and $x_2 = 2$ gives

$$[J]_i^{-1} = \frac{1}{8} \begin{bmatrix} 1 & 4 \\ 1 & -4 \end{bmatrix}$$

The functions are now evaluated to give

$$\begin{Bmatrix} f_1 \\ f_2 \end{Bmatrix}_1 = \begin{Bmatrix} -10 \\ 0 \end{Bmatrix}_1$$

Substituting into

$$[x]^{k+1} = [x]^k - [J]_k^{-1}\} \ f^k$$

gives

$$
\begin{Bmatrix} x_1 \\ x_2 \end{Bmatrix}_2 = \begin{Bmatrix} 2 \\ 2 \end{Bmatrix}_1 - \frac{1}{8}\begin{bmatrix} 1 & 4 \\ 1 & -4 \end{bmatrix}_1 \begin{Bmatrix} -10 \\ 0 \end{Bmatrix}_1 = \begin{Bmatrix} 3.25 \\ 3.25 \end{Bmatrix}_2
$$

The inverse of the Jacobian and the functions are now evaluated at $x_1 = 3.25$ and $x_2 = 3.25$; then, using Eq. A-34, we get

$$
\begin{Bmatrix} x_1 \\ x_2 \end{Bmatrix}_3 = \begin{Bmatrix} 3.25 \\ 3.25 \end{Bmatrix}_2 - \frac{1}{13}\begin{bmatrix} 1 & 2.5 \\ 1 & -2.5 \end{bmatrix}_2 \begin{Bmatrix} 3.125 \\ 0 \end{Bmatrix}_2 = \begin{Bmatrix} 3.0096 \\ 3.0096 \end{Bmatrix}_3
$$

Clearly in just two iterations, we have achieved an acceptable level of accuracy.

References

1. I.S. Duff, "A Survey of Sparse Matrix Research, "*Proceedings IEEE,* **65-4**, p. 500 (1977).
2. J.R. Rice, *Mathematical Software III.* New York, Academic Press, 1977, p. 319.
3. R.S. Varga, "Matrix Iterative Analysis," Prentice-Hall, Englewood Cliffs, 1962.
4. E.L. Wachspress, "Iterative Solution of Elliptic Systems," Prentice-Hall, Englewood Cliffs, 1966.
5. H.L. Stone, "Iterative Solution of Implicit Approximations of Multidimensional Partial Differential Equations," *SIAM J. Numer. Anal.,* Vol. 5 p. 530, 1968.
6. Grimes et al., "ITPACK 2A - A Fortran Implementation of Adaptive Accelerated Iterative Methods for Solving Large Sparse Linear Systems," University of Texas, Austin, Report No. CNA-164, 1980.

APPENDIX B

MAXIMIZING THE CIRCUIT PERFORMANCE OF LONG-CHANNEL MOSFETS THROUGH DEVICE DESIGN AND PROCESSING TECHNOLOGY

The desired circuit characteristics of active MOSFETs in digital ICs include the following: high output-current drive, precisely-manufacturable and stable threshold voltage (V_T), very small subthreshold current (I_{Dst}) at $V_{GS} = 0$, high gate-oxide breakdown voltage, high drain/body breakdown voltage, low source/drain-to-substrate junction capacitances, and high reliability. For the parasitic (field) MOSFET structures threshold voltages (V_{TF}) need to be large enough to prevent leakage between devices. For long-channel MOS devices ($L > 2.0$ μm), the relationship between these electrical parameters and the various MOS device structure is provided by the relatively simple long-channel models of MOS circuit behavior given in chap. 4.

B.1 CHARACTERISTICS OF DIGITAL IC MOSFETS

It is useful to list the desired circuit characteristics of submicron MOSFETs in digital VLSI and ULSI CMOS chips. Depending on the circuit application, the relative importance of each characteristic can vary. In subsequent sections of this appendix we provide examples of how these device characteristics impact circuit performance. Specifically, we would like a MOSFET designed for use in digital applications to exhibit the following characteristics:

1. High output-drive current (e.g., $I_{Dsat} > 400$ μA/μm) when the device is ON.

2. Symmetrical I_D behavior (i.e., I_D should be unchanged if source and drain are reversed).

3. Low leakage current when the device is OFF (e.g., I_D of individual devices should be 10^{-9}-10^{-12} A when the applied gate voltage is zero).

4. Small parasitic capacitances (i.e., junction and overlap capacitance).

5. Small parasitic resistance (the sum of the contact resistance and the source/drain tip series resistance [of an LDD] should be much smaller than the channel resistance).

6. Uniform threshold voltage V_T (e.g., ± 0.1V) throughout each circuit, as well as from circuit to circuit. V_T value should also remain stable (i.e., within $\pm 10\%$ of its original value) over the expected operating lifetime of the chip.

7. Small-valued body-effect coefficient (i.e., this makes V_T less sensitive to source-body bias).

8. High device reliability (e.g., devices should not exhibit hot-carrier-induced degradation or inadequate time-dependent dielectric breakdown, TDDB).

B.1.1 Output Current (I_{Dsat}) and Transconductance (g_m). The long-channel models indicate that I_{Dsat} in MOSFETs can be impacted by various device parameters. First, increasing the gate width linearly increases I_{Dsat}, making this the most obvious way to raise drive current. However, when minimum-sized devices must be used (e.g., for maximum packing density), this avenue may not be available, and the impact of the other parameters on drive current must be examined.

From the dependence of I_{Dsat} on μC_{ox}, both the mobility of the carriers in the channel and the gate-oxide capacitance should be as high as possible. Since electron mobility is greater than hole mobility, circuits using NMOS devices will exhibit higher performance than those built with PMOS devices. In fact, long-channel NMOSFETs of the same width provide roughly 2.5x the drive current of PMOSFETs. In addition, the mobility of carriers decreases as the doping concentration of the channel increases beyond ~1×10^{17} cm^{-3}. Hence, lighter doped channel regions are also favored.

Because the value of C_{ox} is inversely proportional to t_{ox}, as thin a gate oxide as possible (commensurate with oxide breakdown and reliability considerations) is normally used. I_{Dsat} is also inversely proportional to L, and minimum channel lengths are therefore desirable. On the other hand, as the channel lengths become shorter, device operation will be altered so that new models must be developed, as described in section 5.5.

Although the equations indicate that (V_{GS} - V_T) should be as large as possible for maximum I_{Dsat}, $V_{GS} = V_{DD}$ is usually fixed by system specifications and material limitations, and is not alterable by the device designer. Similarly, V_T is selected primarily by other circuit considerations.

B.1.2 Effect of Parasitic Series Resistance on MOSFET Performance. Parasitic resistances consisting of the metal-to-Si contact resistance and the series resistance of the path in the source and drain between the contact and channel also exist in MOSFETs. Since they are in series with the channel, their value R_S is added to the channel resistance R_{ch} to give the total MOS dc output resistance. This implies that R_S may adversely impact I_D and the transconductance (g_m). An approach for minimizing this impact is to keep R_S small compared to R_{ch}. For example, the maximum value of R_S could be limited to 10% of R_{ch}. (While this 10% percent limit may seem arbitrary, it is approximately equal to the R_S/R_{ch} ratio in 1.0 μm MOS devices. Thus, maintaining this ratio as devices shrink seems reasonable.)

Since R_S is normally much smaller than R_{ch} in long-channel MOSFETs this goal is automatically satisfied. However, as devices get smaller, R_{ch} (which is directly proportional to L) also shrinks, while R_S grows larger (because of decreased contact sizes and shallower source/drain junction depths). Eventually, it becomes necessary to determine the channel lengths at which R_S may be a significant fraction of the total MOS resistance. Here we summarize how estimates of R_S have been derived for devices with $L<1$ μm.

To begin, the relation used to calculate the MOS channel resistance, R_{ch} (with the device operating in the linear region of the I_D vs. V_{DS} curves), is normalized to unit width, and is therefore expressed in units of Ω-μm. Then, the value of R_{ch} in the linear region is selected to represent the channel impedance, as it provides the worst case comparison with R_S. An expression from which R_{ch}(linear) can be calculated is

$$R_{ch} \text{ (linear region)} = [(L_{eff} + \{V_{DS}/E_c\})/[\mu_o C_{ox}(V_{GS} - V_T - V_{DS}/2)] \qquad \text{(B-1)}$$

where $\mathcal{E}_c$ represents the critical field at the onset of velocity saturation (see chap. 5). Note that this equation is a modified form of the MOSFET channel resistance equation, which includes in the numerator the term V_{DS}/E_c, whose origin stems from the mobility dependence on the longitudinal electric field. That is, in Eq. B-1, instead of including $\mathcal{E}_c$ in a factor also containing L_{eff} and V_{DS}, the term V_{DS}/E_c is added to L_{eff} to obtain a simpler formula. This leads to a mobility decrease as being equivalent to an increase in L_{eff} for channel resistance or transconductance calculations.

A graph of the values of R_{ch} versus channel length calculated using this equation for NMOS devices and PMOS devices is shown in Fig. B-1, assuming $V_{GS} = 5$ V. In this figure, the 10% value of R_{ch} is also plotted. We note that as the devices get smaller, the value of R_{ch} also decreases. These graphs indicate that the maximum allowed values for R_S for submicron devices will thus be in the 300-500 Ω-μm range.

A more sophisticated constraint than the simple limit on R_S was proposed by Ng and Lynch.[1] They performed an analysis in which an estimate of the decrease in switching speed was calculated as R_S was increased and L_{eff} decreased. Overall, they found that the intrinsic series-resistance effects will negatively impact the speed performance of MOS devices as the devices are scaled below 0.5 μm. Nevertheless, they predict that it will be possible to build devices that demonstrate improvement of speed performance as they are scaled to 0.15 μm. The use of self-aligned, silicided source/drain regions to reduce the contact resistance will be important, as will the development of processes that produce junctions with more steeply graded doping profiles. In addition, contact technologies that provide smaller contact resistance and lower sheet resistances of the diffusion layer under the contact window (or the silicided region) will need to be developed.

B.2 Desired Circuit Characteristics of IC Interconnects

Circuit performance characteristics of the IC interconnect scheme are also important. These include:

1. Low sheet resistance values of the conductor lines.

2. Low conductor-substrate parasitic-capacitance values.

3. High reliability of the interconnect system.

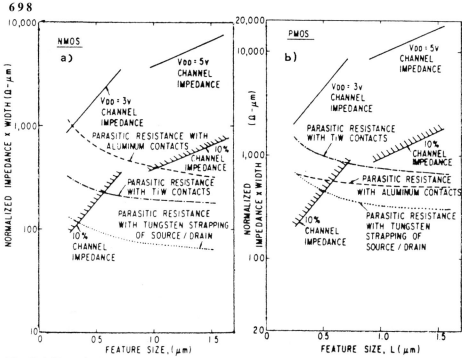

Fig. B-1 Plot of minimum channel resistance and parasitic series resistance versus design rule feature for (a) NMOS, and (b) PMOS. The parasitic residences are calculated for three different contact technologies: (1) Al --- ; (2) Ti:W alloy ··· ; and (3) self-aligned W strapping of source and drain.[4] (© 1986 IEEE).

B.2.1 Circuit Speed as Impacted by MOSFET Device and Interconnect Conductor Characteristics.
Speed performance is especially important in densely packed static logic and dynamic logic (digital MOS) ICs. *Static* logic circuits* are often found in the data path and control sections of digital ICs, and examples are the digital multiplier and the static arithmetic logic unit.* *Dynamic* logic circuits** are functionally the same as static logic circuits, but employ dynamic circuit

---

* In CMOS static-logic-circuits the logic function of each gate is implemented in both *p*- and *n*-channel devices. The use of complimentary MOSFETs in each gate results in larger area circuits per function and larger input capacitive loads since both *p*- and *n*-channel devices must be driven. However, the dual-device types give a major advantage to fully-static logic circuits, namely they exhibit a large noise immunity (which is necessary for fast turnaround designs, where detailed circuit design is not practical).

** Dynamic logic circuits offer the advantage of speed and functional density at the expense of extra design time. The output nodes of the logic gates are precharged to a particular level when the clock has a value 0. During this time (i.e., when the clock value is 0) the inputs to the circuits also change. Then, when the clock goes to value 1, the output may be pulled down to the complementary value, depending on the input conditions. Both functional density and speed are improved because it is not necessary to use a pull-up *p*-type transistor. This leads to almost a 50% savings in silicon area compared to static logic, and a reduction in output capacitance.

techniques such as domino logic. An example of this type of circuit is the ALU in the Belmac 32-bit processor.

A fundamental measure of digital circuit speed is the delay time per gate τ_d. We will perform a rudimentary analysis of the factors that impact τ_d in a MOS logic gate so that the main device characteristics that establish this parameter can be identified.

In MOS logic gates the MOSFET output current (assumed to be I_{Dsat}) is used to discharge the load capacitance C_L (as shown in Fig. B-2). If the incremental change in output voltage is defined as ΔV and the incremental discharge time as Δt (and if we neglect the current through R_1)

$$I_{Dsat} = C_L \, \Delta V/\Delta t \qquad (B\text{-}2)$$

where $\Delta Q = C_L \, \Delta V$ is the charge stored in the capacitor. Therefore, the delay time

$$\tau_d \sim \Delta t \; = C_L \, \Delta V/ \, I_{Dsat} \qquad (B\text{-}3)$$

if I_{Dsat} is constant. This indicates that an increase in I_{Dsat} will decrease the logic gate delay time, and exemplifies the desirability of large I_{Dsat} in digital MOSFETs.

By using the simplified form for I_{Dsat} (see Eq. 4-68), and approximating $V_{GS} - V_T = V_{DD}$, we have

$$I_{Dsat} = \mu \, Z \, C_{ox} V_{DD}^2/2L \qquad (B\text{-}4)$$

where μ, C_{ox}, L, and Z are the carrier mobility, oxide capacitance (in units of capacitance per unit area), channel length, and width of the MOSFET, respectively.

Next, assume the logic swing ΔV is equal to the power-supply voltage V_{DD}, and C_L is roughly the sum of the gate capacitance of the next stage ($C_{ox}ZL$) and any other parasitic capacitances C(parasitic) of the next stage and the interconnect path. That is

$$C_L \sim C_{ox}Z \, L + C(\text{parasitic}) \qquad (B\text{-}5)$$

If C(parasitic)$<<C_{ox}Z \, L$, the load capacitance is essentially just the gate capacitance

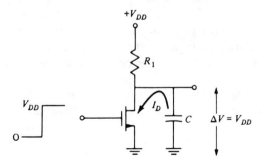

Fig. B-2 Load capacitance discharged to output current in an FET circuit.

of the next MOSFET. In this case, substituting Eqs. B-4 and B-5 into Eq. B-3 and simplifying, we find

$$\tau_d = 2\,L^2/\mu V_{DD} \qquad\qquad (B-6)$$

Equation B-6 shows that if a circuit is dominated by intrinsic capacitance the delay time is proportional to L^2. Thus, significant improvement in switching speed can be realized by downsizing L, but decreasing t_{ox} will have no impact.

On the other hand, if C(parasitic)$\gg C_{ox}Z\,L$, τ_d will be decreased if t_{ox} is made thinner, because this will make I_{Dsat} grow larger, and the improvement will not be offset by the increase in C_{ox} [since C_{ox} is insignificant compared to C(parasitic)].

In either case, we can see that the speed of MOSFET logic gates can generally be increased by increasing I_{Dsat} and/or decreasing C_L. If C_{ox} dominates, shrinking the MOSFET dimensions will decrease the gate delay time. If C(parasitic) dominates, gate delay will be decreased by decreasing C(parasitic). Thus, it is also useful to examine the nature of C(parasitic).

B.2.2 Components of the Parasitic Capacitance.

There are several effects in a MOS IC that contribute to C(parasitic), including the gate-drain overlap capacitance C_{gdo}, drain-substrate junction capacitances C_j,* and the capacitance associated with the interconnect lines (or wiring) C_w. In long-channel MOSFETs G_{gdo} was relatively small, but in submicron MOSFETs C_{gdo} can become significant. This is because C_{gdo} can be increased by such drain structures as LDDs. While these are designed to reduce hot-electron degradation in MOSFETs, the best structures in terms of hot-electron resistance may give rise to the largest C_{dgo} (see chap. 5). C_j is reduced by reducing the drain-to-substrate junction area and also by keeping the substrate region under the drain as lightly doped as possible.

In large VLSI chips, the delay caused by the $C_w R_w$ product can dominate, where R_w is the resistance of the interconnect line. The delay resulting from various interconnect materials per millimeter of length running over a 1 μm thick field oxide is graphed for some of these materials (assuming a 1-cm-long interconnect line) in Fig. B-3. This shows, for example, that if a polysilicon line having a 20 Ω/sq sheet resistance is used to connect one corner of a 0.7-x-0.7 cm chip to the diagonal corner, the propagation delay will be 1.4 μs. Even if Al is used as the interconnect layer, the delay caused by 1-cm-long interconnection lines will limit the circuit speeds once device dimensions fall below ~2 μm.

The latter data indicate that in order for circuit performance to be increased as device dimensions shrink, two goals must be met. First, the materials used for transmitting

---

* When the MOSFET in Fig. B-2 is turned on, electrons flow through it to the positively charged load capacitance C_L tied to the drain. The electrons discharge C_L, causing the drain voltage to drop. As the drain voltage falls, the drain-to-substrate junction must also discharge. Thus, the drain-to-substrate junction capacitance adds to the load capacitance and, therefore, increases τ_d.

signals over long distances on a chip must have the lowest possible resistance values. This has been the key motivation in the drive to replace polysilicon interconnects (20 Ω/sq) with polycide interconnects (1.7 Ω/sq for TiSi₂). It may eventually cause refractory metals (0.5 Ω/sq for W) to be used as the first-level interconnect layer in multilevel-interconnect systems. In addition, it also points outs why Al will continue to be used as an interconnect material, even as devices shrink further.

Second, the length of interconnect lines on a chip must be made as short as possible. The RC delay can be shown to be proportional to the square of the length of the interconnect line. That is,

$$R_W = (\rho\, l)/(w\, t_m) \tag{B-7}$$

and

$$C_W = \varepsilon\, w\, l\, /\, t_{ox}, \tag{B-8}$$

and therefore

$$R_W C_W = (\rho\, \varepsilon\, l^2)/(t_{ox}\, t_m) \tag{B-9}$$

where ρ is the resistivity, l the interconnect line length, w the line width, ε the permittivity of the insulator film, t_m the thickness of the metal, and t_{ox} the thickness of the oxide. Multilevel-interconnect structures can effectively be used to reduce the longest interconnect lines.

B.2.3 Drain Current in OFF-State MOSFETs. The drain current of the MOSFET in the OFF state (i.e., I_D when $V_{GS} = 0$V) is an undesired, but nevertheless important leakage current device parameter in many digital CMOS IC applications (including DRAMs, SRAMs, dynamic logic circuits, and portable systems). In

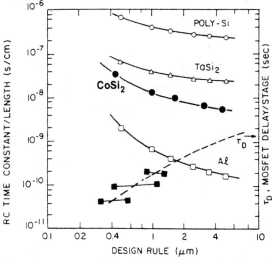

Fig. B-3 $R_W C_W$ time constant per unit length for several conductive materials as a function of feature size. Also shown is delay per stage of NMOS ring oscillators as a function of feature size. The $R_W C_W$ time constant is calculated assuming a field oxide thickness of 1 μm. Copyright AIOP.[5] Reprinted with permission.

addition, in any large device-count MOS IC, leakage currents in OFF-state transistors must be kept small to keep heating under control. (The standby power consumed by devices in the OFF state adds to the total power consumed by the IC, increasing heat dissipation problems in the chip and package).

In DRAMs, SRAMs, and dynamic-logic circuits, charge is stored on nodal capacitances isolated by access transistors or transmission gates (Fig. B-4 shows a transmission gate in a dynamic CMOS circuit). Once the capacitance is charged, the transmission gate is turned off by setting $V_{GS} = 0V$. The charged nodes must not be discharged during the time of a clock cycle by a leaky, nominally-OFF transmission-gate MOSFET. The allowable leakage is determined by how long a time the transmission gate must hold a voltage on a capacitive node. In portable systems, low standby-power-dissipation is needed for long operating times under battery-power.

The value of I_D when $V_{GS} = 0V$ consists of several components, including the subthreshold leakage current of the MOSFET I_{Dst}, the leakage current of the reverse-biased drain-substrate junction, gate-induced drain leakage (GIDL), and leakage currents due to loss of device isolation. In well-designed devices and IC processes it is possible to keep the latter three components smaller than I_{Dst} (procedures to accomplish this are discussed in chaps. 4 and 5). The value of I_{Dst} in long-channel devices when $V_{GS} = 0V$ (per unit width of the channel) depends on the device threshold voltage V_T, the subthreshold swing S_t, and the temperature of operation. As devices shrink, several short-channel effects arise that can increase the long-channel I_{Dst} value.

B.2.4 The Need for Precise Control and Stability of V_T in MOSFETs.
Since the MOSFET models of section 4.5 indicate that I_{Dsat} is proportional to $(V_{GS} - V_T)$, it might appear that V_T should be as close to zero volts as possible. However, as V_T decreases, I_{Dst} will increase at $V_{GS} = 0V$ (see section 4.7), and the noise margin of the logic gate will decrease. Thus, the minimum V_T is

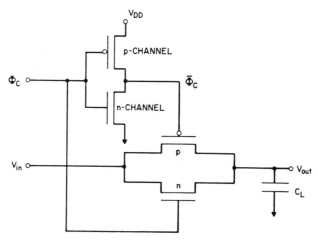

Fig. B-4 CMOS transmission gate driven by a clock signal φ_c, and its complement $\bar{\varphi}_c$, generated locally by an inverter.

generally selected to ensure either a sufficiently small I_{Dst} when $V_{GS} = 0$, or a sufficiently large noise margin.

Once V_T is selected, the need for V_T stability during the normal lifetime of the device (e.g., 10 years) can be inferred from the previous discussion. If V_T decreases, I_{Dst} will increase (giving rise to problems associated with excess leakage), and noise margin will decrease. On the other hand, if V_T increases, I_{Dsat} will decrease since ($V_{GS} - V_T$) will become smaller. Hot-carrier trapping in the gate oxide is the chief mechanism causing shifts in V_T during the life of the device, a topic discussed in chap. 9.

Another example of the importance of being able to control V_T involves semiconductor memory devices. In these circuits, charge flows from the memory cells to the sense amplifier. The sense amplifier is a delicately balanced flip-flop whose voltage-sensing capability is directly related to the threshold-voltage variation between the transistors. Hence, such circuits would not function reliably unless V_T in the circuit devices was highly uniform and stable.

B.2.5 Junction Breakdown Voltage (Drain-to-Substrate). The source and drain regions are heavily doped to minimize their resistivities. Thus, the breakdown voltage of the drain-to-substrate junction will be determined by the lighter doping concentration of the substrate. The breakdown voltage decreases as the doping increases. Hence, as substrate doping is decreased, the junction breakdown voltage will increase.

While the current in breakdown also represents a form of subthreshold I_D, it turns out that the $\mathcal{E}$-field needed to cause breakdown of the drain junction in submicron MOSFETs is smaller than that allowed by hot-carrier degradation limits. (As is discussed in chap. 9, hot-carrier degradation becomes excessive at $\mathcal{E}_{ymax} \sim 0.2$ MV/cm, whereas drain breakdown is estimated to occur for fields of the order of $\mathcal{E}_{ymax} \sim 0.6$ MV/cm.)[2] Thus, breakdown voltage is not considered to be a major limitation of submicron MOSFET design.[3]

B.2.6 Gate-Oxide Leakage and Gate Breakdown Voltage. Submicron MOSFETs with $L = 1.0$-0.5 μm use gate-oxide thicknesses of 12-25 nm. High-quality SiO_2 films typically break down at electric fields of 8-12 MV/cm (the exact value is a function of oxidation and anneal conditions, oxide charges, surface crystallographic orientation, surface preparation and a number of other factors). This corresponds to 8-12 V across a 10-nm-thick oxide.

As discussed in chap. 6, oxide breakdown may also occur at smaller electric-field values, due to process-induced flaws in the gate oxide. Such defects include: metal precipitates on the silicon surface prior to oxide growth; high defect density in the silicon lattice at the substrate surface (e.g., stacking faults and dislocations); pinholes and weak spots created in the gate oxide by particulates; thinning of the oxide during growth caused by the Kooi effect; and oxide wearout due to failure mechanisms related to hot-electron injection.

Charge transport through such oxides without breakdown can occur under high electric fields by Fowler-Nordheim tunneling (i.e., electrons tunnel to the oxide conduction band, and are then transported by drift current to the gate). Below around 4 nm (at less than 3V), some electrons will tunnel directly through the oxide. If oxides thinner than ~3 nm are used, tunneling increases to the degree that an inversion layer cannot form in the MOS capacitor (i.e., the tunneling current removes the inversion layer carriers faster than they are supplied by thermal generation). Direct tunneling therefore sets a fundamental lower limit of about 3 nm for the thickness of the gate oxide. A search for alternative gate dielectric materials to mitigate this limitation is being conducted.

REFERENCES

1. K.K. Ng and W.T. Lynch, *IEEE Trans. Electron Dev.*, March 1987, p. 503.

2. F. M. Klaassen, "Design and Performance of Micron-Size Devices," *Solid-State Electronics,* **21** (3), 565, (1978).

3. W.S. Feng et al., *IEEE Electron Dev. Letts.*, July 1986, p. 449.

4. D.M. Brown, M. Ghezzo, and J.M. Pembley, *Proceedings of the IEEE*, Dec. 1986, p. 1678.

5. A.K. Sinha, *J. Vac, Sci. Technol.* **19**, 778, (1981).

APPENDIX C

DERIVATION OF THE BSIM I_D MODEL

The *ionic-charge model* of Ihantola and Moll described in chap. 4 is the basis of the Level 2 MOSFET model in SPICE. The I_D equation in linear region of this model is given by Eq. 4-57 and is repeated here as C-1 for convenience:

$$I_D = \frac{\mu C_{ox} Z}{L}(V_{GB} - V_{FB} - 2\varphi_B)V_{DS} - \frac{1}{2}V_{DS}^2$$

$$- \frac{2}{3}\gamma [(V_{DS} + V_{BS} + 2\varphi_B)^{3/2} - (V_{BS} + 2\varphi_B)^{3/2}] \qquad (4-57) \quad (C-1)$$

This model predicts I_D in strong inversion but it is too complicated for hand calculations and even for most applications involving computer simulation of large circuits. The complexity of Eq. C-1 is due to the 3/2 power terms in the right hand side of the equation, leading to long execution times if the model is used in the SPICE program to simulate the circuit behavior of a large circuit. Thus, a simpler model for this application is desirable, even at the expense of some accuracy. The Level 3 and Level 4 (BSIM) models of the MOSFET in SPICE utilize such a simpler model. Here we show how this model is derived starting from Eq. 4-57, as is done by Sheu.[1]

The 3/2 power terms of Eq. 4-57 have their origin in the square root term of Eq. 4-10, repeated here as Eq. C-2 with V_{BC} replaced by V_{BS}

$$Q_I = -C_{ox}[V_{GC} - V_{FB} - 2\varphi_B - V_{BC} - \gamma(2\varphi_B + V_{BS})^{1/2}] \qquad (4-10) \quad (C-2)$$

which, in turn is due to the expression for Q_B given by Eq. 4-9 (Eq. C-3 here)

$$Q_{Bmax} = [2\kappa_{si}\varepsilon_0 N_A (2\varphi_B + V_{BS})]^{1/2} = \gamma(2\varphi_B + V_{BS})^{1/2}] \qquad (C-3)$$

The solid line of Fig. C-1 is a plot of the $-Q_{Bmax}/C_{ox}$ term of Eq. 4-10 versus effective reverse bias in the channel.[2] Since the slope of this curve is seen not vary very much, it is reasonable to attempt to approximate the $-Q_{Bmax}/C_{ox}$ term by the first two terms of its Taylor series about the point V_{SB}.

Likewise, if we were to plot the two terms containing V_{BS} in Eq. 4-57 [which we write here as $F(V_{DS}, 2\varphi_B + V_{DS})$],

$$F(V_{DS}, 2\varphi_B + V_{BS}) = \frac{2}{3}[(V_{DS} + V_{BS} + 2\varphi_B)^{3/2} - (V_{BS} + 2\varphi_B)^{3/2}] \qquad (C-4)$$

we would also see that the slope of their plot would not vary much. Thus, it is appropriate to approximate these terms by using the first two terms of the Taylor series of $F(V_{DS}, 2\varphi_B + V_{DS})$, which are

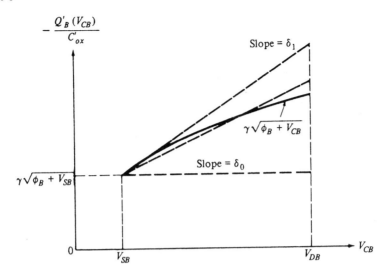

Fig. C-1 The quantity $-Q_B/C_{OX}$ in strong inversion versus effective reverse bias in the channel. Solid line: accurate calculation (i.e., using Eq. 4-56); upper broken line: first-order approximation from a Taylor expansion at $V_{CB} = V_{SB}$; middle broken line: improved first-order approximation; lower broken line: zero-order approximation (i.e., Square-law model - Eq. 4-63).[2] Reprinted with permission of McGraw-Hill Book Company.

$$F\left(V_{DS}, 2\varphi_B + V_{BS}\right) = \sqrt{2\varphi_B + V_{BS}}\ V_{DS} + \frac{0.25\ V_{DS}^2}{\sqrt{2\varphi_B + V_{BS}}} \qquad (C - 5)$$

This expansion, however, is invalid if $(2\varphi_B + V_{BS}) \gg V_{DS}$. To alleviate this problem, the expansion is changed to

$$F\left(V_{DS}, 2\varphi_B + V_{BS}\right) = \sqrt{2\varphi_B + V_{BS}}\ V_{DS} + \frac{0.25aV_{DS}^2}{\sqrt{2\varphi_B + V_{BS}}} \qquad (C - 6)$$

where $a\ (2\varphi_B + V_{BS})$ is determined by requiring the expansion in C-6 to give the best fit to $F\ [V_{DS}, 2\varphi_B + V_{BS}]$ in the desired voltage range.

The value of $(2\varphi_B + V_{BS})$ is considered in the range 0.7V-20.7V at 2-V increments. For each fixed value of $(2\varphi_B + V_{BS})$, the value of the parameter a is determined such that the expansion

$$\sqrt{2\varphi_B + V_{BS}}\ V_{DS} + \frac{0.25\ a\ V_{DS}^2}{\sqrt{2\varphi_B + V_{BS}}}$$

will give the best fit to $F\ [V_{DS}, 2\varphi_B + V_{BS}]$ in a least-square sense, over a range of V_{DS} from 0V to 10V at 0.5V increments. It is found that a can be accurately expressed as a function of $F\ [V_{DS}, 2\varphi_B + V_{BS}]$ in the following form:

$$1\ /\ (1 - a)\ =\ P_1 + \{P_2\ (2\varphi_B + V_{BS})\} \qquad (C - 7)$$

where P_1 and P_2 are determined by a least-square fitting over the range of $(2\varphi_B + V_{BS})$ from 0.7 to 20.7V. The results are

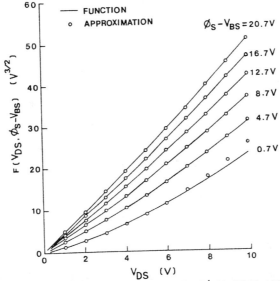

Fig. C-2 Approximating the function $F[V_{DS}, 2\varphi_B + V_{BS}]$.[1] (© IEEE 1987).

$$P_1 = 1.744 \qquad (C-8)$$

and

$$P_2 = 0.8364. \qquad (C-9)$$

The approximation (C-6) is compared to the function $F[V_{DS}, 2\varphi_B + V_{BS}]$ for various values of $(2\varphi_B + V_{BS})$ in Fig. C-2. The agreement between them is quite good, with the root-mean-square error of the approximation being 2 percent when the values of P_1 and P_2 given above are used.

The values of P_1 and P_2 are substituted into Eq. C-7 and this expression is then solved for a. The approximation (C-6) is used in Eq. C-1 for the terms given by Eq. C-4. Thus C-1 becomes (with additional terms also added for mobility degradation and velocity saturation effects as described in section 5.5):

$$I_D = \frac{\mu_0}{[1 + U_0(V_{GS} - V_T)]} \frac{C_{ox}\frac{Z}{L}}{(1 + \frac{U_1}{L}V_{DS})} \left(V_{GS} - V_T\right)V_{DS} - \frac{aV_{DS}^2}{2}) \qquad (C-10)$$

where

$$a = 1 + \frac{\gamma}{2\sqrt{2\varphi_B - V_{BS}}} \left[1 - \frac{1}{1.744 + 0.8364\,(2\varphi_B - V_{BS})}\right]$$

REFERENCES

1. B.J. Sheu and D.L. Scharfetter, "BSIM: Berkeley Short-Channel IGFET Model for MOS Transistors," *IEEE J. Solid-State Circuits,* **SC-22,** August 1987, p. 558.

2. Y.A. Tsividis, *Operation and Modeling of the MOS Transistor,* McGraw-Hill, New York, 1987, p. 124.

APPENDIX D

DERIVATION OF THE DISCRETIZED 2-D POISSON EQUATIONS USING THE BOX-INTEGRATION METHOD

In chapter 2 we showed how the difference-operator method (one of the two finite-difference discretization techniques) is used to discretize the 2-D Poisson equation. However, we noted that in such device simulators as GEMINI and PISCES-II the other finite-difference discretization technique (the box-integration method) is used instead, primarily because it permits non-planar device structures to be handled more easily. Here we show how the 2-D Poisson equation is discretized using the box-integration method, as well as how it facilitates the treatment of non-planar surfaces. As is done in the GEMINI device simulator, we assume a rectangular grid is used, together with the five-point approximation method. We mention, however, that in PISCES-II the box integration method is applied to an irregular (i.e., triangular-based) grid. Note also that the derivation given here is a close adaptation of the method presented by Greenfield and Dutton.[1]

In the box integration method the domain is divided into a set of rectangular subdomains, as well as a rectangular grid structure with nonuniform spacing in both spatial dimensions, as shown in Fig. D-1. The four nearest neighbor nodes are used in the discrete approximation to the continuous Poisson equation, as described in chap. 2. Figure D-2 depicts a node surrounded by its four nearest neighbors and defines the locations and potential values associated with these nodes. The perpendicular bisectors C_m of the lines joining the center node to the outside nodes defines a rectangle with four triangular subregions S_m. The finite difference approximation at the center node is derived by integrating Poisson's equation over the rectangle S. That is, the Poisson equation is first integrated twice on each side as follows:

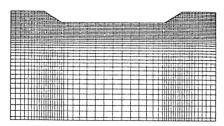

Fig. D-1 Non-uniform, non-planar rectangular grid.

$$\int_{y_0-\frac{h_4}{2}}^{y_0+\frac{h_2}{2}} \int_{y_0-\frac{h_1}{2}}^{x_0+\frac{h_3}{2}} \nabla \cdot [\varepsilon \, \nabla\varphi \,(x,y)] \, dx \, dy = -\int_{y_0-\frac{h_4}{2}}^{y_0+\frac{h_2}{2}} \int_{y_0-\frac{h_1}{2}}^{y_0+\frac{h_3}{2}} [\rho \,(x,y)] \, dx \, dy \qquad (\text{D-1})$$
$$\underset{S}{} \qquad\qquad \underset{S}{}$$

By applying one of Green's theorems the double (surface) integral on the left-hand side of Eq. D-1 can be transformed into a line integral C of S. That is,

$$\int\int_S \nabla \cdot [\varepsilon \, \nabla\varphi \,(x,y)] \, dx \, dy = \int_C (\varepsilon \, \nabla\varphi \,(x,y) \cdot \hat{n} \, dl = \int_C (\varepsilon \frac{\partial\varphi}{\partial x} \, dy - \varepsilon \frac{\partial\varphi}{\partial y} \, dx) \qquad (\text{D-2})$$

The line integral on the right hand side must be split into four parts because of the discontinuous edges of the domain S. In addition, the surface integral over S (the right hand side of Eq. D-1), can also be broken up into four parts, each one representing the integral of the charge density in one of the four triangular regions of S. Thus, Eq. D-1 can be written as

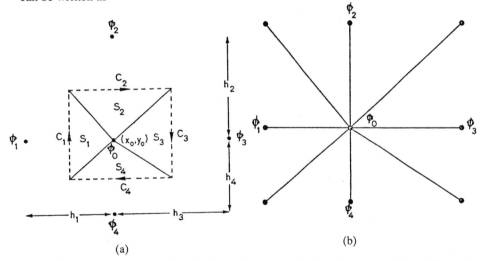

(a)   (b)

Fig. D-2 (a) A node and its four horizontally and vertically adjacent neighbors. The node locations and potentials are indicated. The C_m are perpendicular bisectors of the lines joining the center node to the outside nodes and define a rectangle S with triangular subregions S_m. (b) The eight line segments joining a node to its nearest and next nearest neighbors. Surfaces and material interfaces are composed of sequences of these segments.[1] (© IEEE 1980).

$$\int_{y-\frac{h4}{2}}^{y+\frac{h2}{2}} [\varepsilon \frac{\partial\varphi(x_0+h_3/2,y)}{\partial x}] \, dy \; + \int_{x-\frac{h1}{2}}^{x+\frac{h3}{2}} [\varepsilon \frac{\partial\varphi(x, y_0-h_4/2)}{\partial y}] \, dx \; +$$

$$\int_{y-\frac{h4}{2}}^{y+\frac{h2}{2}} [\varepsilon \frac{\partial\varphi(x_0-h_1/2,y)}{\partial x}] \, dy \; + \int_{x-\frac{h1}{2}}^{x+\frac{h3}{2}} [\varepsilon \frac{\partial\varphi(x,y_0+h_2/2)}{\partial y}] \, dx$$

$$= - \sum_{m=1}^{4} \left\{ \int \cdot \int [\rho\,(x,y,\varphi)]\, dx\, dy \right\} \qquad \text{(D - 3)}$$

Approximations are introduced to Eq. D-3 in terms of the potential values at the five nodes. The integrands on the left hand side are approximated as

$$\nabla\varphi\,(x, y) \cong \frac{\varphi_m - \varphi_0}{h_m} \qquad \text{(D - 4)}$$

and it is assumed that its value is constant over C_m (i.e., the component of the electric field $\nabla\varphi$ normal to each side of this rectangle is taken to be constant along that side).

The simplest approximation to the term on the right-hand side of Eq. D-3 is obtained by assuming that the impurity concentration and free carrier concentrations [and hence $\rho(x,y,\varphi)$] is constant in each triangular subdomain S_m, with its value being determined by evaluation at the coordinate of that node (i.e., using φ_0 and $N\,(x_0, y_0)$). These assumptions transform Eq. D-3 to:

$$\sum_{m=1}^{4} L_m \frac{\varphi_m - \varphi_0}{h_m} \; = \; -\rho\,(x, y, \varphi) \sum_{m=1}^{4} A_m \qquad \text{(D - 5)}$$

$$\sum_{m=1}^{4} B_m\,(\varphi_m - \varphi_0) \; = \; -\rho\,(x, y, \varphi) \qquad \text{(D - 6)}$$

where

$$B_m \; = \; L_m\,/\,(h_m\,A) \qquad \text{(D - 7)}$$

and

$$L_m \; = \int_{C_m} \varepsilon\, dl \qquad \text{(D - 8)}$$

and

$$A \; = \; \sum_{m=1}^{4} A_m \qquad \text{(D - 9)}$$

When the center node does not lie on the device surface or on a dielectric interface, A_m is the area of S_m. The handling of nonplanar surfaces and interfaces may be described in terms of their effects on L_m and A_m in Eqs. D-5 to D-9. Only the calculation of L_1 and A_1 is described as the other pairs are computed in a similar fashion. Figure D-2b illustrates the eight line segments joining a node to its nearest and next nearest neighbors. We assume urfaces and interfaces are constructed from sequences of these segments.

For a n ue lying along the surface, a difference equation is only necessary when the boundary condition used at that node specifies the normal gradient of potential. Figure D-3 shows three orientations of the left portion of the surface which affect L_1 and A_1 in Eqs. D-5 to D-9 for a surface passing through the center node. The presence of the surface may eliminate part of C_1 and S_1 in Fig. D-2a, modifying L_1 and A_1. The dielectric permittivity below the surface does not affect S_1. In Fig. D-3a, the presence of the surface does not affect S_1. In Fig. D-3b, the surface eliminates the upper portion of S_1. In Fig. D-3c, the surface entirely eliminates S_1. Table D-1 summarizes the values of L_1 and A_1 for these cases.

Figure D-4 depicts three orientations of the left portion of the interface which affect L_1 and A_1 in Eqs. D-5 to D-9 for a dielectric interface passing through the center node. The dielectric permittivities above and below the interface are ε_i and ε_s respectively. In Fig. D-4a, S_1 is entirely within the semiconductor. In Fig. D-4b, the interface divides S_1 between the semiconductor and the insulator. In Fig. D-4c, S_1 is entirely within the insulator. The values of L_1 and A_1 for these cases are also listed in Table D-1. As an example of the derivation of the complete finite difference equation, consider Fig. D-4c where the center node lies at a bend in the dielectric interface with the interface

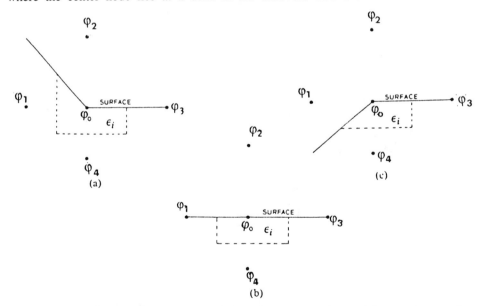

Fig. D-3 Three surface orientations which affect L_1 and A_1 in Eq. D-5 for a surface passing through the center node. (a) Surface is above S_1 and has no effect. (b) Surface passes through S_1 and eliminates its upper part. (c) Surface is below S_1 and eliminates it entirely.[1] (© IEEE 1980).

charge density Q_{tot} taken to be nonzero in the semiconductor beneath the surface. The coefficients L_m and A_m are as follows:

$$L_1 = \varepsilon_i (h_2 + h_4)/2, \qquad A_1 = 0$$
$$L_2 = \varepsilon_i (h_1 + h_3)/2, \qquad A_2 = 0$$
$$L_3 = (\varepsilon_i h_2 + \varepsilon_{si} h_4)/2, \qquad A_3 = h_3 h_4/8$$
$$L_4 = \varepsilon_i (h_1 + h_3)/2, \qquad A_4 = h_4 (h_1 + h_3)/8.$$

Table D-1   Discretization Coefficients for Figs. D-3 and D-4

	Surface Node (Figure D-3)		Interface Node (Figure D-4)	
	L_1	A_1	L_1	A_1
(a)	$\varepsilon_i (h_2 + h_4)/2$	$h_1(h_2 + h_4)/8$	$\varepsilon_s (h_2 + h_4)/2$	$h_1(h_2 + h_4)/8$
(b)	$\varepsilon_i h_4/2$	$h_1 h_4/8$	$(\varepsilon_i h_2 + \varepsilon_s h_4)/2$	$h_1 h_4/8$
(c)	0	0	$\varepsilon_i (h_1 + h_3)/2$	0

REFERENCES

1. J.A. Greenfield and R.W. Dutton, "Nonplanar VLSI Device Analysis Using the Solution of Poisson's Equation," *IEEE Trans. Electron Dev.*, **ED-27**, p. 1520, Aug. 1980.

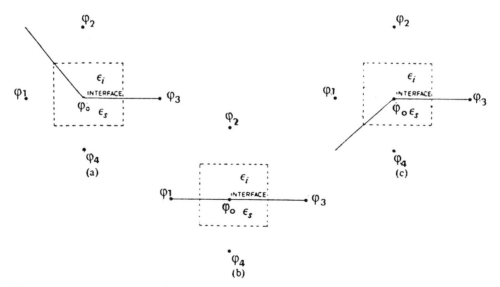

Fig. D-4 Three surface orientations which affect L_1 and A_1 in Eq. D-5 for a dielectric interface passing through the center node. (a) The interface is above S_1 and places S_1 in the semiconductor. (b) The surface passes through S_1 placing the upper portion in the insulator and the lower portion in the semiconductor. (c) The surface is below S_1 and places S_1 in the insulator.[1] (© IEEE 1980).

INDEX

NOTE: FOR MAJOR SUBJECT HEADINGS ALSO CHECK THE **TABLE OF CONTENTS**. THE LISTING ARE NOT ALWAYS DUPLICATED IN THE INDEX.

ORDER FORM

LATTICE PRESS
POST OFFICE BOX 340-W
SUNSET BEACH, CA 90742, U.S.A.

Please send the number of copies indicated below of **SILICON PROCESSING FOR THE VLSI ERA - Vols. 1, 2,** and/or **3 (please specify!).** A check or money order for the full amount for the number of copies ordered is enclosed. Make checks payable to: **LATTICE PRESS.** I understand that I may return any book within 30 days for a full refund if not completely satisfied.

_____
NAME (and COMPANY - if part of your address)

_____
ADDRESS

_____
CITY

_____
STATE, ZIP CODE   COUNTRY

_____
Daytime Phone Number

_____ copies **Vol. 3** @ $ 94.95 each, plus $4.00 for each copy, shipping-handling fee.
(*California Residents*: Please add $5.80 per copy for Sales Tax)

_____ copies **Vol. 2** @ $ 89.95 each, plus $4.00 for each copy, shipping-handling fee.
(*California Residents*: Please add $5.40 per copy for Sales Tax)

_____ copies **Vol. 1** @ $59.95 each. plus $4.00 for each copy, shipping-handling fee.
(*California Residents*: Please add $3.60 per copy for Sales Tax.)

Allow 30 days for delivery

International Ordering Information:

Overseas Prices: Volume 1 - $69.95; Volume 2 - $99.95; Volume 3 - $99.95. Enclose full payment with order in Travelers Checks (US dollars), International Money Order, or by a check payable to **Lattice Press** in **US dollars, drawn on a U.S. bank.** Include a $4.00 shipping /handling fee per copy for overseas orders shipped via surface mail. (Allow 6-10 weeks delivery.) Include a $20 US shipping /handling fee per copy for overseas orders shipped by airmail. (Allow 2 weeks delivery).